WHO'S WHO AMONG STUDENTS IN AMERICAN UNIVERSITIES & COLLEGES® 2016

The 82nd Volume

A biographical compilation of the year's most outstanding men and women in American Universities and Colleges.

WW Scholars, LLC
PO Box 1398
Tuscaloosa, AL 35403

CONTENTS

HISTORY

The Who's Who Among Students program exists as a testimony to the idealism and dedication of Henry Pettus Randall Jr. (August 23, 1911–April 25, 1976) to make an ideal into reality.

In 1934, as an undergraduate student at The University of Alabama soon to be entering law school, Mr. Randall was tapped into various campus honor societies. Having been an outstanding student in every area of campus endeavors, he valued these honors bestowed upon him by his alma mater. However, with a poor farming community background hard hit by the Depression, he was unable to accept these honors because membership dues and initiation fees would have imposed further financial burden. He discussed this financial drawback of these honors programs with the university president at that time, Dr. George Denny. As a result of such conversations, Mr. Randall conceived an honors program whereby outstanding students are recognized and accepted for their accomplishments without required dues or fees.

While still in his campus years, he created *Who's Who Among Students in American Universities & Colleges*®, a distinguished biographical volume honoring the nation's most noteworthy students of higher learning institutes. As a law student, Mr. Randall struggled to gain acceptance of this new concept in university recognition programs. He and his wife comprised the entire staff for several years in the beginning. As one prominent educator remarked, "If a bright young student had an idea like Who's Who Among Students today, he would probably get a government grant to implement the idea. It must have been a monumental task during the Depression."

After graduation from law school, Mr. Randall entered the business community and founded a number of successful companies. His heart and efforts remained with the Who's Who Among Students program. It was his dream that he struggled for and brought into existence. *Who's Who Among Students in American Universities & Colleges*® is a tradition which continues as a testimony to one man's dedication and his willingness to work to make an ideal a reality.

STATISTICS

NUMBER OF COLLEGES IN EACH STATE/TERRITORY

Alabama	39
Arkansas	22
Arizona	6
California	27
Colorado	8
Connecticut	11
Delaware	6
District of Columbia	1
Florida	36
Georgia	33
Illinois	28
Indiana	18
Iowa	14
Kansas	22
Kentucky	25
Louisiana	15
Maine	6
Maryland	16
Massachusetts	22
Michigan	17
Minnesota	5
Mississippi	42
Missouri	25
Montana	2
Nebraska	8
Nevada	1
New Hampshire	3
New Jersey	14
New Mexico	6
New York	56
North Carolina	38
North Dakota	8
Ohio	20
Oklahoma	29
Oregon	4
Pennsylvania	58
Rhode Island	3
South Carolina	31

South Dakota	3
Tennessee	36
Texas	63
Utah	3
Vermont	2
Virginia	30
Washington	3
West Virginia	15
Wisconsin	13
Wyoming	1
Puerto Rico	5
Virgin Islands	2

RESIDENCE OF STUDENTS

Alabama	2279
Alaska	19
Arizona	430
Arkansas	895
California	1335
Colorado	390
Connecticut	352
Delaware	226
District of Columbia	23
Florida	1568
Georgia	1835
Hawaii	18
Idaho	43
Illinois	960
Indiana	921
Iowa	613
Kansas	723
Kentucky	1029
Louisiana	725
Maine	249
Maryland	1435
Massachusetts	737
Michigan	676
Minnesota	338
Mississippi	1938
Missouri	1178
Montana	86
Nebraska	354
Nevada	52
New Hampshire	115
New Jersey	743
New Mexico	268
New York	2229
North Carolina	1658
North Dakota	210
Ohio	1051
Oklahoma	1120
Oregon	133
Pennsylvania	2507
Rhode Island	116
South Carolina	1425
South Dakota	243
Tennessee	1405
Texas	4363
Utah	88
Vermont	129
Virginia	1222
Washington	230
West Virginia	746
Wisconsin	401
Wyoming	24
Puerto Rico	226
Virgin Islands	34

PREFACE

Earning a college degree is a major accomplishment. It represents a high level of education and opens doors to varied careers. Perhaps more importantly, the process of earning a degree helps students learn more about themselves and their world. A college degree also means that you were able to overcome the challenges put before you as you worked toward your goal. Did you have to work to put yourself through school? Did you struggle to achieve as both a parent and a student? Did college force you away from home for the first time? Whatever the obstacle you faced, you can be proud of your perseverance and know that your experiences have made you a stronger person.

But additional challenges lie ahead. As you interview for your first full-time job, you will have to show your worth. New graduates can no longer anticipate a competition among companies seeking their skills. Yet there always will be opportunities for people with talent and drive. As you pursue your career, you must strive to accomplish your career goals. You must make meaningful contributions to your industry. You must give back to your school and your community. And you must do it all while supporting your family and maintaining your other relationships. You already have a history of doing what must be done in the face of disappointment, anger and near defeat. Despite the challenging times that have confronted our nation, you have stayed focused and moved toward your goals.

There is another way in which you are part of an elite group: You were one of the few students at your school nominated and recognized in the pages of *Who's Who Among Students in American Universities & Colleges*®. This is an academic and personal honor you can claim throughout life. So hold your head high and be proud of your accomplishments. Be proud of your new college degree and the doors it will open. Make sure those whom you encounter know that it wasn't simply handed to you. You overcame obstacles and have every right to consider yourself a success.

'Tis not in mortals to command success,
But we'll do more, Sempronius; we'll deserve it....
—Joseph Addison

STAFF

**ADMINISTRATIVE DIRECTOR
CONTROLLER & OFFICE MANAGER**

A. J. Simpson

TECHICAL STAFF

Amy Smith

WEB DEVELOPEMENT

Chris Honiball

EDITORIAL & PRODUCTION

Vanessa Rusch

**CUSTOMER SERVICE &
ALUMNI SPECIALIST**

Amy Smith

Lacy Davis

The staff wishes to take this opportunity to acknowledge with sincere appreciation
the work of many who have assisted in the publication of this book.
Without their help, our task would have been impossible.

UNIVERSITIES & COLLEGES LISTINGS

This is an alphabetical listing of the Universities and Colleges who have participated in the 2016 volume of *Who's Who Among Students in American Universities and Colleges*®. The names of the outstanding students selected to appear in this publication are presented beneath each school alphabetically.

AANIIIH NAKODA COLLEGE, HARLEM, MT

Kaye L. Brown

Jacob D. Doney

Christen Falcon

Shannon L. Healy

Lacey N. Kulbeck

Aryn G. Longknife Jake

ABILENE CHRISTIAN UNIVERSITY, ABILENE, TX

Karley Adrion

John Michael Allen II

Benton Barrow

Cheryl Bell

Rebekah Bell

Sara Bishop

Candace Brooks

Tessa Cave

Hannah Rae Chappell

James Churchill

Nathaniel Cole

Austin Cotton

Cale Bradley Crass

Conner Nelson Cross

Julia Curtis

Ashton Darrow

Emily Dosa

Nathan Michael Dougherty

Kenneth Downey

Marcia Edwards

Cierra Fitzgerald

Kaitlin Jane Foster

Hayden Frazier

Marina Guerrero I.
Puigdevall

Marc Anthony Gutierrez

Catherine Isabel Harrington

Savannah Hipes

Rachel Hurst

Brittany Jackson

Alyssa Quinn Johnson

Tina Johnson

Bethany Jones

William Keenan

Melody Landrum

Shanice Latham

Christina Lee

Kinsey Brooke Lee

Kirby Lemon

Rachel Alyssa Lopez
De Castilla

Jennifer Christian Magill

Jennie Magner

Bryan Maier

Brandon Cole McCarty

Kelly McClanahan

Amanda McCormick

Austin Gabriel McCuistion

Melissa Meyer

Celeste Montelongo

Kendra Morlan

Riley Morrow

Shera Niemirowski

Kendra Day Oregon

Griffin Pedigo

Chelsea Peer

Amy Pinegar

Shannon Porter

Ashton Pruitt

Alexandra Ann Rakestraw

Kylie Dane Richter

Kelsie Roberts

Morgan Leigh Ruble

Aaron Salcido

Alexis Sauceda

Alyssa Shaffner

Lauren Jade Shrader

Cooper Spruill

Mandy Stratton

Jessica Tedford

Paola Teran

Courtney Thate

Gabrielle Thompson

Erika Thrasher

Deanna Romero Tuttle

Claire Elise Tyrrell

Lindsay Rachel Urban

Hayden Walker

Alyssa Wasek

Paris Webb

Miranda West

Danielle Woods

Luke Woods

Regine Yaites

Soo Hun Yoon

Erin Elizabeth Zachary

Jiang Zhu

ADELPHI UNIVERSITY, GARDEN CITY, NY

Tristan Michael Baharally

Victoria Eleisa Caselnova

Deanna Marie Dubinsky

Ewelina Gadek

Victoria Khaimova

Kalsey Sanford

ADRIAN COLLEGE, ADRIAN, MI

Devin Alexander

Wallen Augustin

Haley Logan Barnes

Robert Bodette

Morgan Brandt

Katrina Christine Callus

Patricia DeFelice

Kallie Derrer

Jordany Deus

Karissa DeVore

William Dowdy

Lindsay Durdel

Kelly Dziekan

Javes Escalera

Nicole Fredrich

Rebecca Greco

Blake Hairston

Austin Hinojos

Rachel Jason

Katherine Jenkins

Emily Karaba

Brittany Kerr

Christopher Liberati

Miranda Micallef

Nicole Sue Motz

Morgan Pendleton

Lydia Reedy

Demi Russo

Laura Samuelson

Jane Schlievert

Chelsea Shellman

Lauren St. Andrew

Rachel Wathen

AGNES SCOTT COLLEGE, DECATUR, GA

Chanice T'nisha Alexander
Mecca Soleil Danet
Victoria Holland Forbes
Ana Cristina Garcia
Camila Isabel Hernandez
Nana Nimako
Ugonna Ume

AIB COLLEGE OF BUSINESS, DES MOINES, IA

Bligh Williams

ALABAMA SOUTHERN COMMUNITY COLLEGE, MONROEVILLE, AL

Caleb A. Bonner
Brequetta R. Boykin
Jacobs R. Brewer
Hannah L. Carter
Stevie Alexa Cole
Laiken M. Culp
Jordan Boyd Dyess
Katlin M. Heath
Jacob H. Herring
Nicholas S. Herring
LaMeshia M. Hunt
Alexandra B. Lambert
Robert D. Lankford Jr.
Ada M. Lewis
Brandon Scott Litzinger
Tia M. McMillan
Lea-Cameron Nipper
Willie C. Nugent II
Jon G. Ott
Shanna Nicole Presley
Kendall M. Steele
Maribeth M. West
Raven K. Whitsett
Constance Leighann Wilson

ALABAMA STATE UNIVERSITY, MONTGOMERY, AL

Trey Dominic Adams
Kehinde Ugoemiwei Batife
Kourtney Bernard Berry
Lori Davis
Darren L. Dubose
Ebony Durham
Brianna Lee Fairley
Johnny Garner
Qiana Turquoise James
Damian Tobias Love
Hunter Riley McIntosh
Shenavia Je'Cion Moore
Muriel S. Pannell
Shawan M. Parks
Paige A. Rankine
Celeen Mahane Robertson
Lottriana Marvia Scarlett
Alayna Smith
Mariel Alexandra Smith
Myron L. Smith II
Julianne Keona Trawick
Noni Michelle Trent-Gogins
Arantxia Wijngaarde
Maegan Whitney Williams
Shantia Alexis Wilson

ALBANY STATE UNIVERSITY, ALBANY, GA

Jamal Abd Al-Qadir
Cedric Ashe
Telitita Burley
Jaquel Ciarra Eley
Jonatan Ernesto Galan
Damarkus Green
Artisha Holston
Amber Chalise Little
Kennedy
Alexius KaDeshia Lampkin
JaQaundria Mosley
Morgane Rainwater
Tiffany Roesler
Demetri Wheeler
Shaqeira Wilson

ALBERTUS MAGNUS COLLEGE, NEW HAVEN, CT

Zackery William Barker
Jasmin Burgos
Georgia Conley
Yesenia Cuevas
Erika Nicole Donoso
Emili M. Dubar
Sharon Dunkley-Gentles
James Anthony Higgins
Victoria Elizabeth Hunter
Elizabeth Lamour
Debra J. Laster
Lykeyia Lesane
Shewunikki Q. Moton
Jennifer Rose Owen
Nicole Payne
Christina Pearson
James John Salemme
Christopher Jonathan Shine
Benjamin Jacob Spilka
Karyn Marie Stokes
Jodie Lynne Szarmach

ALBION COLLEGE, ALBION, MI

Autumn E. Bernicky
Ninjin Bilegsaikhan
Jackelyn B. Cubalo
Candace J. Cullens
Blake A. Darling
Justin K. Duchene
Melanie Brooke Fodera
Kylie R. Heitman
Theresa E. Hencsie
Timothy M. Langholz
Jessica V. McKindles
Mitchell W. Moore

Julia L. Roberts	Elisabeth K. Sears	Rhiki L. Swinton	Alexis N. Tillery
Nicole E. Schnabel	Taylor A. Sokoloskis	Safiya N. Syed	Elizabeth G. Witkowski

ALDERSON BROADDUS UNIVERSITY, PHILIPPI, WV

Ottie Justice Barr	Clayton Ralph Heath	Kelsey Dawn Mathis	Adam Lee Sharp
Casey Jo Cleavenger	Daniele Virginia Hoffmaster	Maureen Elaine Muth	Ashlan Rayne Thompson
April Maile Fabrizio	Alycia Marie Horner	Emily Elizabeth Porter	Elisabeth Jordan Thorne
Adam Blake Gillespie	Katharine Ann Lewis	Catherine Anne Rainey	Britney Ashley Wildish
Christian Raldine Gongob	Cassandra Leigh Linn	Zachary William Ransom	Aurora Rose Winwood
Katelyn Michelle Haupt	Kimberly Rae Lupton	Cooper Allen Schroeder	Brandon Robert Wisman

ALICE LLOYD COLLEGE, PIPPA PASSES, KY

Whitley Taylor Albury	Daina Merea Gilbert	Kelsey Nicole Logdon	Angela DeRae Shepherd
Maegyn Danielle Bates	Shantel LaChe Gonzales	Brittany Pearl Lyons	Nicholas Hunter Short
Lydia Renee Bickham	Keniston Drake Grizzell	Zachary Andrew Marcum	Avery Blake Shrum
Kaitlin Denee Calhoun	Jacob Nathaniel Haddix	Kaelyn Sierra Martin	Jacob Hunter Sifers
Kristen Rose Campbell	Ian Tyler Hall	Brooklyn Dawn McCall	Alyn Jabe Smith
Morgan MacKenzie Castle	Kiana Shanice Hall	Katie Elizabeth McFarland	Cody Wayne Smith
David Boyd Cavins	Kyler Gator Hazelett	Makayla Kennedy McNew	Kelcie Logan Smith
Melinda Jean Collins	Kristina Ruby-Louise Helton	Hayley Lynn Mills	Cynthia Denise Taylor
Logan Alan Condra	Makayla Rae Hubbard	Savannah Jayde Minor	Weston Alexander Taylor
Steven Mcdouglas Conley	Olivia Hubbard	Clay Lucas Montgomery	Olivia Brooke Tyree
Courtney Ann Craft	Matthew Tyler Huffman	Brittany LeAnn Newsome	Stephanie Leighann
Holden Luke Dalton	Mary Ann Isaac	Maddison Nicole Niece	Vanhoose
Matthew Thomas Dempsey	Shiloh Ann Jekel	Rachel Danielle Rice	Caitlin Alexis Woody
Jackson Marshall Driskill	Joshua Ray Johnson	Gabrielle Mariah Schwartz	
Matthew Prentice Fields	Elizabeth Hannah Langlois	Desiree Shelton	

ALLEGANY COLLEGE OF MARYLAND, CUMBERLAND, MD

Jennifer Benton	Carrie Glardon	Jessica Lynn Lowery	Dakota Rugg
Harry L. Benton IV	Renae Guenther	Brandi Lynch	Yasai Sallah
Samantha Boatman	Kellie Hadley	Tina McCoy	Rebecca Smith
Lindsay Brady	Heath Heffley	Wendy Merkel	Cody Sullivan
Logan Brooks	Krystal Hobbs	Lisa Mills	Sonya Thomas
Carlee Bussard	Morgan Danielle Hott	Melissa Murray	Jessica Tokarczyk
Bryna Calhoun	Sarah Johnson	Jaren Neat-Washington	Kerah Umbel
Amy Campbell	Ula Kay Keech	Brittania Oakes	Carol A. Watts
Michaela Castle	Amanda Renee King	Akeem Owens	Arian Whetzel
Catherine Clark	Mariah Kline	Airica Paugh	Jennifer Whitman
Taylor Clingerman	Alyssa Lantz	Brittany N. Paugh	Dylan Wilson
Shannon Durst	Allison Nichol Lebeduik	Shinaya Prince	Larry Wilson
Donna Jean Earley-Wolfe	Jamie Lewis	Sierra Raines	Linda Yoder
Alexandra Edwards	Emily Livingston	Monica Rounds	

AMARILLO COLLEGE, AMARILLO, TX

Nicole S. Arias
Jessica C. Austin
Tiffanie C. Boggs
Phillip A. Boothby
Lauren L. Brannon
Jordan D. Byars
Katelin D. Carter
Elani N. Cooper
David Q. Do
Lance O. Duncan

Nicholas A. Durante
Elliott D. Evalle
Larissa J. Fenstermaker
Lily K. Gamble
Mariah N. Glidewell
Meranda L. Graves
Kendra Elizabeth Hanson
Emily S. Henriquez
Daniel Hernandez
Matthew S. Huddleston

Darian P. Irons
Brad D. Johnson
Madison S. Martin
Ciarra R. Melendez
Kien T. Phan
Jenna L. Pickard
Tonjua Marie Pope
Caleb O. Prestwood
Emily Beth Prisk
Lexie M. Reyes

McKayla B. Robinson
Abraham P. Tenorio
Katherine L. Toycen
Noah K. Truelock
Austin G. Ulen
Samson B. Wood
Citlaly R. Zamarripa

AMERICAN BAPTIST COLLEGE, NASHVILLE, TN

Deborah Adedoyin
Adewola-Moss
Winston Guerney Davidson
Bernita Rucker Moore

Marc Leonard Quarles
Tremaine Timotheus
Sails-Dunbar

Brandon JaDarius Smithson
Juquan LuShard Stewart

Monique Shaunte' Wells
LaToya Diane Williams

AMERICAN INTERNATIONAL COLLEGE, SPRINGFIELD, MA

Saraiy Acosta-Meza
Cameron Akers
Karlbuto Alexandre
Aubri Bailly
Kaila Barnett
Jillian Bedard
Romina Bell
Grace Belt
Kathyria Michelle Beltran
Antwan Bluster
Andrea Boczon
Ileana Casillas

Emily Cormier
Marina Del Carmnen Cruz
Tyler Gaynor
Rebecca Gray
Myah Green
Bridget Grim
Josue Guerra
Emma Heroth
Melika Jackson
Chelsea Kemembin
Jenny Labossiere
Jessica Lawler

Crystal Mallett
Anna Mbengam
John Mbengam
Kevin Milla
Amoya Morris-Berry
Nikki Naccarato
Marisa Najarian
Sierra Naughton
Megen Navone
Dolores Perez
Rebecca Rousseau
Michael Schulze

Shannoya Scott
Jerrod Shelby
Saradgine Sincere
Samantha Tabak
Meimi Tomochika
Ricardo Valentin
Lamont Waites
Aaliyah Wright
Lydia Yohannes

AMERICAN MILITARY UNIVERSITY, CHARLES TOWN, WV

Ashley A. Bell
Ian Boehm
David D. Bruce
Stacy Drew Buchanan
Yevgeniy Chystyakov

Jennifer Lynn Snodgrass
Clinton
Esamu Cooper
Paul Costinett
Trevis Day
Ronald Elwell

Victoria Fife
Myles Fry
Frank Sharp Hooton
Randolph Prince
Stephen Quintana
April Rimmer

Vaigalepa Ripine
Marina Rivers
Jamie Simmons
Robert Alan Talenti
Madison Zimmerman

AMERICAN NATIONAL UNIVERSITY, MARTINSVILLE, VA

Lisa A. Bowman

Kimberly J. Hanks

Barbara Kinnaird-Portlock

April J. Morrison

AMERICAN NATIONAL UNIVERSITY, PRINCETON, WV

Carmella E. Akers
Carolyn A. Alexander
Gary W. Anthony
Jessica Shannon Carrillo
Randy S. Carter
Tiffany D. Carter

Victoria E. Cook
Shavonne D. Garrett
Brian L. Handy
Megan D. Heldreth
Virginia A. Hymes
Vanessa R. Lusk

Stefanie L. Martin
Tracy A. Matney
Jaclyn K. Mercado
Megan N. Morgan
Lakan N. Newman
Robyne L. Ramsey

Phillip S. Riffe
Teresa S. Sharpe
Ronald E. Thorne

AMERICAN PUBLIC UNIVERSITY, CHARLES TOWN, WV

Lauren Baldasari
Windy Calvert
Tracy Latrelle Castle

Tracy Dransfield
Veronika Fournier
Stephanie Friend

Matthew Getridge
Edna Goldberg-Fenollal
Nikolaos Kostakis

Veronica Naranjo
Sonia Rebek
Greg Williams

AMRIDGE UNIVERSITY, MONTGOMERY, AL

Michael D. Abbott
Tracy M. Adams
Addie Adkison
Brent Lee Arnold
Darryl E. Arrington
Charles Ballard III
Roy Kenneth Bell Sr.
Donald L. Berry
Thomas Glen Berry

Andrea Gilson Bevill
Samuel Logan Byers
Libby Jaqunn Byrd
Benno Jay Capshaw
Garrett Corey Carlisle
Johnny Jay Davis
Nora Elizabeth Eggers
PJ Green
Cynthia Dianne Guy

Jonathan Glenn Hewett
Corey C. Holmgren
Thea Barnes Langley
Bryan Eric Lewis
Gary Lynn Long
Jason Scott Longstreth
Chaddrick B. Manning
Autum Rebekah McBrayer
Jewel Faye Melton

Jonathan Moore
Patsy A. Moretz
Michael Ray Roberts
Randolph W. Senkle
Kristoffer R. Talley
Thomas Alexander Webb
Joel Stephen Williams
Matthew A. Wolf

ANCILLA COLLEGE, DONALDSON, IN

Nellie Marie Alexander
Benjamin Beers
Kristine Binkley
Barbara Jean Caudill
Jacqulin Debra Jean Collins
Jade Farley

Joshua Felty
Aileen Fleck
Felicia Goodsell
Sandra Harlamert
Caleb Heckaman
Brayann Nikole Ingersoll

Casey Johnson
Andrew McCarty
Kayte E. Miller
Bryce Eric Nickell
Morgan Peoni
Angela Redman

Abigail Renner
Sheyanne Scheffer
Sophia Noel Smith
Adam VanMeter
Valarie Lynn Whiteman
Amanda Zehner

ANDREWS UNIVERSITY, BERRIEN SPRINGS, MI

Hannah Elise Abbott
Charles M. Abreu
Luz Virginia Baez
Emily-Jean E. Bankes
Christian Bardan
Alaryss Marie Carla Bosco
Arleni Miguelina Calderon
Richard Andre Clark
Saharsh Dass

Reginald Jose Desrosiers
Jonathan Edward Doram
Vanna Yasmine Giddings
Amante Jordan Gonzalez
Courtney-Lynn Harvey
Michael L. Hess
Cooper Benton Hodges
Shanelle Eunbyul Kim
Lukasz Jan Krzywon

Joanne Jee Yeon Lee
Julie Margaret Logan
Adrianne Rae Magsipoc
Hannah Mumbi Mbungu
Mindy J. McLarty
Rufaro Cathrine Musvosvi
Robert M. Polski
Ashley Anne Reichert
Zachary Michael Reichert

Genessis Saenz
Brian Dean Shockey
Jason Robert Shockey
Isabel Staples Stafford
Joshua Lee Stahl
Abigail Esther Tejeda
Sumiko Kay Weir
Jonathan Morgan Wheeler

Mercedes Marian Louise Wheeler
Amanda Michelle Whitlow
Eui Bin You
Hyelin You
Juliette Michelle Young
Dillon Cray Zimmerman

ANGELINA COLLEGE, LUFKIN, TX

Sheridan E. Adair
Erick J. Alamo
Frank E. Alamo
Cindy R. Antimo
Garrett R. Augsburger
Bethany G. Baldwin
Ghazi Balis
Debbie M. Barlow
Amelia N. Birdwell
Kaydee M. Burgess
Hannah L. Cain
Kasandra F. Cartwright
Sarah Chaput
Martin F. Chavez
Kim L. Chong
Jack L. Clark
Tanner W. Cockrell
Amanda R. Collie
Deniese R. Comeaux
Daniel Compean

James W. Copeland
Raymond D. Corbett
Eric S. Crane
Gina M. Dameron
Paola Delgado
Kimberly R. Divins
Karen N. Duran
Pamilia J. Estrada
Kayla N. Francone
Cady E. Fuller
Branndon T. Goodson
Christie L. Gore
Erika D. Gregory
Aida C. Griffin
Misty M. Griffin
Jacqulyn A. Grimm
Shannon R. Groce
Dionisio Guerrero
Wanda Gulley
Steven C. Harbuck

Kathia M. Harris
Cheyenne Hart
Kami R. Hart
Cristal A. Hernandez
Angelic A. Horton
Sabrina L. Johnson
Amber L. Jones
Hannah E. Jones
Kelly L. Kapraun
Ysleta Denise Kapraun
Emily T. Keller
Amanda Leann Kendrick
William S. Kolb
Aneshia N. Lamb
Paul C. Lane
Kristina N. Loftin
Asucena Lopez
Joany Y. Lopez
Aldo C. Luna
Nicole L. Markle

Franchesca R. Martin
Lindsay S. Messner
Jessica L. O'Neall
Esther R. Parrott
Paloma Perez
Emily J. Piotrowski
Angela J. Powell
Uziel C. Rendon
Sofia Reyes
Jazmin A. Robles
Taylor Blaine Scott
Anna R. Shuffler
Rebecca C. Small
Katie M. Staggs
Daniel P. Stringer
Jacob S. Taylor
Brenda D. Taylor-Wilson
Abigail Tlamasico
Hayden V. Woods
Jennifer J. Zarate

ANGELO STATE UNIVERSITY, SAN ANGELO, TX

Benjaman Clayton Adams
Marissa Aguilera
Stedman Allen
Marissa Vazquez Anaya
Cynthia Brooke Andrews
Isaiah Aneke
Grant Aschenbeck
Dillon J. Bagnall
Kayla Brooke Ballew
Charles Bennett
Mallory Blauser
Stephannie Bledsoe
Amber Rose Bohr
William Brown
Ryan Blake Burge
Megan Camacho
Andrea Carolina Chavarria

Elizabeth Chavarria
Laura Childs
Adam Joseph Coffman
Maci Margaret Colley
Kamryn Cummings
Sara Currie
Rachel Dahl
Tiffany Dang
Tristan Lane Davis
Dustin Dodson
Brittany Nicole Dowd
Jacqueline Marcella Dowell
Maigan Dunlap
Devin Dunn
Jose Haejin Duran Jr.
Angel Enriquez
Alfredo "Freddy" Felipe

Leah Fisher
Prince Foster
Samuel Fowler
Theresa Freitag
Ryan Glover
Stephen Jake Gonzales
Julie Riley Gray
Tina M. Griffith
Omari Gudul
Jacob Hallenberger
Sarah Harrelson
Hayden Harris
Sarah Katherine Hartman
Joe William Hauser
Melissa Rae Hawkins
Shannon Heinz
Cadyn Heinze

Jasmine Hobbs
Alex Holguin
Blake Holle
Jonathan Hood
Akujiuba Raulings Inyanma
Jake Jackson
Axel Jacquesson
Martin Jaso-Perez
Kelly Johnson
Samatha Jones
Dallas Kaiser
Maggi Jo Keffury
Ilyssa Avelina Kisa
Alexis SuAnn Latham
Morgan Lira
Hope Marie Long
Mercedes LeAnn Lopez

Jarett Lujan
Abbie Rae Lynn
Kris Martin
Jesus Martinez
Theresa Jocelyn Maskill
Lindsey Maurice
Taylor McDermott
Reagan McGee
Chelsea Blain McGinnis
Haley Mendel
Leah Meza
Brittney Miller
Ashley Mohesky
Bolton Morales
Kaylee Rene Morgan
Lexi Nicole Murphy
Cameron Niblock
Nathan Nicks
Kami Lyn Norton

Kristy Gale O'Keefe
Makenzie Allison Ocker
Napoleon Onyeje
Barrett Pace
Alyssa Parisette-Sparks
Keshia Parker
Danielle Patillo
Catalina Perez
Luis Perez
Veronica Perez
Kathrine Plagens
Prasanna Polite
Devonte' Pratt,
Mattie Price
Gustavs Puhovs
Katy Jane Ralph
Mindy Ralston
Alexandria Ramirez
Daniel A. Ramirez

Jarred Ramon
Elizabeth Rapstine
Cecily Elise Real
Shaquan Rhoades
Haley Rhodes
Lusia Rico
Hannah Robertson
Christina Denise Robinson
Corina Ashley Rodriguez
Elizabeth Rodriguez
Allison Romo
Michelle Rosewell
Vincent Jose Salazar
Hilary Sanders
Shelby N. Sanders
Barton Schroeter
Deontae Vashaune Scott
Taylor Lee Seaton
Sara Shirai

Tracy A. Simmons
Hunter Spear
Madison Sudduth
Amber Sullivan
Mary Tapia
Jessica L. Tharp
Dimitra Tsambasis
Cassandra Turner
Gary Jason Turner
Kelsey Rae Velez
Emily Ann Vidal
Dundy J. Walker
Brandi Washington
Travis Whitehead
Skyler Wilt
Kade Harrell Wimberley
Michael Wren
Charles Wright

ANNE ARUNDEL COMMUNITY COLLEGE, ARNOLD, MD

Emily Renee Dreszer
Rashad Ferguson
Adrian Gusky

Annalisa M. Hite
Michael Lee Houck
Victoria Janka

Maria Sandra Johnson
Michelle J. Moore
Jacob A. Murphy

Laura Sydney Romulus
Christopher Charles Swift

APPALACHIAN BIBLE COLLEGE, MOUNT HOPE, WV

Brittany Nicole Best

Briana Michelle Bortner

Brandon Scott Parker

APPALACHIAN SCHOOL OF LAW, GRUNDY, VA

Seth E. Allen
Taylor A. Hay

Adam Jacob Perkinson

Jennifer D. Polk

Daniel A. Williams

ARCADIA UNIVERSITY, GLENSIDE, PA

Jillian Colby Arenson
William Jay Breeman
Jennifer Silvius Clark

Alexander Colton
Megan Conley
Theresa Dewa

Stephanie Feinberg
Allison O'Neil
Jennifer Retter

Amber N. Williams
Steven John Zellers Jr.

ARIZONA CHRISTIAN UNIVERSITY, PHOENIX, AZ

Mckenna Arensen
Timothy Bailes
Brenda Barry
Christopher Bates

Victoria Bates
Amy Beck
Kevin Brown
Becky Ann Capps

Erica Cecil
Breana Duhamel
Emily Dulas
Amber Faulkner

Kyle Allen Finley
Alyssa Gruber
Ryan Hargrove
Jackson Helms

Andrew Hook	Nicholas Dean Martin	Jesse Poweziak	Jesus Silva
Edward Hufford	Selah McAvoy	Eli Jonathan Quintana	Elizabeth Sparks
Desiree Nicole Jackson	Laura Nava	Carla M. Razny	Phillippi Sparks
Alexandra Karl	Miguel Navar	Rachel Redding	Carrie Stephens
Kalyn Rashel Kovacs	Chelsea Oglebay	Ilene Ruiz	Nancy Stocking
Erin Layman	Sarah Ohlman	Cristina Sandell	Alyssa Belle Turner
Erik David Lindahl	Anne Palmer	Bailey Dawn-Michall	Brittany Vanderdrink
Keila Llanes	Danielle Parker	Seltzer	Presley Page Whetman
Matt Lombardi	Jesus Pino Perez	Timothy William Shaffer	Jacob Wilson
Brianna Rea Lopez	Eric Louis Pote	Abigail Silva	Tamara Yanke

ARKANSAS STATE UNIVERSITY BEEBE, SEARCY, AR

Crystal Leighanna Briner	Ayrien Johnson	Sarah Mikula	Emma A. Thompson
Kelly Cook	Kaleigh Kyzer	Dylan Pratt	Tammy Thompson
Johnathan Covington	Mykayla Ladd	Soundra Rogers	Allison Faith Warner
Michael Crawford	Michael Anthony Martin	Cody Young Salmon	
Savannah Finch	Taylor Nicole McKinney	Deana Renee Sowell	
Lunora Cathrine Harrington	Adrienne Kathleen McNally	Allison Rose Sweet	

ARKANSAS STATE UNIVERSITY JONESBORO, STATE UNIVERSITY, AR

Stephen D. Berry	Rebekah A. Frayer	Gary B. Jackson	Destiny L. Quinn
Erica A. Blackford	Bethany Joy Gallimore	Erin A. Langley	Amber D. Ray
Justin S. Carothers	Rebecca M. Galloway	Najwa T. Lee	Erin E. Wadley
Christina M. Chen	Ellen M. Hakenewerth	Angel T. Livingston	DeAnna L. Watson
Hunter M. Clampit	Brandon M. Haley	Cesar A. Marroquin	Jason E. White
Miles Joseph Clover	Anna Hermes	Marshall K. McDaniel	
Drake H. Cullum	Christopher Jordan Hooks	Sahitya Pattigadapa	
Taylor N. Duvall	Oluwayinka O. Iseyemi	Emily Anne Peters	

ARKANSAS STATE UNIVERSITY NEWPORT, NEWPORT, AR

Christopher L. Allred	Edwin B. Brietz	Katie M. Collier	Alicia Danielle Dyer
Zackery C. Angelo	Steven L. Brimlett	Michael A. Conatser	Linda Darnell Dykes
Dalton M. Armstrong	Amanda L. Broglen	Ashlyn B. Cook	Ryan A. Eich
Amanda C. Atkins	James M. Brown	Cristal X. Coronado	Brinkley P. Ference
Brittani N. Baber	Santosha Burton	Christopher R. Cox	Macee Claire Fivecoat
Elizabeth H. Ball	Tiffany J. Byais	Courtney L. Crawford	Elizabeth M. Forkum
Megan Elizabeth Ballard	Chad V. Campbell	Clarissa X. Cruz	Gabrielle L. Fortenberry
Trinity M. Barber	Meghan Jennifer Cantara	Candace M. Dean	Zach J. Foust
Katie M. Barnes	Abbigale B. Carlyle	Armaan G. Dharani	Katherine N. Gann
Chelsea R. Barnett	Shawnda K. Carpenter	Jeremy D. Dowdy	Wesley R. Garrison
Krystal E. Barrett	Sarah G. Chambers	Corey P. Doyle	Latoryia S. Gilmer
Tipton L. Boling	Cailyn G. Cliff	Jason P. Drake	Stephanie Glenn
Tiffany A. Brewer	Kimberly D. Cole	Nathan P. Duncan	Susana J. Gonzalez

Daniel H. Green	William G. Light	Joseph M. Prinner	Tanna E. Tacker
Joy Gregory	Rico Lowery	Andrea M. Qualls	Haven K. Taylor
Stephanie L. Gregory	Morgan L. Malugen	Ronald D. Ragsdale	Christopher J. Tilley
Riley C. Grogan	Kasin Rae Mann	Jamaal R. Rainey	Emily D. Tinker
Mary N. Grubbs	Coley J. Masters	Madison B. Randleas	Bradley W. Tounsand
Anna M. Hackney	Felecia L. McCall	Aaron B. Redmond	Haley L. Trinidad
Kennedy J. Haden	Brian W. McGirr	Dezare'e M. Reel	Bethany C. Tyner
Lee T. Hammell	Madelyn N. McMickle	Renee A. Reese	Chandler T. Vance
Al-Fredia C. Hampton	Deborah E. Metheny	Miranda A. Reynolds	Laura C. Vargas
Jesseca L. Harvey	Cali L. Milligan	Devon L. Richards	Braxton T. Vaughan
Sara N. Helms	Anna Claire Mitchell	Katelyn M. Richmond	Dakota W. Vickers
Phillip S. Hitchcock	Candace A. Montgomery	Cali D. Rogers	Darcey A. Vinson
Summer N. Holden	Preston B. Morgan	Amy M. Rogles	Daniel R. Walker
Mary E. Hollands	Katrina A. Morris	Jessica L. Rucker	David R. Webb
Abigail G. Houston	Bryanna I. Murphy	Cassandra C. Saddler	Seth D. Weisenbach
Terrin T. Huggins	Kelby R. Nicholson	Sarah E. Sanford	David A. Wells
Erika M. Immel	Trisha A. Null	Katelyn B. Sharp	Dylan R. Whitehurst
Peyton S. Inman	Jane Otivere	Natasha L. Shepherd	Sheila Anne Whitlock
Ashley N. James	Onovwerosuoke	Jackie L. Simpson	Conrad T. Williams II
Mikayla S. Jones	Ryan J. Patterson	Amber M. Smith	Tabitha L. Williamson
Tangula R. Jones	Autumn C. Perkey	Taylor B. Smith	Taelor B. Willie
Nathan J. King	Brianna E. Phillips	Timothy J. Snodgrass	Andrew C. Wilson
Hannah G. Knight	Kayla D. Platt	Katelyn M. Sparkman	Garrett C. Woods
Kayla Adalene Knoll	Coy T. Poag	Robert A. Stone	Cheyenne N. Yarbrough
Jonathan W. Lewis	Monique N. Pope	Jeremy A. Summers	

ARKANSAS TECH UNIVERSITY, RUSSELLVILLE, AR

Haven Nicole Brock	Morgan Nicole Earp	Katie Elaine Huff	Ashleigh Lauren Pettit
Terrionna Reshell Brockman	Dylan Scott Edgell	Samantha Ann Hurlburt	Xintong Ren
Hayden Seth Carlton	Tyler Nathaniel Emerson	Kyle Michael Jones	Hailey Elise Robinson
Toni Kaylen Cody	Elvys Ferrufino-Mejia	Jim Taylor Loggins	Audra Marie Schluterman
Allison Luise Congleton	Jocelyn Flores	Dillon Edward Miller	Zachary Lee Schwartz
Caitlin Nicole Dean	Suede Videl Graham	Elijah Austin Moreno	Emely Evette Arias Sierra
Luke Edward Dooly	Evan Blake Gray	Kelsey Elizabeth Nilsen	Bethany Danae Skaggs
Leslie Victoria Dunmire	Christopher Blake Hoover	Tulsi Bhaveshkumar Patel	Julia Christine Smith

ARLINGTON BAPTIST COLLEGE, ARLINGTON, TX

Susan Brown	Kassidy Amber Culver	Lloyd Melvin McCarroll	Ashton Pleasants
Kelsie Mae Carnagie	Emily Glenn	Hannah Jill McGaughy	Hannah Salazar
Elizabeth Joy Combs	Morgan Lea Hale	Micah Depree' Minkina	Alexis Brooke Villanueva
Jeb Alston Cornelius	Parker James Kleinert	Hope Diane Moncibaiz	Ashley Cierra Wade
Kimbra Marie Counts	Caleb Robert LaPointe	Brittany Nicole Morgan	Frances Helena Watson
Dustin Aaron Crawford	Abigail Marvin	David Paul Patrick	Tori Nicole Wise

Jocelyn LouAnn Zornes

ASBURY UNIVERSITY, WILMORE, KY

Meredith Lucille Anderson	Paula Andrea Diaz	Jacob Sherman Meece	Todd Jesse Yoder
Jorge Saul Castorena	Audrey Mabel Gray	Joseph Steven Reese	
Stephanie Ji Chen	Caitlin Taylor Maumenee	Gabriel Morgan Willison	

ASHFORD UNIVERSITY CLINTON CAMPUS, CLINTON, IA

Brittany Acree	Brittany O. Cross	Alex Miner	Nathan Govinda Singh
Ama A. Agyabeng	Jalyn Deering	Keyona Moore	Sahota
Raymond L. Anderson	Rochelle Douglas	Michael Murphy	Katlyn M. Schimerowski
Lenell Andrews	Taylor Ellestad	Elizabeth Nicole Nardi	Nicole A. Schmidt
Joshua Anim Anno	Jordan Flowers	Jasmine Nelson	Marquel R. Schultheis
Corinne Mae Armbrust	Jason R. German	Zouzou Nsemi	Tanner C. Seeley
Courtney J. Babut	Charles R. Holsinger	Jacob-Allen Lee Oldaker	Angelica K. Stonehocker
Lucas Benites	Corrine Gail Hubbard	Anna June Olson	Erich Taach
Megan Black	Efrain Ibarra	Cristian Pacheco	Alicia M. Tamburro
Clarissa Lynn Blick	Md Rashedul Islam	Spencer Fredrick Pfeiff	Sara Vach
Kimberly Borowczyk	Jessica D. Jackson	Fatima Y. Pinedo	Madison Wagner
Danielle L. Boyd	Kelsie Kluck	Patrick Pinlac	Danielle Ariel Wall
Kailai Brantner	Tim Krautheim	Aubree Pirello	Andrew Watts
Courtney A. Bredlow	Yoonsun Lim	Eden R. Pirello	Chelsea Jolene Whitmore
Amanda K. Briese	Froilan Marchan Jr.	Javier Ramirez Bautista	Verron Williams
Megan Casagrande	Celeste McKay	Sierra C. Romero	
Charity M. Corcoran	Diamond J. Merboth	Talia A. Rossi	

ASHLAND UNIVERSITY, ASHLAND, OH

Katelyn Louise Addair	Allyson Marie Coyne	Alison Mackenzie Green	Michelle Marie Koziura
Daniela Noronha Gustavo Alves	Cassandra Jayne Craig	Hannah Catherine Green	Cole Arren Lautzenheiser
	Rachel Estelle Crow	Catherine Ekaterini Hatzigiannaki	Sonya Marie Leishman
Alayna Elizabeth Anderson	Kelly Ann Crowl		Zachary Jeff Lindesmith
Alyssa Ann Angie	Cassandra Louise Curtis	Halee Heironimus	Ashley Marie Lorah
Natalyn Jade Baisden	Davida Crescencia De Fatima Mesquita	Kristen Nicole Herrick	Olivia Macek
Jillian Marie Bajaksouzian		Julianna Leigh Hritz	Hannah Frances Mattar
Joseph Michael Barretta	Emily Elizabeth Embrescia	Janessa Sha Huffman	Kate-Lynn Michelle May
Zebulun Zacheriah Beam	Maria Therese Falorio	Edward Elliott Hunt	Aaron Joseph McKinney
Tyler James Dana Begley	Kentee Fitch	Erica Kelsi Jones	Anna Marie Mion
Kylee Ann Bernthisel	Steven Anthony Forbush	Stephanie Julian	Emily Rose Mussmann
Grace Carolyn Brown	Bailey Lynn Fullwiler	Britney Kandel	Gabrielle Marie Nau
Rhema Ruth Centanni	Brett Jordan Garand	Alexander Todd Kaple	Holly Rose Nowlin
Jennifer Nicole Cipra	Ashley Lynn Gies	Ashley Nicole Keres	Katelyn Darlene Osborne
Molly Reeves Clapper	Kristy Lynn Glanc	Natasha S. Kirkbride	Beverly Sue Paramore
Tarin Jade Cook	Olivia Eileen Glass	Laura Marie Knisley	Paul K. Pernici

John Ramsey Porter
Kelly Elizabeth Ranttila
Shannon L. Read
Cameron Gibbs Ressel
Danielle Justine Rhonemus

Janice Richards
Allyson Nicole Rorrer
Megan Elizabeth Salatino
Olivia Ann Sprague
Danielle Renee Stickler

Mary Kazuko Theus
Brittney Kay Thorne
Christian Allen Tomasik
Kayla Toth
Kristin Nicole Van Dyke

Gabrielle Nicole Vitel
Jamie Lynn Waltz
Devyn Jo Wilson
Heather Brooke Wray
Madison Paige Wright

ASNUNTUCK COMMUNITY COLLEGE, ENFIELD, CT

Nicolette Christine Bailey
Michael Allen Bemont
Krista Campisi
Marissa Campisi
Nicole D'Angelo
Tommi DeMichael

Marissa Gagne
Ruben Garcia
Danuta Krajeqska
Diane Wytenus Kuzmickas
Kellianne LeBlanc
Alexandra Mokrzecki

Ryan Munn
Thomas Nadolny
Kevin Ray
Debbie Roberts
Hana Saleh
Ryan Tetrault

Dean Thomas
Connor Troy
Keith Wiggins

ATHENS STATE UNIVERSITY, ATHENS, AL

Kayla Aaron
Pamela Abercrombie
Peyton Allen
Mark Ryan Anderson
William Anderson
Ramona Banks
Elizabeth Becerra
Shelley Bess
Kethry Blaylock
John Tyler Blevins
Loren Hunter Bookout
Britney Braund
Jennifer Michelle-Gates
Bravo
Jacob Brown
Margaret Brown
Danny Browning
Stephen Bryson
Devin James Buchheister
Dylan Burleson
Nicholos Butts
Marcus Carson
Connie Cart
Allison Chambers
Angela Jordan Christopher
Tammie Clark
Brad Clarke
Trevor Cleckler

Patrick Clontz
Roger Collum Jr.
Jovana Combs
Christina Cook
Joni Corbin
Dallas Brianne Cornett
Randy Corsbie
Jessica Cosby
Erica Michelle Cottingham
Shu Chin Covick
Shawn Craddock
Stephanie Crews
Kaylin Crider
Amy Crosby
Roxi Cunningham
Marta Cristiane
Dilbehbahani
Kesha Dotson
Mary Dougherty
Martha Marie Ellzey
Dalton Farmer
Candice Ora Fawcett
Mary Fouse
Allison Fowler
Brittany Fox
Donnie Frazier
Georgiana George
Pamela Gifford

Kayla Allyson Goad
Franklin Goodwin
Tiffany Afton Guin
Chelsea Haggermaker
LaKrishia Hailey
Jessica Brooke Halcomb
Olivia Hale
Antonio K. Hamilton
Martha Hamm
Haley Hardwick
Jarrod Hardy
Judith Hartis
Dylan Harvey
Becky Hilderbrand
Molly Kathryn Hogeland
Ricky Holden
Vanitey Hundley
Mallory Bauer Jackson
Stephen Jefferson
Demitrius Johns
Alfred Wendell Johnson
Daniel Johnson
Misty D. Kennedy
Billie Jo Knowles
Kari Knox
Brooke Kuykendall
Amanda Lunsford
Caroline Malone

Katlyn Mason
Zita T. McCall
Patrick McCarty
Savannah Taylor
McCullough
Alexander McKechnie
Keighan Gweniviere Melton
Shelby Middleton
Richard Milliken
Kevin Morris
Taylor Morris
Katie Nabors
Ryan Robert Nelson
Benjamin Jacob Nichols
Adam Novoa
Stephanie Owens
Cassie Beth Parker
Steven Patrick
Clara Pesnell
Leigh Chandler Phillips
Lyndsey Pierce
Tara Ponder
Lori C. Pulley
Clara Rainwater
Aaron Rathz
Amberly Loren Reese
Amber Reynolds
Amy Richardson

Max Risner
Chelsey Roark
Jacob Roop
Ivonne Rosado
Amanda Salter
Marilyn Sanchez
Audra Sanders
Christie Sanders
Alyssa Schultz
Elizabeth Self
James Cameron Sharp

Melissa Silvey
Linda Simon
Melinda Simpkins
Andrew Sivak
Amanda Catherine Smith
Haylee Blair Smith
Janiece Smith
Jason A. Smith
Jenise Smith
Jordan Smith
Kendall Blaine Smith

Jennifer Lynn Stanley
Tiffany Stevens
Amanda St. John
Joshua Strange
Glen Strobach
Meagan Sutton
Audra Tanner
Sherry Taylor
Clifford Terry
Rae Ann Testi
Rachael Towle

Patricia Anne White
Austin Wilkins
Alexa Williams
Matilda Williams
William Wood
Mallory Woodall
Corey Woods
Timberlin Jeanette Zink

ATHENS TECHNICAL COLLEGE, ATHENS, GA

Kadi A. Barclay
MacKenzie Boaz
Shuntekia L. Byrd-Haynes
Kimberly L. Calhoun
Amanda T. Cooper
Aydee Hydeia Elam-Polk
Alejandro A. Gonzalez
Melissa L. Greeson

Bonnie M. Griner
Victoria S. Jaquet
Randall P. Keen
Sheronda Kessler
Patricia A. Maynard
Hannah B. Merchant
Brittany A. Narey
Abigail Q. Ogino

Paul M. Ohmer
Jennifer L. Palmer
Ahmad H. Person
Stephanie A. Roberts
Latonya D. Robinson
Shantreis M. Sams
Carissa M. Shubert
Bonnie J. Sims

Cheryl L. Smith
Thomas J. Stein
Shannon M. Stevens
Katie M. Tavernier
Rebecca K. Verhine
Tabbatha Ward
Christina M. White

AUBURN UNIVERSITY, AUBURN, AL

John Chaeho Ahn
Skylar C. Albritton
Amber Ayana Arthur
Benjamin Tanner Baker
Caroline Parkman Barr
Baylor Webb Bishop
Sydney Brooke Blankenship
Whitney LeAnn Brown
Evans Carr
Jordan Michaela Charles
Lauren Chastain
Alisa Chauhan
Andrew Jeffrey Clark
Maiya G. Clausen
Carrie Ann Cochran
Jonathan Michael Corona
Claire Marie Cressman
Susan M. Dean
Darrell Deas Jr.
Lucas Allen DeBaets

Shivam Salil Desai
Katelyn A. Donahue
Marla Katherine Ebert
Morgan Brooke Evans
Margaret Asleigh Ferguson
Alexandra Lauren Gibson
William Thomas Gibson
Katherine Elizabeth Goebel
Jonathan David Gray
Erin Anne Gready
Morton Adam Gurley
Caitlin Michelle Halperin
Francie Claire Harris
Hannah Rose Hashimi
Sarah Hirschfeldt
Nicholas B. Hoisington
Breanna Lynn Hollaway
Andrew Shelby Holman
Andrew David Hungler
Samuel Caleb Johnson

Elizabeth H. Jones
Priscilla Maurine Maurine Kaestner
Mizna Nicole Kanafani
Raegan Andrew Keith
Jonathan M. Kittle
Mason Stephen Langenbach
Adriana I. Larsen
Amanda Celeste Lawson
John Kevin Lazarus
Grace Ann Lenox
Tiffany M. Lewis
Elizabeth Hui Yi Lim
Christian Anne Lloyd
Catherine Elizabeth Lumb
Ellen H. Marsh
Laura Ann Mayhall
Sara Emily McCarty
Hunter Knight McClain
Laurel Elizabeth McCoy

Dion Alexander Moore
Matthew Dean Moore
Elizabeth Maria Morris
Anslee M. Palmer
Devyn M. Parker
Sarah Plantz
Jaime Coryn Preston
Samuel Price
JoAnna D. Propst
Lydia Margaret Purcell
Jami Myong Reece
Megan E. Reynolds
Hilary E. Rizk
Emily Ann Ruggles
Amelia Q. Schuyler
Amy Margaret Shaw
Kristin Nicole Sheehan
Kelsie N. Shipley
Marci Caroline Sims
Ross Cameron Stephens

Allison Nicole Stewart	Daniel Toner	Kristen Marie Warman	Kingslea Corry Younker
Anna Jane Taylor	Julia Alton Tubbs	Elizabeth O'Connell	
Emma Katherine Thompson	Jessy A. Tucker	Yannakakis	

AUGUSTA UNIVERSITY COLLEGE OF ALLIED HEALTH SCIENCES, AUGUSTA, GA

Alejandro Aguilar	Willie L. Davis Jr.	Haley Elizabeth Jones	Sarah Parker
Bryant C. Alonso	Morgan L. Deal	Jennifer Kukharchuk	Stacey Mullen Perry
Clarissa Rene Barry	Daniele Nicole De Lessio	Shelby Jolene Lake	Ali K. Seigler
Brian Berl	Kimberly Ann Deloach	Michael S. Lavantucksin	Jessica Lynn Stewart
Phillip Boatright	Christina Eggleston	Savannah X. Lo	Justin Suttles
Brittany Leigh Brockelbank	Selin Engec	Adrian Malave	Ashley Michelle Taylor
Elizabeth Bryan	Reginald Tyrone Forrest	Jaqueline Nicole Mayberry	Amanda B. Thomas
Alyssa Bryant	Kelsey Fynaardt	Amanda McNamara	Jordan Thrasher
Christopher Andrew Carter	Hannah N. Gay	Hannah Elise McTier	Jahan Threeths
Lauren O. Clayton	Rachel M. Glore	Kacee Camp Morris	Huy Tran
Sophia L. Conboy	Heather Hagler	Samantha L. Murdaugh	Victoria K. Valencia
Kristyn Joy Coogler	Victoria Arasi Hauff	Lindsey Panter Niknezhad	
Abigail Doris Dalis	Kathryn Johnson	Samuel Oloba	

AUGUSTA UNIVERSITY THE GRADUATE SCHOOL, AUGUSTA, GA

Connie Chung	Trevor Hardigan	Amy Paschall	Matthew A. Walker
Ryan Crislip	Bianca Islam	Robert Schleifer	Kan Hui Yiew
Jason Eugene Davis	Jason Lee	Roshni Thakkar	

AUSTIN PEAY STATE UNIVERSITY, CLARKSVILLE, TN

Damilola Ruth Afolami	Davey N. Edmaiston	Amber Christine Heady	Courtney M. Melton
Brooklyn D. Allen	Kimberly R. Escue	Danielle D. Hunter	Josephine Saffert
Karen Rachele Bartlett	Bennett R. Evans	Rebecca A. Illig	Maritza Gayle Suddeath
Keedy L. Burdeshaw	James R. Fields	Rebecca R. Jacks	Elizabeth G. Upshur
Heather Marie Burkeen	Christalynn D. Hamer	Whitney M. Jenkins	Darlene Lanette White
Breanne M. Campos	Allison N. Hamilton	Robert Drew Large	Kelsey A. Zadick
Courtney S. Cousin	Ashley Nicole Hayes	Megan M. McGill	

AVILA UNIVERSITY, KANSAS CITY, MO

Daniel J. Adams	Olivia Ann Deeken	Grace Jochims Miller	Aurora Margot Ramirez
Haley Lynn Baer	Talia Raquel Gonzalez	Patrick Oliver Moore	Sebastian Rock
Shane Steven Bartels	Kayla Renea Grieshaber	Kenneth Clark Moorman Jr.	Hiyori Watanabe
Yesenia Esperanza Beltran	Courtney Nicole Hansen	Elizabeth A. Olinger	Nicholas Osman Yonter
Jasmine Ann Colhour	Michael Gerard Hudson	Elise Marie Pates	Tiffany Lee Zinn

AZUSA PACIFIC UNIVERSITY, AZUSA, CA

Landon Spencer Abernathy	Marc R. Abou Assali	Rebecca A. Allen	Asti M. Altenritter

Tristan Avila	Kaylee S. Fink	Russell W. Mellen	Kathryn E. Schifferdecker
Michael A. Ayala	Kyle D. Fish	Benjamin J. Miller	Allison Smith
Brandon R. Barudi	Collin Friesen	Marissa Miller	Joshua J. Smith
Caroline Bebawy	Kelsey S. Hager	Stephen T. Miller	Owen S. Smith
Sean Patrick Brennan	Christopher Hale	Cole Mizel	Jacova Kathleen Snyder
Alexander T. Brouwer	Jeffrey Thomas Hansen	Margaret Niewoehner	Gretchen S. Stout
Sara M. Brown	Jackson P. Harbolt	Tori O'Connor	Kelyn F. Struiksma
Taylor R. Brown	Hayley J. Hawkins	Sarah B. O'Dell	Michaela B. Summers
Maryanne Burr	Amber Noel Hofland	Amber Overholt	Ryan Sumner
Stephanie Alison Catlett	Daniel Hogue	Jessica L. Palmini	Rebecca L. Tanis
Taylor R. Cole	Quin S. Johnson	Caleb Parker	Sarah Terwilliger
Kathryn Craig	Hanbit Lee	Maren Plog	Allison M. Updike
Abel De Castro	Josiah Lehman-Schletewitz	Alma R. Plunk	Gavin J. Velez
Anna M. De Graaf	Alexis E. Leicht	James P. Porter	Maxwell H. Walden
Linda S. De La Fonteijne	Jared C. Le Shana	Allison Roberti	Austin Welty
Lauren M. Easter	Juan Limon	Veronica E. Roberts	Lauren Werderman
Tori Edwards	Briana N. Lovett	Hannah J. Roth	Heather Wilson
Ray J. Evangelista	Sarah Marie MacIntosh	Aaron P. Russ	Kaitlyn G. Wright
Katie E. Filby	Gabriel Martin	Jessica Sauceda	

BACONE COLLEGE, MUSKOGEE, OK

Seanna Arredondo	Catherine Puckett Givens	Sarah Caroline Maxwell	Ashley Marie Smith
T. Vann BigHorse	Leslie Jean Hodges	Erick Manuel Medina	Junitress JoAnn Smith
Elsie Frances Ceasar	Faith Louise Holestine	Felipe De Nava	Reno Dean Smith
Kristi Lynn Chase	Van Sui Hu	Thang S. Piang	Ashley Renee Stout
Hunter Leann Colburn	Kaiden Benjamin-Castillo	Trevor Wyatt Piearcy	Tessa Marie Strange
Amy Louise Dobbins	Hudson	Tu Reh	Sonia Van Peng Sung
Makenzie LeeClair Flaska	Mu Htee Klee	Tyler Wayne Reid	Corey James Swift Jr.
Jeffery Don Fryer	Pah Lar	Timothy Jaymes Ryan	Tanner Christopher Theriot
Eddie Major Fullbright	Jake B. Manus	Brianna Ruth Seale	Jennifer Lynn Wilson

BAINBRIDGE STATE COLLEGE, BAINBRIDGE, GA

Jenny Louise Harrell (Whitaker)

BAKER UNIVERSITY BALDWIN CITY, BALDWIN CITY, KS

Ryan D. Akin	Laura Grace Bynum	Lora A. Finley	Gunnar C. Hays
Taylor M. Baum	Danielle M. Carlson	Danielle M. French	Brenna K. Herdman
Olivia A. Beins	Clinton J. Chapman	Jake M. Gesling	Robert J. Hoeven
Preston E. Beiser	Taylor M. Chase	Aaron J. Greenbaum	Sarah R. Hollis
Shannon M. Bond	Amanda S. Conrade	David J. Guerrero	Aaron E. Howard
Callie K. Brabender	Michelle E. Critchfield	Jessica L. Harvey	Eero T. Johnson
Sloane C. Brady	Andrew M. Dare	Heidi J. Hayen	Taylor H. Johnson
Spencer L. Brown	Andrew F. Emanuels	Ethan C. Hays	Melissa L. Kinzer

Emi L. Kniffin

Kayla S. Kohn

Sarah M. Lambert

Miranda P. Lindmark

Cambry T. Lynch

Lindsey Mateer

Shannon L. McCarty

Brenda J. McCollum

Jordan E. Miller

Luke C. Miltz

Natalie J. Minchow

Matthew J. Mogle

Jamison E. Montes de Oca

Rachel N. Moore

Sarah A. Mullins

Mallorie A. Nelson

Jasmine Parra

Benjamin H. Pepper

Andrew C. Poindexter

Megan L. Pontius

Darrell T. Randall

Jenny M. Robbs

Haley J. Roberts

Patrick J. Rydberg

MacKenzie A. Sammons

Samantha L. Schroeder

Caylea N. Siler

Rebecca L. Simkins

Ericka J. Simpson

Cody W. Sliva

Lynae D. Soderholm

Steven F. Stendebach

Kaitlyn N. Stout

Collin W. Studer

Daniel J. Sumler

Jacob A. Tompkins

Danisha M. Turner

Gavin M. Webster

Madison R. Wendt

Audrey L. Willis

Layne A. Wilson

Taylor M. Winkler

Hillary A. Yoder

BAKER UNIVERSITY SCHOOL OF NURSING, TOPEKA, KS

Tyler A. Bessey

Megan Elizabeth Decker

Malaya Reyna Deemer

Teresa Elaine Drovetta

Marci Lynn Flory

Tanner McCrary

Holly Santee

Gillian Mary Trotter

Amanda Dawn Vickers

BALTIMORE CITY COMMUNITY COLLEGE, BALTIMORE, MD

Temitope Abdou Moumouni

Tariq Abdul-Akbar

Hajr Abdul-Aziz

Clara Abit

Mariatu Abramani

Francel Paulo Acalain

Krishina Acharya

Toe Adama

Rose Adams

Sharon Adams

Adetayo Adebayo

Tolulope Adedeji

Paulinah Adegbehingbe

Olafunsho Adekanmi

Kehinde Adekoga

Oluwakemisola Adeleye

Margaret Adeloye

Mary Adenusi

Nike Adesina

Olawumi Adetoyese

Alex Adeyeye

Shoshana Afrah

Hannah Agbor

Marcellin Agbor

Deluara Ahmed

Tatek Ahmed

Adetoun Aiyeloja

Mary Ajibade

Olawale Ajigbotafe

Jennifer Akanno

Adrian Akerman

Abdulrasheed Akinniyi

Esther Akinola

Jonathan Akoi

Akuele Akwei

Maryam Alabi

Abayneh Alemu

Misrak Alemu

Andreana Alexander

Paul Algire

Danielle Allen

Maxwell Allen

Katherine Allman

Bukola Alofe

Bettye Alston

Karen Alvarez

Mauricio Amaya

Eunice Anaele

Lucres Andele

Priscilla Anderson

Edirin Aneni

Chukwuemeka Anisiobi

Margaret Anyaoha

Cheryl Anyaorie

Wanda Arbaugh

Tewebeshal Arbi

Analicia Archibald

Faith Aregbesola

Tsegaye Arficho

Rasheedat Arulogun

Nawsath Asharaff

Raphael Asinyang

Adeline Asonganyi

Sean Augustus

Constance Austins-Onyijen

Francis Ayehfor

Dilip B.K.

Kwaku Baah

Moussa Bagayoko

Tekle Bahta

Kaoue Bakanho

Olayiwola Bakare

Tiffany Baker

Daniel Baleho

Trevon Ball

Dieudonne Bamboneyeho

Sally Ann Banfield

Michael Banks

Sewella Barnes

Tahirou Barry

Anlyn Baughan

Evelyn Bawuah

Anastasia Beach

Joshua Beckett

Feleke Belay

Hannah Belcher

Terri Bell

Nkemaka Bella

Christina Berry

Shreeja Bhattarai

Ladimae Maulin Biaddang

Francois Bikoye

Joy Blackwell

Elijah Blank

Paula Bogier

Olubunmi Bolarinwa

Irene Booze

Guy Borden

Asia Bosley

Nong Bouh

Alida Boukondzo	Purna Chhetri	Aasem Deiab	Terrance Fliggins
Bernard Branch	Yitzhak Childress	Tewabech Dejene	Zackary Flores
Latarsha Branch	Anton Christian	Reena Delrahim	Alfred Fondjo
Maegon Braxton	Orogbuo Chuku	Galen Dennis	Ayuk Forchap
Erica Bridgeford	Apolonia Chukwu	Debora Diaz Diestra	Sharron Foreman
Courtney Briggs	Binika Chunara	Robin Dickson	Olive Forteh-Ngochi
Angel Britton	Mohamed Cisse	Prince Loren Diculen	Natalya Fortune
Earl Brooks	Shanira Clark	Deidra Diehl	Serge Fotie
Jesir'E Brooks	Chuchu Clarke	Cynthia Diggs	Tayvon France
Tina Brooks-Quickley	Breanne Cobbins	Megan Dillon	Saleemah Franklin
Erica Brown	Derrick Coe	Obiageli Dimonye	Sharyn Frederick
Jenee Brown	Stella Coker	Margaret Dipipi	Isabella Fuanyi
Jeraka Brown	Avonelle Colbert	Felicidad Doverte	Tamara Fudge
Latonya Brown	Alberta Cole	Abosede Dowling	Adebola Fujah
Maia Brown	Rhea Comninos	Clayton Drummond	Kharl Rainier Galarpe
Ryan Brown	Serenna Conic	Shamira Drummond	Hannah Gallardo
Shawnte' Brown	Terence Conklin	Emily Ducote	Pandora Gallop
Ram Budhamagar	Jinika Conley	Keyvonia Dudley	Mei Gao
Sade Buie	Jonathan Conley	Natasha Duncan	Nicole Gardner
Taria Burr	Latasha Cooper	Catawba Edwards	Anthony Gaskins
Ashley Burton	Diane Kristy Cortez	Kelvin Edwards	Kele Gatling
William Bush	Darrell Cottman	Veronica Edwards	Abravi Gbemafu
Ashley Butler	Troy Cottrell	Temitayo Egbeyeye	Koffi Mensah Gbemafu
Kenneth Butler	John Coyne	Uchechukwu Egboluche	Sisay Gebrie
Shalonda Butler	Tanya Crawley	Joy Eghaghe	Marjory Gelin
Sharon Butler	Karol Venice Cubebe	Jamal El Badaoui	Bekele Gelleta
Peggie Butler-Watson	Gail Cuffie	Suzanna Eldridge	Araceli George
Queenta Bwang	Malik Curtis	Joy Emelumba	Nioka Ghee
Igor Cannon	Vincenzo D'Agata	Ataya Emmanuel	Gregory Gist
Niesha Carr	Melissa D'Amato	Brian Eskridge	Kelly Givens
Wendy Carr	Rahwa Daniel	Patricia Etienne	Abdulmatin Giwa
Darryl Carter	Karl Daniels	Carl Evans	Fausat Giwa
Geneva Carter	John Darden	Candace Everette	Aron Goitom
Stephanie Carter	Elton John David	Rosita Ezemma	Genieve Goodall
William Carter	Jenina Ezra David	Yetunde Fakinlede	Hanzel Timmy Gotia
Elizabeth Cash	Cynthia Davila	Bukola Falana	John Martin Gotia
Randy Chambers	Angela Davis	Maria Falodun	Danielle Grab
Sirak Chamiso	Kiterria Davis	Chaz Faltz	Malcolm Graves
Quiana Chandrasekar	Lisa Davis	Simon Fanuel	Latin Graves Jr.
Elton Charles	Marcia Davis	Mekdela Fekadu	Tiyanna Gray
Thea Chase	Michael Davis	Joshua Fine	Agasia Green
Agnes Che	Sangeana Dawes	Krystal Fitch	Carmen Green
Sedeny Che	Jeffrey De Cola	Matthew Fletcher	Dru Green

Emmelyn Green	Denisha Hunt	Amrit Kafle	John Lucas
Takerra Green	Douglas Hunt	Farah Kalaiselvan	Jean Pierre Lutsheto
Arianna Gregg	Sherry Hunt	Hilina Kalegeta	Karine Lyle
Briana Griffin	Kaanita Hussein	Susan Kangethe	Donnalisa Lyons
Naheed Gul	Sylvia Ibeadogbulem	Amos Karter	Teresa Mack
Delores Gupton	Modupe Idowu	Rose Kastah	Corinthea Madden
Ann Guy	Ramat Ikharia	Olushola Kazeem	Gregory Maddox
Bobga-Herman Gwanvoma	Yonas Imer	Brian Kelley	Mabele Madiba
Jacqueline Gyebi	Gabriel Imonikhe	Keirra Kennedy	Emeka Madueke
Ernest Hackett	Robert Inghram	Tysheria Kennedy	Rosanne Magne Kougoum
Eric Hall	Monique Ingram	Wilde Ketchatang	Esther Majekodunmi
Kerri Hall	Shannon Ismail	Yasaman Khakshoor	John Majors
Latonya Hall	Bisrat Issack	Aysylu Khaliullina	Abdourazakou Mamane
Sandra Hall	Fatouma Issifu	Damaris Kifude	May Maposa-Nyoni
Sierra Hall	Onyeka Iwudyke	Chaunce' King	Charles Marshall
Venus Hall	Gloria Iyaki	Kyong King	Rashike Martin
Richard Hanna	Glory Iyere	Phyllis Kinuthia	Tara Martin
Cassandra Hargrove	Connie Jackson	Salome Kioko	Ryan Mason
Malcolm Harris	Ladonna Jackson	Matthew Kirk	Markita Massey
Julian Harrison	Emma Jacobson	Sofiya Kivenzor	Dmitriy Matrosov
Tonya Harrison	Girma Jaleta	Janel Kleinpeter	Laron Matthews
June Haskins	Han Na Jang	Diane-Aurelie Koagne	Prisila Maundu
Isaac Haskins IV	Jerrod Jaramogi	Evelyn Kotey	Carmen Maxwell
Cynthea Hayes	Naomi Jeruto	Lisa Laidlow	Jeremy McCann
Mariah Heath	Shenglu Ji	Surya Lama	Preston McCargo
Cynthia Hemby	Maryam Jimoh	Ronnie Lambert	Letia McClain
Christine Hemminger	Olanrewaju John Day	Shaquente Lambert	Wesley McCutchen
Candice Henderson	Bryant Johnson	Chrispine Lando	Shawn McKay
Crystal Henderson	Juan Johnson	Omotoni Laniyan	Kimberly McKenzie
Jemill Hester	Keenan Johnson	Moshood Lateef	Lakiesa McLean
Danita Hicks	Kwana Johnson	Lateef Lawal	Mary McLemore-Bowen
Adrienne Hickson	Latina Johnson	Amy Leak	Bianca McNair
Aisha Hill	Mica Johnson	Aleisha Lee	Addis Mengistu
Shabray Hobson	Angelica Jones	Kevin Lee	Alex Mensah
Christopher Hoff	Darell Jones	Kyle Leech	Berhanu Merga
Adrian Holmes	Lashawn Jones	Mihaela Leonard	Nabil Mesbahi
Patria Holmes	Letisha Jones	Sherri Lewis	Augustine Metchoum
Gloria Holt	Martez Jones	Tequilla Lewis	Yvonne Miles
Keyuanna Houchens	Myeisha Jones	Deborah Liberto	Candice Miller
Hayward Hough	Nicole Jones	Antonio Little	Gerald Miller
Rafiq Howard	Vanessa Jordan	Linda Loftin	Romana Miller
Jane Hube	Andrew Joseph	Colette Longmire	Vonzella Mills
Kenneth Hube	Uaenenisa Kaambo	Chareeka Louis	Kheri Mobley

Peter Mochu	Nzeme Nkwelle	Bruno Opara	Shawntrice Reese-Chapman
Mungwi Mofor	Jordan Nnabugwu	Sophia Ossei Boateng	Svetlana Reeves
Tigist Mohammed	Gaelle Nono	Ebere Osunwa	Roslyn Richardson
Maria Mojica	Falonne Nsiala	Raphael Outlaw	Alicia Roberts
Sushma Moktan	Vivian Nushann	Sarah Owens	Antoinette Roberts
Saida Mollel	Kevin Nwachukwu	Temitope Owoyemi	Courtney Roberts
Melanie Monkam	Chinenye Nwosu	Ogechukwu Oyediran	Nakeisha Robertson
Giovonni Moore	Sandra Nwugo	Emmanuella Oyogoa	Joseph Robinson
Sandra Moragne	Doreen Nyanzi	Olga Pach	Nichole Robinson
Theresa Morgan	Eutychus Nyoike	Matth Carlo Padla	Twyla Robinson
Thermon Morris Jr.	Juliette Nzene	Jean Padonou	Olivia Rocquemore
Andrea Morrison	Iyobosa Obasogie	James Pair	Lakisha Rodgers
Kerry Morrison	Ogochukwu Obi	Alreatha Palmer	Rene Rodgers
Beverly Morten	Gabriel Obidiran	Kousalya Pannuri	Kannika Rodmanee
Melissa Morton	Andrew Obiefule	Srijana Panta	Jaminson Rodriguez
Evelyne Moti	Godwina Odigie	Brent Parker	Stephanie Rogers
Shadrack Moti	Oladapo Odusanya	Reginald Parker	Nancy Roman
Corine Mougoue	Omotayo Oduwole	Esther Paseda	Miriam Rosen
Adamou Mouiche Lamanje	Chukwuemeka Ogbodo	Rachel Pastuszek	Shantel Rouzer
Emmanuel Muhammad	Akinyemi Ogundana	Autumn Patton-Sanders	Kianna Rowell
Catherine Mukantabana	Helen Ogunduyile	Gilbert Payne	Patrick Ruble
Fefe Mukendi	Jiyoung Oh	Nneamaka Payne	Paul Ruble
Nada Mukhtar	Emmanuel Ojeanelo	Dante Pennix Sr.	Beatrice Rukenwa
Joy Munoz	Funmilola Ojekanmi	Elizabeth Penny	Lauren Russell
Ekaterina Muranova	Oluwaseun Ojimi	Abdul Pewa	Jemal Sabir
Nancy Murimi	Folarin Ojowa	Emily Pierce	Azeezat Sadiq
Warens Enelly Mvuezolo	Chuchi Oka-Zeh	Sunayna Plummer	Mikias Sahilu
Margaret Mwakazi	Evelyn Okwese	Sijan Pokhrel	Whitney Samuel
Jessica Myers	Anna Okwesili	Judah Polak	Selena Santos
Sajjad Nadali	Gladys Olabamiji	Alicia Polk	Ronald Satterfield
Susan Nanyonga	Wilson Olabamiji	Terrell Poole	Rasheed Savage
Dieudonne Ndashi	Oluwatosin Olaore	Danielle Powell	Abdoulaye Sawadogo
Caroline Ndegwa	Ganiyu Olofi	Star Powell	Addelana Sawe
Amy Ndione	Pauline Olorunfemi	Yvette Powell-Pink	Emily Schutschkow
Gilbert Ndip	Joseph Oluigboka	Sewavi Prince-Agbodjan	Chazz Scott
Stanley Ndunagu	Abiodun Olukini	Monaye Pulley- Gethers	Josephine Scott
Marcey Newsome	Iredele Olusola	Katrina Purnell	Renee Scott
Joy Ngene	Oluwakemi Oni	Terry Purnell	Jenee Scruggs
Prisca Ngenyi	Agnes Ononye	Zhou Qin	Francis Segbo
Quyet Nguyen	Ezinwa Onuoha	Kierra Radcliffe	Angela Sellers
Erica Nicholas	Edna Onword	Neeta Rajbanshi	Nurudeen Settles
Moses Njau	Ngozi Onyekuru	Daniel Ray	Shubhalaxmi Shakya
George Njoroge	Abigail Opara	Joseph Reed	Wei Shang

Shima Sheshbloki
Victoria Shodipo
Laila Shrestha
Sameer Shrestha
Michelo Siachoono
Dmitri Sibanov
Anastasia Sidorenkova
Fouad Sika
Binita Silwal
Denetria Simon
Shelly Ann Simpson
Boruch Singer
Alena Sinitsa
Aaron Smith
Cathy Smith
Douglass Smith
Latonya Smith
Shawniece Smith
Tache Smothers
Shanna Solese-Ragsdale
Selam Solomon
Blanca Soto
Monika Spoerner
Paulina St. Rose
Kenneth Stagge
Ebony Stavis
Michelle Stephens
Andrea Sterner
Robert Stevens
Michelle Stevenson
Marva Stewart
Niamki Stewart

Kelli Strand
Kasim Sulemana
Jinat Tabasum
Wuede Tadesse
Suhadatu Tahiru
Carine Tajocha
Daniel Takele
Soila Takona
Veronika Tamfu
Samuel Tapahuasco
Elizabeth Tapia
Alyx Taylor
Dorethea Taylor
Mary Taylor
Warren Taylor
Tonya Tazewell
Jacqueline Tekwe
Bola Temowo
Tsgereda Tesfu
Shandal Thomas
Genevieve Thompson
Kelli Thompson
Nicole Thompson
Victoria Thomson
Nelius Thuita
Denise Tires
Bethel Tom
Shoshana Topas
Tyrone Toran
Diem Tran
Thanh Thuy Tran
Bekaye Traore

Kellin Trinidad
Montressa Tripps
Diafie Tubah
Roslyn Tucker
Sovit Tulachan
Adamsay Turay
Flora Uwineza
Elena Vaiman
Xiomara Vargas
Apoorva Verma
Jason John Villaver
Paula Vincent-Peterson
Minh Trang Vo
Elizabeth Waleola
Tiffany Walker
Adanma Waller
Luchelle Ward
Lavette Washington
Tychauna Washington
Karen Washington Malone
Josi Waterman
Mable Waters
Jennifer Weaver
Eleanor Webb
Moira Wellons
Sylvia Wells
Irene West
Anthony White
Cathryn White
Dashawna White
Jasmin White
Joyce White

Kameron White
Kimberly White
Re'Gene White
Angela Wicks
Barbara Wilkins
Sonia Wilks
Christopher Williams
Ingra Williams
Jonathan Williams
Patricia Williams
Taylor Williams
Devora Wilson
Samuel Wilson Jr.
Antwon Winder
Theodore Witherspoon
Martha Woldesilassie
Terry Woodfolk
Draketina Wright
John Wroten
Lin Xiong
TaSean Yeargin
Joseph Yingling
Debowrah Yisrael
Louison Yonkeu Kougang
Cynthia Young
Jennifer Young
Wanda Young
Donald Zapanta
Misikir Zenebe
Feng Zhang

BAPTIST BIBLE COLLEGE, SPRINGFIELD, MO

Riley Ayers
Kenneth Brock
Tyler Carleton
Katherine Elizabeth Casey
Tabitha Clapp
Paige Collier
Emily Cresswell
Jonas Crump

Justin Curtis
Austin Davidson
Kadi Dickey
Savanna Edwards
Bethany Inge
Kolter Klass
Bethany Joy McGuire
Zachary Mendenhall

Frederick Mierow
Shannon Mulford
Janay Nogalski
Naomi Oliger
James Pentecost
Shane Phillips
Miranda Rebarchik
Kelsey Shruck

Kelsey Simmons
Rachel Simmons
Reba Snyder
Tyler Storz
Adam Van Becelaere
Wesley Wilson

BARCLAY COLLEGE, HAVILAND, KS

Emily A. Entz

Susan Friesen

Elizabeth N. Herbel

Corbin E. Kellum

David Truman Miller

Sarah N. Miller

Ruth M. Price

Sharese A. Smedley

Nathaniel D. Vanderploeg

BARTON COLLEGE, WILSON, NC

Samantha Brooke Bass

Carley Brook Brantley

Dori Jillian Brooks

Candice Nichole Bunch

Ryan Thomas Canoy

Amy Elizabeth Cogan

Jordan Taylor Cooper

Zachery Austin Corbett

Rhode Desauguste

Linda Eldridge

Emily Nicole Evans

Malorie Lynn Evans

Brenda Felton

Brooke Raquel Fernandez

Hannah Max Finkelstein

Nicolas Charles Genest

Sarah Catherine Hall

Teresa Renae Holland

Virginia Laura Howard

Marylynn Iwanowski

Leighanne Nicole Jones

Smiljana Kljajic

Janice LaRue Lacy

Brianna Michelle Le-Mon

Maximilian Albert Leppert

Brenda Kay Light

Ashley Paige Locus

Felipe Giovany Martinez

Kristin Elizabeth McCarrick

Christina Marie McQuoid

Sammantha Danielle Murray

Nahia Zhaimara Navarro

Latifah Graves Nixon

Allison Marie Pate

Natalieann Josephine
Pellegrino

Lindsay Nicole Pittman

Terreessa "Terry" Purvis

Vanessa Chapman Rawlings

Jonathan Kent Raynor

Lindsay Marie Rembecki

Taylor Marie Rivenbark

Juana Oliva Rivera

Brooke Rivers

Samantha Leigh Roark

Brittany Nicole Robinson

Kelsey Michele Rothwell

Rafael Ruiz Velasco

Jacob William Andrew
Sarvey

Nicholas Maxwell Scalia

Rachel Anne Schoonover

Nicholas Edward Sharp

Mahala Killette Shields

Myra Leigh Stotesbury

Christianna Nicole Taylor

Brittany Lee Thomas

Mihnea Stefan Tomos

Xiomary Torres-Zayas

Michaela Ashten Trefethen

Debra Cherry Whitlark

Benjamin Steve Williams

BARTON COMMUNITY COLLEGE, GREAT BEND, KS

Susie Vanessa Aguilar

Madison Bangert

Leslie Bell

Adam John Birzer

Mary Bitter

Travis Mitchell Bowers

Riley Chrisler

Connor M. Copley

Sophie Crisp

Raegan Cross

Camelle Iliene Deege

Carley Joann Deege

Coryell Lynn Deege

Casey DiVito

Kaylie Doll

Kelsie Doll

Holly Edds

Jordan Edelman

Tasha Lavon Frazier

Brooke Nicole Henning

Jessica Hillegeist

Blake Huxman

Alyson Klug

McKinna Kraus

Morgan Rae Kurtz

Grace Lawrence

Nicklaus Lawrence

Catelynne Castanea LePage

Brooke Louderback

McKenna Mauler

Mallory McQueen

Sara Morris

Jared Oelke

Marissa Oglesby

Allyson Kay Patterson

Holly Pierce

Holly Posegate

James Proffitt

Edith Real

Luke Reeder

Katrina Allene Roenfeldt

Kade Sander

Presley Smith

Natchapol Srinoon

Diane Stone

Katie Tammen

Ashlie Thill

Breanna Dawn Towers

Jamie Waters

Sharonda Wilkins

Colton Allen Zink

BAYLOR UNIVERSITY, WACO, TX

Lindsay Adams

Grantham Akerly

Erica Amos

Marianna Arana

Miguel Astello

Samarth Asthana

Lauren Azan

Rebecca Baker

Erin Barbour

Tate Barrett

Nancy Bearden

Meghan Bell

Connor Blandin
Brittany Bonner
Shelby Booth
Allison Boyd
Brooke Valerie Brady
Philip Austin Brakebill
Pearson Brown
Katherine Carriveau
Cait Casteel
Taliyah Mozell Clark
Carla June Cook
Meredith Dana
Madeline R. Danielson
Alicia Duval
Yara Farah
Amy Feind

Maya Fontenot
Alejandro Gonzalez
Patrick Hall
Daniel Headrick
Serina Hernandez
Jackson Hollis Hornbeak
Danae Hughes
Annelise Ingram
Nicole Kosakowski
Nisha Kurani
Taylor Lahey
Katherine Landgrave
Evelyn DoanTrang Le
Michael LoSasso
Tajwar Majeed
Andrea Manzanares

Julianna Marraccino
Caitlyn McClellen
Danielle N. Miller
Hallie Million
Steven Newcomb
Margaret Odunze
Savan Patel
Natalia Perez
Tyler Pharris
Laura Phipps
Brittany Rollins
Danielle Rutherford
Kimmie Sandusky
Stephanie Shull
Jonathan Siktberg
Ali Sohani

Bryan Solis
Dom Lee Steinmann
Jeffrey Tamburello
Kylie Terry
Graham Throckmorton
Jessie Trespeses
Evan James Ward
Matthew Willis
Reid Wilson
Alexis Winchester
Catherine Woerner
Dan Woodward
Dusty Wright
Hannah Wulfsberg
Yulin Xiao

BAY PATH UNIVERSITY, LONGMEADOW, MA

Kayla Ann Chuba
Brianna Marie Clyne
Kimberly Drahushuk

Amanda Emet
Elizabeth Haylette
Abby Jo Krobot

Anna Meyer
Kimberly Raymond
Kayla Riel

Yismel Rosario
Rose Marie Scalzi
Katherine Sperry

BELHAVEN UNIVERSITY, JACKSON, MS

Blanche Bernice Adams
Annie Katherine Andrews
Pamela Laverne Banks
Brian Wayne Benn
Jeremiah Charles Blough
Cynthia Kay Brasher
Rita Ann Castillo
Melinda Jo Champion
Natasha Dionne Collins
Kathryn Ann Cummins
Jonathan David Dickson
Corey L. Dillard

Rachel Anne Driscoll
Katherine Campbell Gardner
Alexander John Haick III
Bradley Eugene Hamil
Justin Cooper Harris
Dorothy Jean Henson
Richard Keith Levia
Deborah Anne Loo
Jordan Denee Manuel
Arianna E. Marcell
Natasha Luz Maurice
Medavarapu, Harika

Stefanie Marie Medina
Daniel A. Moody
Shawnita LaFaye Neely
Manuel Nunez
Minchun Park
Tabetha Nichole Perry
Emily Caitlin Polson
Julie Magee Powell
Ronnie Reese Jr.
Kaleb Scot MacAlan Reilly
Alexandra Evonne Sahli
Jessica Curtis Stovall

Anna Claire Thaggard
Marie Ann Theisen
Mondria Yaneick Tyler-Sheriff
Jerry Louis Virgil
Kelly Marie Weber
Evangeline Grace Wilds
McKenzie Renee Williams
Jessica Joy Ziegelbauer

BELLARMINE UNIVERSITY, LOUISVILLE, KY

Austin Michael Adam
Michael Ryan Adkerson
Cecily E. Allen
Drew R. Bilodeau
Amy Marie Bontrager
James Evangelos Boukas

Sarah Mary Louise Bowley
Amber N. Brown
Mary Alice Brown
Heather Danielle Campbell
Meghan Elisabeth Corder
Victoria Marie-Louise Crick

Rachel Louise Daniel
Sarah Phillips Dunman
William A. Edelen
Thomas J. Finch
Emily Ann Gahafer
Chasiti N. Gaines

Elizabeth Ellen Gatten
Kelli Ann Goings
Mary Elizabeth Gorham
Mackenzie Corinne Harrison
Dylan Tate Hart
Lexy Green Hazle

Sara Jane Elisabeth Hubbard
Haley Marilyn Hunt
Kevin Josef Jeffrey
Franeisha Jones
Megan Elizabeth Kanter
Megan Marie Kimbley
Matthew Douglas Kirk
Heather Ann Kissel
Claudia Meghan Lab
Maris Anna Libera
Caroline Susan Link

Travis Ros McEachern
Corbin E. McGuire
Kesley A. Moorefield
Ashley Ann Morris
Caroline Marie Mueller
Calli Anne Paydo
Michael Liston Plisco
Alysha Kristina Rauen
Olivia Dawn Reibel
Rebecca Elizabeth Renn
Jessica Renee Ringlein

Tyler Quin Ruch
Thomas Austin Sapp
Kaylynn Yvonne Schwamb
Erica Nicole Shelley
Craig William Skinner Jr.
Christopher Jacob Smith
Thomas Hunter Smith
Grant Thomas Snell
Dulce D. Solorio
Christopher Llewelyn
Robards Spach

Kayla Rachel Stephenson
Adam D. Sterrett
Lauren Michelle Thomas
Aliya Catherine Marie
Thompson
Bethany D. Traynham
Brooke Logan Vaughn
Allison Lynn Welp
Carly Elizabeth Winn

BENEDICTINE COLLEGE, ATCHISON, KS

Christina Barth
Shanon Biwer
Melissa Borsh
JonElliot Brubaker
Adriana Carlson
Bridget Faustina Collart
John Matthew Denton
Andrew Doyle
Jordan Francescon
Darren G. Handy Jr.

Anna Hegenkord
Tyler Henness
Rachel Marie Hernandez
Sadie Hilliard
Julia Johnson
Krista Kosek
Jordan Kramer
Mehan Lancaster
Daniel Langenfeld
Zach Leonard

Katie Lind
Mary Minnis
Elena Teresa Moore
Mary Moore
Christin Elizabeth Noffke
Clare Nowak
Carlyn Olson
Emily Elizabeth Papini
Jessica Pavlik
Phillip Pick

Josh Rhodes
Jerome Roehm
Danielle Shanahan
Maria Starrs
Gabriel Suthoff
Alexander John Van Keulen
William Wallace
Kendall Williams
Lauren Williams
Kallie Woodward

BENEDICTINE UNIVERSITY, LISLE, IL

Mahmoud Abdel
Fatjona Aliaj
Tatiana Arturo
Lauren M. Burish
Miguel Caballero
Alexandra Cascone
Kelsie Dearing
Sally Jo Detloff
Jose Eduardo Dieck
Kirstin R. Dufour

Jermeen El-Zabet
Cory James Evans
Alanna Ferry
Aimee Michelle Ford
Francesca Guido
Shajwa Hussain
Erica Nicole Kotsovos
Kristin Jean Kubelsky
Peter Lee
Rabia Mahmood

Kathleed Miller
Tanushree Nair
Rachel Nicinski
Andrew Nordbye
Uzonna Valerie Olumba
Sarah Oprondek
Ignatius Payne
Ann Pendergast
Angela Regan
Mary Roach

Abigail Rodriguez
Jonathan Dean Schram
Rachel Morgan Scianna
Hafsa Sirajuddin
Mitch Tuthill
Nayeli Vazquez
Rachel Warren
Kelsey Zimmerman

BENEDICTINE UNIVERSITY AT SPRINGFIELD, SPRINGFIELD, IL

Giancarlo Faidutti Alvarez
Brittney Arkebauer
Anthony Dwayne Bellin
Kathy Canaday
Amanda Coniglio
Heather Elyse Crowcroft

Shelby Lynn Dial
Chien Doan
Blake Fawns
Eric Fitzgerald
Samantha Horn
Laura Horton

Sara Howerter
Betsy Ingram
Hui Jiang
Ashley Johnson
Nathania Laier
Duc Le

Linh Le
Kyra Nicole Leinberger
Ashley LeVault
Brittany Limper
Amanda Mandeville
Tyler McEvoy

Hung Nguyen
Anthony Nika
Sonya Lei Perkins
Emily Perone
Mary Richardson

Constance Rybak
Bryanna Stevens
Elizabeth Sullivan
Kelsey Taul
Erica Thies

Linsey Torchia
Duong Hong Tran
Meghan Tribout
Jessica Vonachen
Hai Hoang Vuong

Katherine Webb
Jon Wingo
Morgan Zachary

BENNETT COLLEGE, GREENSBORO, NC

Jazmyn Lynnette Alston
Lanna Nichole Anderson
Angbo, Joy Ann-Destiny
Shaquierra Ny'Asia Baker
Yahnick Nichola Joell
Barclay
KeYona Taryel Barton
Bianca LaBelle Best
Christiana Bockari
Kenji LaShae Bonner
Antachia R. Brown
Danielle Nylia Brown
Kye Elizabeth Brown
Deidra Rose Burton
Aaliyah Janell Carter
Ciara Mashee Chavis
Felisa Jordan Coates
Shemiah Katrice Curry
Casie Koddise Edwards
Kadi Egharba
Jasmine Danielle Everett

Jasmine Monique Exton
Brea Symone Fields
Chanelle Lajoy Gainey
Brianna Marie Gamble
Deneisha Amber Lashawn
Gillard
Bria Janae Hawkins
Kala Regina Hill
Karla Patrice Hines
Taylor Brihanna Hogue
Anjuna Nadia Holloman
BriAnna Leigh Holmes
Kee'Aera Shuneil Hood
Alexandra Julianne Huggins
Precious Shekinah Hunter
Courtney AmberLouise
James
Danielle Sheree Jeffries
Janay Alysah Johnson
Janessa Mina Johnson
Brothely Malique Jones

Kelly My-Angel Jones
Aaleah Renee Lancaster
Amra McKinsey Marshall
Angel Lashawn Mason
Taneil T. Mays
Amber Patrice McGill
Akillah Symone Miles
Kiara Renee Mills
Chelsea Lynne Moore
KeArra Dominique Nunnery
Jariana Oluyemisi Olukoga
Janae Elaina Peats
Kamari Jordan Reid
Areaona Roberson
Shacora LaTisha Rorie
Olivia Portria Rubin
Keirra Michelle Sedgwick
Kyanna Shaquanna Simon
Nana Natasha Sloan
Hakimah S. Smith
Shannon LeAshley Steward

Ladaysia Renee Sturgis
Brittany Shaniqua Tabron
Sharnelle Amaris Taylor
EMoni Shaela Thomas
Adera Evelyn Toye
Addison Lynne Turner
Ashlee Aliyah Vann
Ambria DeJanae Webster
Jaiza Rene Wesley
Charell ReJean Williams
Jamelia Quartzetta Willis
Kadrien Lakwisha Wilson
Kira Ayana Wilson
Vanessa Allison Wilson
Bria Ivy Wortham
Julia Ann Yancey
Danae Monique Young
DeMarise Mone Young

BEREAN BAPTIST COLLEGE, GLEN ST. MARY, FL

Alyssa Sierra Hershey

Jedidiah Andrew Scott

Brian Christopher Stanley

BETHEL SEMINARY, ST. PAUL, MN

Chris James Adams
Matthew Laurence Allinder
Cassandra Kae Bloyer
Bryan K. Button
Kyle S. Christopherson
Taryn Chevonne Cleaves
Benton Cole
Michelle Margaret Couture
Joel David Crandall
Jenna I. Daniels

Erik Stephen Dees
Aaron DeMaster
John Joseph Foley
Karen Day Fournier
Jamie Lynn Fredrickson
Bethany Joy Goetz
Daniel J. Grams
Mary Lisa Guyton-Baker
Timothy Robert Haas
Tara L. Harrison

Avery Marie Harshman
Laura Michelle Houlton
Erik Robert Johnson
Priscilla Kibler
Aaron Van King
Danielle Tara Koehler
Timothy David Kooiman
Bonnie Jeanne Kristian
Ibyi Akkiva L'Bert-Parris
Gregory Robert Ley

Peter Frederick Mades
Jill Meents
Sarah Beth Mikul
Beatrice Naa-Abashie
Moreaux
Meng Mua
Rocky Christopher Muñoz
Karla Kristine Nelson
Daniel William O'Neill
Nkiruka Catherine Okafor

Jeremy Wayne Hilding
Peters
Andrew David Powell
James C. Racine
Kelsey Anne Remple
Nicholas Robert Ruport
Mary Susan Schuelke

Karyn Bernice Sciortino
Johnson
Laura Ann Selker
Jeremy David Shank
Hickory Paul Elijah Smith
Deborah Lynn Spidle
Laura Jean Steege

Samuel Mason Warren
Townsend
Anna Nicole Tucker
Austin Joseph Walker
Robert Kenneth Wendt
Devin John Westhause
Laura Dawn Wiens

Eric Arthur Wilder
John Andrew Williford
Ka Yang
Joanne Elaine Young
James Reuben Yutzy

BETHEL SEMINARY SAN DIEGO, SAN DIEGO, CA

Karla Alonso
Kyleigh Baker
Krista Bergesen
Christopher James Bodiford
Walter Colace

Carolyn Gardella
Roy Inzunza
Daniel Jarrell
Gloria Elysia Kerr
Sung Kyung Esther Kim

John King
James Kubiak
Eric Lam
Jo Ann Lapp
Cara Ann Maeda

MaryAnn Nguyen-Kwok
Mark Olkowski
Carmen Pat
Stacy Liane Roome
Jeremy Spain

BETHEL UNIVERSITY, MCKENZIE, TN

William Cody Atkins
Priscilla Faith Bowden
Sarah Alyse Brawner
Muhase Dorcas Buzigire

Heather Caitlin Hamblin
Paula Marie Holmes
Lorna Whitney Hudson
Carol Andrea Marulanda

Briana Danielle Morrow
Brittney Cierra Morrow
Emily Paige Murphy
Candace Nicole Newman

Shannon Monique O'Mayes
Audra Paige Wallace
Cadence Nariah Whaley
Sydney Claire Wood

BEVILL STATE COMMUNITY COLLEGE, JASPER, AL

Dalton L. Absher
Holly Aultman
Yancy Lane Beard
Matthew Besley
Nia Danielle Blanchard
Anna Grace Bonds
Tonya Justin Bowen
John Bray
Jacob Shane Burns
Jeana Marie Burton
Jedadiah Ryan Canida
Zac Zac Carter
Jarred Hunter Causey
Spencer Lewis Clary
Dwayne Lee Collins
Jessica Bridgette Cook
Blakeney Dallas Cox
Christopher Micheal Cox
Kayla Nicole Davenport
Justin Davis
Erica Nicole Dobbins

Cicely Noelle Dodd
Jake Dozier
Brooke Ashley Driver
Stevi Lyn Drummond
Dana Louise Dutton
William Thomas Earnest
Sabrina R. Eddy
Lindsay South Elliott
Daniel Kash Ellison
Kaly Heavin Flora
Dylan Franks
Casey Danielle Giambrone
Rachel Harley Glasgow
Justin Lynn Goldsmith
Michael Jarrod Graham
Katherine Alexandra Gregg
Jacob A. Guthrie
Hope Elizabeth Hartsfield
Skyler Wade Hawkins
Jordan E. Henderson
Zachary Allen Henson

Dakota A. Herron
Matthew Ishan Hijazeen
Roger Allen Hill
Logan Horne
Karlee Lane Ivey
Jacob Ross Jett
Ashton Suzanne Jones
Jake Wayne Jones
Kimberly Amber
Killingsworth
Morgan Nicole Kilpatrick
Mary C. Kinard
Shirley Virginia Knight
Destin Rogers Lancaster
Arry Lawler
Chelsea Nicole Leonard
Brianna K. Lichtenauer
Autumn Logan
Emelio Madero
Mandolin Rain Madison
Samantha Ashley Madison

Ryleigh Anne Malone
Carlos Luis Marbot
Jacob Markham
Cheri Lynn McAvoy
Ashley Nicole McCraw
Jacob Ellis McDonald
Mark Laney Merrill
Daniel Scott Mertens
Kelsey Morgan Miller
Landon Lee Miller
Autumn Brianne Morris
Makaela Loree Mote
Kaytlin Grace Noles
Chandler Blake Oates
Lena Conswalla Odom
Mahlon Wayne Odom
Eddy Ortiz
Millie Leighann Owens
Zachary Dylan Parvin
Talbert Brent Pate
Frankie Young Payne

Taylor Marie Pendley

Emily Grace Perrin

Adam James Phillips

Jenna Lea Pierce

Drake Pollard

Samuel Samuel Prescott

Jacob Purdee

Amber Michelle Quick

Kristen Michelle Randolph

Jason Rayburn

Megan Elizabeth Reeves

Nathaniel Heath Rice

Stephen Jacob Richards

Jessica Marie Robbins

Catherine Victoria Roberts

Jessica RaShae Roberts

Jacob Robinson

Javan Andrew Robinson

Hannah Grace Roos

Quaishia Lashunn Samuels

David Sanderson

India Shiniece Sherrod

Sekeitha S. Sides

Casandra Tywan Simmons

Karla Rae Simmons

Alexander Dennis Sims

Joshua Irvin Smith

Stephen Jackson Nails Smith

Trevor Smith

Jordan Alexis Stanberry

Shyanne Shayla Stewart

Marisa Paige Stiles

Daniel Jay Thigpen

Tonya M. Thomas

Sarah Madison Tidwell

Hannah Leigh Tingle

Ashley Anita Tran

Jase Bryant Trotter

Franki Shay Troutman

Alexander Christian Tucker

Pamela Valle

Andrew Paul Vice

Joshua Thomas Vinson

John Aaron Wade

Penelope Cathryn Walker

Trevor Chase Walker

Ricky Lee Walton

Amber LaShae Washington

Emily Alaine Wilhite

Hunter Bowden Williams

Latoshia Michelle Williams

Hanna Lee Wilson

Seth Gregory Wilson

Tiffany Raye Wilson

Andrea L. Winters

Anne Elizabeth Wolf

Lena Claire Woodley

Caleb Ray Woods

Drew Christopher Wright

Matthew David Wright

McKenna Scott Wright

BIG SANDY COMMUNITY & TECHNICAL COLLEGE, PRESTONSBURG, KY

Ericka L. Allen

Nathanuel Auxier

Andrea Danielle Bauer

Bruce Begley

Kaci Richelle Bentley

Kendra Marie Boyer

Jessica Marie Branham

Lisa Jean Branham

Edmund Shane Brown

Angela Marie Bryant

Megan Nicole Caldwell

Kaitlyn Elizabeth Campbell

Courtney Deanna Case

Courtney Morgan Casey

Maddisson Brooke Casey

Kolby Wayne Charles

Derek Lee Christian

Gatlin Gabriel Clark

Emily Kristin Coleman

Stevi Lynn Conn

Keisha Ann Crum

Joshua Lafe Daniel

Kristen Nicole Daniels

Leann Nichole Deboard

Salma Diarbakrli

Andrew Matthew Emmers

Kelsey Marie Fields

Kevin Tyler Fields

Bridgett Alexis Fitch

Haylie Moriah Fitch

Kassidy Marie Frasure

Kelsie Brooke Fuller

Casey Gayheart

Nathan A. Gudino

Caleb A. Hall

Nicole Lynn Hall

James Lincoln Hamilton

Randy Dillon Hamilton

Coreen Kirby Hayes

William Samuel Hayes

Courtney Liane Hayton

James Braxton Hensley

Terry Austin Hinkle

Felicia Paige Hopkins

Crystal Michelle Horn

Kristie Leighann Houston

Darian Alexandra Howard

Effie Shannon Howard

Jessica Faye Howard

Kevin Wayne Howard

Joshua Franklin Howell

Brittney Nikkole Hughes

Denisha Breshae Hughes

Tabatha Michelle Hunt

Bentley Michelle Isaacs

William Matthew James

Selena Gaye Jarrell

Roger Lee Johnson

Justin Dylan Jones

Randy Tyler Jones

Gina Sue Joseph

Miranda Nicole Jude

Hunter B. Kinney

Heather Lashae Kiser

Jokeisha P. Lemaster

Montana Leanna Lemaster

Angela Gail Lester

Darian DeeAnn Lewis

Jeffrey Tyler Little

Karen Edith Lovern

Makayla Ann Lykins

Amanda Brooke Manns

Coty McShane Marcum

Kayti Ellan Maynard

Amy Nicole Mccausland

Melissa Ann Meade

Elmer Ray Mills

Destiny Cheyenne Moore

Kristin Cari Moore

Jayme Leigh Morgan

Chassidy Lee-Ann Moses

Dalton Xavier Mullins

Haley Elizabeth Mullins

Joshua Todd Mullins

Harriet Clementine Music

Kennady Lenn Newsome

Cindy Owens

Nathaniel Haze Pack

Zachary Tyler Patrick

Melissa Dawn Pauley

Linnea Ann Pease

Erica Dawn Pelphrey

Chelsey Brooke Pennington

Cortney Breann Perkins

Heather Michelle Perry

Gordon Lee Porter

Megan Rachelle Potter

Charlie Nichole Prater

Madison Bailey Preece

Heather Sue Puckett

Billie Ranziena Ramey
Dustin S. Ramsey
Brittany Nicole Ratliff
Jacob Michael-Byron Ray
Matthew Byron Ray
Kaleb Dwayne Rodebaugh
Bethany Amber Scarberry
John Field Scott
Taylor Paige Scott
Joseph Samuel Shannon

Tabatha Louise Shepherd
Kayla Sizemore
Haley E. Skaggs
David Harrison Slone
Joshua Ryan Slone
Whittney Payge Slone
Bradley William Smith
Chelsey Leigh Spears
Rachel Elaine Stacy
Amber Nichole Stanley

Amber Nicole Stepp
Haley Briana Sullivan
Megan Paige Syck
Tristan Thomas Syck
Mikita Clinton Tackett
Christine Louise Taul
Brittany Nicole Taylor
Brittany Leann Thacker
Amy Marie Thompson
Matthew Nathaniel Toler

John David Toole
Lonnie Richard Trainer
Sarah Elizabeth Vanover
Sara Beth Walker
Lindsay Shea Wallen
Bobby Allen Weighman
Mercedes Layne Whitaker
Tiffany Michelle Whitaker
Kayla Marie Worthington

BIOLA UNIVERSITY, LA MIRADA, CA

Sierra L. Allen
Jonathan W. Alwine
Amanda Barber
Sarah Boerner
Nicole Braski
Spencer Camp
Kristin Taylor Campolongo
Chloe Carlson
Susan Carmichael
Morgan Carr
Jeannie Choi
Joycelyn Choo

Yvette Alice Fries
Conrad Frommelt
Torie Hamilton
Cameryn Hara
Soorin Hong
Herrin Jou
Ken Kahunahana Jr.
Sean Kakigi
Angela Jean Kirschner
Sarah Koes
Caleb J. Lai
Joseph Luigs

Elizabeth Malott
Alejandra Martinez-
Sandoval
Daniel Martinez-Sandoval
Joanna Masopust
Tessa McQuillan
Jessica Mendoza
Samantha Ruth Miller
Crystal Mohr
Nathan Mueller
J. D. Neal
Lauren Nicole Pickering

Spencer Pierschbacher
Eleanor Poltorak
Annah Pritchett
Megan Reade
Lindsay Elizabeth Reed
Rachel Dorothy Rohm
Gavin Sweeney
Melody Tan
Carla Veliz
Mystiana Victorino
Gavin Wong
Sarah Yuen

BISHOP STATE COMMUNITY COLLEGE, MOBILE, AL

Courtney A. Brooks
Tommy E. Caves
Quentin T. Crockett
Dejaih M. Daniels
Kenadria J. Evans

Nathaniel T. Fedor
Tyler X. Hale
Lauren K. Holsenbeck
Kyana L. King
Heather A. Macdonald

Daijah A. Merkerson
Cyle R. Miller
Haley A. Mindler
Nicole L. Moore
Namunyere E. Muhubao

Leticia E. Patton
Amanda C. Perryman
Brittney C. Reed
Dena L. Sanford
Hunter A. Stewart

BISMARCK STATE COLLEGE, BISMARCK, ND

Connor Candrian
Braeton Erhardt

Caroline Jacobson
Kimberly Jarabek

Jessica Kleinsasser
Adam Long

Kelsey Nicholson
Marcie Woehl

BLACKBURN COLLEGE, CARLINVILLE, IL

Brianna E. Bednar
Ashleigh C. Clendenny
Jessica M. Cramer
Jordan Danielle Foor

Clark W. Johnson
Brooke K. Kinroth
Ethan Klaffer
Desiree McCollum

Elizabeth Meehan
Ajay Minton
Kaitlyn Pugh
Elizabeth D. Quick

Morgan Stein
Abigail Sutton
Catherine E. Young

BLOOMFIELD COLLEGE, BLOOMFIELD, NJ

Nelly Fleur Djrehonon Beugre

Tiayanna Ashley Boston

Morgan Collingwood

Tysha Lyn Crosby-Washington

Daniel Garcia

Fara Gaston

Dy-Nashae K. Gunthrope

Mariline L. Jean

Danielle Leslie Johnson

Marcus Leak

Kimberly Luna

Ariel Madera

Zamel Mitchell

Rachael Jessica Neilan

Jennifer Diana Orellana

Yojaira Orozco

Dhrupa Rathod

Samantha Rios Marie Rios-Nieves

Petra Semelova

Johnny Vega

BLOOMSBURG UNIVERSITY, BLOOMSBURG, PA

Rebecca Anderson

Gabrielle Balaguer

Kristina Balla

Christopher Bastardi

Kendra Dorothy Betz

Nicholas Bilski

Lauren Marie Bond

Mikala Jo Britt

Abigail Brown

Leah Marie Cameron

Kahli Castagnera

Lauren Chamberlin

Kelly Cope

Jon Dekovitch

Monica DePaul

Sharnise Dozier

Brooke Elliott

Amber Elsner

Kira Sophia Helene England

Brooke Esbenshade

Jose Escarfullery

Emilie Fauber

Francesca Marielle Gates

Jasmine Gonzalez

Yuliya Goss

Marisa Griffith

Brittany Hardy

Jahlil Hardy

Alex Hazzard

Zymirra Herrin

Clarissa Hoke

David Hooker

Ryan Karpinski

Megan Keefer

Timothy Keiper

Maura Kranzel

Amanda Anne Kuzmak

Bret LePard

Morgan Lewis

Alison Martino

Natalie Ann Mayo

Lexie Elizabeth Mendall

Luke Millan

Nicole Miller

Shawn Miscioscia

Madelyne Morrison

Katherine Mullen

Phelan Neuciler

Samantha K. Newton

Gabriana Nisiotis

Abigail Novak

Nicole Oman

Anthony Patrick

Molly Payne

Carissa Pupo

Alexis Riffel

Nicole Salviolo

Cassidy Sangrey

Madison Scripture

Ashley Lakeisha Shawver

Tye Eder Sheets

Emily Smith-Schretlen

Joseph Stover

Devon Suiter

Caitlin Sullivan

Rebecca Swisher

Jerrin Toomey

Justin VanDerMolen

Nathanael Weaver

Tyler Wenger

Abigail Willcox

Katlyn Wise

Jennifer Kingsley Young

Rebecca Zamonas

Stephen Zbyszinski

BLUEFIELD STATE COLLEGE, BLUEFIELD, WV

Hope Adams

James V. Agee

Tanairi Airey

Clayton L. Akers

Fred Jamaan Alkhodidi

Waleed Abdullah Alosaimi

Michael B. Baker

Angela C. Beck

Charles R. Beckelhimer

Alyssa D. Bishop

Nathaniel I. Blankenship

Rebecca C. Bradley

Kayla Marie Bragg

Marta Briales

Paige A. Brinkley

Kristin L. Brown

Haley Brianna Browning

Timothy Kyle Burks

Jacob P. Carey

Tabatha S. Carter

Michele A. Charnow

Sarah A. Church

Kirk John Collins

Sierra L. Davidson

Kayla D. Davis

Ivy J. Dawson

Micah Sean Denton

Donna A. Deskins

Rosanne De Vries

Deny R. Doss

Derek E. Dotson

Stephanie E. Duncan

Brandon M. Dunn

Katelyn R. Ellis

Benjamin K. Fraley

Kristy L. French

Charles M. Gibson

Benjamin D. Goffin

Jason B. Goodell

Shanti Gurung

Ann M. Hamer

Joseph D. Hanna

Bryana Michelle Hawley

April E. Herald

Anita S. Hughes

Joshua Alan Husband

Eugenia Marie Jones

Tammy S. Kidd

Katie M. Lester

Coty A. Lilly

Autumn Leigh Lively

Alexandria L. Massie

Jimmy S. McPherson
Thomas J. McVey
Caylon J. Minor
Traci D. Mitchem
Katie L. Morton
Cory T. Neese
Amanda R. Nichols
Tiffany Noe
Emily M. Parisen
Kimberly A. Pendry
Jerry D. Perdue Jr.

Jeremiah L. Poff
Deanna L. Radford
Elizabeth R. Rasnake
Charles Millard Reeves
Kathryn L. Scott
Kenneth H. Scott
Joel R. Sharp
Amber N. Shirley
Jordan G. Shrewsbury
Ridge A. Sibold
Michael A. Sifers

Heather D. Simmons
Autumn D. Smith
Cassandra Nicole Smith
Cynthia A. Snow
Laura Faith Stevens
Earl C. Stracener
Brittney N. Thomas
Elizabeth A. Thomas
Kala N. Thompson
Angelina M. Treadway
Jessica A. Turner

Arron Quentin Umberger
John Michael Walker
Sashane Tameika Watson
Jeniffer R. Wickline
Megan L. Wickline
Tabitha A. Williams
Raychel Wood
Makayla B. Zutaut

BLUEGRASS COMMUNITY & TECHNICAL COLLEGE, LEXINGTON, KY

Savannah Beth Adams
Kristie Renee Anderson
Lindsay Marie Baker
Marvin Baker II
Crystal Danielle Barish
Roger C. Barkley Jr.
Jessica Kate Birdwhistell
Kelcie Katherine Brophy
Cynthia Lorran Brosius
Imani Niara Bryant
John David Butler
Jamie Lynn Cammuse
Michael Keith Cardom
Susan Lee Coalter
John Adam Colceri
Michael Thomas Colwell
Courtney Lynn Comroe
Judy Marie Deal

Neil Anderson Dees
Sarah Elizabeth Delaney
Ashley Linnea Dunaway
Liberty Mallare Edwards
Daniel Collier Elkin
Tasha Nicole Elliott
Michael Ray Esham
Mohamed Mahmoud
Ibrahim Farag
Jessica N. Farhat
Corin Foster
Houston Thomas Green
Susan Gail Grotenhuis
Brent Hatton
Jessica Lynn Hatton
Sara Jo Hedger
Roger Hisle
Marly Grace Jenkins

Chassidy Paige Keeton
Maggie Kimani
Didon Wema Litanda
Olivia Grace Marshall
Shannon Michelle McSorley
Melissa Marguerite Myszka
Christopher Michael
Nardelli
Hillary Ann O'Neal
Andrew Simon Osborne
Chris A. Pendleton
Georgina B. Perez Arambula
Evan William Pettit
Joshua Scott Pettyjohn
Emily Nicole Plummer
Heather Jacqueline Pujol
Jacob Peter Reiter
Codie Lee Roe

Daniel Anthony Rogers
Cynthia Marie Rose
Kristina Louise Rose
Benjamin Willburn Russell
Benjamin Joseph Sepko
Richard Benjamin Sills
Glenn Phillip Steder III
Jeanie Marie Sutton
Assan Suwareh
Jacqueline Carol Walden
Amy M. Watson
Alicia Marie Watts
Kari Lynn Weisenfeld
Crystal Suzanne Wicks
Stephen Joseph Wiggins
Jessica Lynn Yates

BLUE MOUNTAIN COLLEGE, BLUE MOUNTAIN, MS

Courtney Leigh Carter
Joshua Levi Cox
Jamieon Morgan Davis

Derek Benjamin Hunter
Jake Louis Omedeo
Micah Clay Russell

Nikki Lauren Taylor
Rachel Leanne Walker
Brandon Douglas Webber

Shiloh Wree Wehrstein

BLUE RIDGE COMMUNITY COLLEGE, FLAT ROCK, NC

Colleen Adams
Arden Avery
Sarah Blackburn
Holly Blackwell
Jacob Tyler Bradley

Katina Antionette Braswell
Betty Brown
Rahma Brown
Mishelle Calvillo
Chelsa Danielle Cannon

Laura Chapman
Christopher Chavez
Melissa Ann Cook
Maira Dubon
Heather Finster

Samuel Frady
Kelly Freeman
Leah Nicole Graves
Kay Henson
Michael Hooper

Kathleen Johnson
Caleb Lee Jones
Alexander Jung
Summer Kelley
Paulette Laberge

Mary Laughter
Shaula Marie Morris
Mary Murray
Brenda Oviedo
Cheryl Lynn Plott

Elizabeth Prince
Manuel Roman-Antunez
Mark Phillip Rubianes
Tarah Singh
Morgan Suttles

Mindy Brooke Roberts
Tavel
Kimberly Wilkie

BMA THEOLOGICAL SEMINARY, JACKSONVILLE, TX

Angeleta Louise Beekman
Michael Eugene Book
Joshua Caleb Defoore

James Rey Hendricks
Felix Lane Knott
Cristian Israel Martinez

Stuart James Priest
Jared Anthony Shaw
Jake Allen Steele

Robert Lee Stokes

BOB JONES UNIVERSITY, GREENVILLE, SC

Jennifer Leigh Allen
Samuel Russell Barnard III
Eric Kristianson Boley
Jessica Denae Bonnema
Casey Elizabeth Brighton
Isaac Frederick Bryden
Kayla Anne Bullock
Laura Ann Bush
Timothy Lawrence Carroll
Kathryn Michaela Chapin
Elizabeth Ruth Fei Yin Chu
Christopher Michael Coker
Deborah Elizabeth
Dahlhausen
Timothy Randall David
Brittany Noel Dechant
Scott Christian Farley
Kayla Leigh Fenstermaker

Bernard Clinton Fowlkes
Jonathan Eli Fremont
Auria Joy Garland
Karen Marielle Girton
Hosanna Marie Gonzales
Emily Ruth Harris
Luke Philip Hollis
Matthew Aaron Hughes
Kristen Leanne Ince
Kendrick Paul Manabat
Infante
Benjamin Joseph Jacquot
Rebecca Danielle Jones
Lydia Louise Kassales
Jae Yoon Kim
WooJoo Kim
Matthew Heyward Ledbetter
Stephen Matthew Lynn

Rachel Grace Madeira
Ryan Andrew McCarty
Ashley Lorraine McNally
Jeffrey Gustavo Medina
Dylan Kristopher Mills
Julie Estelle Mission
Kenneth James Morgan
Holden Thomas Morter
Billy Rae Iris Murphy
Lauren Victoria Musselman
Dakota Grayson Price
Bethany Ann Pursel
Shelley Renee Redlinger
Edward Roy Robinson
Katie Marie Roukes
Abigail Joy Rysta
Zachary Scott Sigmon
Andrew Joseph Smiley

Cameron Raymond Smith
Timothy Daniel Smith
Jessa Mackenzie Stratton
Deijha Monet Swanson
Jennifer Elaine VerWay
David Ethan Wallace
Ciara Dawn Weant
Laura Elizabeth Weier
Matthew Daniel Wells
Jessica Brooke Wentworth
Joel Edward Whited
Elizabeth Ann Whitford
Bethany Lynn Williams
Robert Russell A. Wilson
Vincent Michael Wilson
Caleb Gregory Wright
Zolian Sang Zoong Lwe

BOWLING GREEN STATE UNIVERSITY, BOWLING GREEN, OH

Adriana Davis

Michael Smith

Ryan Kenneth Sowers

BRADFORD SCHOOL COLUMBUS, COLUMBUS, OH

Matt Bibler
Laura Buntmeyer
Pam Darr
Hope Alexandra Deal

Taylor Eilers
Jessica Marie Elliott
Christine Foster
Christina Harrison

Megan N. Miller
Jennifer Rutherford
Sophia Marie Stati
Megan Stewart

Melody Truitt
Morgan Ulery
Mark Zach Williams

BRENAU UNIVERSITY, GAINESVILLE, GA

Riham Abutweima

Rachel Mercedes Adam

Elvira Moya Aguilar

Brittany Michelle Aikens

Adil Abdullah Alghamdi

Rana Saleh Alghamdi

Anecia Dishel Allen

Britney Allen

Cynthia Rae Allen

Hind Salem Alsaedi

Margaret Njanji Ashu

Tatiana Valeria Ayala

Hogai Balouch

Jennifer Barnett

Kaitlyn Batchelor

Susan Shields Baumann

Jimmie Michelle Beasley

Austalia Beaufait

Kimberly Michelle Benn

Abigayle Claire Berryman

Greta Jean Blankenship

Amanda Nicole Bonilla

Nathan Christopher Borne

Lacey S. Borum

Thomas Bowne

Margaret Kathryn Bronaugh

Keri Lynn Broughton

Chelsey Brown

Emily Bruce

Elizabeth Grace Burch

Patricia Dawn Cantrell

Terry Annette Capers

Taylor Annette Carden

Amanda Irvin Chapell

Jamie Elizabeth-Rhodes
Chapman

Kayla Leigh Childers

Katherine Clark

Kelsey Nicole Coates

William Barham Cook

Morgan Copeland

Caitlin Wilbanks Corley

Nipa Mansukhlal Cothran

Rebekah Marie Cox

Jenny Marie Crouch

Michael Crouch

Charmain Theresa
Cummings

Staricka Breonn Cummings

Stephanie Daniell

Amanda Spiece Davis

Brittnie Olene Davis

Christopher James Davis

Jensen Davis

Shawnika C. Davis

Juliann Beth Landers Dean

Rachel Elizabeth Deline

Kayla DelPizzo

Rebecca Susan Del Plato

Amelia Heather Dodd

Hannah Doster

Alina Dumbravicean

Charlotte Deloris Dunagan

Hillary Taylor Earls

Amanda Allyson Ellett

Mary Farrow

Jordan Melissa Ford

Chelsea Morgan Foster

Krista Anita Fox

Ashley Nicole Franklin

Andrea Michele Gaines

Brenda Katherine Godfrey

Emily Renee Goman

Roxanna Gomez

Kimberly Gray

Bryson May Green

Dana L. Greiser

Fatimah H. Hafiz

William Thomas Hall

Sarah Elizabeth Harber

Caitlin M. Hardegree

Donald Graham Harden Jr.

Janae Nichole Harper

Inga Haut

Jana Hood Heaton

Shineitha Kidd Henry

Kristin Henson

Fatima Heravy

Yarden Alleluia Hixson

Ann Marie Holman

Olivia Maxwell Holz

Brittany Shay Hughes

Shelly Ann Hughes

Caylene Ingram

Elizabeth Interiano

Janifere James

Kyunti James-Thorpe

Jenna M. Jansen

Dominika Jasova

Edmark Bradley Jeffrey

Mary Allison Jennings

Melissa Mitchell Johnsa

Kayla Rebecca Jump

Paige Kean

Maggie Mae Rose Keller

Tameika C. Kelley

Lindsay A. Kelly

Justin Wayne Kennedy

Phillip Nelson Kinsey

Casey M. Kozozemski

Alan Antonio Latimer

Emily Lemons

Yixuan Li

Bhumi B. Limbasia

Amy Stephenson Little

Kimberly Dianne Llorens

Bethany Elaine Lochner

Kassidy Reagan Locke

Marshil B. Locklear

Katie Beth Lomma

Savannah Rose Marie Long

Carmen Mineo Lorenzen

Jonathan Dawson Lynch

Kayla Brooke Madsen

Angie Kay Mallory

Bridget Danielle Marlow

Rebecca Josephine Martell

Elizabeth Anne Martin

Erin Jessica McClure

Tammy Sharay McElhaney

Jessi Denise McFarland

Rachel McFarland

Sharon Dione McFarland

Megan Louise McNeal

Leslie Kaye McRoberts

Kristen Anna McVey

Stacy K. Meadows

Michael Ray Mellinger

Maria Fidela Mendiola

Samantha Renee Miles

Jackie Christine Mileson

Hannah Paige Miller

Fallon Jayde Mills

Eric M. Minter

Ronald Edward Moore

Nicole Moses

Nicole Marie Naccarato

Aissatou Ndiaya

Joanna Ngov

Thuy Vinh Nguyen

Kristin Bennett Nix

Bart Allan Noll

Jane Elizabeth Norwood

Ashley Ann Nowak

Amanda Leigh O'Neal

Charles Thomas Ottosen

Jie Pan

Dawn Denise Panowich

Mark Castillo Passmore

Truptiben Hiteshkumar Patel

Alexandria Noelle Patton

Abigail Capri Paul

Maria Perdomo

Alisha Lashay Pinkins

Jordan Pittman

David Heath Pitts

Katayon Qahir

Margie Lynn Reed

April Michelle Reid

Billy Edward Roberts

Courtney Leigh Robinson

Valerie Rodriguez

Sarah M. Rooker

Shelby Shay Rumker

Chantal Brooke Russell

Janet Sanderlin
Kelly Michelle Satcher
Jordan Saylor
Vyacheslav Slavic Sazhko
Elizabeth Schneider
Megan Ann Schultz
James Fulton Sennett
Stacia Kathleen Sexton
Lindsey Shadburn Simpson
Kelly Lynn Smith

Carey Jessica Spurgeon
Marissa Hewatt Stephens
Sasha DeAnna Stovall
Madison R. Strickland
Javaye Devette Stubbs
Xiaoxi Sun
Denise Sunga
Tonya S. Teel
Kassandra Barbara Thomas
Mary Elizabeth Thomas

Linda A. Toomer
Alaina Troha
Kelly Ann Turner
Ashton Michelle Umberger
Karla Joan Utterback
Olivia Varnson
Maribel Vazquez
Amy E. Walls
Yanyu Wang

Thomas Ambrosius Maria
Weirich
Devyn White
Kristine Cleo Williams
Kelsey Nicole Williamson
Rebecca Belle Willis
Amy Elizabeth Wilson
Tiffany Wilson
Diane Alma Wood
Brittany Dyan Zimmerly

BRESCIA UNIVERSITY, OWENSBORO, KY

Emily Adkins
Italo Arruda
Carleigh Jean Bright
LuTisha Buckner
Kelsey Burr
Chase Carrico

Patricia Crespo
Amber Estes
Embra Hawkins
William Johnson
Jordan King
Marketa Kreuzingerova

Cynthia Leonardo
Donita Mallory
Mary Katherine McClure
Erica McFarland
William McKenzie
Courtney Naas

Nicole Ralph
Alexxis Ross-Logan
Jacob Whitfill
Julie Whitfill

BREVARD COLLEGE, BREVARD, NC

Samuel Hobson Blakley
Fatina Gharachorloo

Stepheny Grey Hine
Jamie Lynn Hrobak

Kayla Christine Leed
Hannah Young Leonard

Juan Carlos Mascaro
Stephen Douglas Olson

BRIDGEVALLEY COMMUNITY & TECHNICAL COLLEGE, SOUTH CHARLESTON, WV

Chastity Hope Adams
Jason M. Belt
Kayla Bilak
John Drew Blackburn
Candace Boggs
Samantha Danielle Brewer
Kingsley Israel Brown
Randy Brown
Gregory F. Cade
Matthew Jay Campbell
Tara L. Carder
Erika J. Carroll
Mary Beth Chaplin
Natalie D. Cinalli
Angela D. Cole
Shane M. Cox
Lindly Paige Crawford
Amanda W. Davis
Mark M. Davis

Steve L. Dilworth
Heather Dawn Dolin
Gretchen Sue Drake
Shirell L. Duckworth
Derek A. Dufour
Tammy R. Durrett
Tiffany Amber Edwards
Brad A. Fallecker
Janet M. Foster
William E. Gaskins
Amy Lynn Gentry
David R. Good
Jason Robert Gum
Brendon J. Hamrick
Gary Lee Hartman
Wayne Robert Heavener
Adam Martin Hoff
Hunter Adam Hughes
John Rodney Johnson

Paul Allen Kelley
Bailey S. King
Leon E. Kinney
Sara Nicole Klein
Ian Scott Leary
Frances Lesher
Kevin G. Lewis
Dayton S. Lister
Terry Kenneth Logsdon
Lila G. Lydick
Christen Mylinh Maalea
Anthony L. Markley
Jennifer Joanne Matics
Shaun Douglas Maynard
Billy Ray McLaughlin
James R. L. Meadows
Denzil J. Miller
Lana J. Miller
Charles Adam Moody

Yilmar Chaverra Moreno
Christina M. Musick
Michelle L. Perry
Randy L. Redmond
ODell Scites
Harrison Dale Scott
Larry Brooks Scott
Vanessa Lynn See
Candy M. Sigley
Thomas L. Simmons Jr.
Danielle N. Smith
Randall David Stark
Donald M. Stewart
Kenneth J. Stewart
Leslie Taylor
Morgan Leigh Thomas
Melanie Sue Truslow
Jeffery Tucker
Chadwick L. Vance

Kendra L. Wagner

Nicholas Ray Wamsley

Robert William Wheeler

Aimee Beth Yates

Zachary Michael Walker

Jacob W. Weese

BRIDGEWATER COLLEGE, BRIDGEWATER, VA

David Samuel Bates

Morgan Leigh Bender

Andrew Stephen Bollinger

Jose Martin Cardoso Martinez

Terrence William Chambers

Tracy Lynn Chapman

Shelby Vaughn Edmisten

Desiree Lyvette Elliott

Thomas Connor Fairburn

Emily Claire Helms

Emily Elizabeth Higgins

Samantha Lamas

Kelsey Elizabeth Limbert

Melissa Adele McMindes

Dominee Aria McNerney

Victoria Grace Minnix

Caleb Levi Roderick Quinn

Caroline Frances Reid

Katie Scarlett Rexrode

Emily N. Schmidt

Brooke Allison Smith

Andrew Robert Summers

Katherine Yvonne Thompson

Andrea T. Walker

Shelley Nadine Weachter

Austin Taylor White

BROWN MACKIE COLLEGE LOUISVILLE, LOUISVILLE, KY

Etropia Allen

Matthew Angle

Seyborn Billings

LaDonna S. Bowens

Stephanie Burkhead

Leslie Clifton

Kendra Denise Coleman

Alyssa Dages

Shamika Nicole Davis

Dominique Drayton

Julie A. Elrod

Ashley Farris

Lutfiya Feyzulova

Jennifer Fortner

Kristin French-Marzian

Jordan Fullen

Vicky Furman

Sonya Tonette Gaither

Amber Heun

Timothy R. Hill Sr.

Freda C. Houck

Kaelly Jonason

Selina Justice

William Karl Kannenberg

Jessica Lynn Kendall

Jeffrey Langan

Betty Mahoney

Dana Scruse Malone

Courtney LaShelle Moon

Terri L. Mozee

Athena Pellman

Gregory Poehlein

Wes Priddy

Ezreyona Reed

Vickie Regenaur

Christopher Reynolds

Rebecca Schlegal

Paige R. Skelton

Cherrish Taylor

Darion Taylor

Leslie Tipton

Cristina Vazquez

Jessica Whitworth

Jacqueline Williams

BROWN MACKIE COLLEGE SALINA, SALINA, KS

Lacy Alderson

Julie Allen

Melody K. Bohn

Marissa D. Budke

Denise Catania

Mikale Doherty

Christeena Ferguson

Brenna N. Goddard

Addison Marie Houchin

Candace E. Kattes

Jessica D. Lash

Kourtney Ludlum

Emali McGee

Kevin Morris

James L. Parker

Amber Ponder

Tiffany Riffel

Sara Marie Roberts

Carol L. Rosenboom

Sophie Louise Snow

Taylor Stout

Sara E. Venters

Majak Wenyin

Ilea Windhorst

Haylie Zima

BRUNSWICK COMMUNITY COLLEGE, SUPPLY, NC

Hunter Jefferson Absher

Morgan Elizabeth Alford

Amanda Danyale Alsbrooks

Eli Ray Alvarez

Nancy H. Applewhite

Erika Lynne Ashley

Olivia Diana'lane Babson

Brianna Nicole Baham

Billie Jean Bailey

Mitchell Scott Baker

Charlee Rebeccca Baxley

Abigail Caroline Bentley

Debra Leanne Biggs

Charlotte A. Blakemore

Hoyt W. Booth

Debra Singleton Bordeaux

Heidi Lea Bowling

Christian Hinson Boyd

Chelsey Christina Bozeman

Fallon Jade Bradsher

Alicia Elaine Bryant

Anetta Bryant Bryant

Melanie Lauren Byrd

Karan Herrin Cape

Nathaniel Alexander Carmon

Rebecca Robin Castaneda

Fred Marvin Caulder

Candice Cheryll Chavis

Andrew Blake
Chomiczewski

Erica Leigh Citrullo

Amanda Nicole Conley

Amber Leigh Craig

Marshall Alexander Creech

Chelcie Matia Cruce

Anton Cruz

Kristen Demaris Cully

Patrick Taylor Dame

Blaine Lynden Deabenderfer

Nichole Drayton

Abigail Leigh Dyson

Eric Kent Eason

Kelly Beth Enis

Kobi Dee Etheridge

Julia Capria Faye Eubanks

Amy Nicole Evans

Cameron Jordan Fitch

Olivia Marie Flowers

Karlie Rose Floyd

Carolyn Marie Foggan

Danielle Mello Ford

Heidi Keren Formyduval

Marie A. Forrest

Crystal Amanda Fullwood

Christopher Michael
Garrison

Christina Lee Gillum

Alexander D. Gore

Anastasia Danielle Gore

Hayley Morgan Grimes

Krystal Marie Grissett

Alexandria Gurganus

Cherish Faytth Hardy

Lauren Rae Haugen

Emily Beatrice Hemmings

Connie L. Hensley

Brandon Lane Hewett

Dallas Rose Hewett

Amber M. Hill

Otis Lorenzo Hill

Jeffrey Alan Hillwig

Delois Ann Hines

Eric Daniel Holland

Bret Forrest Horne

Jason Mitchell Huff

Ashley D. Inman

Jacob Dansie Jensen

Amy Kathleen Johnson

Gregory Alan Johnson

Meredith Anne Johnson

Candace Ashlie Kane

Kristina Helene Keller

Britne Knox

Nathan Daniel Kuester

Aaron Gregory Lewis

Jaidenia Bulaga Light

Janet Pigott Little

Kiersten Wylie Lomosad

Anna Marie Mancinelli

Annah Mae Maynes

Ashlee Dianne McCall

Kyle Bryant McCann

Nakese Shajuan McCoy

Kayla Nicole McDaniel

Donald Carlston McKeithan

Brandon Raeshion
McMillian

Kathleen May Melton

Justin Tyler Collins Miller

Amie Marie Milliken

Angel Kay Milliken

Colleen Polk Mitchell

Jasmine Evora Morgan

Kristen Mary Nazzaro

Jacqueline Michele Nunes

Diana Leticia Nunez

Courtney Snell Nygaard

Grayson James Oakley

Christopher Michael
Ochtyun

Julia Allison Orr

Amy Renee Overman

George M. Overy

Michael Stewart Ozier

Christopher Dean Parrish

Christopher Anthony
Pihlgren

K-leigh Morgan Prevette

Mary Kathleen Ratliff

Jonathan Alexander Ray

Eleanor Elaine Register

Joel Adam Reibert

Larry Allen Rivenbark

Carolina Rivera

Achelle Sharea Robbins

Ashley Lydia Robbins

Holly Lou Robertson

Megan Nicole Robinson

Brandy Grace Russ

Dianna G. Schaeffer

Dawn M. Shivers

Corina Anastacie Sierra

Benjamin Ward Simmons

April Lennon Simpson

Fallon Emily Smiroldo

Chelsea D. Smith

Matthew J. Spano

Jordan Michael Spitler

Edith Tapia

Donavan Eric Testerman

Adrian Dawn Tharpe

Jessica Lynn Todd

Elizabeth Jean Van Meter

Christy Lynn Walker

Emily Nicole Weaver

Morgan Lynne Wheeler

Craig Antona Williams

Jermario Derelle Williams

Hannah Louise Wilt

Donald Waylon Wise

Hallee Noelle Worthington

Lindsay Jordan Wrenn

Rebecca L. Wynne

Crystal Brooke Yates

Ashley Morgan Yurek

BRYAN COLLEGE, DAYTON, TN

Bryan Daniel Alderman

Daniel Steven Cadiz

Kristin Nellie Hall

Michael Elizabeth Sherrill

Luke Daniel Smythe

BRYANT & STRATTON COLLEGE ALBANY CAMPUS, ALBANY, NY

Renee M. Brisson

Michesha Lashone-Marie
Cancer

Trenesia Goodwine

Susan Hassett-Sporko

Marcus Robert Henderson

Amanda Lynn Kindlon

Karl E. LaBarge Jr.

Thomas F. Moran

Susan L. Neumann

Mary Kay Overbaugh

Alisia Premchan

April D. Rowley

Shawnta Nicole
Scarborough

Christina Marie Skokan

Lisa M. Stewart-Green

Heather Lynn Torrey

Nancy L. Tortorice

Stephanie Tumi

BRYANT & STRATTON COLLEGE ASSOCIATE DIVISION, EASTLAKE, OH

Tina D. Amos
John M. Brinkley
Eugene Carroll
Katie M. Chorba
Karrie-Ann E. Clay
Amanda M. Futkos
Ma'Cyla M. Hollis

Blaire E. Horvath
Dominique M. Huggins
Candence N. Hughes
Tara L. Irish
Adriana C. Jefferson
Diane Kocka
Princess Y. Mitchell

Christal R. Morrow
Amy R. Murphy
Tabitha S. Nickels
Andrea Padovic
Nicole L. Parson
Marina Puselja
Gina M. Roberts

Kristine Sivillo
Anthony J. Swartz
Angela M. Taylor
Michalynn Thompson
Donna M. White
Selina V. Wooten

BRYANT & STRATTON COLLEGE BACHELOR DIVISION, EAST LAKE, OH

Vatisha Cook-Washington
Joyce A. Maikut

Teresa Lee McCurry
Rayette F. Monte

Katrina E. Tunkara

Angela D. Valdez

BRYANT & STRATTON COLLEGE CLEVELAND – DOWNTOWN CAMPUS, CLEVELAND, OH

Diane L. Bailey
Shondra P. Black
Renee Blackwell
Elizabeth A. Blakely
Monica B. Bradley
Jedidah D. Brooks
Helen J. Cole
Aliyah M. Debose

Carolyn Debow
Khia J. Dixon
Gwydion Morgan Seth
Gilbert
Brenda K. Gregley
Jessica B. Hall
Nicole Y. Hamilton
Darryl C. Hardy

Jean M. Haussman
Latonya M. Humphries
Crystal D. Kelly
Charmyka L. Lewis
Sharmaine R. Martin
Naima F. Omar
Charlotte M. Perkins
Karla D. Rhodes

Catherine C. Swope Blade
Jeffery G. Tucker
David L. Vaughn
Tiffani D. Ware
Cynthia M. Wilson
Dana A. Zerby

BUENA VISTA UNIVERSITY, STORM LAKE, IA

Kacee Leah Baker
Claire Isabelle Boston
Carlee Rae Brown
Patrice Ann Crall
Austin Allen Delp
Chelsey Kathrina Goetz

Joseph Daniel Hindman
Callie Alexis Hoffman
Robert Patrick Ivey
Bonnie Sue Keller
Elizabeth Nam Kim
Tarynne Elizabeth Kinghorn

Carolyn Elizabeth
McDermott
Jamie Lynn Rich
Sarah Lee Schlichte
Zachary Taylor Schmidt
Alec Thomas Sindelar

Stephanie Marie Steiner
Paije Jeslyn Wee
Austin David Wegner-Groth
Hanna Elizabeth Zinn

BUFFALO STATE, BUFFALO, NY

Kenise Adams
Courtney R. Blake
Antonnea S. Bolden
Zoe C. Bolden
Devan V. Brady
Mario J. Cataffo

Jeremy B. Catania
Tiffany A. Chang
Ashley C. Etienne
Jholane R. Haber
Megan R. Haefner
Leanna Marie Kalinowski

Elizabeth A. Malinowski
Derek C. Jorden Jr.
Christine Matos
Alexia D. Matos Mateo
Samuel M. Merriman
Takisha J. Morancy

Miguel A. Pereira III
Lyndsay M. Raymond
Afolabi Soetan
Jennifer J. Steinhorst
Sasa E. Vann
Ashley L. Weselak

BUTLER COUNTY COMMUNITY COLLEGE, BUTLER, PA

Danielle Baker
Brianna M. Bedillion

Jordan Tyler Blum
Alycia E. Brehm

Courtney Callen
Alexander S. Campbell

Stefan M. Carlsson
Christina Marie Davis

Lauren Marie Denny
Thomas Paul Dimun
Leanne Duncan
Nathan William Falchetti
Bryson Fox
Jessica Fox
Curt Greene
Mary Jean Greene

Shawna Grossman-Mershimer
Darian Brooke Gruver
Jennifer Harris
Olivia Margaret Hershberger
Terry Judd Johnstone
Paul Jones
Sarah Dorothy Kasunic
Kendra B. Kepple

Danielle Langley
Cory A. Lautenschlager
Nicole Mansfield
Shyana L. McCommon
Austin W. Miller
Saydie A. Moore
Heather Morida
Codi Elaine Reed
Chad Alan Ryan

Holly A. Schaefer
Cierra J. Shirley
Kelly Dawn Strutt
Rachel Michelle Suddoth
Olivia R. Terwilliger
Kyra E. Walters
Nathan K. Weckerly
Jamie Wiggan
Maizee Rose Zaccone

CABRINI COLLEGE, RADNOR, PA

Erica Ann Abbott
Amanda Boccelli
Madeline Coutu
Alexis Drew

Gabriella Glenning
Mackenzie Harris
Justin X. Juliano
Colin Kilroy

Anthony Michael Lauder
Molly Rose McDougall
Danton Moyer
George Louis Nave

Dana Catherine Peterson
Caitlyn Poole
Abigail Pressimone
Brianna Ridgely

CAIRN UNIVERSITY, LANGHORNE, PA

Okanniwa Babayemi
Josiah Richard Buss
Kristy Raquel Douglas
Jennifer Lynn Dunning
Amanda Lee Fry
Wayne Aaron Hailstone
Emelie Harvey
Franklin Edward Hinson III

Eric Justin Hodges
Timothy James Holland
Charles K. Hopkins
Spencer Michael Kulhanjian
Daniel Laubach
Natalie Livingston
Daniel J. Loch
Adam N. Martin

Carlos Matos
Alyssa Joy Mowery
Catherine Marie Murawski
Katherine Esther Nofsinger
Nicole B. Nutting
Seth Lawrence Richardson
Grace Schmoyer
Joshua Smith

Carol Straub
Nemeh Kamal Sulaiman
Daniel Robert Vandzura
Rachel LeeAnn Warner
Sophie Marie Weber
Shelby Eileen Wischan
Rebekah Joy Zimmerman

CALIFORNIA BAPTIST UNIVERSITY, RIVERSIDE, CA

Grace Priya Ali
Rosette S. Baloy
Nicole Renee Bell
Amber Marie Boetger
Haley Marlene Bogers
Michael Jacob Callahan
Sarah Teresa Campagna
Tessa Beatrice Cannon
Araceli Cortez
Cheyenne Linnea Denison
Peter Aaron Diaz Jr.
Joyeuse Dufitumukiza

Camille Cooper Finnerty
MacKenzie LaRae Freed
Sirena Aghavni Garabedian
Jacob H. Graff
Elad Gunya
Brittany Hale
Michaela Leigh Helinski
Khai Chi Ho
Joan Uwase Kalimba
Catherine Michelle Knight
Jennifer Marie Kolander
Jordanne Paige Laky

Rebecca Joy Lam
Makenna Lammons
Jonah Jonathan Lay
Leigh Ann Lindsey
Zachary Winslow Long
Aliah Averyl Marshall
Alicia Massaro
Alison Nicole Parrott
Matthew M. Powers
Paighton Lorraine Priest
Xavier Ambrose Putnam
Ashtyn Carol-Ann Robidoux

Kayla Nicole Ruiz
Jessica Marie Schoellerman
Corwyn Christian Singleton
Danielle Nicole Snowden
Kyle Brandon Sugimura
Jessica Dawn Troyer
Gabrielle Elizabeth Ward
Amber Faith Wetherford
Rachel Lillian Wong
Nora Marie Zinn

CALVARY BIBLE COLLEGE & THEOLOGICAL SEMINARY, KANSAS CITY, MO

Sarah Noel Blais
Jesse Chapman
Un Joo Alison Li
Christopher
Sarah Catherine Davis
Virginia Lynn Dodd

Dustin Allen Garrett
Amy J. Harmer
Nathan Thomas Harmer
Emily Alyse Harris
Rebecca Chatham Hessel
John D. Huxman

Timothy James Huxman
Christopher F. Johnson
Brenton Mitchell Klassen
Chad D. Nightingale
Marlene Oleksak
Rebekah M. Parker

Lance Matthew Rensberger
Jinshu Shi
Matthew Macpherson
Skinner

CAMERON UNIVERSITY, LAWTON, OK

Mariama Jane Abramson
Chima Aghaulor
Agnes Ajose
Akinola Akinlawon
Timothy Dean Alaniz
Shilo Allen
Lisangela Arroyo
Mark Bannon
Courtney Barden
Lauren Taylor Barrett
Andres Berber
Victoria Boudiette
Ashley Brinck
Jaime Brown
Makenzie Fran Burk

Chidinma Favour Eunique
Damilola Chykugwu
Casey Curtsinger
Richard Dailey
Josey Dennis
Rachna Dy
Mike Fletcher
Bambi Hampton
Saranah Isenberg
Jacob Jardel
Ayush Lal Joshi
Bishaka Karki
Oluwatoyin Toluwase
Kayode
Nikki Kirk
Alexandra Kolinski

Robert Cary McCoy
Casey Meek
Kelsee Beth Monroe
Chelsey Morin
Samuella Anita
Odartey-Addo
Sijalu Paudel
Kynzie Pierce
Rebekah L. Pullicar
Jacob Quickle
Makayla Kristine Rafferty
Misty Robinson
Holden Rowe
Natalie Ruiz-Castillo
Megan Louise Skulski
Lindsey Ann Smith

Vicky Smith
Jared Stokes
McKenzie Talley
Brigette Thompson
Morgan Thompson
Zoie C. Timothy
Nisha Wagle
Sarah A. Walker
Tanner Weston
Brianna M. Wiginton
Donnet L. Williams
Philip Worthen
Nicole Jane Wright
Jeein Yoon
Zachary Ty Young
Sonora Zukerman

CAMPBELLSVILLE UNIVERSITY, CAMPBELLSVILLE, KY

MacKenzie Brook Arrasmith
Erin Elizabeth Benton
Holly Michelle Bowles
Julian Wesley Cain
Maggie Rae Calvert
Luke Alan Camp
Bryana Paige Carkin
Brittney Ann Casey
Katelyn Rose Chalk
Orgil Chinbat
William Trevor Cook
Victoria Leigh Decker

John Robert Eastridge
Ufuoma Zikora Elvis-
Okukowho
Rosemary Anelix Flores
Mhairi Margret Fyfe
Ashley Nicole Goodin
LeeAnn Elliiot Grider
Hanna Kay Hall
Wade Crawford Harris
Joseph David Hartlage
Emily Brooke Hunter
Saori Kataoka

Shelby Rae Knuckles
Erik Zachary Krivitsky
Holli Jeannette Lindsey
Tyler Scott Magruder
Isaac Nathaniel Marvel
Trent Paul Massey
Aaron Christopher Nosich
Taylor Diane Ohlmann
Caroline Jane Owen
Olivia Christine Parrott
Lucas Ryan Pepper
Jade Reanna Perry

Brett Evan Pierce
Caleb Andrew Queen
Kevin A. Rothacker
Alaina Marie King Royalty
Jenna Katherine Rueff
Jacob Freeman Russell
Heather Brook Sabo
Hannah Margaret Sadler
Jai Cassidy Scantland
Jordan Laree Snider
Kathryn Elizabeth Thomas
Mary Katherine Young

CAMPBELL UNIVERSITY SCHOOL OF LAW, RALEIGH, NC

Kelsey Alcide

Seth Elliot Barefoot

Amanda J. Brookie

Emily C. Cauley

Mary F. Dudley

Kathleen Dunn

Paige Miles Feldmann

Danielle Rae Feller

Rachel Goodling

Evin L. Grant

Joshua R. Hall

Toni Hardin

Jeremy Harn

Ana-Alicia Hopper

Josue Jimenez

Devon Howell Karst

Thomas Lamm

Sean R. Madden

Chelsey Marie Maywalt

Meredith Mercer

Samuel Morris-Bloom

Jacob Murray Morse

Kathleen O'Malley

Michael Palombo

Alex Paschall

Cynthia Schafer Pela

James L. Porter IV

Katherine R. Reason

Aaron Michael Seagroves

Arista Jamil Sibrey

Taylor B. Simmons

Sloan W. Smith

Troy Stone

Jamie L. Thomas

James R. Todd

Lauren Elizabeth Travers

Melissa Tulis

Landon Van Winkle

Jonathan Brian Winslow II

Melissa Pekrun Woodard

CANISIUS COLLEGE, BUFFALO, NY

Kate Anticoli

Jessica Dieter

Moyla Halimy

Ashrita Tejy Hanmiah

Alexandria M. Iwanenko

Dilpreet Kaur

Steven Michael Kawalerski

Courtney L. Koba

Robert Lepertine

Joseph J. Lesh

Katherine M. Murphy

Elizabeth M. Sawka

Julia M. Sementilli

Jeffrey M. Spencer

Gina M. Trippe

Alex J. Valvo

CAPITAL COMMUNITY COLLEGE, HARTFORD, CT

Augustine Appiah Mintah

Elizabeth Bishop

Brenton Browne

Shawntoll Buchanan-Boothe

Shane Cianci

Corey Cockfield

Leslie Lionel Flippen Jr.

Patti Garwood

Stephanie Yvette Gary

Chrisline Tyla Gedeon

Kevin Charles Hale

Natalie Tegtmeier

Ida Long Villarreal

CAROLINA COLLEGE OF BIBLICAL STUDIES, FAYETTEVILLE, NC

Amber Nicole Carter

Carol Yeager Church

Stacie Ervin Cole

Michael T. Longson

Gary Rowe

William Taft Wallace

Lewillis Q. Wilson Sr.

CARROLL UNIVERSITY, WAUKESHA, WI

Nicholas Michael Alessi

Peter J. Burress

Daniel Michael Drzewiecki

Frank N. Gorichananz

Jordyn A. Herzog

Alison B. Lambrecht

Samuel E. Simpson

Alexander J. Sperry

Alexandra N. Zogran

CARSON-NEWMAN UNIVERSITY, JEFFERSON CITY, TN

Harold Zachary Ballard

Anna G. Barry

Payton N. Blankenship

Kara L. Cabbage

Ashley D. Carrier

Austin R. Carrier

Eduardo Rafael Carrillo
Salinas

Rachel B. Clingenpeel

Ryan S. Eberle

John C. Echols

Sarah M. Edwards

Jordan J. Elliott

Augusto W. Gil

Rachel V. Harmon

Jalinie Ellen Hensley

Emily H. Hickman

Mark Reede Isaacs

Kendra Lynn Ivins

Sara Beth E. Maddox

Andrew David Mast

Leanne C. Mattie

Amie Michelle McGaha

Katherine E. Moore

Ana Paola Oliveros

Paula Oliveros

Jared P. Reed

Lauren Nicole Sharpe

Leah Grace Wilson

Emily K. Wood

Daniel A. Zellers

CARTHAGE COLLEGE, KENOSHA, WI

Grace Allen
Jessica Kaitlyn Anderson
Lauren Baca
Michelle Balcerzak
Justin Barhite
Morgan Samantha Bashford
Hannah Becher
Jessie Bingaman
Daisy Bower
Josh Brandt
Cody Brant
Aliyah Caraballo
Desiree Selena Carlson
Dana Chartrand
Megan Darrow
Cara Dohse
Anna Domalewski
Teylor Elicia Douglas-Perkins
Emily Jane Duex
Nicole Durante
Josiah Eschbach

Kendra Everts
Ryeshia Rajanee' Farmer
Sarah Fedzko
Kaylene Felton
Kayla Fleming
Stephen Gulinson
Malorie Harder
Cecilia Hernandez-Ruiz
Emily Heuerman
Robin Hill
Lee Hollman
Megan Horst
Anthony Jordan
Elli Kaufman
Laura Kelly
Laura Krings
Sabrina Lato
Jordon Lippiatt
Haley Longley
Dominic Darian Lorann
Benjamin Nathan Massat
Shayla Danielle Mehta

John Meisenger
Rachel Mickey
Adam Milano
Michael Moen
Abigail Moss
Ricky Muhammad
Paige Myers
Alysha Newsom
Annika Nielsen
Maggie O'Toole
Erin Elizabeth Oakland
Amanda M. Ostrem
Gina Pacenti
Karra Pessetti
Michael Pobiecke
Rachel Post
Ian Privett
Alysia Regas
Kristen Reynoso
Helaina Rosenmayer
Krista Rumfield
Carl Saenger

Emily Lynn Salzman
Taylor Sanders
Robert Schwerdtfeger Jr.
Saige Scott
Daniel Setzke
Sarah Singer
Michelle Lynn Spiewak
Richard Stauffer
Tyler Strohl
Aaron Tajnai
Samantha Thone
Brooke Tonyan
Herbert Triplett
Natasha Gabrielle Urbanowitz
Rachel Utt
Kristen Verdoorn
Benjamin Weber
Erlan Wheeler
Samantha C. White
Lauren Taylor Wolfson
Iftou Yoya

CASE WESTERN RESERVE UNIVERSITY, CLEVELAND, OH

Kelsey R. Aamoth
Alexis L. Attinoto
Adhithya Baskar
Gina M. Belli
Andrew M. Blasius
Spencer Tyler Burton
Samantha K. Butler
Vanessa Y. Chen
Vivian G. Chen
Catherine A. Clair
Connor F. Collins
Bethany N. Cook
Catherine J. Culp
Erika L. Cyphert
Barbara Erin Deasy
Michael A. DePietro
Chang Yoon Doh

Michael S. Douglass
Anne E. Drake
Janny V. Evenhuis
Aviva H. Gersovitch
Aditi Gore
Sydney E. Gray
Daliah Jaye Greenwald
Neha Gupta
Jonathan M. Healy
Laura M. Hertz
Shuying Huang
Natasha A. Jacobson
Slater A. Jameson
Tyler S. Jenkins
Emily K. Jensen
Haley L. Kauffman
Dominic Joseph Kizek

Alayna M. Klco
Pavan S. Krishnan
Danielle M. Kulpins
Rachel E. Laveson
Yuhan Li
Angela R. Liu
Christina N. Liu
Qiaoyi Liu
Clarine S. Long
Andrew J. Lopez
Nikhil V. Mallipeddi
Ondrej Maxian
Michael R. McKenna
Corey W. Meyer
Laura J. Mummey
Chinweoke C. Osigwe
Sijie Peng

Elizabeth M. Perea
Aaron G. Peterson-Greenberg
Jason C. Pickering
Rahul Ramraj
Margaret A. Rodriguez
Aradhika Sarda
Sapna S. Shah
Victoria E. Simon
Cara S. Smith
Nishant Uppal
Vincenzo G. Volpe
Lauren K. Wichman
Grace L. Xu
Matthew A. Zembas
Jiayuan Zhang

CATAWBA COLLEGE, SALISBURY, NC

Johnathon Christian Boles
Kathleen Marie Burris
Ashley Marie Everidge
Rachel Elizabeth Gallup

Jevgenij Gamper
Kristina Juliette Hoff
Alex Thomas Lee

Trevor Joseph Loudin
Shannon Leigh Morton
Taylor Elise Spillman

Brinsley Morgan Stewart
Carley Blake Tysinger
Elizabeth Jean White

CAYUGA COMMUNITY COLLEGE AUBURN CAMPUS, AUBURN, NY

Cooper Arnink-Lader
Dominique Baker-Lanning
Ryan Baldwin
Erika Barcomb
Steve Brewer
Angela Bringley
Alexandra Cassick
Martha Caster
Trudi Caster
Georgianne Centore
Rebecca C. Chamberlin

Melissa Clink
Stephanie Michelle Cobb
Heather Crouse
Schyler Delamarter
Sarah DeLapp
Ashley Marion Edmunds
Kevin Gauthier
Andrea Jodeit
Duanna Neileice Johnson
Mitchell Lepianka
Brandon Malone

Benitta NIcole Martin
Alexas McBride
Rebecca Colleen McDonald
Laura Lynne Mocyk
William Mosier
Doug Nedza
Laura Nerau
Louise Anne Partin
Edward Pickard
Max Pinchak
Kelsey Raymond

Mary Reese
Raeann Elizabeth Rhode
Molly Sharples
Caleb C. Slater
Francis Smith
Frank Smith
Zach Steele
Rebecca Tracy
Ed James Vivenzio
Amy Walker

CAYUGA COMMUNITY COLLEGE FULTON CAMPUS, FULTON, NY

Jennifer L. Allen
Jennifer L. James

Maureen A. McCann
Raymond M. Mertens

Kelly L. Newton

Sandra L. Pelkey

CAZENOVIA COLLEGE, CAZENOVIA, NY

Michael William Gill

Bobbi Jo Hannan

Tangie Marie Muncil

Katherine Rosso

CECIL COLLEGE, NORTHEAST, MD

Babette A. Becker
Racheal Boyd
Ronald Brooks
Jamie Cherwaty
Morgan Cochran

Daniela Edge
Becky Franklin-Haas
Krystal Greco
Nicholas Aron Hankins
Julia Harden

Caroline Hicks
Mary E. McLaughlin
Marissa Phillips
Susanna Reyes
Delana Ringer

Tracie D. Strack
Morgan Paige Taylor
Angeline Kay Teoli
Andrea Zartler

CEDAR CREST COLLEGE, ALLENTOWN, PA

Bria Ashley Boyd

Gabrielle Josephine
Kennedy

Sarah Elise Slaw Kiewe

Kristen L. Spencer

CEDAR VALLEY COLLEGE, LANCASTER, TX

Stephanie Alejo
Katherine N. Alexander
Lula Virginia Anderson
Latonia Ayers

Justin M. Bacon
Jessica D. Barajas
Virginia E. Beegle
Caitlin C. Blaine

Devin M. Blair
Carol Bracken
Tiffany N. Briscoe
Alphonso Brooks

Aurynn M. Busby-Baker
Kierra D. Byrd
Phillip K. Cagle
Sarah E. Caldwell

Charles M. Campbell

Sandra A. Carter

Cheryl A. Cauley-Ingram

Latresa K. Clark

Robert B. Clawson

Ariel R. Contreras

Rosa A. Contreras

Rossana Corea

James Cox

Joyce A. Cummings

Teresa L. Daniels

Oluwasiji O. Deleawe

Jose L. Delgado

Tiffany M. Draper

Ellen Drummond

Jennifer Elizalde

Patrick Ely

Larry Emmons II

Lagail Erwin

Paula Evans

Susan J. Fisher

Marisela Flores

Kathleen J. Francis

Latoya N. Freeman

Eian J. Gallegos

Alan R. Garcia

Miriam B. Gaytan

Paul D. Gorish

Kelly H. Gosse

Orlando C. Greene

Erma Jean Griffin

John D. Griffin

Jacob C. Gutierrez

Silvia Guzman

Jeremy D. Hamilton

Bailey A. Hawkins

David Heftman

Khalid K. Hill

Jeremiah J. Hines

Felicia L. Houston

Sandy Earl Hudson

Damian E. Iwuala Jr.

Jacquelyn N. Jackson

Taylor T. James

Amanda J. Johnson

Addison D. Jones

Cheyenne N. Kennedy

Victoria R. Kilguss

Fiona J. Kiprop

Marilyn Knapp

Nickolas C. Kyles

Tania C. Landa

Jatoya E. Land-Williams

Tricia Langehennig

Adrianna N. Lawson

Annabreeze Mykuche Lee

Ka'von D. Lee

Jacob R. Lusk

Hannah E. Manning

Johnnathan I. Melendez

Christanne Middleton

Joshua W. Miller

Patricia M. Minyard

Danielle D. Mitchell

Richard Moffitt

Courtney S. Morgan

Alexander C. Mullins

Mia D. Muniz

Vanessa D. Orr

Omar Ortiz

Dezee E. Overstreet

Mario A. Perez Jr.

Carolyn Ward Peterson

Cornelia D. Peterson

Precious Faith T. Pimentel

Princess T. Pimentel

Aaron L. Powell

Mauri Prather

Gilbert Pritchett

Jaylynn M. Randall

Nicthe A. Rebollar Gaytan

Linell L. Remekie

Alma D. Renteria

Aaron M. Riggs

Lola M. Robinson

Roderick D. Roddy

Maria C. Rodriguez

Ontiveros

Cynthia L. Ross

Shatrudhan P. Sah

Jorge Salazar

Peggy L. Salgado

Tiara N. Sank

Kathryn D. Schmidt

Summer B. Schwing

Markiesia S. Scott

Ki'mii Sellers

Melissa D. Shead

Shohei Shinohara

Manuel Sifuentes

Lina V. Sims

Jaimi L. Singleton

Joseph Slaughter

Cassaundra Smith

Gloria Smith

Patrick D. Smith

Gavin Spain

Sarah L. Spiller

Sterling Michael Spralls

Carol E. Stephens

Natavia S. Stinson

Brad V. Sugg

Shannon Tadlock

Cynthia L. Tamez

Holly B. Taylor

Amon Thapa

Brandi N. Tharp

Whitney C. Thorne

Azia M. Tisdale

Brian E. Walker

Latisa Walker

Clare G. Washington

Rodney West

Justin D. Williams

Chemary N. Wingo

Dusty M. Womack

Michael S. Wright

Shermondra La'resse Wright

Vanessa Wright

Randy Young

Christina I. Youngers

Ashley Zambrano

Irene Zavala

Zantana L. Zuniga

CENTENARY COLLEGE, HACKETTSTOWN, NJ

Melissa Marie Avecillas

Blaine Bergman

Brooke Boetticher

Micheal Clinton

Samantha Darling

Breanna Durkin

Jessica Marie Ervey

Marisa Galfo

Marcus Michael Garcia

Justina Gun

Brenda Horetsky

Aryoung Jee

Se Won Kim

Jessica Ann Martin

Lori Elizabeth McSherry

Amy Lynn Miller

Jennifer Picinich

Ebony Christina Randall

Alan Sciarrillo

Jessie Sharr

Amber Nicole Sporer

Kelsey Stevens

Tyler Thurgood

Lisa Anne Wilbur

Zachary E. Wolff

CENTENARY COLLEGE OF LOUISIANA, SHREVEPORT, LA

Katelyn Alexander
Corey Paul Arcement Jr.
Collin Baker
Max Beilke
Lauren Alice Benoit
Hannah Bergeron
Kyle Boston
Desiree Boyd
Alexandra Britten
Simone Michelle Byrd
MarvKevea TroyMontrell Campbell
Raquel Candal
Chris Cates
Robin Chailland
Katie Chopin
Toby Crouch
Justin Zachary Cueto

Gage Dabin
Calvin King Davis
Trey Davis
Abigail Dillard
Heather Dotting
Carie Dupree
Shane Lee Edmondson
Ryan Flanagan
Kaitlyn Frantz
Rebekah Frazier
Chelsea Glaspie
Ben Green
Dei'Anna Lee Hall
Hannah Nicole Hastie
Elana Hibbs
Deavonte' Jarmole Hicks
Alexandra Nicole Hornsby
Collin Hughes

Kalie Hughes
Sarah Tucker Irons
Princes Meshay Jones
Mason Kay
Mary Ellen Kidd
Hannah Kimbrough
Steven Knight
Stafford Lyons
Bailey Martin
Anthony Patrick McDonald
Mattie Milner
Kaity Mussio
Richard Norem III
Rachel Perkins
Sarah Pinney
Laurie Priftis
Michael Pullano
Hannah Rachal

Mary Katherine Robertson
Tyler Cameryn Sanders
Allison Scates
Logan Settoon
Alexander Michael Shannon
Chloe Snow
Halen Elyse Sumner
Brittney Thomas
Alysea Gabriel Velasquez
Dellanee Wade
Brittany Wagner
Sadie N. Wallace
Joanna Warren
Garret Wick
Jamie Michelle Wright

CENTRAL ALABAMA COMMUNITY COLLEGE, ALEXANDER CITY, AL

Morgan L. Browning
Jalynn Nicole Carter
Chelsea T. Gordon
Shauna Leighton Harrelson

Diane Daniels Jackson
Heather Marie Jennings
James D. Marsh
Joshua R. Nowland

Destiny Faye Perry
Latrell Marquis Rembert
Craig Marion Shells
April Cooley Still

Kenan Marquis Strong
Jordan Shiann Thomas
Celeste G. Virges
Daniel Riley Whatley

CENTRAL ARIZONA COLLEGE, COOLIDGE, AZ

Edward Aguirre
Paris Brianna Alford
Darius Allen
Jesus Anaya
Finn Anderson
Destiney Angelique Armenta
Guadalupe Arroyo
Kenneth Baldwin
Alicia Giselle Bandala
Breanna Bartlett
Marco Antonio Becerra
Jordan Tailor Bell
Alexandria R. Bumm
Gilberte Bussey
Carlos Campos

Alejandra Cano
Kendal Carr
Marilyn Carter
Kendrick Devion Coker
Cinthia corina Corral
Bailey Crenshaw
Elisa Cruz
Aiesha Shantel Curley
Dallin Darger
Cheyenne Dickey
Jalan Dukes
Ember Eck
Austin Tyler Ely
Lizeth Escarcega
Angelina Flores
Quiana Chiffon Flowers

Cameryn Renae Fossell
Jamie Elizabeth Gee
Jaimi Suzanne Gillespie
Jordan Golemon
Salena Gomez
Tarynn Gragg
Joselyne Granillo
Joseph Elijah Gray
Savannah Harrison
Kyan Lee Helmic
Taylor LeeAnn Hires-Caulk
Cassandra Josie Holcombe
Marcene Hoover-Bennett
Victoria Marie Iniguez
Sierra Jackson
Brenna Janssen

Olivia Jaqua
Dana Jessup
Esperanza Jones
Gilbert Kigen
Brandy King
Alexander Koltz
Mared Koral
Andrea Laguna
Cory Lehman
Leonardo Lopez
Cassandra Madrid
Bailey Mahan
Jesseca Mares
Ashley bryanna Martinez
Celisa Martinez
Maria McBride

Jasmine Marie Medina

Melvin Miles

Autumn Miller

Wayne Miner

Jennifer Lee Montreuil

Danielle Taguiang Moore

Monica Munoz

Benjamin Noriega

Brendan Onquit

Quenton Orozco

Nykia Owen

Anthony Parrish-Lacson

William Partridge

Jose G. Pelayo

Jorge Perez

Quinton A. Prunty

Leticia Reidhead

Sarah Reimus

Cherise Darsjoune Robinson

Hezekiel Romero

Benjamin Sagisi

Cordero Alexander Salazar

Roberto Salazar

Dominic Savana

Hayden Searle

Cheyenne Sherwood

Jessica Shirley

Ruby Sierra

Jess Krista St. John

Kennedy Stanfield

Jordan Stark

Ryan Stilwell

Tyrza Alexis Stout

Madeline Sulka

Tracy Lynn Swander

Alysha Terry

Caitlin Thomas

Jennifer Torres-Ramirez

Magaly Lauranne Ashley

Tshipopo

Richelle Anette Villegas

Katilyn Volk

Sophia Von Braun

Mekaela Elizabeth Ellen

Walters

Quinn Waltz

Portious Kerisha Darnica

Warren

Jordan Washington

Maraya Webster

Dylan Weddell

Patrick Lee Wessel

Timothy Martin Wickert

Kyle Wiegert

Shandiin H. Yazzie

Sancia Luann Zavatta

Sarah Ziemba

CENTRAL BAPTIST COLLEGE, CONWAY, AR

Krista L. Abel

Pranay P. Borde

Benjamin E. Brandon

Joshua S. Buczek

Lok Sze Cho

Lauren L. Eyre

Taylor D. Farber

Christopher S. Fields

Alyssa C. Fontillas

Amanda L. Glover

Yolanda D. Harris

Cassandra M. Hawk

Theresa K. Kelley

Lori W. Lee

Ozell L. Lilly

Carter L. Mayo

Wendy L. Minett- Cope

Rosemary "Cookie"
Moncrief

Clay B. Nance

Dillon A. Nix

Jason A. Pierce

Chelsea P. Reichert

James E. Simpson

Pamela S. Sims

Elvin L. Sprankle

Galja Veleva

Colby A. Waites

Tabitha K. Ward

Phyllis Washington

Gwenda K. Williams

CENTRAL CAROLINA TECHNICAL COLLEGE, SUMTER, SC

David Adams

Gregory Albert

Casie Anderson

Shannon Ardis

Henry Arrants

Brandie Atkinson

Kevin Back

LaKeithea Bailey-Nelson

Cristi Ballard

Andrew Beaty

Tonika Shantae Benbow

Cathleen Benehaley

Shelby Boykin

Keli Braddock

Latoya Briggs

Alvin Brown

Jannie Brown

Jayson Buchanan

Mandy Wyer Burke

Kathy Cabrales

Victoria Campbell

Lori Chiarello

Angela Clark

Garrett Coleman

Brittany Collins

Margaret Ellen Conant

Austin Cromer

Ralph Daly

Tristen Dave

Jimmie Delecki

Lisa Dombrowski

Skyleigh Dugener

Terry Badger DuPre

Angela Durant

Travis Dyer

Theresa Egbunine

Tonya Gill Evans

Zoey Heather Fletcher

Michael Gallimore

Jennifer Geiser

Natascha A. Giles II

Kelly Gills

Whitney Graham

Jimmy Griffin

Kenya Harper

Tawania Harvin

Tamera Hawes

Jodi Haynes

Susan Hillsman

Jay Hoff

Jeremy Holland

Brittany Houck

Lindsey Howard

Madison Huckabee

Lacie Hughes

Daley Jackson

Daniel Jackson

Kedrick Johnson

Dave Jones

Shirley Jones

Joshua Jordan

Moneisha Junious

Justin Keefer

Wendy Horne Lawson

Jamie Letterman

Kayla Levy

Jose Maccou

Caleb McCalla

Ashley McDuffie

Tanya McFadden

Nasheeta McIntosh

Chantele Meade

Nicholas Miller

Briana Mitchell

Clayton Mixon

Anna Lorraine Moore

Christopher Morris

Faith Morris

Amanda Nicole Moseley

Jakob Donald Nabholz

Alicia Nave

Emily Charlene Newton

Christian D. Nolff

Kaleena Ortiz-Velez

Ryan Owens

Shaun Parker

John Rawls

Odell Reuben

Lekita Rhodes

Stacey Rippy

Arielle Short

Melinda Smith

Paula Snyder

Baxter Stanley

Marisha Statham

Kevin Stogner

Tyler Sullivan

Dustin Robert Tate

Rebekah Taves

Johnathan Taylor

Shannon Lee Thurston

Trevor Tollison

David Tuders

Dale Turner

Melanie Turner

Holly Michelle Vasquez

James Wandtke

Brianna Marie Washington

Cameron Watson

Vincent Watson

Cydney Welch

Nikki Werre

Ashley West

Clara West

Teresa Williams

Rhonda Winter

CENTRAL CHRISTIAN COLLEGE OF KANSAS, MCPHERSON, KS

Ciara Michelle Alderson

Elizabeth Marie Brooks

Adrianna A. Brown

Dale Newton Butcher

Grace Tillman Chaires

Heather A. DeLaurentis

Dennis Kenyon Dodd

Sam Paul Edwards

Travis Ryan Elder

Cynthia Evans

Kimberly Field

Michelle Lee Flaming

Ryan Michael Freeman

Stuart Douglas Fritz

Michael T. Golden

David Michael Groves

Travis Wayne Hearne

Theresa Marie Heberer

Timothy Heisler

Mark D. Hershberger

James B. Hills

Sarah Kay Johnson

Daren R. Kendrick

Melissa Gail Kent

Jennie L. Kuoha

Samuel K. Kuoha

Matthew Joseph Lee

Kathryn Henley Lott

Ryan A. Massey

David Paul Noren

Richard Lee Norman Jr.

Abigail L. Palmer

Michael Panter

Stevie Rae Penn

James Perez

Haley Mariah Prow

Victoria Blaire Rigel

Brooke Danielle Roberts

Scott Rutter

Charles Palmer Seawood

Paul Anthony Shepherd

Edwincia M. Slater

Richard Paul Sorondo

Shelby Lynn Sparks

David Joseph Stellers

Alicia Stone

Thomas M. Thompson

Jeffrey Neil Worley

Eric Von Yahn

Mark Thomas Young

CENTRAL CHRISTIAN COLLEGE OF THE BIBLE, MOBERLY, MO

Martha Diane Burton

Traci Joy Coquillard

Ian Michael Costandi

Jared Lee Delagrange

Aaron John-Lee Dowell

Adam Nathaniel Fincher

Katelynn BriAnne Frazier

Taylor Diane Salmons

Glenn Samuel Shelton

Jake Wayne St. Clair

Catherine Anna Totty

Rebekah S. Weidenaar

CHARLESTON SOUTHERN UNIVERSITY, CHARLESTON, SC

Skylar Aaron

Sarah Altman

Chanel Bell

Crystal Leigh Bright

Jeffrey Crosby

Logan Crowder

Anna Maria D'Annunzio

Jessica Ann Downing

Cassandra Dunworth

Allyson Dye

Hillary Kaitlyn Evans

Robin Fenters

Autumn Dimple Marie

Hanna

Jennifer Haupt

Kristen Johnson

Rachel Kotzin

Dallas Ladd

Laura McAvoy

Keith William Millender

Aaron Neuhaus

Michelle Danielle O'Connor

Abigail Rauch

Benjamin Robinson

Keenan Juan Rosado

Tiffany Nicole Scott

Cathleen Theresa Stanley

Taylor Stevens

Lindsay Taylor

Benjamin Stewart Teal

Rebekah Joy Witt

Hannah Zech

CHESAPEAKE COLLEGE, WYE MILLS, MD

Phillip Anthony Brunecz Jr.

Etta Marie Cook

Jill Davidson

Timothy Wayne Dignen

Armanda Lee Fooks

Carole Lorraine Halbig

Mackenzie Marie Joyce

Lyndy Christina Mothershead

Richard Anthony Rahilly

Brian Joseph Saucedo-Merida

David Alan Schmidt

Sydney Rae Serwatka

Cassidy Renee Stewart

Stephanie T. Thompson-Leitzer

Katie Lynn Worm

CHEYNEY UNIVERSITY OF PENNSYLVANIA, CHEYNEY, PA

Rayven Armstrong

Jasmine Kachele Cooper

Jasmine Frazier

Tariq J. Furbush

Theresa Harmon

Akia Harris

Makkah Hayes

DeWhitt Jones III

Lugene Kennebrew Jr.

Anwar-Nasser Hutty Mathis

Jahleel Muhammad

Kwadwo Ampong Ofori

Jada B. Phillips

Crystal Baker Roach

Jarely Rosario

Shalaina Renea Sutton

Wesley M. Thorn

Catherine M. Young

CHIPOLA COLLEGE, MARIANNA, FL

Yasmin R. Adderson

Alicia M. Barton

Lexie Basford

Delilah C. Bass

Andrew Bennett

Melinda L. Blechinger

Josiah H. Brooks

Victoria N. Brown

Susan A. Burns

Antonio M. Camacho

Bradach A. Carlson

Angie Caitlyn Carpenter

Odra N. Chapman

Krista M. Chastain

Charles W. Dinkins

Donavan K. Ebersole

Christin E. Fowler

Courtney F. Fowler

Shareem T. Goodlet

Deborah S. Graham

Isaac James Guettler

Angerita Q. Hayes

Bethany R. Horton

David A. Horton II

Hayden B. Hurst

Antwain Martavius Johnson

Bethany L. Kerr

Chelsea A. Kuhajda

Madelynn A. Lytle

Michael A. Marotta

Calen P. Masai

Tiffany A. McAdams

Joel C. McKinnie

Kaylee R. Messer

Steven D. Miller

Louis A. Miranda III

Keionna D. Mitchell

Anastasia A. Mote

Emaleigh M. Munn

Joshua D. Myers

Hannah A. Plazarin

Taajwar J. Pope

Mary E. Raines

Diana C. Ramirez

Elynora A. Sapp

Olivia S. Saunders

Antwan D. Siples

Tatum L. Skipper

Natasha A. Smith

Austin C. Spears

Patrick Demario Spires

Riby A. Stephens

Elizabeth C. Varnum

Samuel K. Wells

Khirsten L. White

Lydia M. Wiedeman

Margaret Wiedeman

Colby H. Wiggins

CHOWAN UNIVERSITY, MURFREESBORO, NC

Des'monay My'chelle Barnes

Calvin Jerome Bowe Jr.

Sierra Janee' Burston

Suraya Ann Chase

Rodney Lee Countryman Jr.

LeAnne Frances Crabtree

Victoria Denise Cragan

Issa Michael Farhoud

Haley Elizabeth Haggard

LaTarryl Renay Hall

Melanie Gail Harris

Melissa Merry Hernandez

Adriea Lalece Herndon

Sierra I. Jones

Shannon Cullins Lassiter

Elonga Adida Manseka

Trevor Lane Marshall

Alisha Veronica Mobley

Kinsey Michaela Modlin

Kaitlin Elizabeth Moore

Mackenzie Ann Reid

Zulay Andrea Romero

Crystal T. Sarnor

Ashley Jane Tackett

Christina Eve Thomas

Sierra L. White

Courtni Cecilia Williams

CLAFLIN UNIVERSITY, ORANGEBURG, SC

Sherlene Latoya Brown

Jabian Mon'tell Cooper

Jason Shem Cummins

Amaris Beraiah Gilchrease

Tiarra Joell
Rachel Faith Johnson
Abigael Jesang Kosgei
DaShawn Rayvon Lortz
Adia Raichelle Louden

Annette R. Mack
Gift Chiamara Nwokeji
Asfar Rashid
Dennis Edward
Richmond Jr.

Pamela Denice Robinson-
Duckson
Patel Kwisha Sharad
Marshae' LeAnna Smith
Robert L. Steedley

Monica Thapaliya
Curtis Lee Thomas
Linh My Tong
Ifeanyi Kingsley Uche
Stephanie Yolanda Wyche

CLARION UNIVERSITY OF PENNSYLVANIA, CLARION, PA

Ashley Louise Cassano
Kayleigh Rae Collier
Audrianna J. DeLacour
Devin J. Forgey
Krista N. Healey

Riley C. Ivol
Evign F. Kile
Amanda Rose Maze
Sinead P. McAnallen
Cole D. Ordiway

Shelby S. Pepmeyer
Emily A. Pfendler
Gloria S. Pytlak
Wade C. Reichelderfer
Devin L. Shellhammer

Matthew A. Tofani
Mariah A. Treiber

CLARK ATLANTA UNIVERSITY ISABELLA T. JENKINS HONORS PROGRAM, ATLANTA, GA

Frank Adams
Stephanie Renee Alexander
Jalan Andrews
Simone Angus
Adrain Artary
Kaia Bailey
Angelina Barden
Ayana Barrett
Mahalia Barrow
Sherace Bartholomew-
Calder
De'Ericka Bertram
Latonya Beverly
Caitlin Boyd-Ragin
Vonnick Boyogueno
Lanese Brackenridge
Andrece Brady
Summer Branch
Brianna Brantley
Carey W. Brock IV
Jasmine Brown
William Jamal Burnette
Armani Caldwell
Charnae Caldwell
Alexis Carey
Junae Carmichael
Austin Casillas
Aaron Chambers
David Emmanuel Chapman

Destiny Coleman
Deneisha Cook
Qiana D. Crenshaw
Br'Shawn Davis
Joselyn Davis
Kenyatta Dixon
Zachary Ahmad Dixon
Sierra Doucette
Madisyn Dudley
Corey Dutch Jr.
Amber Easley
Sydni Falconer
Iyanna Daje Ferguson
Yasmyne Fisher
Stephanie Frampton
Olivia Freeman
Essence Frieson
Eunique Gaines
Alyssa Marge' Gilbert
Stephanie Kaye Gillenwaters
Briana Granger
Jasmyne Grissett
Julian Grissett
Shiane Guziman
Brianna Hale
Warren Hallmon
Warren Hawkins III
Kelcey Hines
Asha Holder

Simone Howard
Bryson Hudgins-Owens
Sheena Huggins
Renee Jennie Ingram
Luetisha Ethelin Jacobs
Tylisha James
Vasthi Jean-Michel
Cierra Johnson
Jaraad Johnson
Moandra Johnson
Sabreen Jasahn Jolley
Kennedi Jones
Marcus D. Jones
Nia Jones
Keyshanna Jones-Coleman
Ania Kight
Bryant King
Byron Lawrence
Allen Lee IV
Claressa Lesley
Henry Robert Carter Lubin
Antonio Mallard
Ronald Thomas McCullough
Zoe Mcdowell
Terence McElwee
Dana McKenney
Ashlee McLaurian
Quenten McNair
Jessica Melton

Zaynah Miller
Tiffani Moore
Laurence Morreale
Amoni Moses
Kayla Newsome
Markenna Novembre
JaMon Helene Patterson
ShaRon Kuhne Patterson
Kierra Perry
Stephen Phillips
St. George Pink
Allen Lugunda Pitts Jr.
Breighlynn Polk
Tori Pradier
Danielle Randall
Erica Ann Rawlins
Le'Zaire Reese
Rashad Revere
Richie Revere
Khyro Reviere
Shamsiya Robe
Deja Robinson
Cailan Sandusky
Shylien Ranae Sandusky
Jessie Scott
Abdoulaye Sidibe
Kortne Simmons
Kanem Frederick Sims
Racquel Sims

Brieanna Nicole Smith
Erika Smith
Riana Smith
Charnelle Snetter
Trinity Spicer
Epiphany Krystal Storey
Dekiera Denae Suknanan

William Joseph Taggart
Lyrique Taylor
Tyree Thompson
Donte' Thrasher
Anessa Trask
Imara Vaughn
Kayla Walker

Aaliyah White
Alexis White
Tanya White
Afiya Williams
Asia Williams
Taylor Williams

Rashida Ashlynn
Williamson
Jahde' Wilson
Tenicia Winston
Jakayla Woolridge
Jasmine Lei Wynn
Elijah Jamal Younger

CLARKE UNIVERSITY, DUBUQUE, IA

Calista K. Beyer
Bryan Byerly
Diana A. Clark

Sean D. DeVries
Shanna Desirae Forbes
Michaela M. Hennings

Thomas D. Keene
Alexandra L. Kurauskas
William James Schwalb

Jonathan Wendell Shepherd
Allison L. Smith
Johnathan E. Sturtz

CLEAR CREEK BAPTIST BIBLE COLLEGE, PINEVILLE, KY

Joshua Keith Blanton
John Jacob Haller

Gabriella Ann Kahkola

Jonathan James Kinner

Diana Kathrine Myers

CLEVELAND COMMUNITY COLLEGE, SHELBY, NC

Clayton Atkinson
Romelle Blanton
Kaitlyn Sierra Bolin
Torrie Brown
Jesse Browning
Brad Bumgardner
Donna Camp
Michael Canipe
Whitney Clark
Holly Celeste Conner
Megan Cook
Jonathan Jacob Costner
Amanda Alexis Creech
Deborah Curry
Nathaniel Alvah
DeDominicis
Levi Duncan
Max Ezzell
Savannah Finger
James Flynn
Jacqueline Gardella

Erinn Garner
Carlos George
Jennifer George
Ewelina T. Gibson
Christopher Gillespie
Emily Grant
Angela Greene
Serella Greene
Linda Gregory
Russell Hamilton
Robert Hartley
Bonnie Hepler
Juanita Hernandez
Peter Hindall
Daniel Hogan
Michael Humphries
Michael Johnson
Jon Katen
Gregory Lebelt
Lynda Ledford
Willie Little

William Martin
Lindsey McCoy
David McCracken
Winston McKee
Malena P. Modirzadeh
Jason Morrow
Tony Mote
Virginia Okonkwo
Valmore Omondi
Savannah Owens
Bobby Parker
Rebecca Parsons
Gregory Pena
Adam Poole
Horace Porter
Alyssa Proctor
Lisa Proctor
Justin Rent
Sandra Rich
Brandon Robinson
Gina Robinson

Karen Lillian Roy
Mary Ruff
Valerie Scruggs
Taylor Ebonee' Smith
Aaron Stroupe
Jonie Stumbo
Jeremy Suits
Amanda Sweezy
Betty Tellefsen
Joseph Tuong
Emmanuel Wallace
Charles White
Joel Williams
Jason Winslow
John Witherspoon
Madison Wray
Ian Yarbrough
Chasty Gray Young
Christina Young

CLEVELAND STATE COMMUNITY COLLEGE, CLEVELAND, TN

Holly Allen

Kayla A. Allen

Steven Christian Lee Amos

Mikala Ard

David Barnes
Ruth Ben-Judah
Taylor Bentley
Luke Boler
Dallas Bowers
Christian Burnett
Nicholas Allen Clark
Jacob Cook
Drew Curtis
Elizabeth Davis
Amanda J. Glenn
Hannah Godfrey
Caroline Goins
Benjamin David Halstead
Kara Headrick
Matthew Henshaw

Christina Ann Hernandez
Bryan Hidalgo
Kelsey Ivey
Jobanna Jimenez
Michael Johnson
Trevor Blake Jones
Brandi Kilpatrick
Kimberly M. Kinter
Charles Kramer
Cody Michael Langford
Micaela Lauth
Stacy Ryan Mahaffey
Alexandria Danielle
Manders
Genecy Liliana Martinez
Anna McDade

Will McDade
Alex Troy Metaxas
Bryson Mitchell
Colton Morgan
Nathan Andrew Myers
Kara L. Owens
Austin Phillips
Emily Grace Phillips
Koltyn Plumb
Shirley S. Poteet
Caleb Mathew Rench
Rachel M. Richardson
Maria Carolina Roman
Alex Rominger
Jennifer Saucedo
Courtney Lyn Seiter

Stephanie Nicole Self
Stephanie Sparks
Shadia Suarez
Colby Tatum
Kristin Jade Thompson
Victoria Nicole Townson
Laceica Turner
Brittany Lorene Umphrey
Ashley Heather Underdown
Johnna Varner
Sabrina Walker
Tayla Wattson
Hagen Wilkey
Jennifer Wright
Miranda York

CLEVELAND UNIVERSITY KANSAS CITY, OVERLAND PARK, KS

Truemon J. Barger
Jerad Barth
Hannah Lee Beran
Whitney J. Brummond
Jessica Leigh Campbell
Justin P. Cook
Matthew DeFroda
Dezerae C. Deis

Brittney L. Donn
Alisha L. Fletcher
Michael Scott Godsey
Nathan T. Hamilton
Weston E. Hielscher
Natalie L. Horton
Angela Imgarten
Bethany P. Long

Mitchell L. Maire
Lauren E. Palmer
Kaylea Pearson
Deborah D. Perkins
Sarah M. Peterson
Angela R. Segovia
Robert A. Selvaggi
Sean W. Smith

Shane M. Smith
Emily E. Toppass
Cliff H. Van Buren
Brea Van De Pol
Melissa N. Volk
Hunter E. White
Ike Woodroof

CLOUD COUNTY COMMUNITY COLLEGE, CONCORDIA, KS

Deborah Kaylene Ames
Danielle Jennifer Andrews
Keisha DeLois Boykin-
Griffith
Boone Joseph Cady
Jace Allen Coppoc
Lisa Ann Davis
LaTanya Marie Didas
Zane C. Downing

Kristina Renae Farber
Courtney R. Freed
Bryce Alan Golightley
Rogelio Moises Gomez
Carrie Renee Green
Darcy Elaine Griffiths
Elora Allain Kay Hardacre
Tracy Elaine Hill
Jaci Liane Kolm

Jarreth Joshua Martina
Leyla Matyakubova
Sagar Minesh Mehta
Sarah Anne Mize
Brittany Jean Murrelle
Brandon Craig Paredes
Brett Allen Peters
Ashley Dawn Seifert
Micayla Marie Sjolander

Joshua Evan Skocny
Brett Melvin Slater
Katelyn Annabelle Thomson
Alexandria M. Walters
Gary Lee Watson
Daisy Linda Lagamia Weber
Christina Kay Wilken

COASTAL CAROLINA UNIVERSITY, CONWAY, SC

Colton John Aksomitus
Shayla Claire Anderson
Amanda Rena Carter
David James Chase

Brett Daniel Cooksey
Suzanne Lynn Crass
Jenna Alexandra Curcura
Shelby Rose Dangerfield

Rachel Anna Ferrara
Nicholas Lucci Fiorella
Matthew Peter Gahagan
Chante Nakysha Gore

Blake Brockington-Dane
Graham
Dekira Monaye Hemingway
Rachael Belle Houston

Ashlyn Eugenia Inman
Essence Lakia Jennings
Rebekah Elizabeth Kelley-Tavernier
Korina Koci

Stephen Joseph Markee
Jaimie Lynn Mataosky
Megan Elaine McGuire
Amy Alison Moody

Deloris Uzo-Amaka Nwadeyi
Misty Marie Porte
Jocelyn Felicia Reedus
Connor Everett Roy

Lena Schaeffner
Steven Orrie Vanden Heuvel
Maura Ann Walbourne
Madison Tricia Warren
Charles Hollis Whittington

COCHISE COLLEGE, DOUGLAS, AZ

Jonathan Abbate
Ericka Aguilera
Annahy Alvarez
Dielcia Arredondo
Jesus Lauro Barreda
Angelica Borquez
Louis Boyd
Edna Campos
Cindy Gallego Carrillo
Christian Soto Ceja
Alma E. Chavez
Francisco Coronado
Jason Joel Cota
Jasmin Diaz

Maria Iliana Diaz
Oscar Diaz
Marco Espinoza
Ruby Estrada
Raquel Espinoza Flores
Ivy Victoria Gibson
Fernando Gomez
Fernando Gomez
Cesar Grijalva
Hilda Gutierrez
David Guzman
Andrea Hernandez
Maggie Hernandez
Betsaida Holguin

Molly Hottel
Scarlett Hughes
Laura Hurtado-Salinas
Jacqueline Lafon
Jaqueline Lafon
Laura Lengel
Miguel Antonio Martinez
Marcela Matuz
Gilda Munguia
Francisco Ovies
Alma Pina
Fernando Pineda
Jacqueline Portillo
Ella Quinones

Marcela Quinonez
Stephanie Robles
Juan Sanchez
Jennifer Skinner
Blake Spencer Suarez
Michelle Valenzuela
Joseph Vasquez
Ruby Vega
Daritza Beatriz Villalobos
Jonluke Villasensor
Symantha Whaley

COKER COLLEGE, HARTSVILLE, SC

Walker Aaron Barfield
Heather Helena Blaschke
Alexi T. Boehme
Mauree Fore Brunson
Artur Bessa Cabral
Katharine Elizabeth Cooper

Adam Leland Coyle
Midori Anike Darr
Cierra Katherine Davis
Savanna Holly Edwards
Angelica Marie Faucette
Emma Marie Ferguson

Taylor Anne Gaskins
Andre Leon McMillon
Marcellus Leroy Moore
Deondre Leman Parks
Janie Olivia Shaw
Tammaka Oli'Shai Staley

Cierra Stinson
Jamez Malik Taylor
Regina L. Torain
Alexis Nicole Wiseman

COLBY-SAWYER COLLEGE, NEW LONDON, NH

Nathaly Abreu
David George Ayotte
Jessica Nicole Baker
Erin Elizabeth Bennett
Sara Anne Berry
Amy Sigrid Blazej
Meghan Elizabeth Bosley
Carrie Rose Brewster
Jaclyn Elise Cinelli
Scott Charles Cooper
Emily Christine Crow
Danielle Christine Duhaime

Anh Phuong Duong
Sarah Rae Fields
Christopher Ryan Gagne
Luis Felipe Garzon Manco
Jaclyn Elise Goddette
Johann Julius Graefe
Sarah Jane Harlow
Rebecca Leanne Hashem
Naomi Eva Humphrey
Kaitlyn Flynn Jackson
Jillian R. Jacobs
Olivia Rose Jones

Zachary Taylor Kershaw
Abhineet Kumar
Anh Phuong Le
Xiaoxiao Lu
Nicole Flora Machado
Benjamin Allan Maines
Jennifer Karen Martz
Olivia Ellen McAnirlin
Zachary Michael Melisi
Allyson Grace Mullen
Morganne Krista Murphy-Meyers

Erica M. Pantaleo
Kylee Morgan Parker
Rachel Anyama Quaye
Barsha Rajbhandari
Dikshant Rajbhandari
Gabrielle Marie Rodriguez
Alexandra Jane Stefan
Bibek Thapa
Margaret Shannon Tucker
Phuong Dong Vo
Lydia Madeline Walker

Menbere Yisfashewa Wendimu

Skylor Hanna Widschwenter

Hannah Elizabeth Willcutt

Kenneth Carlton Wilson

COLLEGE OF CHARLESTON, CHARLESTON, SC

David Coulter Ahnen

Emily Morgan Beck

Michael Faikes

Lucas Freeman

Ciera Gordon

Trevor D. Jones

April Levon Kelly

Ashleigh Kirker

Morgan Larimer

Katherine Lawson

Dylan Lefkowitz

Jessica Mercier

Patrick Mitchell

John Nix

Kalene Parker

Emily Pasko

Zach Sturman

Emily Torchiana

Hannah Katherine Wagner

Meredith Wohl

COLLEGE OF OUR LADY OF THE ELMS, CHICOPEE, MA

Samantha Nicole Alvino

David Opoku Antwi

John-Marc Austin

Joshua Erik Brunson

Samantha Rose Dibbern

Jalen M. Hicks

Phoebe Ann Hobbs

Sirvaughn Khalil Hobdy

Chandra Denise Jackson

Samantha Rose Licursi

Kassandra Nicole Masilamani

Ashley Rose Menslage

Andrew Jerry Mercado

Kelan Roark O'Brien

Jacqueline Sorell Quetti

Taylor Rose Simpson

Mary Kate Sullivan

Dimitri Tessier

Olivia Caroline VanEpps

COLLEGE OF SAINT ELIZABETH, MORRISTOWN, NJ

India Alexander

Shams Nazzal Alshloul

Marie Ceus

Rosa Chilquillo

Fatimah Fisher

Marissa Gioffre Gioffre

Shervonne Angelica Gittens

Keyonta Shannon Hall

Lynette Lynn Hardy

Claudia W. Ip

Shanayah Laquan Jones

Nicole Marie Lacherza

Joelynn Marie Locasto

Donna Maria Manno

Erin Nicole McAuliffe

Evelyn Minolfo

Alicia I. Mitchko

Jamie Alyssa Perrucci

Triana Rego

Marissa Lynn Sherman

Ellen St. Pierre

COLLEGE OF SAINT MARY, OMAHA, NE

Anthonia Ajibola

Rebecca Bagwell

Colleen Bernal

Jennifer Brach

Elizabeth Carraher

Elizabeth Casey

Rachel Connelly

Jordan Ann Copple

Demi Eble

Lindsey Ann Fiegenschuh

Haley Marie Habegger

Kristine Hain

Carolyn Hanus

Alexis Hupp

Mitzi Infante Magaña

Aysha Janssen

Erin Kruger

Mercedes Lewandowski

Brooke Love

Sr. Gertrude Kavugwi Majani

Christa Manning

Maria Martinez

Cynthia McCroy

Brenna Meyer

Haden Mikesell

Erin Elizabeth Nicol

Nicole Pardinas

Dayna Pulver

Abby Danielle Purintun

Elizabeth Rashid

Lauren Rempe

Payton Johanson Roby

Mayra Roman

Amanda Rose Rundgren

Karen Saavedra

Cory Stevenson

Jackie Straube

Savannah Marie Williams

Taylor Williams

Katie Wingate

COLLEGE OF ST. JOSEPH, RUTLAND, VT

Mallory Davis

Angela Jeffrey

Alexandra Jones

David LaRoche

Justin Thomas Lemanski

Samantha Gabrielle Perry

Kimberley Rupe

Nicole Sparks

Gino Agnese

Ahmed Ahmed

Zain Ali

Islan Allan

Salsabeel Allan

Basilio Allen

Muhammad Amir

Stacy Appiah

Steve Arriaga

Justin Atos

Sonny Baialardo

Zana Barrow

Kristen Battiato

Nico Cu Baylosis

Cathy-Ann Borges

Matab Brahimi

Erica Brogna

Alexandra Bruno

Christopher Buonocore

Aissata Camara

Andrew Capizzo

Brandon Cardella

Arthur Cardinale

William Carey

Dana Cariddi

Jurandir Chan

Sonanika Chouhan

Diana Ciavarella

Anna Cieslik

Catalina Colon

Francis Colonna

Irma Cruz Velez

Faith D'Alessandra

Christina Daquieno

Paige DePrimo

Evan Donovan

Kadiatou Drame-Sheriff

Carolyn Drew

Xingru Duan

Lucia Edwards

Kaitlyn Egan

Nadia Elattar

Hassan Fares

Christine Fisher

Christine Taylor Fisher

Diana France-Beurnier

Allison Fremer

Kimberly Gaglione

Mirna Germano

Elena Ghelan

John Gioeli

Valerie Giuffre

Leidona Gjonovic

Tedhar Goldgraber

Erica Golin

Andrea Gonzalez

Joelle Grunblatt

Fitore Halili RN

Katrina Hannan

Mitchell Dean Harris

Sue Ann Herrera

Brittney Ashley
Hollingsworth

Laura Hollingsworth

Stephen William Hongach

Abeer Husein

Maryam Ibrahim

Alexandra Marie Imbesi

Alexander Improta

Fatima Inusa

Muhammad Ismail

Praisey Jacob

Shani Jankelovits

Stephanie Michelle Jara

Korpo Jo-Joe

Christopher Jones

Kellie Joseph

Farzeen Kanwal

Sari Katzen

Luiza Kayumova

Shahrukh Khan

Moriel Khaykin

Megan Kohlsaat

Ewelina Kolakowska-
Salamon

Ousmane Kone

Evgeniya Koshelyaevskaya

Oscar Krol

Xiomara Kurian

Jennifer M. Kurulgan

Dennis Lam

Kristina Lam

Veronica LaManna

Rin Zhi Larocque

Hajung Lee

Xue Qing Liang

Tayla Lugo

Laura Lund

Sally Mach

Janet Magnuson

Joseph Mansur

Victoria Manzo

Dorothea Barbara Martin

John McAllister

Malcolm McPherson

Renee Merritt

Julianne Millen

Kevin Mione

John Murray

Natallia Murzich

Adriane Musacchio

Dona Wasana M. Navinna
Kottage

Bassem Nawar

Yunchao Niu

Amanda Noto

Anna Nowicka

Kristian Nunez

Anita Ohemenggyan

Devon Oliva

Christina Olsen

Guenael Roudjerry Oristel

Maria Pagani

Richard Pallarino

Dakota Paxton

Iranthi Peiris

Carlo Pepia

Amanda Peraccio

Amanda Percaccio

S. Tharuki Perera

Rachel Postiglione

Joseph Potenza

Anthony Raguso

Catherine Raio

Merlin Sara Raj

Olga Rius

Adriana Robledo

John Rubino

Hina Sajjad

Shiqirije Salaj

Ibrahim Sangare

Ada Saqe

Omolola Saula

Mallory Scerbo

Danielle Scozzari

Natalie Semenovski

Tomoaki Shimada

Scott Shouldis

Daniella Sicilia

Dajah Smith

Michael Sutera

Sean Thatcher

Cristal Torres

Alima Toure

Karolina Truchel

Emmanuella Ulasi

Emily Vaughn

Erica Villamar

Ella Viola

Arianna Virone

Stacey Weiner

Robert White

Masha Abhayarawana
Wickramasinghe

Gail Wodkiewicz

Inessa Zakariashvili

Ramy Zakir

PeiPei Zhang   Xian Zhao   Luyao Zheng

COLLEGE THE ALBEMARLE, ELIZABETH CITY, NC

Liliia Abram

Melissa Amber Allard

Dorothy Ansell

Andrew Archibald

Jhasmine Aguilar Arellano

Marcella Dee Arnold

Uliana Bakhtiyarova

Ethan S. Bateman

Christopher Scott Bean

Ross Frederick Becker

Alyson Leigh Berry

Isabel Virginia Beteta

Crystal L. Blake

Olga Alexandrovna Blyum

Sara Bowden

Terrence Boyce

Alexandra K. Brindle

Kylee Renee Brooks

Rebekah Joy Brown

Lisa Ann Bryan

Mihaela Simona Bungete

Barbara Burley

McKenzie Kyle Byrum

Su Cai

Erin Siobhan Callahan

Danielle Callaway

Athena Mikaila Capacite

Stephanie Marie Carroll

Tammy Louise Cayton

Mary Katherine Cheesman

Angie Chen

Megan Kay Chory

Christopher J. Colvin

Melody Elysia Contreraz

Jennifer Nicole Cook

Quiana Victoria Cooper

Joshua Lee Copeland

Kenneth Brian Crowson

Tiara Ronne' Cummings

Sandra Ann Day

Dina Demasi

Josiah Ray Derby

Donna Elizabeth Dewhurst

Dawn Marie Dodson

Maxwell Dominick-Novak

Jennifer Domke

Malwina Dudek

Lizeth Antonia Elizondo

Vargas

Kelsea Naniloa Fallon

Elana Ann Fauth

Steven William Fecker

Cetria L. Felton

Tiffany Louise Felton

Crystal Diane Ferebee

Olga Fesenko

Lacey Breann Fields

Emma Finley

Amy Fish

Codi Babette Fleming

Annette Ward Friel

Xueyan Gao

Altazera Delaney Goldberg

Daniel Spencer Griffiths

Martin Gabriel Guzman

Corienne Elizabeth Haggard

Portia Noel Hardy

Laurel Gabrielle Harrington

Charles E. Havenar

Nolton Raymond Hill

Merrie Holcomb

Cecil Eric Holman

Martha Hoppe

Michael Lucus House

Jessica Lauren Hudak

Chardonnay T. Hurdle

Samantha Ingram

Elisabeth Schiskie Jarvis

Steven Connor Jordan

David Lee Joyce

Izabela Joanna Kajari

Noah Hamilton Kight

Renata Kuzmickaja

Jeffrey W. Laughlin

Nancy Leanne Leary

Phoebe Lease

Elizabeth Livingston Lee

Hannah Grace Locklear

Bettie Worth Lowe

Tristin Loxley

James Christopher Lynch

Kristie Diane Markham

Oleksandra V. Matviichuk

Katelynn Ann May

Floyd H. McGowan

Cody A. McKinney

Cammie McMahan

Amanda G. McMillen

Jennifer Marie Merrick

Richard Miles

Andrea Dawn Miller

Lakeisha Moore

Elizabeth A. Morrissey

Claire Paije Mumma

Mary White Newsome

Starla Louise Newton

Miranda Harris Oliver

Jackson Osebreh

Nina Owens

Sarah Harris Pendleton

Vestel Boyce Pendleton

Cameron Austin Pierce

Olesya Alkeseevna Pkhakina

Courtney Taylor Potts

Dumitru Pruteanu

Justin Regel

Shainelle Cross Robinson

Yahor Rodzin

Sandra Saltirova

Ashley Sampson

Sumeyra Sariboga

Carlee Renee Sawyer

Maria Christina Schwartz

Ricardo Antonio Segura

Quilca

William David Sharber

Sheila Shiflett

Hannah Lenore Elizabeth

Sloate

Brenna Smith

Patria S. Smith

Yurii Pavlovich Sokolov

Carlie Elizabeth Spear

Cassandra Stevenson

Natalia I. Titenkova

Caden Trueblood

Aidan Liam Tumlinson

Ludmila Turcan

Jacob Austin Valentine

Yuliya Vishneuskaya

Ljupka Vuchevska

Marla Wales

Jacob T. Walton

Tamara Janelle Walton

Sishi Wang

Elexis Hunter White

Tara Britton Wilkins

Robert A. Williams

Caitlin Godfrey Wilson

Robin Leigh Woodard

Heather Leigh Woodley

Caston Elizabeth Young

COLLEGE OF THE SEQUOIAS, VISALIA, CA

Mansour Alshahari
Andrea Alvarez
Lisa Anderson
Burcin Arslan
Dieddra Atondo
Irma Barba
Maritza Barragan-Melecio
Daniel James Beauchamp II
Vincent Billings
Timothy Bird
Jorge Bueso
Melody Cabral
Mayra Camarillo
Louie J. Campos
Candelaria Cardenas
Lisanne Carrillo
Connie Cavazos
Mercedes Caroline Cavazos
Danyell Chavez
Lila Chavez
Jennifer Cho
Jianhong Deng
Rayane De Souza Silva
Caner Duzenli
Kyle Edwards

Summer Marie lynn Elston
Theresa Figueroa
Daniel Flores
Andres Martin Flores-Valero
Meghan Franklin
Sadie Helene Garcia
Edgar Godinez
Serina Gomes
Christopher Gomez
Jessica Gonzalez
Emily Guilbeau
Bridgette Harrison
Venancio Hernandez
Collean Holloway
Kaitlyn Holmes
Lauralee Huber
Nicholas Jaramillo
Christopher Jensen
Jacqueline Johnson
Angela F. Jones
Melissa Jurado
Joseph Koster
Kyle cameron Lewis
Madison Therese Loehner
Scarlett Looney

Maricela Lopez
Aracely Lozano
Steven Eugene Lusk
Sean Mavricakis
Mahmonir Mazaheri Jajaei
Hector Mendoza
Adalberto Meza
Emily Miller
Joyce Marie Mondry
Andrew Pacheco
Brianna Marie Pauls
Fabian Perez
Izaac Perez-Solorio
Philip Perkins
Lizzete Plascencia
Ellyn Prado
Hilda Ramirez
Joel Reynoso
David Rivera
Julius J. Rojas
Marilu Romani
Cecilia Ruvalcaba
Jessica Nicole Salinas
Veronica Sanchez
Alejandro Santillan

Samantha Saucedo
Kenneth Seeger
Rachel Shimmin
Maria Silva
Susan Singkeovilay
Gabrielle Sorea
Kathleen Spaunhurst
Tyler McKenzie Stuhaan
Cara Sutherlan
Cinthya Montserrat Torres
Melano
Nancy Elizabeth Umana
Christine Marie Valencia
Aubrey VanSickel
Daniel Villafana
Pablo Villagrana
Yesenia Villasenor
Caylie Watson
Krista Janai Whitaker
Victoria Elizabeth Rene
Williamson
Brooklyn Wilson
Jose Luis Zaragoza

COLORADO CHRISTIAN UNIVERSITY COLLEGE OF UNDERGRADUATE STUDIES, LAKEWOOD, CO

Emily R. Adams
Erin N. Amsberry
Kayla C.A. Baker
Isaac D. Baldwin
Kiana M. Benson
Heather Christina Benton
Amalee Mae Bowen
Carolyn J. Brown
Megan C. Budd
Jillian K. Buell
Josiah M. Bussing
Emily N. Carper
Kelsey Charlene Cook
William A. Corzine
Lindsay C. Dee

Kaitlyn Edison
Matthew P. Erickson
Benjamin Taylor Essells
Jaimie Joy Fabling
Nicole A. Faktor
Myrisa A. Garcia
Marcela Garcia Lopez
Kimberly A. Gilbertson
Madalyn Carol Graeve
Nathanael S. Grasz
Megan L. Hallett
John G. Hansen
Dean R. Hawkins
Rylie D. Helweg
Nicole L. Hooks

Isaac J. Imig
Lydia E. Johnson
Wesley Parker Jones
Hannah E. Joslin
Joyce J. Jowers
Hudson Caleb Jungck
Naomi K. Ketchens
Joshua D. Kuest
Nicolas C. Leland
Marissa M. Lumpkin
Talene J. Magee
Alisha D. Mahon
Leah R. Manee
Hannah Marcy
Hilary Keller Masters

Seth A. Maxwell
Michael J. McGraw
Brenna Marie Moore
Alise Kathleen Murray
Katie L. Murrey
Rachel Ann Nakamura
Kelsey E. Powell
Molly L. Rumbyrt
Maria A. Scheffel
Stephen Thomas Scheffel
Tylor Kaylee Schmitt
Christina A. Seraile
Joshua W. Sherwood
Amy Elizabeth Smith
Stanton D. Spaulding

Kayla M. Stanga
Madison Caroline Stinnett
Taylor Christine Sturms

Nicole N. Versaw
Emily R. Webb
Mesa J. Westlake

Libby L. Whittemore
Taylor E. Wollenberg

Sadie Kirsten Young
Briana M. Zimmerman

COLORADO MESA UNIVERSITY, GRAND JUNCTION, CO

Chris Aiken
Abby Akin
Alyssa Marie Albrich
Laura Andersen
Keren Angeles
Nichole Barban
Kathryn Rose Chovich
Beckel
Kasey Benish
Katelyn Ann Boelke
Bianca Bolcato
Mikayla Marie Bradshaw
Joel Micah Brown
Bryan Bunner
Renee Cameron
Taylor Cecil
Melinda Chenoweth

Drew Michael Collins
Maurice Comer Jr.
Cody Daniels
Alberto Delgado
Sarah DeLong
Dena M. Dolson
Marie Dreher
Jordan Paul Fisher
Marayna Flemming
Avery Gallegos
Emily Morgan Glen
Zoe Nicolette Haney
Sandra Heley
Jordan Hitshew
Jordan Hoffman
Shanna Hoopengardner
Kevin Makanalani Kahuena

Kailey Eileen Kaiser
Bethany Ann Kanesky
Tessa Madalyn Kester
Connie Kim
Kelsey Leffel
Andrea Lopez
Kristina Renaelyn Massey
Katlyn McKeogh
Kristina McLeslie
Keri Metcalf
Dany Minchow
Johnathon Douglas Olivas
Whitney Pigao
Jennifer Ranus
Kiersten Ridgel
Ryan Paul Ruark
Meghan Marie Sanger

Logan Saruwatari
Karis Elizabeth Scroggs
Ericka Lee Sebring
Kyle Anthony Serrano
Meagan Singh
James A. Stulc
Lisa Terry
Kendall Tillman
Jacob Roy Todd
Sarah Volk
Hadleigh M. Wailes
Kelli R. Wilder
Brittany Gerilin Wilson
Eric Ziegler

COLORADO NORTHWESTERN COMMUNITY COLLEGE, RANGELY, CO

Jamie Lynn Bair
Ripley Updike Bellio
Owen Neil Fairchild
Guadalupe Holguin
Jessica Karren

Johana Lara
Taylor Denae Lott
Jesse Michael McCann
Donna Medina
Daisen Noelle Murray

Darian Kristin Price
Alyssa Michelle Reeves
Olga Belova Vaughn
Bailey Kathryn Nicole
Walker

Brittany Walker
Roza Woldemariam

COLORADO NORTHWESTERN COMMUNITY COLLEGE CRAIG CAMPUS, CRAIG, CO

Katherine R. Berkoff
Staci V. Blair
Jeremy P. Chambers
Geraldine L. Collins
Katherine S. Ellis

Robert A. Mackey
Robert L. Meyers
Elishah M. Miles
Teasha S. Moody
Ashley N. Moon

Mariana Morales
Rachel R. Murphy
Jacob D. Prescott
Heidi L. Reiman
Katelyn A. Sadler

Sarah D. Scott
Barry A. Steadman

COLUMBIA COLLEGE, COLUMBIA, MO

Jennifer Avila-Gonzalez
Sarah E. Barris
Elizabeth M. Bishop
Shalonda L. Blanchard

Antonio M. Brown
Ladarryon T. Brown
Kristina E. Cross
Kimberly R. Donnell

James M. Dorman
Trent Everett Finley
David J. L. Glenn Sr.
Jennifer M. Hoch

Emma E. Langham
Kaitlyn C. McHughs
Jordan L. Nigus
Mercedes L. Nute

Anna D. Ralls
Hoyt L. Ross
Josh M. Saffa

Ethan C. Veit
Erin N. Weaver

Anna M. Weeden
Morgan N. Wilde

Elaine Wohlgemuth
Krystle A. Young

COLUMBIA COLLEGE, COLUMBIA, SC

MyLeah Adella Barriteau
Danielle Marie Blackwell
Jessica Jazmin Bonilla
Garcia
Mattison Lott Brantley
Destra Adrienne Capers
Julianna Justine Cobb

Kaela Maeve Coleman
Brianna Leah Cook
Ashley Renee Cox
Wendy S. Early
Marian Nell Easler
Meda Ashley Gause
Taylor Alexis Jeffers Gray

Jennifer Rose Lunsford
Bethany Deborah Martin
Chloe Catherine Mattison
Jacqueline Mayorga
Mayorga
Katherine DeAnn Ready
Kayden Lane Reilly

Paige Arianna Riggins
Eneyda Badessa Solis Cubas
Venelina Hristova Vateva
Jessica Danielle Wagoner
MacKenzie Taylor Wood

COLUMBIA-GREENE COMMUNITY COLLEGE, HUDSON, NY

Kelley Bentley
Chad Bleich
Regina Borfitz
Kimberly Carlew
Christine Cashell

Natalie Dair
Alexis Marita Deeg
Rebekah Michele Dempsey
Wendy Barlow Dufkin
Dominick Fiducia

Jessica Matthies
Beatriz Musong
Sarah Myhre
Jessica Lynn Rivenburg
Tammy Robinson

Chance Moeteaph Ryan
Katie Ray Sambrook
Majella Schaffer
Tina Marie Scism
Jacqueline Scopa

COLUMBIA SOUTHERN UNIVERSITY, ORANGE BEACH, AL

Idaresit Adesewa Adele
Joan Brittain Albert
Melinda Kaye Anderson
Tajudeen Oladele Ashafa
Deborah Jean Boyce

Lori A. Brooks
Wendy Lou Bundy
Jeremey Seth Criner
Sharon Elaine Dolinger
Paula Jo Engel

Stephanie Nicole Gamble
Eric Sean Hampton
Michael E. Hanuscin
Roland Wilson Hubert III
Dunta F. Moore

Ashleigh Liston Oliver
Jessica H. Shoup
Scott Edward Thovson
Jesse Lee Willoughby

COLUMBIA STATE COMMUNITY COLLEGE, COLUMBIA, TN

Hillary G. Allen
Shananikohl F. Alsup
Alejandro Angel
Rachel C. Ansley
Joseph R. Arnold
Braxton L. Bonds
Abby S. Brown
Andrew K. Brown
Logan M. Calvert
Aleaha F. Chapman
Emily T. Coleman
Joshua D. Crist
Kasandria E. Cruz
Jacob D. Curry

Tarissa D. Duke
Brooke R. Eason
Kaitlyn R. Ester
Lauren B. Feichtinger
Shayla A. Fisher
Aleta K. Fowler
Brandon S. Gandy
Robert L. George
Sahel Gingerich
Gretchen C. Greer
Lucas W. Griggs
Matthew R. Hall
Joshua L. Hamilton
Alison N. Helson

Dalaney F. Hollis
Forest S. Holsinger
Kaleigh R. Holt
Ella J. Hudson
Ariellah L. Huisinga
Chandler L. Jones
Destiny K. Juarez
Rebecca L. Kelley
Ryan T. Kemp
Daryan F. Killen
Mackenzie R. Ledford
Abigail K. Lewis
Andrew D. Long Jr.
Hannah N. Luna

Alison N. Mabery
Chelsea R. Marshall
Krizten D. Martin
Taylor L. McKinney
Jasmine S. Meriwether
Adam R. Moser
Kyra J. Newton
Heather L. Nordland Page
Alexandria M. O'Daniel
Shonda E. Parks
Jacob Q. Penix
Lauren E. Perry
Madison M. Pitts
Cadence B. Ray

Sacha E. Reeves
Abbey Nicole Richardson
Jessika H. Riddle
Breanne R. Robertson
Tucker M. Robertson
Peyton T. Russ
Ryan A. Russell
Catherine A. Sisson

Lindsey B. Skinner
Courtney F. Smith
Lauren N. Smith
Morgan Staggs
Tyler H. Stewart
Matthew Stooksbury
Tyler R. Stricklin
Michael A. Stutts

Ora LaShay Stutts
Holly G. Taylor
Julia H. Taylor
Ryan A. Taylor
Mariann Tease
Taylor N. Thompson
Sierra D. Tinin
Hunter L. Tyree

Lacey A. Weeks
Spencer Wise
Tyler A. Woodside
Gregory S. Wunner
Justin T. Young
Joshua R. Yumul

COLUMBUS STATE UNIVERSITY, COLUMBUS, GA

Asha Nichelle Alexander
Delor "Dee" Anderson
Mary Arnold
Molly Avary
Kayla Ayuso
Marc Baker
Jared Jack Bies
Chamaine A. Bjornson
Chatil Bradford
Brittney Kiarra Browning
Joycelyn Cañedo
Destini Cofield
Meagan Marie Corcoran
Tyler Davidson
Brandon J. Davis
Cailee Davis
Jacquelyn DeLauder
Nathan DeMarco-Jacobson

Shirin Felfeli
John Thomas Fellows
James Fielding
Shytara Fields
Brandi Fine
Heather Fournier
Christopher T. Galvez
Jacob Greene
Katherine Grego
Bethany Hansen
Pamela Merritt Harvey
Katherine A. Holmes
Jessica Howell
Yumei Huang
Heather Ivery
Kate Jacoby
Janell T. James
Taylor N. Jenkins

Comfort Johnson
Jasmine Daneria Johnson
Taeler Demoin Klimp
Aina Kumar
Robert Monfort
Kaitlin Moye
Caroline Patricia Moyer
Emily Catherine Murray
Osamienwenfan Blessing
Obasuyi
Akinola Ololade Oladipo
Anisha Patel
Mansi Patel
Chudney Patrick
Staren Pierce
Brittany Nicole Reeves
Thomas Cameron Rice
Shelby Anne Rolling

Shaunquelle Antionette
De'Janae Sapp
Jewell Scott
Meagan Shelnut
Andrea Skipor
Jessica Smith
Krista Marie Snead
Joshua Staples
Jonathan Ross Tew
April Marie Trawick
Emily Vaughn
Chelsea Wakefield
Belinda Louise Walton
Lauren Whitehurst
Mary Kathryn Wright

COMMUNITY COLLEGE OF ALLEGHENY COUNTY, MONROEVILLE, PA

Danielle E. Andring
Eric Norman Arbogast
Choonghwa Sarah Baldwin
Katerina Solodina Bentley
William T. Branch Jr.
Glenn E. Bush
Jacquelynn C. Carnes
Denise N. Cattley
John Trevor Cox
Carina Elizabeth Crane

Erica J. Deitrick
Elizabeth Eva Eger
Maureen E. Fechik
Carol A. Fisher
Christine Gapinski
Poupak Haghighi
Rachael Hoffman
Michael L. Klein
Rebecca Marie Laero
Carissa Rose Machi

Mark Michael Mastervich
Danielle Marie Mazur
Mariah Joanne McDade
Audryana K. Phillips
Roger J. Pogoda
Adam M. Salandro
Ashley Santavy
Marisa Leigh Santucci
Lauren A. Siefers
Kevin James Stapleton

Samantha Kate Stough
Dominique Thomas
Thompson
Megan Marie Tkacik
Jessica Diane Tomlinson
Michelle M. Wadsworth
Angela N. White
Elizabeth Anne Wick
Ian E. Wissinger
Courtney Mae Wojcik

CONCEPTION SEMINARY COLLEGE, CONCEPTION, MO

Christopher Riley Davis

Kevin Anthony Lenius

Ty David Taylor

CONNORS STATE COLLEGE, WARNER, OK

Michael K. Anderson
Jeremy Ryan Barnes
Madison Michelle Bright
Paul L. Bright
Rachel Leeann Brock
Shayne R. Brown
Bailey Marie Bryant
Emilee Raelynn Burdge
Justin Heath Burney
Rebekah Marie Burress
Tyler C. Burton
Kori Lynn Carmack
Makenzie Kaye Carpenter
Desiree Nicole Carter
Kaylee Ann-Rose Casey
Jordan A. Cochran
Julie D'Anne Cones
Brayden Gage Cox
Morgan A. Craig
Baylee Brooke Dosh
Emily Nicole Dowdy
Sydney Blake Edwards

Zalin Keith Edwards
Baylee Maria Evans
Tyler Blake Fletcher
Jacob Allen Flourney
Clayton James Fobber
Kristie Ann Gines
Savanna L. Goldman
Samantha Renee Graves
Elizabeth A. Gresham
Jacob L. Grossnicklaus
Michael Lyndell Handley
William Jake Henson
Payton Lea Anne Hill
Randy Earl Hopson
Ashley Dawn Hough
Bailey Shae Hulet
Justin A. Jensen
Jennifer F. Johnson
Colton W. Keel
Sarah Elizabeth King
Robert Lightfoot Latta
Javier B. Ledezma

DeShawnta Lyday
Philicea L. Mack
Kambri Nikole Martinez
Zadie Rae McElhaney
David Scott McGuire
Gregory Michael Metcalf
Johnny C. Miles
Brook N. Miller
Janessa Joy Moore
Ashley Marie Odom
Brookelyn N. Patrick
Danny Allen Bishop Phillips
Kylie E. Powell
Ashley L. Pritchett
Clark William Reuter
Myranda Dawn Rowland
Kylie E. Sanders
Mayra Sandoval
Amanda Scott
Baylie L. Short
Hannah Elizabeth Smith
Timothy C. Smithson

Brandy Garland Sockey
Grant Sontag
Paige Stevens
Hannah Jill Nicole Strain
Amanda Lynn Stroud
Zachary Wayne Studer
Shannon Coup'e Tacy
Destiny Daniel Towe
Jamicia Lyn Trammel
Drew C. Vandiver
Elizabeth Hope Van Orsdol
Maty Jo Wade
Britten Montana Wallace
Maegen D. Wallace
Justin Ryan Wasson
Jacob Aaron Weatherby
Zachary D. Wilhite
Jace Kyler Wilkins
Shelby L. Wilson
Tyler Shane Wood
Vicki Denise Woodall
Jacob W. Yochum

CONVERSE COLLEGE, SPARTANBURG, SC

Bibiana Ashton Loza
Kandice Elizabeth Miles

Christie Rose Monahan
Jordan Quinn Raska

Ashly Sommer Sutherland

Lauren K. Ziegler

COPIAH-LINCOLN COMMUNITY COLLEGE, WESSON, MS

Destiny Allen
Kelley Ann Allen
Michael Allen
Jordan Antley
Hannah Ashely
Thomas Ashely
Mattie Slade Avants
Carlee Ballard
Brittany Barbay
Andrew Bates
Carletta Battle
Carlotta M. Battle
Victoria Amber Blakeney
Jeffrey Bond

Ashley Boyd
Audriana Bozeman
Danielle Brady
Lauren Rachell Brashier
Wanda Briggs
Michael Buckels
Jeremy Buffington
Greta Carley
William Graham Carter
Harley J. Chandler
Thomas Cole
Brittany Crosby
Michael Curtis
Katie Davis

Benjamin Douglas
Brady Dunaway
Lashard Durr
Kashalyla Edwards
Shelby Edwards
Rebecca Leann Ellzey
Joseph Este
Jonathan Farnham
Matthew Ransom Gill
Brittny Glasper
Kalie Green
John Hamilton
Dustin L. Hart
Lauren MaHaley Hatcher

Perquisha Henderson
Braxton Hinton
Haleigh Hux
Austin Irby
Chloe Johnson
Madison Johnson
Thomas Jones
Christina C. Knott
Cole Langdon
Chelsea Lewis
Kira Marlow
Dedric May
Lindsey Mccardle
Brandi Mcinnis

Christa Mclendon

Cory Mcnamee

Si'Edriq Sha'Ron Middleton

Jasmine Miller

Troy Morgan

Hoby B. Mullins

Zayne Mullins

Ashley Munn

Daniel Nasif

Tony Nelson

Riley Newton

Gregory Wayne Nickles

Kenya Norwood

Austin Odom

Stephen Owen

Marico Paige

Jacob Patrick

Perry Pennington

William Pennington

Shawanda Porter

Joseph Pryor

Samanta Ramirez-Garduna

Anna Richardson

Newton Riley

Katelyn Delanie Roberts

Courtney Robinson

Destini Rollins

Nikki Rowells

Christopher Samuels

Brittany Sharp

Bentley Sills

Colby Sims

Aubrey Smith

Coty Smith

Erin Smith

Haley Smith

Miesha Smith

Phillip Smith

Chelsie Spears

Markeita Ashley Stapleton

Latrece Steward

Paula Stewart

Katlynn Abigail Sullivan

Kaitlyn Taylor

Reed Taylor

Haley Thomas

Travis Brenton Thornton

Tyler Turner

Jackson Twitty

Kayla Elizabeth Tyler

Caitlyn Upton

Kaitlyn Upton

Emily Walker

Jacynto Walker

Bailey Warren

Madison Marie Warren

Allison Watson

Donte Watson

Lauren Brouillette Westrope

Anna Whittington

Zachery Williams

Willow Yakush

COPIAH-LINCOLN COMMUNITY COLLEGE NATCHEZ, NATCHEZ, MS

Helen Victoria Allen

Rachel Page Allred

Cedarius D. Bailey

Emilian A. Bate Ashu

Jamie M. Bertelsen

Edwin J. Blackburn

Tyler Mathew Blank

John Allen Brooks

Laura Ann Brown

Derick Scott Brumfield

Tyler Lee Buckles

Diane Cason Butler

Rebekah Elizabeth Cade

Catherine Sadie Cavin

Kaitlyn Faith Cloy

Taravion Me'Shun Cosey

Kaylee Elizabeth Crain

Reagan Denny

Natrisha A. Dixon

Jesse Larton Dorsey

Patricia Dottery

Joseph Dottery Jr.

Brittney J. Evans

Taheaven C. Fountain

Calli Marie Fuller

Candace A. Green

LaTara L. Griffith

Jessica Lynise Harris

Keola L. Herrington

James David Hollowell

Jonterial T. Johnson

Tamla Sade Johnson

Shanjeanlyn King

Joseph Lee Knight Jr.

Dejanira G. LeBouef

Jason Michael Mann

Jessica Rae Matthews

Isaac Marlow McIntosh

Makeba Shane Mitchell

Alexis L. Moore

Gwendolyn Rose Morgan

Charlotte A. Perry

Jackie A. Phillips

Ryan Garrett Porter

Cole A. Radzewicz

Patricia M. Richards

Tricia Lynn Sadler

Derek William Saxon

Tanisha K. Smith

Brittany N. Strahan

Jonathan Mark Taylor

Quarneshya Monique Taylor

Aaron J. Uram

Catherine Vanderslice

Dorothy Vaughn

Kirby D. Vaughn

Brianna Claire Walker

Breanna Sade Ware

Michael Anthony Ware

Angenel D. Washington

Gwenetta Y. Washington

Alicia Ann Wells

COPIAH-LINCOLN COMMUNITY COLLEGE SIMPSON COUNTY CENTER, MENDENHALL, MS

Nicholas Merrick Allen

Kelsey Elizabeth Baughman

Phillip Patrick Benton

Andrew Tyler Berry

Crystal Deanna Boone

Malia Lakyn Bynum

Krista Gayle Chambers

Madison Taylor Cliburn

Laurel Elizabeth Crawford

AmBrea Kaitlyn Davis

Jessica Hannah Davis

Donnell T. Feazell

Martha Taylor Gable

Hope Katherine Huff

Hayden Lee Jones

Natalie Brooke Jones

Jamilia Latae Keys

Savanah Noel Little

Makeha T. Magee

Marissa Christine McDonald

Tori Ashton Mott

Taysha Roshundra Rivers

Cornelius Dontray Robinson

Daneisha Keera Sanders

Caylee Elizabeth Smith

Savanna Marie Staggs

Victoria Blair Sullivan

CORNERSTONE UNIVERSITY GRAND RAPIDS THEOLOGICAL SEMINARY, GRAND RAPIDS, MI

Kyle Matthew Boase
Andrew Thomas Bolkcom
Joshua Carpenter
Elizabeth Davidhizar
Audrey Christine Filson

Charnel Marietje Houben-Hopp
Andrew Kischner
Kara Strohm Lilly
Paul E. Miller

Ashleigh Rebekka Munch
Andrew James Panaggio
John-Thomas Richards
Erick Arthur Solomon
Seth Michael Stadel

Matthew Daniel Williams
Charles Wineman

CRISWELL COLLEGE, DALLAS, TX

James Clayton Cox
Dawna Lynn Duke
James Knox

Tarrick McGuire
Kelly Renae McLeod

JamesThomas Christopher Riley

Melinda Robinson
Timothy Stone

CROSSROADS COLLEGE, ROCHESTER, MN

Korey Eugene Harris
Jennifer J. Karow
Nawsitar Khinphan

Amanda Lynn Kirchner
Jason Mehring

Kiana Jade Mehring
Nicole Ann Peloquin

Rachel Joy Sternke
Samantha Jean Stuve

CROWDER COLLEGE, NEOSHO, MO

Zayne Mitchel Aldrich
Heather Lynn Allen
Gayle A. Alverson
LeeRoy Clinton Anderson
Tamatha M. Araya
Kerrigan Brianne-Kukal Arnold
Sarah Ann Aulick
Oluwasayo Excel Ayeomoni
Karly Dawn Bain
Crystal Dawn Baker
Monica Elizabeth Ballay
Matthew Scott Bible
Kelly Richard Blotter
Amber Nicole Bogardus
Kayla Marie Brattin
Kaitlyn Paige Brewer
Christopher Robert Bridges
Lindey Erin Broyles
Arieal Lynn Butler
Jennifer L. Campbell
Davin Antony Casados
McKayla Gray Clark
Michael Edward Coberley

Amy Lynn Cochran
Jacqueline Marguerite Cole
Kendra Ann Cole
Melissa A. Collins
Karen Sue Cooper
Carmen C. Creswell
Lana Kathleen Desmond
Douglas H. Dickey
Drew Wayne Dirks
Hannah Lynne Dodson
Cynthia Marie Dominguez
Christopher Lyn Dooley
Amber Marie Doubek
Greggory Grant Drew
Emily LouAnn Dunlap
Dana Lynn Eador
Cristy Leigh Edens
Jacqueline Engelbrecht
Ginelle Sue Esry
Fata Fall
Kaycia Dawn Feller
Kaitlyn Christine Fieser
Kristyn L. Finocchiaro
Hayden Leighann Fisher

Matthew Scott Forbes
Brenda S. Ford
Kayla Forkner
Jessica Lynn Galardo
David William Galvan
Madelaine Paige Giebler
Shasta Liberty Gift
Sharon L. Gilmore
Alyssa Michelle Goddard
Chelsea Rene Gustafson
Amanda Lacy Hall
Deana Marie Hall
Rhonda G. Halleran
Erika Kristan Handley
Kirsten Nicole Hargis
Amy Kaye Harkey
Jessica Morgan Harvey
Jessica Joy Hazelwood
Megan Brooke Heman
Jaqueline Hernandez
Samantha May Hester
Nathaniel Alexander High
Jacob Noah Holliday
Chasity Lynn Huff

Karen Renee Hunt
Macajah Leeann Irwin
Caitlyn Rose Jacks
Jered Keith Jackson
Christopher Kyle Johnston
Logan Gabriel Johnston
Karen Elise Jones
Kathryn Elizabeth Juracek
Matthew James Keeton
Catherine Ailene Kelley
Breonna Renee Knorpp
Tanner James Larsen
Alyssa Dawn Lawson
Robert Mikal Lee
Marissa Ann Lekarczyk
Eric A. Letts
Breanna Rachelle Lewis
Timothy Lingenfelter
Kylie Joy Littlefield
Vira Volodymyrivna Lytnova
Ethan Axel Manke
Rocio Martinez
Misha Leigh McAnally

Austin Brian McCleery

Kristofer Aleksander Miljan

Tiana Shanei Millard

Katie Jean Mitchell

Jared L. Moore

Joanna Lynn Moreland

Courtney Nicole Morgan

Amanda Dawn Munday

Caitlin Brianna Murphey

Tori Elizabeth Murray

Emily Ann Nichols

Christie Mae Ogle

Imalay Marisol Osorio

Vaughn Paul Payton

Kalyn Blakelee Petty

Tiffony Jane Pinaire

Aaron Joseph Porter

Mary Jane Reding

Jacquelyn Leanne Ritchie

Karen Sue Robbins

Jaycie Lee Roberts

Amanda Ann Rowden

Ashley Guadalupe Sandoval

Derek Noah Sandtorf

Michele Renae Sanko

Robert John Schancer

Alexander Wade Scheppert

Sandra Anne Scheurich

Paije Mekenzi Scotten

Lauren Brooke Sebastian

Draven Delaney Sharp

Nash Elijah Smalley

Sue Ann Stanley

Andrea Renee Stanley-Mcginnis

Christian Daniel Stewart

Amber Rose Stout

Loyd-Michael Lubow Sullivan

Emily Eve Swisher

Theresa D. Thorade

Eliza Grace Tidball

Briar Steele Tiller

Emily Elizabeth Trejo

Mercedes Marie Vogel

Saundra Ann Wallace

Cody Lane Ward

Chelsea Diane Webb

Amanda Pearl Wecker

Kristan Victoria Wellesley

Donavin Blake Wilson

Sarah Marlene Wilson

Somer Kay Wilson

Shelli Jean Wimer

Cuy Yang

Drew Jamison Young

CROWLEY'S RIDGE COLLEGE, PARAGOULD, AR

Brandy Michelle Alls

Heather Paige Bronc

Amanda Diane Broom

Kathie Elizabeth Cable

Tristin LeShae Clayton

Kolton Brandon Douglas

Kaylnn Marie Duley

Erica Christine Ewing

Savannah Johns

Hannah Kirk

Kassidie Jean Lawrence

Blake Edward Murphy

Deidra Hope Pillow

Kiefer Calaway Ramsey

Kaitlyn Nicole Roberts

Austin Dean Schwyhart

Wilson Thomas Teague

CUMBERLAND COUNTY COLLEGE, VINELAND, NJ

Stephanie Alvarez

Brooke Ambert

Kylee Bagley

Bianca Birney

Kristin Lynn Borges

Cleo Burrus

Nicholas Caregnato

Joshua Carll

Gabrielle Castellini

Anthony Chesebro

Matthew Colon

Danielle Cornman

Gabriela Cuadra

Adriana Lee DeBartolomeis

Angelo DeCesero

Jose DeJesus

Carly DiDonna

Lauren Fazenbaker

Sarah Rose Galzerano

Jeannie Candelaria Garcia

Vincent Giardino

Meagan Lindsay Haddock

Melissa C. Haddock

Jennifer Ann Hallgren

William Latcham

Sahara Lopez-Dublin

Terron Mitchell-Green

Raul Perez-Duran

Juan Perez-Perez

Jaime Oscar Roman

Georgia Iris Salvaryn

Kellie Lynn Santoro

Courtney Saul

Zachary Scull

Emily Jordan Shropshire

Justin Smith

CUMBERLAND SCHOOL OF LAW SAMFORD UNIVERSITY, BIRMINGHAM, AL

Stewart James Alvis

Hilaire R. Armstrong

Ross S. Barbier

Walker M. Beauchamp

Andrea N. Bolton

Sarah F. Bothma

Jessica Bradi-lee Catlin

Sarah C. Chamberlain

Rachel H. Cobble

Caroline Mills Collins

Ashley L. Crank

Collin D. Hatcher

Jacob J. Key

Mark Andrew Kilgore

John D. Marsh

Julie A. Musolf

Austin L. Nichols

Kyle Anthony Scholl

Cody B. Walker

DABNEY S. LANCASTER COMMUNITY COLLEGE, CLIFTON FORGE, VA

Chelsea Dudley

Brandon George

Windell Austin Gibson

Jennifer Hicks

Rachel C. Lyle   Cody Warren Plecker

DAEMEN COLLEGE, AMHERST, NY

Ellen Marie Banks | Rebecca E. Haley | Stephanie Renee Parwulski | Sarah Elizabeth Rohe
Julianna M. Brnik | Nina M. Jobert | Rachel R. Pawlak | Ann Marie Rose
Shi T. Chow | Maryan A. Jumale | Mark J. Poblocki | Samuel B. Rugg
Brittany R. Denton | Lumeshwar Kumar | Christopher S. Ponichtera | Thanaporn Sae Tang
Mackenzie A. Donahue | Sarah E. Lang | Jordan L. Quinones | Hayle R. Scanlan
Amber J. Drzymala | Meghan L. Lipinoga | Kelsey M. Reeder | Aman R. Shamaa
Daniel B. Gertis | Gregory M. Lowe | Richard A. Reid | Morgan E. Villnave
Paige M. Gilbert | Anna M. Lyons | Breanna C. Reilly | Emily N. Yeager
Kathryn J. Haessner | Maria C. McGrath | Hannah T. Rice |
Ramel H. Haines | Morgan L. Montgomery | Justin C. Richmond |

DAKOTA COLLEGE AT BOTTINEAU, BOTTINEAU, ND

Kelley P. Amsbaugh | Tiffany Lee Hummer | Tanner M. Mundahl | Mattie Bree Schmitt
Joacelyn Antoine | Quincy Kenshan Jones | Leslie Ostreim | Paulo Fiatele Ta'a
Danielle Rita Nichole | Tina Marie March | Jessica Leigh Pigeon | Lucas C. Walsh
Belleau | Macy Beth Martinson | Briana M. Priest | Cole T. Wilhelmi
Sheena M. Ellingson | Phoenix Riley McElroy- | Megan L. Saville |
Daniel John Fyckes | Scott | Sara M. Schaefer |

DAKOTA STATE UNIVERSITY, MADISON, SD

Sarah Alfson | Carmen Ana Davis | Cassandra Marie Lynn | Victoria Rae Sopko
Alex Bangasser | Joshua Dosdall | Morgan | Trent Steen
Laurinda Rene' Bennett | Annalesha Kalis | Len Mutzenberger | Allison Thielsen
Casey Bethke | Mark Korabelnikov | Jessica Mashaun Phillips | Brittany Vlaminck
Elizabeth Eilene Bitterman | Harley Rose Lindell | Jennelle Pueppke | William Joseph Yager II
Kelly Ann Brusven | Jason Lucas | Brooke Relf | Haeun Yoon
Jamie Christman | Jenilee Sarah Mary Misko | Christian Ries |
Alexis Clevenger | Sid Moorhead | Eric Ruppelt |

DALLAS BAPTIST UNIVERSITY, DALLAS, TX

Keila Barrientos | Mary Dolan | Hannah Louise Hollabaugh | Jacob Austin Murphy
Stephen Lawrence Boyd | Marcus Dooley | Ryan Humphrey | Cashlee Alexis Rayas
Shih-Ya Chang | Rebecca Ruth Duitsman | Myles Anthony Johnson | Briana Rene
Shaina Noel Cheever | Nicole Marie Faulkenberry | Song Kim | Jacob Scott Rohrer
Zachary Clarke | Melanie Florian | Jessica Marie Kowalski | Thompson David Smith
Ben Ford Cocherell | Raelynn Goodman | Taylor Jane Mansour | Brian Kent Spann
Emory Cothen | Nicole Greene | Charles Matthews | Sydney Elizabeth Sumpter
Dean Matthew Dahlsten | Emily Jayne Guerra | Jansen Seth McDonald | Daniel Joshua Sweet
Jillian Elizabeth Dodderer | Christian Boothe Hill | Cassidy McKee | Wing Man Tang

Catherine Walker Annie Wells Stratton M. Williams Lauren Elizabeth Zackary

Layne Watson

DALLAS CHRISTIAN COLLEGE, DALLAS, TX

Ruud G. Boijseauneau Rojas Ashley Nichole Hudspeth Erin Holly Parks Daniel Vrooman

Joshua Thomas Bower Benjamin Lester Lantzer Joshua P. Smith Adrianna Walton-Rogers

Selah J. Burnett Chloe Grace Lantzer Mercedes Nicole Soto

José Lucien Gonzales Caitlin Joy Martin Kyle Naaman Spurgin

DALLAS THEOLOGICAL SEMINARY, DALLAS, TX

Levi D. Anderson Jeremy Collings Jeremy Ronald Koleba Benjamin Rounds

Herman Baker Derek George DeMars Hannah-Leah Lambert Zachary Roy

Luana Baptista Aaron Seth Farmer Ryan Landis Lydia Qiuge Shen

Lisa Bowe Sarah Eleanor Frase Danny Lee James Chung-Chien Su

Brittany Bowman Kent Freedman Jordan Parker Mike Trabun

Chad Bradley Carolyn A. Harris JoJo Qiao Kathy Whitthorne

Shiju Simon Cherian Johanna Horstman Hannah Rigel

Samantha Childs Ian Kissell Phillip Ross

DARTON STATE COLLEGE, ALBANY, GA

Daniel Anders Amanda D. Denton Nicholas B. Harvey Amanda Nava

Hope A. Bond Felicia Dunbar Amber A. Hawkins Richard Norman

Amy Borrero Austin T. Duncan Aileena Nicole Holcomb Sara Pickett

Shelley Brooks Courtney A. Engle Deshod M. Holley Mary Radford

George Camp Jillian R. Fiedler Chrystal Hunter Mahlon Randolph

Tyler Cartwright Gustavo Gonzales Britani Lambert Victoria Blaine Richards

Tomomi Colquitt Christopher Graham Allison JoAnna Lewis James Robinson

Matthew Copeland Carson R. Gregors Rae'keymia M. Lewis Fariela D. Sambo

Madison K. Daughtry Michael Hall Genevieve Gennie Marcus Savannah Tappin

Haley Davidson Maggie Hancock Dorothy R. Mitchel Moshonda Todd

Kathryn Deaton Katlyn Dena Harris Samantha Nagy Keirston B. Williams

DAVIDSON COUNTY COMMUNITY COLLEGE, LEXINGTON, NC

Montanna Alexandra Berrier Sarah Katelyn Janus Charlotte S. Pacheco- Taylor Olivia Rierson

Chloe Marie Binkley Charles James Love Sahagún Yesenia Rojas

Mamie Salesta Gates Kinsey Erynn Milsap Emily Brianna Porras Natalie H. Snincsak

Nicholas Christian Gore Zoe Francis Richardson

DAVIS & ELKINS COLLEGE, ELKINS, WV

Amber Nicole Abbott Rhys Lawrence Begley Zachary Bradfield Hannah Carl

Nicholas Akins Oliver Bienias Mary Braham Andrew Carroll

Colton Allen Grayson Blythe Elise Cardot Samuel Casto

Alexander Cheuvront

Emily Coffman

Guilherme Condolo Hubsch

Mark Cordle

Sara Davenport

Jacob DeMotto

Cassidy Dickens

Luka Djordjevic

Ryan Donchez

Elizabeth Noel Estes

Taylor Fealy

Thomas Fletcher

Jennifer Fredell

Gerald Camden Furby III

Jonathan Gainer

Kirsten Linnea Gateless

Natalie Green

Mia Rae Gresak

Katelynn Hanek

Kaylee Harris

Trisha Higgins

Olivia Hudok

Madalyn Humphrey

Aerial Jarvis

Mads Kaiser

Elliott Karr

Kaia Kater-Hurst

Sierra Kelley

Scott Leach

Paul Louzy

Sarah Marshall

Joshua McGlothlin

Nicola Merriman

Halima Michael

Stephen Mihalyo

Alexandra Miller

Ryan O'Connell

Elizabeth Ojanpera-Lynch

Zayd Othman

Benjamin Pastur

Austin Pillado

Sabrina Poessl

Jenniffer Lee Ridgeway

Marlene Ridgway

Kaylee Rosencrance

Sonja Skinner

MacKinzie Smith

Heather Snead

Chelsie Stover

Christopher James Swank

Julia Tenney

Aleksandar Vasiljevic

Kora Mikeal White

Jessica Kailee Williams

Trevor Wratchford

Autumn Victoria
Wunderlich

Elena Zanella

Matthew Zorn

DAVIS COLLEGE, JOHNSON CITY, NY

Alainey Banks

Elijah Buie

William Conboy

Joseph Daniels

Jessica Haenisch

Kendra Joy Krissel

Ashley Lane

Katarina Eva MacFadden

Alyssa McMahon

Joshua Michael Presley

Jenny Ann Saysanam

Harrison Strickland

Derrinda Strohm

MaryAnn Weaver

Mary Beth Weaver

Natalie Wright

DAYMAR COLLEGE OWENSBORO, OWENSBORO, KY

Joelle Barnett

Shayla Crook

Mary Miller

Melissa Pile

Steve Smith

Erin Thomas

Penelope Kaye Vinson

DAYTONA STATE COLLEGE, DAYTONA BEACH, FL

Austin Albro

Kaylee Allen

Megan Quinn Anderson

Sache Juanita Bascome

David Bellish

Madeline Bertelson

Amanda Thierry Bolton

Brian Brooker

Michael Brown

Oscar Cabrera

Sabrina Collins

Kerrie Lorae Dunn

Tivon Faneyte

Gilarys Garcia Milan

Bryanne Gardner

Rosemilie Goulding

Megan Hammett

Morgan Hammett

Joshua Tolson Hasker

Beily Hernandez

Joel Hinton

Alexandra Hollabaugh

Sue Hopkins

Landon Hutchinson

Celyne Isidro

Hailey Jackson

Preston Johnston

Alicia Kandler

Ji Sun Kang

Nana Kani

Elizabeth Christine Kirkland

Mohga Kodsy

Devona Leeks

Emily Linton

Brittany Monderen

Justina Newman

Drew Peden

Norma Poole-Bland

Cynthia James Puckett

Evan Scherr

Corrine Scott

Brad Skibo

Willow Sprague

Annika Thomas

Oliva Thomas

Michael Tirpak

DEAN COLLEGE, FRANKLIN, MA

Meagan Simone Allen

Dominic Ballard

Haley Blair

Alexander Boyle

Alyssa Branciforte	Akeem Jean-Pierre	Marina McHugh	Patrick Anthony Surillo
Paige Carskaddan	Elijah Jones	Raylin Jean Medina	Yim Wing Tam
Yan Lam Chan	Sean Kaiser	Jessa G. Mulman	Hoi Hong Billy Tang
Evan Crocker	Kengo Kawashima	Lexi Ann Newton	India Terrell
Alexis DeVogt	Chandler Keville-Wagner	Alex Park Ostroff	Ryan Tinney
Tara Kathryn Digiovacchino	Candice Coco Lam	Brianna Park	Morgan Turner
Paige Fontaine	Kin Meng Lam	Christina Polanco	Brandon Valls
Michaela Ann Fraini	Silvia Laracca	Justin Rezendes	Jonathan Wickman
James O. Hansen	Chiu Shing Lau	Brenna Robinson	Chi Shan Wong
Hannah Heinzer	Kenisha Memorie Lee	Caitlin Robinson	Ching Nam Yim
Kok Hei Hui	Hiu Hok Leung	Olivia Taylor Rodrigues	Tsz Shun Yip
Michita Inoue	Cody Robert Maynard	Alexis Saar	Murilo Santa Helena Zanette

DELAWARE COUNTY COMMUNITY COLLEGE, MEDIA, PA

Carlo Armando Alcaraz	Armoni Carter	Nata Mansaray	Mario Salgado-Ojeda
Frantzcia Batichon	Gina DiLuzio	Edgar Pena Olivo	Alicia Stearn
Vanessa Beltran Velez	Kahlia Hughes	Yonahandi Pineda	Jonathan Stout
Grace Marie Bernardo	Vicky Lim	Meriana Regis	Gina Thomas
Isabella Elizabeth Cabibbo	Jeffrey Manner	Guadalupe Rios Perez	Katie Thompson

DELAWARE TECHNICAL COMMUNITY COLLEGE GEORGETOWN, GEORGETOWN, DE

Jamin R. Adkins	Enrique Escalante	Marisa K. Lowe	Shelly K. Paxtor Matul
Ruth Adorno Robinson	Taylor R. Ewing	Shannon D. Maner	Jordan K. Perry
Bahaa Al Banna	Walter L. Floyd	Anthony D. Marinelli	James Patrick Pickard
Ryan M. Amsley	Austin W. Frazier	Dana J. Marshall	Jeremy S. Redlich
Lisa V. Badur	Timothy P. Goslin	Maria Donita M. Matias	Samantha A. Reed
Elnara Bagaeva	Ligia Graner	Seosaimhin Aine	Karen M. Reese
Kristin N. Bailey	Mantas Grigorovicius	McGoldrick	Jennifer D. Reis
Rebecca M. Bennett	Alicia V. Hale	Kayla L. McGuire	Blair L. Rogers
Esther M. Betz	Matthew E. Hallowell	Taura S. Melvin	Sonia E. Rosa
Brandon Bishop	Amber R. Hitchens	Tyler J. Merritt	Anthony J. Rousak
Sean J. Breslin	Brittany M. Hoffecker	Haley L. Mitchell	Jennifer L. Rowan
Elizabeth S. Butterly	Dawn S. Humphrey	Elyse F. Moore	Leanne E. Rowe
Teshree Chandradat	Marisa K. Jacobs	Isrelis Navarro	Sarah E. Russo
Ashley M. Cheeseman	Candice T. Jamps-Waples	Sarah E. Neilsen	Almira Salimgarieva
Ashley M. Chupp	Jalisa L. Jenkins	Nathaniel W. Nichols	Shelby E. Scott
Caitlin M. Cook	Brian R. Jennings	Virginia L. Nitsch	Jonothan A. Scotten
Peggy A. Cronic	Jordn A. Justice	Stephanie D. Noll	Travis M. Sewell
Sydney D. Draper	Ashley E. Keith	Nadezda S. Orth	Rebecca M. Sharkey
Britney Edwards	Maryia K. Komar	Alberto Pacheco-Alverez	Robert W. Silvagni
Tristan Engle	Irina V. Kurkina	Brandy M. Parks	Victoria A. Steele
Courtney A. Ennis	Meghan N. Lewis	Samuel L. Parsons	Stephanie J. Tucker
Samuel W. Ernst	Robert Anderson Livingston	Jamie C. Pase	Jerico A. Turner

| Shelby Lynne Vincent | Luz Y. Ward | Shamika A. Wesley | Adam J. Wright |
| Kelsey E. Waid | Dustin M. Warren | Derrick A. Wimbrow | Chanah L. Zrien |

DELAWARE TECHNICAL COMMUNITY COLLEGE STANTON, NEWARK, DE

| Kadeija Griffin | Blake Johnson | Courtney Shatley | Mary "Molly" C. Williams |
| Alan James Hitchner | Robert Overmyer | | |

DELAWARE TECHNICAL COMMUNITY COLLEGE TERRY CMAPUS, DOVER, DE

Sharon L. Allen	Daniel R. Evins II	Alexis Breanne McQuaid	Bruce E. Strother
Desiree Alexandra Aurillo	Brian Gamm	Aaron Mears	David Traxler
Casey Bankes	Roland John Gillette Jr.	Kimberly Mendoza	Joel P. Troyer
Clara A. Beckel	Louisa J. Goehringer	William R. Muffley	Alexander Stephen Twigg
Lisa A. Brown	Timothy S. Howell	Christopher Dennis Myles	Carmen Walls
Michael J. Bukavich	Machaela Shea True Huber	Natalie Osorio	Herbert E. Welday IV
Sarah Clark	Heather Jester	Angel Marie Piecuch	Crystal Marie Welsh
Katherine Elizabeth	Casey Ann Jones	Marcos A. Pou Jr.	Steven Wiltshire
Dacheux	Tyler Kent	Rachel Marie Roderick	Cheryl Wright
Ajahnique Dandy	Jessica Marie Larscaro	Jacob M. Rose	Norma Jeanette Wyatt
Donald R. Daut	Coralys Lozano-Reyes	Morgan L. Russum	
Harryson Domercant	Jessie S. Mbah	Elaina Snyder	
John Denzel Drane	Alexandria J. McLaren	Paul Stitik	

DELAWARE TECHNICAL COMMUNITY COLLEGE WILMINGTON, WILMINGTON, DE

Noah Andrews	Samantha Jones	Morgan Patrick	Walter Ruth
Ashley Arms	Zoe Parente	Charles D. Robinson	Carolane Smith
Joel Crooks-Deforrest			

DELGADO COMMUNITY COLLEGE CHARITY SCHOOL OF NURSING, NEW ORLEANS, LA

Brad Abatte	Richard L. Dubourg	Helen T. Howard	Jacqueline A. Rapp
Savannah Bentley	Derryl I. Dunn	Anne P. Jansen	Joshua Samford
Patrick S. Beshears	Nikki L. Fank	Myisha S. Johnson	Sabrina G. Seals
Lan Anh T. Cao	Matthew O. Feldbaum	Jeanie L. Jones	Lorie L. Seruntine
Britny C. Coste	Tracey J. Galassi	Lauren R. Lane	Alissa L. Smith
Delaney M. Davis	Christina A. Girau	Claudia Dioselina Paguada	Jaime V. Taylor
Scarlett Desselle	Katie Hodas	Hannah Price	Justin R. Tiemersma

DEL MAR COLLEGE, CORPUS CHRISTI, TX

Alexandria Abraham	Blanca S. Canales	Chelsea Cornwell	Katelyn M. Gutierrez
Cori N. Acosta	Judy Canon	Allysa K. Flores	Kimberly Kissoon
Bayley Allen	Lisa Carpenter	Joel Galindo	Yuliya D. Klochkova
Alexis F. Benavides	Jaclyn E. Castillo	Stephanie M. Garcia	Jammie Lopez
Anthony Bucciarelli	Kimberly E. Co	Victoria Gibbons	Shinwin A. Numfor

Daniel Van Pelt	Desiree C. Perez	Jessica Marie Startz	Holly S. Woodall
Lirva A. Pena	Katherine Reynolds	Sarah Tyler	Chelsea L. Wren

DELTA STATE UNIVERSITY, CLEVELAND, MS

Emily Brennan Barham	Hannah Belle Core	Lauren E. Mansour	Joshua James Stubbs
Cathryn Marie Beck	Trey Kimble Densford	Tavelle Montez Marion	Cody David Upchurch
Justin Clark Boatman	Jenna Leigh Anne James	Brittany Danielle McGee	Jessica Faith Wishard
Gregory Braggs Jr.	Allen	Lisa Nicole McLaughlin	Sarah Catherine Yawn
Katie Blair Busby	Alice Chepleting Koech	Christopher Reece Pecou	
Tyler Gilbert Comans	Bethany Keller Leininger	Carrie Lynn Stanford	

DENVER SEMINARY, LITTLETON, CO

Chinwenwa U. Agorom	Angela Marie Blattner	Tady Emmanuel Engulu	Kristy Ann Lapp
Joseph Barlow	Timothy Andrew Brygger	Mary Christine Feeney	Kelsey Anne Randel
John Benjamin Bell	Allison Noel Christie	Laura C. Flores	
Brandon C. Benziger	Daniel Geoffrey Cross	Aaron Joshua Kadavy	

DOANE COLLEGE, CRETE, NE

Jordyn Atwater	Lance English	Julie Jirovec	Amanda Petersen
Garret Borcher	Megan Fletcher	Cassandra Kennedy	Taylor Ruzika
Heather M. Broman	Breanna Bea Fye	Nathan Klein	Kayleigh Schadwinkel
Blake Bunner	Kevin Gunter	Zachary Kucera	Zachary Swanson
Erin Burrows	Phillip Hamburger	Brooke Ann Ludemann	Rebecca Vossler
Sara Cushing	Kaelli Hedgpeth	Allie McConville	Delta Wilson
Allison Dobson	Sydney Holtmeier	Tara Lynn McGinnis	Kale Wolken
Shaylen Doremus	Amy Hung	Marissa Moore	
John Michael Douglas	Amanda Jackman	Katelyn O'Brien	

DOMINICAN COLLEGE OF BLAUVELT, ORANGEBURG, NY

Brianna Elizabeth Arends	Amanda Jean Hallstein	Jamie Elizabeth McGinn	Destiny Padilla
Jenna M. Balsamello	Tatiana Carmen Henriquez	Brian Thomas McGuigan	Ebony Renee Vonwolfolk
Tamara Benoit	Stacey S. Jacob	Katie Ann McLaughlin	Norville Neil Yearwood
Joseph Edward Clinton	Chet Alexander Kleynowski	Brett Armand Mitchell	
Kayla Marie Grodzicki	Vanessa Maria Lorenzo	Thomas Matthew O'Brien	

DOMINICAN COLLEGE OF BLAUVELT GRADUATE SCHOOL, ORANGEBURG, NY

Michelle Allen	Michele Coffey	Sandra Kewcharoen	Meghan Moore
Joanne Pascual Alvarado	Soleidy Estevez	Brianne E. Macalena	Raina Paolini
Brittany Ann Austin			

DREXEL UNIVERSITY, PHILADELPHIA, PA

Dana R. Bloom	Katherine M. Boudreau	Katie L. Delaney	Marko Durica

Yikai Fang
Lynn M. Gotuaco
Gabrielle Housel
Ziyin Huang
Paulina R. Khodak
Zachary L. Lazeu

Tiffany T. Liao
Sean C. Marks
Kevin J. Murray
Bill Nguyen
Nicholas A. Pescatore
Azwad F. Rahman

Alissa N. Reichert
Matthew W. Robinson
Antonio Russo
Austin M. Sacks
Christina Lynn
Schweingruber

Elisabeth R. Sulger
Yonghwan Um
Amy Wongso
Alexandra T. Zeitz

DUQUESNE UNIVERSITY, PITTSBURGH, PA

Victoria Abbondanza
Emtinan Alqurashi
Octavia Renee Anderson
Brianna Antonucci
Hannah Astley
Nicholas Barone
Kathryn S. Barr
Michelle Bartha
Stephanie Bartus
McCall Behringer
Regis Bender
Frederick Bentzel
Laura Brickett
Paige E. Brocious
Elizabeth Brown
Erin Browne
Andrew M. Callan
Maryanne Capp
Taylor Cavalovitch
Hannah Cawoski
Megan Chapman

Zachary Dehm
Emerson Ea
Katelyn Emigh
Autumn Ficklin
Aubrey M. Flynn
Andrew Gaiser
Kenneth Girty
Jessica Glas
Elif Gokbel
Katherine Guido
Scott Heinemann
Julie Herr
Katherine Marie Hilton
Jason T. Hoffmann
Clement Kanu
Anna Virginia Kemper
Mary Kern
Olga Klimova-Magnotta
Heather Konstanzer
Chelsea Kwong
Jeanmarie C. Larkin

Jane Lemmo
Jacob R. Leonowitz
Holly H. Lyons
Tami L. Mack
Kayla Madler
Lauren Mahokey
Michael Mash
Amanda Matkovic
Olivia McCall
Mora McLaughlin
Kiana Motto
Ellen Moysan
Bekir Mugayitoglu
Kevin M. Neumar
Lukas Nunnery
Nosarieme Osagiede
Shane M. Peterson
Sarah Polantz
Rebecca L. Polinski
Timothy Porter
Rachelle Poth

Susan Poyo
Anthony Priore
Joseph Ratay
Erin Rentschler
Rachael Richter
Meredith J. Risati
Julian Routh
Emily Rupprecht
Erik J. Schmitt
Matthew Sears
Kaylyn L. Shearer
Monika Spangenberg
Sara Speedy
Caitlyn A. Stratman
Aaron M. Thomas
Emily Tripi
Elizabeth A. Tuttle
Julie Valentine
Megan L. Wall
Katheryn Wendekier
Marcella Williams

DYERSBURG STATE COMMUNITY COLLEGE, DYERSBURG, TN

Jared T. Anderson
Katherine E. Azlin
Leonard D. Bailey
Franklin J. Bales
Elke A. Barnes
Heather M. Barnett
Savannah L. Beard
Heather J. Bell
Kimberly J. Bevis
Kelsey R. Blackwell
Kayla N. Bolden
Elester D. Boyd

Ashley L. Bradberry
Sara N. Bradberry
Jeffrey M. Brewer
Cassidy A. Brown
Marygrace T. Burnett
Andre M. Burns
Libby A. Butterworth
Amanda N. Carmack
Carling M. Champion
Lara B. Cherry
Kaitlyn M. Clark
Chaise M. Claudio

Haley B. Crossnoe
Christopher L. Davis
Gabriel L. Davis
Priscilla G. Deverell
Candie L. Doss
April S. Dunevant
Lametria D. Dunn
Sandra L. Eaves
Karissa S. Elmore
Jonathan L. Enochs
Allison C. Evans
Kaitlyn S. Fair

Brittany J. Franks
Jonathan W. Goodman
Noah F. Goodwin
Justin T. Gray
Kaci L. Hall
Emily J. Hartley
Jessica Rose Haskins
Timothy A. Hatchcock
Patricia M. Hill
Nicholas Brandt Holland
Jackson W. Hollinshead
Lauren B. Holloway

Jodie L. Holmon
Stephanie Johnson
Lauren E. Jones
Victoria Jones
Richard A. Keenan
Monica Louise Kemp
Mariah J. Kimes
Christian T. Koob
Jon B. Laxton
Veronica C. Layne
Khaliyah K. Lee
Dana M. Lewis
Rebecca L. Lopez
Katherine E. Manning
Sandra K. Martinez
April D. Mason

DeMarius C. Mason
Courtney R. May
Ashley B. McGuire
Matthew D. Miller
Michael R. Moffatt
Chadliss M. Mosby
Laura A. Moss
Mallory Murdaugh
Pachita Northington
Joshua F. Pickens
Shelby Pleasant
Sarah Poiner
Jason C. Poston
Kaci A. Powers
Taylor P. Poyner
Cody L. Purvis

Hailey M. Riley
April Roberts
Jennifer Leigh Rodgers
Anna Rogers
Lauren Rogers
Tanya D. Sampson
Anne Sauer
Randal S. Savoy
Blake T. Schunk
Stephon Small
Radona D. Smith
Stephan T. Smith
Bradford E. Starks
Samantha R. Steele
Rebecca D. Stockdale
Paxton L. Stover

Odi M. Suleiman
Brittany K. Tate
Judith C. Thomas
Vicky Truong
Sara K. Uttz
William A. Uttz
Christopher J. Vanbeukering
Mattheu D. Vanwormer
Matthew D. Vaughan
Dvennio K. Warner
Hannah L. Weathers
Justin R. Weaver
Kinsey Wilder
Beverly J. Wyatt
Natalie K. Yarbro

D'YOUVILLE COLLEGE, BUFFALO, NY

Tristen Chiarmonte
Emily Choate
Brianna Rose Cuthbert
Joseph Day
Sadie Marie Deveau
Joseph Franz

Jonathon Gemerek
Durga Maya Ghimirey
James Goode
William Goode
Jordan Johnson
Rachel Komrek

Ashley Ledwon
Mei Yun Lin
Sarah Marino
Kaylee Elizabeth Martin
Kalie Terese McHenry
Kristen Rebecca Petrushesky

Jennifer M. Spors
James C. White
Shaquita Wimes

EAST ARKANSAS COMMUNITY COLLEGE, FORREST CITY, AR

Tyler Douglas Archield
Thomas Joseph Avila
Jessie Michelle Bouland
Meredith K. Bowers
Lenetta Brown
Tiye Nefartari Butler
Amanda Danielle Coffell
Marquill Danielle Daniels
April Marie Duncan

Kelsey Danielle Ferguson
Seth Bowman Goff
Anita Louise Green
Tyler Wesley Grubbs
Russell Seth Harper
David Thomas Harris
Kimberly Denise Harris
Autumn Courtney Heep
Celine Leah Hooker

Adam Arrington Hoy
Dorothy Kiyumbi
Jordan Brianna Matthews
Jamela Mykeashia McCaster
Derek Shane Moore
Emily Rebecca Odom
Tori L. Parnell
Elizabeth Jane Perry
Kaley Elizabeth Robinson

Jailn Marie Rolfe
Kristen Nicole Silver
Miranda Ariel Sims
Jerry Lee Stegall
Khadijah Janee Walker
Leslie Tai Weatherford
Erin Kristen Wright

EAST CENTRAL COMMUNITY COLLEGE, DECATUR, MS

Caitlyn Aldous
Kayla Anderson
Austin Anderton
Tanesha "Niecy" Barham
Bethany Barnes
Blake Barnes

Madison Barnett
Candace Barrett
Fallon Lyshay Beckham
Louise Berryhill
Erick Bishop
Brittany Black

Rashada Boler
BriiAnna Christine Bout
Sharon Diann Bout
David Boydstun
Caleb Brown
Brittany Bryan

Christy Bryan
Kaley Bufkin
Caitlyn Bree Burnley
Peyton Cain
Joseph Clark
AnnaLea Clarke

Randy Creighton
Skylar Davidson
Michael Davis
Caitlan Dearman
Jayson Dempsey
Evan Cooper Derrick
Shelly Lee Dowell
Katlyn Duke
Benjamin Duty
Maegen Ellis
Anthony Emmons
Ariel Enoch
Allen Lamarr Fails Jr.
Lacey Field
Everett Fisher
Reagan Dawn Fleming
Katherine Fortenberry
Mahalia Gibson
Erin Golden
Carlos Gutierrez
Omar Gutierrez
Zachary Hammons
Andrea Hannaford
Leslie Heath
Lindsay Hedge
John Bruce Hedrick
Grecia Hernandez
Joelie Hill
Lacey Hill

Kathryn Hillman
Jesse Hosket
Eddie Houston
Jacob Huff
Kegan Humphries
Elias Braden Jimmie
Tatyana Johnson
Tallie Johnston
Amber Jones
Dylan Jones
Sherry Keith
Pashien Simone Kelley-
Johnson
Samuel Kelly
Brandi Kilpatrick
Nina LaBue
Summer Lavender
Mallory Alexa Lee
Layne Lepard
Mary Elizabeth Levin
Tanya Lewis
Taylor Lott
Hannah May
Keri Mayfield
Garrett Mcdill
Lalah McMullan
Jacob McNeil
Michael Miller
Hannah Mitchell

Matthew Mitchell
Samuel Mitchell
Patrick Morrison
Karleigh Moss
William Mott
Cayla Myers
Taylor Nazary
Thomas Nazary
Durham Norman
Morgan Orr
Benjamin Derek Pace
Megan Parrish
Brooke Elizabeth Payne
Jelisa Pearson
Madison Pettigrew
Chandler Powell
Bryce Power
Brittany Leigh Rasco
Brittney Rawson
Alexa Roberts
Alisha Tamara Savell
Christina Marie Shoemaker
Lillian Shuler
Tyler Sistrunk
Devin Skinner
Clarissa Smith
JoHannah Whitney Smith
Kaitlin Smith
Mackenz Smith

Shala Smith
Dylan Snypes
Gabrielle Stapp
Carrissa Stevenson
Stephen Coleman Stewart
Haley Elizabeth Taylor
Madelon Taylor
Rebecca Tero
Caleb Terry
Chloe Grace Thaggard
John Abel Thames
Kaitlin Thrash
Allie Turner
Caleb Vaughn
Kimberly Renee Watkins
Anna Claire Webb
Anna Wells
Bay White
Michael Anthony Whitlock
II
Courtney Williams
Devontae Malik Wilson
Christopher Michael
Yarbrough
Megan Leigh Yarbrough
Kara Yates
Kaylee Yates

EASTERN CONNECTICUT STATE UNIVERSITY, WILLIMANTIC, CT

Nicholas R. Aconfora
Justin Milton Ahern
Olayinka Atinukie Black
Hunter Lawson Brochu
Abigail J. Caselli
Karolina Chrzanowska
Alexander R. Cross
Devon Gerald Daniotti
Sabrina A. Davis
Jennifer N. DuBois
Talia R. Erris

Kristina M. Forsman
Danielle Paige Fountain
Bryan Anthony Frankovitch
Alexander Frederick
Sarah E. Froehlich
Clint Patrick Gosselin
Damon Robert Gray
Destiny Jessica Hartmann
Kelly Lynn Huhtanen
Dajoun A. Jones
Alexis Victoria Kurtz

Samantha Nicole Landry
Cole Denis Letourneau
Laura A. Markley
Michael Charles Marshall
John Keith Maura
Kylie Alexis McCartney
Meaghan Elizabeth McFall-
Gorman
Chad-Michael Muirhead
Vivian T. Nguyen
Jessica J. Patrizi

Lauren M. Polansky
Kelvin D'Andray Powell
Haley S. Roberts
Lindsey A. Schaffrick
Lindsey Armstrong
Schaffrick
Anthony P. Testi
Anthony Peter Testi
Quanece A. Williams

EASTERN NAZARENE COLLEGE, QUINCY, MA

Elizabeth Anne Aliotta
Mikayla Rael Birnstiel
Tressa J. Burrello
Julianna A. Cameron
Kristen Elaine Farley
Jordan Leilani Grays
Amanda Lee Hiittner

Krystal Claude Holl
Jaime Lynn Hultgren
Steven Drew Lester
Joshua Michael Lojzim
Beatriz Marques Oliva de
Morais
Jordan Martinez

Jessica Rose McCaffery
Gerald Thomas McNeil III
Emily Donna Morin
Michael Kenneth Peter
Kathryn Elizabeth Pulham
Jill Elizabeth Russell
Christina Saint-Pierre

Caitlin Marie Schesser
Tyler John Spencer
Jeremy Ryne Wagner
Justin Garrett Wagner
Rebekah Harriet Zolkosky

EASTERN NEW MEXICO UNIVERSITY ROSWELL, ROSWELL, NM

April Avitia
Shaye Duran
Adrianna Celina Espinoza
Joseph Albert Gonzales
Bailey Gonzalez

William Kolker
Crystal Medrano
Ruby Miramontes
Kathryn I. Morgan
Noemi Reyes

Hannah Robertson
Kathryn Ross
Jonah Sanchez
Amanda Sosa
Linda Kaye Urie

Diamantina Villa
Rocio Zavala

EASTERN OKLAHOMA STATE COLLEGE, WILBURTON, OK

Angelia Dawn Berry
Kelsey Rae'Gene Chambers
Guy Folger
Connie Grantham
Rebecca Henderson

Gwyn Anntoinette
Honeycutt
Brenna Jade House
Mykaela Lynn Jones
Kareesa Kennedy

Ashley Manning
Taylor Erin Odom
Chelsie Peckio
Lauren Kayley Ragan
Garrett Rogers

Djulinda Then
Monique Shauntay
Threadgill
Courtney Wall

EASTERN UNIVERSITY, WAYNE, PA

Drew Brubaker
Glenn Creamer
Derek Davis
Maria Emanuele

Mary Franks
Elky Fuentes
Frances Greenlee
Peter Herron

Mary Kulikowski
Karl Martin Leisch
Vusisizwe Ntonga
Cara Scandrett-Leatherman

Derek Speese
Abigail Storch
Nicholas Trombley

EASTERN WYOMING COLLEGE DOUGLAS, DOUGLAS, WY

Nancy Lynn Igo
Terrence James Meagher

Lauren Nichole Nachtman

Timothy B. Parks

George "Hunter" Wortham

EAST MISSISSIPPI COMMUNITY COLLEGE, MAYHEW, MS

Savanna Alford
Shelby Anthony
Mary Atkins
Kelli Aurell
Tanner Bailey
Vivian Barksdale
Brittany Jane Bontrager
Colter Branton

Henry Caleb Brown
Caitlyn Buford
Bridget Carlstrom
Morgan Castaneda
Prentess Chancellor
Emily Grace Coggins
Caitlyn Faith Croft
Chad Crowley

Kenyata Davis
Maxwell Davis
Mary Decker
Angela Delain Depew
Johnny Douglas
Taylor Madison Dunn
Jessica Dyson
Genna Edmondson

Ethan Ewing
Anna Lee Fairley
Heath Barrett Fisackerly
Erin Gatlin
Kyle Gordon
Michalina Gullett
Paulina Gullett
Jordan Elise Harmon

Haileigh Hodges	Dixie Caroline Morgan	Sonmondra Alexandra	Julia Thompson
Brandon Johnson	Subrina Oswalt	Quinn	Trest Underwood
Kingdom Kamanda McGee	Braxston Perrigin	Walter Shepherd	Mary Kendall Ware
Tabor McGee	Anna Pittman	Lanie Stokes	Leah Wilson
Philip Milner	Angela Price	JoAnn DeMoville Thomas	Lacy Young

EAST MISSISSIPPI COMMUNITY COLLEGE, SCOOBA, MS

Cody Allsup	Zachary Hanna	Thomas Luke	Jared Shaw
Valiree Ann Blair	Jaleesa Harris	Malik Mayweather	Christian Shelby
Holly Borntrager	Stanley Haynie	Molly McLeod	Christopher Standland
Hailey Bowie	Emily Hughes	Darren Miller	Kasey Stanfield
Cambrielle Campbell	Keishana Dionne Johnson	Melissa Miller	Aliyah Staten
Cassie Dee Campbell	Katherine Jones	Kristen Mitchell	Lauren Stephens
Hanna Christopher	Marilyn Kelly	Raylee Moore	Jeremy Sumrall
Ava Renee Cumberland	Kelsey Kennemer	Montrael S. Nabors	Tia Sykes
Hannah Daugherty	Marissa Landrum	Raven Necaise	Genna Wall
MacKenzie Davidson	Anna Lane	Allison Elizabeth Newton	Jacob L. Ware
Juan Davis	Kailey Lavender	Kasmine Nunn	Abby Watson
Anna Dudley	Zoie LaVergne	Lisa Patel	Haley Whitehead
Amanda Eaves	Briana Danielle Lawrence	Pauline Pimolle	Nathaniel Willers
Clyde Emil Ellis	Sarah Danielle Lolley	John Redden	Jelani Ishmael Kamal
Joseph Fenner	Hayley Lowery	Corley Reynolds	Williams
Mallory Storm Griffith	Shanna Lowrey	Kimberly Rigdon	Jonathon Wynne

EAST STROUDSBURG UNIVERSITY, EAST STROUDSBURG, PA

Melissa Harlie Ciment	Savannah Doyle	Rachal Lachow	Xena Mei
Katelyn Clancy	Nicole Holley Friedberg	Erica Mastrogiovanni	Alyssa Ruth Simeone
Emily Creveling	Eric Januszkiewicz	Dylan Joseph Matsago	Brittany R. Washington

EAST TENNESSEE STATE UNIVERSITY, JOHNSON CITY, TN

Hannah Haney	Jessica P. Martin	Billy Quinlan	Haven Ashley Spanyer
Brandon Tyler Johnson	Jasmine Kaye Parks	Pooja Manesh Shah	Troy David Unland
Casandra Johnson	Rikesh Patel		

EAST TEXAS BAPTIST UNIVERSITY, MARSHALL, TX

Haylie Amison	Tyler Burge	Katharine Cox	Lynlea Grace Hansen
Corrie Gale Andrews	Jessica Nicole Burrell	Caroline Donica	Kaitlyn Belle Iseminger
Alexis Lea Baggett	Shelby Campbell	Caleb Erron Dorsey	Ashley Johnson
Tiana Ballard	Miranda G. Chapman	Morgan Lee Garrett	Sasha Joyce Kotowych
Taylor Bankston	Madison Kay Cockrill	Kayla Michelle Green	Joseph Latham
Gabrielle Besch	Conner Combs	Elizabeth Ann Greenwood	Leticia Louise Manriquez
Cody Jackson Blankenship	Sara Elise Corley	Anastasia Grimaldo-Bachtell	Tanner Matthews

Kevin McConnell
Megan Merrill
Austin Craig Odom
Natile Marie Orr
Shelby Peeples
Jayme Perez

Katelyn Nicole Pope
Jaxon Rader
Crystal Rimes
Morgan Michelle Rupp
Halen Sanders
Mallory Nicole Sanders

Katrina Ann Schulte
Stevi Slaughter
Cheyenne Lane Summers
Lauren Tomchesson
Brady Clinton Tomlin
Kirsten Shannon Waller

Morgan Walters
Anne Warke
Zachary Whitlow
Kristin Williams
Briona Jeane Wilson

EDGECOMBE COMMUNITY COLLEGE, TARBORO, NC

Ndey Jama Badjan
Dakotah Lynn Bilky
Monna Brinkley
Hattie Bullock
Daniel E. Butler
Ryan Chatt
Mack Cherry
Andre Cooper
Gregory Cole Craft
Amanda Demers
Kimberly Alice Dickens
Meagan Elizabeth Flora

Amy Fowler
Leslie Caroline Frazier
Chelsea Nicole Gaston
Jamie Grant
Jean Grimes
Lauren Sledge Holloman
Jessica Baylee Hudson
James Jenkins
Juan Antonio Johnson Jr.
Randall Newman Jones
April Joyner
Kimberly Laughrey

Perla Mata Mata-Reyes
Kelly Wilson Moore
Maria Mosso
Genesis Munguia-Valencia
Anna Claire Musick
Margaret Louise Nash
Brittany Opacinch
Allison Bailey Parks
Annie Alexandria Perry
Nancy Ramirez
Tanasia Sha'Quoya
Richardson

Erica Rodgers
Kevin D. Rook
Michael Carter Rose
Joshua Sears
Bianca Solomon
Dan Stroud
Lucinda R. Weathersbee
Justin White
Angela D. Williams
Brittany Wright

EDGEWOOD COLLEGE, MADISON, WI

Federico Barrionuevo
Marissa Blackmore
Janae Buege-McClain
Kensie Burreson
Paulina Stephanie Chavez-Hemaidan
Rachel DeJongh
Dominic Egizi
Lindsey Elsing
Giuliana González

Robyn Haggerty
Hannah Olivia Hathaway
Brianna Nicole Jacobson
Kammi Kangas
Idah Karonga
Marcus B. Kennedy
Tessa Grace Lake
Ashton Edward Lareau
Ashley Ligman
Megan Elizabeth Lyneis

Trixie Maples
Haley E. Massey
Reg Mortimer
Johanna Novich Leonard
Hope Quade
Shelly Ann Sarauer
Kaley Rae Setzke
Erin Sincox
Kelsey Smith
Carsyn Nicole Soderstrom

Emily Elizabeth Swanson
Yesenia Isamar Villalpando-Torres
Vivian A. Washington
Madeline Ann Winkel
Sara Ann Wojtak
Wolly Wollinger
Michelle Ziegler

ELGIN COMMUNITY COLLEGE, ELGIN, IL

Akemi Almeida
Jennifer Arroyo
Gema Atta
Austin Isaiah Bernat
Sarah Blanchard
Jacqueline Chagoya
Kristen Corcoran
Jordan Alexis Duarte
Jennifer Esparza

David Friedman
Miguel Garcia
Diego Gonzalez
Lisa Lilianstrom
Jesus Omar Martinez
Stephanie Medina
Vanessa Nunez
Hugo Olvera
Eliana Penafiel

Vanessa Perez
Kamie Peterson
Linh Nguyen Khanh Pham
Tammy Piotrowski
Chris Reetz
Jeremy Lennard Baltazar Robles
Alexis John Gesulga Sanchez

Christina Sanchez
Emma Elizabeth Soroka
Crystal Sucato
Janine Szerszen
Ulises Alejandro Zamora

Michael Adams	Cody A. Fox	Francisco Jaimes	Brian Lawson
Juan Felipe Aguila	Eric Friedner	Patrick James	Andrew Lawton
Ryan Akers	Oscar Garcia	Alvin Janton	Malana Doris Linton
Jeremy Heath Allen	Karen Glover	Shawn Jarvie	Steven Lovewell
Alejandro Joseph Amezcua	Jack Glowen	Claire Jeffrey	Tom Lu
Jesse Anderson	Liam Goodall	William Jenkins	Brandon Kyle Lynch
Lloyd Ankrum	David Gorski	Dennis Jensen	Olivia Anne Lynch
Joanne Arciaga	Brian Granruth	Nathanael Johnson	Andrew Gerry Marsh
Mathew Scott Arrell	Darius Orlando Grays	Tyler Johnson	Corey Joshua Mason
Timothy Avery	Stephen Griffiths	Travis Joyner	Sabelo Mathebula
Anthony Bailey	Travis Grimit	Emil Kacura	Cheyene Brittany Matthews
Elizabeth Bailey	Liam Owen Gunter	Josheel Amar Kainth	Priscilla Antoinette
Carolyn Barber	Brandon Guthinger	Wazin Karim	McDonald
Curtis Frank Barber	Timothy Haynes	Benjamin Kastning	Matthew Joseph Miller
Elizabeth Barcus	Janina Helwig	Nikolaos Katsogiannis	Paul Montgomery
Joel Barlow	Edward O. Hermida	Joel Howard Keefer Jr.	Leonard Nalbone
Michelle Bassanesi	Jacquelyn Hicks	Jacob S. Kelderhouse	David L. Noble
Munatsi Bawa	Richard Hickson	Jesus Kelly	Nadia Numa
David Harley Bench	Travis Warren Hill	Dougal Kenagy	George Olusa
Evan Andrew Boggs	Heath Ryan Hilleshiem	Pwint Kay Khine	Marcelino Ortiz Cermeno
Daniel John Brigante	William Hilliard	Christopher Kidd	Justin Douglas Outten
Kamouy Brooks	Bradford William Hinton	Yabi Miki Kidibu	Tavaris Jackson Owens
Brittany Jean Brown	William Ho	James Kimley	Austin Parker
Debbra Brown	Victoria Regina Hodges	Thomas Kinnaird Jr.	Alexander Jonathan Pascoe
Stefan Sho Byland	September Hodgson-Murphy	Jimmy Kitchens Jr.	Abigail Pasmore
Chase Michael Capron	Ryan Hoffman	Peter Joseph Klempka	Jeremia Lee Passmore
Crystal Evelyn Cortez	Erin Hogan	Jason Matthew Klip	Scott A. Patterson
Jeremy Curbey	Darrell Holding	Kaes Kniestedt	Dustin Peltolad
Kelley Dehart	Cassidy Lynn Hollowell	Robert Koehling	Calvin Conney Pereira
Benjamin Dillahunt	Todd Holt	Daniel Konshak	Barbara Peters
Melani Elango Pandian	Joshua Robert Hooten	David Kover	Rohan Peters
Dalton Esselman	Griffin Hoover	Robert Arthur Krauss	Harish Prasad
Samuel Eurich	Amber Elizabeth Hubert	Kenneth Kring	Nathalie E. Quintero
Allen Myrland Fausch Jr.	Thomas Joseph Huntt III	David Krueger	Ajay Raghavendra
Taylor Caroline Fazzini	Gregory Hurley	Zachary Labate	Justin Reuter
Edwin Orlando Febo Jr.	Wolde Husbands	Jeremy Paul LaFlamme	Trever Swish Rizzo
Dwayne Fernandes	Benjamin Hutchings	Richard Laidlaw	Sarena Daniell Robertson
Joshua Fetherland	Sean Gene Ihnen	Jordan Byars Lamar	Abraham Salcedo-
Charles Flammini	Sankrit Iyer	Michael Lane	Valladares
Juan David Florez	James Jackson	Timothy Lange	Joseph Salerno
Jacqueline Anne Flynn	Stacey Lynn Paquette	Joshua David Langschied	Joseph Sambiase
Jordan Foster	Jackson	Mariane M. Larson	Ana Sanchez

Bianka Sanders

Tenzin Sandop

Albert Sandoval

Austin Sanford

Gabriel Santos-Colon

Hemant Saria

David Schell

Joshua Lee Schmeck

Jennifer A. Schrader

Miguel Antonio Seeley

Paul Serafini

William Shrader

Timothy Sikora

Nicolas Simila

Jaspreet Singh

Denver Sizemore Jr.

Jonathan Skoloda

Erin Edi Smith

John Camden Smith III

Daniel Alan Solomon

Sergio Sabastian Sovero

Richard Sparks

Nicholas Sprankles

Cameron Springston

Preston Stone

Todd J. Stubblebine

Timothy Michael Vino

Newman Wanyagah

Nicholas Jerrod Wedlow

Lankford Jefferson William

Christopher Williams

Jason Christopher Williams

Jeremy Wulff

Barak Yaniv

Pola Younan

Jaewon Yu

Raymond Michael Zahler

Mohammed Zaid

Anthony Zalucki

Michael Zarate

EMBRY-RIDDLE AERONAUTICAL UNIVERSITY GRADUATE, DAYTONA BEACH, FL

Adegoke Joshua Adelabu

Ryan Gauthier

Tyler Huntington

Jenna Michele Ludwick

Sultan Raml

Lynsey Schroeder

Richard Tubbesing IV

EMBRY-RIDDLE AERONAUTICAL UNIVERSITY PRESCOTT CAMPUS, PRESCOTT, AZ

Jesse Eugene Andrews

Antony L. Angueira

Michael Alexander

Apfelzweig

Marquina Kaye Araquistain

Josue Arriaza

Jonathan David Bahr

Peter John Bailey

Zack Ray Barkell

Andrew Peter Beal

Michelle Monica Bennett

Joseph Anthony Benoit

Kenneth Michael Blair

Charlie Brett Bomkamp

Brennan Lowell Boss

Kevin Michael Boyle

John A. Braun II

Patrick Claude Bright

Evan Burgess

John Michael Carosello

Christopher Hammond

Cerrillo

Alex Chambers

Dan Lee Clark

Kevin Matthew Cloonan

Shawn H. Connor

Carsen Rayne Cooper

Abigail R. Couto

Ryan Allen Cox

Zoe Zahara Crain

Joshua Chase Crow

Shane Adam Croy

Joshua Daniel Dallam

Kurt David Dalton

Jonathan Douglas Daniels

Jared A. Davis

Russell Lee Davis

Dan Delaney

Cody Emil Johnson Denver

Sam David Dettman

Robert John Didilus

Michael Dorthalina

Spencer Douglas

Victor James Ebuen

Gregory D'wayne Edwards

Tobias Fauser

Luke Alan Feenstra

Kyle William Ferral

John Ford

Tessa Mary Frederick

Walter William Gallaty

Erik Enrique Galvez

Danny Garcia

Dustin George

Scott A. Green

Meredith Hainsworth

Jennie Lynn Halverson

Charles Robert Hannaman

Bradfoard Harris

Micah Heathcock

Travis Yuki Heinrich

Jessalyn Jane Hernandez

Russell James Husarenko

Ronnie Jamison

Cheyanne Tana Kadrmas

Mark Piotr Kajpust

Aaron M. Kinder

Caleb Donald Krolak

Peter Anthony La Russa

Carl D. Leake

Joseph Richard Livingston

Keaton Lee Lyon

Alex Jesse Mangum

Michael Justin Matter

Sterling Maynard

Joshua Anthony McClafferty

Keagan McGill

Steven Fraser McHenery

Michael Anthony Mendez

Grace Alexis Miller

Ryan Parker Miller

Benjamin Milller

America Monge

Celeste Hope Moreno

Eleazar Nepomuceno

Micah J. Olsen

Madelyn B. Powell

James Pratt

Jeremy William Rhoads

Edward Alexander

Robertson

Richard Rodriguez

Benjamin James Salisbury

Claire Schindler

Alex Seung

Scott Leroy Snyder

Winarto Sofian

Lemonte Montra Stills

Austin M. Sverdrup

Mark J. Szpak

Justin E. Tamashiro

Milton Tan

Devin S. Taylor

Matthew J. Taylor

Anthony Valentine Velasco

Jose Fleming Villagomez

Matthew C. Wallace

Ray Wang

Hannah Marie Warren
James Austin West

Kyle Andrew White
Niven MacKay Williams

Austin Wise
Michael Charles Woodard

Nathan J. Youngbeck

EMMANUEL COLLEGE, BOSTON, MA

Kendel Amari
Keith Baillargeon
Sarah Barnard
Maxwell Bukowiec
Jennifer Leigh Burgess
Sarah Nicole Como
Christopher Coutsoukis
Meghan Farley
Marissa Fiumefreddo
Stefano Gambino
Juliann Gavin
Alison Gilbert
Katelyn Taylor Guill
Marianne Halas

Katherine Harrington
Rebecca Lynn Harris
Corey Joseph Hebert
Tabinda Khan
Jessica Kibbe
Danielle Scene Laferriere
Emma Lea Lessard
Emily Lewis
Coleman Lynds
Aastha Mahajan
Jenna Marcello
Krysta Marinelli
Marie Christine Mattano
Kayla Matthews

Garrett Michael McGarry
Amelia McGuire
Khelsea Marie O'Brien
Cian O'Sullivan
Joseph Ouellet
Laurie Paul
Marielle Peace
Amelia Ashley Pease
Allyson Preble
Kurt Pruner
Danielle Rose
Aimee Sanford
Carolina Santamaria
Meghann Soby

Emily Solup
Eric Spargo
Elisabeth Marie Staal
Gabriella Steffenberg
Alyssa Marie Taubert
Christine Anne Tuohy
Carissa Tuozzo
Morgan Joan Van Lingen
Sarah Liynda Walmsley
Sean Walsh
Carly Lynn Ward
Brittany Mahalie Williams
James Carlton Withers Jr.

EMMANUEL COLLEGE, FRANKLIN SPRINGS, GA

Marena Christian Bleech
Preston Cole Braswell
Jonathan David Bryan
Madison Nicole Bulger
Mychael Renee Cain
Eliza Jane Chapman
Brianna Shay Colby
Samantha Ellen Cortese
Kelssie Taylor Dickerson
Ben Tyler Eavenson
Courtney Michelle Floyd

Clayton Michael Fulbright
Brooke Ileene Gaither
Breanna Elizabeth Grizzle
Courtney Michelle Guest
Cassie A. Hall
April Michelle Hardin
Kiara Del Mar Hernandez
Gabriella Monique Hill
Lucinda James
Trenton Randolph Jones
Jazmin Konnick

Meshach Tafari McKnight
Hannah Elizabeth Morrison
Nikolas Joseph Nelson
Katlyn Anne Oliver
John David Patton
Clarence Darren Pegues
Courtney Elizabeth Price
Christina Ejade Reese-
Campbell
Socorro Ruiz
Mark Daniel Shrosbree

Emily Michelle Smith
Olivia Nicole Smith
Callie Christine Sorrow
Emma Jane Tamblyn
Shanice Letrice Teasley
Ashley Nicole Thor
David William Wood

ENTERPRISE STATE COMMUNITY COLLEGE, ENTERPRISE, AL

Karen Elaine Barrett
Kelly Lynn Commerfold
Trey Hull
Saege Johnson

Laken Elizabeth Maulden
Taylor Andrew Murray
Andrew Blake Revels

Noah Riley
Marvin Ripp Jr.
Joseph Tanahey

Taylor Alexis Ward
Sarah Webb
Katlyn Nicole Yates

ERSKINE COLLEGE, DUE WEST, SC

Rachel Maurice Barham
Sarah Rachel Baroody

Maria Catherine
Bedenbaugh
April Marie Bussey

Amelia Chassevent
Samuel Thomas Cothran
Clara Barrow Formby

Darby Kathryn Gentry
Connor Colle Gibson
Elinor Townsend Griffin

Miranda Kaye Guthrie
Christina Grey Holbrooks
Michaela Layne Jackson
Jennifer HaleLee Jennings

Jennifer Ashley Karel
Kate Helen Keukelaar
Foster Jensen Krebs
Kate Marie Macsay

Sarah Frances McDonald
Claire Elyse Mueller
Margaret Vaughan Randall
Bonnie Katelyn Reagin

Casey Christina Rosborough
Krysta Lauren Schaus
Phillip Michael Wood
Ronald Brant Young

EUREKA COLLEGE, EUREKA, IL

Alysha Marie Basel
Oakleigh Beard
Lindsey Brianne Bertrand
Leah Anne Bohlmann
Heather Broyles
Emily L. Camden
Elizabeth Anne Chavis
Kayleigh Janelle Choma

Hilari Catherine Elzy
Whitley N. Gregoire
Joanna Elizabeth Guevara
Emily Grace Harrod
Joseph D. Hasler
Erika Mei Chua Holum
Jeanna Kehl
Seth Douglas Koll

Julianne Miao Xian
LeFebvre
Morgan Dean Long
Grace A. Mahasi
Audra K. Martin
Joshua Michael Matzke
Mary M. McCarthy
Jessica Lynn Merrill

Kirstin Ruth Meyers
Rebekah Nabors
Joshua James Newell
Aaron Pearlman
Brooke Poling
Kelsey Lynn Shoemake
Gabriel M. Swords

EVANGEL UNIVERSITY, SPRINGFIELD, MO

Boyd Derrick Allen
Devon Mikel Andreasen
Brittany Kathleen Arnold
Jeremy Shane Arnold
Darryl Ballew
Quinton Alexander Barnes
Alletha Renee Barnett
Hannah Rachelle Beers
Justus Charles Boever
Rachel Deanne Boyd
Wesley Mitchell Brown
Kaelin Brianne Brueseke
Jason Robert Buschman
Christopher Chandler
Joy Cole
So Young Lee Davies
Lindsey Elizabeth Davis
Kelli Elissa Delong
Larenda Haden de Orellana
Maria Ann Donnay

Joshuah Martin Anthony
Earle
Ashlyn Nicole Edmisten
Amber Lena Edwards
Jenna Elise Elliott
Hannah Jane Flora-Swick
Dennis B. Gamble
Kellen Ray Gillaspy
Charisse Elizabeth Green
Amanda Helen Gribben
Chloe Jo Hadley
Kaitlyn Renee Hong
Rebekah Houseknecht
Jennifer Marie Hungerford
Danielle Altes Huver
Julia Ann Johnson
Jason Michael Johnston
Danielle Rae Kepler
April Joy Landry
Danielle Morgan Latt

Athena Taylor Lester
Alexandria Grace LeZion
Hannah Marie Lorts
Lance Mitchell Loughridge
Jourdan Nicole Lunsford
Joel Manzi
Jill Elizabeth Marler
Kevin E. Mau
Christopher Daniel May
Rebecca Simone Maycock
Cassandra Julianne
McConnell
Benjamin James Moore
Sarah Michelle Morris
Aria Marie Morton
Michael Dean Muench
Kameron Philip Nettleton
Richelle Joy Olson
Anna Catherine Pageler
Aaron Arnold Parrales

Gianna Lyn Perretta
Brianna Theresa Petersen
Laura Ashley Prosapio
Roman Purshaga
Spencer Wayne Ray
Caleb Joshua Smith
Jeremy Christian Sparks
Justin Phillip Stockam
Brittany Paige Sylvester
Korry Matthew Tillery
Katelyn Ann Tollefson
Amy Vance
Janna Clarice Walla
Kara Marie Walla
Ally Faith Walsh
Haley Angeline Watson
Todd Michael Willhite
Cody David Yanez
Ryan Nathaniel Zafiroff

FAITH BAPTIST BIBLE COLLEGE & THEOLOGICAL SEMINARY, ANKENY, IA

Jonathan Ray Balasa
Joelle Clarisse Byers

Martha Grieselda Hartog

Joshua Jordan Gonnerman
Huang

Lydia Joy Patefield
Zachariah Warren Singletary

FAULKNER UNIVERSITY, MONTGOMERY, AL

Erichea Barnes

Briana Bailey Bartlett

Savannah Burns

Eran Cean East

Adam Michael Gifford

Katelyn Nicole Harkness

Jacob Hendrix

Treasa Ho

Alysa Klassen

Alyson Kay McCollough

Bethany Parker

Leslie Renee Parrish

Hanaria Qualls

Aaron Reynolds

Lacey Marie Sargent

Riley Colt Schrader

Sophie Slemp

Larissa Jane Strath

Allison Trovillion

Patricia Wampol

Cori Carolyn Woods

FERRUM COLLEGE, FERRUM, VA

Tori M. Akers

Adreanna N. Alsop

Matthew Tyler Anderson

Samuel T. Belcher

Morgan J. Brown

Kala Brubaker

Brittany Leigh Brummitt

Kelsey L. Carlton

Cameron D. Clark

Whitney A. Clifton

Amber E. Coffin

Brittain D. Conde

Courtney N. Cox

Bailey L. Cribbs

Jazzmin D. Dabney

Hannah J. Davis

Jonathan C. Dickey

Layne Gregory Dillon

Samantha R. Goad

Divante Alex Hamilton

Emily M. Hargrove

Sarah N. Hendrix

Breanne N. Kretzer

Michaela D. Martinez

Ethan R. Mills

Alphe D. Peabody

Galdina R. Prado

Anna S. Richardson

Dresden Ann Scott

Heather A. Smith

Kenya M. Smith

Victoria N. Taylor

Brett Andrew Weiss

FITCHBURG STATE UNIVERSITY, FITCHBURG, MA

Daniel J. Beaulac

Kaitlyn A. Burnett

Corey Coleman

Jason Cook

Holly Elisabeth Cormier

Heather N. DeLucia

Emmanuella Janita

Demosthenes

Sarah Doyle

Ashleigh Dube

Julia Lynne Gimenez

Kaitlin Harnden

Alex R. Hochstrasser

Luke Herbert Jackson

Johnathan P. Jena

Michelle Keohane

Roxxanna Destiny-Marie

Kurtz

Kaylie LaRiviere

Annika Leydon

Fiona Mangan

Shantel R. McGrade

Daniel Ryan O'Donnell

Victoria Ashley O'Kane

Nicole Pelzer

Alicia Randall

Yvonne Nicole Renard

Nathanael Rojas

Dominique Mildred Saulnier

Hannah Elizabeth Siden

Erin Simon

Mollie Delena Tobey

Elijah Aaron Tucker

Kathryn Eva Zimmerman

FLAGLER COLLEGE, SAINT AUGUSTINE, FL

Yasmeen Abou El Seoud

Jared Atherton

Kylie E. Austin

Katherine Baer

Amanda Rose Balzano

Jordyn Barrett

Shelby Barton

Adelaide Bertrand

Patrick Bissell

Jessica Black

Christopher Boissenin

Jonathan Buck

Jake Burton

Lorenzo Frazier Butler Jr.

Kinsey Camelio

Caroline Rebecca Cappuccio

Ryan Carroll

Carolyn Cassidey

Talia Childs

Jillian Marie Cicalese

Mackenzie Conley

Jonathan Cosgrove

Roland Cuculiza

Kaci Cyr

Makensie Danaher

Rachel Davis

Chelsea Elizabeth Day

Tyler DeBorde

Emily DeMerchant

Cassie Deogracia

Emily Dietz

Toby Donaldson

Anna Dow

Sarah Michele Dowler

Stephanie Duncan

Matthew English

Ashley Englund

Katharine Evans

Jacob Stewart Eyer II

Cassandra Fernandez

Courtney Fisher

April Foley

Grace Folts

Rhian Franchebois

Katie Frazier
Giacomo Gamble
Mary Garrard
Shelby Morgan Gillis
Maryrose Hall
Sarah Harding
Nancy Harms
Laura Henning
Manon Marie Herbinet
Sarah Hernandez
Lyne'qua Hodge
Cassandra Honour
Nathan Jaynes
Bailey Johnson
Dylan Jones
Savanna Jones
Makeda Joseph
Renessa Kate Kangalee
Jack Michael Kegelmeyer Jr.
Paige Nicole Kelly
Daniel Killackey
Robert Kirkeby
Hannah Klaus
Madeline Paige Kornack
Michele Lachner
Leslie Lalonde
Maclain Larson

Mary-Jo L. Lendering
Kayla Lindsay
Jennifer London
Angela Josephine Mazza
Dallas Lianne McClellan
Keira McDonald
Jordan McKenna
Mieke McQueen
Carly Mills
Jose Mizrahi
Meghan Mohon
Amelia Catherine Morgan
Amanda Margaret Nalbone
Elizabeth Napolilli
Annie Narducci
Kristen Nichols
Victoria Nolen
Alanna O'Rourke
Hanna Olsen
Miranda Lynn Orlando
Jan Ortiz
Katherine Ortolani
Abbey Osley
Hannah Ostrus
Sadie Owens
Andrew Tobias Palmer
Aaron Pavloff

Jessie Lynn Paye
Austin Perri
Courtney Peters
Tiffany Pindell
Ashley Popp
Melissa Procaccini
James Provenza
Joseph Provenza
Brannon Pruett
Matthew Quann
Maria Teresa Raimondo
Kara Reed
Chelsea Reppin
Angel Edelberto Reyes
Allison Riley
Tanner Roebig
Madyson Rynne
Montana Samuels
Susannah Schloss
Angelica Seaman
Kierstyn Selig
Sierra Shahan
Deborah Shaw
Jacquelyne Rose Shelley
Caroline Sikkema
Taylor Singh
Miranda Slusser

Jedidiah Smith
Ariella Smolin
Monica Stauffer
Kelly Stewart
Kassi McLaren Studds
Genel Sturgeon
Tate Swanson
Amanda Tatum
Stephanie Nicole Taylor
Kayla Tenboer
Lauren Thibert
Lindsay Ugast
Alexis Rene Valladares
Angelique Ventura
Ana Villada
Michelle Theresa Volpe
Emma Voss
Kara Walter
Linn Weber
Alexander Westcott
Alexandra White
Colin Wood
Shannon Young
Melissa Christine Zeise
Tyler Zulewski

FLORIDA COLLEGE, TEMPLE TERRACE, FL

Jesse Thomas Bingham
Victoria Morgan Bingham
Haley Denise Bowman
Christina Holly Caudill
William Michael Christian
Olivia Lee Cook
Madeline June Craig
Simon Mitchel Crim
Conner Francis Crispell
Timothy Daniel Dow

Joshua Quinn Dunn
Mary Elizabeth Gant
Daniel Jeffrey Hooton
Solomon Johnson
Noelani Christiana Lee
Erica Beth Mackey
Hannah Kelly Mitchell
Juliana María Parra
Tanner Scott Pearson
Katherine Alyssa Pruitt

Olivia Marie Roberts
Jesse Michael Roy
Jennette Lee Sink
Cody Michael Slamans
Sarah Kathryn Smith
Breanna Leigh Stackpole
Tania Breanna Steele
Leah Mae Stout
Rachel Allison Tharp
Katherine Emily Thompson

Donna Virginia Trask
Joseph Regan Venuso
Ashlen Jade Weltz
Heidi Christine
Wickersheim
Amanda Michelle
Williamson

FLORIDA GATEWAY COLLEGE, LAKE CITY, FL

Jose Luis Ayala Jr.
Arielle Clara Bernstein

Clinton Wayne Black
Sandra Christine Deleonardo

Bryce Ronald Denham
Winston David Dix

Hawke Maddix Thadrich
Forbes

Katelyn Nicole Greer
Kimberly Susan Heninger
Sierra Diane Holland
Caroline Olivia Horvath
Mariah Beverly Hubert
Khang Chi Huynh
Trey Alexander Johnson
Alexa M'Lyn Lyons

Emily Grace Mauldin
Kara Elizabeth McInally
Michael Houston Means
Debra Ann Melgaard
Elisabeth Marie Micke
Charles L. Miller
Brandon Micheal Nobles
Hannah Elizabeth Nowlen

Mittal Raju Patel
Cheyenne Patterson
Kennedi Zion Perez
Kendell Dirk Pidgeon
Jodi Lynn Schwab
Noah Natale Schwab
Latrice Orlean Smith
Lauren Nicole Spencer

Emily Beth Stoerkel
Danielle Ann Thomas-
Rodgers
Callie Savana Ward
Jamie Sue Weaver
Donald Carl West
Algenon Christopher
White Jr.

FLORIDA KEYS COMMUNITY COLLEGE, KEY WEST, FL

Carlos A. Alvarez Gonzalez
Ashley A. Cowan
Marcel Hatter

Barbariza Kariuki
Heather R. Kenyon
David S. Kidney

Ravenne Leclair
Christopher E. Olson
Breanna M. Peak

Timothy J. Sanders
Jeffrey M. Shirreffs

FLORIDA SOUTHERN COLLEGE, LAKELAND, FL

Michaela Rae Bass
Rachel Kristie Belli
Abagail Katarina Bowman
Paul Bretton
Ashley Nicole Buckley
Yawei Chang

Taylor Cox
Jessica Finocchiaro
Kimberly Gallagher
Lauren Elizabeth Harris
Jordan Honc
Samantha Hymson

Brandi Jones
Margarete Lamons
Virginia Machado
Shannon McKew
Rachel Mostert
Ayumi Sakaue

Amy Sherrod
Christine Sniffen
Brianna Chantelle Turbeville
Kelley Wilson
Joy Elizabeth Wolfahrt

FLORIDA SOUTHWESTERN STATE COLLEGE CHARLOTTE CAMPUS, PUNTA GORDA, FL

Gisella Marie Alcazar
Desiree Marida Alicea
Emilie Jean Booth
Austin Paul Bouhebent
Charles Joseph Brennan
Victoria Danielle Burbage
Brianna Alexis Burkhart
Rose Mary Campanale
Charles Wesley Clarke

Morgan Cox
Faith Lenee Davidson
Laura Ann Ferrell
Joel Fuentes
John Anthony Giamanco
Christa Helper
Katina Henry
Won Jaegal
Shawn Michael Johnson

Ann Melissa Jolivain
Carisa Kay Keller
Jennifer Danielle Knight
Kendra Michele Kotlarski
Jacob Alan Lange
Anna Silvia Medina
Linda Marie Perez
Dominic Robinson
Haley Michell Saine

Jake Taylor Smith
Sarah Rose Haiying
Thornton
Lisa Nancy Upright
Christina M. Willoughby
Megan Caroline Wong

FLORIDA STATE UNIVERSITY, TALLAHASSEE, FL

David Joseph Petrantoni

FRAMINGHAM STATE UNIVERSITY, FRAMINGHAM, MA

Levi I. Alves Jr.
Sara Lynne Bartlett
Tremain J. Bell
Zoe Raija Coburn

Geraldine Lissette Cortez
Emily Paige Crocker
Kathryn Olivia Crow
Christina Hatzopoulos

Kourtney Kacian
Francis "Frank" Legere
Carolyn Magee Mase
Calvin Taylor Ridley

Sara Sullivan
Amanda Vallee
Rachel L. White

FREDERICK COMMUNITY COLLEGE, FREDERICK, MD

Brooks Quinn Barry
Raymond Becraft
Jennifer Beeman-Mueller
Matt Berman
Kelly Billigmeier
Leria Bingham
Joshua Boyd
Scot Bracewell
Danielle Brown
Camilla Brunet
Courtney Buchanan
DeMario Carter
Joel Chung
Alexandra Correia
Claudia Cruz
Alexandria Cummings
Danielle Dixon
Rafealla Dkhar
Ashley Edwards
Matthew Fanning
Ashley Fletcher
Nicholas Foundas

Matthew Ganley
Ashley Geisbert
Rachel Elizabeth George
Joseph Ghaderi
Crystal Gieryna
Guissella Fabiola Gonzaga
Dianne Marie Goyco-
Deynes
Angeline Griffin
Lisa Hadley
Noelia Hall
Brent Jarrett Harwood
Dawn Householder
Dustyn Icard
Olivia Imirie
Tawnya Ireland
Jon-Michael Johnson
Jackie Kase
Kellie Kuykendall
Jennifer Lacko
Dennis Jose Lee
Stephanie Loyola

Heidi MacDonald
Mayleen Marchany
Matthew Marcus
Saida Martinez
LaTosha McGee
Payton Hope Mills
Luca Mochi
Savanna Moler
Ashley Nichole Moore
Dominique Moorer
Owen Walker Moreland
Bridget Myers
Trinh Nguyen
Christian Steeve Ntienou
Sean O'Dell
Spencer Paire
Melifan Parandoush
Alexander Alden Penn
Caitlyn Audra Ray
Lauren Regulinski
Kayla Richardson
Maria Rivera Retana

Sergio Rodas
Stephan Andre Salvadori
Alison Catherine Schwartz
Rachel Elizabeth Schwartz
Mikaela Shelton
Joshua Smith
Mostafa Soliman
Corey Sunday
Brian Taylor
Vanessa Tchabert
Jeremy Torrisi
Fernando Trujillo
Adriana Verdecchia
Lisa Wagner
Jackie Wantz
Dustin Welsh
Vicki Whitmore
Jeramey Williams
Jordan Wood
Jessica Woodward
Darryl Zimmerman

FRONTIER COMMUNITY COLLEGE, FAIRFIELD, IL

Audrey M. Aman
Dena L. Carter
Terry J. Chrtt
Leslie L. Conover
Robert W. Dunlap
Barbara E. Fell

Amy L. Galiher
Trevor S. Guthrie
Chloe M. Hinkle
Millie A. King
Laurissa A. Kinney
Alyssa A. Kollak

Jennifer M. McNeil
Kathryn J. Reuss
Sabrina M. Seitzinger
Regina M. Stewart
Samantha L. Thomason
Christina S. Tullis

Tammy M. Warren
Colin R. Webb
James A. Whitte

GADSDEN STATE COMMUNITY COLLEGE, GADSDEN, AL

Oluwagbemisola Gloria
Aderibigbe
Matthew Blake Adkins
Kervenguly Allagulyyev
Rovelyn Araza
Santiago M. Balma
Rebecca Johanna Barnard
Marlene N. Bigham
Christina Blake
Robert James Blaker

Jonathan L. Broom
Heather V. Burgess
Jessen Mechell Burk
Jaleel M. Burton
Summer Brianna Burton
Chelsea L. Butler
Joshua L. Butler
Tracy D. Cheatwood
Xiaodan Cheng
Kaleb M. Clark

Morgan Alexander Cobb
Robin B. Davis
Sharon M. Davis
Julian A. Diaz
Tammy Renee Donaldson
Amory Q. Dudley
Joaquina R. Esono Nchama
Jessica N. Fears
Samantha G. Frost
Colin J. Gaines

Tammy C. Golden
Carmen Grace
Joel Evan Greene
Alvin Harris
Bryan A. Hawk
RayAnne E. Hill
Jiawei Hoang
Kelsey G. Hood
Christy L.ynn Howell
Ashlyn Brooke Hubbard

William Roby Johnson

Joseph M. Jones

Maya Chanell Jones

Morgan D. Kelly

Anna-Marie C. Kennedy

Shannon M. Lawler

Brandon J. Logerquist

Ferendez R. Lowery

Alan Edwards Luna

Brooke L. Maltbie

Judson Alecander Martin

Jennifer Lea McGinnis

Kerri M. Moore

Kaytlyn E. Naugher

Sarah Kathryn R. Norris

Robert Wayne Norton

Katelen D. Oakes

Aramide Halimat Okunowo

Jade M. Oliver

Christopher Jace Pankey

Kaylan R. Perry

Caley L. Ponder

Carly R. Rich

Allison Daytona Richards

Collin B. Robinson

Jamarco Tyron Rudolph

Kenton L. Russell

Branton A. Schomburg

Dylan Blake Scott

Joe R. Sears

Madison Harley Shanks

Dianna Moon Sharpe

Maggie L. Sheeler

Robert L. Simpson

Andrew A. Smirl

Joshua C. Smith

Melissa A. Smith

Robert Craig Stillwell

Kevin Taylor Triplett

Sara N. Wade

Kristina Jaide Walker

Justin Robert Wilkes

GANNON UNIVERSITY, ERIE, PA

Emina Alicusic

Alex Andrea Bohman

David G. Cimino

Scott Warren Cloudy II

Jillian Ann Kaleal

Ashley Irene Kruise

Deborah Doyle Labesky

Victoria Lavery

Andrea Mancuso

Allison Rose McGinnis

Amber Rose Stilwell

GARDNER-WEBB UNIVERSITY, BOILING SPRINGS, NC

Jill C. Blank

Caitlyn Rose Brotherton

Meredith E. Byl

Andrew P. Campbell

Darrell Maurice Currence Jr.

Emily DeVries

Lacy N. Frank

Jeremiah J. Hamby

Ruth A. Housand

Katherine Elizabeth Hudson

Devin D. Judge

Mason S. Kellar

Brooke M. Kelly

Jacob L. Kirby

Anna Grace Kullmar

Nathan Wangerin Lile

Katie Elizabeth Faith Loftin

Olivia M. LuVisi

Sarah G. Lynch

Joseph E. Martin

Mariana I. Mellado

Kevin A. Mills

Tyra Montour

Elisabeth A. Moore

Daniel J. Napier

Anna Pashkova

Brooke Margaret Rampy

Taylor R. Schwartz

Mary E. Toohey

Samuel Morris Vining

Jacob C. Walker

Jonathan W. Walker

Adam C. White

Dewayne D. Wray

Erica Joanne Wright

GARRETT COLLEGE, MCHENRY, MD

Sarah Hope Baker

Pamela Kay Barchers

Jeffrey Thomas Bittinger

Kyle Andrew Bowman

Tiffany Erin Bowman

Courtney Paige Burdock

Collin Louis Caprini

Jessica Ann Cooper

Winston Emmett Ernst

Olivia Marie Fike

Halei Lauryn Filsinger

Nicholas Shane Fogle

Jordyn Lee Folk

Jamar Kenneth Goggins

Timothy Harrison Gotsch

Kyra Mei Griffith Newlin

Angela R. Guthrie

Daniqua Nicole Harrington

Marinea Rose Heindel

Nadja Denique Henry

Ivy Lynn Iden

Krystal Dawn Jacques

Sebastien Clebert

Jean-Charles III

Cristey Dawn Kordyban

Mariah Kay Kulak

Jennifer Michelle Lambert

Anna Rebecca Martin

Cambria Nicole Martinez

Kelly Joy Mast

Lynette Jean Maust

Tyler Kenneth Moon

Ashley M. Murphy

Christopher Joseph
Nakashima

Alexandria Nicole Nicklin

Olamilekan Nyklel Ojo

Brianna Renaye Opel

Tracy Marie Park

Sara Nicole Paul

Katelyn Elizabeth
Petersheim

Abigail Jeannette Porter

Ashley Elizabeth Powell

Madilyn E. Riesco

Brittney Nicole Robinson

Tonya Lynn Sanders

Alexander Jacob Savopoulos

Britani Paige Sebold

Dwayne Shillingburg

Shelby Lynne Simmons

Megan Tori Stone

Sara Marie Sweitzer

Ryan Scott VanNosdeln

Nathan Earl Watt

Adam Luke Wilkinson

GENESEE COMMUNITY COLLEGE, BATAVIA, NY

Tarik S. Allicock
Maria A. Ammarell
Ashley L. Aureli
Connor F. Barleben
Arion Bashir
Heather M. Bombard
Jatawny A. Briggs
Colin L. Brillian
Natalie M. Brooks
Annesia H. Bruno
Gina R. Buda
Dean Byrne
Pamela J. Cady
Celia A. Caleb
Kah F. Chan
Erica M. Cheman
Chantal I. Christina
Sarah Church
Lauren M. Countryman
Simone M. Davis
Courtney E. Deeren
Seth W. Deeren

Iesha Donyelle DeLesline
Rachel A. Diel
Heather M. Dries
Kasey D. Edgerton
Maria K. Frieday
Marymagdalen T. Gabalski
Vanessa E. Gayle
Haylee L. Glor
Nina R. Haenle
Kira R. Hargrave
Laurel L. Hendershott
Virginia L. Henning
Jaclyn L. Higgs
Tiffany Hill
Reed S. Hnidy
Kelly Hubbard
Evan Jacob
Madeline M. Kay
AnneMarie R. Kelsey
Lilia E. Kesterke
Kristi A. Knutson
Alexis N. Krinkie

Fany L. Loughlin
Mackenzie R. Marinaccio
Thais Matte
Danielle M. Milbrand
Jacob Miller
Hannah Morrison
Ryan A. Napieralski
Cynthia Y. Navarro
Katherine I. Nicot
Jenny Odessa
Andrew J. Ohlson
Johnathan Peritore
Jordan Reese
Taylor F. Relyea
Morgan K. Ripley
Deborah R. Rivera
Hailey A. Rizzo
Mitchell P. Robinson
Jessica N. Rush
Jorguino A. Savio
Kelsey L. Schmitt
John C. Schumacher

Daniel J. Scott
Rebecca Anne Sheets
John R. Sherman
Yu Shimizu
Robert B. Skrzypek
Jennifer A. Smith
Megan A. Smythe
Anthony Stampone
Amanda A. Starczewski
Isabella G. Steinmetz
Karli A. Stekl
Cody Michaels Sumeriski
Daniel R. Telban
Hanna E. Tischer
Katelyn E. Trowse
Michael L. Tucker
Johnathan J. Warne
Sharaisa L. White
Danielle Wilshire
Jacob Wittmeyer
Danielle M. Zale

GEORGE C. WALLACE STATE COMMUNITY COLLEGE, DOTHAN, AL

Katie Banister
Macey Barney
Christina Baxley
Megan Brafort
Riley Brooks
Aaliyah Ty-sha Burks
Karla J Burris
Megan Coles
Jerry L. Daniels Jr.
Lonnie Alan Demien
Zinnia Y Guzman-Delgado
Sidney Hall

Patricia Harris-Hodge
Patrick Herndon
Tiffany Megan Jones
Jaleah Kennedy
Ashlynn Kimbro
Melanie Knight
Katie Kowalsky
Shannon Lord
Zachary Loyed
Samuel Maddox
John Mason
Anne McCready

Johnnie McDonald
Elizabeth Suzanne Meadows
Kimberley Melanson
Candace Moore
Thomas Morelli
Alisha R Morrison
Mickey Nelson
Alicia Parsons
Christine Lee Raddatz
Adam Rinehart
Mason Robinson
Laderius Sanders

Shaquilla Sewell
Nick Shelley
John Steven Simpson
Mary Hannah Smith
Bikeem Spann
Jada Starling
Natori Tyson
Flora Vail-Lopez
Deanna Williams
Kimberly A. Williams
Shakiera Williams
Margaret Young

GEORGE FOX UNIVERSITY, NEWBERG, OR

Koh Baugnon
Elizabeth Berger
Brenna Brutscher
Chandler Brutscher

Jay Cornwell
Alexandra Diehl
Keiko Christina Fujii
Mikayla Greenwell

Heather Harney
Shealtiel Hart
Julia Howell
Kosette Isakson

Ryan Lacky
Sijia Liao
Erika Christine Lopez
Jonathan Lee Switzer

Jake Vanier   Kyle Webster   Dylan Yamamoto   Yu Zhang

Kelsey Vaughn

GEORGIA HIGHLANDS COLLEGE, ROME, GA

Jerry Achille	Halle Rebekah Hanks	Blake Leatherwood	Jorge Tinoco Ramos
Jordan Appel	Adam Hatcher	Jessica N. Lee	James Rosser
Taylor Barton	Marquis Holmes	Jahmelia Louis-Jean	Wesley Sanders
Auriana Broughton	Caleb Howard	Joshua Mabry	William Adam Scott
Lydia Chandler	Neilie Jace Jace Armstrong	Shadrack Marion	Kaneisha Smith
Holly Chaney	Aujhati O'Leon Jacquette	Zach McCrum	Oluwaseun Oluwabenga
Eriq Lesean Colon	Jared Johnson	Stacey Moffett	Subulade
Sarah Cousar	Justin Jones	Marquis Nixon	John Henry Thomas
Karicka Culberson	Khalil Jamal Jones	Chrysanthus Nkengfack	Tanner Thomson
Mary R. Demesquita	Laura Ashley Jordan	Tina Marie Noles	Brandon Vallean
Michelle Edwards	Wesly Lahens	Cory Norman	Darrel Wilson
Lorenta Everhart	Olivia Lauzon	Tochukwu Nwokike	David Tyler Wright
William Griffin	Faruq Abayomi Lawal	Roderick Presswood	Angel Zarate

GEORGIA MILITARY COLLEGE WARNER ROBINS, WARNER ROBINS, GA

Brittany Aldaz	Deanna Fondren	Hayden Miller	Hannah Taylor
Evander Banks	Kelsey Gore	John Tyler Moreland	Machaela Verhage
Travis Batchelor	Jori Genae Karen Green	Rudy Mosely	Haley Viles
Najma Rasjeen Bennett	Brianna Higginbotham	Roderick Paschal	Brandy Ward
Alexander Bittle	Kenneth David Johnson II	Olivia Remillard	Elizabeth Ann Wheeless
Kelly Deann Brantley	John Kennedy	Portia Ridley	Carolyn White
Lydia Faith Brown	Jessica Kettlewell	Aaron Rogers	Ciara White
Matthew Austin Buckley	Ashley Brooke Killebrew	Caitlin Romanowski	Sandi Whitworth
Bailey Churchwell	Catrina Michelle Lee	Teryn Rumph	Magie Williams
Bruce "Greg" Colburn Jr.	Keeley Linch	Benjamin Saunders	Ciara Ann Young
Raven Colon	Johnny Luong	Heather Small	
Sarah Cooke	Britney Martin	Markisha Strobridge	

GEORGIAN COURT UNIVERSITY, LAKEWOOD, NJ

Camilla Bach	Keashan Gordon	Alexis Jenkins	Efthimia Stefanou
Takiya Boyette	Amanda Graga	Andrea Marie Lewis	Juliann Suckow
Deanna Briganti	Edwana Hallowanger	Kassandra Lillo	Tiffany LaShawn Thomas-Rogers
Janae Butler	Jaamirra Hamm	Ivan Lingat	
Jaclyn Marie Cusack	Jamie Hand	Anna Katherine Borba Mead	Beatrice Annlovina Thompson-Quartey
Logaina Elattar	Christine Hedgebeth	Patricia Pagan	
Bethany Elizabeth Felicie	Nicole Hoagland	LeeAnn Pilot	Angel Whaley
Angeline Monica Flores	Tenaya Hughes-King	Ashley Reilly	Luka Zgonjanin
Brian A. Ford Jr.	Miriam Hunte	Milagros Ivelisse Sims	

GEORGIA REGENTS UNIVERSITY COLLEGE OF NURSING, AUGUSTA, GA

Mario A. Aguinaga
Margaret Elizabeth Allred
Megan Brooke Barnes
Josie L. Bass
Sara Kate Beecham
Callie M. Bibb
Emily M. Boggus
Bonnie M. Boutwell
Sierra E. Brink
Brianna Alexandria Brooks
Jordan F. Brown
Gabby A. Brown Reece
Sarah M. Buffaloe
Craig Devon Taylor Burton
Marlene W. Call
Charlie Elizabeth Campbell
Anthony W. Capozzi
Karis Casseus
Alexandria C. Cassidy
Amanda J. Chapman
Michelle A. Clum

Hannah J. Costantino
April C. Culler
Sarah Cutcliff
Josie Deason
Sarah K. Denney
Lauren Elise Dodd
Calen B. Duncan
Cheryl Ann Elliott-Dawe
Geoff E. Franqui
Hannah Lindsey Galt
Emily K. Gay
Shena B. Gazaway
Rebecca M. Gee
Miranda Rose Hawks
Daniela M. Hazelwood
Lauren E. Heffernan
Kaylee B. Hennelly
Tina Lynn Holden
Natalie P. House
Sara Rebekah Houston
Chi Chi G. Ijebuonwu

Jesse Garon James
Sabrina C. Judd
Philip Matthew Knauer
Lacy Elizabeth Lally
Dawn L. Langley-Brady
Putchararporn P.
Lavantucksin
Donna Teresa Linck
Jessica Samantha Litton
Christina Nicole Love
Susanna M. Mathew
Christen E. McCabe
Brandi J. Middour-Oxler
John James Milner
Ashley M. Montag
Elizabeth A. Novak
Colleen Ann O'Brien
Caitlyn M. Oellerich
John C. Ohanu
Quyen T. Phan
Jessica Lavonne Pruitt

Tracey Sue Puig-Baker
Clair S. Reed
Ashley Conner Reeves
Matthew Kelly Robinson
Jacey L. Salley
Robert Sarfo
Sarah E. Sather
Dtawahn P. Sexton
Larry Tyler Shealy
Gabby G. Stapf
Ben L. Stapleton
Brooke V. Szoch
Jamie L. Threatt
Kathryn Wallace
Haley M. Waters
Aimee J. Wheeler
Amelia R. Williams
Cory Randall Zeller

GEORGIA SOUTHERN UNIVERSITY, STATESBORO, GA

Alexandria Rita-Ann Bryce
Faith Ann Buchanan
William Taylor Carrick

Ashlee Leighann Charles
Cooper D. Largent
Damilola Elizabeth Olatunde

Abigail L. Ormsby
Mackenzie Paige Payne
Russell Tyler Rogers

Eddison James Smith III
Caitlyn E. Stouder
Cera Morgan Weaver

GEORGIA STATE UNIVERSITY, ATLANTA, GA

Aderonke Abidoye
Shivam Agarwal
Tomi Akinmola
Alyssa Ames
Eduardo Aviles
Stephen Ayiro
Daniela R. Baker
Gabriela Batista-Vargas
Imani Dominica Bethel
Lawrence Blair
Sibilla Blair
Alexander Blanco-pence
Grace Elena Bondy
Reaghan Elizabeth Braun

Sarah Buckalew
Eugene Butler
Terri Arjuana Carroll
Whitnie L. Carter
Julianna Casabonne
Marlena Collins
Alyssa Combs
Micah Lee Costello
Danielle D'Auria
Shiwali Daryapurkar
Karla DeSantos
Fatoumata Diarrassouba
Orhan Bahadir Dogan
Beruk Edris

Kimberly Erukunuakpor
Sean Robert Evans
Rosalyn Falkner
Andres Fernandez
Amber Fields
Stephan Fitzpatrick
David Flynn
Sony Fortune
Rachael Frank
Ciara Frisbie
Sandeep Gande
Beverly Gilliard
Herbert Goodwin Jr.
Ramona I. Grad

Jana Haddad
Saira Sidra Hamid
Katherine Hammaker
Madison Hanberry
Chinmay Handa
Jennifer Miranda Harris
Penny Harvey
Grace Sara Harwood
Akil Hawkins
Alexandria Heenan
Tiffany Rae Hendricks
Calla Fasano Hensley
Thakshila Madushani Herath
Victor Daniel Hernandez

Kenneth Herock
Maaeah Howell
Kysa Huddleston
Ari Jones
Janisha Jones
NuLuv Jones
Catherine Joseph
India Janay Kelly
Joshua Kim
Taihan Kim
You Ji Kim
Noreen Kloc
Saraka Cyrielle Kouame
Andrea Kunze
Gregory LaFortune
Quan Le
Grace Leach
Marisa Lew
Xu Li
Qian Liu
Lina Maria Machado -
Bejarano
Karuna kumari mahato
Natasha Malize

Marcia Denise Mallory
Suzanne B. Maner
Miriam Martinez
Ishaka Maskey
Dream McClinton
L'Dominique Nikole
McDaniel
Sharon McLean
Kate McPhee
Diego Meneses Gomez
Ameer Muhammad
Mary Murray
Stephanie Marie Nakamura
Jody Noll
Ayse Ozturk
Anraya Palmer
Anita Pansari
Rashad Parmer
Tyler Patrick
Tyiesha Patterson
Churamani Paudel
Amy Elizabeth Pelissero
Victoria LaRae Penney
Deborah Pierre

Terri Pines
Britney Pitter
Grady Poole
Tiffani Reardon
Kristen Reinkemeyer
Terrance Bernard Render
Jonathan Paul Richardson
Alexandra Taylor Richmond
Kimberly Rodriguez
Leonardo Julian Rodriguez
Noel Salaices
Bonnie Colleen Sams
Hannah Sauber
Benjamin Schaefer
Karen S. Scott
Glorin Sebastian
Amalesh Sharma
Tonya Shells
Prescott Sidney Madison
Stephanie Skinner
Anatou Soumahoro
Amy Summerlin
Brooke Alexandria Thedford
Angela Thomas

Devrick Alexander Thomas
Joshua Thomas
Tristen Trevino
Amairani Vaca Lopez
Joseph Velazquez
Kaitlin Wade
Raquel B. Walker
Daniel Washington
Bianca Wentt
Sasset West
Laneesha White
Maranda Whittington
Bradley Williams
Nakia M. Williams Jr.
Ting Shuo Wu
Shiyu Xiao
Wei Xu
Gao Nou Yang
Harold Young
Pamesha Young
Silvana Young

GLEN OAKS COMMUNITY COLLEGE, CENTREVILLE, MI

Elizabeth A. Arrington
McKenna M. Bowdish
Mary L. Bright
Kendra K. Classen

Brittany V. Harman
Kyle A. Kuzmick
Hans W. Miller
Raul Morales Jr.

Johanna Lee P. Orca-
Handyside
Isabella Palhoni de Lima
Kathleen T. Shackleton

Amber M. Speece
Robert Edward Tomlinson
III
Walker Isaac Truckey

GOLDEY BEACOM COLLEGE, WILMINGTON, DE

Cindell Aguirre
Richard Bayless
Daniel Bernal
Emily Bitondo
Alexa Boyer
Matthew Joseph Cavender
Cori L. Conner
Rebecca Cordo

Ciera M. Crafton
Daniel Dunlap
Renee Dunn
Ryann Farley
Jane Ann Grimley
Sarah Grzybowski
Kelsey S. Guinnup
Eric Patrick Johnson

Melissa April Kahn
Alexandria M. Kennedy
Charlee King
Dante Manerchia
Paulynn Mao
Grace McCarthy
Amina Mrad
Deanna Nardi

Valarie Orth
Mikayla Paul
Blanca Azucena Rodriguez
Nina Sengl
Matthew Streitz
Kaitlyn Marie Townsend
Amber Nicole Wroble

GOLDEY BEACOM COLLEGE GRADUATE SCHOOL, WILMINGTON, DE

Binod Baral

Lu Cai

Anand Choksi

Filipa Correia

Ihab M. Farag
Meezie Foster
Kara Handlin
Mona Hassan
Rasha Salah eldin
Abdelhammed Hassan
Charles Hilyard

Vanessa Leon
Eric Magarov
Ahmed Mohammed
Mahammoud-Salem
Christopher R. Marinangeli
Elsayed Fathi Moussa
Mohamed

Sayed Mohamed
Fatma Osama Mohammed
Danielle Nourie
Ayda Stephanie Puentes
Ryan Quann
Katarzyna Ross
Shaimaa Nagy Shalaby

Amanuel G. Teclehaimanot
Tripti Upadhyay
Marta Iris Watson-Vidot
Zachary Wise

GORDON COLLEGE, WENHAM, MA

Oyedolapo A. Anyanwu
Robert Wesley Arning
Shakia Artson
Zachary Auwerda
Sarah Bailey
Alexandria Charlene
Beckvermit
Lauren Berg
John Buckley
HanByul Chang
Kelley Chang-Fong

Jennifer Coverdale
Austin John Drukker
Mollie Enright
Lauren Entwistle
Andrew Farley
Juvenal Fils
Courtney Jaclyn Gingras
Henry Hagen
Elaine Joyce Hong
Daniel Hurley
Chelsea Kapes

Nathan Landis
Marina Lavender
Zoey Meyer-Jens
Hans Nicolaas Miersma
Abigail Nash
Yearim Oh
David Popa
Megan Quackenbush
Victoria Quay
Rachel Ryder
Sarah Marie Sessa

Samuel Sherratt
Truett Josiah Smith
Rachel Stalker
Jesse Steele
Peter Story
Libbi Wilson
Monica Wong
Nathaniel Youndt

GRACE BIBLE COLLEGE, WYOMING, MI

Victoria R. Anderson
Samantha J. Argutto
Briana V. Bailey
Camron C. Befus
Erin H. Befus
Jacob D. Blauwkamp
Jonathan S. Blosser
Sydney R. Brown

Morgan D. Carlisle
Travis J. DeWall
Holly V. Haney
Kimberlee J. Holstad
Dicia A. Horner
Shannon C. Hupp
Kali J. LaHaie
Anna D. Lange

Josie N. Lange
Jillian K. Luplow
Zachary D. Niles
Jessica L. Pegg
Mary G. Pryer
Ellie N. Ratter
Lisse B. Schuerman
Abigail E. Schultz

Jonah P. Sherstad
Jordon T. Sherstad
Allyssa L. Thompson
Mandy L. Todhunter
Alyssa A. VanStrien
Cahara A. Williams

GRACE COLLEGE & SEMINARY, WINONA LAKE, IN

Drake Darrah
Laura Dewlen
Bryce Glock
Kyle Hamlin
Ashley Rose Herrington
Ethan K. S. Higa

Hannah Jeffreys
Darcy Johnston
Elizabeth Manko
Julia Marsh
Jordan Nathaniel McIntyre
Rachel Meader

Kelly Nemec
Alexandra Grace Sanford
Hannah Scott
Christopher Sharrock
Elisa Stump
Brett Taulbee

Alixandra Marie Underwood
Jarod M. Ward
Lauren Watt
Hannah Wehrle
Mary Wick
Katherine Yoder

GRAMBLING STATE UNIVERSITY, GRAMBLING, LA

Ross H. Adelsperger
Bello H. Ahmadou

Ebony J. Aiken
Damilola E. Akano

Alickson T. Alexander
Bradley E. Alexander

Kenneth L. Allen
Ali M. Almukhtar

Ali A. Alqahtani

Zillah N. Anagho-Tah

Kanedria L. Andrews

Alexis N. Ashley

Jordan C. Bailey

Willie Balancier

Joshua R. Beatty

Brionna Bedford

Tisinquea C. Bell

Shareika A. Benjamin

Darius K. Berard

William M. Besselman

Corinthia Blanson

Barry R. Bontiff

Jacory Boozer

Michael R. Bradley

Teara S. Breaux

Terence L. Brigham

Sharon Brown

Jullone S. Burnette

Percy L. Cargo

Raven Catholic

Koree N. Ceruti

Briauna L. Chambers

Hassan K. Chepkwony

Amber N. Coleman

Haley M. Comeaux

Lala Aicha Coulibaly

Hui Dang

Alannah M. Daniels

Agnita Ruth M.
Degallerie-Peters

Sammu Handi Amila
De Silva

Shaciarra Drake

Courtland R. Fields

Abyssinia N. Flores

Gerals J. Gafford

Riccie L. Gray

Endiah D. Green

Nadisha H. Guavo

Robynn A. Hadley

Raven N. Hampton

Tyson L. Hardy

Tara E. Harris

Andre D. Hawkins

Jalen Heath

Breianna Heims

Jeanelle Z. Hilaire

Kennedi M. Hildreth

Sheronda F. Hill

Jonathan G. Holston

Biyu Hu

Joseph C. Hurst

Amanda W. Hypolite

Merlissa M. Hypolite

Timothy Ismael

Jakelia M. Jones

Ke'yon K. Jones

Tyra Jones

Rochelle C. Joseph

Montana J. King

Rasheedah D. King-Parm

Ethan R. Lambert

Keisha Nicole Laville

Dao T. Le

Jennifer L. Lesage

Jazmyne D. Lewis

Krystal E. Lindsay

Justin L. Malone

Kisha Louisa McCoy

Melanie S. McCrory

Jharrayne I. McKnight

Jennifer O. Meregini

Kassandra S. Merritt

Britnee L. Montgomery

Morganie L. Montgomery

Taryn Adele Moreno

Yunique R. Murphy

Alicia G. Nanthan

Paul A. Nosworthy

Linda N. Nwodo

Jack A. Ocwieja

Ariana J. Oliver

Onajite J. Owhe

Larissa N. Penn

Destinee Perkins

Chasity M. Perry

Samara A. Perry

Essence L. Peterson

Phillipa J. Phillip

Brianna O. Phillips

Ashley M. Phlegm

Kaitlin Porter

Jordan S. Powell

Kiara K. Redeau-Harris

Jeirlyn Remie Augustine

Brianna L. Ridgell

Jimmitriv R. Roberson

Shameka D. Roberson

Taylor S. Robinson

Rita R. Rogers

Greyya Rushing

Sheneaqua S. Russell

Delana D. Saint-Jean

Rashandra Self

Anthony G. Shillingford

Jodeen S. Shillingford

Ashirah C. Simpson

Prentiss C. Smiley

Roosevelt A. Smith

Emerals D. Stanford

Vaughn W. Stroman

Makesa K. Tavernier

Auslyn M. Taylor

Cindy T. Tran

Jonathan L. Wallace

Breonna M. Ward

Kenisha L. Warrington

Kessa A. Warrington

Muridia S. Washington

Breanna Wayne

David West

Devin D. Williams

Marrianna D. Williams

Zarita R. Williams

Ciara C. Wilson

Lanhia S. Young

Emad M. Zeni

GRAYSON COLLEGE, DENISON, TX

Bethany Anderson

Cristina Quintanilla
Beamesderfer

Logan Andrew Beauchamp

Cynthia Beck

Michelle Linette Beckcom

Jamie Beckett

Loretta Bertrand

Michaela Bledsoe

Matti Bolin

Lisett Bond

Hannah Borg

Joi Bowers

Rebecca Nicole Braden

Brayden

Johnny Brito

Matthew Brown

Scott Bruton

Kristy Burden

Stephanie Michelle Canaday

Joshua Carpenter

Michael Carr

Caitlin Cato

Whitney Chaney

Justin Choitz

Amber Clay

Jaden Coffin

Kaley Camille Cox

Antwon Craddock

Elizabeth Crawford

Ricky Crow

Robert Santino DeMarco

Dasia Jaqae' Dunlap

Angela Dwyer

Samantha Ellett

Brittney Emerson

Rui Moe Emerson

Anthony Eskue

Manda Lynn Esparza

Carlos Espino

Brandy Fair

Sarah Fisher

Audrey Dawn Fox

Amanda French

Andrea Galvan

Natalie Brinee Gann

Samantha Gaskill

Elvis Gonzalez

Robert Graham

Miles Greenway

Bobby Griffis

Shelley Griffis

Michael Grove

Irene Gudorf

Matthew Gudorf

Sierra Haley

Amber Hamilton

Deborah Hardin

Christina Marie Harper

Rebekah Hartwell

Amber Hayes

Abby Joy Hendrix

Eric Henricks

Cade Hess

James Hix

Estelle Ayaba Houndanou Kokou

Britney Hubbard

Gabrielle Marie Hundley

Jenner Philip Jackson

Tani Johnson

Ashley Jones

Brandi Jones

Cana Marissa Jones

Rebecca Jones

Shelley Jones

Curtis Kaven

Kayla Kent

Shawna Klassen

Carinda Lea

Cody Land Lenderman

Taylor Leslie

Taylor Lester

Ronald Little

Jennifer Littrell

Melissa Lynn Lorensen

Hannah Love

Jason Lyons

Erik Magee

Brenda Marshall

Breaca Mason

Alec Raye Matteson

Karen Maxwell

Dymond Mayhew

Caleb McCanlies

Brenda Mejia

Denise Mohling

Thalia Molina

Jesse Moore

Roya Morakabian

Yaressi Moran

Kasandra Morris

Barbara Morton

James Newman

Phuong Nguyen

Amber Northcott

Angelia Oglesby

Delaney Ortega

Madison Pankey

Bobby Parker

Mark Pedigo

Nia Petrus

Tana Pirtle

Stacie Pope

Randi Prutch

Kasandra Puebla

Samantha Lee Ramsey

Melanie Renee Rayburn

Gabriel Valentino Rendon

Ana Roberts

Daniela Rodriguez

Brandy Lee Rose

Dalen Rosenow

Carolyn Ross

Anna Marie Roush

James Rucker

Dave Young Sanderson

Raine Schinkel

Chelsea Schock

Lori Schoenbeck

Morgan Alexis Scribner

Jennifer Shindler

Laura Lee Shuman

Jesse Sloan

Mallory Smith

Spencer Snow

Deborah Fay Souther

Joseph Scott Spindle

Samantha Stanek

Ashley Brooke Stephens

Kasi St John

Brandon Stockton

Christy Strawn

Joshua Tai

Elizabeth Taylor

Amber Terrell

Heather Trimble

Mark Valentine

Shelby Madison Via

Kyle Weatherly

Cheyanne Wells

William Whisman

Bailey Michelle Whitehead

Steven Wilt

Michelle Winkler

GREENVILLE COLLEGE, GREENVILLE, IL

Dylan Edwin Antila

Nicole Ashley Baker

Jasmine Kamilah Bavaro

Alexus Morgan Baysinger

Jacquelynn Faye Bleisch

Jason Daniel Borntrager

Susanna Claire Bowers

Jennifer L. Brakenhoff

Roman Tavarez Butler

Devin Lemuel Chaney

Mary Todd Christian

Timothy Carl Daniel

Melissa Joy Deal

Mary Lois Deterding

Reed Johnson Durley

Brian Roy Ehresman

Emily Nichole Foster

Kyle Eldred Freeze

Logan Lee Freitag

Taylor M. German

Chelsea Marie Gilles

Heather Nicole Henderson

Charles Christopher Herrick

Joshua David Herrick

Dustin James Higginbotham

Sarah Elizabeth Holliday

Elizabeth Lynne Johnson

Lincoln Gregory Johnson

Morgan Lee Johnson

Kristen Paige Kanaskie

Bailey Alyssa Keim

Kathryn Leigh Kelley

Deonte L. King

Tyler Young Kohrs

Kieley Marlene Leach

Xu Li

Brent Adam McCollum

Kaleb Lee McCullough

Amanda Marie Muehlberg

Justin Daniel Mulholland

Rebecca Lynn Munshaw
Logan Patrick Nelson
Kirsten Enet Norsworthy
Timothy Benjamin Osborne
Kayla Nicole Parker
Taylor Renee Paulin
Aaron W. Phillips

Miranda Jo Prichard
Corbin Mikel-Cornelius
Quinonez
Emily Rebekah Rauch
Rachel Leigh Renshaw
Annie Lee Reyes
Katie Marie Schmierbach

Claire Victoria Schmitt
Elle Claire Shaw
Cory Paul Snyder
Kami Elizabeth Suess
Joshua David Thomas
Keli Cecelia Marie Totton
Joseph N. Watson

Leanna Grace Westerhof
David Philip Weyers
Darlene Marie Wilson
Benjamin Michael Wiltse
Molly Elizabeth Works
Parker Matthew Wray

GROVE CITY COLLEGE, GROVE CITY, PA

Alexandra Khourine Abel
Ariel Abir
Laura Kathryn Ames
Evelyn Lee Andersen
Evan Alexander Avery
Kelsa Hope Battig
Caroline Grace Bennett
Katherine Gayle
Birmingham
Azzama Azzamovna
Bochenkova Bell
Dalton Isaiah Bowser
Madison Young Bowser
Andrew Hoober Brackbill
Jessica Elaine Brinling
Jessica Jordan Bryan
Marco Crispolto Campelli
Daniel Stephen Casselli
Anna Magdalene Cessar
Justin Cha
Daniel Stephen Chapman
Emma Elizabeth Cinatl
Julia Louise Connors
Elijah Lain Coryell
Erik David Covert
Kelly Marie Cowher
Shelby Virginia Davenport
Alyssa Marie Davies

Danielle Leigh Dennis
Emily Ann Denton
Shawna Beth Fiscus
Katherine Anne Flenniken
Natalija Marija Galens
Lauren Elizabeth Gillespie
Matthew William Glasscott
Logan Robert
Hammerschmitt
Colton Thorne Henry
David Joseph Hindman
Annie Laurie Christy
Holfelder
Jonathan Lee Hoyt
Jon Robert Lee Huff
John Barnabas Hughes
Shayla Paige Hunker
Jordan Ellie Jensen
Amanda G. Johnson
Sooyoung Jung
Rebecca Lynn Kennedy
Thomas Holden Kutz
Karolina Sofia Lagerquist
Timothy Richard Lagoy
Rachel Alyson Lapp
Benjamin Paul Leavitt
Emily Louise Leavitt
Mary Grace Leone

Grace Peggy Jean
Leuenberger
Eliza Marie Lowe
Madalyn Marie Lutz
Aimee Nicole Lynch
Benjamin Nicholson
Marasco
Alaina Dianne Marr
Abigail Jeanette Mathes
Jonathan Duncan Mathes
Liesl Carter McClintock
Shannon Marie McDade
Kenton James McFaul
Amy Ray Mitch
Ryan Daniel Mott
Peter Andrew Nesbitt
Amy Constantine Noll
Megan Rose Obley
Christopher Scott Parry
Samantha Dawn Parry
Elizabeth Anne Parsons
Erin Nicole Pechacek
Justin Edward Pennypacker
Ryan Andrew Pietryga
Grayson Stone Quay
Emily Elizabeth Rabenold
Andrew Russ Risinger
Lydia Quinn Rittenhouse

Evlyn Mae Roper
Emily Faris Rothbard
Travis James Royer
Amy Grace Rumbaugh
Daniel Isaac Rzewnicki
Daniel Scott Schafhauser
Alexandra Anne Schellin
Kimberly Joy Schlabach
Joscelyn Eva Seaton
Caroline Grace Sedmak
Sarah A. Stites
Paul Timothy Sundman
Mariah Gail Syre
Stephen David Tam
Jonathan James Thomas
Kristin Anne Thomas
Julia Rose Tolson
Emily Rose Townsend
Joshua Kurt VanEerden
Michaela Felicia Velloney
Joseph Ray Vermilya
Megan Marie Walters
Abigail Frances Weaver
Lauren Diane Whitmire
Samara Rae Wild
Cody Robert Work

GUILFORD COLLEGE, GREENSBORO, NC

Michael Oliver Aberle-
Grasse
Aaron Tyler Abts
Adrianna Maria Allred

Moises Alvarez
Alexandra Trent Barbour
Timothy Claypool Barrows
Karen Michaela Beggins

Nicholas Kenan Blackwood
Graceon Elias Blondeau
Hannah Elizabeth
Brewer-Jensen

Sydney Leigh Brown
John Liam Brvenik
Tesia Burton
Stephanie Lauren Byer

Nicholas Leonard Caputo
Kiernan Barnes Colby
Lillian Rain Collins
Katie Marie Copeland
Stella Daniel
Samuel Clay Dawson
Allison Marie Debusk
Britton Nathaniel Dunn
Nicholas Patrick Eckstein
Samantha Marie Evans
Suzanne Helen Farmer
Mitchell Francis Ferrick
Adam Christopher Fiore
Nathaniel Curtis Fulbright
Katharine Hope Fullerton
Julia Mae Geaney-Moore
Austin John Girting
Maria Fernanda Gonzalez
Haley Elizabeth Griffith
Cristina Renee Guttersen
Emily Judith Haaksma
Laura Renee Hall
Wilson Burton Hamilton
Tyler Denzel Harris
Elizabeth Hillary Harrison
Walter Hassell
Daniel Lane Haupt
Dylan Close Haupt
Lillian Marie Hayward
Keara Gordon Henault

Brooke Elizabeth Herr
Zana Nicole Hicks
Seren Marisa Homer
Daniel James Hulburt
Justin Lee Ivey
Wesley Ray Joseph Johnson
Jonahs Sarah-Annah Jones
Abraham Peter Kenmore
Jarrett Brooke Knepper
Dannielle Josephine Krsak
Karlen Michaela Lambert
Kristian Joseph Laureiro
Nathan Andrew Redvers Lee
Nicholas Christopoulos Lent
Amanda Lynette Libby
Fiona Rosa Lloyd-Muller
Colin Patrick Macintosh
Naomi Jeanne Madaras
John Joseph Madden
Quincy Leah Malesovas
Connor Ferris Manning
Jaylan Martin
Noah Rebbeck McDonald
Eleanor Howard McTigue
Erik Ludwig Meiler
Leah Noel Meservey
Cara Elizabeth Messina
Sarah Ann Miller
Katherine Maile Munro
Jordan Lee Musick

Brett Robert Myers
Moira Ann O'Neill
Anna Julia Opaleski
Zackery Mitchell Parris
Calli Jo Pastor
Matthew Ryan Pawlowski
Sara Angelina Pearson
Ian Patrick Penny
Lucas Perez-Leahy
Kahlil Omari Perine
Michelle Elise Perine
Natalia Faye Petkov
Eryc Joseph Pierrelouis
Landon Carson Pope
Marinda Catherine Popp
Adele Erin Price
Lucas Prillaman
Aaron Chase Quate
Rohini Rajnarayanan
Hayden Read
Rebecca Mariana Reyna
Kelsey Marie Rice
Lucy Rice
Anna Dean Rider
Carson Alexandra Risser
Elizabeth Love Robbins
Elena Ana Robles
Dakota Rock
Emma Eileen Rountree
Kelsey Curtis Ruehling

Emma Grace Rumpl
Madison Stewart Ruppenthal
William Douglas Sands
Victoria Maria Saraldi-Gallardo
Vincent Schueren
Maggie Taylor Shaffer
Beatriz Carrie Shropshire
Ryan William Siebens
Lee Kathleen Sisson
Margaret Ann Slater
Matthew Adam Smith
Gray Nathaniel Stanback
Tess Lorraine Sophia Stryk
Laura Mary Todd
Nina Charles Troy
Eli Brooke Tuchler
Grace Dalton VanFleet
Cassandra Marie Vaughn
Nellie Clare Vinograd
Alice Elena Waller
Rachel Paskin Wieselquist
Katelyn Elizabeth Williams
Jared Emerson Willis
Edgar Guy Woodliff
Caitlin Joan Young
Davia Young

GUILFORD COLLEGE CENTER FOR CONTINUING EDUCATION, GREENSBORO, NC

Ulric Gregory Aristide
Amanda Gail Bailey
Matthew James Banville
Meghan Brittany Barrett
Chrystal Brannon
Phillip Lindsay Bray
William Andrew Burton IV
Presley Byrd
Jennifer Campos-Marquez
Pablo Luis Carranza
Joshua Chavez

Melissa Coley
Brittany Ann Cominos
Megan Laine Daniel
Rena Davis
Ana Alicia DeLeon
Mittie Arista Dodge
Holly Duke
Jose Jaquay DuRant
Anthony Eckemoff
Nick Fakhoury
Jeremy Floyd

Brian Free
Caleb Gardner
Todd William Gillen
Steven Grice
Marshall Lee Grossman
Shameka Gumbs
James Earl Hall Jr.
Lindsey Brooke Hedrick
Jessica Hilliard
Beverly Ann Holmes

Richard Hugh Connor
Huntwork
Deborah Ferguson Imbler
Antoinette James
Janet Regina Johnson
Carolyn Jones
Jessica Brooke Jones
Ray Anthony Knirs
Dale Nicholas Koch
Sherri Lovin Kress
Paul Joseph Ksieniewicz

Wilbert Lennon Jr.
Scott Allen Lewis
Kelsey Walker Lindeman
Miranda Louise McDowell
Libby Parks McGee
Natasha Nicole McKinney
Marla McNear
Precious Nicole McNeil
Colin Wasson Miller
Daniel Matthew Mohr
Marc Joseph Muraski
William Nemeth
Matthew Michael Oberg

Lily Orive
Stephen Perrone
Sheree Michelle Raya
Christian Matthew Reid
Gregory Rierson
Ana Nicole Robinson
Lakeisha Nicole Robinson
Ryan Dennison Robinson
John A. Russell
Jessica Leigh Self
Joo-Hurn Shim
Kimberly Gold Shores
Kristy Marie Simonetti

Brian Russell Smith
Trina Ann Smith
Jason Stanley
Benjamin Eric Stinson
Tara Strefling
Melissa Kirkman Sumner
Gloria Regina Taylor-
Williams
Thor Hege Tobiassen
Sofia Holmgren Tull
Amelia Uffelman
Brooke Van Der Giessen
Brett Van Horne

Katie Voss
Kathryn Walters
Nicholas Charles Warfield
Judy Elaine West
Adam David Williams
Josiephine "Josie" Alston
Williams
Kerri Williams
Monica Harvey Williams
James Bradford Wilson
Teresa Sturdivant Wing
Jaime Leigh Wright

GUILFORD TECHNICAL COMMUNITY COLLEGE, JAMESTOWN, NC

Lori Thompson Bolden
Ron Brooks
Peggy Elaine Browley
Blessing Byll Daku
Daniel B. Dawson

Daphnie D. Donnell
Mary Lee Hedrick
Jamie Nicole Helander
Nicole Chariesse Hicks
Katie Bea Keene

Brent Matthew Kempke
Joel Michael Kidd
Mary Martin
Shavon Salari
Sharon Tully Saunders

Acorea Darren LaMont Sims
Ra'anan Jordan Sistare
Chrystal Sue Smith
Ibrahim Soumana Garba
Barbara I. Walden

GULF COAST STATE COLLEGE, PANAMA CITY, FL

Abigail Kathryn Akins
Johnathon K. Alleman
Dawn M. Bailey
Adam Brian Casey Boone
Victoria Michelle Bradley
Allison Kaylee Burks

Kimberly Therese
Carstarphen
Melissa G. Carter
Nathan A. Chaffee
Bruce F. Ferris Jr.
Sara Lachayne Hagood
Savannah S. Hasty

Linda C. Howell
Jazmine C. Lewis
Stephanie M. Mason
Christina M. Maynard
Kyla G. McKenzie
April D. McLemore
Erica Lee Morgan

Curtis Lawayne Oxley
Colleen L. Pazakis
Francine Jessie B. Quiguyan
Jayden Stansberry
Michael S. Wright

GWYNEDD MERCY UNIVERSITY, GWYNEDD VALLEY, PA

Amanda Jane Gramiak

Kaitlin Marie Jobba

HALIFAX COMMUNITY COLLEGE, WELDON, NC

Patrick Adams
Derricke Allen
Brittany Baggett
Edward Banks
Kendra Battle
Baylee Sue Baugham
Keely Beal
Gina Bechtel-Hicks

Cody Birdsong
Nicholas Blackmon
Brittany Bolton
Erick Bowen
Lisa Branch
Morgan Branham
Dominic Brickhouse
Lacey Renit Bridges

Carolina Broady
Dennis Broady
Joseph Brown
Tre Brown
Cynthia Bryant
Jacob Bryant
Kelsey Burd
Ryan Burke

Jayia Burse
Christopher Bynum
Kevin Bynum
Shauquwanda Bynum
Angelica Castro
Jason Chandler
Marcus Chichester
Raymond Chin

Dexter Cofield
Elizabeth Collins
Tamekia Conner
Kaley Copeland
Sumner Cox
Amber Crafton
Jordan Cutrell
Brandon Davis
Charlene Davis
Jarrett Davis
Mary Davis
M'bechi Davis
Shanna Deloatch
Corey Dickens
Whitney Dickens
William Dickinson
Lydia Jaclene Edmonds
Kwatika Ellis
Darrian Epperson
Ashley R. Evans
Brenda Everett
Kelsey Faison
Stephen Farmer
Latesha Fields
Shanta Fields
Ashley Garcia
Reagan Gardner
Antwan Garner
Tyrone Garner
Meredith Glover
Ashley Gorham
Sharkeita Green
Anthony Justis Harder

Courtney Hardin
Jessica Harris
Reginald Harris
Trassie Catina Hewlin
Caitlin Hicks
Heather R. Hughes
Jacqueline Jacobs
Holly Jenkins
Jalyssa Jenkins
Jessica Johnston
Jestestric Jones
Kaylen Jordan
Aniya Kee
Hailey Kidd
Kendall Kidd
William Killian
Morgan Kinsey
Derrick Lassiter
Erik Lassiter
William Lassiter
Charnella Leary
Joseph Liles
Kelsey Livesay
Brittany Sharelle Lopez
Jeffrey Lyons
Allison Majors
Victoria Majors
Andrea Mason
Alicia Massey
Dakota McKeel
Jonathan Meads
Nichole Medlin
Alonzo Melton

Natara Michael Velanzquez
Tanner Miles
Danzel Mitchell
Sherrill Moss
Denny Nicholas
Matthew Owen
Jacqueline Panton
Charlie Parker
Ruhi Patel
Jaime Pearcey
Jessica Anne Pearson
Shirley Pernell
Evelyn Phillips
Douglas Pitt
Brittany Poythress
Kawayne'a Pugh
Alice Quille
Charmaka Randolph
Deantre' Richardson
Ashilan Riddick
Christopher Robinson
Charnekia Ann Rudd
Zaquantai Sears
Kristen Shaw
John Short
Teneisha Silver
Patrick Simmons
Christopher Sledge
Justin Smith
Matthew Smith
Zoe Sparrow
Lashawn Speller
Silvester Squire

Teresa Squire
Steven Stansberry
Chassity Stephens
Amy Stokes
Taylor Strickland
Olivia Tann
Christian Taylor
Sarah Taylor
Melissa Thompson
Ronald Todd
Gretchen Tretheway
Michaela Turner
Jacob Twisdale
Larry Vaughan
Sarah Vick
Nicholas Vore
Colby Walls
Danielle Webb
Miranda Wheeler
William Wheeler
Trionti Whitaker
John White
Kendall Wier
Daniel Williams
Destinee Williams
Kristina Williams
Monique Williams
Jonathan Wilson
Toby Wilson
Stephanie Witten
Timothy Worrell

HAMPDEN-SYDNEY COLLEGE, HAMPDEN-SYDNEY, VA

Alexander Vincent Abbott
Lawrence Brantley Bowers
Conrad Wilson Brown
Alex Scott Crabtree
William Reed Echols
Westley Davis Eure

Kyle Irving Fraser
Robert Byrne George
Robert George Kerby
Ryan Allen Kluk
Benjamin Wei Lam
Joseph Anthony Lantagne

Joseph Nehemiah Link
John August Stevenso
Mohay
Melchior Francis
Savarese IV
Shaquann Saddat Seadrow

Joshua Davey Taylor
Jefferson Connor Thompson
Benjamin Branch Edward
Vincent
Cody Eugene Wright

HAMPTON UNIVERSITY, HAMPTON, VA

LaQuayle Domonique Agurs
London Coleman-Williams
Muniratu Fujah
Brendon James
Maya K. Jordan
Ryan Jordan
Kentaysha Anita Lane
Francine Marquis
Racquelle Charlene Perry
Serena Nicole Rudisel
Kristin Carver Samuels

HARCUM COLLEGE, BRYN MAWR, PA

Novena Chanzu
Sydell Damas
Monica Kelly Dougherty
Amber Eberhardt-Brown
Erin Gilliland
Rose Jeanette Hampton
Veronica Phoebe Hegerman
Shannon Hughes
Travis Hughes
Zachary Juliano
Cerise Kacensky
Sharifa Lloyd
Alexandra Logue
Alissa Manion
Courtney McKinney
Cristina Mitchell
Sebastian Paredes
Audrey Reyes-Schneider
Stephanie Sanchez
Laura Story
Brianna Yakscoe

HARDING UNIVERSITY, SEARCY, AR

Megan Breanna Albers
Mary Allen
Olivia Bissell
Alissa Buckner
Hannah Cochran
Daniel Crouch
Bethany Brooke Daniel
Esther Nohemy De La Cruz Gamez
Michael DeSalvo
Angela Nicole Duggins
Andrew Eller
Kayla Ellis
Nathan Enix
Aundrey Flewellen
Hunter George
Peria Gipson
Corbett Scott Hall
Bethany Luanne Harris
Elizabeth Heffley
Jesse Michael Hixson
Drew Howerton
Meredith Hyde
Tandy Jo Jackson
Christiana Jenczyk
Steven Kyle Johnson
Luke Kays
Brooke Kehl
Kaitlyn Leonard
Hannah March
Elizabeth McIlroy
Rachel Miller
Nakisha Marie Milton
Janae Mock
Jenna Ann Montgomery
Cassondra Kaylene Morris
Rosemary Mumbua-Michael
Kevin Naceanceno
Jacob (Michael) Michael Nesbit
Austin Nightengale
Meghan Norris
Jonathan Oden
Aristides Ortiz
Lillie Victoria Parrett
Madeleine Perry
Sophia Pickle
Andrew Pyle
Elena Rabago
Victoria Jayne Reinhardt
Paige Ried
Sydni Ilyse Sansom
McKenna Smith
Kelly Melissa Spangler
Rachel Stone
Emily Mae Strandvold
Kelsey Sumrall
Carly Taylor
Jantzen Teague
Peyton Templeton
Lauryn Tobias
Alex Traughber
Monica Paige Whitman
Devan Wilkerson
Carrie Wingfield
Jeffrey Wright
Robert Austin Yates
Cordell Joseph David Zalenski

HARDIN-SIMMONS UNIVERSITY, ABILENE, TX

Bikram Bhandari
Katie A. Brown
Yueh Xuan Alexis Chuah
Stephen R. Clark
Caitlyn K. Cloy
Timothy L. Deaner
John M. Dodge
Joshua Malacara
Bailee McCann
Courtney Elizabeth Mentzel
Shiloh Brianne Reaves
Brianne Michelle Repko
Kenneth L. Schuessler
Joel K. Templeton
Stephen Twilleager

HAZARD COMMUNITY & TECHNICAL COLLEGE, HAZARD, KY

Tori Anissa Adams
Jacob T. Addison
Keisha Nichole Amburgey
Kelly Nicole Asher
Sydney Blair Back
Alaina Sue Bailey
Dakota Brooke Baker
Kristin Nicole Baker

Rebekah Lauren Baker
Ashley L. Banks
Kimberlin Kaylene Barnett
Kasey Cheyenne Barrett
Tessa Michelle Beder
Susan Marie Billingsley
Kari Lynn Bingham
Lakyn Tashae Bolen
Gabrielle Bowling
Ronald Wayne Bowling
Sarah A. Brashear
Hannah Elizabeth Brewer
Michelle LeeAnn Brewer
Robert William Brigman
Ernest A. Brown
Ronnie Allen Burke
Michael Dylan Burton
Christa Lynn Campbell
Kaylee Hannah Campbell
Kelsey Paige Carico
Kayla Lee Carroll
Christina Helen Childers
Dan Ryan Cody
Alyce Dot Combs
Charlotte Faye Combs
Flossie Louise Combs

Jeffery Scott Combs
Joanie Lynn Combs
John Edward Combs
Taylyn Geneil Combs
Vicey A. Combs
Zachary Taylor Combs
Anthony Hwan Comito
April Dawn Dixon
Laken Sue Dobson
Matthew Izak Dyal
Megan Cheyanne Farmer
Holly Lynn Feltner
Ronald Joe Fortney II
Ellora June Franklin
Sylvia Elyse Fryman
Kevin Ray Fugate
Solomon Edward Fugate
Sharon Raylonda Gibson
Lisa Renee Hamilton
Blake Alexander Jackson
Kimberly Renee Jacobs
Kelsey Nicole Jarrell
Scott Jonathan Kelley
Rebecca Jean Kilbourne
Robin Lynn Lane
Destiny Nicole Lewis

Gary Wayne Lewis
Laura Mae Logsdon
Lily ReVena Maggard
Sara N. Maynard
Cassity June McCool-Solis
Paula Ann McDaniel
Latoya Nicole McIntosh
Savana Mable McIntosh
Jeremy Ryan McMahan
Megan Denisa Meade
Daniel Floyd Messer
Shalene Nicole Miller
Makayla Richelle Morgan
Corey Wayne Mullis
Kati Nicole Noble
Sophia Dawn Noplis
Chasidy Lynn Palacios
Patrick Timothy Patula
Rhonda Yvonne Perkins
Gregory Lee Perry
Kaitlyn Deann Perry
Kayla S. Perry
Shawn Douglas Porter
Kimberlee Claire Ray
Cody Nathaniel Ritchie
Starla Brooke Roark

Brandon Keith Roberts
Sherrianne N. Robinson
Donna L. Rocca
Brianna Lynee Russell
Christopher Micheal Sanders
Kacie Lynn Schott
Kenny Wayne Scott
Jon Setzer
Kaitlin Marie Simpson
Bethany Lee Sizemore
Pheyten Brooke Smallwood
Jocelyn C. Smith
Whitney LeeAnn Stamper
Donald Edward Swisher
Jessica Renae Taulbee
Jennifer O. Thompson
Jacob Isom Tucker
Jacqueline K. Vires
Samantha Brooke Walker
Michael Watkins
Autumn Skye Weisbrodt
Leah Frances White
Jamie Dewayne Wilder
Brooklyn Michelle Wilson
Anthony David Wooton
Melissa Sue Wright

HENDERSON COMMUNITY COLLEGE, HENDERSON, KY

Deanna Adams
Andrew Richard Bengert
Zakary Thomas Lee Bengert
Lillian Celeste Brown
Erin Bailie Campbell
Lauren Jenae Carney

Lesley Ann Cohron
Alecia Dawn Crawley
Madison Nicole Darnell
Donald Robert Heard
Jodie Renee Heierman
Macey Ann Klauder

Melody Ann Kloke
Amber Renae Lucas
Brandy Ray Mason
Hannah Nicole May
Jordan Miller
Lindsey Renee Morris

Lisa Kay Moten
Allison Paige Petterson
Crystal Jayne Sanford
Meagan Elizabeth Sigler
Faith Ann Whitledge
Helen Mariah Windhorst

HERKIMER COUNTY COMMUNITY COLLEGE, HERKIMER, NY

Ashley Brown
Thomas Callister
Jacob Cardinal
Andrew Cieply
Teddi J. Cromling
Connor Doogan

Patrick Dorrian
Cavon Elias
Esteban Galvez Ospina
Tonya Susan Hayes
Lauren Elizabeth Leone
Ashley Marshall

Timothy Vernon McKenzie
Jordan Claire Mercer
Anthony Mincarelli
JaNay Mucitelli
Seth Olson
Lindsey Parese

Michael James Sarpen
Daykota Rae Snyder
Tianderah Twichell
Kelsey White
Meghan Elizabeth
Whitmoyer

HIGH POINT UNIVERSITY, HIGH POINT, NC

Savannah Angel
Jennifer Armstrong
Hannah Bailey
Matthew Beck
Kara Ann Benkovich
Laura Bernitsky
Jeffrey Berwager
Eliana Maria Betzios
Anthony John Boucher
Jacob Brooks
Chandler Louise Brown
Michele Burns
Jacqueline Cafasso
Elizabeth Carlson
Rodrigo Catalan-Hurtado
Lilliana Chalfant
Tyler Michael Cook
Christen Cothran
Emily DeLena

Hattie Dougherty
Corinne Eckert
Samantha Paige Entwistle
Caitlin Ferguson
Sarah Elizabeth Field
Lucas Fogaca
Kira Noelle Foglesong
Nicole Alexandra Font
Nicole Forman
Jessie Giaquinto
Ainsley Gompf
Hannah Grau
Jordan Delanie Green
Kimberly Nicole Greve
Gabrielle Hayes
Shirley Headen
Bridgett Renee Hess
Christina Grace Honeycutt
Andrew Jansen

Rolonda Kelly
Summer Kiesel
Sara Kirkpatrick
Dan Lomas
Lilla Lorand
Jennifer Rose Marshall
Meredith Diane Matsakis
Sierra Middlebrooks
Paul O'Donoghue
Kelly O'Sullivan
Clara Joan Osmont
Hailey Ann Parry
Emily Louise Pearl
Lynde Pepper
Kelsey Perrell
Nicholas Anthony Pierle
Lydia Prior
Lauren Quintal
Aria Shanee Real

Elizabeth Reichart
Christine Rickert
Madeleine Romano
Heather Lynn Rossi
Lauren Rubenstein
Cailyn Scanlan
William Shaw
Brandon Sloan
Deanna Smith
Elyse Rhea Stoner
Nicole Straley
Erin Margaret Sullivan
Stuart Nelson Swinford
Sara Kaitlin Thompson
Rachel Townsend
Alyssa Carmela Walker
Matthew Warrick
Jasmine C. Williams
Allie Rose Zambito

HILL COLLEGE, HILLSBORO, TX

Morgan Michelle Ballew
Michelle Canright
Whitney Lynn Chandler
Justin Crabb
Nika Davis
Darion Diggs
Kyndra George

Cole Hatfield
Justin Hendrix
Michaela McCord
Kristen Miller
Brookelyn Shae Newkirk
Marisela Ochoa
Emalee Payne

Anthony Rhodes
Andrea Rivera
Susana Rodriguez
Olivia Santos
Joanne Schroeder
Brandt Shilling
Kyle Taylor

Riley Harold Wikel
Angela Willison
Matthew Willison
Abigail Wilson
Casi Wood
Emily Zimmerman

HILLSBOROUGH COMMUNITY COLLEGE, TAMPA, FL

Stephanie Agard
Pablo Alameda
Carlos J. Alers-Fuentes
Hatim Alghamdi
Ameer D. Ali
Deborah S. Andrango
Teresa Armel
Abdoulaye Ba
Kate M. Balandrano
Kristen A. Bates
Jolene A. Batson
Raquel M. Baudrit

Antonia D. Bell
Tara A. Belzung
Andrea Bencardino-Florez
Abby M. Bernaldo
Mary K. Blanchard
Eric J. Bledsoe
Zach L. Bonner
Alexandria L. Burton
Ashley Childress
Nicole H. Cluck
Emmanuel O. Coker
Michelle Colson

Leonardo K. Constante
Taylor Corder
Ricardo Cox
Stevie N. Dailey
Jamie P. Daring
Leomar Davila
Melissa De la Cruz
Yzael De La Cruz
Yazmin A. Diaz
Charles Dickens
Haley Dixon
Elizabeth A. Duran

Razia J. Fayiz
Ivelisse Feliciano
John M. Fernandez
Matthew R. Flanagan
Marc A. Flecha
Christopher Flowers
Selena J. Fournier
Ramesh P. Francis
Taylor A. Ganio
Leslie N. Gilley
Sarah M. Gilliam
Natalia T. Glover

Noah Van-Cleef Grant
Cody W. Grantham
Devany A. Green
Carolina Grimaldo
Adrianna K. Grow
Shannen Hagemann
Amanda M. Hash
Amberlyn M. Hauck
Nelly Hernandez
Paul Herz
Thomas J. Hill
Natasha Ariel Infante
Donnelle Lezaldy January
Kelsie L. Johnson
Brittany A. Judson
Daniel J. Krupa
Pak Hin K. Lee
Daria A. Leon
Edmond Luckenson
Irene M. McAlvanah
Andre L. McNeal Jr.
Claire P. Meitzner
Lilibeth Melendez
Landon Messick

Evelyn Modl
Adam Mustafa
Joanna Negrete
Phuong M. Nguyen
Kylee M. Noss
Aoife B. O'Reardon
Gabriel A. Obinyan
Naomi Ogidan
Cheyenne L. Olson
Lisa L. Olson
Victoria Orellana
Emily J. Otten
Devon D. Parke
Tyler K. Parke
Garvin O. Payne
Huriel Perez
Chi K. Pham
Austin A. Polk
Jorry Powery
Mary E. Presley
Landon J. Purvis
Rachael H. Pyram
Amal Qaadoun
Alexander A. Rana

Je'Vonte M. Reaves
Laramie L. Renew
Cynthia A. Reyes
Syttney R. Richards
Emma Jane Richardson
Arely Rodriguez
Nelson Sanjuro Rodriguez
Maria C. Rojas
Lizette Marie Roman
Tyrek C. Royal
Matthew J. Russell
Heyam Shalabi
Leeanna L. Siegmund
Darius A. Sillart
Zurania Simon
Courtney L. Smith
Desaran M. Smith
Emanuel D. Sotomayor
Andrea St. John
Gabrielle K. Steinig
Matthew O. Sugrim
Hannah E. Tallent
Hung Quoc Tang
Alicia K. Tannis

Nicholas P. Tersigni
My T. Thai
Arstella B. Timmons
Kayla M. Toole
Elena A. Torna
Antonino Travia
Kasey A. Traylor
Imanol Trigo
Ngoc B. Truong
Amanda J. Twigg
Rachel Valdes
Vimary Vera
Adrian Vicente la Lande
Aleksandrina A.
Vodenicharska
Eric L. Walker
Kimberly A. Werkheiser
Darius L. Wilson
Nyasia C. Wray
Freddie D. Wright
Yuying Xian
Asmahan Yacoub
Shahriar Zamani

HILLSDALE FREE WILL BAPTIST COLLEGE, MOORE, OK

Mason Shane Anderson
Kayla Renee Bradley
Brooke Ashley Davidson
Jonathan Kemper Combs De
Aquino
Anthony Michael Dillard
Tiffani Marie Dorman
Taelor Monyque Drew

Courtney Suzanne Findley-
Anderson
Jordan Haylee Frazier
Levi Alexander Harrell
Joshua M. Hein
Ryan Edward Hickerson-
Davis
Chelsea L. Johnston

Quinton Avery Ray
Alex-Andria Maureen Rooks
Mark Joseph Seiter
Andrew W. Shipley
Joshua Edward Sloan
Robert Edward Thompson
Rachael DeAnne Travis
Mason Wade Walkingstick

Jimmy Lee Wisdom
Katie Joy Woerz
Ryan Paul Woerz
Taylor Renee Youngblood

HINDS COMMUNITY COLLEGE, RAYMOND, MS

Jordan Adekweh
Eddie V. Anderson
William Hosier Anderson
Shaunell Marie Applewhite
Betty M. Barnes
Elijah Kane Beatty
Mary Kelli Bethea

Natalie Ruth Blakely
Matthew Eric Bobo
Classie D. Bradford
Chaz Michael Breaux
Cortez Brooks
D'Cha'Ray Jamerick Brown
Kadaisha J. Brown

Talgat Michael Brown
Anthyone Burrell
Gladys M. Burrell
Connie Evalyn Burril
Bracken Nicole Carroll
Rachel Alexandria Carroll
Erika Sarahi Chacon

David Walton Ching
Kennedy Elayne Collier
Brittany Shabrion Colllins
Amber Brielle Davis
Madeline Nancy Davis
Mercedes A. Davis
Shelby Gene Dearing

Jessica Nicole Decell
Olivia Ann DeGrado
Andrea Erin Delbalso
Karan Prem Dhawan
Jason Duane Dillon
Lena Yvonne Dixon
Mishael Israel Drake
Naarah I. Drake
Samson Israel Drake
Kristen Danielle Dunaway
Courtney Brooke Evans
Kirstyn D. Ferguson
Gracie Gayle Fletcher
Asiah Simone Ford
John Barron Garbo
Jayden Taylor Gardner
Famie Cheyenne Gaseb
LeBreonna LaCheryl Glenn
Callie Lanelle Godbold
Mary Caitlyn Graham
Jacob Aaron Hale
Tyrus Larae Hamilton
Georgina Danielle
Hammons
Erica Shantres Harris
Jasmine Harris
Symphonia Amanda Harris
Walter Harris
Cara Joy Harrison
Isola Camelle Hartman
Sherry Lynn Haughton

Courtney N. Helom
Michael Jwan Henderson
Sabrina Victoria Henry
Joshua KaMon Hodge
Ashlie Nicole Hollingshead
Brittany Leighanne
Houseworth
Yolanda Nicole Hudgens-
Simmons
Hunter Benjamin Huff
Robert Harrison Hunter
Selena J. Hunter
Abbey Marie Irwin
Corbin Dwayne Jamison
Brandon RayLee Jenkins
Lindsey Brooke Jeselink
Cristen Elizabeth Jiles
Samuel Lamar Johnson
David Wilmon Jolly III
Jarvis Jerell Jones
Marcus Dewayne Jones
Timothy Cruise Jordan
Trevor William Jordan
Kaylyn Danielle King
Benjamin Carlisle Koestler
Tory Elizabeth Laird
Christin Michelle Lang
Marion Wade Lee
Rebekah Imani Lee
Ashley N. Louis
Olivia Victoria Lovvorn

Aubrey S. Lynch
Rebecca Jean Machost
Mary Louise Manard
Jonah Reed Masterson
Amelia Faye Matthews
Williams
Darione Maxie
Kyisha Lynette Mayfield
Anna Grace Maynard
Jalen Nicole McArthur
Taylor Reann McClain
Taylor Nicole McCracken
Amber Lydia McCullough
Kathryn Suzanne McKinion
Ty Lausan Mohler
Precious F. Moore
John Kyle O'Keefe
Samantha Kathryn Pace
Mackenzie Lynn Page
Lineasia M. Palmer
Jessica Anne Paul
Michael Thang Hong Pham
Sidney Morgan Phillips
Cortney Shuree Powell
Bryden Michael Reed
Rachel Elizabeth Rhett
David D. Robinson
Carl Brandon Ross
Hannah Wyvonne Ross
Eric Joseph Rush
Alexander Owen Shoemaker

Kimberly Bridges Smith
Theary Kun So
Christina Briana Spencer
Kasakia A. Spencer
Hailey Rae Stacy
Carly Grace Stocks
Megan Nicole Stockton
Taylor Lynn Stockton
Rebecca Diane Strong
Amber Leigh Thomas
Chasity Jaronda Thomas
Phillip Ryan Thomas
Rocio Gomez Torres
Megan Leigh Valentine
Marcus Robert Valles
Giovanny Varela Nunez
Rafael Vidana
Abigail Elizabeth Walters
Crystal Nicole Ward
Gabrielle J. Wells
Valerie Lauren White
Ciara B. Williams
Keunte T. Williams
David A. Wilson
Robert Evans Winschel
Diana Julissa Wox
Nahgee Sahleem
Yeroozedek

HIWASSEE COLLEGE, MADISONVILLE, TN

Maritza Cuevas
Shana Ann Debty
Johnathan William Dickson
Susanna Dimmick
Kelsey E. Donoho
Brad Mitchell Gandy
Paul Selman Goodman

Sarah Gail Goodman
Tevin Jamal Henry
Haylee Marie Kennedy
Kendra Rose Pearl King
Halei Gayle LeQuire
Jennifer Hayden Lester
Rachel Hanna Moody

Jaylon Juwon Moore
Jessica Raven Moore
Miranda LeShell Morrow
Danica Leigh Proulx
Danielle Lynne Proulx
Samantha Nicole Ray
Natasha Marie Robinson

Jordan Darnell Sexton
Breck K. Sheaffer
Skyler R. Tallent
Drey Dillon Tipton
Eric Wayne Wolfe

HOLMES BIBLE COLLEGE, GREENVILLE, SC

Godwin O. Agbo

Lucius D. Hand Jr.

HOLY FAMILY UNIVERSITY, PHILADELPHIA, PA

Lisa Abramski

Alicia Marie Alvarado

Claudia C. Boggi

Jaclyn Boileau

Hana Agnieszka Britland

Catrenia Marie D'Imperio

Nikki L. Dwyer

Jeanette Marie Einspahr

Rachel Fediuk

Jovannalee Fernandez

Meghan Frederick

Emily Gilmour

Sara Lobley

Rachel Lee McAnany

Marianna McKenna

Erin Ann Miller

Andrew Orapallo

Adam Lee Price

HOPKINSVILLE COMMUNITY COLLEGE, HOPKINSVILLE, KY

David N. Aman

Zavier M. Atkins

Richard D. Braem

Adam M. Brewer

Amber V. Bruce

Jamie J. Buckner

Derek E. Burkhart

Mitchell W. Calvin

Vincent M. Collins

Rickey D. Cupp

Katie M. Drake

Brooklyn E. Gardner

Veronica Gee

Mary V. Johnston

Jessica R. Keenan

David N. Langner

Jusdan D. Lynch

Kaitlyn B. Mathews

Stacy H. Mathews

Dawson O. McDonald

Zoie A. Merren

Erica R. Palowitch

Piers B. Peeler

Caleb A. Poe

Lori A. Powell

Timothy M. Schmitt

Brittany F. Simpson

Caitlin L. Starr

Brittni R. Tichenor

Marylynn V. Webb

Iyona T. Woodard

Christopher Daniel Young

Genevieve M. Younger

HOUSATONIC COMMUNITY COLLEGE, BRIDGEPORT, CT

Mario A. Castiello

Betzabeth Enid Castro

Juliet Chin

Nyrasia Unique Lomax

HOWARD COLLEGE, BIG SPRING, TX

Kayla Bell

Arielle Charuk

Angelica Diaz

Brittany Dover

Annabel Faught

Alexandra Gibbs

Tyler Green

Brittany Henderson

Katie King

Patrick Laws

Jackelina Martens

Victoria Martinez

Jordan Matthews

Shazay Norris

Cassidi Redlin

Cory Remschel

Katherine Reyes

Bryce Short

Sara Stevenson

Laura Thieme

Shelby Ume

Leksey Yarbar

HOWARD COLLEGE AT SAN ANGELO, SAN ANGELO, TX

April J. Amine

Aimee T. Armendariz

Kami D. Bailey

Sybilla B. Baker

Mary C. Baty

Tyler B. Benbow

Kailey P. Berube

Mustafa J. Carlisle

Danny S. Cervantez

Heather L. Coyro

Jessica R. Cuellar

Diana R. DeHoyos

Tylin G. Farris

Haleigh R. Finch

Joseph L. Flannagan

Kacelyn Ann Follis

Rahegyn E. Franke

Amparo Gonzales

Lorenzo G. Govea

Vanessa D. Griffith

Kelsie R. Harrington

Roger L. Henson

Melissa Hernandez

Candi K. Homer

Dana Hughes

Kevin S. Johnson

Joshua J. Leenerts

Arron M. Mattes

Yvonne Minjarez

Jeanelle M. Montez

Anthony Moreno

Alondra F. Perez

William E. Pippin Jr.

Dustin A. Proctor

Britnee C. Raley

Angelica M. Ramirez

Cheyenne M. Sikes

Bianca R. Titus

Angel Vasquez

Brent E. Wesley

Christopher W. Wheeler

Jonathan D. Williams

HOWARD COMMUNITY COLLEGE, COLUMBIA, MD

Liliana Aviles

Christine Ballou

Arzoo Bassal

Jay Brilliant

Sandra Carr

Brooke Chung

Michael Cieplak

Joseph Devera

Furo Dublin-Greene

Jose Egea

Alethea V. Franklin

Katrina L. Gazo

Jolanda Graham

Jody Gross

Melissa Helsing

Jonathan Hudson

Elizabeth Jennemann

Benjamin Law

Deb Leib

Jonathan Lessels

Michelle Ludlow

Petrina Miller

Kevin Moreno

Kelly Morgan

Sasha Nemchinova

Timothy Adam Newton

Himadri Patel

Maricruz Perez

Aleksander Petrov

Abigail Pollock

Freddy Ramirez

Jane Rawls

Valerie Rose

Zulekha Sayyed

Angela Serdula

Jayson Shiamraj

Pooja Singh

Kara Stoner

Ephrata Temesgen

Akbar Tolbert

Kristin Jenel Watson

Alex Webster

Hanna Welsh

Lorraine Wiggins

Terrell Willis

Mallory Wilson

HOWARD PAYNE UNIVERSITY, BROWNWOOD, TX

James Abbatiello

Callie Adams

Tammy Arreola

Katie Ash

Morgan Ashmore

J Bailey

Michael Bailey

Olivia Belsher

Jaclyn Rose Bonner

Chandler Condra

Abraham Cooper

Ruth Davis

Keaton Fletcher

Elliott Gray

Kristin Haman

Rebecca Nicole Hamilton

Victoria Hardin

Doug Hurt

Jerry Hurt

Rachel Ann Mahagan

Vanessa Mae Marquez

Xavier McFalls

Ivyanne Alyssa Nichols

Emily Peisker

Diana Rebeca Puente

Luis Robles

William Rumfield

Amber Rose Shipman

Isaac Conrad Herrera

Sommers

Kelsan Wolverton

Sharon Wolverton

Caitlin Wood

HOWARD UNIVERSITY, WASHINGTON, DC

Brandon Martrel Beasley

Jalyse J. Cuff

Taylor L. Facen

Alexis Kassandea Reid

Grant

Elizabeth D. Jenkins

Na'ima S. Jenkins

Kimberly G. Johnson

Ayotunde A. Odejayi

HUDSON COUNTY COMMUNITY COLLEGE, JERSEY CITY, NJ

Princess Erza Abardo

Jessica Abdelnabbi

Sara Abuawada

Luis Miguel Aguayo

Caroline Aldaz

Anthony Alkuino

Michael Anchundia

Betsy Apena

Julio Faustino Arroyo

Alexander Calle

Christopher Canela

Erwin Catacutan

Hodeia Davis

Hamilton Mikhael Diby

Maggie Farog

Candice Marie Fernandez

Steven Michael Galarza

Victor Enok Gavilanes

Edward Gotia

Shawn Hartrum

Aaron Kates

Adrian Kayanan

Melissa Kleckner

Elizabeth Kotinsky

Monique Longoria

Providencia Lopez

Kimberly Luciano

Felicia Theresa Lyons

Gina McHugh

Jose Ramon Melendez

Mary Yvette Mercado

Amaalah Ogburn

Kinal A. Patel

George Damian Pauljohn

Andres Pinargote

Angline Christian Plummer

Thalita Real

Fiorella Rodriguez

Cindy Ruberto

Hamza Saleem

Nakiya Marie Santos

Katherine Yessenia Sorto

Marc Surujballi

Taylor Thomas

Jazmin Gavrielle Vergara   Katherine Laura Willman-   Kian Wilson   Jocelyn Shirley Wong-
Godfrey   Castellano

HUDSON VALLEY COMMUNITY COLLEGE, TROY, NY

Lisa A. Clevenger	Stephen M. Hatalla	Vivica C. Paull	Amy J. St. Clair
Lennox Degrasse	Melanie P. Hecker	Laura A. Pierson	Alicia M. St. Germain
Josiah J. Dillon	Liesl Hull	Brigitte S. Pryor	Molly Kathryn D. Stenard
Caleb J. Ducharme	Rebecca M. Johnson	Abigail E. Radliff	Sandra R. Thomas
Joseph A. Dugan	Levi W. Kelly	Matthew G. Roden	Robert K. VanNess
A'Chynee Z. Edmundson	Bryce S. Kirk	Helen M. Schneider	Victoria A. Weinhold
Teresa M. Edwards	Shreshta Kota	Haley J. Scott	Hali C. Winch
Gabriel M. Father	Kresimir B. Krtalic	Krista L. Seeberger	Chancey A. Young
Shawna M. Fitzsimmons	Everett C. McNair	Alexander J. Shannon	
Caleb N. Gregg	Brody P. O'Connor	Erica L. Shudt	
Jessica D. Gruss	Luelushee L. Pa Thaw	Robert L. Song	

HUNTINGDON COLLEGE, MONTGOMERY, AL

Andrew Michael Ackerman	Anna Margaret DeMedicis	Lauren Marie Lugen	Jassmine Parcilleea Riley
Elexis Monique Arnold	Alicia Nicole Gauker	Farrah Rachelle Mahan	Oliver Gabriel Saywah
Jenell Amber Buckner	Christopher Joshua Glennon	Brooke Nicole Meadows	Jorgi Amelia Sims
Brantley Colvin Carr	Emily Lindsay Grinstead	Carlee Elizabeth Nobles	Jeremiah Cash Stone
Melanie Blair Casebere	Caleb Paul Hart	Madeline N. Pendley	Britni Danielle Thibodeau
India Chaney	Donna Nichole Kennedy	Tachera Breone Porter	Lamar Alan Thompson
Jordan Keith Criswell	Heidi Yvonne Knecht	Jennifer Lee Price	Michaela Joy Tillery
Jessie Ray Culey	Bridget Mary Lee	Anna Corinne Raley	Candace Renee Williams
Kristen Renee Curtis	Barrett Ewing Leverette	Eliza Kaye Richardson	Stephanie Marie Yasechko

HUNTINGTON UNIVERSITY, HUNTINGTON, IN

Benjamin David Blum	Anne Marie Hacker	Lauren Lee Kirby	Abigail Sarah Thiebaut
Bronwen Ellen Fetters	Tyler Robert Herber	Kelsey Grace Kruse	Brice Andrew Urschel
Lauren Alexa Frischman	Amy Ellen Hetrick	Lucas Jay Lengacher	Olivia Anne Watkins
Brandi Lyn Girod	Kody Michael Hope	Luke Michael McConnell	Krista Kaylinn Wood
Haley Brooke Glinz	Clarissa Meredith Hunter	Megan Jeanne Schueler	
Rebecca Leila Grimes	Tyson Bailey Kalischuk	Rachel Nicole TerMarsch	

HUSSON UNIVERSITY, BANGOR, ME

Heidi Schnee Bauer	Daniel Cole	Paul Forand	Anthony McLaughlin
Jeremy Boutot	Gretchen Crockett	Michelle Humphrey	Owen Miller
Troy Cantalupo	Amber Davis	Kateri Jeffery	Kelsey Nason
Marissa M. Charette	Julianne Davis	Kelsey Livermore	Scott Peacock
Marleah Blair Clark	Kayla Ashlen Day	Hannah Lugdon	Olivia Plaisted
Rachel Clark	Nicole Duplessis	Melissa McKenney	Melesa Punsky

Kristen Roemmich	Sarah Smith	Natasha Thompson	Danielle Violette
Erin Rollins	Aaron Somers	Jennifer Tracy	Alan Wardwell
Miranda L. Shepherd-Bussiere	Aisling Stephenson	Mikala Elizabeth Varela	Cassandra Lynn Webster

HUTCHINSON COMMUNITY COLLEGE, HUTCHINSON, KS

Tyler Jacob Balsters	Michael Hendricks	Bailee Marie Porter	Dallas Thompson
Megan Renee Bartley	Hunter Maverick Hill	Mary Brigid Reilly	Madison Nicole Watson
Ryan Ethan Bengston	Nathaniel Hoefer	Jenessa Nichole Rose	Logan Alanzo Weppler
Max Carlson	Brooke Ranae Keller	Kendra Selzer	Morgan Wheeler
John David Colclazier	Adam Joseph Konen	Sara Shaban	Nicholas James White
Maddi Elizabeth Cumpston	Kayla Koop	Kirsten Showalter	Sarah White
Stein Desir	Dalton Ray Luce	Ulises Silvestre	Ian Williams
Aaron Wayne Ewy	Karrie Renea McNutt	Ty Joseph Simons	Matt Willis
Marcus Gaeddert	Leah M. Nelson	KateLynn Rose Spencer	Jon Yates
Jovita Garcia	Makenzie Paige Nisly	Kacie Michelle Stuever	
Hunter Wayne Guthrie	Jason Paine	Andrew Thompson	

HYLES-ANDERSON COLLEGE, CROWN POINT, IN

Caleb Josias Amorós Mejia	Jessica C. Garcia	Kimberly McCroskey	Menahem Naituli
Catherine A. Beal	Kevin Gonzalez	Fletcher	Tuiolosega
Jonathan Samuel Beil	Brittany Joy Guin Beil	Gabrielle Nicole Rhodes	Loran A. Wilson
Katie Ann Chavez	Marissa Anne Howell	Abigail Marie Stamatis	Zachary Yelton
Jacob Robert Doan	Omar Lopez Ramirez		

ILLINOIS STATE UNIVERSITY, NORMAL, IL

Jennifer Brauer	Connor Joyce	Lorena Lopez	Fabiola Rosiles
Bridgette Edmonson	Lauren Koszyk	Javier Padilla	

IMMACULATA UNIVERSITY UNDERGRADUATE, IMMACULATA, PA

Kenneth Anderson	Alec Butler	Lauren Degnan	Jessica Hudoka
Megan Alice Aslanian	Marissa Casella	Matthew DeLallo	Mark Hueber
Kyle Beideman	Shelby Clare	Matthew Tyler Dunn	Chelsea Irwin
Jon Bernhard	Adam Connor	Shannon Rose Dunphy	Nisha Jacob
Caroline Elizabeth Biondolillo	Rose Theresa Corcoran	Gabe Dwyer	Fatmata Kamara
Amanda Boselli	Lucio Rocco Costantini	Roy Ferrell	Annaliese Kambouroglos
Gabrielle Kristen Bourne	Diana Marie Cusick	Jenna Lynn Fratterelli	Kathleen Kennedy
Marianthi Zannis Bousses	Allison Rose D'Abbraccio	Patrick Friend	Rachael Kitchens
Erica Marie Buckley	Carleigh Dabritz	Anne Giorgio Gorman	Emma Koontz
Sara Marie Burke	Joanne Daris	Rachel Lyn Graham	Alicia Lawler
Cory Burkhart	Angela DeAntonio	Hailey Elizabeth Gustainis	Allison Leonard
	Anne Marie DeCarolis	Kelley Hennessy	Justine Leschke

Sandy Luna Lopez
Kristin M. Lynch
Alyssa Malitsky
Colleen Martin
Christine Nicole McIntyre
James McLean
Laurence Stryker Messler
William Nelson
Marissa Lin Nihill
Kaitlin O'Reilly

Stephanie Katherine
Olzinski
Jennifer Orlandi
Kevin Parsons
Matthew Pascarella
Michael Pascarella
Lucia Pasternak
Sarah Pasternak
Nicholas Pezzotti
Michaela Raffaele

Wilmarie Rodriguez
Matthew P. Ross
Olivia Ross
Kasey Rossell
Danielle Rulon
Lauren Shaffer
Dylan Katherine Shelton
Sarah Silverman
Stephen Smith
William Xavier Smith

Sarah Stepanchick
Marina Melissa Stolarczyk
Michael Sturdivant
Laurel Brooke Trevena
Adam Wheatley
Abigail Wilson
Meron Tesfaye
Woldearegaye
Jingchen Zhao

INDEPENDENCE UNIVERSITY, SALT LAKE CITY, UT

Nathaniel M. Abram
Tyrion Renee Adams
Genevieve Alonge
Monique Aponte
Lorraine J. Armstrong
Shannon Danielle Ayzie
Cristine M. Babcock
Junko I. Barker
Stephanie L. Barnard
Joseph Barsic
Aime Bateman
Amanda Rae Becker
Shawnalee K. Bennett
April F. Black
David Brooks
Shonda Brooks
Elizabeth M. Budenberg
Dominique D. Burns
William L. Busch
Pamela K. Carruthers
Gabriel Carvajal Vargas
Erik Casarez
Katie J. Cheatham
Jennifer M. Christian
Carly Clement
Roy L. Compton Jr.
Nancy Cope
Cynthia A. Crawford
Iris Cruz
Amanda L. Dashner
Mary Ann Delaloye

Christina Moreland Devine
Carisa Duru
Justin K. Echols
Kristine Eckert
Nicol A. Elder
Denise Elliott
Edlena Jeanette Faison
Robert J. Fate
Mandy Ficarra
Julia A. Fussell
Mindi Garcia
Cheryl Gearin
Koshy George
Ranell Lou George
Whitney Giles
Corrie M. Goranson
Emily K. Grill
Richard L. Guy
Drew Alexandra Haag
Kelli Ester Hall
Mary A. Halstead
Kendra M. Harris
Sandra J. Hartman
Victoria A. Hassler
Kelli Ann Hawkins
Connie Haycock
Tammy Hennison
Taylor J. Henry
Joseph Charles Hogue
Daniel W. Horvath
Shanen L. Hughes

Tonya R. Huntington
Samantha Hutchings
Patricia J. Imperiale
Dianna L. James
Scott T. James
Kelly M. Jewell
Cherie N. Johnson
Joshua Johnson
Vickie T. Johnson
Joseph Timothy Jones
Nathaniel S. Kane
Michael Stephen Kasuboski
Amy S. Kelly
James Earl Kennedy
Amy Alison King
Kenneth H. Kinsler
Sharese M. Lance
Michelle J. Landaverde
Melissia R. Lindemann
Sharon Kaye Little
Jannaye Ramona Macias
Ronda Lynn MacNeil
Lynnora Mahle-
Talayumptewa
Jason L. Marks
Nicole Yvonne Marleau
Sharron Martin
Lexie S. Martinez
Paul-Michael Martinez
Mary Evelyn Mcgehee
Leeza Anne McGowan

Stephanie J. McGuire
Sandra J. Mejia
Michael A. Mieure
Keri Moore
Sarah Ann Morris
Kelley Ann Napper
Rachelle Diane Napper
David A. OConnor
Kristopher M. Overturf
Laura Palomino
Ryan S. Pavlak
Samantha Pelkey
Elizabeth Perez
William Perez
Matthew Bradley Po'oi
Kierstyn N. Ratliff
Brian Jensen Redling
Tammy L. Ries
Rose M. Riffle
Dave T. Roberts
LaDonna Robertson
Tony J. Roddy
Juan G. Rodriguez
Jessica Rodriguez Monroy
Catherine Romeo
Jodi D. Rotter
Suprena Russell
Elizabeth M. Sanchez
Kimberly R. Schilke-
Pinckney
Melanie E. Schmidt

Ryan A. Schneider	Jossi R. Stanley	Douglas Thompson	Tina R. Wilborn
Susan Sebranek	Margie J. Starling	Diana L. Thorne	Ethel M. Wilkes
Sara M. Shupert	Katherine A. Stine	Stephanie M. Townsend	Stacie L. Woodall
Dwayne Sippio Jr.	Tamera A. Strieter	Tito J. Trujillo	Bobbi J. Wright
Weston M. Sorenson	Cheryl Taylor	Samantha Turner	
Lawrence A. Spann	Jessica Taylor	Lenora Underwood	
Cayla R. Staman	Samantha J. Thomas	Kimberly L. Wadsworth	

INDIANA INSTITUTE OF TECHNOLOGY, FORT WAYNE, IN

Brandon Bailey	Fernando Antonio	Kayla Morrell	Haley Toliver
Muhammad Harith Bin	Fernandez Bello	Jonathan Mueller	Rayana Villalpando
Jalalluddin	Aubrianna Hazen	Brian Nichter	Tyler Wells
Donald Bittner	Marcus Hobbs	Megan Alexandra Perrey	Brock Wheeler
Molly Bolt	Zachary Katter	Nicole Price	Nathan Wilz
Chad Brooks	Fabian Kaufmann	Steven Remesnik	Michael Winans
Quinton Burnett	Jamie Nicole Kilps	Jeremy Michael Rice	Kaleigh Young
Tayler Campbell	Charun Lee	Idontea Ancacia Richardson	Ashley Zeabart
Anabell Cordero Rovelo	Adam Lehn	Morgan Sage	Jessica Zurcher
Amanda Dicks	Emily Mancos	Wiebke Schlender	
Kassidy Eberhart	Milos Milidragovic	Eli Shultz	

INDIANA UNIVERSITY EAST SCHOOL OF NURSING, RICHMOND, IN

Erica Baden	Katherine Collins	Christa Maitlen	Carol Stephens
Mary Barton	Paula Gerth	Tonya Miller	Rachel Tressler
Antoinette Brewer	Anthony Goodpaster	Lisa A. Monroe	Shanna Via
Christina Burks	Annalisa Keene	Brenda Singleton	Katherine Jean Wadsworth
Casey Callahan	Susan Klein	Natalie Smith	Lynette Faye Weidner

INDIANA UNIVERSITY SOUTH BEND, SOUTH BEND, IN

Eman Alkotob	Jared Nicholas Campbell	Corey Geyer	Craig Alan Johnson Jr.
Eduardo Alvarez	Kelsey Carmack	Sarah Geyer	Jennifer Jones
Desmond A. Atem	Sierra Conklin	Natasha Renee Grove	Christine Jordan
Monn Paul Andre Valery	Damon Javier DeJesus	Nicole Hassinger	Michael Joy
Avoaka	Brian Duffy	Yoshimi Hayashi	Michaela Kapala
Allan Barnes	Jenna Early	Pamela Flores Hernandez	Lois Kassem
Shail Bhagat	Jasmine Ensz	Randy Hewitt	Holly Klopfenstein
Amanda Bogard	Kala Erickson	Alexandra Nicole	Kilee Knafel
Christine Mary Elizabeth	Jessica Fennen	Hochstetler	Meagan Jane Kowalik
Bohlmann	Patrick Finnigan	Madison Hofferth	Emily Mari Kozinski
Willard Bontrager	Danielle Lyn Fishburn	Alexandra Grace Humphrey	Wesley Kuric
Bethany Brewer	Alicia Ashley Flores	Elyssa Kate Hurdt	Roberto Leal
Matthew James Burnham	Traci Foster	Charles Jackson	Michele Lentner
Danielle Cagle	Luke Gaboury	Elaine Jackson	Leslie Lestinsky

Ross Linton
Scott Joseph Linton
Ryan Lohman
Susan Long
Carter Lubelski
Jordan Lucas
Emily Macellari
Kaitlyn Mcdonald
Jazmine Medina
Renae Michalski
Tiffany Milnes
Miren Mosteller
Alaina Leigh Myers
Alyssa Coral Neece
Jessica Lynn Nelson
Emily Nix
Ryan Novak

Rachel Ann Nuner
Kerianne O'Donnell
Sergio Ortiz Cardoso
Ashley Painter
Jacob Michael Parker
Kristina Partridge
Sheel Patel
Bradley Stephen Pontius
Shannon Marie Porowski
Alec James Radecki
Rhonda Redman
Michael Reece
Janelle Rehlander
Devin M. Roach
Aaron Louis Roeder
Lindsay Romwalter
Darla Rowe

Brady Christopher Ruffing
Stephen Michael Salisbury
Jaime Andres Sanchez
Rachel Santos
Anthony Sergio
Melia Shisler
Taylor Silveus
Kayla Smith
Luke Smith
Gninhinninchionni Fatima
Soro
Bethany Soto
Josiah South
Jennifer Stahl
Cheri Dee Stalcup
Jacquelyn Stalder
Riley Stichter

Emil Talic
Emily Tavares
Laura Karen Taylor
Andi Trowbridge
Hannah Van
Cassandra VanSky
Kimberly Vegh
Shawn Wagner
Susan M. Ward
Emily Wilson
Jane Wise
King Wong
Sarah Woods
Halie Zartman

INDIANA UNIVERSITY SOUTHEAST, NEW ALBANY, IN

Kirsten Lea Black
Megan Black
Hannah Dailey
Deven James Estes
Christian Ryan French

Aubrey Elizabeth Garman
Samantha Grayson
Jessica Holbrook
Bethany Hoskins
Morgan Elizabeth Kaiser

Aimee Breanna Kelmel
Alicia Ledington
Ginnie Lee
Cortney Perkins
Hugo Enrique Sanchez Juan

Victoria Anne Swank
Alicia Thomas
DeAnna Whittinghill

INDIANA WESLEYAN UNIVERSITY, MARION, IN

Adam Warren Burggraf
Erin Naomi Elting
Angelica Rose Huffman
Sarah Jane Kerrn

Heidi Joy Kolberg
Janice Marie Murray
Ubong A. Ntewo
Keith A. Rogers

Shannon M. Rogers
Kaylee N. Sills
Ryan Christopher Smith
Nicole Joy Turcotte

Randall "Milt" Van Natta
Seth Emerson Walker
Bethany Rose Williams
Tracey A. Zimmerman

INDIAN HILLS COMMUNITY COLLEGE, OTTUMWA, IA

Brandee Achilles
Carla Kay Adams
Lisa M. Akers
Nicholas Alexander
Rebecca Appleget
Jeffrey Alan Ashmore
Marisa Basham
Justin Beach
Thomas Bebernes
Alison E. Bennett
Cory Bennett

Cynthia Beverlin
Jordan Billups
Tom A. Blunt
Jordan Bossard
Kathryn Box
Tristan Boyer
Andrea Breckenridge
Tara L. Brewer
Ringgenberg Bridget
Cory Burdette
Courtney A. M. Burgess

Maria I. Burkle Gonzalez
Cole Campbell
Karishma Cavanaugh
Jaden Chalupa
Cynthia A. Chavarria
Skyler M. Crosby
Nathan Crump
Lara Davis
Rachel Ann Decook
Irina A. Demeneva
Zeynep Deniztoker

Thomas Wayne Derby
Kacey Y. Duffield
Breanna L. Eaton
Dayton Bradley Fears
Carlos A. Fernandez Soto
Shannon L. Finneran
Christopher M. Fisher
Trevor Fitzpatrick
Tonya Fletcher
Foncham Buma Foncham
George Francis

Daniel Fredrickson	Yekaterina Krongart	Colette Niyang	Colby Starr
Jacob Glasscock	Mikayla E. Lanman	Misti Novak	Brian St John
Marissa Greenfield	Amber Lewis	Cameron Oehler	Stephani Danielle Stockton
Jesse Griffel	Jonathon Liles	Haylie N. Owens	Jonah Stovall
Aaron Michael Hackett	Austin Linder	Tony W. Parker	Noah Stovall
Daniel Haffner	Matthew D. Lucas	Heidi Perlberg	Paige L. Stroud
Mikayla Hance	Charity W. Luke	Cheyenne Phillips	Yinga Talla-Takusi
Tyler Heifort	Jonathan Earl McArtor	Angela Pohren	Breanna L. Terpstra
Joelle Henning	Kathleen McGinity	Kailyn R. Risher	Leona Thomas
Charles Hoenig	Haley McKay	Kathleen Robertson	Teri Trueblood
Samuel L. Hofstetter	Jacob McLain	Courtney Ryan	Justin Truitt
Nevada Horner	Amanda Jo Meier	Paige Ryan	Shelby Vallen
Aaron Huff	Katherine Membreno	Paul Ryon	Adam C. Vander Vort
Allison T. Hulsizer	Karla Jackeline Mercado	Nathaly Salinas	Naomi Vandervort
Bogdan Iftinca	Barahona	Nicole Sanders	Austin T. Versteegh
Lana Inderski	Tamara Merseli	Tyler Sanders	Katherine Anne Walker
Angus Janssen	Brandy Millikin	Dallas Schumann	Sidney Waller
Jesse T. Janssen	Michael Mosbey	Charles J. Severson	Tonya Ward
Jordan E. Johnson	Delphine Munji	Bradley Shearer	Calista Wegner
Kylie Johnson	Cody Murphy	Seth A. Simmons	Gayla L. Whisler
Adria G. Jones	Kasey Murphy	Jodie Sirovy	Michael Wide
Kandi Jones	Brendah Muthoni	Lance Smith	Christian Williams
David Kish	Ashley M. Nelson	Katie Smothers	Karley Williams
Katie Konrad	Dylan J. Nelson	Alicia Snyder	Cody Wintermote
Adinda Koopmans	Spencer Nelson	Lorna Snyder	

INDIAN RIVER STATE COLLEGE, FORT PIERCE, FL

Noelle Adams	Rajul Brahmbhatt	Ryan Coppedge	Ivan Garcia
Jennifer Addeo	Pamela Brannen	Carrie Mae Daub	Melinda Garcia
Ashton DeLEE Adkins	Tara Gracen Brown	Shaylin Demers	Jordan St. Germain
Claudia Aguilar	Keona Mone't Cadore	Mary Donnelly	Cori Gondola
Michael Anderson	Meghan Callahan	Mary J. Dorey	Felicia Gordian
Hannah Artille	Andrew Caputo	Cayce Douthitt	Holly Hensley
Dominique Barral	Ryan Daniel Carley	Aiden Dowell	Sansiago Hernandez
Mary Baumbach	Kacy Carvajal	Shelby Durden	Paige Highstone
Christie Beck	Kasandra Castle	Joshua Eads	Nathaniel Howard
Tessa Bellamy	David Casto	Craig Emslie	Curtis Humphrey
Amanda Blanchard	Jackson Casto	Areli Enrique	Olivia Jacobi
Jennifer Bonan	Yamilet Cendejas	Vincent Esposito	Margaryta Rzhevska
Kathryn Borruso	Hua-Lin Chen	Madison Evans	Jernigan
Hanna Bostwick	Christina Clerc	Kaylyn Fells	Amali Kadur
Brittany Bowen	Patrick Connell	Shannon Nicole Fies	Catarina Elizabeth
Ashley Bradford	Christie Cooper	Chelsea Fruggiero	Kaltenhauser

Alexander Kamentz
Hali Keller
Mikaela Elizabeth Kelly
Grace Kenny
Kateryna Kopylova Radomski
Laura Mercedes Kutey
April Marie La Mattina
Jasha Lee
Tyler Leonard
Colin Leung
Tayla Elizabeth Jesse Lovemore
Barbara Lutjen
Grace Lynch
Katherine Mackey
Brian MacNaught
Heronaldo Marcelin
Melissa Cay Marcinek
Rana Fadi Mardini
Joah Massey
Courtney McCreary

Tana McDaniel
Christine McGrath
Jason Megnauth
Valeria Mendez
Meghan Miller
Alton Mills
Cassandra Moore
Zane Moreland
Craig Allen Muchow
Claudia Munoz
Jason Myers
Keegan O'Malley
Ashley Mary-Elizabeth Orr
Troy Palmer
Charles Parker
Coy Patterson
Josey Lyn Pearce
Shelby Lynn Pelkey
Joseph Phelps
Christopher Preston
Arthur Quinn
Jovanni Lazaro Rabelo

Sarah Rahming
Udishtir Ramcharan
Michael Richard
Sarah Ann Rider
Rickey Rodriquez
Manuel Rubio
Melody Anne Saepae
Joshua Saffomilla
Alicia Christine Sanders
Elizabeth Rose Santelices
Maria Sarria
Andrea Sempsrott
Delfilia Serrano
Joseph Share
Matthew Shipley
Leola Simmonds
Leah Sims
Maria Sofikitis
Emelie Maria Stenhammar
Emily Stone
Madison Paige Stowe
Amelia Strazzulla

Blessy Tamayo
Keith Taylor
Rachel Tompkins
Kimberley Toperzer
Natalia Varanavicius
Ivette Vega
Matthew Francis Vigilio
Krystal Villalobos-Ayala
Sophie Vitale
Emily Walker
Manuel Larry Ward Jr.
Karyn Wells
Nadia Westerik
Cameron White
Megan Wichern
Michael Wilson
Jennifer Wolfe
Mark Woodruff
Sindy Wu
April Zamora
Christopher Joseph Zermeno
Geoffrey Zheng

INTER AMERICAN UNIVERSITY OF PUERTO RICO, SAN GERMAN CAMPUS, SAN GERMAN, PR

Amy Lee Agostini-Gracia
Gerald Almodóvar-Méndez
Joshua M. Álvarez-Peña
Jennifer M. Antonetti-Ramos
Michelle M. Arenas-Vega
Stephanie Arroyo-Rivera
José F. Avilés-Acosta
Yuritza Ayala-Mercado
Norberto A. Báez-Muñoz
Holly Marie Bevagna Ospina
Janice Tilo Bianchi
Isamari Bonafé-Ramos
Karla M. Bou
Naomie Burgos-Vega
Carmen Buxeda-Pérez
Mariangelly Caraballo-Cancel

Katiana N. Castillo-Camareno
Gladys Mary Castro-Santana
Esteban A. Ceara-Tomei
Tania L. Cosme-Renovales
Natalie Creitoff González
Frank Cruz-Vélez
José D. Curbelo-Arocho
Nichole Del Toro-Morales
Andrea Devaris-Martínez
Yamilette M. Díaz-Ferreira
Daileen Diodonet Zapata
Sindy M. Dorelien
Tatiana Erazo-Flores
Eugenio R. Fajardo-Acosta
Raymond Feliciano-Rodríguez
Adrián O. Figueroa-Vargas
Denise García-Ortiz

Joffre E. Gómez-Frontera
Alejandro González-Ayala
Abimael González-Guzmán
Karlisbett González-Quiñones
Alex J. González-Torres
Lynnette E. González-Vargas
Lorraine Michelle Henríquez-Quiñones
Jimmy A. Hernández-Ortiz
Patricia Jiménez-Mojica
Kalesha A. Jiménez-Santiago
Stephanie Justiniano-Santos
Nichole M. Laracuente-DelGado
Kermit A. López-Cancel
Iván A. López-Justiniano

Alejandra Lozada Martín
Diemarys Lugo-Cintrón
Andrea Lugo-Ruiz
Wanda Esther Martínez
Keyshla Medina-López
Keyshaliz Meléndez-Monsegur
Thalia F. Méndez-Sánchez
Diameliz Mercado-Mercado
Claudia I. Molina-Aponte
Keyla Montero-Mercado
Graciela M. Morales Cuevas
Erica Morán-Moreno
Astrid Marianne Muñoz-Centeno
Jennifer Nazario-Irizarry
Haydemar Nazario-Meléndez
Jailene Nazario-Rivera

Wilcely Ocasio-Rodríguez
Zuleika Quiñones-Albino
Kristine M. Ramírez-Acevedo
Génesis K. Ramírez-Pérez
Noemí Aynith Ramos-Centeno
Carlos J. Ramos-Morales
Miguel A. Ramos-Ortiz
Mónica Ramos-Padilla
María T. Ramos-Pagán

Wilmarie Ríos-García
Julio J. Rivera-Báez
Aixa M. Rivera-Rivera
Sebastián J. Rivera-Torres
Nashalie M. Rodríguez-Almodóvar
Emily C. Rodríguez-Morales
Leyinska Rodríguez-Torres
Giledmarie Sáez-Ortiz
Zuleika Sanabria-Delgado
Mariana Santana-Cosme

Génesis Santiago-Acevedo
Jiomar Santiago-Feliciano
Emanuelle Eric Santiago-Martínez
Tamara Santiago-Olavarría
Guimarie Santos-Orengo
Ricardo Omar Segarra-Irizarry
Mirnaliz Segarra-Madera
Emanuel Serrano Cancel
Susette M. Sosa-Ortiz

Roberto A. Soto-Olmeda
Nandy Toro-Hernández
Bárbara Torres-Santiago
Zoralis N. Troche-Rodríguez
Ana M. Tubéns-Pérez
Jannybeth Vázquez-Ocasio
Keimilly Vega-Sánchez
Erika M. Vélez-Lugo
Ginmarie Vélez-Rivera
Sebastián Vélez Ruiz
Lisa M. Vélez-Vélez

INTER AMERICAN UNIVERSITY OF PUERTO RICO, SAN GERMAN CAMPUS GRADUATE SCHOOL, SAN GERMAN, PR

Isabel Abreu-Chon
Nereida Acosta-Cruz
Gladys E. Arcelay-Figueroa
Juan L. Arocho-Llantín
Glendalee Arroyo-Colberg
Amarelis Bonilla-Couret
Joanna Camacho-Acosta
Carlos J. Camacho-Montalvo
María Cintrón-Rivera
Richard Cruz-Irizarry
Grisel Cruz-López
Julio A. Cruz-Rodríguez
Coralis D. Cruz-Toro
Philip Flores-Vializ

José L. Frontera-Suau
Norma I. Gómez-Echandy
Maritza González-Quiñones
Efrén Lamberty-Cruz
Rachel K. Larusso
Helga E. Maldonado-Domínguez
Arleen Marchese Pérez
Diana I. Martínez-Santiago
María Medina-Amador
Luis E. Mercado-Cintrón
Desirée Morales-González
Eyda L. Muñiz-Rivera
Lisette Oramas-Soto
Reinand Ortiz-Feliciano

Iván R. Pagán-Toro
Expedi J. Peña-Checo
Glenda R. Pérez-Domínguez
Edgar Pérez-Matías
Nitza Y. Ramos-Cruz
David Ramos-Matías
Néstor Reyes-Colón
María Del C. Rivera-Cáceres
Jamilet Rivera-González
Evelith Rodríguez-Cordero
Reinaldo Rodríguez-Pagán
L. Carolina Rodríguez-Ruiz
Lisnel Rosario-González
Annelisse Ruiz-Aponte
Alismiriam Santana-Cancel

Verónica Santiago-Beauchamp
Daniel R. Shanklin
Clarissa Soto Morales
Frank A. Suárez-Caro
Jenesther Torres-Olmeda
Lizette M. Torres-Rodríguez
Luz C. Valenzuela-Rojas
Josué Valle-Quiñones
Luis D. Vega-Rodríguez
Zullymar Vélez-Llantín
Laurie N. Vélez-Rivera

INTER AMERICAN UNIVERSITY OF PUERTO RICO, PONCE CAMPUS, MERCEDITA, PR

Alvaro Ferriol Alonso
Isabel Ricart Alvarez
Mariálix Cancel Bonilla
Nashaly N. De Jesus Burgos
Berenice Mercado Caquias
Karen Torres Cardenales
Katherine Vega Flores
Zujeirly Vega Flores

Carlos Lefranc Garcia
Javier Maldonado Lopez
Mariel Rodriguez Lugo
Martha Lopez Martha
Allan David Mercado
Carlos A. Lanzó Mercado
Kamil Alvarado Montes
Joseph Matos Ocasio

Benjamin Colon Ortiz
Eduardo Santos Perez
Carlos Santiago Ramos
Adeline Rivera
Janette Ortiz Rivera
Ricardo Noriega Rivera
Roselin Pérez Rivera
Diego Guerrero Sanfilippo

Jean Gonzalez Santini
Gabriel Cascante Suarez
Agnes Cruz Torres
Alexander Rosado Torres
Keyla Maldonado Velez

INTERDENOMINATIONAL THEOLOGICAL CENTER, ATLANTA, GA

Alexis Blackwell

D'Jaris Canty-Wallace

Dietrich Carroll

Cynthia Marie Crawford

Audrey Lee Calhoun Daniels   Vanessa Hardin   Nathalie N. Nelson   Geoffrey Stoff

LaTonya Dash   Derrick Lakeith Henderson   Troy Parris   Christopher Blake Trent

Diane Taylor Edwards   Renetta Hobson   Brittany Powell   Veronica Wiley

Karla Frye   Brandon Isome   Marcus Alexander Price

Anita Green   Jonathan Devone Miles   Michael Sands

INTERNATIONAL BAPTIST COLLEGE & SEMINARY, CHANDLER, AZ

George Binoka   Joshua Asael Mendoza   Stephen Andrew Shumate   Mariah Nicole Yarnell

Heather Nichole Braswell

IOWA CENTRAL COMMUNITY COLLEGE, FORT DODGE, IA

Maggie Mary Anderson   Shelby K. Fechner   Zachary D. Klimesh   Hailee N. Richardson

Alexie Brooke Bagley   Tanner J. Felton   Nicole R. Kline   Marshall R. Richardson

Laura J. Baltazar   Ashley K. Finken   Calista D. Koeneke   Paige E. Savery

Abigail M. Becker   Clare M. Flattery   Hailey S. Konecne   Devon A. Schuster

Brett L. Becker   Rachel Marie Fosbender   Sean M. Kramer   Nicole M. Schwarz

Cassandra R. Benjamin   Luis E. Godinez   Jessica N. Kuebler   Cole Thomas Scieszinski

Abigail S. Bishop   Hannah L. Groshens   Melanie J. Lambert   Andrew C. Stover

Kierstin Allana Bloom   Austin J. Halligan   Nolan J. Lepel   Malachi B. Swanson

Shae L. Blum   Thomas A. Hartley   Alexander E. Markov   Teresa J. Thomas

Fourtytwo D. Chotper   Sherri S. Hefley   Laura E. Martin   Rebecca J. Vohs

Kara M. Cipperley   Haleigh B. Hood   Louie J. Miller   Maxwell J. Widmar

Alyssa K. Clark   Amber M. Huffman   Hasbiallahu Mohammed   Andrew L. Wiechmann

Kelsey L. Crosser   Tiffany J. Hull   Catalina Perry   Tangy E. Wiseman

Macy A. DeVries   Alexander J. Jackson   Bailey M. Porter   Amanda N. Wymore

Abbigail L. Dobernecker   Rose M. Johnson   Konrad P. Powell

Naomi M. England   Ben B. Kenobbie   Amanda L. Propst

ITAWAMBA COMMUNITY COLLEGE, FULTON, MS

Tiana J. Allen   Julianna M. Garner   Imani D. Morrison-Clark   Jordan A. Wade

Andria N. Barnes   Rachel McKenzie Garrison   William Tanner Palmer   Schyler B. Watson

Victoria N. Bobo   Ryan J. Gillentine   Mallory L. Pannell   Jamie N. Wilburn

Gabrielle M. Cannon   Alexis E. Guy   Hunter N. Payne   Stephanie Wilson

Joseph Drew Carter   Eleanor Kate Hester   Jansen Bridger Thomas   Joshua Zaragosa

Michaela L. Cooper   Holly M. Jones   Evangelin Ruth Von

Megan M. Corrie   Judi Beth McMillen   Boeckman

ITAWAMBA COMMUNITY COLLEGE, TUPELO, MS

Toni Byars   Kelsey Crump   Amy Gray   Margaret R. Hudson

Patrick Campeau   Alexis Flowers   David M. Henderson   Bethany A. Jernigan

April Clark   Michael Foley   Stephanie Hernandez   William Bryce Krumcke

Elizabeth Crowder   Katelyn Gordon   Andrew Hill   Jacqueline S. Langford

Alicia Marie Lovelady	Randy Morgan	Devin Roe	Jose Vazquez
Sara Malmberg	Lakin Patterson	Melissa Tackett	Steven B. Ward
Kayla McElhenney	Michael Pippin	Afton B. Trimm	George W. Washington

ITHACA COLLEGE, ITHACA, NY

Kailee R. Abdou	Sara Larkin Elwell	Daniel S. Leap	Michael A. Rizk
Jamina M. Abillar	Catherine Felicetti	Amanda J. Lee	Marci Rose
Christine Zihui Adams	Tak-Man Kimberly Fung	Michelle A. Lee	Miriam E. Rosenthal
Ashley Ahl	Benjamin Gaynor	Sabina Leybold	Meredith K. Ryer
Brittany Asito	Hannah M. Goodman	Carrie Lindeman	Rachelle A. Sartori
Thomas Barkal	Natalie Grande	Sarah Elizabeth Loeffler	Brandon R. Schneider
Katie Beaule	Veronica Griesemer	Ciara V. Lucas	Felicya M. Schwarzman
Jamila M. Carter	Katelyn Marie Gualtieri	Carson L. Mohler	Ella Sciocchetti
Timothy Conners	Samantha Guter	Arham Muneer	Eli Serota
Katherine R. Crowe	Kenute J. Hammond	Lia Ynes Munoz	Jamie Ingrid Shum
Madison Crowe	Lima Hossain	Zachary A. Myers	Olivia Sod
Natalie B. Dionne	Julia Imbalzano	Alyssa Marie Napier	Mackenzie Stevenson
Tate Dremstedt	John Jacobson	Lexa Pennell	Daniel J. Tjie
Lee Anna Drown	Sara Y. Kim	Irma Aurora Perez	Rebecca K. Veninsky
Maya Drummond	Nicole Kristina Kuzdzal	Alexis E. Powell	Caitlin Wormsley
Ashley L. Ellis	Allison B. Latini	Dominick S. Recckio	Sara Yagan

ITT TECHNICAL INSTITUTE NORTH CHARLESTON, NORTH CHARLESTON, SC

Louis Blake	Soffiann Hawkins-Barnett	Walter Odom	Andrew Taylor
Janet D. Del Valle	Tracy Lee Judy	Dan Owsley	Jason Weldon
Tiago Dos Santos	Ronnie Leviner	Nikia Perry	Ronald White
Brian Lee Durden	Charles Mack	Hitaishi Persaud	Corey Womack
Justin Armond Edwards	Jerry A. Melendy Jr.	Adam Rice	
Irving Givens	Robert Mitchell	Nicholas Rogerson	
Leo Goden	Ryan Munn	Sean Styron	

IVY TECH COMMUNITY COLLEGE OF INDIANA SOUTHWEST, EVANSVILLE, IN

Tatiana E. Adams	Michael G. Bugher	Dennis R. Dyehouse	Carla K. Gray
Kassandra L. Appel	Kelli E. Bumbalough	Crystal G. Elderbrook	Christine L. Hamilton
Julie K. Ashby	Jacob W. Carver	Craig M. Englert	Stephanie F. Hardiman
Lavern Austill	Allisia A. Cline	Breihan Fetcher	Cassie Hart
Krimson R. Bailey	Geraldine Cobb	Andrew A. Fickas	Shelby M. Hicks
Haley N. Baker	Cathy A. Condi	Meaghan K. Fluty	Carley Hollander
Corey L. Beck	Chastity Coomes	Shelby C. Forston	Matthew H. Hubachek
Savannah Faye Benton	Shannon C. Daniel	Aaron Funkhouser	Katie M. Hulett
Teaira Bloodworth	Jeremy Dillon	Jonathon H. Gahimer	John D. Hutchison
Ronni N. Bowman	Jonathan Duff	Raymond Gibson	Paul A. Ippoliti
Wade A. Bryant	Kara A. Duncan	Owen J. Gogarty	Brent M. Irwin

Jamie R. Irwin
Clarise Johnson
Marie J. Johnson
Christopher Jones
Joshua C. Jones
Emma R. Joshi
Amanda Junker
Mike E. Keeney
Caitlin M. Lashley
Mark A. Lowery
Miranda K. Marks
Destinie Martin
Kelly McBride
Sabrina M. McCarty

Mary C. McCutchan
Miyoshi D. McGuire
Regina A. McKinney
Talisha K. McKinney
Jeremy R. Melton
Kelly J. Merry
Sarah M. Miller
Sara L. Miller
Christopher A. Mills
Nickolas A. Mills
Kaylee D. Mowry
Amy M. Mutz
Sarah Elizabeth Nalley
Grace Nankwenya

Michael T. Nickel
Matthew P. Notter
Jacquelynne M. Piekarski
Kristina R. Porter
Pamela L. Powell
Urhonda Latrice Presha
Cain L. Proudfoot
Bianca J. Rankin
Jason D. Rankins
Lisa A. Redmon
Zacharey R. Render
Amanda R. Riggs
Katie J. Rister
Trent M. Rodgers

Breanna S. Scales
Joseph J. Schnee
Preston C. Sharp
Magan A. Sheldon
Alannah B. Smith
Adam M. Tepool
Darrion J. Terrell
Stephen A. Todd
Megan Utley
Cherise M. Williams
Angela C. Woolsey
Kati S. Young
Erin R. Zimmer

JACKSON STATE COMMUNITY COLLEGE, JACKSON, TN

James M. Adams
Jessica Lee Arnold
Leah E. Austin
Samantha L. Austin
Rebecca I. Blackwelder
Jillian Elise Bland
Jessica Danielle Burkhart
Billy Walker Cherry
Jonathan Paul Chin
Jason Collins Coffman
Seanna Elizabeth Creech

Kathy Daniel
Kristy R. DeShazier
Crystal DiBenedetto
Lisa Mary Doyle
Donald J. Ducheny
Caitlyn R. Elder
Jon Marc Gowan
Megan Michelle Harris
Taylor Lea Harris
Abra Ann Hindman
Michaela C. Holloway

Lisa Beth Hopkins
Jessica Lyn Johnson
Faith S. Kirk
David Cain Lindsey
Alex Clay Lingelbach
Jeremy Mayo
Tyler McCaskill
Linley Helen McClain
James D. Mitchell
Aneetria Deshawn
Montague

Daniel W. Pillow
Wanda Lorene Scott
Emily Ann Stricklin
Jacklyn Sulock
Katelyn E. Thomas
Macy Elaine Thompson
Carey J. Whitten
Brooke A. Young
Madison Rish Young

JACKSON STATE UNIVERSITY COLLEGE OF BUSINESS, JACKSON, MS

Rebekah O. Adewumi
Pamela M. Alston
Asmae Bennis
Eroncia M. Berry
Dimitri B. Bien-Aime
Calvin L. Brown
Tyrannie D. Coleman
Anthony R. Cornish
Amber L. Davis
Ashley S. Davis
Faith D. Donaldson
Gaston J. Douglas

Kaneisha S. Gilmore
Taronecia T. Graves
Cleorissa C. Griffin
Anissa Hidouk
Tiffany Tiara Holland
Na Tausha S. Jefferson
Jonathan E. King
Kristy S. Mason
Elissa A. McCool
Delaka C. McDonald-Dixon
Larry T. McGhee
Erin S. Miller

KeTyria A. Moore
Jasmine S. Neal
Tayanna J. Purnell
Benjamin J. Quinn
Aubrey D. Scott
Natasha G. Simmons
Bria N. Sims
Richelle R. Smith
Ben-cuda R. Stowers
Jonathan E. Terrell
Natalie A. Thompson
Nicole A. Thompson

Sterling C. Thompson
LaWanda M. Tolliver
Arden R. Toney
Jaleel L. Tyler
Breana N. Viverette
Siara L. Wells
Chrishae M. Whitehead
Raven S. Wilson
Nikis Danielle Wright

JACKSON STATE UNIVERSITY COLLEGE OF EDUCATION & HUMAN DEVELOPMENT, JACKSON, MS

Ashley N. Adams

Shaboria L. Akins

Gabrielle R. Anderson

Mari'Onna L. Bailey

Melissa L. Banks Walker

Shirrell P. Black

Anita A. Bonilla-DeMari

Brittney S. Brooks

Lakeitha S. Brown

Monica M. Brown

Sharon D. Brown

Raquel R. Burns

David Burns Sr.

Eboni M. Butler

LaQuinte Rochelle Campbell

Shakira J. Caston

Ray A. Chambers

Aretha R. Chandler

Binyoka B. Collins

Shonika M. Cooper

Courtney M. Darden

Jamencia C. Day

Alice T. Dortch

Ferzandra L. Edwards

Adina D. Ellis

Brionna Z. Epes

Jennifer P. Ervin

Rosaland L. Evans

Sharon D. Freeman

Andrew Lewis Freeman Jr.

Tiffani L. Gilford

Jonquill L. Griffin

Laterrica D. Griffin

Brittanie A. Hales

April C. L. Harris

Jazzlyn E. Harris

Jeremy M. Harris

Ke'Aira S. Herron

Inez A. Holmes

Tyinnia T. Jenkins

Ralph V. Johnson

Shujondra L. Johnson

Corlette K. Jones

Jorrie C. Jones

Rashida Jamila Jones

Flora L.ynn Lawson

Shandolyn A. Lawson

Denise C. Love

Marquita S. Marshall

Amy T. Martin

Jerry LaVell McDonald

Lottie L. McDonald

Quartilya C. Mosley

Victoria R. Norwood

Betty K. Paty

Matthew A. Person

Kristen M. Powell

Latonya R. Rankin

Felicia S. Reed

Elanda W. Robinson

Joyce Marie Robinson

Shuretta R. Shippings

Carleigh E. Smith

Jasmine A. Smith

Anne B. Stevens

Larry D. Strickland

Shatavia S. Stricklin

Alicia S. Terry

Natasha Q. Williams

Jasmine S. Young

JACKSON STATE UNIVERSITY COLLEGE OF LIBERAL ARTS, JACKSON, MS

Emmanuel B. Amponsah

NaTosha D. Barron

Courtney N. Body

Rashad C. Bogan Roberson

Mia D. Brooks

Frettina K. Brown

Tamera Y. Cain

BreAnna H. Causey

Arlene C. Caviness

Laura L. Coleman

Laporshan S. Conerly

Amber M. Cooper

Grace A. Cowan

Nigel D. Davenport

Cory L. Davis

Kesicia A. Dickinson

Chereigna N. Dixon

Latoya M. Donerson

Allyson J. Durr

Nafeesa M. Edges

Candi J. Ellis

Kiara R. Flantroy

Zachariah J. Givens

Sarah A. Gore

Jada N. Henderson

Jocelyn O. Henderson

Princess K. Hollins

Jasmine C. Jackson

Tia S. Jackson

Shanel Jenea James

Charmane K. Jenkins

Ann L. Johnson

Tiffany Y. Johnson

Tyrone C. Journey

Keith L. Kennard

Monique C. McGahee-Norwood

Aleka S. Mitchell

Bradford M. Moore

Monica A. Moore

Briana K. Morrissette

Kordia J. Mosley

Jhade' B. Norris

Marla A. Nottingham

Kiara N. Owens

Carlene J. Parker

Alexis S. Pauline

Cherese A. Pendleton

Lydia E. Plumpp

Meyonsha R. Riddles

Keiven J. Russey

Alexis B. Scott

Lindsey R. Shaw

Brianna Lynn Smith

Kionna C. Steward

Elizabeth M. Taylor

Jamika A. Thomas

Mia M. Thompson

Cliffaniqua S. Towbridge

Tristian D. Trask

Courtney M. Walker

Kristi M. Walley

Mallory Whitfield

Chanel U. Wilkerson

Jordyn A. Williams

Keleigh Y. Williams

Shamiraca L. Williams

Ceaira E. Wilson

Dashawna L. Wright

Marlina M. Yarbrough

Bianca T. Young

Merina L. Young

JACKSON STATE UNIVERSITY COLLEGE OF PUBIC SERVICE, JACKSON, MS

Latesha W. Allen	DeShonda L. Fortune	Brandi M. Jones	Violet J. Powell
Charlicia R. Anderson	Theresa A. Gardner	Jasmine Qwaunta Jones	Peaches K. Roberson
Aaliyah M. Brown	Rita L. Gibson	Levella Kelly	Wessie B. Sims
Deidra A. Bullock	Neikeya C. Glover	Kaylin D. Kinchion	Patricia A. Slaughter
Jarmikco Z. Bullock	Aliah T. Green	Emanami M. Kirk	Cheryl D. Thompson Gray
Lindsey A. Busch	Jessica T. Griffin	Denae R. Lee	Daphne L. Tinner
Kristin J. Castilla	Olivia K. Griffin	Naesha M. Lidge	Regina S. Wilcox-Lewis
Demeturis A. Collins	Carey L. Gunn	Mu'Nesha G. Lott	Constance R. Williams-
Kristina L. Collins	Lateshia S. Hammond	Wilma J. May	Jones
Cassandra D. Cowart	Mary A. Haralson	Christina N. Mayo	Antranekia J. Willis
Taija T. Craft	Roy C. Harness	Jerry L. McDonald	Alise U. Wilson
Rachel C. Denson	Jasmine S. Harvey	Denitra Chervon Mitchell	Ashley A. Wilson
Natasha N. Durr	Alisha M. Hoggatt	Kiana P. Moore	
Victoria D. Dyson	Mikel L. Jenkins	Oprah Lea Neely	
Claire A. Enow	Vinechia L. Johnson	Rachad Damon Neyland	

JACKSON STATE UNIVERSITY COLLEGE OF SCIENCE, ENGINEERING & TECHNOLOGY, JACKSON, MS

Anwuli N. Anazia	Tsegereda K. Esatu	William Kayitare	Hannah M. Scott
Meron G. Asnake	Amanuel E. Faris	Stella A. Kelvyn-Olowola	Aaliyah T. Sibley
Jasmine M. Barnes	Naphateria D. Farrow	Raven A. Lawrence	Marcus D. Sidney
Taylor A. Bramlett	Deion K. Fields	Alexis E. Lee	James W. Simpson IV
Aniecia Annette Brewster	Myeisha R. Fountain	Brittany N. Lynn	Amber N. Stokes
Michael T. Brooks	LeSamuel J. Gardner	Brittany N. Martin	Canessa J. Swanson
Kiara J. Brown	LaShayla T. Gilbert	Kevonce F. McDonald	Tadele F. Tadele
Tyesha S. Bynum	Eugena R. Grigsby	Jarrett R. McElroy	Mireille L. Tankoua
Arianna R. Cargin	Patrice J. Harris	Olivia D. McNeal	Sandjong
Latrista T. Carter	Portica D. Harris	Carmel Laetitia Mobio	Jamon M. Thomas
Victoria E. Casher	Marsella W. Hatfield	Ryan B. Montgomery	Laura M. Uzzell
Kanisha A. Cooley	Breanne D. Hendricks	Jala Michelle Morrow	Jacob E. Vandervelde
Paris O. Cooper	DeQuan J. Henry	Labresha S. Naylor	Kory B. White
Samaria A. Cozart	Shantwanza F. Hill	MiaNwi S. Obioha	Janine A. Wiley
Santana S. Creese	Jordan D. Hubbard	Joseph A. Owusu	Miracle M. Wiliams
Rodney D. Daniely	Maya K. Hughes	Camilo A. Patino	Erin K. Williams
Ebony A. Davis	Alesha RoChe' Jackson	Angel J. Patterson	LaShay C. Williamson
John A. Dearman	Jared J. Jackson	Destiny R. Pounds	Zajvé Quiana Woods
Ryan A. Deising	Jasmine S. Jackson	Lufat Rahman	Whitney J. Yarborough
Meghan LaTrice Donald	Dymonn J. Johnson	Alexander Rivera	Ji H. Yoon
Davesha A. Doty	Jalen I. Johnson	Jeida K. Robertson	Myia K. Young
Jamey A. Douglas	Regina M. Johnson	Devonte A. Robinson	
Dominique Edwards	Shaquetta M. Johnson	Yasmeen L. Robinson	

JACKSONVILLE COLLEGE, JACKSONVILLE, TX

Joseph Allen	Cody Grimes	Lukas Lampe	Humberto Rodriguez
Austin Anderson	John Hale	Maria Delgado Lara	Amanda Self
Richard Berry	J.T. Harris	Verlo Levels	Danielle Stricklin
Zechariah Cogburn	Zachary Harris	Rhys Main	Lenka Styblova
Aaron Franks	Correy Hemphill	Mayra Martinez	Tyler Thackerson
Cameron Franks	Kwajual Jones	Brittany Chantileah Reyes	Brittany Trowbridge

JACKSONVILLE UNIVERSITY, JACKSONVILLE, FL

Alexandra Abreu-Figueroa	Mae Davis	Jia-Siang Leong	Kirstin Margaret Purdy
Juan Arguedas	Charla La'Tia Dixon	Jennifer Lince	Christina R. Robb
Savannah Victoria Bates	Graham Michael Dobbs	Kelsey Martin	Christina Roldan
Evens Blanc	Faith Doski	Brittany Mathis	Jayla Shelton
Stanley Blanc	Bailey Flynn	Allison McClain	Ashlyn Taylor Sparks
McKenzie Bolin	Jonathan Bradley Glover	Zane Miller	Roy Starr
David Borelli	Kateri Goldammer	Taylor L. Montgomery	Alex Stoetzer
Jack Burns	Gabrielle Hickman	Shannon Morin	Natalie Swaim
Brittany Bush	Ashley Hirt	Luke Myhree	Ryan Tyler Wagner
Nolan Carney	Stephania Landaeta	Shawna Newman	Kelsey Wiglesworth
Hannah Clay	Gutierrez	Jessica Parker	
Michelle Davidson	Stephany Landaeta Gutierrez	Anne Pinto	

JAMES H. FAULKNER STATE COMMUNITY COLLEGE, BAY MINETTE, AL

Blakely Kenzie Barnes	Courtney Coppell	Emilia Khismatova	Laquasia Rogers
Joseph Hall Barnett	Kendra Holt Coppoletta	Anthony Kucera	Shavia Mayola Safford
Collin Barrett	Emma Marie Cotney	Kaylyn Michale Lary	Janel Salanoa
Baylen Beck	Bria Antoinette Cox	Tristan McAnally	Kristen Seales
Jennifer LeAnn Biediger	Caleb Eugene Cox	Shelby McCreedy	Ashleigh Shaw
Kirsten Binegar	Emilee Marie Cunningham	Brandon McGrew	Mary Emily Shelby
Amanda Black	Denae Flowers	Lauren Gabrielle Moorer	Annie Shook
Miranda Nicole Black	Kayleigh Gardner	Laura Mosley	Adam Simte
Kaitlyn Blubaugh	Harley Geddes	Quintarius Munnerlyn	Megan Taylor
Dominque Bousquet	Lauren Godbold	Colby Myers	Mary Elizabeth Thompson
Misty Dawn Brown	Jaycee Nichole Goins	Sarah Reynolds Nielsen	Aren Valrie
Lauren Bryant	Braiden Paige Gottier	Morgan Parker	Angela Wade
Eron Orlando Burrell	Andrea Gravely	Brittani Peacock	Ashli Weide
Nicholas Godwin Bush	Gabriela Gross	Racheael Rafferty	Caroline White
Jennifer Ann Campbell	Kacy Holden	Makayla Valencia Reed	Matthew Stephen Wigal
Angel Te'anna Carthen	Ebonee Keturah Jackson	Alexksandra Richardson	Alissa Williams
Lisa Jeanne Case	Alexandria Danielle Johnson	Alec Riley	Kela Wilson
Cassidy Comstock	Courtney Johnson	Cody Roberts	Megan Zulli

JAMES SPRUNT COMMUNITY COLLEGE, KENANSVILLE, NC

Shamika Renee Andrews
Charsha M. Anthony
Kenneth Paul Boney
Jorge Luis Castaneda
Tamara Fletcher Donnelly
Chancey Frederick Earp
Bailey Mae Giddeons
Nina Mae Jones
Marixell De Los Angeles Kauffman
Brianna Johnson Knox
Kassie Brooke Maready
Kimberly Bates Miller
Michael Lamont Murray
Crystal Nicole Norris
Hunter Kennedy Pope
Margaret Pollock Turner
Tracy Thompson Tyndall
Alexander Scott Webb
Pamela S. Whaley
Amanda Worley White
Karen Isabel Zuniga

JEFFERSON DAVIS COMMUNITY COLLEGE, BREWTON, AL

Robert Michael Arrant
Tristen Ashleigh Boothe
Tiffany Rae Bryan
Keelan Chase Burnham
Tracy Gregson Champion
James Crockett Dailey
Amber Dawn Davis
April A. Dorriety
Brandy Nicole Dunlap
Angela Shalaine Flowers
Madeline Arlene Frazier
Samantha Denise Gunn
Taylor Michelle Harris
Alanna Irene Johnson
Tyler Jeffrey Joyner
Joshua Chandler Kendall
Drew Ann Lambert
Taylor Deston Lane
Richard Paul Norris
Elizabeth Ashley Pugh
Dakota Ryan Sheets
Tyler Lane Smith
Kimberlee Jene Walter
Brittany Nicole Wasdin

JOHN BROWN UNIVERSITY, SILOAM SPRINGS, AR

Emily Barden
Jeff Branson
Kenneth Crane
Audrey Dearien
Elizabeth Marie Flora-Swick
Stephen Gilmour
Alyssa Goddu
Leah Guy
Emily Lynn Hackett
Steven Hamilton
Walter Javier Hernandez Cruz
Bradford Johnson
Ashley Kunze
Rebekah Lindstrom
Daniel Joseph Loganbill
Kyriana Lynch
Luke Howard Macfarlan
Lauren Martin
Cesia Stephanie Melendez Orantes
Elyse Partee
Ethan Penner
Meaghan Ranz
McKenzie Raub
Maria Angelica Serrano
Derek Stout
Peyton Margaret Weaver
Olivia Wheelock
Sara Elizabeth Whitlock
Ethan Zuck

JOHN C. CALHOUN STATE COMMUNITY COLLEGE, TANNER, AL

April R. Asher
Shafisha Orolla Natasha Bamfield-Cummings
Cynthia Bishop
Nicholas Ryan Brown
Franco Camarillo
Brandon Chatman
Samantha D. Cherni
Sara D. Coble
Jay Michael Copeland
Miranda M. Defoe
Victoria Denslow
Brenda S. Dockus
Ashley Nicole Donahue
Timothy Edge
Sarah Beth Everett
Kelsei Alonna Farmer
Daniel Gawlak
Catherine A. Guthrie
Justin Hall
Bethany Elaine Hammond
Julie Harris
Amina Hassan
Bridget Renee Haynes
Abigail Claire Hickinbotham
Sidney Hodge
Livia Marie Hogue
LaLonne Chantel Humphrey
Emsley Peyton Jones
Shereitta Lockhart
Marissa Lucento
Preston Mann
Mackenzie Mathews
Larry Maxfield
Jamison Drake Maxwell
Dylan S. Miller
Guy Lawrence Miller
Shelby Miller
Veronica J. Moss
Nasren Hassan Musa
Maegan Louise Osborne
Zachary David Page
Kristin Parsons
Raveen Symone Patterson
Hayden Pressnell Phillips
Christine Provancha
Jeffrey Tanner Reed
Athena Catherine Reese
Yumna Riyaz
Dashia Sharie Rothwell
Ashley L. Sanders
Jonathan Everett -Anthony Schiavone
Scott Austen Shipley
Stephanie Ann Sparks
Hannah Elizabeth Spencer
Hannah Sullivan
Nedyelka Sumner
Katherine Marie Swamp
Marnie Lynn Tabor

Austin Blake Terry	Amanda Shadai Tisdale	Jennifer R. Wallstead	Nicholas Gene Zupancich
Maretta Christine Thompson	Avery Elizabeth Townsend	William Patrick Woller Jr.	

JOHNSON C. SMITH UNIVERSITY, CHARLOTTE, NC

Jana Ajdukovic	Mayra Isabel Hernandez	Brooklyn Danyell Miller	Imani Rae Scott
Breanna Nicole Archibald	Kahina Nzingha Hood	Gail Raven Mills	Khadijah Segura
Patricia Ann Armstrong	Waynee Hyman	Eboni Darnella Moran	Alana Dion Seldon
Hajira Fosua Attah	Tovea Anetia Jenkins	Oshauna Sherise Morgan	Korey A. Smith
Jacques Michael Austin	Allen Edward Johnson	Christina Danielle Morrison	Bernard A. Smith Jr.
Kenrisha Ashleigh	Andronica M. Klaas	LaTondra V. Morrow	Khaliyah De'Andra Stroud
Brathwaite	Carmen Teresa Knight	Manmikan Cynthia N'dri	Jibra'il Sutton
Tillery Briahunah	Shamara Kyham Knotts	Nompumelelo Mpumi	Surya Jai Swilley
Corina Buenaventura	Vernon Lawrence Koger	Nobiva	Khadijah Lachelle Tart
Cody C. Byrd	Felicia Ann Ledbetter	Jean-Marie Nshimiyimana	Ashenafi Abera Tsaudu
Craig Jeffery Cannon	Renato Leon	Francoise Ntakirutimana	Jane Tukia
Stephany Daniel-Lopez	Cierra Brianna Levias	Yasmeen Qeche Parker	Handis Rosibel Umanzor
Sherri Lynn Davis	Joshua Linson	Javari LeVonte Parks	Rhynea' Kandyce
Victoria Paige Davis	Jheanelle Melissa Linton	Jordan Michael Parks	Underwood
Karen Diaz	Lesly Lizeth Luque	Toi Nicol Parks	Rodrigo Vazquez
Zachary Dickey	Quinesha Mone' Lynch	Carlista Sherr'ee Patrick	Juan Carlos Venegas
Cynthia Denise Douglas	Kenneth E. Mabry	Patrick Arlando Patrick	Esthefani Alexandra
Marissa Alicia Duff	Thomas Trevon Martin	Terrell Bouvier Pearson	Villacorta
Fellan Felicia Ferguson	Tinyiko Vallerie Nicole	Aaron Iman Pendleton	Raquel Villatoro
Joshua B. Fernandez	Maswanganye	Ayanna Perry	Tia Joselyn Wash
Edgar A. Garcia	Sandy Mathurin	Frantzcise Prince	Tatianna Sadia Watts
Damara Elizabeth Garcia-	Vonicia V'Nes McCollum	Warren Sithembeka Radebe	Krista Danielle White
Garcia	Theresa Wilhelmena	Trudy-Ann Stephanie	Kamauri Dai-jah Whitmore
Ramon Garibaldo-Valdez	McCormick-Dunlap	Richards	Acacia Wilson
Chelsea Storm-Elaann	Kimberly Ciedah McFadden	Kyle Leonard Anthony	Jessica Vanesa Wiltshire
Griffith	Itzel Medina	Robinson	Darche Tyieka Witherspoon
Keyon M. Handley	Alexus Nikkol Melton	Gabriel E. Rosario-Garcia	Alana Nichelle Adele Worth
Morgan Mikenzie Hasty	Laura Andrea Meneses	Perry Xavier Rowdy	Daron Rashad Wright
Jada Imani Haynes	Andrea Veronica Meneses	Njeri Adenike' Rutherford	Nikhiya R. Young
Sydney Ruth Leftwich	Diaz	Dalia Violeta Salinas	
Henry	Alfred Alexander Mickle	Tania Yasmin Salinas	

JOHNSON COLLEGE, SCRANTON, PA

Thomas Francis Abrams	Anthony Carachilo	Dylan P. Haberzettl	Kenneth Kocher
Jonathon P. Beckage	Marissa Coleman	Patrick Connor Hannon	Jenna Lehman
Kara A. Boles	Joseph W. Devers	Andrew Hart	Jonathan Kim Maxwell
Emily Erin Brown	Shauna Nicole Fahad	Nicholas Jerome Hojnacki	Patrick Joseph Munley
Matthew Burke	Brian Foytack	Jacob francis Kalinay	Shannon M. Noll

Frank M. Polumbo   Jared M. Rude   Dustin Schroeter   Zachary Taylor

Richard J. Reddock   Jesse James Santarelli

JONES COLLEGE JACKSONVILLE CAMPUS, JACKSONVILLE, FL

Tetesha L. Bostic   Debra C. Lutz   Toshua Kawonya Reed   Margaret Nell White

Michelle I. Harris-Chisholm   Jennifer R. McKenna   James Glenn White   Jeremiah Young

Catina Jacinda Henry   Latiesha Nicole Raines

JONES COUNTY JUNIOR COLLEGE, ELLISVILLE, MS

Faith Anderson   Jeana Graves   Kiana De'Marius McFadden   Jenna Smith

Emily Revé Batley   Hannah Hampton   Dallas McKinnon   Alden Jae Swindle

Emily Bedwell   Karlie Hart   Justin Ra'Shad Moody   Lindy Tabor

Hannah Boyte   Joshua Phillip Hester   Jennifer Niemeyer   Hanna Da'Shae Tolbert

Illisia Breazeale   Harley Hilton   Denice Renee Pearson   Luke Tucker

Krystal Brown   Thedford James Hollis   Austin Allen Perkins   Tabitha Jo Flora Wade

Geneva Ellyn Catlett   Sierra LeeAnn Holmes   James Ponder   Crystal Watkins

Ethan Davis   Amy Hosey   Anna Price   Adam Wigley

Alexa Blake Deas   Mason LouAllen Irby   Sabrina Claire Rounsaville Ashley Brooke Williamson

Virginia-Leigh Donohue   Matthew Ishee   Clinton Thomas Sasser   Fredrick Woodruff

Yasmine Sha'Neca Fairley   Jordan Alexander Jones   Natalie Beth Seales   Joanna Word

Kaylie Suzanne Flynt   Bryce Kinzer   Thomas Luke Sims   Robert Steven Zugg

Danielle Girod   Marianna Lunsford   Cady Nicole Smith

JUDSON UNIVERSITY, ELGIN, IL

Ethan Adams   Serena Ching   Phillip Lindsay   Rebekah Tabb

Gavin Buckland   Scott Layton   MaryJane Reilly   Eshcol Thomas

JUNIATA COLLEGE, HUNTINGDON, PA

Jonathan A. Altland   Lindsey M. Cundiff   Steven T. Guetzlaff   Stevie L. Kitching

Adrienne E. Ballreich   Morgan T. Decker   Ethan L. Habbershon   Alexis S. Klein

Madeline K. Bennetti   Adena K. Delozier   Natalie A. Hager   Mitsuki Koh

Courtney J. Bickel   Paige M. Dennison   Garrett C. Hain   Kate J. Lorenzen

Sarah E. Bilheimer   Gordon W. Dimmig   Garrett C. Hain   Julia A. Mathis

Anna K. Bistline   Conor P. Dimond   James R. Hemminger   Rachel M. McCloskey

Jillian J. Bloise   Catherine A. Douds   Samantha N. Hendricks   Kathryn A. McElwee

Jason D. Boblick   Caitlin C. Emslie   Denisse E. Herrera   Brittany Nicole Meier

Paige A. Bohn   Christina A. Estright   Morgan A. Horell   Sierra N. Mellish

Andrew R. Burlingame   Katelyn D. Fisher   Hannah D. Hrobuchak   Hannah Sanae Morris

Rachel P. Carnicelli   Carissa A. Flook   Brittany R. Jasper   Ryan T. Mull

Haley M. Chandler-Reed   Erin S. Gaines   Hannah R. Jeffery   Megan E. Myers

Trevor R. Clune   Taylor J. Garraffa   Suzanne Jlelaty   Stephanie W. Njeru

Kristin Ciara Collins   Nakita A. Gearhart   Nicole E. Jordan   Khadejia A. Norman

Kyle M. Pannebaker	Katharine N. Shelledy	Petro Sokirniy	Maris K. Wilson
Holly M. Renninger	Ryan M. Shelton	Alexis L. Stone	Thida Win
Kelly A. Reynolds	Jacob Daniel Sinclair	Bailey O. Swogger	
Eleanor P. Rice	Christopher M. Sinisi	Nikea J. Ulrich	
Alexandra San Miguel	Anna E. Small	Cameron E. Westerlund	

KANSAS CITY KANSAS COMMUNITY COLLEGE, KANSAS CITY, KS

Jonathan B. Allee	Dustin C. Eby	Hannah E. Moore	Brandon S. Reid
Conor G. Behrens	Chase M. Holle	Flora H. Nyakatura	Marisol Salinas
Andres De Avila	Dalton A. Kincaid	Afua N. Owusu	Daulton D. Smith
Savannah Hayley Dungan	Allyssa B. Lutgen	Matthew R. Perez	Shawn M. Smith

KEAN UNIVERSITY OF NEW JERSEY, UNION, NJ

Lydia Abdelsayed	Deanna Dell-Bene	Ilianna Maria Jimenez	Christina Papetti
Edward B. Adams IV	Dolores DeLuca	Milfre Jimenez	Kenan Pierre
Caroline Antonio	Gabriel De Luca	Jonathan Ray Journett	Yasmine Reed
Requel Avena	Michelle Diaz	Casandra Lambert	Eduardo Sanchez
Shawn D. Bragg	Bianca Dossous	Sarah Marie M. Takla	Kyle Seales
Austin Brecht	Joseph C. Fernandez	Nisha Mahase	Emily Thomas
Jacquelyn Anne Cali	Ashley Field	Olivia Angela Maltempi	Quoc Anh Tran
Ana Claro	Abby Gallego	Isaiah M. McClain	Katheryne Wall
Jake Daniel Cocchiarella	Brandon Gooden	Camille McCoy-Gilliard	Steven W. Walters
Chelsea Dalesandro	Taylor Grier-Johnson	Shruti Nadkarni	Whitney Wanton Sotolongo
Karen Damoah	Aerianna Hardy	Kimalee Nichol-Ford	Taylor A. Williams
Al-Mujeeb Danmole	Judy Jacobs	Alex Nunoz	Xia Xue
Daisha Davis	Kayla Ayanna James	Nicole Anne Olearchik	
Cadene Delisser	Alexis Jimenez	Julio Cesar Olivo	

KENNESAW STATE UNIVERSITY, KENNESAW, GA

Melanie Elizabeth Abel	Claire Bohrer	Camille Carpenter	Brittany Cordaro
April Adams	Whitney Boring	Henriquez	Isabela Correa de Castro
Kelsie Adams	Austyn Brock	Wil Caruso	Lauren Crabtree
Laura Alford	Briana Brown	Kristen Cash	Jaiva Crawford
Crystal Elizabeth Allinger	Joseph Brown	Vitale Kyle Castellano	Clayton Fairchild Currier
Angel Alejandro Almodovar	Kimberly Brown	Cindy Chamberlain	Dionye Curry
Omar Husein Almutlq	Mallory Brown	Di Chang	Daniel Dantas
Alishia Anderson	Nicholas Bullard	Hongyu Cheng	Bertram Davis
Jack Baker	Anthony Burnette	Yeju Choi	Ryan Delaney
Jonathan Baker	Matthew Ross Buxton	Laila Cohen	Anisha Dinani
Arielle Balkcom	Marion Cannon	Chelby Coley	Askari Dobbs
Emily LaRae Bishop	Rebecca Cannon	Allante Collier	Lindsay Douglas
Kensie Blackledge	Myles Christian Cardenas	Glendale Collins	Nadine Duncan

Carl Duperval

Michelle Edward

Ashley Marie Edwards

Justin Farmer

Rachel Elizabeth Feltner

Stephen Andrew Fields

John Fitzpatrick

Gerard Foka

Reagan Foster

Leslie Franz

Aspen Glanville

Breanna Gleeson

Krista Goettig

Debani Gordon

Anne Goulart

Rachel Nicole Gragg

Sydney Green

Matthew Greene

Brooke Rena Grier

Corrie Griffin

Candace Grof

Zachary Gruca

Abigail Gustafson

Morgan Hague

Dallas M. Hall

Meghan Harkins

Chelsea Harris

Thomas Christopher Hartwell

Joshua Hashemi

Micaela Hays

Wanhua He

Malinda Ann Hernandez

Jeremy Hudak

Precious Chiamaka Igboneme

Tobore Imarah

Lauren Jacques

Cooper Jordan Jannuzzo

Daniel Johnson

Jessica Jouria

Carol Kahrmann

Alan H. Kazemian

Morgana Ann Kennedy

Tanasia Ayana Kenney

Simoine Kenya

Morgan Knowles

Alayna Lynn Kolb

Melissa Kramschuster

Kristin Lauterbach

Martin Leak

Jamie Lee

Stephen Lococo

Lathrop Lougheed

Andrea Lovett

Sydney Lydia Jeanine Lyman

Ashley Maag

Shennell Monique Mack

Ngozi Onyinyechi Maduoma

Kaitlin Maginnis

Emily Manross

Jared Martin

Carolyn Mayes

Kayla McClung

Sarah McCuan

Briana McCullough

Megan McDowell

Paiton McDuffie

Taylor McGhee

Yancey Dobbs Miller

Jenny Minter

Blake Miranda

Michelle Swyers Mitchell

Lindsay Montgomery

Caroline Renea Moore

Nicholas Austin Moore

Matthew Morrissey

Sarah Elizabeth Muncy

Andres Munoz

Shannon O'Dell

Vivian Okere

Nicholas Pape

Adrianna Leigh Parson

Divanny A. Pena

Angelica Eloisa Perez

Melissa Perkowski

John Michael Pledger

Sala Elizabeth Prain

Madyson Price

LaNadia Rumania Pugh

James Pyle

Danna Qasim

Anna Reyes

Wenceslao Andrew Rincon

Corshae Robinson

Katrina Robinson

Malachi-Chaim Robinson

Nicole Robinson

Sherrie L. Rodriguez

Farhad Sayedzada

Alikeh Kweli Shaw

Ludmila Silva

Tyra Skinner

Brittiny Slicker

Samantha Slicker

Taylor Sloope

Laina Esprit Smith

Cheyanne Sotelo

Jessica Stewart

Rachel Elizabeth Stignani

Richard Sykes

Tori Tabor Antem

Karina Tates

George Thomas

Andilyn Nichole Tichenor

Melanie Valentine

Carmen Joy Van Ameringen

Victor Villanueva

Amanda Vincent

Veronica Vredenburgh

Brianna Chantel Westland

Debra Lynn Wetherhead

Joelle Furcha Whitener

Brittany Demi Williams

Gabrielle Williams

Micahl Williams

Daniel A. Wright

KENTUCKY MOUNTAIN BIBLE COLLEGE, JACKSON, KY

Boonchalit Chokdeepusit

Rachel Marie Graves

David Jennings

Joanna S. Pyle

Tara Silecchia

KENTUCKY WESLEYAN COLLEGE, OWENSBORO, KY

Holly Nicole Blackburn

Amber Marie Bryant

JoCarol Bunch

Seth Thomas Burnette

Matthew Charles Chestnut

Kylie Rae Davis

Kathryn Ann Dishion

Erin Leigh Dorn

Aaron Christopher Eaves

Taylor Elizabeth Gaddis

Makayla Elaine Gish

Connor Alexander Goodwin

Wei Hu

Dylan Michael Jeffery

Breanna Lindsey Jones

Lydia Ann Kaminski

Griffin James Kelley
Jordan Blake Key
Heather Nicole Lacy
Seth Lawrence Lasher
Elizabeth Anne Martell
Rhiannon Michelle Moore
Michael A. Mosby

Andrew Logan O'Bryan
Kaci Michelle Ovelgoenner
Daphne Jewell Parker
Claire Elizabeth Payne
Kaitlyn Rebecca Pelletier
Monica Celess Pentecost
Simeon Alexander Pogue

Ronnah Briana Richards
Tyler Allen Shewmaker
Emmalee Rose Speer
Haleigh Elizabeth Stringer
David Wayne Thompson
Jennifer Dominique Walker-
Crawford

Mackenzie Brooks
Weedman
Taylor Carol Wilson
Bria Michelle Wright
Emily Anne Yocom

KETTERING COLLEGE, KETTERING, OH

Alyssa Lynn Adams
Gabriel Alvarado
Nana S. Amoabea
James Allen Ashcraft
Brian Astor
Melanie Jane Bainter
Justine Melodie Benjamin
Emily Jane Benton
Emily Boldman
Olivia Renee Booher
Sarah Brad
Angela Marie Britt
Alverna Hess Bugh
Madison Rae Buxton
Veronica Calhoun
Jacob Tyler Callahan
Bonnie Campbell
Stacie Chandler
Ricardo Chujutalli
Katharine Marie Clark
Sarah Craycraft
Michele D. Delamater
Shasling Delgado
Michael Anthony Deyhle
Jerry Dean Dickess
Alicia R. Doty
Christopher Douglas

Brandon Douglass
Adrienne Ehrhart
Joshua Eley
Jade Marie Elking
Michael Elson
Danielle Leigh Engle
Jeremy Michael Fanberg
Tyler Farr
Kyle Fenner
Mareike Ferguson
Seth Foote
Jamie Foster
Brett Friesen
Jade Morgan Garcia
Ashley Gayheart
Danielle Nicole Gillium
Michelle Givan
Rachel Emma Goldman
Emily Grace
Christine Grimme
Alicia Gurtz
Kristen Marie Heitman
Paul Caspar Hess
Jacob Huddleston
Jiries Yousef Jaraiseh
Jill Nicole Kerns

Mahshid Mogtehedi
Khansari
Terra Kreiner
Alicia Nicole Ledford
Abigail Lesoine
Stacy Maag
Rachel L. Mack
Christine Marriott
Chelcia Celeste Maul
Aileen Kathryn McCormick
Jessica Michaels
Danielle Marie Moeller
Nicholas Scott Mullen
Susana Ofori-Buadu
Rachel Olding
Trey Thompson Overla
Rebecca C. Page
Jason Andrew Pennington
Brandi Pogue
Jessica Ann Purkey
Jessica Pykosz
Zachary Ranly
Brandy Cheyenne Ravert
Morgan Elizabeth Riese
Jennifer Roan
Billy C. Robbins
Deborah Ruff

Chelsey Sakal
Paige Julian Schmerber
Andrea Denise Schneider
Abby Rapking Segbers
Olivia Suzanne Snell
Rachel Snelling
Rachel E. Sowder
Justin Thomas Stafford
Erin Marie Stelzer
Samantha Lynn Stidham
Ryan Paul Stocum
Samantha Szopo
Karla Tapia
Justin Earnest Lee Taylor
Krisha Thomas
Allie Thompson
Allison Trabue
Mara Vajen
Ian Patrick Valentine
April Margaret Whitman
Erich Thomas Wiggershaus
Julie Wilson
Kathleen Kelly Yeary
Sydney Michal Yendell
Jessica Lauren Yoshida
Lindsay Makayla Yount

KEYSTONE COLLEGE, LA PLUME, PA

Rachel Balon
James Blockberger
Gabrielle A. Bosshard
Lindsey Bucklaw

Sarah Canavan
David Catlett
Kelly Ann Corcoran
Jennifer E. Davis

Summer Demcevski
Tara Dix
Kelsey Edelmann
Alicia Englert

Winnie Evans
Jacquelyn Eyster
Terry Fleming
Shannon Renee Giedieviells

Ivala Lyn Gilman
Tyler Gilroy
Micole Gumpper
Richard Hardy
Dulvanese Innecco
Jordan Joyce
Danielle Karwaski
Kaila Ketchum
Megan Malena Lewis

Kimberley Bryn McGuire
Bryan McIntyre
Jasmine Mercedes
Lauren Nardelli
Katelyn Osborne
Christina Lea Pomaquiza
Louis Reyes
John Rock
Amanda Lee Russo

Heidi Lynn Saxton
Vika Gloria Shpolyansky
Christina Sinibaldi
Joel Skivington
Dane St. Duran
Jessica Rachael Surace
Gina Marie Szymczyk
Brian Toda
Erin Westervelt

Danielle Wheeler
Carly Williams
Lori Williams
Zipporah Elizabeth Williams
Bethany Youshock
Stephanie Marie Zdimal

KING UNIVERSITY, BRISTOL, TN

Jeffrey N. Albrycht
Rachel Mae Arrowood
Samantha Dawn Austin
Austin S. Bilbrey
Catherine Marie Blackwell
Donna Gaines Boxell
Rachel Beth Burke
Jonathan Daniel Carrier
Amy Renae Chisom
Donna A. Coffey
Rachel Suzanne Coleman
Wesley Scott Collier
Sarah Ruth Collins
Cathy Patricia Cowan
Stephanie Michelle Creech
Talitha Nicole Davidson
Shirley Davis
Booby H. Dotson
Linda Denise Edwards
David Alan Farmer
Samuel Issac Fennell
Devan Laura Fox
Victoria Suzanne Franklin

Rebekah Lynne Frye
Joseph Ryne Ganger
Caleb Wiley Greene
Callie Ruth Greer
Kimberly Arden Guy
Susanne Nicole Hall
Medea Elizabeth Harr
Julia LeAnne Hayes
Mark Louis Hencken
Thomas Downs Henry
Jenny Maria-Lee Hensley
Holden Wayne Herrell
Victoria LaSha Hinican
Samuel Henry Hobday
Austin Arthur Hogle
Amber Jean Hoots
Anita Haulsee Irvin
James Tyler Irwin
Matthew Keith Jackson
Lindsay Marie Kihnel
David Ray Kilgore
Amy Elizabeth Kiningham
Tessa Anne Klingensmith

Daniel Joseph Krause
Pamela Diane Looney
Ashleigh Nichole Manke
Robert E. Mann
Jessica Robin Marcus
Donna Lynn McManis
Arista Noel Metcalf
Ashley Briget' Millsap
Konica Renee Moore
Nicole Marie Neilson
Bridgette Renee Nelson
Risner
Makayla Renee Newberry
Cindel Breanne Oakley
Vanessa Leigh Odom
Deborah Okyere
Tamra Lynn Oliver
Geoffrey Stuart Ormston
Julie Katelynn Perrine
Stephanie Anne Rhea
Bethany Danelle Rhudy
Spencer Andrew Robinson
Bethany D. Rose

Kelly Louise Rose
Charles Kennith Ryan
Genna Toney Scalf
Tiny Rena Shortridge
James R. Sircy
Hanna Colleen Smyth
Jennifer Wyatt Stanton
Joshua Edward Stephens
Victoria Rose Stephens
Elizabeth Anne Swallow
Heather Kay Testerman
Rebekah Danae Triska
Olivia Joy Underwood
Amanda Hope Vaughn
Haley Elizabeth Venable
Joshua Blake Vestal
Marietta Yoakum Wells
Aaron Matthew Wiggins
Casey S. Williams
Christopher Ryan Yates

KUTZTOWN UNIVERSITY, KUTZTOWN, PA

Jessica Adamczyk
Alyssa Blasko
Jaron Sebastian Bradley
Isabella Marie Canova
Katherine Clauhs
Christopher Vincent Erthal

Kelsey Greth
Melissa Anne Gump
Rachel Megan Hammersley
Jennifer Hill
Christopher John Kalbfell
Elaine Katherine Knox

Joel Leibensperger
Kelsey Taylor McGuire
Megan Elizabeth Mehalick
Shane Murphy
Waskar Paulino
Diedra Alexandria Pile

Kevin Lee Ruppert
Dana Lynn Salanik
Jacqueline Hayley Schor
Shelby Schwoyer

LABETTE COMMUNITY COLLEGE, PARSONS, KS

Chelsi Arratia

Abbie Atkins

Janel Marie Baker

Sheldon Balocca

Alixandria Nicole Boulanger

Kerri L. Butler

Kelsie Coltrane

Kendall Elliott

Mary Gathoni

Emmalee Kayann Handshy

Toni Alexandra Hurst

Hunter L. Kellar

Sacia Kelsey

Abigail Kreighbaum

Sharai Larry

Bria Maples

Andrea Kay Palumbo

Brett Perez

Chris Robert Ponce

Bianca Carolina Rodriguez

Holly Ryan

Kiersten Sailsbury

Tera Kay Spear

Ashley Lynn Stalford

Megan Maire Thompson

Jill A. Troy

Whitney Nicole Wolken

Ashton Kristine Wood

Jennifer Wood

Grace Workman

LAGRANGE COLLEGE, LA GRANGE, GA

Sara Emily Arnold

Abigail Catherine Bowen

Carolyn Brianna Bridges

Christopher Jacob Dunn

Carmen Brooke Findley

Benjamin David Fuller

Kyle Robert Gutowski

Peyton Madison Hanners

Victoria Blessing Harison

Cortney Larane Head

Anna Catherine Morman

Kara Alyssa Patterson

Andrea Lee Richard

Blake Thomas Schuck

James William Scruggs

Justin Perry Slay

Chandelle Doreen Ulmer

Summer Alexandria Vo

Ella Ileen Weymiller

LAKE LAND COLLEGE, MATTOON, IL

Brittany L. Ballinger

Layna J. Bond

Bryse R. Bugger

Shirley J. Davis

Mara L. Dearnbarger

Cassandra L. Eilers

Erica J. Grant

Benton J. Hakman

Matthew P. Kuhns

Samantha P. Lloyd

Sarah Jean Locke

Chelsy M. Lorance

Cody L. Morris

Kayla N. Peterson

Clyde M. Powell

Gracia L. Ramp

Chandra F. Smith

Janessa N. Watson

Allison J. Wheeler

LAKELAND COLLEGE, PLYMOUTH, WI

Amanda M. Bagnall-Newman

Trista R. Barron

Steven John Canales

Megan E. Gomez

Bailey E. Grayvold

Le'Shay L. Jones

Emma L. Landowski

Danielle M. Livingston

Peter J. Ludolph

Karalee J. Manis

Jacob A. Nault

Suzette Rosas

Heather E. Ross

Amanda N. Smith

Brooke L. Wilder-Corrigan

Samantha J. Williams

Katherine A. Zielsdorf

LANMAR UNIVERSITY, BEAUMONT, TX

Jeremy Allen

Nidal Alsayyed

Stephanie Abella Bermudez

Emily Blanke

Kristin Lee Bolser

Christian Brent

Jessieca Brock

Keyana Carr

Paige Carter

Adharsh John

Chundammanal

Devyn Marva Coleman

Maegan Collins

Christina Craft

Brian Glen Curran

Zach Defrancis

Erica Alyse Edgerly

Robert Alton Ehrlich

Linda Ann Esch

Johanna Kristyn Figlia

Mason Gardner

Chelsey Gates

Nirmal Chandra Gope

Brianna Graffagnino

Ayah Hamza

Jason Hatton

Eric Hernandez

Jacqueline Hernandez

Rebecca Marie Higginbotham

Jonathan D. Hodges

Michael Dalton Holly

Zach Holt

Charles Huynh

Odera Ibekwe

Sarah Irwin

Aaron Spencer Lavergne

Lauren Leshikar

Brittany Lopez

Linda Drabek Marshall

Jacob Thomas Martin

Chassidy Janae Mayo

Matthew McAfee

Trent A. McGee

Colton A. Morris

Levi Kent Morris Jr.

Micah E. Murdock

Shelby Murphy

Elizabeth R. Newell

Gregory Dillon Nicholson

Love Osemwegie

Stephanie O. Oyeka

Jordan Price

Maci Taylor Reeves

Kristeen Reynolds

Deirdre Richardson

Kayleigh Danielle Romero

Lydia Rosario

Richard Rosario Jr.

Molly Ross

Fredrick Ryans

Lauren Schuldt

Kristi BreAnne Sonnier

Matthew Richard Swain

Kara L. Timberlake

Keeley Irene May

Townley-Smith

Kay-Alana Turner

Lowell Conde

Washington Jr.

Joseph August Wells

Shelby Corene Whitehead

Robyn Winkle

Kevin Wayne Zabala

Miroslava Estefania

Zendejas

LANCASTER BIBLE COLLEGE, LANCASTER, PA

Daren J. Baker

Lindsey Allison Blest

Agnieszka E. Braczyk

Ifeoma Brookins-Monroe

Antwoine Clark

Wallace Clayborn

Kathryn J. Coomber

Jessica L. Crist

Hannah P. Derr

Eric W. Dobbins

Elisabeth Marie Florio

Aubrey S. Folger

Phillip Ford

Shelby L. Geraci

Josiah D. Groff

Daniel Harris

Tedd Taylor Holbrook

Jennilea R. Horning

Mariah Etta Keener

Monica R. Kirsch

Pamela Elizabeth Lipscomb

Richard Longacre

Rita Annetta Mabone

Shannon K. McNally

Hannah Lin Reichard

Faith Irene Scheuerman

Grace Helene Scheuerman

Evan Carter Smith

Albert C. Suniga

Brian Taliercio

Louis Anthony Villafane II

Katelyn Alyson Webster

Heather Wells

Bradley Andrew Wilcox

Rebekah Wimer

Abigail Nicole Witherell

Tukker A. Zimmerman

LANDER UNIVERSITY, GREENWOOD, SC

Olivia Catherine Bair

Jordan Leigh Beeler

Stevee Autumn Booth

Stacy Simpkins Condrey

Kristyn Leigh Cumbee

Sara Elizabeth Hix

Victoria Susan Jones

Dan Keown

Kendrick G. Kinard

Andrea C. Marshall

Cameron Hayley Miller

Steven "Sonny" Nodine

John Patrick Nugent III

Amber Marie Opel

Ashley Victoria Redden

Justina Teale

Jessica Renee Trotter

LANE COLLEGE, JACKSON, TN

Jasmine Nakia Armstrong

John Thomas Brownlee

Aliana Clark

Demetrius Cole

Shaquille Duncan

Fantasia Monique
Edmondson

Felicia Fowler

Jaclyn Allison Hayes

Guja Grace Jeong

Ashley Nicole Johnson

Jodi Dynel Johnson

Kyana Johnson

Dayane Louis

Deizarae McCoy

Sheritta Jasmine Mincey

Courtney Roberson

Jamie Ann Robinson

N'dezha Imani Robinson

Niya Jordan Royal

Leonardo Undre Sanders

Carmilah Smith

Jareese Diane Springfield

Ihuoma Tasie

Uchenna Joseph Sylvester
Ugwu

Jakaira Monique Walker

Cortez De'Vonte Williams

LANGSTON UNIVERSITY, LANGSTON, OK

Jasmene C. Abernathy

Lynne Andrew

Brittany Michelle Bailey

Mark W. Barber Jr.

Ebony Barnes

Alexandria Lee Becker

LaShonda M. Bishop

Kathy Blalock

Kiajuana S. Brimer

Jera R. Brown

Tameeka L. Bryant

Cedrick Ladon Carter Jr.

Blongshia Cha

Rico Letrelle Childs

Khyra L. Chiles

Chaste' L. Coppage

Shekinah Cosby

Brandon Craig

Raven Daniels

Jonathan T. Davis

Breanna Rochelle

Edenborough

Ngwese M. Edie

Amanda C. Felder

C. Beautiful-Joy Fields

Joseph-Michael J. Fields

Kwanshae A. Flenory

Tonya L. Flenory

Megan J. Francisco

Moret Regeale Freeman

Alessia A. Gallegos

Halina E. M. Garraway

Kayle N. Golay

Landon Gray

Sha'Breaunnia Q. Guy

Rashad Hall

Rozlyn S. Hamilton

Kristi L. Haney

Aaron N. Hayes

Kichelle L. Henderson

Mira A. Hendricks

T'ara Howard

Dante Luis Huerta

Matthew Jackson

Maya B. Jackson

Jeffrey L. James

Samantha O. Jay

Orlando Johnson III

Asia A. Jordan

Keith E. Justus

John Kalka

Susan K. Kotey

Cheron D. Lewis

Terri A. Link

Sydni D. Long

Octavia S. Lyndsey

Hellen N. Maina

Akran H. Manseh

Chantel Marshall

Alexus K. Mason

Madison L. McGolden

Meochea Mearilon Marie

Mckesson - Pittman

Trevon D. McNabb

Deamonte A. Miles

Doristina C. Moncriffe

Anna E. Morakot

Omar W. R. Muhammad

Antwonette E. Mulrain

Violetta Jenea' Mumford

Lisa Angelica Munnerlyn

Stephanie Newton

Jennifer M. Ninman

Nana A. Osei

Britnee M. Pannell

Christopher D. Pannell-

Hyeche

Eliza D. Payne

Shayla Penner

Dennis Pletcher

Moriah A. Plowden

Lalitharani Rajasekar

Latisha Ramos

Travon A. Reynolds

Sydney M. Rios

Cherjuan Y. Robertson

Quineshia Robertson

Christine D. Rosas

Awet Z. Russom

Sydney D. Scott

Christopher A. Smith

Dwight D. Smith

Tracy L. Smith

Joseph E. Snodgrass

Michael P. Spencer

Aschten Steward

Rachel E. Stinson

Valencia Lynette Tapia

Rhonda A. Taylor

Virgil Teter Jr.

Phyllis B. Thomas

Kristopher Vine

Lynell Walker

Damon D. Wallace

Jeffrey E. Wells

Felecia A. White

Marcus E. Whitfield

Quentin J. Wickliffe

Jennifer R. Willhite

Devin Williams

Gabrielle G. Williams

Danielle S. Wright

LAREDO COMMUNITY COLLEGE, LAREDO, TX

Vicente Rafael Acosta

Evelyn Natalie Aguilar

Maria Alejandra Aguilera

Korayma Alcala

Cody Allan Arnold

Maria Ivette Arroyo

Gonzalo Emmanuel
Astudillo

Miranda Janelle Beltran

Airam Fernanda Bernal

Elida Prissyla Campos

Mariana Cardona

Patricio Carrasco

Amanda L. Castaneda

Kali Dee Castaneda

Karla Michelle Castillo

Gabriela Alejandra Castro

Marina Itzel Castro

Tiffany Nicole Castro

Manuel Cerda Jr.

Megan Chacon

Irma Samantha Chavarria

Jorge Armando Chavarria

Claudia Celeste Colon

Carly Cordelia Comer

Benjamin Orestes Contreras

Jose Abraham Covarrubias

Sandra Janeth Cruz

Alexis Denise Cuellar

Maria Del Rosario Cuevas

Jasmin Damian

James Edward Deliganis

Kamil Diaz

Gerardo Javier Duarte

Dania Aime Elizondo

Katia Elisa Escamilla

Lorna Pamela Espinoza

Pedro Abelardo Espinoza Jr.

Jorge Eduardo Flores

Maria Guadalupe Frausto

Andrea Arizbeth Garcia

Daniel Garcia

Efrain Garcia

Francisco Roman Garcia

Jesus Edmundo Garcia

Nelly G. Garcia

Roberto Garcia III

Jose Alonso Garcia Jr.

Ernesto J. Garza

Melissa Ann Garza

Virginia Gaytan

Violeta Gil

Brizneyra Edelen Godinez

Gabriela Goldaracena

Aida Lizeth Gomez

Denzel Gomez

Diego Gonzalez
Gabriel Gonzalez
Marcos Emmanuel Gonzalez
Roxanne Olivia Gonzalez
Aaron G. Gutierrez
Amy Michelle Gutierrez
Angelique Rikki Gutierrez
Axel Alejandro Gutierrez
Magaly Gutierrez
Maria Esther Gutierrez
Carlos Fernando Guzman
Ricardo Daniel Guzman
Jessica Jakeline Hernandez
Jorge Alejandro Hernandez
Stephanie Hernandez
Obed Hernandez Cardenas
Teresa Juarez
Ingrid Marie Lascari
Yamile Guadalupe Leal
Brenda Loera
Brittany Renee Longoria
Stephanie Jean Longoria

Arlene Lopez
Jose A. Lopez
Luis Madrazo
Joseph Alexander Manzo
Cassandra Marquez
Andres Martinez
Isela Joseline Martinez
Laura N. Martinez
Ferdinand Charles Martinez Jr.
Raul Martinez Jr.
Rogelio Martinez Perez
Aileen Mata
Sara B. Montalvo
Carlos Morales
Kassandra Ashley Murillo
Gabriel A. Narvaez
Luis Ottmar Nudding
Sergio Ornelas
Armandina Ortegon
Abelardo Daniel Ostoa
Claudia Padilla

Maria Eugenia Padron
Jose Antonio Palacios
Amber L. Palos
Abigail Perez
Roman Orlando Quiroga
Jesus Cristobal Ramirez
Roxanna L. Raz
Gilbert Reyes
Jessica Riojas
Guadalupe Lizette Rivera
Rosalinda Rivera
Felipe De Jesus Rodriguez
Braulio Humberto Rojo Martinez
Edgar Javier Romero
Evelyn Melina Romero
Aimee Elizabeth Ruiz
Eduardo U. Salazar
John Michael Salinas
Gabrielle Brianna Sanchez
Jose Luis Sanchez
Kimberly Miranda Sanchez

Mayra Cecilia Sanchez
Alberto Sauceda
Alexandra Sauceda
Lorena Aracely Sepulveda
Kassandra Berenice Silva
Deborah Dennis Solis
Diancil Noraima Solis
Héctor Rodolfo Tenorio
Grecia Yazmin Tovar
Andrea Trevino
Alyssa Denise Uresti
Raul Enrique Valadez
Juan Ely Vega
Ruben Vela
Osvaldo Daniel Verduzco
Brenda Villarreal
Luisa Andrea Villarreal
Felipe Yniguez Lopez
Kristina Mayela Zamarripa
Alejandra Zaragoza
Peter A. Zimmerman

LA ROCHE COLLEGE, PITTSBURGH, PA

Kimberly L. Aland
Justin Tyler Bakow
Mohammed Ahmed Balgoname
Hannah L. Bevington
Peter M. Biernesser
Kelsey M. Brenner
Christine R. Chiodo
Eric Cosmides
Tyler C. Craig
Danielle M. D'Amico
Ana Paula De Marco Teixeira
Danielle M. Demme
Hollie Dickson

Michelle M. Draskovich
Russell Dunn
Katelynn Gazarik
Daniel S. Gebhard
Alyssa J. Haney
Mary Hilke
Heather I. Houseman
Joseph A. Illig
Emily M. Irwin
Cassandra E. Johnson
Shaunese L. Johnson
Rebecca R. Kaminski
Putu Widya Kartika
Dayana R. Lardo
Nicole L. Linkes

Jessica S. Mancuso
Derek E. Meeder
Cassandra A. Nadzam
Kole N. Newcomer
Boniface M. Ngigi
Kiersten R. O'Donnell
Gina L. Pellegrino
Megan Poland
Desirae J. Pope
Celeste I. Reed
Greer A. Reed
Sarah E. Reichle
Dennis Riosa
Eric J. Schmitt
Jessica L. Seidl

Michelle R. Shahan
Hayley R. Shaw
Julia E. Shelton
Cerci Erma Smith
Torin Smith
Hannah Elizabeth Strauch
Rita M. Vinski
Thomas Joseph Wagner
Michael Francis Weaver
Paige M. White
Colin M. Williamson
Stephanie A. Wizorek
Courtney E. Yuska

LA SIERRA UNIVERSITY COLLEGE OF ARTS & SCIENCES, RIVERSIDE, CA

Dawn Agustines

Lana Al Abbasi

Marvin Iaed Amen

Kelanie Aragon

Syria A. Armenta
Maria de Lourde Barragan Channer
Madeline Barrett
Jason Bendas
Christopher Bradley
Brianna Calderon
Jessica Cardona
Diane Castellon
Kevin Castro
Lindsey Char
Crystal Michelle Chavez
Po-Jui Chen
Allison Cheng
Breana Sarah Chin
Yebin Choi
Jennifer Choo
Michael Kimin Choo
Celina Cuevas
Brenda Delfino
Jose Delgado
Shashini Edward
Laurel Enix
Anthony Felder
Pamela Fernandez
Benjamin Figueroa
Andrew Fishell
Katharine Foster
Hannah Garza
Patricia Gerungan
Ryan Gil
Adrian Gonzalez
Daniel Gramling
Samantha Gray

Anne Leah Guia
Justin Guiao
Joseph Kezeli Gyorkey
Tyler Christian Haase
Jordan Harder
Jenessa Headley
Katrina Henry
Daniella Hernandez
Samantha Hernandez
Shehanie Hewawasam
Trace Huang
Yi-Hsuan Hung
Alyssa Hunt
Alexandra James
Hyein Ji
Kevin Jimenez
Maurice Joseph
Neil Joshi
Kevin Kawamoto
Nicole Jessica Khoe
Eunice Kim
Katrina Kim
Kevin Kim
Michelle Kim
Young Kim
Deeya Paresh Kumar
Jesse Lamog
Daniel Larios
Jane Lee
Julian Lee
Marcus Lee
Nicole Jung-Hae Lee
Chang Chun Lin
Po-Jui Lin

Viktoriia Liu
Stephanie Looi
Hazel Lopez
Victoria Lowe
Linda Lumintaintang
Scott Makorow
Natasha Mandolang
Marcela Martinez
Deborah Matul
Jessica Maynez
Jennifer Miranda
Allan Lim Moreno
Llewellyn Mowery
Bianey Munoz
Ronald Nance
Monica Ochoa
Edgar Padilla
Edward Pak
Kennya Palacios
Jonathon Payne
Nathan Perreault
Lauren Pfenninger
Lauren Prado
Michelle Pramana
Amanda Provost
Alisha R. Pruitt
Elena Rabago
Benjamin Radlein
Yesenia Ramirez
Christopher Ratter
Aleksander Real
Justin Rivera
Debbie Roman
Elisa Romano de Araujo

Andrew Mervin Salgado
Kevin Salgado
Nicole Samila
Tanya Samila
Andriana Michelle Saucedo
Samantha Schales
Stacy Shain
Chandra Shipp
Amanda Shultz
Aldrich Sitanggang
Durrell Smith
Jee Eun Song
Lauryn Marie Stiles
Brady Supriadi
Luke Swartz
Panpana Tangmunchittam
Kylie Teele
Melanie Tripet
Louis Ugalde
Daman Uppal
Sarah Vaca
Alexis Valencia
Stephanie Vera
Chanica Veranunt
Melissa Villegas
Hung Van Vo
Chloe Walker
Cidnee Walker
Iris Wang
Marci Weismeyer
David Wuchenich
Tsai-Wei Yang

LA SIERRA UNIVERSITY ZAPARA SCHOOL OF BUSINESS, RIVERSIDE, CA

Reggie S. Albarillo
Ariana K. Anugerah
Bryanna L. Baroi
Paulo Bechara
Samira Behiyat

Anthony J. Cobos Stewart
Nicholas W. Feldkamp
Morgan B. Frasure
Zoe J. Godfrey
Jessica J. Hunzelman

Sarah Maher Jameel
Lauren A. Johnson
Brian M. Khan
Kevin A. Nicholson
Neil D. Patel

Joshua S. Robinson
Ethan M. Wong
Andrew M. Yoon
Alexander B. Zaykov

Darione L. Adkison

Mojisola Taiwo Agbaje

Walter Aaron Agee

Ariel Dominique Allen

Krystle Danielle Allison

Rubina Saleem Alvani

Antonio Bernard Anderson Jr.

LaJasmine Breanna Andrews

Nabil Yassin Arafeh

Andrena Leigh Barnes

Demarco S. Bass

Eric Lamar Bell

Ashley Elaine Benjamin

Jasmine Alexandria Bennett

Richard jean Berru-Guerrero

Conner Logan Bowlby

Daniel Brian Bowman

Jacquelyn Rae Boyd

Zachery T. Boykin

Byron Alexander Bradley

Hunter Wright Brown

Jessica Chiquetta Brown-Tyner

Justin Lee Bryant

Jessica Burrell

Rodricque Jamal Burrell

Meagan Lynn Byrd

Larry Donell Campbell Jr.

Haley Danielle Cargile

Christen Deauna Carter

Sean James Cascaden

Walter Matthew Castle

Demitric Linnard Christian

Erica Michelle Clayton

Kamesha Shunta Cogmon

Hayden E. Cooley

Randall Bakari Cottrell

Christopher Cody Cox

Janelle Denise Crenshaw

April Michelle Cumbie

Jessica Nicole Daniel

Brandon Wayne Davis

Nicole Davis

Thomanesia Lashae Davis

Robert Lee Dawson III

Julian Kavon Dill

Alnyya Nichole Eddins

Claire Aryonget Emuron

Quiani Shonice Finley

Gentry Isaac Ford

Keith Bradley Foster

Michelle Foy

Eriel Tyeshia Fuller

Latanya C. Giles

Kent Zachary Glass

Tyree Vanessa Gray

Fernisia Marie Green

Taylyn Meeshae Greene

Brittany K. Hall

Jesslyn J. Hall

Chere Amour Hamilton

Jasmine Neche Hanberry

Chiquita Hannon

Jadirha Sophia Hannon

Ayobiyi Abeni Harris

Josiah Kyle Harris

Austin Drake Harrison

Jessica N. Hartley

Jameka Lashun Harvey

Sylvia A. Heard

Juwan R. Henderson

Brandi Marsha Hennington

Joy C. Hill

Dinah Mae Hollingshead

Mary Margaret Horne

Desmund Bernard Horton

James Paul Houston

Brittany J. Hunter

Kieshunta J. Jackson

Kelley Briana Johnson

Michael Ray Johnson

James Edward Joiner

Denise Kelly Jones

Apiffany Monique Kinnard

Austin Wyn Kirby

Camilla Breunka Kirksey

Tyrek Devonte Lake

Joaquin Jamaal Lambert

Steven Keith Lampkin

Stephanie M. Lewis

Courtney Marie Maddox

Devan James Manix

Stephanie Shavonne Marable

Frank Joseph Martin

Jennifer Thomas Mason

Kimberly Nicole Mastin

Lakendra V. Maxwell

Brionna Levette McCarthy

Patrick William McLaughlin

Alyssa Janay Miller

John Alexander Miller

Dylan Lee Mills

Alyssa B. Mullinax

Michael Gathu Ngugi

Naomi Wangari Ngumo

Blessing Nkeiruka A. Nzeocha

Chakahier Oliver

Michael Oliver

Mayowa Mary Otuada

Anthony Martez Outsey

Renathean Owens

Ashley Nicole Park

Latoria Antronet Payne

Braden L. Phillips

Russell Cole Phillips

Alise Renee Pickens

Jesse Cole Pnazek

Tsaiyesi Dante Rhodes

Shannon Smith Riner

Stacy Noreen Roberts

Alexis Alexandria Rowser

Darryl Ty Sherron

Arie Chanteria Smith

Coleman Andrew Smith

Linda Faye Smith

Raymond Smith Jr.

Bernadette Faith Stamps

Alexis Roichelle Streety

Ashlie Shard'e Terry

Shannon Denise Thomas

James P. Thompson

Robert Dalton Tibbles

Johnathan Tyler Tidwell

Trenice Michelle Towns

Jennifer Trice

Toleda Lashae Turner

Jenna Larell Twigg

Kookie Louise Veale

Regina Lewis Warren

Corvette Alise Washington

David Robert Whatley II

Cynthia Diane Williams

Trent McCray Williams

Trikeya Lettiece Williams

Matthew Thomas Wroclawski

William Zachary Yasko

Yi Sheng Ye

Yashica A. Young

Brandon Ryan Zimmerman

LEBANON VALLEY COLLEGE, ANNVILLE, PA

Stephanie Agudelo
Noe Aguilar-Gonzalez
Jeffrey Bates
Jeremy Beaver
Sara Behm
Megan Berner
Eric Bieber
Matthew W. Blanke
Megan Blauch
Sabrina Bomberger
Jennifer Bowers
Cara Breslin
Brittany Brubaker
Peyton Carper
Madeline Chronister
Robert Moran Conlon
David Corvino
Stephanie Cosgrove
Paige Diller
Olivia Edwards
Megan English
Larissa Ashleigh Christine
Eriksen
Michael Ferrara
Andrew Christian Stewart
Flinchbaugh

Ariana Freeman
Alexandra Renee Garrett
John Gething
Lucas Gienow
Victoria Gluszko
Jarrod Goss
Collin Greer
Matthew Healy
Hunter Heath
Clayton Heebner
Paul Hefferin
Dean Howey
Alayna Kalinay
Amy E. Karnes
Joshua Kauffman
Julie Kehs
Cody Kelly
Sarah Kensinger
Aileen Koch
Tyler Stephen Kollinok
Morgan Kratz
Bradley Leer
Brigham Lewis
Sarah Light
Cody Lloyd
Kirstin Lynn Luckenbill

Timothy Lupia
Cody Manmiller
Matthew Maple
Jessica McKelvin
Bradley Mehl
Jessica Lynn Meyer
Miranda Milillo
Timothy Monko
Kayla Muff
Kathleen Organtini
Giovanna Ortiz
Cory James Paternoster
Haley Patrick
Hannah Pell
Carrie Olivia Pfleiger
Laura Ramage
Scott Kinsey Reagan
Hannah Reedy
Amanda Ringenbach
Bridget Rose Rothert
Johnathan Salcedo
Rebecca Sausser
Victoria Seader
Maggi Lee Secrest
Selina Seymore
Eric Sharp

Lyndee Ann Sheaffer
Sonam Sherpa
Clarissa Shoffler
McKenna Sickels
Matthew Snader
Lauren Spelling
Hannah Stone
Charles Thai
Adam Thomas
James Thurby
Dylan Tobias
Vincent Tranchitella
Taylor Umbrell
Sara Urner
Ryan Vaughn
Curtis Washburn
Rhys Watkins
Jeremy Wheeler
Alyssa Wiekrykas
Brittany Wilson
Mary Katherine Yost
Lindsay Catherine Zwally

LEE UNIVERSITY, CLEVELAND, TN

Madison Alexander
Laine Ansel
Nathan Bates
Katharine Noel Bosch
Nicholas Branson
Benjamin Buckner
Jenna Burkert
Morgan Lee Colander
Emily Ann Collins
Connor Craig
Kaylah Annae Cutshaw
Sarah Nicole Davis
Emily Cassandra Dawe

Catherine Margaret Dean
Dylan Dixon
Madison Claire Dressler
Haley Dyar
Hannah Ford
Gabriel Paul Franco
Kaylee Marie Good
Jordan Halperin
Daniel Hardesty
Richard Huynh
Vi Huynh
Jaclyn Joelle Johnson
Melanie Joan Kehrer

Sarah Kelly
Bradley J. LaChapell
Sarah Landrum
Edwin Leon
Laura MacGowan
Blake McGrath
Kristin Mitchell
Carl Montgomery
Brenna Oubre
Dana Diann Pair
Evan Pell
Ashlyn Alexis Poplin
Ellen Porter

Eric Pritt
Caleb Hamilton Redick
Christina Grace Sarmiento
Cody Schoenly
Kaley Schwab
Amanda Seale
Rebecca Marie Serbu
Olyvia Smith
Maggie Stancliff
Jared Christopher Stewart
Ben Taylor
Casey O'Beirne Taylor
Makayla Tedder

Lauren Alexandra Todd
Ruben Villa
Caleb Wade
Rachel Westcott

Kayla Whitehurst
Jordan Wilcox
Kimberly Williams
Mesa Ann Grace Williams

Myia Williams
Camellia Yvonne Wilson
Carly Wingfield
Bailey Withrow

Amanda Yeager
Aubrey Yowarsky

LETOURNEAU UNIVERSITY, LONGVIEW, TX

Melissa Beatrice Ackerman
Erin Elizabeth Arbogast
Shaelyn Kristen Baas
Thomas Foster Back
Darby Joshua Ball
Peter Blackburn Barber
Henri Joseph Barber IV
Hannah Elizabeth Barnett
Stephanie Nichole Berglund
Shauna Michelle Betz
Brandon Michael Brenchley
Morgan Renee Broberg
Azrael Zechariah Brown
Hannah Victoria Brown
Antonio Jesus Bujana
Joshua James Burdett
Mercy Madeline Burklin
Hannah Esther Campbell
Nathan Daniel Canaviri
Marissa Joy Carlson
Janis Lynn Carrington
Cara Leigh Case
Monica Dianne Cerceo
Carmen Chek Jia-Wen
Peter Kaae Christensen
David Andrew Connelly
Sarah Christine Copeland
John Michael Cox
Christopher Andrew D'Auria
Aaron Thomas Dalton
Laura Katherine DeOtte
Eva Grace DiFrancesco
Melanie Ashley Dittmer
Elizabeth Joanne Duffy
Alyssa Brianne Eden
Taylor Lee Empkey
Mariah Nicole Ferkel

Michael Paul Finney
Alex Brent Flanagan
Arbolay OliviaJane Flores
Luke Benjamin Funk
Gregory Nathan Gaddis
Austen Trevor Garrett
Jeremy Kirk Goossen
April Sakura Grafton
Dusty Nicole Green
Shawna Grace Griffin
Chandler John Griscom
Jacob Alan Hall
Elisa Joy Hamm
Matthew Jonathan Hannusch
Benjamin John Heckard
Jennifer Marie Heidt
Nicholas Aaron Henry
Allen Davis Hill
Samuel David Hodges
Jacob Douglas Holm
Jesse David Holmes
Brian Nicholas Howell
Jaron Myles Hrushka
Kara Danielle Huff
Nathanael Charles Hughes
Guerney
Douglass_Holloway Hunt
Martha Mallory Jeske
David Churchill Johnson III
Benjamin Matthew Jorgens
Katie Marie Kamas
Benjamin Charles Keener
Elizabeth Maria Keener
Benjamin Juerg Keller
Nathan Michael Kleoppel
Liana Rachelle Kriebel
Joshua Bruce Kucera

Danielle North Lamphear
Madalaine Rachelle Lane
Cameron Austin Laramee
Leonel Leal III
Diana Katherine Leon-
Arguello
Thomas Joaquin LePoidevin
Jessanne Yuan Lichtenberg
Abigail Ruth Lopez
Nicholas James Malinaric
Austin James McCasland
Austin T. McDonald
Rachel Elaine Metzel
Andrew Isaac Mitchell
Taber Scott Miyauchi
Daniel Ian Moses
Joshua John Mueller
Caroline Elizabeth Nix
Noah Benjamin Nobley
Nathan Drew O'Day
Deborah Oluseyi Osomo
Luke Aaron Owen
Fontagne Jade Paxton
Andrew Nathaniel Pearson
William David Perkins
Christine Catherine Perry
William Edward Peterson
Timothy J. Pickle
Calvin James Pitman
Andrew William Pollard
Emily Christine Powers
Blakely Mitchell Redwine
Shimon Patrick Rigdon
Aisha Jeanne Rigert
Rebekah Shay Rigsby
Micah Erik Ritschard
Daniel David Robbins

Matthew Medd Roberts
Zebediah Del Rose
Jason Christopher Ross
Noah William Russell
Josiah Paul Schiewe
David Conner Schroeder
Emily Schultz
Cody Ty Shamblin
Margaret Joanne Shrum
Joshua Ryan Slagell
Andrew Marcus Smith
Gabriela Abigail Soto
Matthew Brian Staley
Anna Rose Steege
Nathan Daniel Strachen
Matthew Keefer Sturm
Derek Michael Syme
Josiah Wesley Taylor
Israel Mark Terrill
Julia Danielle Thurber
Colin Samuel Tompkins
Lucila Noemi Torres
Timothy Trotter
Emily Kathleen Tutt
Kooten Marissa Kaye Van
Samuel Thomas van der
Hoeven
Kayla Irene VanWagner
Morgan Boone Weaver
Jacob Daniel Weeks
Savannah Storm Wessies
Catharina Elisabeth Whipple
Clifford Nathaniel White
William Maxwell Whitney
Alisa Nicole Wilson
Elisabeth Anne Wilson

Garrick Jason-den Hoed Worrell

Jordan Thomas Wright
Andre Makeen Youngblood

Zachary Zanardi

Margaret Elizabeth Zeitlow

LETOURNEAU UNIVERSITY GLOBAL, LONGVIEW, TX

Jonathan Paul Admire
Lisa Ann Anderson
Sandie Michele Anderson
Bryan Clinton Baldwin
Kellie Marie Beard
Nicole Marie Becker
Kelli Sue Benson
Stacy Nikkole Blackwood
Mary Delle Boudreaux
Nicholas Paul Bowen
Regina Bowens
Kevin Ray Boyer
Emma Rechael Boyum
Kimberly Kay Bozarth
Brandon David Brantley
Keith Barnard Brown
Shannon Eliot Brown
Dena Janine Canaguier
Gina Elaine Cary
Andrea Joy Cooper
Melissa Elizabeth Crohan
Julie Davila
Shelly Lynn Dowell
Michelle Rae Drake
Pamela N. Elliott
Maria Teresa Erlewein

Amber Kay Escobar
Eleonor Martina Espinosa
Teresa Fiedler
Candice Nicole Ford
Brooke Allyn Foreman
Phillip Carruth Foreman
Stephanie Russell Frederick
Walter A. Golding
Matthew Scott Hammel
Kimberly Marlene Hare
Michael Evan Harmon
Leah Rene Hart
Claire Yvonne Held
Rebecca Marie Hicks
Jamie Marie Jack
Alexandria Bianca Johnson
Shlonda Evette Johnson
Joyl Lynn Kimmel
Charlene Kostak Kostak
Susan Kay Lawrence
Jodie J. Leonard
Robbi Jean Lewis
Vanessa Lynn Lockett
William Benjamin Lofton
Cynthia Lorraine McDougal
David Glenn McMurray

Veronica Mendoza
Amy Toyoko Mitchell
Holly Ann Mizer
Bethany Dianne Moers
Monica Molina
Reggie Ruben Montemayor
Aliece Michelle Montgomery
Scott Patrick Muse
Kimberly Nielsen
Cari Lynn Petrea
Tanya Danielle Phillips
Allen C. Pigeon
Ellen Mary Plunkett
Douglas Ryan Potter
Clarissa Quintanilla
Deborah Lynn Reeves
James L. Rivera
Robin Michelle Rodriguez
Nicholas Shane Rogers
Ricky Lee Rogers
Priscilla Darlene Roper
Meagan Rena Rosen
Brian Scott Saddler
Christopher Heath Sanders
Steven Elmo Savell

Whitney Ann Schubarth
Lisa Luwaine Seaton
Annie Faye Shine
Jeannie Frances Sisk
Ricki Ann Slatten
Brittnie Shea Smith
Shannon Lee Solomon
Yasmin Suissi
Danko Anterino Sulpizio
Sheena Shari Tankersley
Jeffrey Scott Thompson
Mitchell Robert Trantham
Brandy Catherine Tudor
Barbara Vargas
Rachel Jeanne Vaughn
Laura April Waldron
Clarette Carter Walker
Cresia Gay Wigglesworth
Douglas Ray Williams
Madai Galvan Williams
Nichole Leshon Williams
Elisa Marie Ybarbo
Blanca Estella Zamudio

LEWIS & CLARK COMMUNITY COLLEGE, GODFREY, IL

Cody Allsman
Trevor Bick
Gillian F. Burroughs

Katie L. Deluka
Ethan Randall Gallaher
Miriah Harris

Laruen Nicol Mullikin
Mackenzie Lynn Rose
Torrey Saxton

Nicole Steiner
Evan Michael Stillwell

LIFE CHIROPRACTIC COLLEGE WEST, HAYWARD, CA

Alicia M. Alvarenga
Stephanie Barbakoff
Keith D. Belliveau
Christopher O. Buccieri
Kevin B. Carey

Daniel R. Ceballos
Jason C. Chesney
Kristen E. Chila
Dylan J. Clements
Caitlin J. Collins

Kenneth E. Crum
Lindsay R. Donaldson
Richard M. Doss
Jenessa C. Dyke
Rebecca D. Ellis

Fabiana Goncalves
Daniel Y. Goodman
Zachary B. Gower
Monica A. Green
Lara M. Hill

Canyon T. Hurst
Bek R. Jarzombek
Rebekah R. Jarzombek
Michael Luu
Matthew N. Marsala
Margaret A. McInnes

Tyler R. Meier
Charlene Gaile Poderoso
Frank Polivka
Fredrick L. Polizo
Tzong Tzu T. Rogers
Nicholas E. Rous

Katherine S. Schlein
Grant J. Schoen
Rachel A. Sullivant
Marisa A. Sum
Eva G. Tang
Benjamin L. Terrano

Steven T. Waltner
Edwin G. Watson
Joseph M. Zingone

LIMESTONE COLLEGE, GAFFNEY, SC

Jonathan Charles Addy
Joel F. Aguilera
Christol Lynne Barton
Gerald William Beasley
Thad Perry Beason
Jeremy Martin Bedford
Marlin Cleavon Bennett
Raphael Thomas Bernard
Candace Sylvia Berry
Rodger DeWayne Blakely
Pamela Brantley
Ester Rena Carter
Anna Carolina Caruso
Caruso Duarte
Gloria Ann Chandler
Michael Francis Chorn
Thomas Earl Clary
Taylor Nicole Cline
Willie Mae Coaxum
Heidi Marie Cobb
Stephen Wesley Cochran
Lyann April Conkin
Maggie Cox
Robert D. Crooks
Nikki Shawnee Daily
Michael Simon Darazi
Terrance D. Davis
Jessica Arlene Diederich
Alayna Paige Downey
Brian Chadwick Dunagin
Tamara Louise Durant
Tonsa Evoria Edwards
Robert Skyler Elliott
Jennifer Norwood Fallaw

Matthew James Farmer
Kacie Lynn Faulks
Deborah Hyman Felder
Richard L. Ferguson
Katrina Nicole Fishburne
Audrey Denise Ford
Tisha Ford-Harris
Sheri Ann Garrett
Adam George Godfrey
Nicolle Mary Grant
Michelle L. Greathree
Almeka Green
David Alan Green
George Brian Hadley Green
Kristina Marie Grossett
Cassandra Mitchell
Hallingquest
Jason Christopher Harvey
Rachel Catherine Simone
Hickey
Teresa Hicks
Rhonda Herndon Hiott
James M. Holland
Ernest Hopkins
James Brandon Hughey
Chadwick Quay Hutchins
Cynthia Stokely Jackson
Manon Janin
Vivette Maria Johnson
Justin Lee Johnston
Blakley Melissa Jolly
Dustin Thomas Keenan
Mary Alice Hackmann
Keller

Tierrieney Elizabeth Kenley
Camilla Jernette Keyes
Crystal Gail Kraft
Christian Jamal Larsen
Ari Benjamin Lascari Diaz
Shakila Byers Lattimore
Stephen Jason Law
Gina Nicole Legaluppi
Maurissa Breanna Lester
Allie Christina Little
Tereshia Lashelle Livingston
Larry Shannon Locklair
Gayla Elizabeth Loudermilk
Tara Craft Manteghi
Mariette Martinez
Brian Conor McCall
Jordan Claire McDaniel
Ira Javon McInnis
Alex O'Brien Meeks
Chelsy Breanna Messer
Julia Correa Moreira
Danielle Marie Morey
Jerry Lynn Morey
Elizabeth B. Moss
Matthew John Mullarkey
Sarah Anne Munoz
Kelsey Leann Nabors
Bradley Carlton Norman
Johnathon Eugene
O'Donnell
Jessica Anne Onken
Melvin Allen Orr
Matthew Lucas Ostermiller
Glenda Williams Parkman

Jose Santos Peraza
Charlton Tyler Petty
Lawanda Denise Phelps
Walker
Ashley M. Piper
Lindsey Renee Plyler
Alex Wilson Poda
Kristofers Pone
Lalaina Jonathan
Randriamanantena
Diana Christina Rice
Brandy Elaine Richburg
Jaylen Christine Schulte
Denis Schulz
Heather Nicole Scruggs
Thomas Brent Shealy
Tonya Eleise Simpson
Mosi Mandisa Small
Kenneth Lamard Smith
Vinicius Finzch Sportello
Kelsey Marie Stanley
Chris Ian Swain
Lindsey Elisabeth Taunton
Roy B. Turner
Carol Evans Vaughan
Sharmaine Wagner
Nancy Dillinger Walters
Luca Sebastian Wanek
Annie Mae White
Jessie Julian Wilkes Jr.
Tommy Harold Windsor Jr.

LINCOLN COLLEGE, LINCOLN, IL

Edward Bowlby

Angus Buller

Molly Buse

Ashlyn Nicole Carroll

Madalyn Cooper

Alexis Crawford

Jeremy Davis

Kayla Dierker

Kyra Doolin

Kristin Engelhardt

Alec Esparza

Alexis Fricke

Blake Haas

Darcie Hawkins

Cory Hull

Cassandra Jennings

Jaedyn Krebs-Carr

Rebecca Lee

Bryant Lewis

Jovalle Mahon

ZoeAnne Marie Nepolello

Emma O'Dell

Austin Picton

Jessica Plummer

Myranda Posada

Josue Ramirez

Shae Ramos

Chelsee Jean Roberts

Ashley Robinson

Kimberly Rosales

Garrad Paul Straube

Mallory lee Tharp

Justus Toussaint

Jessica Marie Van Dam

Breanna Walker

Lauren Dawn Wendt

LINCOLN COLLEGE OF NEW ENGLAND, SOUTHINGTON, CT

Gina Patrice Cassella

Fallyn Lenore Coleman

Rebekka David

IuLiana Garnett

Nicole Harrison

Dana L. Jannetty

Angel Maria LaPlante

Leslie Mantello

Jacqueline Marchio

Meoba K. Nsenga

Irsida Omeri

Ashley Plourde

Ellery Sharlow

Celina Soto

Kelly M. Susi

LINCOLN TRAIL COLLEGE, ROBINSON, IL

Kyle Albaugh

Samuel Calvert

Mary Carter

Gemma Challies

Lauren Monique Elliott

Shelby Ferguson

Preston French

Jason Goodwin

Leslie Goodwin

Drew Michael Halter

Kristi Ham

Sierra Henry

Mallory Kent

Austin Krause

Sungho Lee

Bradley Maurer

Koert William Mehler

Trena Millsap

Jessica Moore

Zachary Scott Allen Murphy

Jay Prior

Miranda Pruitt

Jason Richart

Thomas Romine III

Seaton Sheldon

Erin Beth Swarens

Neil Williams

Joseph Ray Wirey

LIPSCOMB UNIVERSITY, NASHVILLE, TN

Julia N. Allen

Lucas R. Allen

Jenna L. Anthony

Mary Ashley Arendsee

Ashley D. Arledge

Parvin A. Atrushi

Debora N. Baddley

Sarah E. Baily

Gabriela Barboza Azofeifa

Jordan E. Beale

Katelyn J. Bianchini

Shelby A. Blake

Margaret E. Boshers

Lauren A. Brewer

Melba Shavonne Buchanan

Tate K. Burns

Chrisana R. Calandro

Hannah Joy Carignan

Stephanie N. Celada Rodriguez

Claire Mackenzie Coker

Alexander T. Csorba

Ezekiel X. Cutts

Talbott L. Denny

Nhan L. Dinh

Emily L. DuBose

Destinee B. Easley

Chandler A. Eckert

Hannah E. Feiten

Lillian C. Fisher

William Brandon Foriest

Michaela G. Genz

Kiera T. Glover

Malloree H. Grimes

Leah D. Gwin

Henriques M. Hassell

Katherine M. Hedges

Jackson William Hensley

Eric N. Hillstrom

Moriah N. Hollaway

Kenleigh N. Howard

Allyson M. Johnson

Dalton G. Keck

David Tobiassen Keough

Daniel John Lenart

Katherine R. Lopez

Caleb N. Love

Cole A. Meador

Mark A. Mitchell

Amanda S. Myers

Mark M. Naguib

Leslie C. Newman

Whitney M. North

Blake Elizabeth O'Donnell

Hannah J. Passamonte

Diana R. Proffitt

Corey S. Ramsey

Adrian K. Ricketts

Cesar N. Rodriguez Camacho

Natalie A. Shrull
Emily M. Shuler
Hannah Elise Simmons
William T. Sisson

Mary E. Skrabut
Taylor M. Smith
Albert W. Stockell III
Rustin L. Suray

Phetsuvanh Kevin Talatham
Rachel A. Tockstein
Terence Michael Turner
Sarah J. Wagner

Margaret C. Wheless
Heather A. Witt
John W. Womack
Kelly M. Young

LOGAN UNIVERSITY, CHESTERFIELD, MO

Refat H. Abdeljaber
Gregory R. Davis
Andrew W. deBethune
Marcel M. Garcia-Hosokawa
Charles M. Hogan

Jason A. Holt
Weston A. Holzinger
Tember Lenn Hursh
Brittany L. Jauernig
Ryan J. Krokstrom

Shannon E. Kuhn
Lance K. Maki
Jordan D. Mousley
Clayton T. Newberry
Elizabeth A. Paskey

Amanda Leigh Peiffer
Chase Preston Rupprecht
Bret G. Toftness
Samantha Brooke Wideman

LONG ISLAND UNIVERSITY BROOKLYN CAMPUS, BROOKLYN, NY

Elizabeth Aboaba
Stephany Adjei
Dennis Amvrosiatos
Nadeem Baalbaki
Richard Baffoe
Catrina Barnes
Cermone Natterle Baugh
Chaneque Bucknall
Tavajay Campbell
Shlomo Chaya
Jizelle Christolin
Tylena Clinton
Dawnasia Freeman
Jose Fuentes
Rashma Gobardhan
Raffi Gregorian
Lucy Gunton
Carol Jeannette Hanon

Ryan Herold
Nabila Ibrahim
Jermaine Isaac
Paul Salib Isaac
Michael Ivatorov
Moksh Jagia
Natalee Natassia Teresa
James
Vamshi Krishna Jogiraju
Logan Alexander Keys
Rebecca Madeline
Khaimova
Rose Khizgilova
Caroline Lynggaard
Koenigsfeldt
Gargi Lakhwani
Jenna Lasaponara
Kwon Lau

Michelle Lawton
Madison Lukosius
Israel Maldonado
Ana Samely Maria
Sadé Vianney Mc Intosh
Stephen Mensah
Kayla Mohammed-Riley
Brittany Nelson
Amber Nhu Ly
Stephanie M. Nunez
Jackline Okot
Allegra Ondrejka
Matinat Oyewo
Reymont Rafael Proano
Srinivas Ravella
Rachel Robb
Samuel Salib
Darshil Shah

Kushal Shah
Roopali Madhukar Shinde
Anastsiya Shor
Yevgeniya Shulman
Sabrina Simmonds
Sylvester Singh
Dilruba Sultana
Grace Tam
Isabella Wagener
Jasmine Watson
Whitney Lynn West
Devon Wilks
Debra Willner
Aleruchi Wosu
Han Chun Yang
Mengdi Zhao

LONG ISLAND UNIVERSITY POST, BROOKVILLE, NY

Gabriel Amato
Kevin Ammann
Ashley Anes
Michael Aquilano
Corey Ashe
Brittany Avarino
Kelly Anne Backus
Melissa Anne Bantz
Erica Lynn Bergen

Melissa Bianchi
Catherine Rose Bihun
Jena Nicole Bitsko
Caitlin Marie Bowe
Fallon Boyle
Morgan A. Boyle
Benjamin Brinton
Michael Campbell
Kelly Marie Carey

Anthony Caruso
Michael Castagnaro
Divya Chainani
Laura Kaye Chamberlain
Jonathan J. Chambers
Salvatore Ciulla
Ashley Clay
Samantha Coppola
Kelsey Amanda D'Andrea

Maxime DeVillaz
Stephanie Nicole DiPreta
Kristina Dolan
Giovanna Domingo
Vicky Marie Eichhorn
Kyle Fagan
Johannes Forgaard
Stephanie Frobin
Georgia Gantidis

Brianna Gibbons
Janelle A. Gibbs
Peter Grabowski
Lisa Greco
Heather Grova
Laura Harwell
Sarah Hecht
Julia Hogan
Jacqueline Rose Homan
Dominique Netanya Ho-Shing-Mason
Alyssa Hu
Courtney Jenkins
Isaiah Johnson
Seren T. L. Jones
Abel Joseph
Olivia Kavanaugh
Laken Kelly

Kaitlin Kingston
Sarah Rebekah Knapp
Casey Koster
Johann Andri Kristjansson
Eddie Lane
Morgan Lannig
Olivia Paula LaRocca
Tiana Lee Lemke
Coreece Lopez
Philip Lungren
Theresa Marie Lupo
Alexandra Frances Lynn
Kaitlyn Maniscalco
Kirsten Manno
Tine Markar Lolland
Michelle Masiello
Marcelleno Maxwell
Zachary Steven Mazzella

Lauren McGarty
Toniann Patricia Militano
Brittany Nichole Mitchell
Katharina Nisa Muniz
Gabrielle Marie Nau
Michael Nicosia
Kristy O'Connell
Shelby Valerie Obst
Rachel Ojalvo
Christian Oliver
Lauren Palumbo
Zachary Parker
Ketan Parmar
Melissa Peet
Catiana Mendes Pereira
Robert Picard
Brianna Pisano
Serena Puca

Melissa Quintanilla
Alexa Regina
Jessica Rivera
Taylor Rosenking
Courtney Sack
Kasi Scarcella
Nichoals Sieban
Jawaan Smith
Abigail Sollecito
Ryan Spaeth
Samantha Sterling
Aaron Swede-Taillon
Heidi Titko
Vincent Eli Turano
Greg Vavrinec
Talya Mae Williams
Mirna Youssef
Zoey Zibor

LONGWOOD UNIVERSITY, FARMVILLE, VA

Asha Lakshme Bala Krishnan
Mark Stephen Barham Jr.
Emily Catherine Beahm
Jacob Edgar Brumfield
Jennifer Morgan Burris
Sarah Ellen Butler
Hannah Marie Carr
Tyler Adam Cepeda
Williane Charles
Darrius Lee Christian
Olivia Katherine Colella
Jenna Marissa Crummett

Kelli Nicole Everette
Ashley Elizabeth Fox
Kathryn Eileen Fralick
Kelly Marie Frostick
Jessica Erin Gangitano
Constance Michelle Garner
Hailey Marie Gilbert
Quincy Aaron Goodine
Victoria Aliese Gordon
Emily Taylor Grandfield
Elizabeth Kathleen Greenwood
Jacob Joseph Harvey

Shakeyau Brionna Jackson
Brianna Nicole Johnson
Natalie Ann Joseph
Emily Lorraine Krause
Noah Ryan Lovelady
Willie Robert Miles
Kelsey Marie Monk
Shannon Nicole Opie
Vanessa Kaye Parada
Lilly Ann Payne
Brittany Marie Perkins
Nicole Teresa Reed
Karen Elizabeth Richardson

Mary Katherine Richio
Genis Hadden Robertson
Hadiyah Saleem
BharaniVyas Sankar
Jacob Christopher Stanley
Haley Rose Talmage
Chyanne Annastasia Trowell
India Morcelia White
Dillon Shane Yonker
Charles Patrick Duane Zurn

LORD FAIRFAX COMMUNITY COLLEGE, MIDDLETOWN, VA

Linda Marie Austin
Autumn Rose Beck
Jacob Benjamin

Katherine Christian
Eric Keener
Samantha Ann Nicholson

Emmaline Peck
Monica Reid
Abigail J. Stocker

Theresa "Tessie" Van Dyke
Elise Wheelock
Cassandra Wickline

LOUISIANA STATE UNIVERSITY AT EUNICE, EUNICE, LA

Brandi Nicole Alleman
Casey Noel Allen

Jaclyn Gail Boone
Willie Dondiego Breaux Jr.

Allison Dawn Briscoe
Lacey Markeesha Broussard

Stephanie Alaina Cooper
Morgan Eve Doucet

Bobbijo Julia Dupras
Constance Erin Guidry
Catlyn Renee Lauret
Gregory Louis Leger

Abigail Elizabeth Leonards
Donna Louise Leonards
Yadira Ruby Luna

Kaliee Brooke Lyons
Mikelyn Qian Manuel
Halie Danielle Stelly

Ruby Leann Thompson
Savannah Kathleen Watts
Raymond Earl Zorn Jr.

LOUISIANA STATE UNIVERSITY SCHOOL OF DENTISTRY, NEW ORLEANS, LA

Alexandra Renee Burns
Holly Nicole Callahan

Caroline Victoria Cappello
Adrienne Joan Champagne

Erica Lee David
Jennifer Anne Ducharme

Anna Aleena Galjour
Meaghan Marie Marquize

LOUISIANA TECH UNIVERSITY GRADUATE SCHOOL, RUSTON, LA

Jeni Maegan Abrams
Joshua Aaron Adkinson
Jairus T. Ballard
Remington Allen Bard
Chynah Mare Benton
Kaitlin Beretich
Kenneth Berlier
Kara Yoder Berning
Gordon Neal Blackman III
Sara Hahler Blazek
Brian Byrd
Susan Jane Carey
George W. Carpenter III
Christopher Joi Champagne
Christie Clark
Trey Denver Clark
William John Clower
Joshua Michael Coriell
Alana Jeanete Crump
Mattie Thomas Daley
Sonja Renee Davis
David Matthew Debnam
Chelsea Alena Dressel
Jake Dugard
Mary Dunn
Craig Randall Ferguson

Jenna Fincher
John D. French
Andrew Bryan Gardner
Brienna E. Gilbert
Rebecca Joy Graham
Elizabeth Griggs
William Reid Grimes Jr.
Nicholas David Groden
Yuan Guo
Tara Harmon-McElheney
Stephanie Marie Hart
Matthew J. Hartmann
Heather E. Hawley
Ashton Laura Hay
Abigail M. Hennigan
Sarah Henthorn
Kevin Scott Holly
Wilson Garrett Hood
Whitney Irvin
Jamie Lyn Irwin
John K. Jackson
Rowan Rene Johnson
Ben S. Kemp
Andrew C. Kepper
Kevin Dean Kisseberth
Jessica L. Knight

Haley Kormos
Nina Lisa Krey
Kaylee Ann Laitenen
Sandra Lara
Jesse P. Lehmann
Tanya Allen Lueder
Maggie MacDonald
Jacenta Matthews
Stacey Renae McAdams
Zachary McCauley
Justin McDearmont
Hillory Milot
Roiashley J. Molier
Robert H. Montgomery
Aaliyah J. Muhammad
Stuart John Murray
Mason P. Nabors
Gergana G. Nestorova
James Connor Nicholson
Casey O. Orndorff
Molly Elizabeth Page
Amanda M. Parsonage
Stanislav Ponomarev
Nia B. Potier
Saba Ramazani
Brad R. Random

Louis Gustave Reis
Craig Robinson
Douglas C. Schmidt
Blinn D. Sheffield III
Jiani Shen
Jakara L. Smith
James Alan Solow
James Colton Stevenson
Sawyer David Stone
Carter J. Street
Joy Stripling
Hope A. Tarlton
Taylor Warren Tarlton
Nicholas August Todd
Joanne M. Tran
Collin A. Tranter
Herbert Vandenberg
Natalie Vandersteen
Vladislav Voziyanov
Dianne E. Walding
Jeffery Adam Weisman
Rebecca Ann Wickliffe
Shuang Wu
Alyssa Catherine Wylie
Chaoran Zhang

LOURDES UNIVERSITY, SYLVANIA, OH

Zachary Daniel Babb
Dorothea Baumgartner
John Paul Bazydlo
Andrew Brock

Katie Marie Cerveny
Taylor Derr
Brooke Nicole Diekman
Jonathan Farrell

Christina Goellnitz
Tracy R. Harmon
Emily Elizabeth Howland
Beau Kramer

Hanna Sue Mclaughlin
Brianna Marie Megyesi
Megan Mosiniak
Matthew Olsavsky

Sara Marie Ondrus

Brandon John-Harold Oneail

Tiffany Amber Osborn

Kristen Oxender

Alyson Fountain Parker

Maritza Quinones

Alex Samson

Timothy Ryan Short

Eden Marie Smith

Kristi Marie Spiess

Kara Thomas

Elijah Walters

Zachary Zsolcsak

LUBBOCK CHRISTIAN UNIVERSITY, LUBBOCK, TX

Ghaniah Alkul

Shenae Ammons

Marcus Arrington

Ruth Bailey

Kimberly Barnett

Christopher D. Biggerstaff

Jason Blackwell

Markese Bohanon

Taylor Bonner

Jamie Boone

Kimmi Brock

Tucker Daniel Brown

Claire Elizabeth Bruffey

Chelsea Bullock

Elise Buraczyk

Tonya Canchola

Madeline Cannon

Jeffery Carr

Teresa Cockhill

Brandi Copeland

Greg Cowan

Hunter Cox

Adolfo Cuevas

Jonathan Dansby

Jacob Darter

James Dean

Dylan Delaney

RaeAnna Dennison

Komissa Egon

Kayla Emerson

Cassidy Flow

Sarah Fultz

Emily Garton

Serena Camille George

Brandon Greer

Wayne Austin Hancock

Danielle Harms

Haley Hawkins

Brogan Hays

Michelym M. Hereford

Rigoberto Hernandez

Rebekah Herron

Valency Higgins

Jase Hill

Brittany Holloway

Christopher Hornback

Rachel Nicole Hunt

Michael Hutton

Abby Johnson

Chance Juliano

John Knox

Jennifer LeBlanc

Cole Long

Demi Alexis Lorey

Morgan Lowrey

Kyleigh Ann Lucia

Malori Maddox

Lauren Marie Marek

Shonda Mayer

Maci Mayfield

Jamie McClaren

Keely McCrady

Joshua McLemore

Bethany McMillan

Wendi McNabb

Ashton Meeks

Gladys Miranda

Rachel Montgomery

Kayle Morin

Patricia Moulton

Autumn Munoz

Heather Murphy

Paige Nichols

Jeffrey Orme

Andrew Pacanowski

Audra Park

Amanda Perez

Oyuki Perez

Regina Phariss

Kathryn Pierce

Jessica Pool

Taylor Prather

Jonathan Priddy

Samantha Puente

Meredith Ramirez

Isaac Ramos

Jocelyn Richardson

Carsten Russell

Tyler Sams

Amanda Scott

Christopher Severs

Emily Sims

Ashley Slaughter

Monica Renee Smothers

Teal Stark

Kayleigh Steward

Allison Szabo

Mary Kim Thomas

Samantha Torrez

Isabell Trujillo

Gemma Volpato

Brianna Jade Wallace

Jake Talon Walton

Norma White

Kalinda Marie Wight

Dylan Willis

Heather Wood

LURLEEN B. WALLACE COMMUNITY COLLEGE, ANDALUSIA, AL

Chyanne Emily Allen

Starla LeighAnn Ballard

Kenneth Paul Barnes

Hannah Keaghlan Barron

Jennifer Lynn Bennett

Adrianna Shauntel Bradley

Erica Leigh Bradley

Joshua Cole Bush

Cory Michael Cain

Caitlin Patrice Carpenter

Hanna Lashae Chaney

Virginia Rose Chechak

Max Hunter Cobb

Logan Gray Dauphin

Anna Marie Davis

Ryan Patrick Davis

Brandon Lestat Delano

Lyndsee Jo Edwards

Jazmin Danyelle Garrett

Sarah Elizabeth Godwin

Shelby Leighann Golden

Precious Willnel Hamilton

Taylor Ashley Hartley

Brianna Dean Hebert

Lindsey Magnolia Holmes

Detrich Gaige Horstead

Brandon Tyler House

Amber Nicole Hutchinson

Aislinn Olivia Jones
Taylor Abigail Joyner
John Tracey Knight
Joseph Bernard Longmire Jr.
Christine Linette Loveless
Hannah Elizabeth Lynch
Joshua Delano Mathews
Austin Ray Matrullo
Macon Taylor Messick
Katherine Allison Nail

Matthew Ryan Nelson
Kathleen Ann Obrien
Summer R. Peacock-Wingard
Johnathn David Phillips
Matthew Clay Pierce
Akia Kianna Pitts
Chelsea LeeAnne Powell
Zachary Kyle Price
Rayson James Rhoads

Kaleb Allen Richard
Allison Danielle Riddle
Noah James Rider
Frederick William Riedel
Zachary Dylan Riley
Nathaniel Dale Sallans
Joshua Kye Sasser
Savannah Elizabeth Scott
Latanya Santavia Simmons
Rachael Kathleen Stephens

Rhyne David Taylor
Ashley Nicole Tetter
John Tyler Thompson
Tara Nicole Trant
Katherine E. Veasey
Jodie Elizabeth Watson
Katlin Michelle Wiggins
Avery Sha'Mone Williamson
Dalton Bradley Woodyard

LUTHER RICE COLLEGE & SEMINARY, LITHONIA, GA

Charles Ray Banister Jr.
Josiah James Batten
Bennett Eugene Benton III
Ivy Lee Boswell III
Blake Allen Burnside
Amanda Gail Collins
Glenn E. Dire

Carrie Fuller
Troy Heller
Jerald C. Johns
Christopher Clinton Johnson
Richard Sheril Jones
Khari Lanning McElrath
Ryan Matthew McFarlane

David R. Mills
Peter James Mordh
Camille May Neff
Matthew lee Spoon
Steven Robert Steinhilber Jr.
Douglas Myron Stephenson
Jay Allan Stillinger

Jeff Stockett
Charles Jeremiah Tondee
Jurian Jermaine Washington
Victoria Laruth Weathers
Irena Wilkosz
Brian Keith Williams

LUZERNE COUNTY COMMUNITY COLLEGE, NANTICOKE, PA

Austin E. Abild
Danielle Austin
Curtis Herbert Bates
Tracy L. Beers
Jason M. Belack
Amber Blight
Russell A. Carpenella Jr.
Ian C. Corazza
Tara L. Cortese
Mark A. Dickson
Alyssah B. Dombek
Nicole M. Gower

Alexander K. Gregoire
John M. Hall
Kathrine Marie Heady
Richelle C. Hess
Alisa A. Karsko
Tristi M. Liene
Gabriela P. Luna
David T. Matcho
Jaleel McNeil
Marquis M. Morris
Kendall D. Moss
Jeremy Nicholas Nenstiel

Nicole Letukas Nichols
Terie M. Oelke
Geralyn A. Olick
Isaura V. Olivares
Jose A. Osorio Soto
April G. Owen
Valerie J. Piccola
Elizabeth N. Reggie
Anthony J. Roberts
Courtney M. Schaible
Donoven Q. Scott
Kristen L. Stepanski

Rachel M. Stynes
Brittany L. Sugamele
Cassandra A. Swan
Mark A. Swick
Lyndsey M. Szela
Eric D. Thomas
Tiffany Lynn Timmons
Maria T. Villano
Breanna Welch
Mark S. Williams Jr.
Patrick B. Woodruff

MADONNA UNIVERSITY, LIVONIA, MI

Amanda Kalman Arcy
Shannon Dusute

Holly Laginess
A. De' La McClendon

Mariah Morozow
Nathaniel Theobald

Allie Elizabeth Vockler

MADONNA UNIVERSITY GRADUATE SCHOOL, LIVONIA, MI

Racha Alchommali
Seena H. Ankouni
Laura Ashley Arnold

Kathryn Mary Bandfield-Keough
Andrea Madison Biggar

Miranda Leigh Bodnovits
Stephanie Marie Boersma
Alyssa A. Bornheimer

Carol Borowski
Colleen Frances-Boylan Bouren

Sara M. Brock
Kaitlin Grace Brooks
Alan Peter Buelow
Hannah Renee Burge
Jennifer M. Burgtorf
Sarah Burkholder
Jill K. Burress
Lynnette Olivia Cain
Jessica Marie Carlin
Katherine Michelle Carlson
Janice Nicole Centers
Yu Hua Chu
Andrew Richard Ciesielski
Andrew Thomas Clark
Lisa Michelle Cogswell
Donna Marie Coloske
Jamie Craig
Jane Ellen Culp
Josini Devis
Jennifer Kristal DiMilia
Caitlin Donovan
Rochele Melinda Doran
Lindsay Mary Dugan
Christine A. Engle
Loren Kelli Evola
Hardik Gandhi
Shawn Michael Gauvin

Devon Jacqueline Gilbert
Wendy S. Grzych
Stephen Michael Guirey
Amber Hairston
Meghan Hardey
Frank Harrison
Carolyn Noel Hocking
Michelle Renee Howe
Christopher Hurst
Lindsay Carol James
Tami Jensen
Lynn Michelle Jimenez
Deborah Johnson
Wesleyann Patricia Johnson
Audrey C. Jones
Kathryn Marie Kanous
Sukhjinder Kaur
Lauren M. Kelm
Nicole Elizabeth King
Renee Lynn Kiriazis
Colleen Lee Kohn
Sarah Therese Kosel
Lauren Elizabeth Lakin
Norman Peter Lentine Jr.
Sara Elizabeth Leslie
Lisa Marie Loch
Susan Marie Lockwood

Lisa Ann Loger
Ryann Noelle Lowry
Rachel Majewski
Sarah Catherine Malysz
Sherry Lynn Mason
Kristin Mattia
Lyndsey Megan Morgan
Bridget Ann O'Donohue
Thomas George Oliver
Katy Lynn Olsen
Amanda Marie Olson
Jeannine Marie Oynoian
Brian Stuart Paul
Amy Lynn Paulson
Sandra K. Phillips
Nicole Rochelle Pilkins
Wendy Rene Poplaskie
Sara Lynn Provost
Dawn Liese Raymond
Charles Roberts
Denise Ann Robertson
Roxanne L. Roth
Joan Denise Russaw
Lina Nassar Saad
Filloreta Saraci
Bradley Andrew Sassack
Patricia Marie Setnicky

Megan Shaffer
Lynn Paielli Singer
Sarah M. St. John
Kellie Stark
Caitlin Janisse Steele
Jeri Lynn Steichen
Linda Taleb
Bethany Anne Templin
Tracy Allison Thompson
Alyssa Jo Tomasik
Elizabeth Turbiak
Stacey Gail Van Dike
Terri Lynne VanNorden
Elissa Ann Wagner
Lili Wen
Lisa Marie Wheeler
Matthew Brad Wilson
Lance Raymond Woody
Courtney Layne Wozniak
Shalyn Diana Yandura
Sevinc Yucel
David Frederick Yule
Danielle Zachary
Sarah Zajac

MAINE COLLEGE OF HEALTH PROFESSIONS, LEWISTON, ME

Nicholas Boucher
Christine Doyle

Bethany Grant
Kathryn Guerin

Kelly Huston
Ali Lamb

Robin Perkins

MANCHESTER UNIVERSITY, N. MANCHESTER, IN

Lucas Afif Al-Zoughbi
Taylor Martin Anglemyer
Jacob Henry Archambault
DaiJah Money' Asumang
Riley Blake Bannon
Matthew Donald Bennett
Ben Mark Bolen
Jake Thomas Burns
Thomas Zachary Dean

Jamie Lynn Dowdy
Wade Michael Dunn
Mitchell Eby
Hannah Marie Field
Kathleen Elizabeth
Fitzgerald
Nathan Lyne Frantz
Martin Garcia
Chad David Gindelberger

Ryan Michael Hawkins
Kate Nichole Heath
Jaspreet Kaur
Cole Edward Kellogg
Glynnis Dionna King
Kalie Jean Lastagarkov
Abigail Louise Lynn
Mackenzie Lynn Mance
Raj Kishore Manglani

Karmen Reed Marquardt
Claire Elisabeth Miller
Zachary Brock Newcomer
Jessica May Noll
Alexah Kay Parnin-Choisne
Cheyenne Renee Ramsey
Jacob Alexander Ray
Danielle Marie Robertson
Allison Paige Rowe

Suede Anthony Daniel Schiffli

Katherine Elizabeth Skeen Shortt Nicole Sky

Jessica Elizabeth Small

Andrew Ryan Sparger

Sarah Elizabeth Stahl

Haley Marie Steinhilber

Shannon Elizabeth Stephan

Ezri Daniel Stewart

Sam Fraser Torgerson

Gaius Goree Webb

Blake Matthew Woodward

MARIAN UNIVERSITY, INDIANAPOLIS, IN

Demarise Jaqueline Abbett

Christopher Ryan Anderson

Adam Michael Antone

Francesca N. Arguello

Adam Joseph Arthur

Mark C. Babbey

Emily R. Bueno

Natalie Ann Butler

Hannah Elizabeth Carpenter

Jillian M. Charboneau

Claire Alexandra Crane

Jill Marie Crane

Amanda M. Dudich

Anna M. Dudley

Lawrence A. Durchholz

Emilie Rose Esker

Kolten J. Everts

Megan R. Fabbro

Holly C. Freeland

Emily A. Garrett

Molly Elizabeth Gerth

Caroline Olivia Glowacki

Lydia R. Godsil

Brooke Marie Grannan

Sarah Lynn Groves

Alan Azael Guillen

Isaak Edward Haas

Lakan Marie Hasser-Smith

Taylor Elizabeth Helvie

Caitlin E. Hensley

Matthew L. Hess

Aleiza Lefsky Higgins

Elizabeth Kay Hilt

John David Hoffman Jr.

Quinton Alexander Horne

Stephanie N. Hostetler

Jonathon Clark Hosty

Brittany Michelle Kehoe

Samantha A. Koch

Gregory R. Konkle

Ann Catherine Kuntz

Joseph Andrew Kurucz

Kristina Landeck

Zachary Ross Luttrell

Elizabeth Thomasina Marsili

Jeffery A. Mayo

John Casey McBeath

Rita D. McCluskey

Renee B. McDougal

Angela M. Meyer

Emily M. Meyer

Courtney A. Michel

Allison Joan Miller

Hannah M. Molinaro

Grace L. Neathery

Mary Hannah Oberhausen

Elizabeth Olivas

Elizabeth A. Ortlepp

Coryn J. Rivera

Daniel J. Ross

Aubrey M. Schrader

Grace E. Sexton

Mackenzie Lee Sipe

Lauren Jane Sprague

Nicholas G. Stone

Madeline Leigh Weber

Evan Weeden

Alexander Byron Wetmore

Allison R. Willets

Alyssa Mae Witkowski

Jocelyn Cole Young

Casey Ann Zaberdac

Heather N. Zore

MARIETTA COLLEGE, MARIETTA, OH

Kennedy Clyde

Chanell DeJuana Cornett

Kindle Crossley

Ann Goolman

Annalee Haviland

Emily Jones

Erin Noelle McNulty

Lauren Morain

Gene Neill

Trinity Nicole Schlabach

Patrick E. Specht

Morgan Leigh Spradling

Blake E. Szkoda

Eileen P. Walsh

Brittany Waugaman

Miranda Katherine Williams

Jared Woodford

Megan E. Wrbas

MARIST COLLEGE, POUGHKEEPSIE, NY

Genesis Abreu

Matthew Amato

Shannon Nicole Bales

Chelsea Bennington

Alexandra Berg

Audra Boehm

Ignacio Borbolla

Alexandria Brannigan

Taylor Brown

Corinne Bruckenthal

Bryan Buttigieg

Kawailani Calarruda-Nunes

Robert Carreira

Christine Coughlin

Emily Crescitelli

Rebecca D'Antuono

Deanna DeVito

Samantha DeVito

Majay Donzo

Renee Dufek

Anna Durkin

Corinne Echmalian

Briana Flynn

Maggie Gallagher

Sarah Brigitte Gaudio

Maria Gironas

Elizabeth Anne Grisafi

Susan Gugger

Deana Hasandjekaj

Tara Quinn Higgins

James Holodnak

Anna Horrigan

Carli Jurczynski
Madeline Kachou
Lauren Lamadore
Jamie Landry
Jonathan Ronald Licandro
Emily Kristin Lohse
Joseph Marini
Ashley Mast
Kristen Mateja
Marianne Mazza

Alexandra McCahill
Kimberly Logan McVetty
Kaitlyn Meagher
Stephanie Melnick
Dakota Modica
Kristen Mueller
Caitlyn Murphy
Nichole Musumeci
Christopher Rashaad Myrick
Emily Nagle

Siobhan Pokorney
Jennifer Rescigno
Samantha Riccio
Matthew Ruis
Cassandra Leigh Saad
Miguel Nicandro Sandoval
Marisa Scarpitta
Christopher Seiter
Nicole Shanks
Julianna Sheridan

Craig Jesse Soderholm
Samantha Sprague
Nancilyn Stafutti
Joseph Suchanek
Kelsey Taylor
Kimberly Tobias
Melanie White
Tourron Whitfield
Anthony Zanin

MARSHALL UNIVERSITY, HUNTINGTON, WV

Hallie Elizabeth Andrews
Anthony James Bady
Jessica Taylor Beahrs
Erik B. Bjornson
Miracle LeAnna Boltz
Darius Lee Booker
Ryanne Taylor Brown
Chelsey Rae Curry
Virginia Cheyenne DeBolt
Charles Frederick Dobson
Taylor M. Douthitt
Mary-Michael Eberbaugh
Samantha Brooke England
Jordan Vincent Fanelli

Morgan Ashlei Farrell
Elizabeth Marie Finch
Jessica Paige Gambill
Megan Hackney
Tatyana Maria Hall
Elizabeth Keenen Hance
Nichole Janan Henderson
LaChel Shontae' House
Eva Nicole Howden
Victoria Raye Lanman
Christina Marie Lute
Brandon Jon Metzger
Skylar Brooke Midkiff
Lindsey Janelle Miller

Christopher DiCarlo
Monsell
Breanne Lyn Morehead
Mary Katherine Norton
Nicholas Alexander
O'Donnell
Brittany Ann Ochoa
Deborah Jenai Pope
Isabelle G. Rogner
Jacob Nathaniel Roman
Vinay Kumar Sarangandla
Megan Lynn Shiner
Alexis Nicole Smith
John Robert Sowards

Anthony Roberts Spano
Mercedez Janele Speight
Clayburne Anthony Stevens
Elisabeth Ann Tauber
Nguyen Sinh Thai
Alyssa Baily Turner
Tianna Rose Venable
Erin Shae Wroblewski
Ayanna Marie Wynn
Shuo Xu
Dana Zeid

MARY BALDWIN COLLEGE, STAUNTON, VA

Kelsey Allen
Johnna Bingham
Jazmine Brooks
William Douglas Campbell
Alice Facknitz
Taylor Lindsey Frick
Katelyn Goodfellow

Carolyn Huynh
Aaleyah Joe
Jerema A. Lovell
Lea Jasmine Marlowe
Stephanie Elizabeth Mason
Kelley Frances McKinnon
Jan Edlene Te Miguel

Katherine Danabet Narvaez
Mena
Brianne Perry
Dena Ritts
Stephanie Sackett
Kayla Sibold
Shelvey Elizabeth Smith

Elizabeth Suchanic
Shannon Marie Sullivan
Marlena Faye Thorne
Mikayla Waters-Crittenton
Randolph Welch

MARYGROVE COLLEGE, DETROIT, MI

Alyssa Adkins
Wissam Alawi
Deena Allen
Elise Armstrong
Aprell Arthur

Doris Ashouh
Hector Avila
Anna-Kay Barrett
Paige Bennett
Jennifer Billups

Teshia Janiece Bradford
Brittney Bradley
Erica Butts
Erica J. Cracchiolo
Dawn Davis

Raymond Dennis
Felicia Donahue
Theresa Dray
Corey Dunaj
Summer Ellerbee

Shannon Farlow

Keila Flores-Arreguin

Shauntay Frazier-Hall

Rebecca Geersens

Toni Grusser

Dalia Hamooda

Daishonai Jackson

Sabrina Jadallah

Jasmine Jenkins

Dominique Johnson

Patrice Johnson

Nicole Kempinski

Brittany Kihl

Leo Kopack

Mallory Little

Lillian Lucas-Jones

Wanda Manning

Katina McKinney

Melody McLean

Tiaria Meadows

Countessa Michaels

Lenora Miller

Ashley Murphy

Joseph Myrick

Issrae Nabhan

Sara Ophoff

Jeremy Otto

Courtney Ozog

Christian Page

Alixandria Pappas

Rosario Parada

Tina Perry

Karlee Perrymond

Fareeda Rahmaan

Breanne Ranta

Catalina Rios

Oneil Robinson

Sara Faye Ruch

Lydia Sanchez-Puebla

Adam Scanlon

Regynell Sharpe

Sade' Smith

Amber Staudt

Rachel Staudt

Megan Stuart

Jamie Sudak

Khalid Suleiman

Rebeka Sultana

Sarah Suppelsa

Camryn Washington

Cassandra Williams

Dontez Williams

Chaynise Wilson-Simmons

Stacey Zielinski

MARYVILLE UNIVERSITY, ST. LOUIS, MO

Nicolas Andrade

Shehmin Awan

Brittany Jean Bagby

Joseph Daniel Balassi

Joseph Barkofske

Kayla Bayne

Jacob Bizaillion

Evan Booker

Adam Brazzle

Krissy Bryde

Aaron Buettner

Cory Lee Bunger

Aaron Callahan

Brianna Carter

Jordan Coker

Joseph Copeland

Nadia Dawod

Julia Marie DeGise

Kevin Doherty

Jessica Marie Donnelly

Laura Duggan

Jack Emory

Alicia C. Farrington

Erin Finnegan

Kelly Elizabeth Freeman

Shea Lynn Gabehart

Raphael Garcia

Brianna Gardner

Christina Gerst

Luke Gilsinger

Rebecca Girresch

Jordan Green

Emma Gregg

Jenna Griswold

John Grunik

Ashley Hall

Elizabeth Hammond

Samantha Hartnett

Lauren Ann Marie Hawk

Alyxandria Holshouser

Davy Jia

Nicholas Kasparie

Shawn King

Zachary Klipsch

Miranda Knight

Marianne Leano

Katie Malone Wright

Chad Mancuso

Andrew Mandziara

Kellie McCarthy

Hana McGinis

James McGrath

Emily McHenry

Melanie Metherd

Bayli Mooney

Nia Morgan

Malorie Mueller

Andrew Myer

Lynda Nana Gyedua

Oppong

Andy Painter

Rachel Patrick

Bradley David Patz

Sydne Peck

Joshua Pellikan

Taylor Poole

Nicole Alexis Pruett

Michelle Ray

Garrett Dale Reifschneider

Abigail Reilly

Victoria Reinders

Michael Scharf

Hollistyn Schlaikjer

Ryan Schlick

Morgan Schumer

Melanie A. Self

Laura N. Steiner

Jessica Stuart

Lauren Melissa Sullivan

Jennifer Susnic

Jaclyn Marie Terbrock

Jessica Sue Tobin

Chinyere Turner

Stephanie Turntine

Miranda Marie Valleroy

Jeffrey Vaske

Joshua Venner

Nathan Vorel

Laura Genevieve Welling

Jennifer Ann Wellman

Kayla Yettke

MARYWOOD UNIVERSITY, SCRANTON, PA

David Christopher Bonomo

Stephanie Borger

Brianne Brady

Kathleen Brogan

Meghan Tenore Brown
Despina Bubaris
Amy Buchala
Natalie Burke
Jaye Alexandra Cannon
Daniella Castellanos
Ellen Clauss
Austin Collignon
Karlie Contrera
Christina DeCola
Cherish Dellatore
Amelia Marie DeMasi
Alison DeMelim
Satara Lynn Dickey
Danielle Marie Di Leone
Francesca Domiano
Markus Donahue
Amanda Donaldson
Laura Drake
Maxwell Vincent Drake
Laura Drapek
Skylar Drexel
Susan Durand
Brigid Edmunds
Jamie Diantha Feaster
Allison Rose Fruehan

Kelsey Gallagher
Colin Ganard
Molly Gardiner
Elissa Gary
Stephen Gaylets
Alexa Gerchman
Danielle Hagin
Ann Marie Holler
Emily Hoskins
Peter Inirio
Heather Michelle Kani
Patrick Kernan
Rachel Kester
Amanda Khozouri
Sydney Marie Kishbaugh
Keandra Alea Koons
Ryan Kozich
Kate Lebo
Rebecca Leighty
Morgan Leitold
Lisa Levanduski
Frederick Loefflad
Kelly Lynn
Alexis Katrina Maylor
Alyssa McCarthy
Meghan McClarey

Julia Carol Meeker
Caitlin Metzger
Amy Micklos
Kimberly Miebach
Valerie Morgan
Megan Morrell
Ariel Muhs
Kayla Murphy
Anthony Muscato
Lexi Rose Myers
Abigail Nadia Canare
Nicolas
Mary Ninivaggi
Casey O'Callaghan
Christopher O'Donnell
Emily Osborne
Sophie Patricia Pauline
Jeannette Pepe
Dominique Aurora Perk
Victoria Pezdirtz
Stephanie Piccoletti
Danielle Plunkett
Julia Polczynski
Mariah Robbins
Deidre Romano
Megan Roper

Ann Ruggiero
Maria Theresa Ryle
Jude Saforo
Morgan Sanda
Emily Jane Scappatura
Valerie Schmidt
Emily Margaret Schweiger
Amanda Shire
Rebecca Siegfried
Anneliese Simon
Veronica Smith
Kimberly Stone
Michael Stracci
Pamela Sutliff
Janet Thompson
Marisa Troiani
Nicole Tucker
Hannah Viparina
Michele Margaret Wadud
Sarah Walker
Mackenzie Warren
Anne Widenhofer
Alyssa Wood
Austin Wright
Nicole Ziegler
Samantha Ziemba

MASSACHUSETTS COLLEGE OF LIBERAL ARTS, NORTH ADAMS, MA

Ryan Baker
Jessica Barcher
Wilhelmina Beeler
Jamie Burdick
Patrick Engle
Paige Fairman
Brittany Gallacher

Paul Groff Jr.
Colby Joshua Harvish
Nicholas Hernigle
Alexandra Elizabeth Kadell
Cassandra Louise LaChance
Monique M. Lemay
Alexander Lopez

Abigail Thacher Lucas
Kelsey McGonigle
Grace Ngobo Toko Mbonda
Jenna L. O'Connor
Allison Pepi
Evan Pirnie
Elizabeth Pitroff

Gabriella Prata
Melanie Rowe
Kathleen Sansone
Veronica Rose Sniezek
Sarah Tefft

MAYVILLE STATE UNIVERSITY, MAYVILLE, ND

Brett T. Bachmeier
Taylor Jordyn Benneweis
Brady Dean Eichelberger

Madeleyne Monzaly
Gallardo Irias

Elizabeth Angela Hoglo
Grace Ann Keller

Hannah M. Ness
Hunter Allen Torgeson

MCDANIEL COLLEGE, WESTMINSTER, MD

Clarissa Balint
Leigh Brownell
Megan Duesterhaus
Rebekah Gerwitz
Roger Gerome Isom Jr.

Leanna Jasek-Rysdahl
Joy Kim
Anna Kokubu
Mariah Ligas
Elizabeth Grace Mann

Laura Maurer
Kelsey Minyon
Andrea Richardson
Ashley Rogers
Morgan Alexis Stanback

Julia Wainwright
La'Bria Wallace
Sophie Marie White

MCDOWELL TECHNICAL COMMUNITY COLLEGE, MARION, NC

Forrest Brook Ledford
Whitney Taylor Penland

Samantha Taylor Reece

Rebecca Ann Vogt

William C. Wohnus

MCHENRY COUNTY COLLEGE, CRYSTAL LAKE, IL

Britney Marie Adams
Andrew Bernard
Carmisha Breanna Chavers
Sara Crain
Madelyn Cysewski
Caroline Diedrich
Colleen Marie Duncan

Matthew Gruse
Mark Handeland
Gavin Jones
Brandon Kuhn
April LaVoie
Mason Martin
Jason Memmen

Daniel Phillip Nick
Brian O'Connor
Ann Ray
Megan Riordon
Benjamin Rohrer
Jamie Lee Sacramento
Cameron Strom

Carlee Udischuas
Kaz Woodward
Alexander Logan Woolard
Lisa Marie Wos

MCKENDREE UNIVERSITY, LEBANON, IL

Cheyenne Autry
Krystiana Clarke
Elizabeth L. Dykstra
Samantha J. Fagerburg

Whitney S. Funk
Merrilee Beth Gibbs Davolt
Allison P. Jones
Zach Loehr

Brooke A. Moore
Kenneth L. O'Dell Jr.
Alyssa Marie Reiniger
Bradley Jerome Schniers

Vincent Ray Spradling

MCPHERSON COLLEGE, MCPHERSON, KS

Miranda K. Clark Ulrich
Dixon A. Cooney
James Covel
Savana J. Cross
McKenzie L. Frank

Lisa M. Goering
Laurina J. Hannan
Tyler Henning
Austin W. Hiebert
Rebecca S. Hornung-Heeke

Addie Roesch Johnson
Alia M. Khalidi
Ashley Frankenbery Long
Ashlee R. Maier
Daniel May

Isabelle A. Moyer
Crystal Jane Osner
Colby L. Patton
Michael L. Rhodes
Rea Nichola Samuels

MEDAILLE COLLEGE, BUFFALO, NY

Tanya Abousaid
Stephanie Appenheimer
Earl Sidney Atwell Jr.
Dymone Tinay Barnwell
Elizabeth Barrett
Mackenzie Berger
Jessica Bessette

Samuel Bloomberg
Brigitte Carrier-Auger
Calvin Crosby
Jacob Denz
Jolanta Dzierzynska
Mark Girardi
Korry O'Brien Jackson

Kadeisha Kellar
Kendall Kent
Nicole Kepfer
Erica Mongelli
Cache Petters-Mathews
Hannah Pomeroy
John Posch

Heather Prior
Kelly Sekuterski
Thomas Daniel Serba Jr.
Taisha Elizabeth St. Jean
Alea Wade

MEHARRY MEDICAL COLLEGE GRADUATE SCHOOL, NASHVILLE, TN

LaTayia Aaron
Christopher Artis
Carlton Baskin
Miajenell Carroll
Amber Cheatham
Aaron Jamal Toomer Childs
Benem-Orom Davids
Brittany Davis
Kayla Dietrich
Dominique Dotson

Christina Eskew
Andrea Flores
Kelly Harris
Kenneth Harris
Shalonda Ingram
Kendria Lataira Irby
Bobby Jones
Alyssa McCoy
Gabrielle McGlathery
Deneshia McIntosh

Emuejevoke Olokpa
Samuel Pellom Jr.
Lauren Pilcher
Stephanie Pulliam
Ariana Renrick
Douglas Robinson
Amber Shaffer
Kevin Sims
Joseph Terrell Smith Jr.
Lakeisha Summers

Jessica Sutton
Chelsie Swepson
Tamkeenat Syed
Chemyeeka Tumblin
Tiffany Turner
Sarrah Widatalla
Amanda Williams
Morgan Zialcita

MEHARRY MEDICAL COLLEGE SCHOOL OF DENTISTRY, NASHVILLE, TN

Lauren Carter
Sanna Charlie
Jerica Cook
Damien Cuffie

Mia Holmes
Huges Jean
Monique Johnson
Yadiel Kinfu

Jasma McDonald
Steffanie Monroe
Bianca Newman
Mark Rice

Pasha Sanders
Temicka Terrell
Shontreal Ward

MERCER COUNTY COMMUNITY COLLEGE, WEST WINDSOR, NJ

Brittni Addye
Christina Bainbridge
Samantha Lynn Barlow
Elisabeth Bernal
Michael Bitonti
Dean Blank
Kristen Nicole Cheesman
Haley E. Cortelyou
Dana Davies
Barri Kathyrn Deptula
Kaitlin Diamond
Gabriel Shianne Douglas
Ivett Figueroa
Yael K. Fisher
Hayley Fletcher

Joseph S. Giambelluca
Julian Gonzalez
Jeffrey Emilio Gordon
Koran Green
Donna Greene
Kellen A. Groover
Brianna Nicole Gurdon
Ousman Joof
Casandra Kniskern
Bonnie Zackson Koury
Carrie Krewson
Malgorzata Lagowska
Carly Layton
Austin D. Lindsay
Gabriel Matt

Jeffrey M. Meckel
Fanhelee Morency
Casey Murphy
Jeremy S. Nass
Nnamdi Nnajiofor
Rose Nnajiofor
Kevin Ortega
Jiahui Peng
Glendy S. Pineda
Anna Prendergast
Ignacio J. Redondo
Anastasia Elizabeth Rick
Taymani Kissling Rivera
Melanie Sachs
Deisy Sasaguay

Autumn Sharkey
Justin Michael Smith
Melissa Smith
Elbia Velasquez
Jennifer Vitella
Richard Ward
Matthew Gregory Wereski
Latasha Nicole White
Qaysean K. Williams
Peira Wood
Lemin Wu
Christina Zeppenfeld

MERCER UNIVERSITY, MACON, GA

Emily Erin Bless
Olivia Marie Boza
Braeden Lee Brettin
Katherine Michelle Morris
Brinkley
Caleb Jorob Brown

Darcy Katherine Callaway
Colleen Kaylynn Closson
Jamie Elizabeth Coates
Victoria Ashley Conley
Nicole Oyedamilola Esuola
Bryana Jenale Ferris

Joshua Randall Funderburke
Jenna Noelle Gipperich
Gabriel Jonas Gonzalez
Leslie Anne Graham
Caroline Grace Hardison
Austin Thomas Harrison

Jordan Bailee Hester
Charleston Adrienne Hurley
Taylor Mackenzie Jolly
Alison Laura Lambright
Caroline Shannon Loos
Christopher Jordan Murdock

Thomas Buie Norton
Aaron Michael Odom
Min Hyun Oh

Devanshi D. Patel
Ashley Nicole Smith
Kiara C. Smith

Sarah Kathryn Ugan
Michael Celin Wagner
Avery William White

Olecia SoRelle Witt
Joseph Knight Wozniak

MERCER UNIVERSITY GEORGIA BAPTIST COLLEGE OF NURSING, ATLANTA, GA

Ryan Bannan
Mitzie Braswell
Jennifer Bresson
Kayla Ann Byerly
Jennifer Capshaw
Carolina Carter
Wardine Cullens
Mehtaab Dobani
Milyon Fears

Heather Grafton
Jeanette Hairston
Zachary Hartley
Casey Hopkins
Pamela Jackson
Emily Ruth McCabe
Kaitlin McColl
Ann McCoy
Sandra Monk

Shayla Monroe
Sonya Moon
Karman Ott
Angana Parmar
Aybree Pugliese
Darlene Rogers
Kaly Celeste Royster
Collin Schalk
Katherine Sly

Gina Solomon
Eileen Thrower
Joshua Antunes Vieira
Margot Catherine Wallis
Megan Williams
Michaela Williams
Avery Winchester
Shelby Wolfe

MEREDITH COLLEGE, RALEIGH, NC

Bailey Cathlin Benge
Jessica Le Sha' Boyd
Kathryn J. Burnet
Jordan Candace Capps
Christina Lynn Churchill
Raven Alexzandra Gregory
Lacey Magdelyn Hambridge
Sarah Haseeb

Alexandra Lee Herel
Kimberly Anne Au Hinton
Alexis Nichole Holmes
Meredith Elaine Hovis
Kasey Lynn Jones
Tia Janae Joyce
Nicole Elizabeth Lawson
Abigail Margaret Lorentzen

Destiny Cherelle McDuffie
Mollie Elizabeth Melton
Rebecca Lynn O'Brien
Zainabu Akinyi Otieno
Brittany Liane Oxendine
Rachel Victoria Powell
Kristen Deann Rivera
Courtney Jean Saunders

Jessie Ellen Taylor
Elizabeth Marie Thomas
Nideara Abriel Tucker
Nyssa Natasha Tucker
Jean McChesney Webb

MERIDIAN COMMUNITY COLLEGE, MERIDIAN, MS

Brittany Allen
Matthew Berler
Jami Daugherty
Reagan Dupre
Rebecca Estes
Brandon Evans
Ashley Fedrick
Ian Garner
Paige Gibson
Clayton Gray
Fisher Gray
Trace Hamby
Tyus Harden

Thomas Walt Harrington
Austin Harrison
Heather Harwell
Daniel Hill
Sophie Hodge
Derek Hoffman
Ronald Holloway
Kristen Hull
Anna James
Joshua Johnson
Lakia Jones
Ryan Lane
Ryder Leifried

Devon Logue
Megan Mallette
Adrianna Mendoza
Michael Meyers
Steven Adam Motes
Kaytee Nelson
Chanler Pickering
Shelby Proaps
Daniel Ray
Grant Renegar
John Ricks
Victoria Riebock
Alexis Rivers

Esmeralda Rodriguez
Alana Sanders
Alysia Shaw
Shamiah Sims
Dalton Smith
Drew Smith
Morgan Wall
Tyler Weeks
Emily Williams
Tori Wolverton

MESSIAH COLLEGE, MECHANICSBURG, PA

Samantha Alderfer

Courtney Lynn Allen

Michelle Aungst

Cassandra Baddorf

Andrew Badgerow

Bethany Baile

Lindsey Ann Barner

Christopher Michael Young
Beam

Christian Becker

Erin Besse

Melissa Jane Biener

Alia Carol Blair

Jonathan Maxwell Bodner

Ellen Brandenburg

Matthew John Bressler

Virginia Brickey

Erin Brown

Emily Budd

Ashley Burkett

Alia Morgan Burlew

Hannah E. Carrington

Emily Carter

Adam Chilcote

Phoebe Chua

Lindsay Elizabeth Coleman

Nathan Dean Conklin II

Elizabeth Alden Demendoza
Conte

Jeffrey Daub

Julia DeNardo

Benjamin W. Derk

Laura Dipaola

Sarah Elizabeth Druck

Nathanael Spencer Eagan

Shaun Egolf

Megan Leah Ekstrom

Hannah Joy Eldridge

Lydia Ellsworth

Mark H. Engle

Jael Elaine Epple

Alex Faus

Lyndsay Feather

Jessica Forster

Caleb Thomas Fugate

Jonathan Fuller

Zachary Dawson Galloway

Kyra Garling

Luke Daniel Gibson

Rebekah Glick

Susannah Goodman

Kathleen Hahn

Quentin Dean Hampton

Stephen Haverstick

Madeleine Heistand

Robin Elisabeth Hennessey

Kia Holly Hitt

Sarah Hoffer

Leah Holzhauer

Michaela Horst

Dustin Innerst

Molly Janczyk

Brianna L. Jewell

Shiloh Kail

Kathryn Kaslow

Courtney Keener

Benjamin Kennel

Rachel Kidwell

Olivia Kimmel

Robin Kline

Natalie Koenig

Stacey La Gatta

Hanna Lazio

Paul Allen Leiphart

Bryan Leong

Rachel Lippert

Kaitlin Logan

Lindsay Longoria

Kristen M. Madore

Caitlin Magaw

Jacob Mandell

Christina Manero

Brady Anthony Marburger

Kathryn E. Martin

Thomas Martin

Anna McArdle

Abigail Grace McBride

Ryan McCann

Sallie McCann

Christina Anne McIntyre

Hing Jii Mea

Jennifer Mikec

Braden Miller

Matthew Ludwig Miller

Sharon R. Miller

Katrina Dawn Neyman

Anh Nhat Nguyen

Douglas Nolt

Tobias Nordlund

Rebekah Notte

Allyson Olkowski

Elena Nicole Patton

Richard Prensner

Arielle Grace Raugh

Monica Reiss

Laura Ritenour

Bridgette Rodgers

Christian Rogerson

Allison Ross

Holly Ross

Julie Noelle Ross

Jared Ruhl

Hannah Ruskan

Joseph Saufley

Jenna Saylor

Timothy Saylor

Kelsey M. Schlegel

Katrina Schrock

Amy Schunemann

Michaela Scotten

Yacoub Seyni

Rebecca Shirk

Alicia Sims

Tiffani Singley

Jeffrey Stiles

Katie Lynn Stoltzfus

Lauren Marie Stratton

Adam Strawser

Justin Swank

Paul Tajiri

Rose Talbot

Duane Troyer

Joseph Willaim Twaddell

Madison Vander Ark

Anthony Watkins

Marisa Joy Weaver

Marcie Webber

Jacklyn Weit

Katrina Williams

Joshua David Wilmot

Mitchell Wirth

Benjamin Wise

Jonathan Barry Wolf

Elisabeth Wright

Mary Wright

Sung Bo Yoon

MID-AMERICA CHRISTIAN UNIVERSITY, OKLAHOMA CITY, OK

Tia Alderman

Kayla Baldwin

Laramie Ball

Nataly Barillas

Blake Barnett

Reese Black

Mason Brown

Jamie Carroll

Elaine Cleveland

Ashleigh Clouse

D'Shala Culberson

Makailee Davis

Leah Jaclyn Dees

Joel S. DeSecottier

Madison Fowlkes

Kathryn Pearl Rose Herald

Joy Howerton

Brianna Jezioro

Hannah Luedtke

Tyler McIntosh

Alana Nicole Miller   Sarah Romine   Sherie Splawn   Dustin Welch
Jenny Pratt

MIDAMERICA NAZARENE UNIVERSITY, OLATHE, KS

Georgia Anderson   Abby Friesen   Nick Newton   Tyler Sparks
Dade Douglas Baker   Hayley Gately   Drake Palmer North   Jonathan Stark
Amberlee Leona Brinkman Michelle Hanna   Caleb Oster   Mark A. Stirling
James Browning   Spencer Hart   Caitlyn Joy Ostry   Tyler Evan Taute
Cale Brubaker   Charlee Holsinger   C. Jazmine Parra-Navarro   Marshall Taylor
Cheryl Calhoun   Kristi Rose Jackson   Ian Perry   Valerie Van Hoecke
Nicole Lynn Conrad   Jenna Keen   Phillip Ramsey   Lenzie Jon Vulgamore
Morgan Couchman   Kensi Kitsmiller   Haley Raydo   McKenzie Elizabeth
Grayson Daganaar   Brandon Patrick Koontz   Carrie Remillard   Vulgamore
Alexandria E. Diehm   Nicholas Lancaster   Alicia Marie Riley   Anita Walkingstick
Amanda Li Doerhoff   Zachary Martin   Blake Robberson   Jacque'Lyn Annette
Lindsey Eaton   Ada Martinez-Medina   Devron Robinson   Williams
Heather Rose Engle   Carrie Lynn McClure   Kori Ann Ross   Rachel Young
Mario Paul Flores   Madison McKay   Ginny Rundberg   Brittany Zimmerman
Heather Fox   Tyler McMahan   Tarynn Rydel
Taylor Fries   Whitney Newman   Stephanie Schultz

MID-ATLANTIC CHRISTIAN UNIVERSITY, ELIZABETH CITY, NC

Wendy Jo Early Ward   Brittany Danielle Harrison James Richard Knight Jr.   Samantha Paige Roberson
Caitlin Dawn Goss   Amy Lynn Isler   Morgan Fawn Nayadley   William Evan Tanner

MIDDLE GEORGIA STATE COLLEGE, MACON, GA

Monika Meyahna Evans

MIDDLESEX COMMUNITY COLLEGE MIDDLETOWN CAMPUS, MIDDLETOWN, CT

Zachary Augenstein   Michele R. Haynes   Benjamin Radcliffe   John P. Tirone
Sarah J. Blum   Michelle L. Irizarry   Noah Radcliffe   Massimiliano Trentini
Lena M. Ciborowski   Ivon N. Kaolnji   Zachary C. Ross   Victor A. Triay Jr.
Benjamin J. Fichman   Loan T. Khuc   Seth J. Sadoian   Alain N. Tshipamba
Sabrina L. Garcia Nunez Emily LaBissoniere   Lisa A. Sanders   Amy G. White
Zachary Giroux   Giovanna A. Lakomy   Jennifer A. Shusterman   Douglas D. Wilson
Timothy C. Green Jr.   Kyle E. Ouellette   Joseph E. Stedman
Jessica T. Grote   Angela J. Pierce   Michael A. Stielau
Paul Gudelski   Deja B. Pierce   Chenoa Summer

MIDLAND COLLEGE, MIDLAND, TX

Lyssa J. Bell   Dora D. Carey   Yara L. Carrasco   Jason C. Conway
Levi Bryand   Jesus A. Carrasco   Patricia L. Chick   Chad Curtis

Heather Mae Dudley	Mercy T. Jama	Tho Nguyen	Ashley N. Spears
Megan C. Ennis	Janet J. Kimuge	Kelly D. M. Rains	McKenzie L. Stubbs
Jayme S. Farmer	Stephen Kyei	Raquel R. Ramirez	Ashley A. Sullivan
Ashley M. Frazier	Breanna Lafoy	Sarah A. Repman	Behrang Tahamtani
Samantha E. Furtmann	Rachel K. Long	Gerardo Reyes	Wendy Tenorio
Larissa G. Gomes	Krystal Lopez	Natasha N. Rodriguez	Shaylee L. Winchell
Kerilyn S. Gomez	Belina C. Martinez	Janeth Ruiz Garcia	Abibat A. Yusuff
Solomon A. Hainna	Clinton A. McCrary	Ramon Salazar	
Tammy J. Hanks	Jeanette G. Medina	Jonathan A. Schwalbach	
Emily G. Hobbs	June A. Moore	Mingming Shi	

MIDLANDS TECHNICAL COLLEGE, COLUMBIA, SC

Elizabeth Brook Albert	Amber Dubose	Fredricka McKinnon	Conner Ripley
Tim Altman	Joel Easton	Kayla Marie Mixon	Phil Rivera
Meredith Atkinson	Erika Engelke	Jaqueta Rona Moore	Megan Roe
Fletcher A. Battle	Amy Fairbank	Joy Beth Morgan	Jorge A. Ruiz Salas
Daniel Bein	Jean Flemming	Tonya Mull	Alejandro Santana
Victoria Hope Bell	Folline Gasque	Bailey B. Mullis	Gretchen Sellers
Stephanie Bellah	Danny Richard Gleaton Jr.	Andrea Marie Murray	Jamie Lynn Shurtz
Carmen Cherise Bethea-Fairley	Kristen Gomez	Dwayne Nabors	Jasmine Sims
	Jessica Grate	Jarrett Adam Nettles	Kaycee Sims
Melissa Raleigh Black	Charline Denise Green	Kolina Nicole Neumann	Anusorn Sirinopwongsagon
Danielle Boland	Nan Hardwick	William Nicholson	Billy Smith
Chante' Zaria Brady	Laura Harrelson	Allison Lynette Odom	Kelsey Megan Solomon
Sharai Vanasa Brannon	LaToyia Harris	Shannon Olsen	Raymond Patrick Stevens
Tara Michelle Brazel	Ashley Hayden	Olivia Louise Ondus	Katherine M. Stone
Natalie Shawn Bright	Jocelyn Hill	Hannah Ott	Peter Strong
Emilie B. Brown	Willard F. Holley III	Chantel K. Outlaw	Daniel E. Tetrick
Natasha Calhoun	Kimberly S. Irtenkauf	Kelly Brock Parrott	James Matthew Thornton
McKenna Rae Cieslak	Angela Jackson	Chineese Perry	Kristopher Alan Todd
Kelsey Lauren Clamp	Lashawnda Jenkins	Dominick Pierallini	Bethany Turner
Jessica Collier	Natasha Johnson	Chaqueta Player	Brittany Turner
Brianna Conn	Alyene Keller	Jonathan Pridmore	Brandon Warczyglowa
Trevor Conner	Jessica Ann Kitchens	Laci Brooke Proctor	Jennifer Anne Langley
Rasheen Crawford	Karen Harris Knox	Daniela Puentes	Worrall
Rebecca d'Erizans	Terry B. Mahl	William Reid	Juliana Wright
Rebecca LeAnn Day	Kristen Matthews	Robert Rhodes	Jordan Yellowdy
Maeghan Dilley	Megan McCoy	Brigitte Richards	Laurel Youngblood
James Brandon Dooley	Jennifer McFetridge	Denisha Richardson	

MIDSTATE COLLEGE, PEORIA, IL

Todd J. Arnold	Maria I. Barragan	Abby L. Beck	Cristina M. Bishop

Jamie R. Brown
Alicia R. Couri
Linda K. Cox
Jennifer Down
Daniele D. Fauser
Kari L. Gattung
Tiffany L. Gazza
Scott W. Glaser
Christopher L. Hansen
Matthew T. Happach
Brigitte L. Harper

Elisa G. Heffner
Pamela J. Horton
Whitney N. Jones
Gabriel J. Koch
Brandon H. Laesch
Adrienne L. Locks
Nicholas J. Maloof
Jeffrey T. Morrow
Matthew L. Morrow
Brent K. Oakes
David C. Ozuna

Jordan B. Rahn
Becky L. Robinson
Craig A. Roth
Rebecca S. Saban
Rebecca A. Schisler
Blaize J. Shipp
Michelle L. Smith
Rachel Maree Stomberg
David R. Strode
Nicole M. Swallows
Jesse A. Thacker

Amanda L. Thompson
Jenna L. Tompkins
Daniel Z. Torralba
Erin J. Totosz
Ryan J. Vaughan
Bobbi J. Wages
Glennas M. Walker
Sheena M. Weatherington
Markel A. White
Michele M. Whitehurst
Chelsea L. Whitford

MIDWESTERN STATE UNIVERSITY, WICHITA FALLS, TX

Joshua H. Aaron
Matthew A. Aaron
Jaime M. Abraham
Maria V. Acosta
Yvonne K. Albert
Akeida D. Alexis
Simone Joselle Ria Alexis
Dayana Amaya
Janice Arriaga
Mai A. Badran
Krishna Mohan R. Bakka
Brandi Baldwin
Ravi P. Baskaran
Katie A. Becker
Suman Bhandari
Sarah B. Bond
Mary M. Brady
Blanca E. Brezina
Anne E. Bristow
Kay K. Brookes
Jocelyn R. Brown
Rachel E. Bullard
Courtney D. Burnette
Nikki R. Bussue
Shelby M. Butler
Cheyenne N. Cannedy
Laura M. Cason
Irvichal C. Challenger
Weiwei Chen
Bethaney C. Clayton

Denzel E. Coipel
Ione Colombo
Kelli D. Cousins
Elascha D. Davila-Hicks
Damian G. DeSilva
Vijaya Madhuri Devarapalli
Ayesha R. Dewalagawa
Madamawatta
Diane S. Eakins
Anthony Chisom Enem
Kessia S. Eugene
Israel T. Ezeodum
Kayla Y. Fells
Sherrima M. Ferlance
Sara N. Finkler
Sarah G. Flagg
Matthew R. Fox
Brendlyn V. Fyfield
John C. Garman
Alexis S. Gay
Kasau L. Gomes
Renatta L. Graham
Michael A. Graves
Andrew D. Gray
Kenneth R. Griffin
Teran M. Griffin
Jn Claude Gustave
Kailey L. Harper
Sierra L. Harper
Shirley L.ouvina Hazel

Andrew Todd Hebert
Ashley Herman
Shelby A. Horne
Candace V. Hughes
Sonia A. Ike
Rachel M. Innes
Gentille Iradukunda
Harley T. James
Cassidy D. Jarrett
Tayler M. Jerrick
Merkern Hirsha Melissa Jn
Panel
Benni B. Joseph
Ali Khalid
Natalie C. Knobloch
Kara M. L'Esperance
Kristin M. Lanier
Kareen La Touche-Phillip
Melissa J. Laussmann
Anna E. Lerew-Phillips
Yanru Li
Gwendolyn C. Lopez
Karina Lopez
Corbin Santiago Matamoros
Maryana B. Mbalule
Andrea Mendoza Lespron
Selena M. Mize
Latham J. Moody
Sharon R. Mucker

Yashwanth reddy R.
Muddireddy
Shawn M. Murray
Shonae W. Musgrove
Juleigh M. Myracle
Iesha O'Loughlin
Cindy A. Onyekwere
Adanna C. Oparaji
Ethan F. Parker
Nikesia G. Pemberton
Katherine A. Pendergrass
Chanuka G. Perera
Cailli C. Perry
Yasmin K. Persaud
Bernard Peters
Nanette T. Philip
Megan C. Piehler
Emerald A. Pierre
Indira S. Placide
Gisselle A. Polius
Shilpa Poloju
Sydnee J. Pottorf
Avelyne "Pinkey" Prince
Rhea A. Randhawa
Coleman L. Reidling
Zeltzin A. Reyes Trejo
Rebecca M. Rhone
Zakary M. Roberts
RuthAnn M. Ross
Deborah S. Roucloux

Ricardo D. Ruiz
Cody W. Rutledge
Demetria S. Samuel
Sarah M. Schloemer
James W. Schrah
Jody E. Settle
Karishma Shah
Nidhi K. Sharma
Eli W. Sheppard

Parker Haden Short
Jennifer M. Sissel
Gyselle R. Skeete-Wallace
Rachel Marie Smith
Brian S. Spence
Ashley P. Stewart
Jahron J. Stuart
Jordan K. Susac
Dyamond Tankersley

Patrick I. Thompson
Kelsey L. Tidwell
Motlatsi K. Tolo
Esmeralda A. Toral
Diana Torres
James E. Trevino
Princess M. Trussell
Andre V. Tyrell
Alexander J. Van Allen

Katelyn E. Vietti
Jordan R. Waddell
Indeesha M.
Wickramarachchi
Rainah M. Winston
Paul E. Yacho
Erick J. Zambrano
Destiny A. Zynda

MILLIGAN COLLEGE, MILLIGAN COLLEGE, TN

Sarah Caitlin Bane
Abigail Faith Bethea
Molly Kate Brannock
Zoey Marie Brennan
Nathan J. Cachiaras

Katherine Elizabeth Douglas
Eden Kendall Greene
Emilee Michelle Leichty
Laura Renee Mixon
Caleb J. Nix

James Joshua Ramsaran
Gabriel David Rees
Casey Lynn Richardson
Katherine Mary Siglin
Andrew James Simonsen

Kerri Slaughter
John Mark Steadman
Micah RheaAnne Stephens
Shayla LeeAnn Wood

MILLSAPS COLLEGE, JACKSON, MS

Lizhou Ai
Anna Lexus Andrews
Kandice Bailey
Will Brewer
Graham Casey
Cheryl Cole
Hunter Coleman
Cadi B.N. Duncan

Pooja Goel
Rajan Hanstad
Sarah Hawthorne
Ryan Henry
Hannah Huval
Madeline Iles
Mary Frances Ivey
Daniel Lamar Furnace Kees

Corissa Erin Lambert
Sophie Lipman
Cali Longo
Adriana Lopez-Esteban
Brooks Marion
Alexandra Summer Melnick
Kenneth Newburger
Emerald Norton

Hirni Patel
Ellen Smith
Anthony Joseph Vernaci III
Lauren Voelker
Erika Wheeler
Theresa Ann Woehnker
Carlos Austin Zamarripa

MILWAUKEE SCHOOL OF ENGINEERING, MILWAUKEE, WI

Logan Ray Bakkum
Nicole Alexandria Baylon
Colin Daniel Bekta
Jonathan Patrick Braaten
Elizabeth Rae Brooks
Karissa Miranda Brunette
Chase Anthony Bryant
Justin Lee Clough
Elizabeth Ann Donohew
Lauren Ashley Dudley
Megan Marie Feilbach
Haily Rain Fernald
Samantha Joanne Fredricks
Alexandra Marie Fuerst

Sofia Ann Garcia
Jason Scott Genz
Mitchell Gieske
Austen Leahy Gross
Kyra Rose Gudgel
Megan E. Hayes
Abigail Paige Heiller
Garrett William Hoeg
Nathan Andrew Howell
Lauren Patricia Itzin
Dylan Arthur Klepps
Alexandra Theofania G.
Klonis
Megan Elizabeth Kroll

Devon Donald Lantagne
Ana Sofia Larraga Martinez
Landon Mara
Kasey Lee Mylin
Savannah Dawn Neu
Seth Ryan Opgenorth
Riley Francis Padron
Michele Pancani
Nathaniel Robert Pedigo
John Mark Ponio
Michael Lee Prochaska
Mariely Ramirez
Logan Rae Readnour
Kathryn Mae Ready

Emily Savela
Evan Michael Schilling
Elizabeth Marie Schmitt
Brandon E. Shea
Arthur Russell Siebel
Camille Rose Somberg
Kai Michael Swanson
Alana Dean Tirimacco
Marlena Kay Trier
Kersey Lynn Uphouse
Kelsey Rae Uuskallio
Johanna Hseng-hsi Wang
Matthew Bryant Weinke
Rachel Louise Wellnitz

Kaitlyn Ann Wolf

MINNESOTA STATE UNIVERSITY, MANKATO SOCIAL & BEHAVIORAL SCIENCES, MANKATO, MN

Aaron Micheal Anderson

Jade Rochelle Anderson

Steven Arriaza

Jake Gordon Aspenson

Haylee LaVae Barnum

Brooke Marie Barrett

Matthew L. Bender

Brandon Anthony
Bergemann

Breanna Mae Bethke

Taylor M. Bird

Crystal Violet Boag

Jolynne Bockman

Krista Nicole Bruns

Keith Andrew Burggraff

Chord Wesley John Buscho

Carissa Carpenter

Grace Centini

Cassidy Paige Chapek

JinJu Choi

Cassandra Leigh Cosenza

Bethany Rae Degner

Sarah Ann Delhanty

Mikyla Jean Denney

Sarah Marie Dickhudt

Katelin Patrice Dietel

Grace Olivia Doyle

Quentina Elaine Dunbar

Judy Lee Duquette

Amanda Dusterhoft

Kelly Eckert

Kristi Ann Edblom

Taylor Farr

Peter Scott Fenske

Brianna Rose Fitzgibbons

Ashley Lauretta Flaherty

Shelby Ann Flegel

Desiree Lynn Frederick

Jonathan Michael Friday

Laura Ann Fry

Lydia Fry

Elisa Kay Gjermundson

Patricia Joyce Glover

Chad Edward Goertzen

Elizabeth Guss

Katelyn Ann Hakinson

Julia J. Hamann

Ellen Leigh Hammerschmidt

Tyler Joel Hammerschmidt

Bryce Hansen

Mary Hanson

Alyssa Marie Hareid

Thomas Richard Harrington

Rosa Maria Consuelo Hayes

Mandee Jo Heiderscheidt

Jacob Eli Hendrickson

Kailie Ann Hinkle

Dustin David Hissam

Rebecca S. Holmberg

Cole Patrick Huggins

James W. Hughes

Thomas Maxfield
Huntington

Zachary Larry Jacobson

Kristen Carol Jaehnert

Janessa Amber Jandt

Duck Woo Jang

Lauren Elizabeth Jenson

Danielle Charlene Johnson

David Jeremy Johnson

Jessica Lee Johnson

Erin Joan Kahnke

Melissa Marie Kangas

Jacob Francis Kerr

Caroline Kienlen

Morgan Kirchner

Krystal Lauren Klement

Bethany Jane Koshak

Rachel Anne Kramer

Sarah K. Kraus

Cortney Kressin

Caleb Jonathan Krochalk

Kevin Michael Krueger

Kami Lynn Kuhns

Ohhyun Kwon

Celine Nadege Kyelem

Megan Elise Lahti

Kiersten Dee Larson

Luke David Larson

Eun Hye Lee

Abbey Mae Linderholm

Erin Linscheid

Shaylyn M. Lyksett

Nicole Tacheny Lynch

Dayan Matthew Maas

Kathryn Dolores Macey

Margaret Madison

Nicholas James Madson

Drake Andrew Malaske

Paige Mallam

Nicole Anne Mara

Laura Katherine Mason

Rina Matsuda

Rachel Marie Mattick

David Thomas Mattioli

Trisha Maust

Nena Ellen Kay McCalla

Zachary Colter McCarver

Ryan John McFarland

Michael Milks

Kevin John Miller

Sandra Lynn Miller

Tyler Joshua Milless

Jason Jerome Francis Millett

Kourtney Marie Mitchell

Taylor Marie Montbriand

Molly Nicole Montgomery

Nicole Marie Moritz

Thomas Richard Mossman

Timothy Jon Mourning

Fartun Abukar Musse

Ezequiel T. Nava

Yang Kalia Nelsie

Amy Marie Niedenfuer

David Rodger Nyhus

Leah Nyirashishi

Claire Otto

Jack William Owen

Dustin Michael Pautsch

Hannah J. Peterson

Heather Marie Peterson

Mark William Pierpont

Kyle Edward Pirron

Brittany Ann Pitcher

Mistin Mary Price

Sandy Kay Prochaska

Amber Nicole Recker

Keaton Patrick Reuben

Haley Jade Rohloff

Jennifer Sue Rubio

Samra Lita Russell

Bethany Rose Rykhus

Casey Scheller

Kyler Tellier Schoner

Anne Schuelke

Alissa R. Shape

Madeline Robin Shaw

Dakota Shepherd

Katherine Sherrard

Katelyn Skrien

Hyun Hee Song

Lydia Rose Stafki

Ashley Yvonne Stangler

Jessica Jo Staricka

Summer Raye Steenhoven

Kayla Beth Stone

Erika Teachout

Luke Thao

Owen Marvin Theis

Jessica Marie Underdahl

Tabitha Jennifer Urban

Joanne VanHaren

Megan Kylie Vergin

Trisha K. Walker

Stephanie Ann Walters

Kristin Weber

Rebecca Louise Wegscheid

Austin Jacob Weinandt

Taryn Wicks

Nathan Wiig

Aftyn Scot Wildes

Hannah Marie Witzig

MaKayla Marie Woller

Ethan M. Wynia

Chengleng Xiong

Nou Chee Yang

Sara Ann Young

Luke Isaac Zabel

Karisa Maria Zachar

Lauren Zappitello

Jessica-Brooke Brelynn
Zehme

MINNESOTA STATE UNIVERSITY–MANKATO ALLIED HEALTH & NURSING, MANKATO, MN

Nicole Marie Amos

Bethany Grace Bishop

Tucker Randall Coil

Emily Ann Cramer

Rachel Marie Eiler

Thate Erica Elizabeth

Kathleen M. Finley

Madeline Elaine Frank

Jacqueline Kay Frederickson

Sapana Ghimire

Vanessa Jean Gubbels

Alexis Janel Haakedahl

Scott Michael Heitkamp

Riley Ann Holmes

Molly Louise Horning

Austin James Lane

Allison Spanier Maleska

Elizabeth Faye Maloney

Kellie D. Metzger

Laura LouAnn Monson

Pa Houa Houa Moua

Emily Jean Mueller

Amanda Marie Murphy

Sarah Aileen Nicosia

Emily Elise Norell

Kayla Rose Patterson

Erin Jo Peterson

Cassidy Lee Ross

Maxwell Lee Schmeling-
Rykhus

Jill Rae Schmidt

Allison Mae Scott

Madeline Marie Smith

Jade Rachel Jamieson
Spenger

Mallory Rose Spier

Elisa Marie Van De Steeg

Danielle Lee Walsh

Amy Nadine Westerlund

Logan William Willhite

MINOT STATE UNIVERSITY, MINOT, ND

Kayla Marie Barke

Christina Marie Beck

Alexander Lee Buchholz

Kelsey Mae MacNaughton
Buchholz

Ashley Michelle Busch

Joshua David Bussard

Danielle Jean Foster

Molly Jane Haagenson

Ismail Abdi Hassan

Savana Talor Kingsbury

Annika Rose Kraft

Meggan Eron Larsen

Miranda Margaret
Lessmeister

Teagan Marie Loppe

Caley Jean Nelson

Chloe Lian Ondracek

Shelby Danielle Pederson

Bob B. Jacob Pond

Vanessa Ramirez

Cassandra Elizabeth Stauffer

Christin-Ann Rose Stoll

Reagan Van Teeling

Keyona Maranda Walker

MISERICORDIA UNIVERSITY, DALLAS, PA

Kayleigh Monica Morein

Caitlin E. Vitale

MISSISSIPPI COLLEGE, CLINTON, MS

James Eric Anderson

Anderson Reid Bensch

Anna Lauren Bicker

Stephanie Elizabeth Bittick

Andrew Mark Borho

Amelia Katherine Brashier

Zachariah Daylin Burns

Avery Elizabeth Caldwell

Colton Richard Caver

Jesse Allen Chasser

Grace Elizabeth Clark

Lynley Cole Clark

Lauren Elizabeth Compere

Bretton Christopher Crosby

Lauren Elizabeth Cullen

Victoria Nicole Danczyk

Hannah Elizabeth DeVries

Elaine Catherine Everett

Myles Darian Faries

Lauren Alexandria Fiegle

Claire Elise Fisher

Alexis Anne Frautschi

Taylor Alyse Gaughf

Shelby Grant Gilliam

Stephen Payton Gray

Charles Cole Gressett

William Brown Gurtowski

Michael Patrick Healey

Mary Ellen Heath

Lynnsey Kay Jackson

Sarah Lindsay Knight

Gerald Lee "Jay" Kucia Jr.

Dudley Ford Lampton

Victoria Kay Langworthy

Lacey Katherine Leddy

Cheng Li

John Benton Long

Shaniqua Denise Love

Kaitlin Veronica McCarty

Melanie Layne McCoy

Dalton Seth McDonald	Sherree Michelle Rayner	Shelby Lynn Sattler	Grady ONeil Turman Jr.
Elizabeth Ann McNeer	Nichole Lynn Marie Rhea	Kawsu Sillah	Katherine Ann Upchurch
Mary Elizabeth McRae	Macy Hart Riley	Weston Andrew Smedley	Caleb Joshua Upton
Tabitha Christian Mizell	Cason Benton Robbins	Carol Ann Stevens	Emma Carroll Waller
Caleb Neal Morris	Christian Ray Robbins	Ashley Brooke Subervielle	Reagan Christine Webb
Steven Sollon Papas	Melissa Corrinne Roberson	Shelby Anne Swede	Joy Waller Welch
Dorothy Elizabeth Parish	Karlee Beth Russom	Abby Jo Thompson	Andrew Steven Wilson
Benjamin Gilbert Peyton	Sara Lauren Rutledge	Qian Tong	Keaton Luke Yeatts
Joanna Lauren Pope	Brian D. Sanders	Anna Katherine Travis	Alexa RaeAnn Zylstra

MISSISSIPPI GULF COAST COMMUNITY COLLEGE JACKSON COUNTY CAMPUS, GAUTIER, MS

Caeleighn Bernard	Rebekah E. Heyer	Bradley R. McGill	Rebekah L. Smith
Cassidy Mackenzie Birchfield	Natalie J. Hopkins	Hallie Nicole Nettles	Dylan K. Spencer
Haley Bradford	La'Kol M. Hutchins	Isaac L. Payne	Shane M. Sullivan
Colions F. Cato	Tyler M. Joiner	Haley C. Ross	Jenna Renee Swift
Brandon C. DeLillo	Cory L. Kiper	Tristan L. Ruppert	Sandra S. Trinidad
Kyndall L. Dobbs	Danielle M. Kuper	Elizabeth R. Sandoval	Cassidy E. Voelkel
Evalyn J. Goff	Noah H. Lafferty	Amber Renee Schulze	Michiru Yamaoka
	Lydia E. McDowell	Tabitha M. Simmons	

MISSISSIPPI GULF COAST COMMUNITY COLLEGE JEFFERSON DAVIS CAMPUS, GULFPORT, MS

Arieonna E. Allen	Yavonnie D. Edwards	Madisyn A. Lanoue	Katherine S. Norman
Tamara S. Bangs	Justin S. Gurka	Jasmine Lindsley	Daniel D. Russell
Andrea M. Bundy	Jenna M. Hayes	Hannah B. Livingston	Dezmon E. Santana
Joanna K. (Jojo) Burnett	Morgan B. Henry	Mallory S. Lyon	Alexandria L. Stevenson
Tyler E. Doussan	Hadley N. Hill	Bria L. Magee	Megan J. Wilson
Corwin J. Drummond	Victoria F. Jones	Cotton M. Massengill	Stacy R. Witt
Adam J. Dunnells	Ailey J. Kirkpatrick	Guy V. Monjure	

MISSISSIPPI GULF COAST COMMUNITY COLLEGE PERKINSTON CAMPUS, PERKINSTON, MS

Tyler Allen	Devin Diane Easterling	Emily Howell	A'Darius Vince Steele
Zundui Badral	Jamaal Elizenberry	Mandalene Marie McKissick	T'Laria Truong
Parker Bond	MaKayla Houston Farris	Diego Munguia	Elston Walker
Charda' Boone	Stosha Sierra Gamble	Alexandria Perkins	Annie Victoria Watts
Aurellia Bourne	Madeline Groue	Keisha Pierre	Sally George Wilson
Jessica Lauren Burrill	Catherine Lynn Murrah	Bailey Purvis	Erika Starbuck Wood
Brittany Cooley	Hasty	Iris Laihmen Quan	Jaycie Yott
Steven Michael Craddock	Devin Havard	Chance Robinson	
Arnel Dujkovic	Daquan Holloway	Anna Scovel	

MISSISSIPPI UNIVERSITY FOR WOMEN GRADUATE SCHOOL, COLUMBUS, MS

Nancy M. Ashford	Jana Berry	Gillian P. Robinson

MISSISSIPPI VALLEY STATE UNIVERSITY DEPARTMENT OF CRIMINAL JUSTICE, ITTA BENA, MS

Katrina Yvette Bell	Ellis Collins	Ashley L. Johnson	Quintarus K. Robinson
Ricardo C. Benson	DeMarcus A. Frazier	Rhodesia N. Johnson	Shota Shalashvili
Denisha L. Byrd	Tanessa R. House	Laura Redditt	Tyrina C. Starlin
Jerry Carter	Jerimesia N. Jackson	Taliyah R. Riddick-Waters	

MISSISSIPPI VALLEY STATE UNIVERSITY DEPARTMENT OF ENGLISH & FOREIGN LANGUAGE, ITTA BENA, MS

Seprela M. Ellis	April Lawrence	Santiadra Dearra Toolie	Valiesha Catherine Wells

MISSISSIPPI VALLEY STATE UNIVERSITY DEPARTMENT OF SOCIAL WORK, ITTA BENA, MS

Courtney Nicole Barnes	Shantell Olds	Tamiko Wilkins
Calvin Brown	Tamatha Lashall Outlaw	
Michelle' Clay	Hawkins	
Glenda Chambers Hampton	Rehoma Spivey III	

MISSISSIPPI VALLEY STATE UNIVERSITY DEPARTMENT OF TEACHER EDUCATION, ITTA BENA, MS

Rebeka Clinton	Halle Gayten	Von Love Jr.	Monchelle Taylor
Jasmine Coats	Dominique Golden	Kateris Alexander	Quashan Terry
Denmariae Collins	Christen BreAnn Green	Shaquoy Scott	Ashley Yates
Yolanda Foster	Willexia Griffin	Jeanette Sewell	Brandon Yepez

MISSISSIPPI VALLEY STATE UNIVERSITY MATHEMATICS, COMPUTER & INFORMATION SCIENCES, ITTA BENA, MS

Joshua D. Bailey	Kalyx N. McDonald	Jatinkumar R. Patel	Rashad L. Williamson
Alexandria C. Garland	Raveen T. McKenzie	Na'Kaila M. Sandidge	
Jabbar A. Lindsey II	Ifeanyi R. Onyenweaku	Jamal R. Stevenson	

MISSOURI BAPTIST UNIVERSITY, SAINT LOUIS, MO

Katherine Anne Alexander	Rebecca Counts	Esther Kathleen Gilliam	Debra D. Lambert
Shannon Nicole Alley	Abigail Rose Crain	Tyler Gerard Greminger	Hannah Louise Lovekamp
Hannah Grace Ballard	Michael James Cutler	Haley Fay Grueber	James R. Maasen
Kelly Devyn Barns	Claire Kahana De Mello	Erik S. Gustafson	Sam Richard Mauer
Allen Michael Berryman	Ann J. Derges	Jereme Matthew Harry	Alan Lee Meyer
Paula J. Bess	Colby Robert Duncan	Jasmine Donsha Jackson	Lydia E. Milan
Casey Bouillere-Howard	Yolanda A. Dye	Brooke Shelton Jennewein	Gabrielle Lee Mitchem
Jonathan David Brown	Dominic Edward Fabrizio	Molly Valnessa Josephs	Miranda Loren Monroe
Shawn C. Brown	Courtney Flanagan	Nika Juricic	David Morris
Darrian Lee Chrzanoski	Elizabeth Ashley Fuld	Matthew James Ketterer	Andrea Paige Mossman
Taylor L. Cook	Megan Nichole Gaither	Courtney C. Kiernan	Elizabeth M. Nelson

Adam Patrick Ney
Faith Victoria Notz
Brittani Nicole O'Connell
Nandi Bose'De Person
Emily Lynn Potts
Haley Elizabeth Pouliezos

Lucas Robert Prichard
Ryan Alan Rerich
Olivia Lucille Rhea
Alexander Roux
Christopher Aaron Rowland
Suheir Osama Shalabi

Kaitlin Elizabeth Shanks
Debbie Sharp
Charles Edward Small II
Toni Elizabeth Stang
Kristen Michelle Strange
Shavon Mona' Swearengen

Katherine Erin Switzer
Hailey Korrine Townsend
Jordan Tempyl Weller
Maxwell Cosmo Kinnison
Wingate

MISSOURI STATE UNIVERSITY WEST PLAINS, WEST PLAINS, MO

Billie Ann Brown
Casey Simon Buehler
Grace Nicole Buffington
Paydan Anne Clayton
Cateland Jade Collins
Abbigayle Faye Evans
Guro Key Froberg

Ashton Nicole Garner
Hannah Christell Grills
Seth Michael Hadley
Shelby Lynn Harris
William Joseph Hatcher
Kathryn D. Henson
April Gaylene Hogan

Ashley Elizabeth Howell
Jessica Elizabeth Jenkins
Curtis W. Kelm
Kaitlyn Taylor Kentner
Morgan Renee Kinder
Sydney M. McBride
Cassandrea L. McCart

Allison Nicole Neely
Heidi Lynne Pettit
Hailey Ashton Shinberger
Shane Aubrey Shulters
Katey Danielle Smith
Danielle Ramona Sullivan

MITCHELL COLLEGE, NEW LONDON, CT

Nicholas Augeri
Tylea Banks

Savannah Jean Boyle
Dorcelle Katia Lawrence

Zachary Marmo
Anthony Jospeh Mastria

Jennifer Marie Neff
Sophie Spiller

MITCHELL COMMUNITY COLLEGE, STATESVILLE, NC

Allison Marie Barkley
Courtney D. Cox-Manser

Jonathan Ray Isenhour
Angela Johnson

William Macnamara

Carol Nettles

MITCHELL TECHNICAL INSTITUTE, MITCHELL, SD

Colin Alley
Cody Ray Bernt
Ariel Dawn Bieber
Kyle Blume
Logan Michael Bordewyk
Cody J. Brake
Jesse Jay Brunmeier
Dylan Brunsing
Travis W. Colbert
Nicholas A. Cundy
Aaron DeHaai
Haley Sue Delancey
Taylor McHale Delker
Cody Eugene Denison
Brandon A. Doyle
Tyler M. Durfee
Jackson James Entringer

Jill Ruth Fischer
Emma Marie Flynn
Michael John Geidel
Kelly M. Gillis
Chet Pierre Glanzer
Jill Greenway
Ryan D. Guericke
Brittney Ann Hansen
Nicole Heier
Ericka D. Hellberg
Aaron Robert Herman
Leighah Faye Hertel
Joseph P. Hetland
Brandon Paul Houska
Tracy Michelle Howe
Adam Lee Hruska
Austin Lee Huggins

Tyler James Hughes
Allen M. Johansen
Nickolas Alan Johnson
Katie Elizabeth Juhnke
Paul G. Kelly
Andrew Mark Kilcollins
Kayla Jolene Kloucek
Tammra Kay Kreth
Lee Ronald Lauck
Kutler Leighton
Sydney Rae Logan
Layne A. Lucas
Benjamin Ray Matzner
Reed Alan McBrayer
Robert Lee McFarland
Liam J. McManus
Dylan Meyer

Jordan Mykah Miller
William Paul Minow
Rachel June Mora
Danny Mullis
Cassie Marie Murtha
Alex Stephen Musson
Joseph Martin Nagel
Chase James Nelson
Katrina R. Nicholson
Aryn Novotny
Kelsey Marie Overweg
Ryan Donald Pearson
Peggy S. Plaatje
Kristi R. Plooster
Brittney Lorraine Priebe
Erin Courtney Ridgway
Jesse Leo Ronke

William Scott Royse
Lacey Schimke
Cassidy James Schnabel
Cory Charles Schulte
Joshua A. Schwingler

Tatyanna Marie Shade
Scott A. Shoemaker
Travis A. Smith
Brady R. Soulek
Benjamin Merle Stevenson

Hailey Leona Sumption
Erin Madelyne Thomas
Mikayla Renae Tolliver
Joel W. Uecker
Angela Anne Vissia

Austin J. Weber
Seth Richard Weeman
Justin Wipf
Eric Zepp
Christopher Zuber

MOLLOY COLLEGE, ROCKVILLE CENTRE, NY

Krystine Abberton
Kezia Andrews
Tracey Balinskas
Maria Gabriela Barandica
Laura Biagiotti
Milan Botte
Kevin Bowles
Ashley Tamara Caffey
Nicholas Anthony Calabro
Andrew Capobianco
Alexa de la Torre
Anna Theresa Delgado

Rebecca Desormeaux
Thomas Dreyer
Elizabeth Duffy
Gemma Clare Erdmann
Natalie Fernandez
Alexandra Martha Grunin
Desmond Guidroz
Grace Healey
Keesha Hill
Sara Jacklin
Anja Marie Jackowski
Scott Jones

Jason Kloos
Timothy Klotsche
Steven Daniel Malinowski
Toni Marie Martini
Mary-Kate Michels
Cassandra Palmer
Kristen Ponticelli
Kerri Robertson
Christian Paul Romanelli
Michael Russo
Michael Schultz
Maryanna Swanson

Robert Brendan Theofield
Sean Troy
Felipe Vargas
Santiago Vargas
Peter Vath
Alexander Vinciguerra
Shakhan Daniel Volmar
Tyler Walther
Karlee Yanantuono

MONMOUTH COLLEGE, MONMOUTH, IL

Amber Berge
Kathleen Brown
Katherine H. Carter
Kayla Cherry
Bradley Thomas Dulee
Jessica M. Fox
Andrea Elizabeth Gasow
Mary J. Gonzalez

Mary Claire Claire Griffith
Megan R. Horack
Brian Johnson
Dillon Lehr
Jade Jazmine Luthy
Jacob Patrick Marx
Rachel Sophia Masch
Steven Murphy

Emily Olson
Barbara Louise Pajor
Kathryn A. Rees
Paige L. Rus
David Erik Ruud
Victoria M. Salyards
Emily J. Sheetz
Miranda L. Shryack

Jaire Sims
Michael G. Smith
Josalyn R. Spagnola
Neriangela Velez
Emily Lynn Watkins

MONROE COMMUNITY COLLEGE, ROCHESTER, NY

Sydney Abbate
Rickie Austin Jr.
Andrew Badura
Mackenzie Bemish
Jennifer Mae Boutwell
Alexandra R. Buchner
Jeremy Carmichael
Lynette M. Collazo
Corrin Ann Collins
Michael Compter
Chelsea Marie Cornelius

Benjamin Andrew Davies
Yvan Del Valle Abreau
Lisa Denmark
Melissa DiFrancesco
Mayasia Elliston
Safari Harris
Rachel Hendee
Sara LiPera
Carmen I. Lopez
Yomary Malave
Justine Mauch

Genesis Maria Melendez
Gloribelise Merced
Claudette Elise Morris
Bekkah A. Najeeullah
Johnny Ogene
Victor Ortiz
Sean Paul
Thomas Peppers
Matthew Preiser
Emmalynne Quinn
Rosalind S. Randolph

Francenia Reynolds
Leon McKinley Rice
Nancy E. Robertson
Victor J.R. Rojas
Chantelle Rothfuss
Nancy J. Santacessaria
Lia Schapero
Tara Scott
Anani Serbeniuk
Nicole Simmons
Nuri N. Simmons Jr.

Daniel Steiner

Randy Lecelle Stevenson

Angel Swaney

Richard Eugene Thomas

Calla VanLuven

Jina A. Walker

Jordan Welch

Caroline Wensel

Kristal White

Corene Wiggins

Irvin Williamson

Jacob Wilson

Cynthia L. Wisor

John Wu

Sabrina Zazzara

MONTGOMERY COMMUNITY COLLEGE, TROY, NC

Thomas John Alt III

Nicholas A. Batten

Edwin Benjume

Mitchell G. Bowers

Mary K. Britt

Addie W. Brown

Toni T. Callicutt

Casey N. Chappell

Evelyn E. Corp

Elizabeth J. Davis

Jodi S. Decker

Amity R. Dyer

Allister P. Ford

Journey J. Hatcher

Chia Her

Kecia M. Islas

Jacqueline E. Jimenez

Lisa S. Lowder

Talia A. Lowder

Jonathan H. Macdonald

Brian M. McGuire

Kenneth J. Morris

Anita W. Munoz

Hunter D. Nelson

Lindi Caroline Outz

Brandon L. Pemberton

Jose M. Peralta

Toni D. Poindexter

Homar Jaimes Rodriguez

Paul Samonekeo

Jake A. Smith

Stephen D. Tableman

Samuel K. Tate

Constance L. Thompson

Tyler D. Thompson

Bobby R. Threadgill

Angela A. Vaught

Kelsey R. Wall

Austin L. Warner

Nicholas A. Woodard

MONTGOMERY COUNTY COMMUNITY COLLEGE, BLUE BELL, PA

Steven Adoff

Janet Askin

Bobbianne Babb

Stefanie Barszowski

Nicole Battista

Thomas Bednar

Kristy Bell

Elizabeth Bergland

Maria Boggi

Kyle Bone

Donna J. Braner

Marion Bucci

Daniel Buttorff

Jacqueline Caddle

Catherine Rose Camuso

Patricia Capizzi

Sarah Ciambrano

Julie Clark

Julie Beth Clark

Kevin Cruz

Heather Marie Curran

Elizabeth Cusmina

Cassandra Davis

Sharon Delporte

Carlos DePaz

Maura Duggan

Courtney Durham

Erin Alker Ehinger

Lori Flynn

Dana Fornicola

Ann Forrestal

Kevin Franklin

Theresa Gallagher

Masynn Gensler

Bridget Geri

Susan Ann Giancola

Allison Giannone

Karen Gratton

Rivka Gross

Joseph Gruver

Debra Haasis

Heather Haby

Kathryn Hall

Eun Kyoung Han

Joseph S. Hartline

Brittany Hewitt

Diane Heydt

Judy Hoffmeister

Ruth Holsopple

Nancy Horton

Holly Hughston

Colin Blake Hurrey

John Ilisco Ilisco

Solange Jacques

Emmett Johnson

Julianne Johnson

Timothy Judge

James Karcher

Monica Keister

Amanda Kida

Jon Kilgannon

Janice Kutt

Lynn Lang

Lisa Leadbeater

Fang Li

Jinman Li

Johanna Licari

Heidi Elizabeth Liebenberg

Carl Lingenfelter

Debra Lockard

Jacquelyn Lutz

Regina Marie MacMurtrie

Donna Maden

David Maga

Brian Maggio

James Mahoney

Kristy Mahoney

Agnieszka Mandosik

Renee Marshall

John May

Eileen McGilloway

Daniel McGlinchey

Lori McIlvee

James Holmes Mearns V

Angelika Mae Morelos

Angelika Mari Mendoza

Morelos

Catherine Morroney

Michael Morrow

Jenna Lynn Moyer

Jaclyn Marie Murphy

Robert Murphy

Audrey O'Keefe

Cameron Michael O'Neil

Martina Oborna

Elizabeth Palesano

Danielle Pearson	Michael Reiner	Anna Short	Richard Vose
Marta Pecharo	Emily Violet Reitmeyer	Sara Shultz	Lee A. Wagner
Courtney Pepe	Jacob R. Robertson	Alex Siwik	Dianarose Weiler
Vicki Peters	Victoria Rosato	Arnette Pendleton Smith	Sarah Marie Welch
Corey Pettine	Andrew C. Rose	Lavinia Lisette Soliman	Eileen Williams
Lindsey Phillips	Michelle Rose	Hui Song	Michaela Belle Williams
Thomas Pittman	Brittni Ruch	Woo Young Song	Jason Wolff
Breanna Potts	Kyle Sapovits	Benjamin Swanger	Martha Wolgemuth
Julie Primavera	Jessi Shaffer	Esther Thompson	Mary Zabriskie
Heather N. Pringle	Silvia Shambo	Margaret Thompson	Amanda Wang Zhou
Tetyana Protsyk	James Sherid	John Timmons	
Victoria Reeser	Gabriel Shoemaker	Wen Trice	

MORAINE PARK TECHNICAL COLLEGE, BEAVER DAM, WI

Jeremiah Alderden	Matthew Robert Grady	Anne Moericke	Dawn Shelly Weber
Anita Irene Bagwell	Gustave Jacoby	Rebecca Powell	Ashley Wimer
Grace Bleiler	Cody Liesener	Natalie Schmitz	

MORAVIAN COLLEGE, BETHLEHEM, PA

Alyssa C. Alessandra	Connor P. Gallagher	Gabrielle C. Marotta	Kristoff St. John Adrian
Zachary J. Arcona	Gina M. Gambacorto	Audrey McSain	Riley
Taylor Mackenzie Blake	Emily R. Hanes	Marie Ann Mikols	Brittany M. Spinosa
Victoria M. Bobyak	Jaclyn R. Hudak	David M. Pasquale	Shannon N. Strohl
Meghan M. Cote	Christina M. Isernia	Peter J. Petrack	
Clint Doyle	Maxwell Korten	Kimberly I. Polanco	
Rebecca H. Eisenstein	Kayla M. Krouse	Bethany E. Rang	

MORENO VALLEY COLLEGE, MORENO VALLEY, CA

Erika Amaya	Michele Gardner	Esly Lopez	Veronica Person
Marco Beltran	Jocelyn Gastelum	Melissa Wanda Jeanette	Kevin Phalavisay
Amofah Brobbey	Ismael Gonzalez	Lopez	Katie Rader
Amanda Broudway	Sandra Gonzalez	Tyrone Macedon Sr.	Ana Rico
Jacqueline Castro	Rochelle Gorman	Sonal Masit	Jose Saavedra
Derica Cooke	Dorothy Ethal Hatton	Sakia McDowell	Monica Satchell
Francisco Cruz	Emily Heath	David Hernandez Montes	Elva Alejandra Silva
LeAnn Davila	Natasha Howard	Tanisha Morrris	Amber Smith
Doris N. Egbo	Vania Iriarte	Steven Oertel	Briana Strohacker
Giselle Esparza	Sean Jackson	Yulda Ogilvie	Casey Thomas
Kristin Feldmeier	Camila Kafie	Andres Padilla	Elizabeth Princess Thomas
Kassity Flores	Deena Moustafa Kamel	Tawanna Marie Parker	Kimberely Tran
Alma Garcia	Erick Lomeli	Jessica Pasillas	Daniela Valdovinas

Bryan Vargas
Alex Vidales

Phoebe Vo
Tekeyah Whitman

Tashie Noelia Marie
Williams-Powell

Karen Zetina

MORRIS COLLEGE, SUMTER, SC

Wesley Michael Alexander
David E. Alston
Olusola Ayodele Awosanya
Shalyssa Bryana Benson
Bridget Jenise Black-Harvin
Johntrell M. Bracey
Ilissa La'Quennitta Brown
Isiah D. Brown
Jessica J. Capers
Lawrence J. Carson
Latavia Janelle Chavis
Shadannia Coachman
Darryl D'ondre Cunningham
RaJohn Lachad Davis
Jasmine Monique Deloach
Melissa A. Dixon
Eniya J. Edwards
Tisheema Ragene Elmore

Brandon Dwight Epps
Brandi N. Garner
Amber S. Gaskins
Betty Denise Geddings
Imani C. Gibson-Aubry
Christopher Alexander Graham
Darnell Christopher Griffin
Tomeka Lashawn Harris
Baylee Z. Hawkins
Calandra R. Ingram
Ashley Renee Jaggers
Dominique L. Jenkins
Charles Edward Jones
Pearly M. Keith
Elissa M. Latham
Fannie B. Lockett
Kerry Leanard Manago

Sondra Shanay McCauley
Kendra Lynette McLeod
Samuel McMahand
Jamela A. Montsho
Kenyatta Tiara Oliver
Patrick N. Outler
Derwin J. Platt
Bazh Amber Ragin
Terrah S. Reuben
Carlton Bernard Richardson
Shawn Derrell Robinson
Lakendric Rush
Jake Sanders III
Destiny Dawn Saunders
Travares DeVante' Scott
Jesika Sharper
Gavin D. Singleton
Dianne Smoot

Federica Keleria Staton
Chassidy R. Stevens
Jazmine Milan Stover
Michelle Angela Sutton
Hannah Michelle Thomas
Eric Leon Walters
Shaquille O'neal Washington
Lenore Michele Waterman-Jackson
Ashley Nicole White
Tywanda L. White
TyShae Wiley
Harold Verdel Williams
Rene Luchinda Wilson
Rontia Genice Wright
Yvonne Chaveau Wright
Belinda Louise York
Kenyetta Ronelle Young

MOTLOW STATE COMMUNITY COLLEGE, LYNCHBURG, TN

Jacob Dale Anders
Katherine Elizabeth Arnold
Amelia Lynne Baggenstoss
Tabatha Brooke Beverly
Katherine Nicole Bidinger
Kasey Le'An Boyd
Bailie Charlene Bradford
Amelia Dawn Cash
Jesse Adam Fanning
Dylan Cole Gilmer
Jessica Gochee

Stephanie Godinez
Charles Vincent Gonzales
Melissa Stark Goodman
Trevor Michael Hudson
Anthony Jerome Humphrey
Amber Dawn Jolly
Ali Mundher Kadhim
Khaila King
Sylvia Baylee Luttrell
Emily Ruth Mahoney
JeanMarie Martin

Toni McPherson
Courtney Samantha Miller
Carrie Neill
Sarah Olson
Elizabeth Prather
Nomi Chith Rettich
Terri Lynn Sharp
Christopher Robin Smith
Jonathan M. Smotherman
Lisa Mary Snell
Lora Annette Sons

Tayhlor Stephenson
Tyler J. Storz
Caitlin Tripp
Katie-Beth Trout
Clinton R. Warren
Taylor M. Warren
Sarah Elizabeth Wester
Shawna Marie Willoughby

MOUNTAIN EMPIRE COMMUNITY COLLEGE, BIG STONE GAP, VA

Kennedy Blake Allen
Christopher Chad Austin
Teena Marie Baker-Dunn
Amanda G. Bentley
Heather R. Boggs

Dalton J. J. Brown
Jennifer Lynn Carter
Pamela Lynn Castle
Amanda Lucille Christian
Amber Brooke Cleek

Linda Ann Cochran
Rebecca E. Cochran
Jason Alexander Collins
Emily Kaitlin Daily
Hannah Lee Fannon

Noah McKeithan Fields
Alex Nathaniel Garnett
Kayla Ranae Gilbert
Meagan Fay Hood
Titus Zachary Houston

John P. Jones
Abbigail Marie Leonard
Misty Alison Mabe
George Gale Merriam
Holie Nicole Miller
Renee C. Morgan
Ronnie Lee Phillips

Maria D. Powers
Cassie Renee Ramey
Brenla Rasnick
Derick Alan Robinette
Sarah Rose
Kala Morgan Rutherford
Chelsea Bryanna Salyers

Sarah Beth Simons
Monteia Brooke Sloan
Rachel Shannon Sluss
Heather N. Stanley
Rachel Marie Stanley
Randy D. Stanley
Christi Ann Stidham

Micheal S. Sturgill
Rachel N. Sturgill
Morgan Ashley Thompson
Megan Denea Triplett
David Matthew Underwood
Jordan Tyler White
Aftyn Mackenzie Woodard

MOUNT ALOYSIUS COLLEGE, CRESSON, PA

Ricky Lee Abbs
Petina Jo Albright
Tara Farouk Appiah
Brianna M. Baker
Dylan J. Baker
Jill Anne Baumgardner
Derek R. Bell
Dillon J. Bender
Valerie M. Bender
Jesse Ryan Betar
Kalyn N. Blake
Amy J. Bomboy
Jesse Bortner
Connor R. Bowie
Kacie Lynnea Burk
Rachel Cain
Kirk A. Davis
Sarah Lynn Davis
Rebekah Joy Dean
Jordan K. DeMasi
Nicole M. Dunn
Jorden L. Eutsey
Jeanine F. Farabaugh

Michelle M. Fischetti
Justin L. Fleegle
Meredith R. Flick
Kelly C. Forsgren
Sydney Nicole Foster
Serena Marie Frew
Mary Jean Friend
Kylie Rebecca Froehlich
Chey Nekol Garvin
Lori A. Gress
Alyssa D. Harris
Abigail Lindsay Hawkins
Ian M. Helsel
Brianne L. Hilger
Stacie Marie Horvath
Evan Robert Hughes
Anna T. Jacobeen
Brittany Lynn Jones
Bobbie Sue Kist
Sean M. Klapper
Brenten S. Knott
Nicholas R. Konior
Jason P. Kopera

Eugene D. Krupa
Cassandra M. Lieb
Katelynn Marie Luciano
Mara B. Lytle
Cheyanne E. Marsh
Katherine D. McCormick
Stefani L. McCormick
Aaron M. McGuire
Ashley Dawn Miller
Ashley N. Miller
Crystal L. Miller
Emily Carole Mills
Haleigh T. Millward
Katelyn Cassandra Miorelli
Stephanie Michelle Moyer
James Petney
Donna M. Plummer
Katie Lynn Reed
Amber Lynn Reese
Melissa May Reeves
David E. Reigh
Jeffery Allen Rickabaugh
Ryan P. Rimbeck

Joseph P. Roland
Michelle L. Ross
Kristan Dawn Rouser
Brenda M. Sanner
Cynthia Janet Santoyo
Jennifer L. Smith
Sarah K. Spaulding
Alicia Rose Strittmatter
Robert J. Swank
Ryan S. Sweet
Austin A. Toth
Julie A. Vitko
Mercedes Lynne Wachter
Katelyn R. Wackerman
Lauren C. Walker
Kolby M. Wasnick
Greg Thomas Wierzbicki
Dorinda M. Wilson
Adam Dale Worthing
Bridgit M. Yothers
Carol Zheng

MOUNT SAINT MARY COLLEGE, NEWBURGH, NY

Joseph Issac Eddie B.
Borden
John Chiaia
Rebecca Ashley Gordils

Kerry Marie Maloney
Kristine Martin
Kelsey Morgan O'Brien
Lauren Taylor O'Neill

Justin Daniel Perez
Olivia Katherine Proulx
Aaron M. Ricci
Isabella Tartaglione

Ilci Giraldine Velarde

MOUNT VERNON NAZARENE UNIVERSITY, MOUNT VERNON, OH

Aaron Christopher Ault
James Barton

Andrew Bates
Jared K. Bohley

Wesley Philip Boston
Konnor Byers

Zachary Clark
Genevieve Michele Crump

Jeffery Culbertson
Amber Lynn Ebie
Jacob Fetzer
Rachel Harmon
Annabelle Harray
Vickie Heath
Mark Howard

Brandon Hull
Tedroy Mevrick Jackson
Melissa R. Johnson
Susan Lee Kessler
Kaitlyn Kilpatrick
Joshua Kirby
Melanie Lombardi

Annette Mary Mahon
Cameron J. Mast
Efrain Montero
Matthew David Musick
Jessica Myers
Clairanne Porter
Hannah Tate Shaffer

Nancy J Jo Speece
Amber Nichole Strickler
Riley Swanson
Kendra Vosler
Logan Weghorst
Douglas Wolfe
Rebekah Anne Wright

MOUNT WACHUSETT COMMUNITY COLLEGE, GARDNER, MA

Alyssa Adoretti
Thayna Aguiar
Joseph Almeida
Marcus Altman
Jasson Alvarado Gomez
Arturo Aponte-Cruz
Bella Ballin
Andrea Bartlett
Thomas Berger
Aleisha K. Berthiaume
Levi Bushnell

Aurea Carrion
Karen Chapalonis
Michel Cocuzza
Emanuel Corbeil
Elizabeth Cross
Kevin Figueroa
Nelida Figueroa Lopez
Jennifer Gariepy
Trevor Hansen
Thomas Hill Jr.
Tatjana Irene James

Alana Jones
Bethany Jones
Sara Khan
Stevie LaBelle
Julia McHugh
Kimberly Lynn Mertell
Nathan James Morris
Jana Murphy
Hillary Nna
Camila Pereira
Marymar Perez Cruz

Shannen Pimental
Rebecca Pincott
Michael Racine
Christian Rossi
Ellen Smith
Benjamin Spurr
Jari Squire
Cathy Teague
Leah Trudeau
Ashlie Nicole Visco
Kelly Williams

MULTNOMAH UNIVERSITY, PORTLAND, OR

Echo Bennet
Abigail Buckley
Tory Ford
Alexis Govert

Lisa Hice
Justin Jones
Randall Jay Mitcham

Elizabeth Ng
Jessica Olwa
Christy Quinn

Jonathan Root
Anastasia Simmons
Alexey Tuchin

MURRAY STATE UNIVERSITY, MURRAY, KY

Bobbie Marie Albertson
Samantha J. Bedard
Breanne Michelle Beisiegel
Victoria Lynn Bertram
Morgan Breanna Bethel
Paige Kathryn Beuligmann
Cameron Mitchell Bishop
Allison Marie Borthwick
Mariah Rose Bradley
Mary Catherine Bradley
Erika Layne Brunson
Justin Dwayne Bryant
Robert Anthony Caito
Rain Marie Carroll

Courtney Brooke Collins
Clinton Franklin Combs
Emily Francesca Conrad
Corie Elizabeth Coplen
Matthew Thomas Crane
Caisey Joelle Dotson
Madison Rae Embry
Aimee Jannette Farquhar
Corey Ryan Fisher
Samantha Joelle Flamm
Skyler Kaitlyn Frye
Taylor Grace Futrell
Katelyn M. Geilear
Landon McKenzie Gibbs

Carlie Nicole Gish
Aimee Kabahizi Habimana
Brennan Kathleen Handley
Emma Beckwith Hanrahan
Kayla Rose Harbin
Hannah G. Harris
Kristin Brooke Henson
Devin T. Hill
Sophie L. Hillier
Amanda Ann Hobson
Paige Alexis Hoffmeister
Alexander Matthew
Hopewell
Tessa M. Howald

Erica J. Howard
Katelyn Marie Jaqueway
Elisabeth Ann Johnson
Drew H. Kelley
Luke T. King
Jarred M. Koerner
Audrey C. Lewis
Ryan M. Limpus
Victoria Elizabeth Marables
Sydney Victoria Meyer
Ronnie Wayne Mills
Meagan Renee Moffat
Victoria Morgan Mohon
Fumihiko Nakamura

Maggie JoAnne Nawa	Vaughn Thomas Reed	Samuel T. Sheffer	Sarah Denise Traylor
Tanner Dale Neese	Jenna Dawn Ross	Christina Marie Sherman	Mallory Nicole Tucker
Amy Parrish Nightingale	Emily Ann Rust	James Tyler Slack	Amanda Jane Valentino
Heatherly B. Paschall	Ashley Ann Samuelson	Rebecca Kalyn Spraggs	Kara Renee Watkins
Erin O. Patton	Brianne V. Sanders	Abigail J. Stamper	Alyssa Renee Wells
Nathan Wayne Payne	Jesse Gabriel Sautel	Taylor S. Stevens	Anna Michae Word
Morgan Pearson	Melissa Kay Schenck	Suzaan Stoltz	Kaitlin Dean Ziesmer
Sydney J. Potts	Emily N. Schmahl	Brandon M. Story	
Lucas Preston Prather	Madeline E. Schmitt	Garris Landon Stroud	
Heather Rochelle Raley	Erin Marie Shaughnessy	Sydney MiRann Tibbs	

MURRAY STATE UNIVERSITY GRADUATE SCHOOL, MURRAY, KY

Hajar Alhajri	Kristopher Durfee	Melissa Kiefer	Crystal Nanney
Fahad Mohammed Alharbi	Dana Ecton	Amanda Kilmer	Chelsea Renee Neale
Amjad Almotaery	Jama L. Eddleman	Christian Klaas	Amanda Neumair
Abdulrahman Alqahtani	Caitlin Edgar	Laura Kopshever	Robert Newman
Asma Alqahtani	Chelsea Edgar	Shelby Kosmecki	Ciara Newsome
Nedaa Alshehri	Renisha Elam	Derek Lawson	Riann Offutt
Marisa Lynn Bedron	Laura Ferguson	Nhu Le	Renikka Owen
Allison Board	Channing Fisher	Pamela Lefko Jones	Allan Paul
Charles Booth	Melissa Tyndall Fox	Nicole Leitch	Victoria Ann Pierpoint
Rainey Bridges	Ashley Fritsche	Carolyn Lewis	Amanda Pittman
Rachel Brockman	Autumn Funkhouser	Amy Ligons	Cassandra Polk
Kendra Bronsink	Wendy Gamblin	Mark Mallory	Shelby Pryor
April Brown	Zachary Garrett	Tiffany Manning	Merrill Punke
Cody Brown	Kenneth Geary	Pamela Manning-Hamilton	Megan Radivonyk
Cynthia Brown	Angela Gibson	Hannah Michelle Martin	Hema Ramachandran
Katherine Byassee	Jessica Gibson	Alexa Martinez	Jody Randall
Kelley Carrico	Julie Gilliam	Lyndi Mauk	Tiffany Ray
Meghan Casey	Rebekah Goemaat	Amanda Maxlow	Elizabeth Reed
Wendy Cayce	Haley Goff	Kate Mayfield	Kayla Rhodes
Joseph Clark	Carol Green	David McDowell	Angelina Romero
Rachel Clark	Miranda Greenwell	MaKenzie McEnroe	Patrick Labrian Saddler
Jeffery Coats	Megan Hall	Molly Melvin	Lisa Robin Sanford
Jillian Rose Cornell	Allen Harmon	Hilary Miller	Amanda Sarles
Tammy Crumble	Kelly Herrenbruck	Melissa Millikan	Lacey Schrock
Megan Daugherty	Jessica Higdon	Melanie Mills	Andrea Searcy
Melanie Degenhardt	Nicholas Hildabrand	Kara Moody	Lauren Shelby
Esther Delos Santos	Holly Hopkins	Kelly Moore	Tracy Sizemore
Kristen Dick	Jennifer Howe	Taylor Morgan	Crystal Skelton
Stacey Dixon	Jeffrey Jones	Staci Morris	Kara Smith
Lisa Downey	Marian Karanja	Heather Moulton	Lynsey Smith
Georgia Dunevant	Megan Kem	Nichole Murdock	Dena Stamper

Andrea Stang
James Stark
April Stern
Brittney Stinnett
Lori Stover

Kristen Strachan
Katie Taylor
Wayne Thomas
Richard Todd
Tara Vann-Schreck

Browder Warren
Deena Whirley
Brooke Wills
Thomas Wilson
Heather Wolfe

Lauren Woolen
Kelly D. Workman
Nancy Wunderlich

MUSCATINE COMMUNITY COLLEGE, MUSCATINE, IA

Bridget L. Anderson
Alison R. Axtell
Lucie K. Booth
Andrew J. Carpenter
Melissa M. Cavazos
Carissa J. Chatfield
Beth Ann Cole
Carrie M. Cottrell
Holly Dobbins
Danielle D. Evans

Kathleen N. Franks
Mason Wayne Fullerton
Clay B. Geise
Dylan D. Golinghorst
Stephanie A. Honts
Patrick James
Eric M. Kahl
Emma L. Kent
Damian J. Klinkenberg
Michelle L. Kottman

Zhi Lin
Mark N. Loveland
Lexys A. Marolf
Zachary M. Mortenson
Amy B. Moss
Brianna S. Newberry
Chelsea G. Parrish
Joshua D. Peddicord
Steven Poppe
Anna R. Rauenbuehler

MacKenzie L. Sanchez
Courtney C. Simpson
Tina Skipton
Adam M. Sterner
Ryan L. Storjohann
Madison M. Sturms
Ezekiel S. Walker
Ashli N. Williams
Amanda F. Wilson
Maci R. Zimmerman

NASH COMMUNITY COLLEGE, ROCKY MOUNT, NC

Kristen E. Akers
David E. Arnett
Ivy Beasley
Michelle R. Bellamy
Chelsey D. Blackston
Wesley T. Brown
Amanda N. Cary-Bunn
Heather Marie Christman
Mark A. Ciolek
John E. Crutchrow
Avonna R. Dickens

Ashley D. Fisher
Nathan L. Griffiths
Joshua W. Hendricks
Lynda L. Hight
Allison B. Jones
Sarah C. Jones
Fallon N. Kehoe
Hannah R. Kendrick
Michaela Lamm
Tyler D. Landry
Charles A. Lanfranchi

Krystal D. Lewis
Marla G. Matthews
Sophia L. Mbacke
Suzanne M. McLaughlin
Christopher G. Mercer
Sandra E. Moss
Kelly R. O'Brien
Justen C. Paul
Ca-Voncha' Marcella Pearce
Yentam T. Pham
Melissa R. Pulley

Jacob A. Sandy
Bennett W. Satterwhite
Chelsey L. Shearin
Graysen Smith
Morgan M. Smith
Tamra T. Snelling
Dustin B. Sweet
Olivia G. Taylor
Kaitlyn A. Wallace
Dana K. Wise
Cyna A. Woodard

NATIONAL COLLEGE BRISTOL CAMPUS, BRISTOL, TN

Jason Baker
Ricky Dean Bubert
Angelia L. Gent
Nathan E. Hawkins
Karen E. Helton

Whitney B. Holcomb
Samantha J. Hopson
Patricia G. Ingle
Jacqueline Annette Mathis
Lauren M. McSwain

Nicole E. Melton
William J. Melton
Brenda Lee Nunley
Melinda D. Perrigan
William D. Roberts

Leah R. Simpson
Amy Michele Vaught
Jamie Leann Williams
Brenda L. Young

NATIONAL COLLEGE RICHMOND, RICHMOND, KY

Cindy Louise Arbuthnot
Lisa Bargo
Kimberly Michelle Cowan

CaSandra Lynn Dyer
Jennifer Guier
Cortney Lynn Hembree

Alaina Justine-Kelley
Johnson
Sara Michelle Johnson

Allyson Brooke Mosley
Sheena Pitman
Rhonda Ponikowski

Jessica Richards	Randi Lynn Short	Melissa Ann Ward	Sarah Young
Tonita Janinne Rose	Tammera Tipton	Jaime Lee York	

NATIONAL LOUIS UNIVERSITY, CHICAGO, IL

Samuel Lankah	Derrick L. Mitchell	Allison Potter	Elsa Victoria Villarreal
Rebecca Mendoza			

NATIONAL PARK COLLEGE, HOT SPRINGS, AR

Savannah Abbott	Alyssa Diggs	Karly Kroening	Kathryn Powell
Heather Nicole Adams	Alexander Lee Ditto Jr.	Brielyn Kulis	Sarah Prince
Carla Arnold	William Dixon	Nicole Kathryn Kunkel	Samantha Ruff
Louis Bader	Brittan Driggers	Stacy Lacefield	Dana Russell
Jessica Ball	Traci Duke	Carson Lamb	Dana L. Russell
Kelly Barnes	Rebecca Lynn Echols	Mathew Lim	Desirae Rutherford
Felicia Beasley	Luke Geoffrion	Jennifer Lowe	Remedios Santos
Kathryn Bennett	Scotti Gerhardt	Jamie Lynn	Corey Scheer
Christina Gail Bias	Daniel Gibson	Mary Lynn	Josie Scheer
Diana Boothe	Laney Gibson	Parker Maghoney	Nikki Scheer
Leah Boyd	Alice Gill	Teresa Manley	Kelsey Schildgen
Hope Bratton	Samantha Goodman	Loren Alise Manning	William Shepperd
Ruby Brawner	Michelle Gordon	Lisa Martin	Marshall Shields
Jessica Bray	Susan Rayburn Graham	Alison Martinez	Leigh Smeltzer
James Briner	Lane Graves	Alicia Matz	Leigh Ann Smeltzer
Trina Brown	Austen Greco	Stacy McBay	Jerrica Speed
Vernon Brown	Hannah Guerin	Leslie McNeal	Leathia Stacy
Rilee Bryant	Lauri Gulley	Kathryn McWilliams	Holly Staggs
Kaycie Bullion	Victoria Hendrix	Tiffany Miller	Baylee Taylor
Angela Burris	Ashley Hennessee	Cody Morrison	Colton Terry
James Byrd	Frankie Hernandez	Rodney Morse	Austin Thomas
Stephanie Jayne Carpenter	Cheryl Christina Holmes	Karolyn Mullins	Tyler Tigue
Terry Cash	Summer Honeywell	Romykia Nelson	Johnny Tillery
Sheena Casteel	Kaylinn Jordan Hutter	Dylan Patton	Kale Tilley
Courtney Castleberry	Wavelon Jenkins	Nicole Pedlar	Jeremy Vaughn
Brett Chanley	Kelli Jennings	Amanda LeAnn Pennington	James Robert Voydetich
Janee' Chomyn	Alexis Jessup	Harriet Pennington	Bailey White
Joshua Coke	Jennifer Johnson	Erica Peppers	Jessica White
Thomas Coleman	MeChelle Jones	Nikki Perkins	Tosha White
Aryn Mathew Cotroneo	Leanne Kelley	Lance Pittman	Christina Williams
Jordan Couch	Charles Kennedy	Kimberly Pointon	Gina Wright
Joshua Crowder	Brittany Kersten	Phoenix Popow	Ling WuDenger
Odeli Davis	Tyler Kinder	Jarren Porterfield	Jacob Yates
Angela Diehl	Beneditte Kouetcha	Okaidi Yasmin Posadas	Andrew Yeomans

NAVAJO TECHNICAL UNIVERSITY, CROWNPOINT, NM

Clifford Allen
Randall Blake Allen
Eric Albert Bailey
Garrith W. Becenti
Kyle Caneil Bedonie
Christina Lesa Begay
Jeremy Begay
Lacey Calvina Begay
Ryanson Taylor Begay
Sandoval Begay
Charmayne Lynn Ben
Gilbert Joel Benally Jr.
Dwight Carlston
Marell Charley
Ronald Keith Charley
Tyrus S. Charley
Jayvion Samuel Chee

Teverrick Vaughn Chee
Kelly J. Chiquito
Nicholas Jay Clark
Fayetta S. Clawson
Jonathan Dan Clyde
Kirsch Davis
Rylan Sean Davis
Shyla Roanna Davis
Michael Shane Dohi
Eron Sorrelman Guy
Gerald R. Henry
Lamonte James
Homer Bronston Keith
Anfernee Edward Kirk
Corwin Rey Largo
Curtis Ray Largo
Derrick Lee

Craig A. Lewis
Myrna Mitchell
Chuck Morgan
Dale Morgan
Nathaniel Murphy
Dana Maureen Nez
Leslie Notah
Shaylene Samantha Paul
Lennie Ray Reynolds Jr.
Donovan Sam
Samual Herman Sam
Jamila Ann Silas
Hansen Tapaha
Erin Michelle Toadlena
Matthew A. Todecheenie
Robinson Loren Tom
Aaron Lane Tsosie

Filiberto Soto-Acosta
Vecenti
Andrew Wauneka
DeRon Mario White
Zachariah Tracey
Whitesinger
Patrick Ray Williams Jr.
Lisa Jean Willis
Wynona Ann Wilson
Angelo Lando Woody
Zachariah Terrance David
Woody
Chad Redfield Yazzie
Destinee Lea Yazzie
Dexter Davis Yazzie
Aldrian Yellowhair
Nicholas Charley Young

NAZARENE BIBLE COLLEGE, COLORADO SPRINGS, CO

Jason B. Bishop
Kelley L. Buckbee-Lutcher

Trevor D. Foley
S. Ryan Foster

Suann Moore
Jonathan L. Parker

Robert M. Parker
Benjamin J. Thelander

NEBRASKA CHRISTIAN COLLEGE, PAPILLION, NE

Hannah Bates
Cole Denne
Jeffrey Dirks
Austin Ettleman

Brandon Grant
Melissa Householder
Corey McCracken
Reid Milliken

Daniel Norton
Jordan Reese
Joel Schwendinger
Jed Shermer

Amy VanDorsten
Alicia Vonckx
Emily Whitney
Libby Wolkow

NEBRASKA WESLEYAN UNIVERSITY, LINCOLN, NE

Aubrey D. Adkisson
Megan M. Albracht
Trey A. Bardsley
Rachel M. Bauer
Kaitlin M. Beck
Connor W. Bohlken
Adam S. Braegelman
Ashley M. Bykerk
Amy K. Christensen
Brianne E. Conover
Elizabeth S. Cox
Madison L. Davis

Edson Inacio Santos Kilundu
de Oliveira
Connor N. Dethlefs
Samantha M. Dolezal
Elenita M. Donley
Andrew J. Farrand
Jessica M. Gehr
Sarah L. Gentes
Christopher J. Harroun
Eoghan P. Hartley
Jordan P. Hiatt
Claire E. Holmquist

Hannah M. Husted
Kurtis C. Johnson
Zachary J. Keating
Rachael L. Kirschenmann
Autumn C. Kunze
Ryan G. Larsen
Chelsi J. Marolf
Kesley J. Marshall
Skyler J. May
Jenna M. Moore
Michelle E. Munoz
Spencer L. Randazzo

Elizabeth D. Reimer
Charli K. Saltzman
Alessandro Schirano
Matthew W. Schmitt
Rachel R. Schmitt
Emily S. Scholting
Morgan B. Schultz
Garrett G. Sellhorst
Wesley J. Smith
Mariah L. Stradley
Moriah M. Thompson
Tarryn K. Tietjen

NEOSHO COUNTY COMMUNITY COLLEGE, CHANUTE, KS

Darian De'Shon Abram
Amy Acuna
Honey Aho
Corey Black
Jordan Taylor Braun
Shelby Brooks
Camri Jacyn Burke
Alec Chenault
Abigael Cheruiyot
Aimee Clawson
Vince Croci
Ramsey Janae Davis
Kayla Drybread

Mona Eden
Patrick Ellis
Regina Evans
Tiffany Folsom
Robin Goodreau
Erika Greiner
Ashley Henry
Jenna Hensley
Sheldon Hill
Darick Allen Jones
Morgan Renee Kistler
Mandy Sue Lewis
Ginger L. Lindsey

Sherri Lucas
Sandra Luna
Kaden Milner
Allyson Nychell Mitchell
Nicole Nathan
Chenae Del Newkirk
Alicia Pepper
Haleigh Nicole Qualls
Madison Ruder
Alexa Kay Ryan
Cynthia M. Schulz
Kacie Ann Shadden
Derek Sharp

Katelyn Shepard
Lok Shrestha
Haley Slade
Alexandra Sluder
Savannah Smith
Melissa Stephens
Zoie Stewart
Tanner Strickbine
Blake Tomasino
Samuel S. Wheat
Kyle Whedon
Sarah Williams
Timothy Williamson

NEWBERRY COLLEGE, NEWBERRY, SC

Catherine Abagail Barrett
Rebecca Lynn Darley

Chelsea Lynne Ellisor
Ajahna Nyema Grosvenor

Carlton LeVante' Kinard
Summer Elizabeth Lane

Emily Jane Perry
Marshall Knight Rentz

NEWBURY COLLEGE, BROOKLINE, MA

Wael Altali
Cindy Alexandra
De La Cruz
Alyssa Donovan

Elizabeth Jill Fox
Tory Hoemke
Isata Jamila Jalloh
Daria Ansley Johnson

Dequila Shante Jones
Olivia N. Kenyon
Katelyn Alexandra Roeser
Paige Nicole Sparks

Mabel Sterritt
Sonya Gwendolyn Theriault
Selina Wang

NEW ENGLAND COLLEGE, HENNIKER, NH

Jessica Barnum
Amanda Biundo
Danielle Blaisdell
William P. Bregonzio
Jonathan Chabot
Keith Michael Cross
Sara Culhane
Demesha Kenyana
Donaldson
Alexandria M. Frisoli

Melissa Marie Gilman
Stephanie Goulet
Allison Frances Granata
Emily Gubbins
Devon Justus Hubisz
Jon Charles Hunt
Hannah Noël Jackson
Demi Latham
Thomas Lott
Bridgett Alicia McIntyre

Mackenzie Alexis Meegan
Caroline Mols
Nicholas Tyler Nelson
Erica Notini
Jessica Paulhus
Emily Reale
John Wesley Reed Jr.
Kelly Ann Robinson
Kathryn Rodrigues
Christina Gianna Rubiano

Lauren Kimberly Smith
Maria Soulios
Lindsey Stewart
Rachel Thomas
Nina Paula Truckenmiller
Rachel Vigliano
Christopher John Whaley
Thomas John Zervos
Zhu Zhu

NEW HOPE CHRISTIAN COLLEGE, EUGENE, OR

Douglas Jay Lindquist II

Alyssa Lynn Sanford

Jacob Scott Thiessen

NEW HORIZONS COMPUTER LEARNING CENTER, PITTSTON, PA

Eric Bottge

Joseph Butryn

Ciro Delucia

Michael Fischetti

Henry Lai

Paul Marx

Rachel Panczyszin

Justin Riffert

Charity Yohn

NEWMAN UNIVERSITY, WICHITA, KS

David Leo Baalmann

Katilyn Danielle Bush

Maureen Elizabeth Hogan

Easton B. Julian

Emilie R. Leivian

Lucas M. Schauer

Nathaniel C. Siple

Mallory R. Vickery

Kylie L. Werth

NEW MEXICO HIGHLANDS UNIVERSITY, LAS VEGAS, NM

Brianne Abeyta

Elisa Abeyta

Joshua Alcon

Julissa Archuleta

Elena Armijo

Larissa Carbajal

Lorenzo Chavez

Gabriel Cordova

Tamlyn Marie Crain

Angelica Gonzalez

Steven Gonzalez

Janel Herrera

Ariadna Izaguirre

Jacob Kelly

Amberly Lopez

Jessica Monique Lucero

Natasha Lujan

Robert Mariano

Celina Martinez

Michael Martinez

Raymundo Melendez

Tarissa Mellin

Julianne Marie Mendoza

Leticia Merrills-Gonzalez

Krystol L.A Myers

Destiny Pacheco

Derek Pino

Desiree Pino

Chantel Rivera

Alyssa Romero

Donna Romero

Katelyn Romero

Maria Alaena Romero

Shyann Romero-Martinez

Flavio Vigil

John Ramon Vigil

Trenton Ward

Rachael Marie Zayas

NEW MEXICO JUNIOR COLLEGE, HOBBS, NM

Mary Acosta

Jessica Nichole Burguete

Rose Jebet

Alicia McComas

Candace Sloane McCraw

Alexis Morales

Angelica Nunez

Valeria Nunez

Taylor Scheller

Jason L. Wagner

Leah Brooke Wagner

Rachel Nicole Wagner

Emily Wood

Nardos Workneh

NEW MEXICO STATE UNIVERSITY CARLSBAD, CARLSBAD, NM

Byanka Arreola

Chance Brunton

Julie Cheatham

Athena Clutts

Anthony Cook

Sabrina Fannin

Amelinda Marissa
Fernandez

Crystal Marie Fine

Paige George

Kristen Harrison

Maritza Bailon Holguin

Zachariah Holmes

Sarah Kater

Amy Lee

Stefanie Martinez

Gabrielle Mathews

Lisa Monk

Marisol Isabel Moreno

Erica Raylissa Navarrete

Jaiden Nesbit

Sandra Yadira Nevarez

Alexsandria Nicole Pearsol

Martinez

Roland Roy

Ciera Samaniego

Michelle Smith

Gabriella Vasquez

Angelica Walterscheid

Staci Westbrook

Jordan Wyatt

Kyliegh Yerby

Zachary Young

NEW RIVER COMMUNITY COLLEGE, DUBLIN, VA

Austin S. Ahmann

Renee C. Albert

Tessa A. Atkins

A'me L. Baber

Ankan Basu
Shrabanti Basu
Jamie L. Bolt
Amanda V. Caldwell
Kevin C. DeHart

Kate A. Feuchtenberger
Jandelle L. Fournillier
Michael Hammond
Chelsea R. Hensley
Suki Mahar

Savanna M. McGarry
Jessica C. Milby
D Cody Rathbone
Lorenzo I. Rios Jr.
Jacob N. Roach

Joanne M. Stegle
Mason S. Turbyfill
Katie L. Waldron
Stacie A. Zoch

NEW YORK COLLEGE OF PODIATRIC MEDICINE, NEW YORK, NY

Nathaniel Alabi
Faezeh Bakhtiari-Nejad
Kurtis Bertram
Elizabeth M. Bonarigo

Raj Kumar Grover
Anthony Jabra
Adel Hassan Kadous
Erin Kunz

Gabrielle Laurenti
Jack Michael Levenson
Caitlin E. Miner
Terrence Park

Alisha Jenna Poonja
Mark Rotenstein
Joseph Cameron Waterhouse

NIAGARA UNIVERSITY, NIAGARA UNIVERSITY, NY

Carl Bailey
Rachel Elizabeth Bailey
Elizabeth Anne Beebe
Kelley Biro
Jacob Blaisdell
Jonathan J. Borek
Kristen Cavalleri
Selena Rose Cerra
Jake Eberth
Janene Ennis
Elena Victoria Feliz
Kelly Fitzpatrick

Erin Geen
Emily Catherine Gibson
Rachel Gromlovits
Dominic Joseph Hannon
Karen Grace Harty
Olivia Herberger
Paxton Marie Hill
Jasmine Hinaman
Kierr Iman Jackson
Anna Krempholtz
Marina Laurendi
Erin Leppien

Khallid Lewis
Kathleen Marie O'Brien
Macari
Christopher Ryan
Mussleman
Briana Lynn Neale
Michael Paglicci
Nick Palisano
Nichole Pascucci
Peter Raimondo
Kyra Rieker
Lexany Rivera

Jenna Roberts
Kyle Schwindler
Jillian Renae Stoessel
Alexis Tymorek
Alexander Xavier Utz
Sarah Volmy
Vivi Vongkhily
Amy Christine Wnuk
Nick Joseph Wojcicki

NICHOLLS STATE UNIVERSITY, THIBODAUX, LA

Brayeah L. Alleman
Lawrence J. Arceneaux III
Fallon Authement
Caroline E. Ayers
Alyse M. Barclay
Stephanie K. Barnett
Jordan R. Bebee
Briana N. Berthelot
Alicia L. Boudreaux
Lillie M. Bourgeois
Beau Brady
Ryan M. Brown
Morgan K. Brunet
Anna R. Busalacchi
Brent Cheramie

Taylor J. Chiasson
Trey E. Clark
Elizabeth P. Clement
Kaylee M. Cole
Camille E. Comeaux
Melanie S. Cowan
William P. Crenshaw
Kristen A. Daigle
Natalie E. Daigle
Kaylie L. Daniels
Josue R. Diaz Juarez
Holly E. Dicharry
Adam J. Doucet
Robert L. Dufrene
Terry G. Dupre

Sydney Esponge
Alayna E. Falgout
Alexis M. Foret
Marcus L. Fox
Jacqueline E. Frederic
Megan P. George
Richard J. Grabert
Jenna L. Graham
Brendon J. Gros
Rebekah M. Gueho
Brooke R. Guidry
Kyle J. Guidry
Megan M. Guidry
Abigail R. Hagen
Meghan E. Hanley

Hannah M. Haydel
Jordan E. Hebert
Matthew D. Hymel
Paige E. Johnson
Trace M. Juneau
Ross Kinchen
Sarah L. Lambert
Sydney M. Landry
Claire R. LeBeouf
Sarah E. LeCompte
Abigail L. Ledet
Adam E. Lefort
Lindsey M. Loupe
Lauren E. Luce
Baileigh Meche

Morgan E. Mitchell	Stuart J. Percle	Emily E. Schexnaydre	Maddie L. Toups
Megan A. Monier	Marisabel Ponce Cordero	Hillary E. Scott	Jacob D. Vega
Carolanne B. Moore	Katherine R. Robichaux	Kade V. Smith	Reece C. Vitale
Paige E. Morvant	Heidi A. Rodrigue	Katelyn L. Smith	Dane P. Vizier Jr.
Celia Y. Ordoyne	Victoria F. Rodriguez	James T. Sothern	Sarah E. Zeringue
Grant A. Ordoyne	Philip J. Roth	Rosalyn M. Stilling	
Anna C. Ortego	Mary A. Sauce	Les B. Theriot	

NICHOLS COLLEGE, DUDLEY, MA

Irving M. Eggleston	Jaime L. Miglionico	Amber Tariq	Mario A. Turner
Brian K. Hancock	Lindsey E. Oliver		

NORFOLK STATE UNIVERSITY, NORFOLK, VA

Haseena R. Abdur-Rahman	Jeremy Everett Carlson	Lanaya A. Lewis	Malcolm Q. Smith
Shaquil V. Adams	Karen Elleyse Clemmons	Brianna LaTreya Lindsey	Ravin K. Vick
Dev'Juan R. Archer	Breanna Y. Dennis	Jackson D. Littlejohn	Rachel F. Webb
Armonee S. Avent	Michael D. Evans	Roshad C. McPherson	Dominicia Angelique
Bryan-Daniel Stuart Barker	Janay A. Frazier	Luvley L. Mosely	Williams
Sr.	Kayla Gross	Miata Marie Palmer	Felasha O. Wilson
Jourdan E. Bethea	Jessica L. Johnson	Lindsey Marie Podd	
Michelle Renee' Brown	Tatiana D. Leonard	Chrys Marie Slaughter	

NORTHAMPTON COMMUNITY COLLEGE, BETHLEHEM, PA

Allison E. Beerwa	Himil J. DeSai	Emmanuel Lee Maxwell	Elizabeth A. Segreaves
Brittany Alyse Brewer	Jennifer Lynne Finn	Irma Ortiz-Astacio	Amira Shokr
Courtney Marie Burger	Julia Anne Kostelny	Logan Johanna Paff	Holly A. Torcivia
Victoria M. Cintron	Caiyu Li	Kimber Lee Rohner	Virginia Mary Welsh

NORTH CAROLINA WESLEYAN COLLEGE, ROCKY MOUNT, NC

Jose Luis Batista	Linda Ann Cooper	Emalyn Marie Jessup	Sherri Perry
Christopher J. Bellinger	Lauren Ashley Gosselin	Barbara J. Jeter	Mary Jane Poole
Kristin Elizabeth Bryant	Azzeddine Hammoussi	Rhonda Tate Kernodle	Justin Allen Stringfield
Darlene Burton	Jordan Nicole Harrell	Saurav Malla	Robin Leigh Todd
Tina Evonne Carter	Douglas Hoggs	Anneta McCoy	Ervin Demonte Whitley Jr.
Aqiyla Caudle	Alexis Danielle Jackson	Mary Elizabeth Norton	Joyce A. Williams
Jamarius Dequell Coley	Ruby Lee Jacobs	Briona Allie Parker	

NORTH CENTRAL UNIVERSITY, MINNEAPOLIS, MN

Josiah West Baker	Jacob Daniel Felstow	Helen A. Hansen	Susan Denise Pratt
Karlee Jo Cox	Zachary Richard Fortunato	Victoria Audrey Iverson	Tania LaNae Rosener
Lydiah Renee Durene	Sean Carlo Francisco	Grace Johanna Miller	Annalise Elizabeth
Katelynn Naomi Fate	Marci Diana Greig	Samantha Rae Olson	Schroeder

Jacob William Singer   Weyer Elizabeth Tera   Benjamin James Wagner   Mekeyah Lashae Wright

NORTHEAST ALABAMA COMMUNITY COLLEGE SOCIAL SCIENCES, RAINSVILLE, AL

Kristen Maria Bass
Forrest Gentry Benson
Austin Tyler Boyd
Morgan Leann Bryant
Ashley Campos
Kathryn Ann Olind Coleman
Josie Marie Crider
Daniel Stuart Dobbs
Tien Ngoc Dong
Latasha McClendon Dove
Zachary Tyler Foster
Hunter Lamar Furgerson

Kennedy Raye George
Lori Kristen Gorham
Nicole Lafaye Gunter
Tristan Scott Hairston
Katie Marie Hatfield
Andrea Marie Head
Natalie Kate Hitchcock
Griffin Scott Horton
Jessica Loren Hullander
Joanna Carla Hurley
Tessa Michelle Hutson
Elizabeth Ashton Kennamer

Teletha Leah Deanne
Lahayne
Trenton Thomas Linderman
Joseph Raymond Markowski
Ashley Nicole McCarver
Kaitlyn Alysse Mize
Savannah Lee Owens
Debra Yvonne Pack
Maleah Ann Parmer
Juana Elizabeth Sebastian
Alyson Rae Smart
Juliana Hope Spears

Caroline Gracen Spigner
Kelsie Lakesha Stinson
Seferina Lynn Valey
John Quaid Westmoreland
Hannah Leann Whitecotton
Matthew Ray Wilbanks
Ethan Thomas Wilkerson
Emma Gabrielle Winkels
Hannah Emily Wootten

NORTHEASTERN JUNIOR COLLEGE, STERLING, CO

Andrea Abarca
Samantha D. Archuleta
Erica D. Arnold
Brady A. Baer
Jordan Blach
Matthew D. Brower
Krista A. Carter
Hannah C. Clark
Cierra Davis
Angelina M . Garduno

Jacob G. Gerk
Necole L. Hampton
Spencer M. Haragan
Brittany A. Harris
Celine T. Hornung
Kristina Horton
Dustin E. Kachel
Jessica D. Lauritzen
Jessica L. Lechman
Hadassah S. Lindstadt

Kayla D. Littlefield
Madison Melvin
Jazmin Montes-Pedrego
Lauren M. Montoya
Brittney N. Pepitone
Holden M. Ramey
Tasha N. Rasmussen
Kalie D. Romero
Thalia C. Rosales-Ortiz
Scott T. Rosas

Michael W. Semler
Kayla R. Smith
Lonny T. Trehal
Taylor D. Upchurch
Yvette I. Velasquez
Taylor N. Weingardt
Tyson J. Weingardt
Austin P. Zink
Jenna L. Zink

NORTHEASTERN OKLAHOMA A&M COLLEGE, MIAMI, OK

Nick B. Abernathy
Macee S. Brophy
Kylie K. Buttram
Anneke M. Carr
Larry J. Cisneros
Charity D. Coberley
MaeKayla K. Cole
Amber L. Cox
April L. Crockett

Deborah R. Crutchfield
Caleb M. Epperly
Elizabeth A. Flanders
Matthew V. Fusselman
Corynne M. Hagins
Shannon L. Hughes
Jennifer L. Isgrigg
Kylie M. Jones
Domonic Josephs

Courtney Alexis Jourdan
David K. Kiesewetter
Lucille A. Kinglsey
Kaitlyn H. McNiel
Sadie L. Morris
Taylor N. Pevehouse
Miguelangel Pineda Soto
Luke G. Preaus
Madisyn R. Rhone

Johannah E. Richardson
Harlie N. Sasser
Mackenzie C. Shamblin
Daniel Gibbon Simmons
Madison L. VanBurkleo
Bailee M. Wolfe

NORTHEASTERN STATE UNIVERSITY, TAHLEQUAH, OK

Taylor N. Adams
Molly L. Bennett

Sarah N. Butler
Gemini A. Creason-Parker

Tyler S. Denton
Jayne R. Gause

Morgan L. Helterbrand
Johnathon J. Ozturk

Cody C. Robinson   Kacie D. Thompson   Brittany M. Trent

NORTHEASTERN TECHNICAL COLLEGE, CHERAW, SC

Tiffany Carol Arant	Connie Chewning	Ronnie Glenn Guinn Sr.	Julie Roscoe
Natasha Austin	Curtis Dalton	Cora Harrison	David Rushing
Mary Jo Black	Ashley DeHaai	Tanasia Holloway	Dawn Schauer Simmons
Dylan Boone	Bronson Eslick	Casey Horton	Keyosha Sellers
Tanya Monique Boyd	Alexis Ford	Andrew Jenkins	Brandi Sessoms
Mary B. Burnell	Francie Freeman	Alonna Lee	Danny Small
Thomas Cannon	Megan Griggs	William David McLaurin	Sydney Wilson

NORTHEAST IOWA COMMUNITY COLLEGE CALMAR CAMPUS, PEOSTA, IA

Shelby Jo Bodley	Tara Lynn Fink	Terry Sawyer	Alex Wehrspann
Evan Fair	Anna Hoins		

NORTHEAST MISSISSIPPI COMMUNITY COLLEGE, BOONEVILLE, MS

Amber N. Anglin	Stacie L. Dunn	DeAndre D. Jones	Lindsey A. Ormon
Andrew R. Ashe	Maggie A. Eaton	John-Stuart H. Jones	Connor B. Padgett
Melanie B. Autrey	Kelsey N. English	Natasha E. Jones	Haley D. Pannell
Charles D. Barnes	Christopher S. Fowler	Sarry-Ann Morgan Jones	Avery Lee Parks
Shelbi H. Barnes	Genia M. Gaar	Kerston L. Jumper	Anthony J. Partain
Darren E. Bass	Grant T. Gaar	Rachel L. Kelly	Rachel C. Peeler
Kayla P. Bell	Emily C. Gafford	Andrew D. Lambert	James B. Phelps
Jacey S. Borden	Nathan S. Gaillard	Trace P. Lee	Madison Bain Phillips
Dantez T. Brock	Abbie-Michaela C. Gardner	Sierra N. Lewis	Caelan D. Pollard
Hunter C. Brown	Anna K. Gardner	Mallory S. Little	Bailey E. Raiford
Sarah E. Brown	Ashley K. Gates	Savanna M. Loveless	Jasmine K. Redmond
Charles S. Carroll	Logan R. Gates	Jennie C. Maddox	Ashley N. Robertson
Brandi N. Clark	Katherine B. Gatewood	Zackery W. Marcinek	Michealla J. Schallock
Erica L. Clifton	Anthony J. George	Cynthia G. Martinez	Hayley M. Schrock
Sara Paige Cooper	Layken D. Greene	Logan R. McAfee	Cade S. Scroggins
Scotty D. Cooper	Keeley K. Groves	Clayton L. McCoy	Grantland R. Searcy
Samantha C. Cornelius	Lindie E. Hill	Angelina C. Meeks	Amanda D. Selman
Breanna N. Crabb	Sarah A. Hill	Landon T. Meeks	Christa B. Sides
Caroline Bea Crawford	Calin A. Holley	Michael C. Mooneyham	Madeline L. Smith
Carolyn L. Davidson	Madison Brooke Horton	Katelyn E. Morton	Brittany G. Stephenson
Anthony T. Davis	Harley M. Hutson	Dennis R. Mullins	Makinley K. Steward
Hannah C. Day	Anna C. Ivy	Katelyn E. Murphy	Kameron J. Talley
Allison P. Dillon	Hunter T. Ivy	Kenneth T. Newby	Johnathan K. Taylor
Jennifer A. Douglas	Cebrina D. Johnson	Mikayla B. Newkirk	Marlee E. Taylor
Jameson C. Droke	Tyler A. Johnson	Mayuka M. Nix	Haleigh B. Tennison
Chase G. Duke	Katie L. Johnston	Randal C. Norris	Kayla M. Thomason

| Mariah L. Turner | Stacy D. Tuttle | Kaitlyn D. Wilbanks | Lindee G. Witt |
| Allison E. Tutor | Nayra O. Whitaker | Alesha D. Willbanks | Parish L. Wright |

NORTHEAST STATE COMMUNITY COLLEGE, BLOUNTVILLE, TN

William John Allen	Kayla N. Egan	Dustin W. Hensley	Haley M. Page
Gabe A. Bombailey	Hannah Lynn Fink	Victoria G. Hewlett	Matthew T. Poole
Shawna L. Burrow	Brianna N. Franklin	Joseph M. Hicks	Tessa L. Ross
John A. Cagle	Jacob T. Gillenwater	Melindalou Nicole Johnson	Stephen N. Shepherd
Trisha Y. Carter	Abigail R. Hathorn	Annie L. King	Polly J. Steffey
Fara A. Childers	Anna R. Heath	Jimmy L. Murphy	Beverly D. Stipes

NORTHEAST TEXAS COMMUNITY COLLEGE, MT. PLEASANT, TX

Miguel A. Buendia	Rebekah Sue Hall	Melody Haruna Mott	Makomborero Tembo
Isaac Earl Burris	Tiler E. Hall	Gabriela Quezada	Maria Guadalupe Torres
Morgan Marie Capps	Athena I. Hayes	Genesis Stefany Quezada	Steven Ray Vaught
Cailee Anne Davidson	Nathan R. Johnson	Orellana	Jessica Velazquez
Angelica Fuentes	William Austin Jones	Andrew Michael Rogers	Scott Thomas Wilhite
Efrain Garcia	Trace Allen Lewis	Cassia Noelle Rose	Hector Eduardo Zuniga
Jaden Brooke Green	Presley Brianna McClendon	Emmalea Ryan Shaw	
Elizabeth N. Griffin	Ryan-Rose M. Mendoza	Mary M. Smith	
Louis Nelson Hall	Noel A. Moreno	Brianna Katherine Stacks	

NORTHERN ARIZONA UNIVERSITY, FLAGSTAFF, AZ

Bailey Anderson	Felicia Fiedler	Jobelle Musni	Celeste del Carmen Tabares
Sarah Brewer	Johrie Lee-Rose Fisher	Oluwayemisi Bolatito	Dorothyrose Vowels
Yoko Chavez	Rachel Harrow	Ogunde	Joseph E. Zodiacal
Margaret Collins	Chelsea Ryan Heintz	Alexander Ollerton	Miriam Zveitel
Cassidy Crews	Kaitlyn Leung	Samantha Orsulak	
Francis DiFranco	Corbett Jordan Light	Jack Poupore	
Sara Leann Ditmanson	Colton Rivers McConnell	Kristy Ann Silva	

NORTHERN ILLINOIS UNIVERSITY, DEKALB, IL

Oluwatimilehin Adeboje	Paige Dowell	Marilyn Koonce	Meghan Tan
Reggie Bates	Sha'Bree Drink	Michaela Luckett	Afreen Warsi
Jordan Danaè Clayton-	Alyssa Dunbar	Gladys Sanchez	
Taylor	Randiss Hopkins	Anurag Singh	

NORTHERN KENTUCKY UNIVERSITY, HIGHLAND HEIGHTS, KY

Amneh M. Alzatout	Natalie A. Conner	Emily C. Kappes	Danielle A. Ott
Maxwell S. Boyle	Yasmeen R. Daher	Rodney Karr	Simon P. Segal
Julie Bridewell	Lucas T. Edelen	Jonathan R. Mangus	Justin L. Siefert
Jason L. Callihan	Hannah L. Hearn	Alma J. Onate	Mariah C. Stanforth

Jacob E. Telesz   Becky Wiethorn

NORTHERN MAINE COMMUNITY COLLEGE, PRESQUE ISLE, ME

Thomas Albert
Heather R. Baker
Brady T. Bubar
Jacquelyn Chevalier
Kennedy Ann Churchill
Crystal Anne Condo
Jesse Cormier
Kayla Cote
Stephen Spencer Davis
Harold Decker
John Dixon
Matthew Farkas

Kala Farley
Brenda Gilliam
Caleb Gordon
Brendon Harmon
Leslie Heath
Kyle Hews
Lawrence Huckins
Chiharu Jandreau
Jamie Rose Kamorowski
Sally King
Karl Kornchuk
Danielle Larrabee

Kelli Lawlor
Jamey J. Lessard
Eric Martinez Mendieta
Peter Michaud
Clarina Nadeau
Megan A. Nelson
Collin Patterson
Katelynn Priscilla Perkins
Anjanette Pike
Ryan James Plourde
Stephanie Marie Plourde
Rachel Rossignol

Meagan Royer
Autumn Saucier
Bethany Shaw
Vanessa Shaw
Benjamin Sipe
Andrew Smith
Nicole Lynn Thompson
Eleonora Toussaint
Jessica Lynn Vaillancourt
Kristy Vigil

NORTHERN OKLAHOMA COLLEGE, TONKAWA, OK

Megan Alexander
Cody Wade Asche
Allyssa Danielle Belair
Cole Burchett
Kaylen Donelson
Reanna Dorsey

Brianna Guffey
Sreyla Heng
Victor Hernandez
Paj Joyce Jackson
Tara Lucas
Cassie Marney

Joshua Mayo
Brittany McBrain
Rebecca Means
Zach Rogers
Amber Scott
Kyla Smith

Clayton Stephens
Ryan Weathers
Kiana Wilcoxson
Baylie Wilson

NORTHERN OKLAHOMA COLLEGE ENID, ENID, OK

Aaron Kyle Beagle
Brittany Lynn Bingham
Logan Paige Burgess
Payton Nichole Calhoun
Casey Randall Cole
Carson Levi Combest
Tiffani Coots
McKinzie Devereaux

Hannah Paige Hedges
Alexis Rae Hill
Rebecca Paige Holliday
Harrison Chandler Hull
Shalyn Cooper Layn
Jamie Michele Lowrie
Asheley Lynn Middleton
Kimberly Jo Miller

Levi Darin Nichols
Hailey R. Parker
Natalie Grace Rapp
Zachary Scott Rayner
Sean Matthew Robison
Katie Lynn Rogers
Kelsey Clarice Schumpert
Addi Renee Shamburg

William M. Sprayberry
Sage Nikole Sunderland
Brooke Michelle Tate
Dakota E. Theilen
Tyra Renee Williams
Kathryn Elizabeth Yunker

NORTHERN STATE UNIVERSITY, ABERDEEN, SD

Katie M. Abraham
Waleed Mohammed Morsy Ahmed
Rachel Lindsey Myers Albright
Dylan James Amdahl
Nicole Lynne Arnold

Channing Randall Barber
Zachery Lyle Barber
Andrew Robert Bell
Taylor Paul Beutler
Anna Cate Bondy
Cassandra A. Bottum
Melissa Ann Brede

Megan Marie Brink
Jackson William Bruce
Abigail Geraldine Burgard
Kelsey Jane Chambers
Travis James Clark
Ian Thomas Coughlin
Logan Jerald Crown

Ashley Lynn Daughters
Trent Bennett Dean
Autumn Marie Deutsch
Addy Elena Diaz
Sophie Christine Doeden
Alexis Joy Doerr
Conner Ward Doherty

Samantha Gabrielle Elbert
Dakota Marie Feller
Tanner Lee Feterl
Hilary Marie Filler
Shannon Lea Fines
Brock Allen Fischer
Candace Leigh Fosheim
Kelsey Christine Gale
Eric John Gerber IV
Katelyn Mae Giedt
Braden Scott Goldade
Katie Mae Graham
Diana Marie Grettler
Tyler Wayne Gripentrog
Carrie A. Gutierrez
Maggie Kristine Hepper
Renee Elizabeth Hoffman
Harrison Wayne Homelvig
Seth Michael Honerman
Sasha Marilyn Hovind
Justin W. Howard
Haley Kae Hubbard
Derek Alexis Hughes
Maria Kalunda Ilolo
Stephanie Ann Iverson

Cody Dean Johns
Carrie Anne Johnson
Cathy Maire Kerr
Ruth Kinyanjui
Corey James Klatt
Elizabeth A. Kolda
Megan Jean Krogman
Lauren Marie Kunz
Jory Allen Kunzman
Bethany Joy Latterell
Adam Robert Leach
Ben Joseph Lickteig
Brittany Elizabeth Limanen
Tanner Tanner Lopez
Dan Phillip Lown
Christopher Edward Malsam
Ashtin Marie McClemans
Taylor Dawn Melius
Danica Ellen Mae Mickelson
Dylan Jon Mickelson
LaRae Lynn Mock
Ben Frederick Moen
Amy Jo Moser
Mathew James Muston
Brooke Christine Nelson

Cody Joe Nichols
Joyce Catherine Nolan
Kayla Elizabeth Nuese
Amber Joy Ogren
Shlomit Emilie Oren-Ross
Devin Joseph Pedersen
Cheng Peng
Darin Matthew Peterka
Thea Jean Rave
Matthew Carl Remmich
Christina Marie Renz
Katelyn Marie Rhodes
Katie Ruth Roberson
Jake David Samuelson
Kaitlyn Grace Sandmeier
Philip David Sauer
Michael Dale Schliewe
Autumn Lynn Schulz
Bailey Lenn Simon
Donavan Thomas Soulek
Jamie Kendal Stadel
Grant William Steen
Mercede Lee Stotesbery
Jordan Ann Stotz
Dreena Lynne Streckfuss

Nathaniel L. Street
Rebecca Ruth Swier
Brianna Atalie Tagle
Lexy Inez Teerink
Matt Scott Thorson
Brittany Danielle Tietz
Jeffrey Scott Tobin
Paige Rose Tooker
Justine Lori Tuscherer
Zachary James Ulmer
Annika Marie Van Oosbree
Brandon Stephen Vockrodt
Cody James Voegeli
Kamie Sue Wagar
Taylor Elaine Wall
Lexi Joyce Ward
Skye Arlan Warwick
Paige Briann Waytashek
Carrie Ann Wegleitner
Chelsea Marie White
Katherine McKenzie
Wollman
Tyson Douglas Zemlicka

NORTHERN VIRGINIA COMMUNITY COLLEGE, ALEXANDRIA, VA

Nowrs Abulhul
Kayla Acosta
Urby Ahmed
Yasmin I. Alamin
Omar Faiz Alamodi
Enas Al-Hadidi
Alia Ali
Yara Al-Swaity
Amina Amisi
Whitney Amo
John Andrews
Stacie Argade
Derrick Arthur-Cudjoe
Adriana Arvizo
Kiran Aslam
Nadia Karolina Avila

Solome Ayele
Hakeem Azoor
Kevin Baisden
Grant Bartolomei
Ridi Barua
Saim Bashir
Rahima Baz
Jessica L. Beausoleil
Yasmin Bekri
Sara Besharat
Graciela Billingsley
Samantha Blain
Courtney Boone
Phanny Bou
John David Bownik
Jennifer Brooks

Valentina Anatolie
Bulavitchi
Adriana Del Rosario
Bustamante Yactayo
Ariana Bustamente
Michael Socrates Cabrera -
Ortiz
Jimmy Alexander Cartenga
Adria C. Carter
Hajar Chokhmane
Samia Rahail Chughtai
Giuliana Coers
Vincent Cordrey
Benjamin Stuart Cressey
Sergio Cuellar
Alyssa Cunningham

Vivian Yvette Dade
Nicolette Sachi Defrank
Randolph Diaz
Donny Dila
Marian Dualle
Salwan S. Elberi
Jennifer Elgin
Nora Elhsiekh
Jeannette Essimi-Menye
Elias Fadlallah
Aurea Galvan
Lorena E. Garcia
Nathan Gaul
Chelsea Geckler
Rebecca Marie Goforth
Valeria Leslie Green

Jami Dawn Gulley

Angel Gutarra-Leon

Heather Hardy

Charlotte Lynne Hepler

Kimberly Susana Hernandez

Syed Hossain

Marwa Osman Hussein

Muhammad Ilyas

Shahrozia Imtiaz

Tomy Isra

Raina A. Jaffa

Reeyia A. Jaffa

Hidayah Jaka

Mohamud Jibril

Trista Leann Johnson

Hyun Suk Joo

Elizabeth Judd

Jasmine Kamole

Alesia Kardash

Manisha M. Khatri

Priya Khatri

Krista Knudson

Maksimilian Kochev

Jessica Kolbe

Sarah Kouadio

Gbenoukpo Etienne
Lakognon

Hannah Rebekah Lane

Soo Lee

Yu-Chieh Lee

Vanessa Linquist-Barrie

Grey P. Madison

Chirstopher Mallace

Shimol Mangawa

Katlyn A. Marshall

Angel Martinez

Sandrine Krystelle Ngono
Mbita

Sahureli Mendoza Khoury

Alison Mikes

Mehdi Mirsoltani

Abdelazeim Mohamed

Insaaf Mohamed

Andre Bernard Moore Jr.

Catherine H. Mosier

Amirkhan Mukashev

Louise M. Murray-Pino

Mariam Myelle

Christine Nguyen

Quynh Nguyen

Tho Nguyen

Trang Nguyen

Juliette Nichols

Leonardo Edward O'Gilvie

Nana Ofori

Payal Panchal

Ganna Pavelko

Sandra V. Pineda

Claudia Jerusalem Pleites
Morales

Jennifer H. Posadas

Ekaterina Prokofeva

Elham Rabani

Patrick B. Rafael

Giulliana Ratti

Stevey A. Reid

Francesca Reilly

Christopher Antonio Reyes

Roberto Jose Rivas Martinez

Rayza Sofia Rodrigo Vargas

Elinorth Rojas

Samer E. Saab

Aina Saiful Bahri

Jason Sanchez

Kevin J. Sanchez

Arvie G. Santos

Amy-Lynn Scott

Linqian Shu

Natasha Simpkins

Matthew K. Southerland

Brittany Ann Spivey

Kimberly Sullivan

Armani Tagle

Ibrar Tariq

Kevin Toe

Thanh Tran

Viet Tran

Pablo Urioste

Jose Antonio Velasquez-
Principe

Thao Vu

Erica Marie Walker

Estera Warrick

Richard Washington

Ahmed Youssef

Idris Zaki

Linwen Zeng

Michelle Zink

NORTH GREENVILLE UNIVERSITY, TIGERVILLE, SC

Emmy Diane Allen

Rachel Elizabeth Alley

Faith Suzanne Auslund

Kenneth Lee Ball

Becklin Marie Blankenship

Sabrina Ann Brem

Sara Ashley Brunson

Sommer Ashley Cagle

Elisha Seth Carnahan

Carlee Alexandria Colvard

Megan Elizabeth Darby

Makayla Rebekah Davis

Taylor Dupes

Suzanna Margaret Edwards

Mary Elizabeth Erny

Emalee Allison Fields

Katelyn Lydia Galyean

Andrew James Gilstrap

Aaron Josiah Harris

Madison Willis Harris

Dillon Foster Hollifield

Daniel Carson Horn

Forrest John Keefer

Julia Grace Klukow

Anna Elizabeth Krezdorn

Elizabeth Lynne Latzka

Rachel Victoria Locke

Mary Ellen Lovin

Emma Elizabeth Maguire

Hannah Mashburn

Casey Paige Owens

Rebekah Hope Pepper

Brittany Leigh Pigg

Jonathan Keith Shorter

Lauren Elizabeth Southards

Linnea Grace Stevens

Margaret Knox Stuckey

Victoria Elizabeth Vazquez

Grace Elizabeth Watson

Kendra Danielle Webb

Kelsey Nicole Wilson

Erica Carolyn Yelton

NORTHWESTERN OKLAHOMA STATE UNIVERSITY, ALVA, OK

Princess J. Adenuga

Jaclyn Cherie Burke

Teris Dangol

Christina J. Erford

Kambri K. Harland

Sam Garrett Harland

Kelsey B. Leveling

Morgan N. Lewis

Logan Rant Lindley Nicole Renee Marema Elizabeth Ann Mouser Bailey Renae Trammell
Sadik Malik Bruno Macedo Miguel Megan N. Sanders

NORTHWEST FLORIDA STATE COLLEGE, NICEVILLE, FL

Marley Burch Rebekah Jo-Ann Foushee Tiffany Mathews Katie Towe
Jennifer Burrage Dylan Garofalo James Meadows Ashley VanAmburg
Robert Franklin Busasrd Jr. Megan E. Garofalo Kelly Moon Victoria Van Hoorebeke
Tristan Colpitts Andrew Hannah Jason E. Mueller Arin Walker
Jennifer DeJesus Omar Hanson Kaitlyn Philmon Amber Wall
David Troy Dobson Amber Hayden Dennie Smith Carson Wilber
Rebecca Edwards Stephanie Hicks James Sweeney Madalyn R. Wilson
Jamie Ellis Cheryl Liddon Sidney Thomas Grace Young
Shae Fountain Margaret Mann Daniel Thornton Christian Zeigler

NORTHWEST IOWA COMMUNITY COLLEGE, SHELDON, IA

Deven L. Bonnema Krista E. Johnson Kyle A. Post Chase J. Vermeer
Amber K. Buren Joanna L. Kruger Zara L. Trigg Alissa M. Walters
Lee H. Gravel Haley J. Morfitt Jasmyn J. Van't Hul
Gabrielle M. Hartog Billi J. Niemeier Casey J. Vermeer

NORTHWEST MISSISSIPPI COMMUNITY COLLEGE, SENATOBIA, MS

Erinn Kelsey Adams Alexis Bryner Audrey Grace Eldridge Karen Roseann Jones
Hunter Reed Ainsworth Faith Susan Buchanan Jordon Donte Elliot Melissa A. Jordan
Lauren Aker Taylor Chase Bulliner Tanya Paulette Etheridge Dominique Batrice Kelly
Karla M. Alfaro Turner L. Bullock Gustavo A. Garrido Olivia Jane Kent
Ginny Rene Allen Robert Brian Burnett Edith Ann Gilpin Vicky Harvey Kerner
Ashley Marie Anderson Natalie Dianne Byas Benjamin Seth Guntharp Kaleb Ethan Kill
Sheree D. Anderson Allison Dawn Byrd Noah James Guntharp Justice N. King
Asante J. Baker Charlene Marie Cain Justine Sarah Hanks Kayla King
Katelin Rose Balentine Kayla Marie Casey Delois J. Harris Hunter G. Lacefield
Kimberly Garner Barbee Maggie L. Cates Shelby R. Harris Lori Houston Lance
Stephanie Barnes Hannah E. Clarkson Amber Lee Hawkins Brian W. Langston
Mallory Paige Bass Sarah Elizabeth Cole Sean Collin Hawkins Robert L. LeMay
Rachel Lynn Bayles Joseph Grant Coleman Wendy R. Hicks Carla Renee Lentz
Christina Ashley Berryhill Lydia Ann Cross Ethan E. Holmes Rebekah Morris LeWallen
Kevin Richard Black Adaria Cunningham Ashley Danielle Hood Mary Lynn Lewis
Kristin Renay Bohanna Amanda Michelle Cursey Austin Houston Jared Thomas Logsdon
Amanda Diane Bolton Drew Taylor Davis Heather Samantha Howard Megan Marie Magadanz
Jaime L. Bowden Tallan Anjel Drewery James Randall Hudson Kelly Alden Martin
Christina Marie Bowler Markevia L. Eason Katherine L. Hunt Savannah D. Mask
Phillip Aaron Brasher Emalee Jean Edmonds Laquan Kartrell Jackson Victoria Lynn Mathias
Dalton Bryant Deandre C. Edwards Linda Anne Jackson Brandy Aileen Mattice

Kristin N. McClelland
Paige Alana McClure
Brianna Jo McDaniel
Bonnie Baran McDonald
Taniya N. McNeil
Tiffanee Sharnaye Merritt
Hailey M. Miller
Melinda Jean Milner
Kiara Nicole Mitchell
Trenton Lee Mobley
Alexis Kate Moore
Andrea Nichelle Moore
Hunter Austin Moore
Cody Wayne Morris
Mathew Martin Morris
Sarah Jo Murphy
Raymie Lane Neal
Wilson Jessica Kay Nelson
Audrianna Nicole O'Dell

Gregory Issiac O'Neal
Rohinibin Patel
Heather Pearl Perryman
Jeremy Wayne Phillips
Jerry Wayne Pierce
April Elaine Pomeroy
Daniel James Pompa
Frankie Laine Pondexter
Skylar Joy Poole
Lindsey Nicole Pugh
Dixie Lee Quinn
Brandon Scott Raines
Lisa Marie Reisinger
Thomas "Trey" Reynolds
Lance Taylor Richey
Peyton Elizabeth Rico
William J. Roberts
Timera Denise Rodgers
Madison K. Rooker

Abigail J. Rucker
Kaitlyn Danielle Russell
Kirill Safrin
Elizabeth K. Sanborn
Rebecca M. Sanders
Leila Savage
Cody Alexander Schmitz
Mollie Kate Scott
James Drake Shaw
Joseph Tyler Shook
Jessica Lynn Sims
Kayleigh Sims
Angela Marie Smith
Lyle Smock
Samantha R. Sprague
Holliann Belton Stevenson
Lauren Elizabeth Storey
Laken Scarlett Suddoth
Timothy Switzer

Jenna Taylor
Rose Taylor
Savannah Brooke Taylor
Jaylayne Telford
Karen Thomas
Katrina Joy Tippins
Sang Truong
Robbie Lynn Vinson
Tatyana Antwanette Wadley
Cassie Marie Walker
Vintasia M. Wallace
Apple M. Walton
Monica Ward
Ashlinn Theresa Webster
Samantha Michelle Whittle
Kristle Deshawn Williams
Tyler Christian Willis
Billy Max Wilson

NORTHWEST–SHOALS COMMUNITY COLLEGE, MUSCLE SHOALS, AL

Algeria Anderson
Gaspariny Andres Pascual
Chase Helton Askew
Sarah Rae Aycock
Kevin Sean Bailey
Meagan Noel Barnette
Matthew Ryan Bevis
Joshua James Bonds
Alexandra Borden
Jasmine Alexus Buckhalter
Tasha Butler
Benjamin Cagle
Mary Camp
Kristen Campbell
Dixie Monserrat Chavez
Griselle Cienfuegos
Ashley Figueroa Cifuentes
Elizabeth Cochran
Candice Copeland
Terrie Cozart
Dillion Creekmore
Carmen Crowden

Kaylea Davis
Macy Davis
Zach Davis
Jamie Dodson
Barbara Dozier
Vera Dragovich
Jessica Duncan
Krystle Duncan
Emily Farris
Yaneliz Fernandez
Nathan Kyle Fiscus
Ivannica Flute
Meanna Fuqua
Destiny Michelle Garcia
Tiffany Garrie
Brian Gibson
Danah Gilchrist
Candice Alicia Gonzalez
Natividad Gonzalez-
Rodriguez
Jessica Guzman
Taylor Hamilton

Kenneth Hamm
Billy Jacob Hargett
Colton Hargett
Jennifer Harrison
Lakin Brooke Hatcher
Andrew Hester
Adam Holt
Alyssa Hutcheson
Anthony Indelicato
Tony Jefferys
Alexis Johnston
Cole Jones
Jordan William Kelso
Desireé Nichole Kerby
Kimberly King
Robert King
Kasey T. Knudson
Tiffany Sue Lane
Ashley Lansdell
Shannon Laster
Christopher Lee
Andrew Michael Lindsey

Adrienne Lourenco
Nina Loveless
Haley Luther
Samuel Lynch
Dylan Kane Mansell
Erin Marsh
Hollie Mason
Ludmila Matmuratova
Steve Mills
Jeff Mitchell
Keisha Mitchell
Ethan Montgomery
Tolonda Montgomery
Blake Moore
Justin Moss
Tyler Myers
Christian Morgan Nelson
Tessa Norris
Carly Priscilla O'Dell
Alli O'Rear
Whitney Alexas Peppers
Rachel Perkins

Larry Pickens
Carson Randolph
Brittney Roccato
Nicole Ross
Chris Russell
Zachary Ryan
Katelyn Shea
Paulette Sledge

Cheyenne Smith
April Softley
Keenan Sparks
Alyssa Springer
Trendy Steele
Kayla Nicole Surratt
Evelyn Swinney
Lana Tatum

Walter Terrell
James Thompson
Madison Tidwell
Taylor Grace Tidwell
Alexus Brianna Tiggs
Jenna Wade
William Walker
Nicholas Wallace

Sarah Beth Warner
Ory Austin Wigington
Samantha Lorraine Wilson
Elizabeth Georgia Wooten
William Wright
Kaylee Young
Michelle Elaine Young

NORTHWEST UNIVERSITY, KIRKLAND, WA

Rachel Bailey
Charles Baimuke
Jaime Baker
Genevieve Soraya Bendeck
Justin Blair
Lauren Bongiorno
Gabriella Markina Bontrager
Aleah J. Bright
Cassidy Brown
Kevin Carpenter
Sarah Clark
Timothy Danhof
Nickolas Josiah Del Degan

Joshua Deshazer
Annelisa Dieterich
Jenna Fox
Stephen Garcia
Victoria Noel Geck
Elizabeth Gideon
Srishti Gilbert
Whitney Goodrich
Lacey Gray
Rachel Hargett
Abigail Hembree
Cinthia Rubi Hernandez
Navarrete

Catherine Jensen
Jeremiah Jones
Brenden Keene
Nathan Isaiah Kennedy
Ryan McClees
Jessica Olsen
Emma M. Petris
Joy Quackenbush
Kristian Ann Rasch
Christine Reatz
Jonathan Michael Reed
Larry Rogers
Rachael Schlimmer

David Erick Sotelo
Colleen Stringer
Kaitlin Swartz
Ronald Swift
Jamie B. Tanner
Tiffany Michelle Taylor
Timeea Turturean
Robin Ullman
Daniel Walton
Rachel Williamson

NORTHWOOD UNIVERSITY DEVOS GRADUATE SCHOOL, MIDLAND, MI

Emily Bagwell
Sadegh Bairami-Mamaghani
Dione Banks
Lindsay Campeau
Michael Condon
Amee Cox
Martin Cumba
Valisa Downing
Matthew Earley

Harry Flotemersch
Tracy Gallo
Rachel Gates
Cheryl Getty
Ernest Gonzales
Ann Hellow
Barry G. Hornburg
Alexandra Kuch
Janet Kummeth

Nicholas Langlois
Megan Manning
Carmen McClendon
Sarah Morris
Sarah Niemeyer
Kelsey Pendley
Johannes Sterobo
Ryan Suszek
Courtney Szelesi

McKenzie Jean Terwillegar
Morgan Ulseth
Aaron Veenkamp
Sally Vlietstra
Michael Wacht
Mary White
Danielle Wilkosz
Thomas Wood
Brad Zapalowski

NYACK COLLEGE MANHATTAN CAMPUS, NEW YORK, NY

Reginald Amicy
Ayodele Naomi Campbell
Erika Castro
Ritchie Charles
Desiree Lorraine Claudio
Sara Donado

Gregory Francis
Graham Girard
Tiffani Janiel Gonzalez
Jazmel Estephany Guzman
Naomi Hatch
Keren Hernandez

Crystal Jo
Deena Elizabeth Maga
Evan Mellinger
Alivia Mae Mendez
Sae Byol (Grace) Paik
Yiseul Paik

James Patterson
Winaldbert Remonvil
Anthony Sandoval
Tessa Tokke
Priscilla Valencia
Lillian Vaquiz

Anthony Philippe Vaval   Nicole Michelle Vega   Eun Young Lee

NYACK COLLEGE ROCKLAND CAMPUS, NYACK, NY

Kyle Amig
Grace Katherine Anger
Amber Arteaga
Daniel Avila
Daniel Bailey
Stephen Bailey
Emily Barner
Christina Battistella
Aaron Beattie
Jessica Ariela Berrian
Alexandria Bisson
Momoko Black
Jacqueline Bourdett
Elizabeth Deon Brumley
Jessica Bryant
Sarah Burnside

Jennifer Cook
Andrea Cuevas
Natalie Dinkler
Luke Eskelund
Tehillah Eskelund
Scott Fagerlund
Ryan Floridia
Jenna Fowler
Shaniqua Freeman
Tyler Harju
Jessie Heinaman
Carly Heinbaugh
Darla Her
Craig Jacobs
Matthew Keller
Rachel Kunker

Brian Lawrence
Jeremiah Murphy
Kassie Neumann
Richelle Ortiz
Kathleen O'Sullivan
Nicole Pagan
Shawnja Pratt
Caroline Proulx
Valentina Pshenichnaya
Natalie Quinn
Andrea Cheryl Reed
Jedidiah Riconda
Gabrielle N. Robinson
Ada E. Sanchez
Natasha Nadia Sayed
Vanessa Sefriou

Laurie Seifert
Dacara Seward
Greggory Siemering
Emily Sigmon
Kathryn Ann Stoehr
Noah Tatum
Kevin Torres
Cynthia Rosa Urena
Kayla Urena
Maria Varano
Rebecca Wakeley
Karly Walborn
Janiece Williams
Kimberly Yano
Jordan Yee
Sarah Yim

OAKLAND CITY UNIVERSITY, OAKLAND CITY, IN

Natalin Rene Akles
Kelsey Michelle Atkins
Jordyn Cassandra Brown
Maria Theresa Cottier
Bradley Austin Douglas
Jamie Ann Dunigan
Emily Elaine Engle
Cori Michelle Fields
Ashley Lynn Forbes
Kendra Marie Gehlhausen

Christina Lynn Glispie
Laban Kyle Graber
D'Nell Ranae Greenwell
Raven Symone Greer
Kayla Ann Houchin
Adam Craig Jenks
Megan J. Klees
Roman A. Lambert
Megan Nicole Larson
Sam Adrian Mitchel Lee

Matthew Adam Lucas
Stephanie Danielle Mallory
Logan Michael Marshall
Marilee Sue Mills
Eleni Claire Moreland
Jaycee Larae Parke
Laramy Macrae Parke
Brittany M. Paul
Michael William Paul
Jessica Marie Reitz

Anthony Paul Retter
Marisa Rachel Rodgers
Alexandra Michele
Schechner
Carole DeAnne Splittorff
Madeline Day Stilwell
Addison Lee Stoll
David Josiah Stroup
Steven Douglas Toepfer
Megan Lynn Wilson

OAKWOOD UNIVERSITY, HUNTSVILLE, AL

Esther Alexis
Anna-Kay Melissa Bailey
Brandi J. Batten
Jodel Abigale Bernard
Raymond Louis Brown
Chelsea Laurette Browne
Tyler Eliot Buford
Da'Asia N. Calhoun
David Keith Camacho

Daniel Ryan Chandler
Kebrina Simone Clark
Carlette Christina Cohen
Devin Cohen
Marcus Christopher Desir
Lauren C. Eaton
Kaiya LeNae Flemmons
Kristoff V. R. Foster
Nathanael Gamal Francis

Ariane Greenidge
Lemuel E. Hackshaw
Monique Jacqueline Harding
Jonathan D. Harrell II
Samantha Allana Asantewa
Harris
Ebony R. Hicks
Safiya M. Hudson
Sesly Huerfano

Khristopher M. Jones II
Kohrissa C. Joseph
Lemont Joseph
Nia Alexandria D. Langley
Jordan Cole Langston
Tahisha Mahalia Latortue
Kamesha Yvonne Laurry
Calvin Lokko
Cristol Lopez-Palafox

Antonia La-Keisha Matthew
Chantal Nicole McHayle
Mallory Christine McHenry
Kristen D. McLean
Jodian Monique McLeod
Gabriellia Elizabeth McNeil
Farrah Melidor
Selina O. Minott
Dionne Monroe
Ashli Brionne Moore

Camille Jervasia Moore
Shurla Marcia Morris
Jotessa Zari Musson
Kristen Nedd
Demetria Brittney Packwood
Eryn Jodell Peeler
Areisa Sadonie Peters
Madell Polica
Jazzmin Joy Pride
Kayla Renee Ramsey

Darnell R. Robin
Kenesha Talby Ryce
Aymeric E. Saint-Louis-
Gabriel
Britney R. Scott
Devon Michael Scott
Kristen Nicole Sharp
Kiel Avery Smith
Rebekah Irene Spann
Samara Kamilah Stagg

Kyndal Elaine Starks
Mallory Breanna Sullivan
Amal Emmanuel Taylor
Jeffrey Q. Taylor
Alexzandra Theresa
Williams
Deneka Shae Williams
Va Shon Ruel Joshua
Williams
Jocelyn Patrice Woodson

OHIO UNIVERSITY ZANESVILLE, ZANESVILLE, OH

Hunter Baker
Colleen Beck
Cameron Corns
Christopher Emmert

Dylan Evans
Kristin Flagg
Tasia Foster
Jade Grubb

Devin Hess
Melody Maynard
Abby Neff
Cassidy Smith

Charles Smith
Samantha Sorg
Krystal Wheeler
Somer Yoho

OHIO VALLEY UNIVERSITY, VIENNA, WV

Dean Albrecht
Kenleigh Ash
Rodney Azu
Allison Irene Berger
Isaac Trent Boles
Justin Boyce
Abigail Brannon
Stefanie T. Brosey
Isaiah Casenelli

Anne Colley
Randall Colson
Povilas Dambrauskas
Kayla Dixon
Kelly Ferneding
Kelcie Garrett
Allison Gherke
Yuki Hata
Jacob Huck

Gabrielle Jordan
Cathryne Kean
Joseph "Scott" Lowe
Brittian Miller
Adessa Marie Morris
Trevor Osborne
Jessica Paulding
Tijana Radman
Carlos Rubio Garcia

Jessica Schoonover
Julia Secoy-Prim
Andrew Simms
Deividas Sinickas
Ethan Smith
Keith Sweitzer
Madison Wallace
Ethan Zimmerly

OKLAHOMA BAPTIST UNIVERSITY, SHAWNEE, OK

Erin T. Arroz
Blaine Andrew Atchley
Sabrina M. Attaway
Chelsea J. Aube
Amy Lauren Barrett
Jessica Danielle Beach
Colin O. Bergeron
Jeremy Allen Bernhardt
Evan J. Berry
Hayden Garner Burnett
Kari R. Callahan
Nolan Daniel Cannon
Samuel Christopher Castles

Katlyn Lane Chambers
Jeffrey Brock Cherry
Wendy Anne Chuning
Amellia Nicole Coffey
Shalee L. Cordell
Denise Nicole Coroiescu
Nathan Alexander Crawford
Taylor Rae Crismas
Sheridan Lynne Crofford
Marissa D. Crowson
Kailynn Shelese Crutchfield
Taylor Ellen Dabney
Krysten Raye Denney

Jessica Elise Dickinson
Katherine Elizabeth Dodgen
Kelsey Jo Doty
Sadie M. Dunaway
Kayan Marie Dunnigan
Grant Ashton Durham
Grace Catherine Eckstrom
Christian B. Edmonds
Rachel Dawn Evans
Allison Kay Everett
Sydnie Loren Gabbard
Dillon E. Gardner
Sierra Lynn Gilbert

Hannah Elizabeth Godsy
Noah Alexander Golaboff
Bruna M. Gomes
Gabriel Nathaniel Gordon
Ashton Mckinzi Gores
Graeson D. Griffin
Emily Grace Guleserian
Andrew S. Halliburton
Sean Anthony Heard
Lydia Kathleen Hodges
Abbie Noel Hooten
Maile Nichole Hopkins
Zhiyuan Hu

Chace Bucklin Ifland

Hannah Jo Jett

Joshua Dennis Johnson

Mandy M. Johnson

Michael Andrew Johnson

Anna J. Jones

Emily Anne Joslin

Adam Christopher Kelley

Courtney Dawn King

Mark Christopher Knapp

Kelsi E. Lancaster

Jennifer Marie Land

Joel Burton Langford

Megan Anne Lawson

Kristen Elizabeth Lee

Juliana L. Leppke

Kelsey Rae Linsenmeyer

Lauren Brianne Long

Kaitlyn Lucy

Molly Crystal Marietta

Kendall L. Marshall

Megan Elizabeth Mattke

Emily Elise McCarthy

Rachel Sue McCloy

Mason William McCormick

Kaylyn Nichole Medcalf

Emily Nicole Montgomery

Amber Christine Morrisett

Molly B. Munger

Leslie Marie Nungester

Hunter Leigh O'Malley

Kyle Andrew Opskar

Angela D. Paige

Kerianne Elizabeth Petersen

Scott Alan Pfister

Daniel Z. Ramirez Carranza

Nathan S. Reed

Meg Reeder

Ines Remersaro

Nathan Patrick Roach

Catherine Sue Roth

Jennifer M. Roubedeaux

Christopher M. Sanford

Hanah Ivy Sheppard

WookJin Sim

Hannah N. Slater

Chad Preston Smith

Jordan E. Spencer

Tracy Cui Yi Sung

Ian Tyler Swadley

Breanna Rose Taylor

Andrew Ronsholt Thomsen

Victoria Christine
Thrutchley

Taylor Brooke Tinker

Marcus William Titterington

Susana Torres

Rebecca C. Tyler

Dakota Quade Unruh

Autumn Dawn Urton

Britton Ryce Shaw
VanBuskirk

Hannah Elsa Marie Vick

Robert S. Walker

James Matthew Walters

Kirstina Marie Ward

Matthew Ray Welborn

Nathan Ogle Whitson

Zachary Christian Widener

Sarah Michelle Wilkerson

Kylie R. Williams

Erin Renee Wilson

Landen D. Wolever

William Benjamin Woodson

Danielle Paige Young

OKLAHOMA BAPTIST UNIVERSITY GRADUATE SCHOOL, SHAWNEE, OK

Chase T. Vencl

OKLAHOMA CHRISTIAN UNIVERSITY, EDMOND, OK

Sherriee Abuel

Yibo Ai

Jamil Al Botros

Kirby Allen

Lindsay Meredith Allenbach

Trevor Austin

Alexandra Autrey

Mary Ann Baker

Travis Battles

Sarah Bell

Andrew Bellcock

Samuel Berridge

Joshua Bilello

Laura Blair

Meagan Elizabeth Bobo

Ian Boyes

Garrett Bremer

Matt Brown

Timothy Allen Burdick

Carl Burmeier

Bryan Buxton

Emily Calvert

Danielle Childress

Allison Chilton

Travis Lynn Clark

Adam Clothier

Sarah Cobb

Preston Coleman

Amanda Margaret Cooper

Cody Cooper

Cody Crossley

Marki Louise Crouse

Phillip Curtis

Abby Delaine Davis

Emily Dick

Katelynn Dickson

Debra Diepenbrock

Chloe Frances Downey

Emmanuel Taylor
Dufitumukiza

Rachel Eppes

Emily Erickson

Gage Ervin

Kaylee Eubank

Kandyce Everett

Kelli Ewert

Eric Falley

Casey Farrar

Alexis Farrell

Marci Frias

Travis Wayne Frost

Emma Gade

Ornella Gashumba

Mitchell Gaylord

Adam Giles

Cecilia Gramling

Rachel Greenlee

Daniel Griffin

Michael Harlan

Katelynn Harmon

Phillip Harris

Benjamin Hartman

Thomas Joseph Hartnett

Magdalyn Hawkins

Megan Brianne Hendricks

Denali R. Hicks

Garett Hill

Rachel Holmes

Jason Huebert

Ashley Huff

Jean Paul Iradukunda

Kyler Johnson

Matthew Johnson	Dontasia Rae-Lynn McAfee	Marina Pendleton	Heidi Vanbenthem
Toria Lin Johnson	Hannah McKenzie	Kyle Porter	Seanhenry Vandyke
Ryan Jones	Alexander McMannama	Jared Punjabi	Christian Robert Samuel
Tanner Jones	Jessica McNeal	Brandon Ramsey	Wright Wagner
Kristen Jorgensen	Matthew Miller	Courtney Redmond	David Walden
Brennym Kaelin	Silas Morris	Seth Reiter	Hayley Waldo
Christina Kaelin	Sylvie Muhimpundu	Meghan Rice	April Wall
Kelly Sue Karguth	Marie Mukashyaka	Rachel Risley	Guangda Wang
Caleb Krut	Michael Murphy	Collin Schnakenberg	Hayley Weaver
Rene Moise Kwibuka	Corbin Murrow	Zachary Shaffer	Kristen Wheeler
Parker LaMascus	Jacey Neagles	Amanda Smith	Lauren Wheeler
Erica Landes	Courtlin Tara Neece	Cody Smith	Brady Wheelock
Elizabeth Lewis	Tracy Nguyen	Lauren Smith	Whitney White
Ashley Lim	Emily Nichol	Tori Dale Smith	Kyle Wood
Kara Litzkow	Michael Nsengiyumva	Jenisha Spivey	Sheldon Scott Yeakley
Brandon Loe	Nicholas O'Sullivan	Tyler William Sriver	Freddy Yemere
Emilio Lopez	Kehinde Ogunwemimo	Sean Steele	Blake Alan Yort
Ryan Lutterloh	Megann Olsson	Deborah Swanson	Corbin Holloway Young
Jayla Marie Luxton	Robert Pabst	Luke Alan Swanson	Timothy Zuercher
Mallory Mager	Michael Parker	Anna Taylor	
Makenzie Markus	Trenton Parker	Moriah Thomason	
Kasey Martin	Renee Pedersen	Tanya Thompson	

OKLAHOMA PANHANDLE STATE UNIVERSITY, GOODWELL, OK

Angelique Rosanna Archer	Cody Fischer	Logan Litton	Ashtyn Leigh Swenn
Samantha Arledge	Sage Fischer	Jessica Lowery	Kevin Tankerson
Anyssa Barbosa	Johnbraden Andrew Frontz	Kendal May Malone	Christopher Lee Thompson
Daniel Mabil Ber	Salina Galindo	Lori Marie Miller	MaKenze Quinn Twyman
Savannah Lauren	Danielle Gonzalez	Jacob Murphy	William VanHooser
Bertschinger	Josh Gordon	Payton Osbon	Brandon Vaverka
Craig Dalton Bohl	Tyler Hall	Willem Pretorius	Shelbie Rose Mae Weeder
Haley Bonilla	Patrick Hallford	Kinsey Puyear	Ashby Nicole Williams
Jade Cathcart	Madison Lynn Heathington	Chanda Parker Reynolds	Kymberly Laurcen Williams
Raymond Claypool	Sarah Henderson	Christina Rodriguez	Darcie Rae Wilson
Kaci Davenport	Kayce Anne Ingram	Kelby Ross	Andreanna Jo Wray
Eva Dye	Ashley Jarzombek	Scot Schwieterman	
Trey Fankhouser	Dakota Lamb	Vanessa Delia Solis	
Abigail Ferguson	Jordan Marie Langland	Tyler Duane Stephens	

OKLAHOMA STATE UNIVERSITY CENTER FOR HEALTH SCIENCES, TULSA, OK

Paul Atakpo	Sarah Bradley	Abigail Cogman	Kelsey Dalmont
Gregory Bradley	Russell Brown	Trevor J. Conner	Colby Degiacomo

Bryan Duell

Clayton Farahani

Jerrod King

Terresa Miller

Michael Thomas Money Jr.

Eric Morrison

Khanh Nguyen

Nadjeschda Nordquist

Tiffany Scheuplein

Jolee Tabatha Suddock

Amru Swar

Elizabeth Tran

Emily Turner

OKLAHOMA WESLEYAN UNIVERSITY, BARTLESVILLE, OK

Jack Billy Arreola Lopez

Alissa Monique Brown

Denton Ray Brown

Kacy Nicole Bryan

Julie Jo Campbell

Chloe Monique Canfield

Molly Marie Card

Miranda Nicole Coffey

Carissa Kathleen Cole

Kyle Lee Essary

Ashley Paige Fargo

Jose Gabriel Flores

Cassandra Elise Frailey

Elijah Gonzales

Katherine Michelle
Goodrich

Jacob Tyler Hall

Jared Ray Hall

Ellen Johanna Harms

Jo-Nieca Daniella Herrera

Ryan James Hill

Spencer Steven Holdorf

Jalen Dominique Jackson

Cecilia Jimenez

Megan Nicole Jones

Jonathan David King

Patrishia Ashley Knott

Maggie Kelly Lannan

Hugo L. Lemus

Daniel Jordan Linick

Shaina Merlin Luke

Will Franklin Price

Krista Shannon Reimer

Kourtney Annetta Rhoads

Sierra Shae Roth

Sarah Alison Sharp

Tyler James Sherwood

Trevor Aaron Stark

Hannah Grace Stedwell

Aaron Lee Terrill

Kaitlyn Elizabeth Thomas

John Thomas Young III

Nemanja R. Zalad

Suzannah Mae Zimmer

OLIVET NAZARENE UNIVERSITY, BOURBONNAIS, IL

Lainee K. Abbott

Abigail E. Allen

Angelique R. Azouri

Madeline G. Bloom

Ashley N. Borop

Amy R. Brown

Annette F. Carr

Caleb N. Cornell

Zane R. DeBeck

Jessica L. Dirkse

Daniel J. Eccles

Addyson N. Emmons

Renee L. Enz

Megan M. Eylander

Shelley Lynn Fellows

Andrew C. Fischer

Tyler S. Ford

Laura A. Fosnaugh

Lucas W. Fritch

Jacob R. Gouge

Laura J. Graven

Karalyn R. Hewett

Austin C. Holton

Kyle M. Johnston

Emily M. Kane

Michael S. Krebill

Madalyn E. Lathrop

Jordan J. Lingle

Taylor N. Logan

Joelle N. Mannion

Joseph E. Mantarian

Brandon N. Maranion

Michaela M. Maris

Megan L. McKinley

Garrett L. Muhlstadt

Gwendolyn V. Payne

Calvin W. Price

Catherine L. Reed

Chelsea L. Risinger

Clara A. Ruegsegger

Emily E. Sauer

Marie C. Sheets

Michael-Andrew T.
Spalding

Shelby L. Wegforth

OLNEY CENTRAL COLLEGE, OLNEY, IL

Kristen Aldridge

Bree Ann Boley

Dalyn Brach

Bridget Brian

Morgan Collins

Sandra Davis

Danny Deimel

Claire Downes

Luke Durre

Jack C. Dwyer

Lexie Erwin

Ariel Renee Flowers

Torri Brooke Frye

Madison Gibson

Linda Goodwin

Zachary Hardin

Jill Humes

Courtney James

Jason Jones

Stephanie Nicole Kirkland

Quentin Klingler

Chelsea Kocher

Will May

Leighanna Miller

Jordan Paige Morris

Brianna Alexandria Nail

Neal Northcott

Nakyung Oh

Kaitlin Mae Rauch

Tammie Sager

Spencer Schultz

Becca Stover

Kevin Douglas Ukena

Kristen Urfer

Heather Nicole Vaupel

Christina Welker

Christy Michelle Wimberly   Rachel Zwilling

ORAL ROBERTS UNIVERSITY, TULSA, OK

Eshu (Josh) Yonan Badal	David L. Floyd Jr.	Jonathan Hutchins	Alexis Muscarella
Brandon Braun	Lyndy Foust	Sydney Ilg	Violet Mwanza
Danielle Lucy Cerminara	Hannah Erin Fruh	Natalie Lackowicz	Peter Wesley Odom
Elizabeth DeVore	Rachel Galfo	Chadwick M. Lukasiewicz	Tamrah Ruth Patterson
Meghan L. Drake	Kirah Heffner	Alexandra Anne McDonald	Charis Anne Schneider
Mary Allison Ekhoff	Grayson A. Hostetler	Grace Sarah Min	Morgan Sutton

ORANGEBURG–CALHOUN TECHNICAL COLLEGE, ORANGEBURG, SC

Brittany Abbott	William Carter	David Fogle	Dallas Hutto
Ashley Adams	Joseph Cecchini	Christopher Alan Foley	Carly Jackson
Matthew Adams	Joshua Chaplin	Adeline Fotso	Gloranna Jenkins
Teresa Amick-Ballard	Kaitlyn Chavis	Mark Daniel Fralix II	Jimek'Que Jenkins
Corinthia Anderson	Samuel Clayton	Brandi Funderburke	Laveda Jenkins
Joseph Anderson	Tamara Cole	Nicholas Furtick	Justin Jennings
Myra Ardis	Rebecca Connor	Angela Gable	Daniel Johnson
Ashley Ayer	Rebecca Corbett	Taylor Given	Ke'Andra Johnson
Katie Baltzegar	Caitlin Crider	Shantanique Ka'Niece	Dorothy Joyner
Tyler Barnes	Dustin Croxton	Givens	Barry Keever
Ashley Baxley	Paul Cullen	Jonathon Godwin	Hollianne Kehoe
Justice Beach	Laurence Cuttino	Seth Goodwin	Shirley Keitt
Ciera Bell	Hailey Dantzler	Benjamin Graham	Lamaranda Kelly
Joy Bellamy	Kasey Dantzler	Andrew Green	Aimee Kibodeaux
Kayla Bennett- Cochran	Roger Darby	David Green	Kristopher Kidd
Sean Bernstel	Bryan Davis	Edwin Gwaltney	Christopher Kinard
Akoeba Biova Biam	April Deaver	Fayequeisha Haggood	Kendra Kirby
Oletha Bookard	Nicholas Dobson	Meredith Hair	Brittany Kovach
Wanda Bowman	Hannah Dockery	Shakira Harley	James Livingston
Alana Bradley	Zachary Drawdy	Amanda Hattler	Sheila Livingston
William Bragg	Samantha Dudley	Leanna Haufler	Crystal Lorick
Katalin Bramblett	Donald Dunkin	Matthew Haulbrooks	Susan Lyda
Christina Brantley	Misty Dyal	Kathryn Hayden	Brandie Lyons
Aaron Brickle	Samantha Edgemon	Kaela Hayes	George Lyons
Mary Brown	Sara Edwards	Shedrick Henderson	Kelly Lyons
Romairo Bryant-Martin	Amanda Eisman-Lindsay	Rebecca Hickman	Susan Macclary
Caroline Burns	Andrew England	Darcey Holladay	Joshua Malejko
Keith Byrd	Thomas Evans	Dalton Holman	Morris Mallard
Daneshia Byron	Caitlin Felkel	Katrice Hudson	Victoria Maltais-Mcdonald
Damilya Ann Capers	Kevin Fisher	Jesse Hughes	Kelly Martin
Ashley Carson	Kevin Scott Fisher	Cody Hutto	Lesley Martinez

Traci Maynard
Robert McClary
Mary Brooks McDonald
Samantha Meadows
Alisa Medlin
Tiffani Miller
Shayquell Mitchell
Destiny Murph
Janet Musselman
Coran Myers
Danielle Marie Nash
Gary Nelson
Tyler Newman
Mary Nnatubeugo
Bernice O'Neil
Andria Odum
Melissa Oneal
Patrick Ortiz
Jimmy Osteen
John Ott
Melissa Parker

Tanna Patel
Kealaysha Perry
Timothy Perry
Kelsey Platt
Sandra Price
Joseph Rast
Lori Reed
Rachel Reid
Heidi Reno
Amy Rinkenberger
Catherine Rivera
Alfreda Rowe
Joshua Rutland
Angelia Ryant
Chelsea Salisbury
Don Sandifer
Joseph H. Sandifer Jr.
Philip Schneider
Ethan Owens Shelley
Latwanda Shivers-
Thompson

Kyle Shore
Jessica Sims
Daniel Singletary
Dustin Lane Singletary
Jamie Sires
Jacquleen Skinner
Joy Smith
Kandice Brienne Smith
Christopher Smoak
Lonnie Smoak
Alison Stevens
Abram Stewart
Willard Still
Kristin Stroud
Aaron Sutton
Adam Sutton
Robin Tabucbuc
Benjamin Thomas
Octavius Thomas
Robert Thompson
Stephanie Thompson

Alisha Treen
Erica Tyler
Don Tyrone
Virginia Walling
Nicholas Wasilonsky
Joshua Waters
Matthew Waters
George White
Samantha Robin Whittle
Kelsey Wiggins
Rhonda Wiggins
Dana Williams
Kimberly Williams
Patrick Williams
Rhonda Williams
Amber Williamson
Thomas Wilsey
Lauren Wilson
Malcolm Wright

OTTAWA UNIVERSITY, OTTAWA, KS

Kaylee Morgan Asher
Bekka J. Bailey
Austin R. Blaue
Jacob L. Brendemuehl
Kent W. Buetell
Jordan J. Calderwood
Melissa J. Clingerman
Jacyn B. Dawes

Garrett Michael Dragoo
Avery M. Enzbrenner
Elyssa L. Esposito
Destinee Lynn Evans
Riley R. Falk
Lisa R. Greer
Bailey L. Griffith
Jessica N. Gunnels

Lane M. Harris
Lindsey N. Henke
Rebecca M. Housman
Michael T. Jones
Austin T. Kehoe
Caleb M. Krueger
Caleb W. Love
Jacob A. Martin

Melanie A. Murphy
Shailendra V. Selvaraj
Joseph T. Siegele
Michael C. Steinbacher
Jenna M. Stigge
Angelica A. Tapia
Kaitlynn M. Walker
Dayton H. Walter

OUACHITA BAPTIST UNIVERSITY, ARKADELPHIA, AR

Nicholas Archer
Jessica Lynn Ashcraft
Elizabeth Bacon
Sam Beary
Joseph Breckenridge
Claudia Marietta Brizuela
Morgan Brothers
Richard Burke
Ellen Butler

Michael Butler
Layne Castleman
Erin Cheshire
Roxanne Easter
Grace Finley
Rachel Gaddis
Suzie Gresham
Emily Harris
Scott Hartley

David Headrick
Allie Hegi
Anna Kumpuris
Dixon Land
Ben Lange-Smith
Bonnie Magee
Jacob Moreno
Brent Northington
Hannah Osborne

Reagan Parsons
Griffin Peeples
Ryan Perkins
Abby Root
Elva Rosas
Josh Rubin
Saddie Sasser
Jordan Sharp
Treslyn Shipley

Lauren Snow	Emily Tual	Rachel Wicker	Sara Catherine Williams
Mollie Taylor	Will Wallace	David Willhite	Karen Wray

OXFORD COLLEGE OF EMORY UNIVERSITY, OXFORD, GA

Lillian Boyer	Cristin Rebecca	Jamani Montague	Layla Tajmir
Stephanie Day-Goodman	Hendrickson	Onyi Ohamadike	Rashika Verma
Diane Glover	Chasen Motte Jackson	Shloka Parvatrao	Mark G. Walden
Carissa Hope Goodwin	Shubhangi Jain	Shoba S. Patel	Bingran Wang
Kereisha Harrell	Jeremy Andrew Male	Athira Penghat	
	John Mizuki	Branden M. Rodriguez	

OZARK BIBLE INSTITUTE, NEOSHO, MO

Courtney Anne Johnston	Jamin Martin

PACIFIC UNION COLLEGE, ANGWIN, CA

Janae N. Bowman	Jeffrey K. Egly	John Mangan	Andres Rodriguez
Sergio A. Caishpal	Abby N. Everett	Emily M. Mathe	Pedro A. Rosillo
Mikyla H. Cho	Jordan D. Fode	Ella M. Melnick	Emilio Rovalino
Soungmin Cho	Timothy A. Giang	Jacqueline L. Millar	Zachary Seifert-Ponce
Hannah A. Choi	Laura M. Helms	Trevor A. Nogueira	Kim R. Thompson
Paul Dahoon Chung	Sue Min Sophia Kwon	Raechel E. Opsahl	Josue A. Tobar
Bethany Jasmine Costa	Byron C. Lee	Dmytro I. Panchenko	Ryan L. Vigilia
Sarah M. Cusick	Sarah K. Lee	Jeong Soo "Chris" Park	Benjamin Chukuma Vincent
Duyen T. Doan	Madison B. Macomber	Brysanna C. Penland	Cyndee L. Westenrider

PALM BEACH ATLANTIC UNIVERSITY, WEST PALM BEACH, FL

Tyler D. Ascenzi	Maxwell N. Carter	Kathryn E. Gentry	Michael D. Leonard
Clara Bailey	Olivia R. Casper	Alyssa Hearing	Abigail Jeannine Lindholm
Erika Barajas	Benjamin T. Colabella	Stephen A. Hedger	Thomas Lucas Lubben
Jessica D. Baureis	Savannah Cook	Jade Heiserman	Alyssa Maddox
Susan E. Bealor	Sherriann R. Cosgrove	Gabriella Hoge	Tonya Mateuszczyk
Evan Berlanti	Justin W. Cunard	Rachael Holehouse	Jenna Lynn McMorrow
Lauren D. Blair	Elizabeth Davis	Laura E. Humphrey	Christopher A. McQueen
Christina Mae Bodensiek	Cody Deboer	Amber Lynn Johnson	Kayla Marie Mendez
Korey Bricker	Sarah Elizabeth Dias	Lindsey Johnson	Caleb W. Meyer
Marion Brito	Andrea Echlund	Aaron M. Katanic	Courtney Elizabeth Miner
Ann-Marie Romona	Maryssa Ellison	Troy F. Katterheinrich	Nicole C. Minott
Broomfield	Chadd M. Feyas	Stella E. King	Jessica Monteiro
Stephany A. Brown	Justin Forcier	Hope Koleczek	Carrie D. Moreau
Josephine Bunn	Alicia M. Fowski	Jake T. Kreamer	Melody Mulligan
Theresa M. Butler	Danielle N. Frandsen	Karina A. Langer	Ryan P. Murray
Alexis S. Cahall	Nicole Freire	Naomi Lau	Anderson Eleanor North

Joseph Louis Nunez
Ashley Owen
Shelby Padilla
Savannah Peiffer
Alexzandra Mary Phillpot
Liana N. Plunkett
Breeze Linae Pollard
Grace Postorino
Alyssa Lane Prew
Suely Rivera

Heriberto Rodriguez
Faith E. Rohn
Julie E. Sandberg
Daniela Santamarina
Jeremiah D. Sater
Gabriella Silva
Megan C. Sorber
Cassidy Stanton
Jordyn O. Strahm
Ashley C. Taylor

Ruth Terkelson
Molly Thistle
Erica Thompson
Paula Throop
Madhav Timsina
Jonathan Taylor Van Oss
Nicole L. Verheek
Kimberly G. Vreman
Angela K. Wagoner
Emily C. Waller

Lori K. Wendling
Karina White
Saija Denay Wilson
Sarah E. Wilson
Bridget Wollrabe
Natalie Elizabeth Wood
Kasey Wyer

PALO ALTO COLLEGE, SAN ANTONIO, TX

Justin Aguilar
Ricardo Almaguer
Alejandro Alvarez
Corina Alvarez
Marissa Antopia
Jennifer Aparacio
Beverly Barrientes
Valentin Barrutieta
Allie Bruster
Demas Cardenas
Amanda Cerda
William Harley Combs II
Carol Crockett
Brandi Nicole Crowell

Melissa Faith Cruz
Isai De Hoyos
Denise Deleon
Jade Escamilla
Briana Esquivel
Elijah Garcia
Hilary Elizabeth Garcia
Joe Gonzalez
Mark L. Harmon
Selma Gutierrez Hernandez
Alexis J. Hodge
Ashley Hoelscher
Nia Eloisa Jaramillo
Misty Jones

Tuk Maya Karki
Michael Laguna
Carol Lankford
Prisilla Ruth Lares
Deborah Leal
Nefi Amulek Magana
Dominik Marfil
Mendoza Maribel
Jonathon Martinez
Brian Mbanefo
Jasmaine Moore
Murillo Murillo
Jo Nieto
Kendra Rainey

Rosalio Ramirez
Emily Rodriguez
Jacqueline Rodriguez
Julianna Sifuentes
Derick Tinajero
Luis alberto Trinidad
Kayla Tuttle
Liliana Valle
Justin Vera
Bryana Wendy Villarreal
Isabella Witherspoon
Darren Taylor Zettner

PANOLA COLLEGE, CARTHAGE, TX

Shelby Allen
Kristina Briann Almeida
Lauren Anderson
Alicia Nicole Ayers
Katherine Baze
Josh Benson
Ursula Candy Betancourt
Lola Boren
Emily Nicole Bounds
David Bragg
Dewey Brannan
Maggie Elizabeth Bush
Stacy Campos Sandoval
Nelly Carrasco Bohorqu

Liliana Castaneda
Austin Charanza
Alaina Paige Christian
Ashley Payton Christian
Melody Cohorst
Jayme Cole
Cameron Coligan
Sierra Collins
Marzaveon Cooper
Rebekah Corley
Robby Cox
Melisa Gayle Cunningham
Lewis Dales
James Braswell Davis

Jennifer Davis
Hannah Deal
Toby Dylan Delgado
Debra Dickerson
Harley Duncan
Michael Elliott
Steven Emmerling
Britney Everitt
Brian Fincher
Janice Fincher
Carrie Ford
Laura Fryman
Amber Gage
Osiel Garcia

Larhonda Garrett
Cameica Gates
Ashley Gay
Luz Gomez
Jordan Gore
Kastley Shayne Greer
Kaycie Gros
Ana Guerrero Rodriguez
Belinda Hamby
Coby Hammons
Destiny Hart
Hunter Hartmann
Stephen Heath
Seth Hendricks

Christopher Henslee
Jason Henslee
Efrain Hernandez
Megan Hogg
Ja'Lea Holland
Hannah Hoover
Taylor Hudspeth
Macie Innerarity
Amber Jarrett
Ashley Johnson
David Johnson
Shene Monique Johnson
Tiara Johnson
Jasmine Jones
Kami Koenig
Tamara Latham
Matthew Letourneau
Taylor Lane Lindsay
Laura Lindsey
Sherrie Lloyd
Jessica Lynn Long

Erica Lovely
Cindy Loyd
Jaxon Lucas
Patricia Maberry
Meagan Mackey
Melissa Mangan
Adine Sarai Mañón
Shajuana Marry
Jennifer Lynn Mayfield
Dana Mcdaniel
Curtis Mckenney
Sara Mendez
Lacy Miles
Jessica Millican
Sierra Marie Moses
Rachel Mukweyi
Shay Mullins
Deanna Musico
Desiree Nitzschke
Gregory Och
Corey Oliver

Sarita Page
Joel Pallares
Ronna Lynn Phillips
Melanie Pinkston
Tyler Powell
Shannon Pruett
Michaela Quinn
Christopher Ramirez
R'Trevia Randolph
Taylor Reeves
Dillon Richmond
Nancy Robbins
Anjelica Rocha
Jason Ryan
Mary Sanders
Tina Sandidge
Madilyn Sanford
Mccartney Satterwhite
Auna Shofner
Carlie Smith
Hannah Smith

Tanesha Javon Smith
Stacie Sonnier
William Spanial
Lyjessica Sparks
Logan Spear
Delisha Strain
Aesha Strong
Rialie Taylor
Jessica Leann Thompson
Meagen Tillman
Brady Tovar
Thomas Trotter
Bobbie Warren
Amber Lynn Weatherford
Tyler West
Taylor Christine Wilkerson
Alexander Willett
Ben Wise
Chantel Simone Woodard
Marie Wynn
Steven Yates

PARIS JUNIOR COLLEGE, PARIS, TX

Cade Armstrong
Dezmond G. Barnes
Stephanie D. Bradford
Amber N. Campbell
Colton B. Clemmer
Denisha D. Crow
Alexandria N. Cruz
Chelsey L. Davis
Stephanie A. Duncan

Alonso Gallegos
Kevin N. Heath
April D. Horton
Chelsie L. Howlett
Debbie D. Huff
Lauren E. Jeans
Kortni C. Johnston
Kristopher Koon
Kaitlin Lewis

Mary E. Lewis
Matthew L. Lunsford
Preston V. Martin
Taylor P. McCloure
Monica D. Montgomery
David R. Parker
Katherine G. Parrish
Tyler M. Pohl
Gail L. Rogers

Chad E. Sherrin
Keith J. Shivers
Magan A. Smith
Crystal G. Snider
Damya Toney
Joshua K. Winton
Frances Christine Worley

PASSAIC COUNTY COMMUNITY COLLEGE, PATERSON, NJ

Mohamed T. Abdelghany
Romeo B. Acevedo
Cameron J. Ameye
Andre C. Avila
Flor Ayala
Shayna I. Barrera-Mercedes
Alexander Lopez Beltran
Erjola Berati

Adiareli Cabrera
Saskia E. Davis
Miguel A. De Jesus Jr.
Cindy Ercolano
Ana J. Fellippello
Josias I. Fraser
Alejandro Galvan
Luisa Gonzalez

Rebecca Hafelfinger
Tiona D. Harris
Michelle C. Hernandez
Evony M. Hernandez-
Contreras
John C. Llerena
Smerlyn Lora
Deyanaris Luzon

William B. Matias
Monica Melse
Daisy Negron
Jimena Nunez
Leisa O. Oliphant
Ramona Padilla-Chalas
Bryan A. Pazmino
Nicholas J. Peterson

Sandra E. Rey

Yeliz Sara

Jovanie E. Simpson

Jordan T. Stack

Miriam Toxtli

Klaudia Udvari

Fabio S. Utrilla

Yhashoda Welcome

PEARL RIVER COMMUNITY COLLEGE, POPLARVILLE, MS

Tyler Alan Abney

Michaela Andrews

Rebecca Applewood

Cheyenne Baker

Leah Rose Balli

Kristen Barnes

Bethany Berryman

Lynnessa Best

Ashley Marie Briggs

Katelyn Briggs

Regan Brown

Tyler Cagle

Thomas Catlett

Kevin Alan Craft

Brianna Dillon

Andrea Donovan

Micah Eastridge

Christopher Edenfield

Leslie England

Rebecca Farmer

Miranda Fazende

Jason Funchess

Elna Garner

Lauren Gentry

Barbara Gipson

John Graves

Kayla Nacole Graves

Stanford Gwin

Carter Hankins

Curtis Hart

Meaghan Nicole Holsen

Kevin Jarrell

Rashawn Johnson

Dana Shondrika Jones

Katelyn Victoria Ladner

Julie Laird

Kale Lancaster

Hannah Landrum

Cindy Le

Tierney D. Manning

Jeffrey Marshall

James Massengale

Houston McMahon

Zachary McPhail

Hannah Miller

Greg Myers

Joshua Patrick Neal

Jerrod Newson

Dana Peavy

Robert Perry

Jordan Kayelin Pharr

Karen Posey

Lauren Robinson

Brian Andrew Rogers

Cassandra Rosser

Rhegan Seymour

Sandra Silvain

Jocelyne Sims

Jessica Stevens

Lane Stewart

Ashley Leeann Taylor

Kayla Ra'quel Theodore

Evan Thornton

Victoria Valliant

Lorrie Warren

Anthony Williams

Anna Wren

PEIRCE COLLEGE, PHILADELPHIA, PA

Janet Andrea Afflick

Wanda Ivette Amaro

Dialya Ruth Avegnon

Emaline Mae Baronofsky

Melissa A. Batchelor

Thomas J. Blickos

Michael Allen Brooks

Lisa Nicole Castano

Dansela Caushi

Nghi Khiet Chau

Judith I. DeFiccio

Analise Jade Dennis

Nicholas A.
DiGianivittorio Sr.

April Dobson

Idowu I. Edeki

Roberto Esposito

Mariya A. Georgieva

Shakira Monae' Gregg

Gabriel Grove

Aqueelah Harris

Chrissie Ann Hernandez

Carol Yvonne Jamison

Jacqueline E. Jones

Maryse Kercy

Ashley Kerekes

Kathleen Kientzy

Thomas J. Kilbride

Diana Delores Kirkland

Joseph Raymond Logan

Theresa A. Lounsbery

Edward Donnell Lyons

Joshua Lytle

Willie Frank Mays

John Michael McHugh Jr.

Nicole S. Neal

Marisol Ortiz

Souroosh Pardakhti

Melissa A. Pasquariello

Rosea Pheap

Mark Jameson Rivera

Anthony Joseph Russo

Jennifer M. Slavic

Quanesha Myniah Smith

Christopher Felix Sutanto

Lamin Swaray

Patrice Lynette Thomas

Mary Ann Patricia Torres

Monica Denise VanWright

Michelle A. Woeller

PELLISSIPPI STATE COMMUNITY COLLEGE, KNOXVILLE, TN

Victoria Culpepper

Hong (Rose) Thuy Kim Do

Christina (Haley) Emitt

April Dawn Gilbert

Liat Koenig

Rebecca Sharon Lengfellner

Carlie Elizabeth Sims

Courtney Marie Young

PENNSYLVANIA INSTITUTE OF TECHNOLOGY, MEDIA, PA

Lakia Allen

Natasha Allen

Jason Bocella

Joanne Cassidy

Anjelica Cervantes

Nina Chernikova

Zachary Chubb

Lynda Kyung Devenny

Marilyn Dutch

Rhonda J. Estep

Jena Ferrigno

Brian Fulginiti

Shawn Fulton

Amber Gallo

Donna M. Girodana-Fedena

Nicholas Anthony

Govannicci

Edison Guzman

Emma Howell

Flora Denise Hunter

Elizabeth Iatesta

Alexander Jackson

Jacob Allen Kamp

Kristen Kendall

Kelly Kenworthy

Tanera Knox

Robert Lamberson

Imareliss Lopez

Nicole Brooke Lord

Bridget McCaffrey

Shakkir McGuire

Marcus Mercado

Natasha Nevarez

Westley K. Otte

Konstantin Pavluchenko

Nilmary Perez

Diane Ricketts

Sara K. Romano

Amber Juaniesha Sheridan

Daniel Spayd

Maiya F. Townsend

Monique Walden

Nadira Wallace

Joseph Wood

Jason C. Worrell

PENNSYLVANIA STATE UNIVERSITY DUBOIS CAMPUS, DUBOIS, PA

Linsie Nicole Adams

Lauren Anderson

Tory Anderson

Aaron Angstadt

Andrew Angstadt

Tamera Louise Anthony

Shane Baxter

Andrew Travis Bigley

Ryan Bish

Carley S. Boice

Anastasia Boleen

Courtney Braunns

Emilee Brown

Hope Elizabeth Buskirk

Amanda Butler

Samantha Carobine

Dylan Clingan

Desmond John Coleman

Gustin Conde

Nathan Confer

Tawnya Cordwell

Jessica Czekai

Robert Denoon

Matthew Duffus

Grace Earle

Robin Laine Foltin

Nicholas Genevro

Tanner Gooden

Clinton Goodwin

Darcie Mae Grenier

Anthony P. Halm

Kristy Hanes

Anna Harkleroad

Howard Hartzfeld

Evan Hatfield

Jacqueline Hetzler

Brett Himes

Jake Himes

Amanda Horner

Matthew Humes

Julianne Inzana

Cory Jamieson

Taylor Jantunen

Brittany Johnson

Brendan Keegan

Scott Berman Kephart

Joseph Knarr

Jennifer Lenze

Dennis Lee Lumadue III

Mandy Marconi

Koren McCullough

Leah McKay

Jeanie McKenna

Amber Lynn Metzger

Jessica Metzger

Linsey Mizic

Dale Louis Moore

Colleen Elaine Mulhollan

Courtney Mullins

Roy Mumau

Gregory Myers

Michael Narehood

Braden Neal

Courtney Newman

Brad Noland

Briana Nussbaum

Ellis Painter

Brandon Pash

Courtney R. Patterson

Zachary Pomeroy

Shalane Read

David Robbins

Justin Rock

Nathaniel Rodgers

Samuel Michael Roselli

Kayla Rossi

Joshua Sanko

Matthew Santaniello

Rachel lee Schreiber

Tyler Scott

Julie Shimmel

Cassidy Sicheri

Amber Siverling

Jacob Skubisz

Justin Smith

Krista Smith

Tiandra Snyder

Noah David Stellabuto

Molly Stoltz

Sadie Viglione

Juliana Vokes

Shelby Volosky

Taylor Walborn

Holly Dawn Wensel

Chelsey Winters

Zachary Wood

Johnny Zheng

PENNSYLVANIA STATE UNIVERSITY NEW KENSINGTON, NEW KENSINGTON, PA

Milagros J. Barta de Brasser
Brandon B. Burchette
Ian R. Callender
Carley Lynn Carnahan
Hon Tak Cheng

Ariel Christine Festa
Laura Ashley Gensamer
Joshua Tyler Gump
Brittany Ann Hydock
Christian Brendan Kamenic

Watipaso Kumwenda
Jiahui Lin
Jonathan Paul McCabe
Brittany Miller
Marissa A. Russo

Madison M. Sedilko
Savannah Michelle Smith
Cheyenne Danielle Swanger
Evan Joseph West
Ashley D. Worlds

PENSACOLA CHRISTIAN COLLEGE, PENSACOLA, FL

Thomas James Andrews
Laura Jane Baptista
Francis Connor Barich
Jesse C. Bilowus
Kathryn Lavinia Black
Sarah Elizabeth Borton
Scott Joseph Brady
Brooke Lori Brauneis
Ashley Marie Brizuela
Cody Benjamin Bryant
Timothy Duwan Burley
Aaron Michael Conley
Micah Lee Farmer
Eric Michael Flanagan
Timothy Daniel Francis
David Gray Fulp
Amanda Noelle Gardner
Dikchhya Gauchan
Tyler Tillman Gellos

Andrew Lee Gowans
Grace Cassidy Greenwood
Patricia Hartono
Jessica Lynne
Hollandsworth
Elyssa Kay Houk
Jacob Lane Jekel
Kody Hayden Johnson
Shauna Christine Kaiser
Elijah Kimmig
Sarah Elizabeth Kozar
Timothy Michael Krug
Mark William Labins
JinWoo Woo Lee
Asupa Tracy Leota
Robert Michael Linstrum II
Timothy Drew Lobdell
Hannah Marie Loo
Hannah Mae Lowhorn

Christina Ann McAdory
Josiah Mark McFarland
Kendra Elise McFarland
Thomas Whittaker Messick
Grace Anne Morrissey
Amber Kay Morton
Michael William Motz
Cody Allan Nagel
Lydia Marie Peplinski
Douglas Edwin Perez
Joy Elise Randazzo
Jacqulyn Brooke Rasmussen
Dan Wayne Ang Reyes
Amber Louise Richards
Bethany Joy Roberts
Joshua Daniel Schlaudt
Trevor Nathaniel
Schumacher
Kelicia Sheree Sellers

Eunkwon Seo
Carrie Ann Shrewsbury
Jeffrey Reagan Limbaugh
Snow
Shivangi Vishnu Soni
Stephen Allen Spilger
Joel Suarez
Brianna Lynell Tewell
Hannah Beth Tewell
Alexis Jade Turner
Kayla Marie Udd
Danae Joy Vandenburg
Mary Elizabeth Ruth
Weinmann
Joy Elisabeth Scheerer
Winston
Matthew Ryo Yamada

PEPPERDINE UNIVERSITY, MALIBU, CA

Edward Adutwum
Laura Ashlock
Aaron Barnett
Matthew Baucum
Trevor Borg
Briana Chmielewski
Luke Collins
Matthew Crowder
Justin Curry
Meghan Cyron
Joel Denning
Matthew Finley
Domenic Frappolli

Ziqian Gao
Jessica Gash
James Gehrels
Lydia Gerard
Abigail Gibson
Max Ginnell
John Edward Hartman Jr.
Rachel Annette Hews
Jonathan Hirsch
Kevin Hoffman
Monica Houweling
Alexandra Howerton
Justina Huang

Ehimamiegho Idahosa-Erese
Amber Jaramillo
Taylor Jarvill
Jeremy Jorgensen
Amy Kahng
Anna Kitsmarishvili
Kailee Kodama
Ngoc Le
Eleanor Lemco
Sara Leonard
Rebecca Lu
Miles Mash
Chelsey Maus

Callaghan Richard David
McDonough
Caitlin McLaughlin
Elise Monroe
Melina Moussetis
McKenna Murray
Sydney Newman
Lionel Ong
Caroline McKenzie Ott
Makamae Palos
Lois Park
Pauline Park
Hannah Patterson

Jenna Pautsch

Danielle Pena

Ashley Royal

Brian Wesley Sanders

Danielle Shilling

Lily Sorourifar

Anne Souther

Daniel Spencer

Haley Marie St. Martin

Jessica Starman

Connor Thompson

Hannah Turpin

Andrew Urias

Austin Vick

Nicole Virzi

Jenna Wall

Zachary Wilson

Sarah Zhang

PFEIFFER UNIVERSITY MISENHEIMER, MISENHEIMER, NC

Janna Kristen Featherstone

Torrianna Lakiesha Foster

Kimberly Marie Goodell

Stephanie Marie Hardig

Matthew Kevin Humphries

Aaliyah Ta'Nae Jackson

Nigel Alexander Jackson

Savannah Leigh Johnson

Ashley Dawn King

Patrick David King

Wayne Darnell Lipford

Natalie Christine Marsh

Christie Elizabeth Mello

Valeria Maria Mendoza

Natalie Joan Miller

Kathryn Elizabeth Peeler

Anslee Erin Smith

Aaron Nathaniel Triplett

PIEDMONT COLLEGE, DEMOREST, GA

Lisa Alexander

Adam Benjamin Arlt

Mary Avants

Sherry Bratten

James Brewer

Christina Brinkley

Isabella Brown

Riley Carter

Savannah Castles

Morgan Cheek

Jessica Dundore

Josie Eavenson

Danita K. Gaudette

Hannah N. Green

Joel Daniel Greenway

Janie Harris

Megan Kearney

Zachary Ryan Langley

Katelin Lovercamp

Miranda Moore

Angela Murray

James Passmore

Charles Reid

Jessie Slusher

Daniel Stepler

Keirra LeeAnn Swallows

Caleigh Teague

Tifanie Dee Thompson

Haley Rae Vasser

Tara Weimann

Jenny Anne Whitmire

PIEDMONT TECHNICAL COLLEGE, GREENWOOD, SC

Jeny Abercrombie

Lisa Ashby

Michala Barnum

Stephanie Michelle Bohland

Joel Oscar Boley III

Matthew Brewer

Jayde Brooks

Melissa Clayton

Charles Jason Cooley

Susan Graham

Tracey Melissa Green

Abigail Hershberger

Kelly Jenkins

Nicole Lawrence

Jana Lawson

Christian Loner

Sherry Mabrey

Cheryl Mackey

Karen Martin

Carl Ouzts

Ashley Owens

Nichole Papinchak

Lisa Perryman

Ashley Polson

Marlee Erin Poole

Jerri Smith

Drake Sorrow

Shannon Stockton

Robert Strawhorn

Jimmy Sweezy

Letesha Tillman

Broch Travis

Walter Wall

Jason White

Logan Wooten

Hannah Wright

PIEDMONT VIRGINIA COMMUNITY COLLEGE, CHARLOTTESVILLE, VA

Stacie R. Adams

Shannon N. Albright

Chiron J. Anderson

Rachael L. Box

Kevin L. Carter

Atlee Faith Catlett

Taylor M. Clark

Vincent J. Coppola

Sarah Cote

Jennifer Y. Davis

Kimberly A. Davis

Mackenzie L. Dovel

Madison R. Dovel

Angelique A. Durham

Heather L. Fauber

Antonia Florence

Megan C. Ford

Deanna M. Funkhouser

Sophie M. Grace

Julia Grammer

Kim Hellems

Malika J. Hill

Deanna M. Insana

George A. Jung

Charles L. Kovacik

Adonis Krasniqi

Cameron P. Krest

Marsha J. Leitzel

Paul Speros Mamakos
Michael May
Mary L. Montgomery
William E. Morgan
Amanda N. Morinelli
Malissa K. Mullins
Reuben L. Neff
Ashlyn M. Norford

Sean P. Norville
Eileen O'Brien
Kristy L. Patrick
Lauren R. Pennington
Sheri L. Pilcher
Christopher D. Randolph
Jessica A. Roy-Harrison
John R. Sanderson

Joshua A. Schrecongost
Maia Sequoia
Jordan R. Shifflett
Susan J. Sorbello
Jacqueline Kate Stewart
Victoria Stow
Candyce F. Tarrance
Carley M. Thorpe

Sarah N. Walls Mathis
Tiffany M. Walton
Mary R. Watts
Teaira N. White
Cristina C. Widder
Julie M. Woodson

PONTIFICAL CATHOLIC UNIVERSITY OF PUERTO RICO, PONCE, PR

Dariana Guerrero Rivera

PRATT COMMUNITY COLLEGE, PRATT, KS

Andrew Connor Beck
Nancy Janeth Chavez Torres
Madison Daily
Mattison Dusin
Dylan Eck
Allicia Rose Hall

Julio Ibarra
Alyssa Kimber
Dylan King
Spencer Kraus
Emily Dee Lucas
Jamye Chanielle McCarty

Megan Mercer
Coral Merlo
Easton Tyler Mitchell
Aubree Nuest
Breanna Leigh Phillips
Nathan Roth

Mariana de Paula Silva
Cole Washington
Ryan Zoglmann

PRESBYTERIAN COLLEGE, CLINTON, SC

Austin Dean Allen
Jordan Olivia Ashley
Mary Katherine Bartlett

Mary Maxwell Ervin
Julianna Grace Franklin
Erika Laine Gotfredson

James Richard Hayes III
Elizabeth Ashford Silcox
Madison Alissa Smith

Kayla Andrea Stanford

PRINCE GEORGE'S COMMUNITY COLLEGE, LARGO, MD

Jennifer U. Akanoh
Zahra Aligabi
Michalah Arnold
Joubel S. Boco
Mervin Keith Q. Cuadera
Jeajout Jean Daniel
Cymonisse

Souhayl Ahmed Ali Diwani
Rachel Ilao Dizon
Ayanna M. Ellsworth
Sade Abigail Ayahna Evans
Abdulfatai Adetola Fakoya
Charles Robert Fongno
Joseph Garner

Jonathan H. Inda
Abdu Kiyaga
Sylvia Rose Marie Klein
Eliane Lakam
Blessing Chiamaka Leonard
Natalia Alexandrovna
Mitiuriev

Favour A. Nerrise-Njunkeng
Miriam Ofoegbu
Nicholas Reid

PROVIDENCE COLLEGE, PROVIDENCE, RI

Ryan Christopher Amazeen
Thomas James
Andrikopoulos
Connor John Barrett
Michael Elmer Burke
Catherine Eleanor Cherry
Danielle Marie Colabatistto

Lauren Lucia Coulombe
Graham Robert Cox
Erin Patricia Curtin
Michelle Ann Fernando
Colleen Grattan Gardner
Lauren Marie Griffin
Abbey Marie Guerino

Kelsey O'Toole Hayes
Kathryn Place Hiller
John Dimitri Jovan
Alyssa Marie Kinney
Patricia Marie Krupinski
Meghan Catherine Lescault
Ramon Eduardo Lopez

Brittany Rose Mandeville
Rebecca Rose Marisseau
Morgan Lindsay McCarthy
Kathleen Bridget McGinty
Amanda Christine Muzyka
Madeline Mylod
Audrey Elizabeth O'Neill

Michelle Catherine Ouellette
Kristen Leigh Perrelli
Christina Marie Perri
Emily Rose Pin
Alana Marie Prinos
Shelby Eckel Scola

Logan Gouveia Serabian
Andrea Lauren Spencer
Tyler Thomas Stein
Cayla Angela Stifler
Katelyn Michelle Sudlik
William Suter

Benjamin David Swiszcz
Hailey Clancy Tavares
Nicole Elizabeth Toscano
Daniel Anthony Tosiano
Grace Elisabeth Twardy
Thomas Edward Upton

Jenna Marie Wahl
Christopher P. Walsh
Reegan Paula Whipple
Jamie Ethan Wilson
Benjamin John Wright

PURDUE UNIVERSITY CALUMET, HAMMOND, IN

Leizel Christine Acres
Samantha Basar
Abigail Bondi
Jacalyn Brabbs
Brittney Nicole Brack
Jessica Castro
Nicole Cichocki

Nicholas Ecsy
Lindsey Joreen Flagg
David Haddad
Caitlyn L. Hayes
Ayden Henderson-Vigil
Hannah Christine Kelly
Bailey Lauritzen

Haley June Loden
Karina Longfellow
Jessica Loy
Seidu Mahama
Patrick Mudd
Zoe Rozich
Melissa Sida Diaz

Haley Smith
Shelisa Thomas
Yvette Lourdes Thomas
Jessica Vankley
Tongan Russel Wang
Jesenia Marlyn Zendejas

QUEENSBOROUGH COMMUNITY COLLEGE, BAYSIDE, NY

Shashi Ahmed
Anisah Ali
Maria Anaya
Maria Anaya
Juan Javier Arcenas
Malaak Chabaan
Suny Dayane Chavarria
Yueli Chen
Yueli Chen
Kyle Chin-How
Margaret de los Santos
Udya Seneviratne
Dewanamuni
Evens Esperance
Eddie Fernandez
Rahonel Fernandez

Jodi-Ann Grant
Weijing Gu
Hyungju Ham
Angelica Usha Harcharan
Tao Hong
Jean Jieun Hwang
Yi Jiang
Yi Jiang
Yizhu Jin
Maria Kakonikos
Haeun Kim
Landen Kwan
Krystal Lee
Julie Leong
Marie Metayer
Moushmee Moniram

Sherwayne Morrison
Wilson Eduardo Nieves
Wilson Nieves Vasques
Ricky Panayoty
Kristina Papacostas
Mathiu Perez Rodriguez
Derek Cameron Perry
Daysi Proano
Rashida R. Farokhi
Chanele Rodriguez
Chanele Rodriguez
Emely Rosario
Silvia Salamone
Moe Thet San
Haseeb Shah
Hyo Jung Shin

Shriromani Sukhwa
Fang-I Sun
Fang Irene Sun
Laura Suriel
Tulasha Thapa
Nelson Tobar
Brian Um
Brian Um
Joselin Vargas
Maria Virginia
Villadiego-Punto
Quanjian Yan
Hyeon Yun

QUINSIGAMOND COMMUNITY COLLEGE, WORCESTER, MA

Cherise Liana Connolly
Phillippee Dashnaw
Aaron Dean
Sonya Fournier

Ozzy Gonet
Brittany Huffault
Erika Marie LaCrosse
Marcelo Lopez

Kristin Maki
Kayla Paige Paterson
Beryl Pettiford
Olivia Rachon

Madeline Vinton

RADFORD UNIVERSITY, RADFORD, VA

Antoinette Bruno

Hyisheem Calier

Sydni Chernault

Kathryn Dillon

Aisha Foy	Brittany Justice	Tyler Pace	Bowen Sheng
Lauren Fulcher	Anjana Koirala	Marta Paulson	Holly Thomas
Jesse Gibson	Priya Lall	Shannon Plante	Alan Ward
Hannah Gullickson	Emily Martin	Ashley Riedell	Samaiyah Williams
Kassie Hall	Krysta Matthews	Courtney Scaggs	Alice Wren
Sara Hammonds	Reuben Miller	McKay Schmitt	
Jessica Henwood	Craig Moseley	Cynthia Schulz	
Rachel Jones	Natnael Nadew	Olivia Sheetz	

RAMAPO COLLEGE OF NEW JERSEY, MAHWAH, NJ

Alyssa Dumatol	Aleksandar Ivaylov Goranov	Wilson Emerson Quiceno Jr.	Dawn Wilkenfeld
David Gardy Ermann			

RANGER COLLEGE, RANGER, TX

Dawson W. Adams	Mariah Leigh Fields	Sarah Mae Manning	Daisy Selena Saldana
Haylie Christine Adams	Chad Curtis Fleischman	Kathy D. Marcom	Jessica Lynn Schulze
Ana Elizabeth Alfaro	Hope Shantal Frame	Luis Martin	Jesus Serrano
Ali H. Alhamadah	Delbert James French	Payton Re'An Matthews	Madeline Taylor Sewell
Daniel Alvarez	Luke Daniel Garner	Mackenzie Hope Mayes	Kelsey Lee Simmons
Bryan Anthony Benz	Baylee Ellason Godfrey	James Acy McGehee	Shelley Dyan Skaggs
Deanna Lynn Black	Kendall Jenkins Gonzales	Yvette Medina	Teresa Anne Smith
Ky Reed Bray	Lourdes Edith Gonzalez-Rivera	Peter Meikle	Tyler Aaron Stary
Tyler White Brooks		Heather Rayeanne Merket	Emily Leann Swain
Jayden Shi Brudney	Jordan Tyler Gray	Makennah Moore	Jiavani D'Naya Thompson
Summer Gabrielle Byrne	Bradley Ray Hall	Marx Idelfonso Mora	Terrin Summer Thompson
Shelby Jordan Cannon	Caleb Wade Hardy	Conner Jacob Motley	Ariel Marie Todd
Kayla Marie Casey	Joy Shelly Hardy	Jonathan Daniel Narvais	Susan A. Travis
Colby James Childress	Dennis L. Harper	Kathrine Neal	Kolbie Rayanne Vaughn
Amelia Alexis Collins	Hannah Elizabeth Harris	Holly Michelle Needham	Thais Simoes Vieira
Denise Daub	Kyle Christopher Haynes	Paul David Neely	Maci Valen Walker
Darby Leigh Davis	Rachel Christine Hazzard	Lee Jay Newton	Katy Lucille Wells
Mercedes Davis	Arielle Rose Heinrichs	Kendell Modena Lee Noles	Stephanie Nicole Wheeler
Brandon Adam Day	Vanessa Hernandez	Jonathan Perez	Bailey Jo Whilden
Shelly L. DelBosque	Tonya Christina Hoffman	JoAnn Carol Pitts	Lynne Whitehead
Hunter Reed Dennis	Jamie Ranee Hollstein	Jessica M. Polka	Emily Marie Willey
Cynthia A. DeRamus	Kendra Brooke Keith	Megan LeeAnn Portnajmer	Daniel Jeffrey Winkler
Victor David Diaz	Cheyenne Noelle Kennedy-Rosche	Joseph Austin Prado	Nicholas Peter Wittkopp
Dawn Marie Dittoe		Kylee Mae Quillin	
Peyton Evan Donahoo	Jon Claude Kirbo	Jessica Mari Ramirez	
Lauren Renae Fanara	Weston Kirbo	Amanda Lynn Reynolds	

Briana L. Abdul-Raqib

Austin Abraham

Haley M. Allen

Macey L. Augst

Brielle G. Autery

Christian C. Babin

Cameron J. Baldwin

Trinity D. Bea

Willa A. Beckley

Sydnee N. Belcher

Bryce R. Bell

Kalin A. Benza

Jacob E. Bethem

Stephen L. Bliley

River H. Boulay

Cole A. Bristow

Jacob T. Brown

Jessica Burch

Allison K. Burgess

Stephen B. Busic

Lark E. Bussler

Allison T. Chism

Kathleen L. Coakley

Bonnie R. Coates

Meaghan E. Cole

Caitlin V. Coleman

Warren Croxton

Alys K. Davis

Lauren N. Devlin

Carlos D. Echols

Sarah G. Edwards

Megan D. Elbourn

Elizabeth B. Ellis

Mary K. Ellis

Campbell Farina

Lisa M. Frush

Alexandra C. Fuccella

Leona J. Gaither

Sean T. Gatewood

Jayson G. Gill

Cassidy Goodwin

Kellyanne Gray

John L. Grindstaff

Austin D. Halter

Bailey Hamilton

Zachary E. Hamilton

Ronald Hansford

Kayla S. Harding

Karlyn M. Harwood

Devlyn M. Haviland

David C. Henning

William E. Hillman

Matthew K. Hodges

Billy B. Hollingshead

Rachel R. Hudnall

Madison A. Huie

Kaylee N. Humphrey

Madison Hutson

Samuel R. Irungu

Christin N. Jaynes

Keondra J. Jenkins

Thomas R. Jenkins

Jillian S. Jett

Zhide Jin

Jonathan L. Jukes

Cullen J. Kettle

Douglas Kodl

Tyler F. Kolmetz

Christian L. Koon

Erik M. Lamb

Brittina O. Layne

Meredith LeBel

Skyler B. Lennon

Esmeralda Y. Lopez

Victoria A. Lowe

Julia S. Mahoney

Deion M. Maith

Ilona L. Marshall-Ulett

Anne C. Mcdermott

Michael J. McGregor

Rachael N. McMahon

Katherine A. Michos

Brittney L. Miers

Madison Miller

Garrett T. Mills

Denzel Mitchell

Hunter S. Moison

Chloe A. Moker

Camryn S. Molnar

Tony L. Morris

Les K. Murray

Alexis N. Newsome

William Edward Norton Jr.

Dalton B. Olson

John N. Olszewski

Matthew H. Osborne

Mallory S. Overstreet

Brian M. Owens

Kenneth T. Owens

Madison L. Packett

Tara L. Padovan-Hickman

Stephen C. Parker

William R. Parker

Connor N. Pemberton

Madison C. Pierson

Latunae W. Pooler

Joseph M. Price

Amanda L. Ramon

Laura M. Redman

John W. Richardson

Vivian A. Sanchez

Shannon Santiago

Sarah H. Saunders

Sydney N. Scherer

LaTesha M. Scott

Morgan N. Shaffer

Mary C. Skinner

Kara B. Smith

Maria S. Spadaccini

Richard E. Spillane

Hannah Stanford

Virginia A. Stoughton

Macy S. Swift

Hallie G. Taylor

Yulisa A. Vasquez

Quran S. Veney

Madeline L. Vest

Elizabeth Eva Savina Walters

David Wang

JunYi Wang

Hope E. Warren

Amanda Craig Washington

Kendall G. Webb

Emilie J. Webster

Cole H. Weigartz

Mary E. Wells

Ethan C. White

Racheal A. White

Claire D. Whitman

Tina M. Willis

Jacob T. Wilson

Micaela A. Wilson

Joseph P. Wolski

Grayson P. Womble

Samantha J. Woodcock

Detty N. Wools

Joel P. Wools

Jason D. Yowler

REGENT UNIVERSITY, VIRGINIA BEACH, VA

Cletus Kpobari Aakol

Tharwat Maher Nagib

Adly Nagib

Sandra E. Alcaide

Emiliano Ariel Alegre

Joyelle Lasheia Anderson

Andrea M. Atkinson

Lance Bacon

Crystal D. Barnett

Richard Mark Bell

Juliette Anne Bjork

Roderick Bradford

Spencer Andrew Brown

Leigh Carter Budwell III

Donald Bufford

Courtney Greer Calvert

Donnovan Isaiah Campbell

Jennifer Desiree Cannon-Murff

Leigha Harper Canterbury

Amy Noelle Carmickle

Dana Cavallaro

Jessica Anne Clark

Rachel Lee Coleman

Robert P. Costello

George Overdorf Cunningham IV

Dale E. Dale

Brittany Lynn Davenport

Debra Jean Dean

Maurice A. Denton

Marie Louise Dienhart

Joseph Lane Donovan

Billy L. Doray

Lindsey Caroline Douglas

Karen Jesuit Drosinos

Barbara Anne DuPree

Luke Eichelberger

Jasmine Hyatt Erickson

Lucas Aaron Erickson

Jeremy Howard Ezell

Laura Catherine Fisher

Matthew Fitch

Malcolm C. Fitschen

Philip FitzHugh

Michelle Elizabeth Freeman

Sara G. Gainor

Anna Elizabeth Gant

Carrie Elizabeth Gantt

Derek Geerlof

Keith E. Goodman

Matthew A. Gribler

Shannon Leigh Grimsley

Racheal R. Guse

Katharine Elizabeth Harden

Brenden Michael Harrell

Anicca De'Anna Harriot

Lynnette L. Harris

Jo R. Hawke

Holly Ann Heath

Linda Ann Heindl

Ariel Brooke Heinsius

Peifeng Mary Ho

Hannah Noel Hopper

Katie Nicole Howard

Robert B. Huizinga

Barrett Narron Jacobson

Lindsey Ann Jennings

Charles Alexander Jones

Richard C. Kao

Shawna Brynn Kelly

Natalie Christina King

Schalk Benjamin Klopper

Kathleen M. Knudsen

Renee M. Knudsen

Daniel Chris Koblitz

Emily Hope Kooiman

Sarah Rae Kretzer

Angie Ku

Kenneth Samuel Kuper

Christina Marie LaPenna

Jonathan Lokhorst

Jennifer Luke

Donna Jordan Mannon

Martha J. Martin

Grace Celesta Masonheimer

Christopher Paul Mateer

Elizabeth Marie Maul

Michael Nathan Maunder

Devon Michael Miller

Elisabeth Joy Moore

Victoria Jean Moreno-Riano

Tranese Denitra Morgan

Elizabeth Mary Morris

Patrick Charles Neidich

Takeisha Shante Newsome

Joshua J. Nierle

Courtney Beth Noble

Christopher Norgbey

Boniface Odong

Gary Ortego

Geneva Lee Oster

Melanie Patino

Michele D. Perry

Gina Elizabeth Pezzuto

Tiffany Lynn Phillips

Heather Lynn Ploski

Emily S. Puder

Hannah K. Puder

Malaika Jean Quarterman

Wilmot J. Rachel

Christina Rainey

Nathen David Ransom

Sean P. Reilly

Bevin Kateri Reinen

Kirstie Lee Robison

Robert Michael Roland

Danny Roman-Gloro

Brian L. Sauder

Sarah J. Schmidt

Sandra Denise Skinner

Angelina Strouss

Shirley Ann Suarez

Beth Marie Symanzik

Jessica Torres-Cedillo

Mary Lucille Troy

Consuella S. Tynes

Amy Sue Upton

Julie Ann Waples

Ashley G. Watkins

Mary Elizabeth Watson

Rachel Jean Weckbacher

Hannah Christine White

Ciara Nicole Whitty

Jay Tyler Wiles

Kathryn Riendeau Worley

Jing Wu

Sara Wilkerson Zimmerman

REGIS COLLEGE, WESTON, MA

Christine Aherne

Jassira Alves

Jennifer Amaral

Shogofa Amini

Lauren Bonagura

Traylon Butler-Neal

Jordan Chusid

Christina Deang

Michael Emanuelson

Riley Fergus

Lauren Ghazal

Cassandra Marie Godzik

Ariel Hansen

Elizabeth Harpin

Brittany Hicks

Melinda Mara

Margaret McCarty
Jordan Monts
Michaela Nejaime
Andrew O'Reilly
Michael Panagiotakos
Anushya Pandian
Uma Patel

Jonathan Paul
Ann Peacher
Wesley Pointjour
Sarah Porter
Jaime Povinelli
Jenna Rocha
Giselle Rodriguez

Renato Rosas
Najat Sandabad
Zachary Sletterink
Katherine Stockton
Evan Stone
Kathleen Sullivan
Alex Tran

Diana Tran
Ashley Ventolieri
Susanna Walter
Johanna Westcott

REID STATE TECHNICAL COLLEGE, EVERGREEN, AL

Sydney Albritton
Richard W. Ausborn
Teresa Jean Barlow
Benjamin John Broich
Nancy Rena Burgans
Joshua A. Burkett
Andrew Cauthen
Jennifer M. Colbert
Kiaira Coleman
Morgan Lynlee Davis
Jelisa L. Dear
Samuel Gareth Dees
Keyarea M. Dixon
Melissa Edwards
Stephena Lavon Ellis

Christian Aleah Felts
Charleetha Fields
Joshua Findley
Samantha Marie Flux
Matt Franklin
Barbara Joyce Gandy
Lauren Short Gipson
Donavan R. Green
Christian Gross
Hunter Harris
Stephen M. Hataway
Susan Elaine Helton
Austin D. Hiers-Johnson
Ahleyah Hollins
Sterling Joe Huggins

April Johnson
Clarence T. Jones Jr.
Steven Reese Jordan
Scotty T. Lindsey
Adam C. McCall
Angel Asberry McGhee
Chalae McMillian
Douglas Colton Morris
Shelley B. Mothershed
James W. Murphy
Nekela Peters
Jessica Pugh
Amanda Brooke Raines
Susan Nicole Reed
Wanda Rudolph

Crystal McCombs Schofield
Jazmine A. Sinquefield
DeVelma Evette Smith
Mykleen Spears
Nicholas Stacey
Kyle Summers
Kyondria Timmons
Leslie Turk
Kasey Bradley Vaughan
Victoria Blair Webb
Shamika Deniece Wiggins
Danielle Williams
Idamesha Vanshay Williams
Jessica Nicole Wright
Kenyell L. Young

REINHARDT UNIVERSITY, WALESKA, GA

Allison Hazel Abernathy
Sante Alana Alfonso
Taylor Danielle Asher
Ansley Michael Avera
Anthony Tanner Ballingall
Ines Yanely Bibiano-
Baltazar
Jocelyn Leigh Blair
Courtney Ann Boggs
John Michael Bowling
Emily Kate Bowman
Kathy Thornton Cater

Hannah Marie Craton
Matthew Charles Duncan
Caleb John Faulkner
Matthew Gordon Freeman
Trenton Hunter Futch
Brittany Nicole Gaddy
Natalee Nicole Gordon
Madeline Carol Gray
Christopher Brad Griner
Carlos A. Guzman
McKenna Rae Haag
Jacob Andrew Howard

Rachel Elizabeth Kay
Rhonda Fay Kelley
Colby Jane LaFever
Marianella Victoria Lopez
Melissa Amanda Martinez
Kadie Anne Mullinax
Lauren Ashley Mullinax
Patrick Hunter Oswald
Diana Fernanda Perez
Taylor Angel Pineda
Tyler Anthony Pineda
Rafael Salazar Cruz

Megan Catherine See
Alyssa Breann Smith
Abigail Taylor Sneathen
Kayla Delaine Spenard
Erika Lauren Szatmary
Shelby Nicole Trotta
Joshua Adam Vavases
Camey Latasha Washington
Callie Elizabeth Wheeler

RENSSELAER POLYTECHNIC INSTITUTE, TROY, NY

Nurleeqa Abdul Latiff
Elizabeth C. Alderman

Samrin A. Ali
Scott H. Altern

Bradley R. Amari
Moses J. Amdur

Vincent L. Arena
Patrick J. Aselin

Danielle N. Balzano

Anthony A. Barbieri

Louis-Xavier Barrette

Gregory M. Bartell

Kirthana B. Bhat

Charles K. Bittner

Rachel Beth Blacker

Samantha N. Bliss

Olurotimi A. Bolonduro

Kianna K. Brevig

Tyler Sterling Brown

Veronika Bychkova

Michael J. Caiola

Elizabeth A. Capogna

Diego J. Carrasquillo

Brian S. Casel

Daniel J. Catranis

Frank W. Charbonier

Trishala Chaudhary

Carolyn Chlebek

Nicholas D. Choi

Yuvraj Chopra

Jennifer W. Church

Michael D. Conward

Mason R. Cooper

Joshua M. Correira

Megan E. Curtin

Heather D. Danielsen

Chandler X. Dawson

Micaila A. Dean

Kelly M. Dearborn

Hannah De Los Santos

Haley R. Derlinga

Niyati V. Desai

Christine S. Desplat

Trent A. DeVerter

Dede Dolkar

Jaire R. Dorsey

Casey L. Doyle

Khalil A. Drayton

John F. Drazan

Brandon P. Drumheller

Jonah E. Duch

Jordan W. Dunne

Nicholas P. Dvorak

Samuel A. Ellman

Alisa Emag

Grace E. Erdman

Justin R. Etzine

Erin E. Evke

Andrew W. Faulds

Valerie I. Fix

Christopher W. Flood

Marcus E. Flowers

Casey H. Fong

Devon M. Forsythe

Tatyana N. Fortune

Jennifer A. Gallego

Alessandro E. Galli

David J. Gardiner

Michael J. Gardner

Kelly M. Gatslick

Mason E. Gentner

Matthew J. Germanowski

Sarah L. Giddings

Laura D. Gillespie

Christina T. Gilliland

Elizabeth A. Gjini

Devin J. Glenn

Nicholas D. Gnitzcavich

Chaz A. Goodwine

Jonathan J. Gottwald

Tyler P. Graf

Ian Geoffrey Gross

Michael Han

Jenna N. Hastings

Patrick M. Haughey

Victoria L. Hepworth

Orlando J. Hernandez

Grace M. Herrmann

Christopher L. Higley

Paolo W. Hockenmaier

Dustin H. Hoffman

Samantha L. Holton

Melissa R. Hyndman

Severin V. Ibarluzea

Paul O. Ilori

Michael Y. Ishida

Zachary M. Jablons

Raymond S. Jacobson

Kayla A. Jones

Harrison C. Kang

Alexander P. Kelleher

Olivia Rachel King

Charles W. Kirchner

Alexandra K. Kotsakis

Morgan L. Kube

Michael S. Kubista

Weixuan Lai

Christopher J. Lamplough

Julia J. Lane

Alison M. Lanzi

Harrison Leinweber

Jason R. Li

Gary J. Liskovich

Seth R. Lowenstern

Amy K. Loya

Valerie A. Lumsden

Allison Ann Luongo

Thomas Robert Ratcliffe

Manzini

Enxhi Marika

Patrick Joseph Martin

Caitlin H. McCleery

Alexander R. McDonald

Kiana Marie McNellis

Rachael L. Melita

Gregory J. Merrill

Donald R. Millang

Andrew L. Moberg

Donna Grace L. Moleta

Conrad E. Mossl

Lucy V. Naslas

Erika D. Nelson

Kyle V. Neumann

Gavin M. Noritsky

Bridget M. O'Loughlin

Barbara D. Padilla

Jesse D. Pelletier

Gabriel Perez

Christine M. Perrone

Victoria N. Phan

Peter Daniel Piech

Kyle R. Pollard

Tarun Prabhala

Ajinkya Puntambekar

Ferheen Qureshi

Andrew Rainville

Thomas A. Rebbecchi

Alexander J. Roaldsand

Ines M. Roman

Victoria M. Ruplin

Brittany T. Rupp

Robert A. Russo

Cory D. Sago

Sarah A. Schattschneider

Arthur J. Schick

John A. Schiel

Hayley N. Schluter

Joshua C. Schramm

Akanksha Sharma

Geena A. Simila

Corinne R. Skala

Daniel P. Spatcher

Heili M. Springsteen

Elena G. Steffan

Lauren M. Stenroos

Dana K. Stevens

Sarah E. Straub

Andrew B. Sudano

Jimmy G. Tabanao

Selina A. Tedesco

Jane M. Thibeault

Fei Tong

Hannah S. Trasatti

Paige E. Trasatti

Keara A. Traylor

Ezra L. Tucker

Erica R. Uhler

Roshni Vachhani

Virag A. Vora

Mary C. Votto

Michael T. Wassick
Amelia L. Watterson
Alexandra K. Wells
Michael R. Wentworth
Shamus A. Wheeler

Ciera J. Williams
Jonathan K. Williams
Jordan T. Williams
Matthew D. Williams
Max A. Winkelman

Zachary T. Wolfgang
David F. Wolmark
Benjamin M. Wright
Haoxue Yan
Natalie Yin Yi L. Yap

Alexander Yin
Cara E. Yocum
Mingyi Yuan
Ziyu Zhou

RICH MOUNTAIN COMMUNITY COLLEGE, MENA, AR

Warren Ray Bellows
Julie Hannah Brown
Krystal Cavelli
Christopher M. Cloud
Candace Jean Ford

Brittany Michelle Frayer
Sydney Godwin
Darla Henry
Shauna Horner
Macey Hubbard

Cody Colt Kaelin
Courtney Ellen Meador
Madison Pettigrew
Eleanor Priddy
Caroline Melissa Singleton

Marion Ashley Smith
Jerusha Christine Tedder
Andrew Tkach
Veronica Vanbuskirk

RIDER UNIVERSITY, LAWRENCEVILLE, NJ

Shaun A. Bartole
Hannah Rose Bass
Amanda J. Bezold
Kyle Bivens
Johanna N. Blume
Alexis L. Bonamassa
Savoia N. Buntin
Diamond S. Carr
Jessica A. Crowell-Graff

Alia B. Danch
Arden E. Dean
Christina L. Diecidue
Sandra N. DiGrazio
Caroline W. Forde
Allison G. Griffiths
Stephen V. Hopson
Matthew D. Howell
Rebecca M. Janicki

Andrew W. Jemas
Haley Kristine Johnston
Matthew Kolbusz
Kayla E. McLaughlin
Hunter M. Morgen
Katharine T. Rella
Tara M. Roach
Olivia A. Rosenberger
Rachel S. Safer

Tarah-Lynn Saint-Elien
Allison H. Sawka
Samantha A. Schimek
Jessica R. Stanislawczyk
Natalie A. Taptykoff
Tyler D. Weakland
Lucia Catherine White
Jenna N. Wilush

RINGLING COLLEGE OF ART & DESIGN, SARASOTA, FL

Luiza Garcia Alaniz
Sara Bicknell
Christopher Arthur Blond
Krystal Boersen
Natalie Anne Constable
Katelyn Liane Hagen

Dania Hammad
Jade Skye Hammer
Muriel Nicole Holloway
Tarun Lakshminarayanan
Carly Lohr
Nikelle Marijah Mackey

Kade Stewart Patrick
O'Casey
Andrés Paz
Jessica Pinns
Jeremy Puttkammer
Patricia Sigmon

Elizabeth Ann Tomashek
Flavio Vincenti
Michale Warren
Michelle Yi

RIO GRANDE COMMUNITY COLLEGE, RIO GRANDE, OH

Isaac J. Andrews
Joao Paulo Antonio
Charlene K. Arrowood
Michael T. Bailey
David I. Bakenhaster
Devon Ray Barnes
Wesley A. Barnett
Elizabeth N. Bearhs
Cortney D. Beaver

Brenden Black
Matthew A. Blair
Lindsay Boothe
Destiny A. Brown
Kayla R. Browning
Michele D. Burton
Steven Chapman
Maggie Clagg
Brandon E. Coon

Julie M. Crace
William Crisel
Kali Morgan Cunningham
Crystal R. Davis
Michael A. Davis
Kimberly Lynn Day
Sarah Jane Delaney
Brittany Durst
Kasey P. Eblin

Colton M. Edge
Bethany A. Evans
Cyndie Few
Deliah L. Fish
Katie M. Glover
Danielle K. Gruber
Jenna L. Hamner
Hannah A. Hawley
Matthew T. Hodge

Thomas E. Holley
Kelly D. Humphrey
Andrea E. Hunt
Shannon R. Jackson
Megan A. Jones
Donald E. Keels
Hope E. Leopold
Floyd Allen Lowry
Rebecca Mace
Cody C. Mattox

Katelyn Christina Meeks
Amy Beth Miller
Cheyenne L. Mills
Andrew Donald Moffett
Samantha M. Nance
Morgan N. Neff
Morgan Faith Nottingham
Larry E. Patrick Jr.
Katelyn Marie Perdue
Brian E. Perkins

Shelby Pickens
Olivia F. Poling
Marissa May Radcliff
Megan Raynard
Gabriel C. Richmond
Brooke N. Rider
Kelsey N. Risner
Elizabeth D. Rutter
Christina Seaman
Heather L. Simpkins

Timothy R. Swann
Chantal Tomek
Brittany Ann Walk
Barbara M. Webb
Heather Whaley
Andrea N. Wines
Kyle A. Young

ROANOKE-CHOWAN COMMUNITY COLLEGE, AHOSKIE, NC

La'Kyra M. Askew
Johnetta Sessoms Chavis
Randy Cunningham
Shanice Donte' Grant
Giovonni De'Shawn Harrell
William Cody Hecker

Quintina Myeater Howard
Jessica Howerton
Gail B. Ingram
Laverne Wilder Jones
Ennis Mitchell
Joel Patrick Murphy

Justin Markel Murphy
Lydia Caye Murphy
Shirley M. Parker
Ronald Mclean Rawles
Marvin Ryan
Tyesha Renee Sanders

Michelle Sandusky
Shannon Denise Vann
Donna Webb
Wanda T. White
Willie A. Williams
Cynthia L. Wilson

ROBERT MORRIS UNIVERSITY, MOON TOWNSHIP, PA

Katie M. Abramowich
Sarah L. Affrica
Khalid M. Alshammari
Jonathan N. Anderson
Hannah E. Arnold
Amanda L. Axelson
Cassidy N. Baker
Damean Omar Barfield II
Jeremy T. Basinger
Jacob A. Bayne
Haley M. Beck
Olivia J. Bello
Cameron E. Bilger
Brooke Birckbichler
Andrew T. Birk
Jarrod E. Blumer
Darius J. Boxley
Lauren E. Brace
Megan M. Brewer
Austin J. Brown
Micah C. Brown
Quaheem T. Brown

Savanah M. Buhite
Asa J. Bull
Ryan N. Bunni
Andrew D. Calve
Hunter P. Carlheim
Denzel J. Carter
Sean Nicolson Cawood
Mara R. Cerro
Jessica A. Chin
Christopher C. Chislom
Lea K. Chrisman
Kylee D. Cigana
Nicki Cillie
Erica R. Cooper
Matthew D. Corkery
Emily G. Day
Monica A. Deluca
Cory J. Desimone
Matthew J. DeVito
Jaime L. Diskin
Kyrstin E. Dittenhafer-Swartz

Merritt O. Donoghue
Robert M. Dougher
Jacob A. Dufford
Cali A. Durning
Brittany Elaine Ericson
Adam R. Etzel
Steven K. Fiadewornu
Ashley T. Finello
Samantha R. Franks
Andrew D. Gerberich
Ashley M. Gerhart
Matthew E. Gornall
Becky A. Hall
Patrick D. Hanlon
Rachel L. Hasselman
Ian T. Healey
Xavier M. Hickman
Jessica A. Hogue
Shawn M. Hood
Andrew A. Horvath
Maura A. Howard
Trae D. Hurley

Randi D. Jackson
Emily M. Jamison
Adam C. Johnson
Jeffrey R. Jones
Zouka G. Karat
Emily M. Kella
Brooke N. Kennedy
Devin N. Kiska
Daniel Z. Kitchen
Rachel Michele Konesky
Samantha L. Kovalyak
Amanda L. Kuss
Matthew P. Leach
Christa B. Lerch
Amanda M. Lewis
Ryan D. Lewis
Hunter R. Lockhart
Marrissa A. Loreto
Stephen Michael Lucot
Katelyn Maione
Matthew D. Marterella
Kaitlyn E. Martin

Amelia M. Mateer	Jacob James Pearson	Sonya L. Selvaraj	Matthew Vona
Robert A. McGlennon	Cody Perlaky	Katie E. Shirley	Megan A. Waleff
Sydnee M. McKeever	Gwendolyn M. Pfleger	Maggie R. Shoup	Daniel G. Walizer
Mitchel B. McPeek	Jessica M. Pollick	Kendra A. Slis	Emilie J. Wasko
Allison N. Meade	Ashley M. Price	Coartney N. Sommers	Robert R. Weir
Douglas R. Mikec	Gianna N. Pro	Daniel H. Spittel	Alvin D. White III
John W. Moore	Myles L. Ragin	Shamoni M. Steadman	Alvin Dinsmore White III
Charles R. Mulvany	Hael Rajab	Sean M. Steele	James Dinsmore White III
Brian D. Murone	Natalie M. Roche	Evan T. Stiger	Megan C. Willey
Bailey M. Neale	Vincent A. Russo III	Isaac R. Swink	Rosie M. Williams
Jordan D. Neusch	Andrew S. Scheidemantel	Krista M. Symosko	Rosie Marie Williams
Anastasia I. Novodran	Heather L. Schrecengost	Jeremy P. Taggart	Taylore R. Williams
Anne Marie Olson	Adehl M. Schwaderer	Yves Justin N. Tiendrebeogo	Ashley N. Wojciechowski
Mitchell A. Ovell	William H. Scott IV	Eileen C. Toribio	Leslie D. Wolford
Crimson J. Pavlekovsky	Evyn P. Selden	Ashley M. Vesci	

ROBERTS WESLEYAN COLLEGE, ROCHESTER, NY

Chloe J. Adrien	Abigail R. Curinga	Keisha Corin James	Nicole M. Puglisi
Michael David Barberi	Angela Marie Cuskey	Naomi Klossner	Lisa Ann Redband
Alexis K. Bauer	Shelly R. Dailey	Melissa LaCelle	Molly Richardson
Carol Sue Beiswanger	(Bernardini)	Bridget A. Lemmon	Molly Starr Richardson
Richard A. Billitier	Andrea Paige Didas	Sumita Leonard	Tahlia Sarrantonio
James Blake	Andrea Fattore	Hannah E. Letterman	Ashley Shellenberger
Rachel Boswell	Elizabeth A. Fenton	Victoria K. Link	Rebecca Noelle Smith
Olivia Grace Bradstreet	Laurie Ferrarese	Kathleen Ann Merz	Sulamita O. Stakhnyuk
Morgan Brown	David W. Fidler	Christy L. Miller	Joanne Thomas
Kerstin Mary Burns	Naomi R. Fillion	Abigail E. Monroe	Karen Thomson
Natalie Rose Burns	Ruth Fisher	Melissa Muldoon	Chelsea Renee Touchstone
Mylessia Candie	Carson Fuhrman	Kathleen Nagle-Roides	Elizabeth R. Valento
Brooke A. Caton	Abigail Frances Gimino	Gabriel John Necoechea	Julia Vitale
Clara Elizabeth Chan	Christiana Goetz	Elizabeth Lynn Newbould	Dylon T. Walbridge
Laura Nicole Ciminelli	Kathryn L. Hollowood	Julia Grace Norris	Brittany R. Ward
Marianela M. Contreras	Brenda Houtenbrink	Elizabeth C. Osborne	Julia Nadine Wilson
Jacqueline Marie Corbett	Rachel Beth Hutchinson	Leah Payton	

ROCHESTER COLLEGE, ROCHESTER HILLS, MI

Laura Elizabeth Corp	Hannah M. Kwiecinski	Stephanie Dee Rhines	Hannah E. Wasil
Olivia Ann Fledman	Nathanael Adam Lefwich	Megan Theresa Saigh	Preston David Watkins
Bethany Joy Hagerman	Lindsey Lee Leppek	Matthew Tate Sanders	Troy David Wilkinson
Hannah Marie Kajer	Anna Grace Palmer	Rachel Leigh Taylor	
Kevin Krawczyk	Natalie Ann Redmond	McKenzie Taylor Walch	

ROCKINGHAM COMMUNITY COLLEGE, WENTWORTH, NC

Tammy T. Cook	Karishma P. Desai	Kristie M. Tripp	Caroline Grey Watkins

ROGER WILLIAMS UNIVERSITY, BRISTOL, RI

Virgina Albert	Andrew Erickson	Brendan J. McQueeney	Jill Kelly Sabrina Scarlett
Veronica Mariela Alicea	Selena Desire Fortes	Kerlie Merizier	Resh
Haya Elise Awwad	Christopher Joseph Gilman	Caleb Milford	Stephanie Ressler
Spencer Zachary Babst	Harry Hall IV	Katherine Austin Mitchell	John Arthur Rice III
Rachel Battista	Neal Hart	Heather Mohamed	Randal Craig Richardson Jr.
Kristen L. Boyer	James Kelley	Alyssa Ashley Otis	Christina Leigh Sargeant
Jenna Marie Brink	Aleksander Kusik	Jonathan David Panella	James Scacco
Sharilynn Brown	Kelly Kwawu	Sadie Peden	Blake Brimmer Hall
Christopher Busby	Henri Tyler Lanciaux	Gabriella Alyssandra Perez	Sherman
Marquis Caesar	Jesse Langknecht	Ashleyann Perez-Rivera	Manveer Singh
Alex S. Campbell	Katie Lowerre	Kristi Perreault	Jessica Soares
Nicole Prescott Capistran	Erin Claire Lyons	Kaelyn Phelps	Michelle Taylor
Haley Carignan	Nataly M. Maloney	Sarah Marie Quinn	Kate Emily Thompson
Danielle Elizabeth Combs	Zachary T. Marcoulier	Kristina Rauccio	Emily Tomczyk
Katie R. DeBlois	Adam Mayer	Matthew Gerard Regan	Rachel Alexis Trahan
Eliza Patricia DiBara	Matthew H. Mazzie	Seth Reiner	Eric Valenti
Megan Elizabeth Dulong	Danielle McCullough		

ROSEMEAD SCHOOL OF PSYCHOLOGY GRADUATE SCHOOL, LA MIRADA, CA

Lauren N. Apodaca	Lilian A. Medina Del Rio	Christopher D. Schadt	Daniel M. St. Clair
Annette C. Chan M.A.	Raquel J. Mendoza	Lindsay M. Snow	Frank Liang-Yao Wang
Hilary J. McCaskill Son	Trinnin F. Olsen	Rebekah E. So	

ROSEMONT COLLEGE, ROSEMONT, PA

Carlos Augusto Aguilo	Noel Higgs	Jordan Lamarr Purnell	Jennifer Paige South
Sarah Ryan Byerley	Carly Ann Hislop	Kyle William Robinson	Travis Benjamin Staples
Matthew Scott Carr	Alana Jeanne Howell	Jennifer Roque	Marygrace Urmson
Kim Tuyen Dinh	Heemali Shailesh Kamdar	Molly Dawson Rowe	Krista Ann Vadaketh
Andrea Marie Dossantos	Brianna Macauley	Dominic Micah Scafidi	Kianna Voorhees
Johnathan Otto Ehritz	Nikki Lyn Maurer	Eric Willi Schaefer	Lauren Whelan
Colleen Anne Flynn	Rookha Mian	Louis Schlecker	
Samantha Lynn Harrer	Nisha Pradhan	Brittney Marie Shupp	

ROSEMONT COLLEGE SCHOOLS OF GRADUATE & PROFESSIONAL STUDIES, ROSEMONT, PA

Angela Anderson	Bradley Ryan Carpenter	Erin Marie Kelly	Phuong Minh Nguyen
Jacqueline Ann Baker			

ROSE STATE COLLEGE, MIDWEST CITY, OK

Venus Atwell
Debbie Babcock
Payton Emma Bailey
Holly Joan Black
Brooke Giovanne Bradley
Kimberly Rae Braknage
Kortney Cheyanne Brown
Laura Anne Cesar

Rachael Lorraine Clark
Traci Janell Conkling
Carey Renee Falls
Jessica Mae Freeman
Cassandra Kate Garrity
Wesley Ray-Alan Jackson
Lindsey Marie Johnson
Leslie Marie Jones

Ariele Nicole King
Jordin Leigh Lippel
Ryan Michael McDonald
Chase Anthony McMillen
Marah Elisabeth Miller
Kimberly Ann Morrow
Grace Njeri Mwaura
Stephanie Denise Osmond

Karen B. Overholt
Delicia Madria Reed
Kaylee Lynn Shaw
Carly Ann Smith
Elizabeth Wallace Tabak
Peyton Hunter Tadlock
Lauren Michelle Zalewski

RUST COLLEGE, HOLLY SPRINGS, MS

Bangura H. Aji
Shirley Ann Bean-Walker
Andea Been
Tyneyla Bolden
Quo-Shayla Brewer
Dominique Brown
Cade Claiborne
Lester Regina Dodson
LaShonda Ervin
Cortia Henry

Pamela Hodge
Jeremy Hubrins
Belinda Ingram-Pegues
Monica Jeffries-Walton
Jordan Emani Jones
Savahn Jordan
Johnathan Lesueur
Shermeka Lewis
Alix Luhunda
Justice Lynch

Monique McKoy-Lewis
JaKayla Mitchell
Janicia Mitchell
Ernest Morris III
Carla Muse
Lakendres Nabors
Jessica Newsom
Jakeyia Perdue
Atiyah Reed
Kayla Reed

Erick Lamont Reed Jr.
Urell Perez Richardson
Melissa Riddle
Jasmine Sumlar
Aaliyah Travis
Aaliyah Travis
Nakisha Williams
Cheston Woodland

SACRED HEART MAJOR SEMINARY COLLEGE OF LIBERAL ARTS, DETROIT, MI

Benjamin Miller Eriksen

David Anthony Pellican

Julie A. Ryan

John Shi

SAINT JOHN VIANNEY COLLEGE SEMINARY, MIAMI, FL

JohnArmon Sabado Antolin

Christopher James
Grevenites

SAINT JOSEPH'S COLLEGE MAINE, STANDISH, ME

Whitney Shaunice Adell
Danielle Ellen Charette
Kelsey Ann Dumond
Aliyah Dominique Gregory

Christopher Daniel Hughes
Lauren Marie Legere
Marisa Eiler Lundy
Nicole Nalani Ouellette

Desiree Jolie Parent
Lauren Rachel Ramsay
John David Rose
Lauren Elizabeth Sharples

Nhu Monica Vo
Erin Mary Weir
Eric Richard Young

SAINT LEO UNIVERSITY, SAINT LEO, FL

Tori M. Aderholt
Alphonso Anderson Sr.
Katlin Marie Arguello
Lisa Ann Bailey
Natalie H. Baker
Lanna R. Barican

Winston Barksdale
Dalan Barzani
Donna Bidlack
Amanda Black
Samantha J. Blumenberg
Kirsten Bozeman

Earl Bradley Jr.
Lang Brenda
Watson Brittney
Corey Brown
Timothy Brown
Trishuna Lavette Brown

Joseph Cabral
McGrath Caleb
Dustin Campbell
Clara Capote
Armogan Carrie
Sadler Carrie

Alvin Carroll

Horace Chandler

Melissa Chardon

Wilbur Cherry

Michael Congemi

Gracemary Cordero

Terry Steven Creason

Allendys Diaz

James Dukes

Cedrick Earley

Tommy Ellison

Kenneth Evans

Danyale Ezell

William Fencl

Harry Fisher

Sativa Fisher

Roberto Flores

Angela Denise Frazier

Robert Walter Fryer III

Anthony Fuller

Billy Gardner

Heath Gardner

Virginia Geiger

Connor Ginn

Tory Glover

Maybelle Gossett

Shanethra Green

Davida Griggs

David Guillen

April Gutierrez

Charisma Harris

Eyob Hawaz

Andrea Hines

Savannah Hotchkiss

Lyndsey Gray Hubbard

Tawanna Jackson

Kyle Monroe Jenkins

Rivers Jennifer

Johnnie Bernard Jones

Linnie Kelly

David King

Tyra King

Jameka Kirkland

Marlon Antonio Knight Sr.

Lacey Kruszeski

Pitter Krystal

Lathanya Lancaster

Nesbitt Landen

Katherine Langston

Rich Laura

Michelle Lear

James Lebrun

Danielle Leslein

Jasmine Levine

Nikita Lewis

Gia Marie Mate

Sandra Brunson McBride

Vena Shikey Claudette McCall

Robert McGill

Michelle McMillan

Patrick McQuhae

Lindsey Meszaros

Marty Miller

Jerry Molina

Karen Monsanto

Jenifer Morales

Leo Myers

Jessica Rose Naccarato

Cristina Natividad

Heather Niedzwiecki

Michelle Nixon

Corey Oliver

Katina L. Oliver

Velarde Oliver

Melissa Orthun

Larry Paul

Thomas Pierce

Melvin Anthony Price Jr.

Na'eem E. Prince

Kathryn Raethel

Zachary Rang

Chandra Ray

Lorenzo Reed Sr.

Matthew N. Rhodes

Shelia Robinson

Rita Rust

Victoria Ryan

Jan Saenvilay

Jennifer Melissa Lyn Salter

Young Savannah

Gregg Anthony Senko

Brooke Nicole Smith

William Stephens

Allison Behm Strouse

Carlos Sullivan

Clintoni Swain

Deedra C. Thomas

Devon Thomas

Sabrita Dian Thurman-Newby

Raysa Amezquita Turner

Yolanda Tyler

Heather L. Vaughn

Joanne Virea

Kendall Wainwright

Rosie Washington

Angela Whilden

Kelsey Whitaker

Tammara Whitworth

Kenika Wiggins

Hayes William

Faberg'e D. Williams

Henrietta Bullard Williams

Lawrence Williams

Lewis Williams

Tyler Joseph Wilson

Sarah Zamora

Detrica la'Joy Zimmerman

SAINT LOUIS UNIVERSITY DEPARTMENT OF BIOMEDICAL LABORATORY SCIENCE, ST. LOUIS, MO

Adam Nikolaus Benckendorf

Christine Deanna Bennett

Nathaniel W. Best

Vikram S. Cheema

Annalyssa C. Fordell

Jordan M. Frye

Stefan J. Gelven

Jordyn L. Huston

Natasha Karishma Khatwani

Syshane S. Lu

Katherine F. Peterson

Marco Walter Rossi

KayKay San

Matthew D. Schulte

Rhena S. Singh

Nguyet N. Truong

Kenn J. Vattathara

Lynn J. Vattathara

Alec M. Weiss

SAINT LOUIS UNIVERSITY DOISY COLLEGE OF HEALTH SCIENCES, ST. LOUIS, MO

Michael E. Brazelton

Frances Cole Deadmond

Nathan R. Fritts

Mitchel P. Kohnen

Kathryn A. Lohmann

Sarah A. Wessling

SAINT LOUIS UNIVERSITY MEDICAL IMAGING & RADIATION THERAPEUTICS, ST. LOUIS, MO

Mashael Abushail	Laura Christine Fohne	Danielle Dael Homan	Britton Kerrig Spiegel
Andrew James Bulla	David James Hannibal	Hilary Michelle Lashmett	

SAINT MARY-OF-THE-WOODS COLLEGE, ST. MARY OF WOODS, IN

Abigail H. Abel	Katie M. Hanley	Sierra I. Lopez	Emma B. Riffe
Traice J. Akins	Vivian M. Hansen	Gabrielle K. Lovins	William J. Riley
Maribeth E. Allen	Lauretta A. Harmon	Amber R. Maness	Artishmie Marie Robbins
Casey G. Anderson	Erin M. Harnett	Ashley N. Mathis	Mandy Roush
Kierra I. Anderson	Amanda L. Hattery	Heyli M. Mattingly	Morgan Samuelson
Kacey J. Barnhart	Hannah N. Hein	Shay E. Mays	Sierra N. Smith-Swickard
Jordan A. Bray	Suitin Cer Hnin	Ciara E. McClain	Maria Sofianou
Devyn L. Burns	Lora M. Hofmann	Nathan A. Mensah	Shannon M. Sonderman
Cecilia Caron	Jessica A. Hood	Mikayla J. Metheny	Melissa R. Stuck
Leah S. Castetter	Chenelle E. Horn	Tammy Meyers	Dawnelle R. Sullivan
Dulce A. Chavez	Madeline N. Howes	Amber E. Morris	Stacy Switzer
Carla J. Chrisman	Jessica L. Hughes	Sarah M. New	Mallory J. Tanis
Michael Coleman II	Emily E. Humphrey	Nicole D. Nichol	Holly Ann Taylor
Haylie M. Davenport	Kelci Hunzeker	Bonnie L. Osborn	Whitney R. Teeters
Casey Lynn Dust	Sarah E. Hutchinson	Jessica L. Paddock	Amanda J. Thompson
Susannah M. Eckert	George Ijames	Shelby D. Parmer	Patricia S. Walke
Teresa A. Eddy	Farrah L. Johnson	Morgan E. Patterson	Amber M. White
Kalea C. Ellis	Rian N. Jones	William D. Patton	Kylee E. White
Hannah M. Endress	Sarah E. Kenderdine	Allison J. Payonk	Sydney R. Wilderman
Kilee K. Fagg	Mikayla J. Kinneer	Amanda F. Pereda	Amy D. Wilson
Brittany Farbo	Ashley Koomler	Amanda L. Perry	Elvira G. Wolford
Ryan J. Ferguson	Cassandra M. Koors	Jacqueline Peterschmidt	Heidi Woodruff
Nyctasia D. Fitton	Gina A. Lanier	Christina M. Pifer	Ciera Yergeau
Dagny J. Gargas	Danielle M. Latourette	Jessica Lee Pitts	Kammi D. Yeryar
Frances L. Garrett	Rebecca N. Latta	Courtney M. Prather	Grace L. Ziegler
Katie Good	Kathryn L. Lewis	Na-Shaunda DaNice	
Caitlin Amelia Granfield	Jennifer E. Linder-Miller	Rayford	
Rebecca M. Hampton	Amanda C. Loebker	Brylie N. Riddell	

SAINT MICHAEL'S COLLEGE, COLCHESTER, VT

Arianna E. Aquadro	Stephanie N. Bonewald	Emily H. Carolin	Owen O. Dayton
Gregory J. Baker	Elizabeth A. Bradley	Casey E. Ciapciak	Jordan C. DeKett
Rebekah L. Balch	Briana M. Brady	Justin T. Colletti	Carter D. Denton
Victoria A. Barnum	Mackenzie E. Breen	Julia B. Crisman	Meaghan C. Diffenderfer
Allison S. Bergeron	Margaret M. Burns	Adrienne A. D'Elia	Benjamin D. DiNardo
Richard W. Bernache	Meghan A. Burrows	Logan P. David	Taylor L. Donnelly
Timothy M. Bolger	Makenzie L. Burud	Brendan P. Davitt	Margaret M. Earl

Curtis R. Echo

Mackenzie J. Edmondson

Robert S. Ettenborough

Bradford R. Farrell

Emily W. Ferver

Conor K. Floyd

Samuel B. Fogg

Mary J. Gannon

Timothy J. Gaudion

Andrea L. Gemme

Elise N. Genereux

Kenneth L. Giangregorio

Keri J. Giguere

Meaghan E. Glendon

Abigail N. Goudey

Denise L. Groll

Robert J. Grosso

Alyssa M. Hamel

Gregory R. Hamilton

Sarah A. Haselton

Brianna F. Healy

James R. Hodge

Nathan A. Hodge

Celina F. Horbat

Abbigail E. Hyslip

Erin A. Irons

Kristen L. Isabelle

Jessica M. Jablonski

Emma T. Kalamarides

Peter J. Keefe

MaryAnn Kelly

Daniel G. Killea

Samuel S. Laves

Daviah D. Lawrence

Natalie S. Ledue

Emily J. Loebs

John L. Loomis

Brian T. Lothrop

William K. Lowe

Celsey L. Lumbra

Meghan S. Lynch

Kristen E. McCarthy

Brianna K. McKinley

Shannon D. McQueen

Jenna E. McQuesten

Charles L. Merry

Catherine M. Messitidis

Kelsie A. Miller

Kathryn R. Miyahira

Roberta S. Molokandov

Jordan E. Moore

Sean P. Morrissey

Ellen E. Murchie

Marianna V. Nowacki

Michelle E. O'Donnell

Michelle A. Oberding

Zaire L. Peoples

Charles J. Phalon

Sarah E. Phelps

Sephorah Pierre

Giussani Valentina Prado

Tanner D. Pratt

Abigail C. Rajotte

Karleen A. Richardson

Tyler G. Rossmann

Kelsey M. Ryan

Rachel G. Sanborn

Alexia D. Santos

Michael C. Schreiner

Alexander B. Shaw

Allison E. Shea

Caitlin I. Shea

Julie Maureen Shea

Susanna M. Shigo

Willow R. Smith

Katherine E. Spilhaus

Jesse A. Suhaka

Lucia M. Thomas

Nicolas J. Thornbro

Tino A. Tomasi

Katharine I. K. Tooke

Maria C. Valentyn

Dylan P. Ward

Cory D. Warren

Candace P. Washington

Cody P. Wasuta

Melissa C. Westland

Sophie R. Zschirnt

SAINT VINCENT COLLEGE, LATROBE, PA

Jacob R. Boros

Patrick H. Breen

Donald J. Cole

Shaina A. Contic

Alaina M. D'Aloiso

Rachel M. DeNino

Jennifer L. Desalvo

Kathleen M. Dillon

James D. Farnan

Samantha L. Fether

Sabrina L. Filkosky

Allison K. Frye

Hannah M. Galvin

Ashley E. Geese

Benjamin J. Grassi

Courtney D. Grondziowski

Lauren E. Harbaugh

Rachel A. Hast

Anna M. Hillman

TuDuc Ho

Samuel E. Homan

Joseph C. Howard

Ryan M. Karl

Jillian Kegg

Brett R. Kurpiel

Matthew S. Loftis

Margaret A. Loya

Katherine E. Lucas

Rebekah R. Musho

Taylor M. Nitkiewicz

Leah M. Poponick

Peter S. Reiter

Anna C. Rifilato

Charles N. Russo

Alexander J. Scialabba

Miranda S. Senchur

Jacob M. Sheehan

Helena Shoplik

James M. Singer

Maura N. Snyder

Abigail L. Stahl

Jocelyn T. Stas

Aaron E. Stein

Shannon M. Tantlinger

Hannah Truong

Marla G. Turk

Rabia Uddin

Hailey M. Umbaugh

Kayla J. Uveges

Joshua R. Vasko

Alexa M. Vercelli

Rachel Vogl

Julian D. Whalen

Rachel Linn Wohar

Jieni Zhou

SALEM STATE UNIVERSITY, SALEM, MA

Christina M. Addonizio

Elizabeth Pina Cabral

Brittany Lee Dingle

Logan Harold Dunnigan

Nadia H. East

James Austin Elliott

Belkis P. Frias

Colleen Suzanne Good

Felicia Marie Hayden
Courtney Rose Lillie
Brittany Violet Locklin

Katie Lynne Lulsdorf
Francis Xavier Norton
Cassandra A. Riva

Yessica Rodriguez Rios
Victoria Anne Sobotka
Gloria Styskin

Jacquelyn Marie Sweeney
Maxime George Theriault

SALT LAKE COMMUNITY COLLEGE, SALT LAKE CITY, UT

Michael Eduardo Baca
Soto Sr.
Lauren Branigan
Nick Carlson

Sera Nilsson Carlson
Emma Lynn Farr
Tami Finlayson
Dom Lepore

David Martinez
Morgan Nelson
Jeremy Trujillo
Jared Wallenmeyer

Ryan Welch

SALVE REGINA UNIVERSITY, NEWPORT, RI

Sasha Arias
Joseph Barbera
Taylor Becchetti
Ethan Boghigian
Megan Bonenfant
Katherine Ann Butterfield
Zachary Cahill
Berlenise Castillo
Adriano Cirioli
Colleen Cloonan
Alexander DiMauro
Ashley DiSciullo

Caitlin Downing
Emilee Duffy
Caleigh Anne Farragher
Melissa Figueiredo
Courtney Flynn
Francesca Galeazzi
Ellen Gensicki
Amy Irving
Kevin Jesiolowski
Sara M. Johnson
Ryan Kelly
Sarah Lavallee

Allison Lavoie
Jay Lopes
Jessica Luisi
Erica Manchester
Michael Marotta
Michael P. McNamara
Allyssa Medeiros
Brittany Melanson
Katherine Ann Mendes
Hayley Morais
Jillian Munafo
Kara O'Riley

Garrett Rupe
Courtney Schramm
Patricia Socarras
Shannon Soule
Thomas Stracensky
Benjamin Tetschner
GinaMarie Tonini
Brittany Withers
Blaine Woodcock
John Wukovits
Sinan Zeino

SAMFORD UNIVERSITY, BIRMINGHAM, AL

Abigail Grace Acker
Sarah Elizabeth Bailey
Victoria Morgan Batson
David Reid Bayless
Laura Catherine Bean
Natalie Lillian Grace Bennie
Brittany Kay Bisese
Molly Rebecca Brown
Brianna Charlene Canady
Matthew Taylor Carrick
Taylor Kevin Chadwell
Regan Elizabeth Chewning

Joshua Aaron Chitwood
Nicholas Ashby Clanton
Victoria Alexandra
Domitrovich
Ross Gregory English
Isaac Cushman Espy
Andrew Jordan Feldewerth
Alyssa Taylor Gallas
Blake Ryan Gardner
Andrew James Graves
Logan Caldwell Greenhaw
Garrett Lee Greer

Sarah Grace Grove
Courtney Ann Hawkins
Caroline Gayle Hinds
Analeigh Elizabeth Horton
Sarah Whitney Howard
Conner Michael Kapperman
Katie Elizabeth Kosan
James Franklin Lowe
Molly Elizabeth McCoy
Kaitlin Rose Moore
Katherine Marie Nelson
Emily Caroline Novkov

Anna Claire Per-Lee
Mary Laura Ann Prickett
Devynne Renae Roahrig
Rebecca Salstrand
Kathleen Elizabeth Sharp
Abbie K. Shimer
Jalen Alexander Spraggins
Michael G. Taylor
Margaret Campbell Terp
Lawren Brianna Ware
Rebecca Louise Womack

SAM HOUSTON STATE UNIVERSITY, HUNTSVILLE, TX

Victoria Adeniran
Samantha Aldrich
Corian Thomas Allen

Ruth Amarachi Amaku
Nicole Elizabeth Aponte
Kenneth Barnes

Melissa Ann Barrett
Justin Basso
Kelley Berger

Patricia Biles
Sarah Black
Darcy Boston

Brittney Boyd
Leah Boyd
Nicole Budnik
Katelyn Bunch
Kaysean Clavelle
Valerie Coronado
Cristina Courcy
Jaren Crist
Hadley Davis
Caelyne Dial
Amy Nicole Douglas
Mary Ellison
Zecharias Embaye
Christina Espindola
Jessica Estrada
Alexandria Marie Falato
Rachel Dianne Farley
Ashley Fluty
Jordan Franks
Paloma Garcia Duran
Alondra Garza
Shelby Genung

Dalton Glass
Michael Gonzalez
Mariah Lynn Gorom
Michelle Griffith
Jessie Harris
Samantha Hart
Camille Hay
Malorie Renee Hegemeyer
Kiel William Heidman
True Hernandez
Hallie Rachel Hicks
Marissa Hill
Nicholas Hollingsworth
Carrie Hopkinson
Hope Dryden Horwath
Larry Irby
Jaelan Jackson
Jacqueline Jaramillo
Manjot Singh Jawa
David Jimenez
Paul Jones
Haley Jozwiak

Cali Justice
Claire Kendrick
Claire Kilpatrick
Holly Kons
Ashley Kopps
Janine Kuwahara
Kyle Laqua
Caroline Marlene Ledford
Celeste Lo
Jacy Brianne Lockey
Elizabeth Lyssy
Jessica Mackey
Briana McCall
Luis Morales
Madeleine Mortimore
Samuel Patrick Murra
Austin Nelson
Joanna Nigro
Olivia Renee Olguin
Meagan Pasket
Tyler Patek
Heather Pearson

Kelsey Powers
Miranda Prado
Peterhao Quach
Callie Renaud
Alice Judith Reyes
Brittany Alexandra Rickard
Avery Alexandra Robinson
Jaclyn Robinson
Joshua Sablatura
Isidro Salazar
Rubin Sandlin
Alissa Scheurich
Sarah Sherman
Kourtney Marie Spriggins
Patrick Stanford-Galloway
Aaron Tipton
Aaron Valadez
Nereyda Vera
Jeremy Villanueva
Brandi M. Villarreal
Bethany Whitten
Hannah Zedaker

SAMUEL MERRITT UNIVERSITY, OAKLAND, CA

Nathan Stewart Boyd

Emma Hoi Lam

Stephanie Mita

SANDHILLS COMMUNITY COLLEGE, PINEHURST, NC

Levi Edward Barnes
Michael R. Boisvert
Eli M. Brewer
Israel Lopez Capote
Aaron Randall Cheek
Kimberlee Farris

Debra Lee Hawkins
Allison R. Hendrix
Jacqueline Hernandez
Barry Lee Hill
Annie Marie Huffman
Jessica Latham Jacobs

Marissa Lupkas
Kerry Sarah Murphy
Russall Jae Noell
Brenda Mae Stenerson
Mary Beth Tempesco
Allen Joseph Thomas

Humberto Farelli Viana
Sarah Katherine Voelker
Kionna Watkins
Vanessa Helen Wright

SCHENECTADY COUNTY COMMUNITY COLLEGE, SCHENECTADY, NY

Breanna M. Aanensen
Christa L. Agans
Sean Allison
Thomas Andreyo
Meghan A. Appleby
Stefanie Y. Bailund-Witty
Ronald T. Baldwin Jr.

Michael J. Banewicz
Hayley J. Bennett
Jacob W. Benninger
Micah Z. Benreuben
Stephanie P. Bink
Kayla M. Boniecki
Jessica R. Bonjukian

Tracy Bowen
Leonard C. Brain
Cody N. Burda
Jonathan D. Burkhart
Shaelei D. Butler
Christina M. Calantone
Elijah P. Casper

Matthew J. Center
John G. Chamberlain
Lauren R. Chiras
Joyce E. Chowenhill
Kyle J. Cira
Julie Irene Collins
Yomaira Colon

Lisa A. Covey
Lorna M. Cragle-Otty
Kelly L. Crosier
Eric M. Cross
Charles T. Curcio
Amanda L. Cuthbert
Sahar Darwish
Bonnie J. Davis
Nicole A. Davison
Suzanne M. Demarco
Rocco J. Demento
Abigail L. Deuel
Caitlyn C. Drumm
Jennifer M. Dugan
Olivia C. Esposito
Elizabeth N. Evans
Michael A. Favata
Benjamin P. Ferretti
Michael C. Filak
Melanie D. Fillerup
Alejandro C. Flores-Howland
Bernadette R. Foley
Kyle E. Folk
AshLee M. Ford
Catherine M. Forth
Thomas M. Franceschiello
Denise M. Fuller
Ciera M. Fylipek
Elizabeth J. Gaffney
Ronald P. Gardner

Joshua H. Garry
Angelica I. Gattgens
Harry O. Gochee IV
Kristin K. Gordon
Shanee Gordon
Heather S. Grogan
Sarah C. Gugliuzza
Grant D. Hackett
Joseph E. Haessig
Shornakay S. Hamilton
Kevin M. Hammer
Linda L. Harbers
Sarah L. Harbour
Brian D. Harkness
Zachary S. Harrington
Sheri L. Hayes
Richard A. Hazleton
Damon C. Hitt
Carl Richard Hoyt II
Troy J. Huggard
Michael S. Hugo
Michael A. Hunt
Ryan T. Hurtt
Deborah A. Ingles
Gan P. Inma
Joshua P. Jablonowski
Thomas R. Jennings
Carly L. Johnson
Rebecca N. Kalicharan
Jeffery T. Karabin
Sabrina K. Kelly

Daniel T. Killion
Dorothy E. Kline
Autumn Kochis
Robert A. Kochis
Swarna L. Kota
Sarah E. Laplant
Jack C. Lather
John Lauterbach
Sharon A. Lemme-Masciocco
Jeffrey S. Lentz
Jerome Daniel Lewis
Luis A. Lopez
Jenelle N. Losaw
Joseph E. McDade
Marcia M. McDonald
Carolina X. Medina
Brian E. Merfeld
Aleksey Monastyrenko
Abysinnia R. Muir
Chelsea L. Neahr
Chik Wai Ng
Danielle P. Nolan
Martina L. Oleary
Dominic J. Orlando
Ethan A. Peterson
Stephen T. Piorkowski
Shantal J. Plass
Rodrigo A. Polanco Perez
Teresa A. Randall
Nathaniel A. Redden

Ashley M. Rickson
Ben A. Riehlman
Chelsi A. Riley
Jocelyn A. Rogers
Eric Sahagian
Cecilia M. Sanchez
Michaela C. Schnore
Gail R. Seise-Boyd
Daniel L. Sheehan
Peggy Y. Siegfried
Gitanjalie Singh
Julianna M. Smith
Wayne L. Snyder
Kimberly D. Sparks Way
Robin A. Steinhorst
Morgan D. Sullivan
Tao Sun
Tracy A. Sweet
Kevin M. Symons Jr.
Sherry L. Talbot
Joshua J. Ten Eyck
Erica M. Toth
Ashley B. Tyrell
Gabriel J. Vega
Marcy L. Vonmaucher
Eric S. Vuignier
Benjamin Walston
Dwayne A. Wilson
Morgan Winnie
Donna A. Wright-Wilson
Valerie Zaloga

SEATTLE PACIFIC UNIVERSITY, SEATTLE, WA

Ian D. Adams
Grace E. Andrews
Haley Ann Balbi
Daniel Lloyd Baldridge
Shamele M. Battan
Benjamin Graham Battles
Andrew Robert Bell
Mikaela Marie Beloberk
Maddy O'Mara Booster
Elayna Nicole Boot

Matthew James Bowden
Shane David Bowman
Tyler Austin Breier
Hallie Anne Brinkman
Jessica Marie Butler
Erica Hope Buzbee
Diana Laura Cabrera
Tiffany Gim-Yain Chin
Hannah Jiamin Chong
Briana Celeste Chui

Mariah Frances Conley
Erin Nicole Creighton
Natalie R. Cunningham
Janissa Leigh Doerscher
Rachel Mary Douglass
Bryce S. Eng
Rose Lauren Ewing
Samuel J. Filby
Gretchen Elise Gelman
Matthew Robert Guchee

Jessica Elizabeth Gunn
Caleb Michael Gustin
Madeline Marie Haugen
Chelsea Elizabeth Heimbigner
Christopher Jay Herron
Emma Ruth Elise Holm
Emilie Grace Jackson
Timothy Joseph Jan
Jacob Leelan Johnson

Kāʻeo-Puʻuwai Castelli
Kealoha-Lindsey
Jacob Tyson Krodel
Jonathan Daesun Kwon
Taelin Kahryn Lanier
Gabrielle Nicole Larreau
Eleah Anna Lovell
Anne M. Macy
Jonathan David Mansen
Sarah EL Martin
Mary N. Mathison
John Benjamin McAuley
Sarah Katherine McDermott

Brendan Stewart McMillen
Hannah Lauren Miller
McClintock John Miller
Macie Elaine Mooney
Garrett Matthew Mullett
Tara Lynn Paris
Anna Elizabeth Patti
Amelie Rebekah Pederson
Deborah Jean Peterson
Elisa Beth Raney
Hannah Marie Rodrigues
Michaela N. Rubenstein
Alexander Scott Russo

Carl Ward Sallee
Jared William Schneider
Lindsey Arella Sieb
Katelyn Marie Siron
Samuel Caleb Stumberg
Scott Gunnar Swenson
Giselle Tayal
Claire Emily Thompson
Kelsey Hanna Tuohy
Tatiana Meneses Ubay
Jonathan David Van
Schenck
Jacob Aaron Van Winkle

Kendall Ann Vignaroli
Katlyn Marie Voss
Jordan Reese Wagner
Jaren Dawn Walker
Carla Jane Walp
Rachel L. Weeks
Aaron Lee Wolfe
Rebecca Rose Wolfe
Alden Ellis Wyland
Emma Ruth Wyma
Alaina Christine Zeldenrust

SEATTLE PACIFIC UNIVERSITY GRADUATE PROGRAM, SEATTLE, WA

Kayla Noelani Aiello
Gaurishri Anantha
Rebekah Anya Appleton
Amber Selene Bryant
Jeffrey Charle Carrier
Cynthia Jobeth Cuellar
John-Paul Honeyford
Denham
Marni Rose DeNike
Mykela Jana Fantone

Sherese Ursula Gamble
Elizabeth Marie Garrett
Jonathan Paul Gerig
Lindsey Elizabeth Hanson
Kari Christina Heinz
Kelsey E. Hinrichs
Nicole Renee Kemp
Nathan Ross McKim
Ashley Claire Miraldi
Kiley Ann Moss

Naomi Theresa Nanez
David C. Palm
Brianne Lynn Pan
Courtney Elizabeth Pullen
Catherine Elizabeth
Rehberger
Brenna Catherine Reid
Jeffrey Aaron Roache
Gini Scott
Natalie Ann Semegen

Samantha Shipley
Joanne Kathrina Sparrow
Corinne Lindsey Spero
Melissa Sue Turtzo
Brianna Joan Weimar
Meghan Suzanne Young
Jessie June Zimmerman

SEMINOLE STATE COLLEGE, SEMINOLE, OK

Jalyn Anderle
Billy Andrew
Melina Baldwin
Ashlee G. Birchall
Elijah Bishop
Sydney Brummett
Kinzey Guinn Bryan
Sandra Childress
Haley Cochran
Bridgette Coleman
Felecia Cope

Timothy Costley
Jacy Cowan
Logan Crenshaw
Ann Epperley
Taylor Kay Factor
Nicole Ferrell
Ksenia Fisher
Maria Goodnight
Johnathan Harrington
Devan Harris
Mckayla Hendrix

Brianna Hilton
Landrea Hixson
Kimberly James
Damera Ann Krenzer
Makenzi Lamb
Jessica Loafman
Asheleigh Brooke Mathews
Beau Kaine McGinnis
Caitlyn Mosser
Janay Nichole Nix
Morgan Palmer

Jennifer Ramsey
Rose Roberts
Shannon Robertson
Mark Sanders
Peyton Scott
Kristin Smith
Alondra Taximaroa
Carter James Towey
Seth Winters
Hanna Zimmerman

SETON HALL UNIVERSITY, SOUTH ORANGE, NJ

Shannon Fitz Alexander
Benjamin Ayzenberg

Veronica Beck
Daniel Chemy

Mary M. Donnelly
Maxwell Dotson

Amy Gao
Lauren Garcia

Christopher Gboji
Timothy Hoffman
Christian Jamandre
Ryan Kane

Monique McDonald
Jamie McIlvaine
Joel Jesus Menendez
Brianna Michelle Monti

Albery Cris Paula
Joseph Puleo
Anthony Scudieri
Kirsten Simmons

Kayla Toomer
Meldrick Von Umahon

SETON HILL UNIVERSITY, GREENSBURG, PA

Stephen T. Barnhart
Dipeeka Bastola
Jesser L. Boulnemour
Emily N. Gilles

Candace A. Hall
Sarah K. Kimutis
Katie C. Kincade
Jonnah Marie Labishak

Michele N. Mellick
Michele M. Morgan
Anthony Carlo Palmiscno
Bradford D. Paquin

Shelby Kristoff Romanik
Erica L. Schweinsberg
Megan R. Shugarts
Molly J. Zindash

SHAWNEE COMMUNITY COLLEGE, ULLIN, IL

Katelynn N. Cook
Jacob Michael Hall
Mildred R. Henderson
Amanda S. Houseman
Hannah J. Hunter
Kendall C. Ivy

Alicia K. Jordal
Eduardo Juarez
AliceAnn H. Kotter
Kaitlyn M. Lipe
Jesse N. Livesay
Hannah K. McClarney

Patrick J. Nesbit
Kalen S. Parker
Angela Mi Peterman
Rebecca M. Reeder
Wyatt W. Robinson
Tara D. Rowan

Courtney L. Sanders
Melody A. Siron
Sherry Y. Trexler
Sahara D. Veach
Saundra J. Wathen

SHAW UNIVERSITY DIVINITY SCHOOL, RALEIGH, NC

Carolyn H. Bell
Mark T. Gibson

Nichole L. Harris Glover
Rogerline P. White

Carol Wilson-Jones

Margie P. Worthy

SHENANDOAH UNIVERSITY, WINCHESTER, VA

Kimberlyn Leanne Abel
Majed Waqit Alharthi
Abdulrahman A. Aljanoubi
Sara Ahmed Aljardan
Andrew Allan Allison
Lama Suliaman Alogaili
Saleh Abdulaziz Alsoghair
Nasser Fahad Alturaifi
Angybell Carolina Andrade
Christian Asinero
Eva Laura Assogba
Gina Thompson Ayers
Molly Catherine Barb
Amanda Lee Barnett
Caleb D. Baxter
Roxanna Lynn Beeler
Emma Rose Benson
Samuel "Joey" Bikkers

Martina Cacciaroni Bingham
Emily Susan Boero
Mitchell D. Bohman
Rebecca Marie Bove
Christine Alana Bowers
Cassie Marie Boyd
Michele Marie Boyd
Katelyn Bridge
Brianna Maria Brophy
Brittany Lynn Brownlee
Jasmine Bryant
Nessyah Adelaide Trudy
Buder Gallagher
Carolyn T. Calleo
Nicole Elizabeth Campbell
Kailbeth Andreina Chacin-Gonzalez
Jeffrey Wei-Ta Chuang

Mary Dorsey Clarke
Anthony Michael Cornet
Christine Elizabeth Cox
Carolyn Stewart Watkins
Crysdale
Christine Marie Daily
Hilda Walesca Darce
Katherine Anne Defiglio
Dylan Andrew Derflinger
Lyly Tran Doan
Sarah Zimmerman Driver
Tyler Schponover
Dunnington
Andrew Eidberger
Mark Mena Fahmy
Jillian Marie Fahrbach
Pamela Jean Fisher
Jessica Anne Flagg

Ashley Foster
Thanveer Reddy Gadwal
Danielle Lillian Gallupe
Syr Charles Gonyea
Laura Nichole Graham
Katelyn Marie Gregory
Gabrielle Marie Haas
Rebekah Hade
Brooke Leigh Hahne
Alexander Edward Haley
Tyler Harvey
Lauren Hawes
Kedra Monique Haynes
Jacqueline Heisey Hemler
Andrew Dalton Herring
Katherine Grace Hood
Stephanie Anna-Marie Jackson

Richard Henry Jeric
Terria Trana Jones
Jing Kang
Shannon Brooke Kelly
Ethan Joseph Koons
Kelli Kunert
Matthew Knight Laird
David Landrum
Kathleen Anne Lasick
Katherine Irene Rose
Lemming
Kristy Marie Lennon
Sarah Christine Levering
Tara Shante Lockhart
Brandon Lee Loos
Anna Ruth Lopynski
Hannah Eileen Makridis
Caitlin Amber Malick
Sarah Hypatia Mann
Abigail Martin
Emily Martin

Jillian M. Masciantonio
Brittany Ann Mason
Peyton Joyce Massad
Andrew Tyler McDermott
Rachael Linda McDermott
Kelynn Powell McPeak
Kamran Mehta
Amanda Marie Menke
David Merola
Victoria Lynn Miller
Demetra Maria Mylonas
Jacob Ryan Newton
Francisco Gabriel Nolasco
Michelle Bach Nugent
Zacharia Daniel Overby
Jeremy Ethan Parel
Philip Alexander Pasco
Levi William Perry
Amanda Roswell Pettyjohn
Kylie Nicole Pooler
Melissa Rae Propst

Jennifer Maddalino Purdy
Erin Elizabeth Puskar
Emily Rafala
Jenna Claire Rampale
Colin Read
Airiel Alexandra Renner
Alayna Rose Ribovich
Miriam Magdalena
Robertson
Aurielle Eileen Rowe
Harley Nicole Ryan
Katie Danielle Salyers
Kelly Ann Scott
Douglas Gerald Shaw
Colleen Shendow
Shelby Rose Shrader
Taylor George
Slaughenhoupt
Elaine Marie Smith
Vanessa Angela Sousa
Rachel Lynne Stalker

Alexandra Helen Steege
Mirana Belle Stoker
Eric Robert Stottlemyer
Cassandra Rose Tabarini
Brandon Lee Thomas
Miranda Camille Thomas
Kathleen C. Tickle
Christopher Tillman
Caitlin Alexandra Tilton
Quang Ton
Erin Vandergrift
Cambria Van de Vaarst
Denver Marie Walker
Seth Walker
Brandi Marie Warren
Erin Allison Weddle
Anna Margaret Wilson
Annie Ka Yi Wong
Hassan Ziauddin

SHEPHERD UNIVERSITY, SHEPHERDSTOWN, WV

Charlotte Lorena Bellotte
Julianne Marie Brown
Natalia Michele Browne
Lisa Andrea Carden-Watson
Keani Chinn

Sarah Elizabeth Conway
Daniel Benjamin Cordova
David William Donohue
Caitlin Sarah Fournier
Jacqueline Kowalski

Leonie Middeke
Jesus Aaron Ruvalcaba
Stephanie Lynn Santella
Emily Austin Spangler
Kelsey Blake Stoneberger

Cassidy Nicole Watson
Jade McKenzie Weaver

SHIPPENSBURG UNIVERSITY, SHIPPENSBURG, PA

Brandon P. Adamson
Jaylen D. Alston
Brielle Arch
Gabriella M. Brackett
Kaitlyn A. Brant
Adrien Cartal
Matthew C. Christman
Caitlin M. Clark
Zane M. Clevenger
Jessica Collins
Crystal J. Conzo
Caitlin L. Deeter

Cortlin A. Dell
Eric DeMuth
Courtney Devine
Brian D. Ettinger
Joseph Farabaugh
Katherine L. Fisher
Julie R. Fuhrman
Brandon Scott Garlitz
Jonathan D. Glennon
Jessica A. Harding
Julie Hendrickson
Brian T. Hoertz

Morgan A. Horowitz
Shaniece Jackson
Lara C. John
Leah E. Johnson
Haley M. Jones
Jacqueline A. Joseph
Jordyn E. Kahlbaugh
Robert P. Kitchen
Zachary Kline
Amanda N. Kuzo
Erick Lane
Jesse J. Lawton

Erica L. Martinez
Mary McDannell
Carolyn N. Meier
Anthony J. Militano
Katherine M. Miller
Madelyn Mae Moyer-Keehn
Christopher J. Mullin
Benjamin J. Myett
Aaron M. Nogle
Colin Ochs
Derek S. Over
Emily J. Owens

Stephanie Pike
Laura Nicole Plank
Hector M. Raya
Aaron R. Rhoads
Paige Lauren Rippon
Dakota T. Ritz

Joshua Robeson
Jorge L. Santiago
Justin S. Schneider
Michelle E. Schultz
Scotty Scott
Ashley M. Seyler

Megan S. Shaw
Holly Spence
Ciara R. Stanley
Stefan M. Szilagyi
Victoria L. Tomlinson
Mark A. Tressler

Lucas M. Van Horn
Patrick R. Wells
Brian M. Wendling
Greggory R. Whitcomb
Brittany Wood
Ryan Word

SIENA HEIGHTS UNIVERSITY, ADRIAN, MI

Emily L. Abbs
Patrick Allen
Amelia R. Balinski
Jessica Behnke
Nick Isaiah Blumenau
Chelsea Coatsworth
Gabrielle Corbin

Amber Lynne Denomme
Phoenix Duncan
Alyssa A. Fausneaucht
Sam Haack
Kayla Herold
Paul Jacobs
Justin Lempicki

Charles Lawrence Ludlow
Daniell May
Jocelyn Near
Kristen Pitts
Andrea Rumler
Erin Russell
Salman Sadi

Amber Maryie Spencer
Brittany L. Trout
Sydney Madelynn
VanHoose
Rachel Wellman-Benedict

SIERRA NEVADA COLLEGE, INCLINE VILLAGE, NV

Morrain Ruby Bauer
Calhoun Rodgers Boone
Terra S. Breeden
Brett Marie Cassel
Timothy P. Curran
Nicholas Galantowicz

Jesse Guess
Kyle E. Kelly
Danny S. Kern
Jordan McNally Koucky
MeiLi Caroline LeRoy
Tom S. Loeschner

Marina M. McCoy
Finlay Bryan Neeson
Makenzie R. O'Connor
Kaitlyn E. O'Hara
Courtney L. Potts
Tayler Marie Robertson

Emma K. Romo
Michael J. Schmidt
Scout M. Sorcic
Lena Gale Stroheker
Elias Stuerz
Ian Robert Wieczorek

SIMPSON COLLEGE, INDIANOLA, IA

Wade R. Adams
Susan J. Alt
Tanner J. Augustine
Sarah C. Beadle
Katelyn M. Behounek
Marissa A. Belau
Blake R. Bergstorm
Taylor C. Besser
MacKenzie K. Bills
Dana W. Bohan
Madeline J. Bosworth
Clayton J. Bowers
Evan O. Braxton-Barto
Geoffery A. Converse
Sean P. Duvall
Joshua D. Eaton

Katelyn R. Eichelberger
Sandra Danielle Fairchild
Ethan C. Frederick
Jeannetta L. Fuller
Kaitlyn M. Gochenour
Jacy K. Gomez
Natalie B. Gordon
Dillon D. Gretzky
Victoria L. Halloran
Chelsea E. Hamerlinck
Nicholas P. Hermon
Hannah M. Hill
Coltyn J. Hunter
Tricia K. Ingram
Tegan L. Jarchow
Kyle E. Jensen

Louis R. Joslyn
Jordyn R. Kelso
Alexandria L. Konig
Robert D. Lyons
Jacob S. McLain
Kelsey L. Merschman
Molly M. Monk
Danielle M. Musselman
Taylor A. Nehring
Sarah B. Noel
Booke C. Panzer
Michael J. Pavon
Hallen Phung
Mariana Quinones
Sara J. Reed
Gage K. Reis

Ruth A. Roberts
Trey J. Scott
Natasha A. Shehade
Cort I. Singleton
Maureen E. Snook
Brenda R. Soto
Dylan B. Struck
Morgan A. Struebing
Grace M. Tshimoa
Hali J. VanVelzen
Abbie L. VanVleet
Colby P. Vlieger
Erin A. Wendover
Colin P. Zidlicky

SINCLAIR SCHOOL OF NURSING UNIVERSITY OF MISSOURI, COLUMBIA, MO

Allison Anbari

Andrea Beth Becker

Abigail Christine Camden

Dominic Joseph Chambers

Dana Kathryn Cruz

Ciara Mary Demings

Zachary Ryan Elmore

Elizabeth Susan Emmert

Michaella Lynn Forck

Erica Nicole Hoeferlin

Gina Koch

Amber Dawn Linneman

Alexandria Ann Mediavilla

Pamela Lynne Ostby

Kelly Renee Queathem

Bailey Ann Ritter

Courtney Denise Robinson

Brittany Ann Sansone

Briana Lynn Snyder

Colleen Marie Tabaka

Meagan Elizabeth Terry

Emily Tesar

Lydia Marie Todd

Megan Elizabeth Voorhis

Brittany Michelle Zee-
Cheng

SNEAD STATE COMMUNITY COLLEGE, BOAZ, AL

Fonda R. Absher

Elisabeth I. Anderson

John S. Archer

Jordan B. Armstrong

Ryan J. Beam

Kyle Bryan Beddingfield

Dean E. Bell

Casey R. Blalock

Brent E. Brackett

Courtney R. Brooks

Jimmy F. Brooks

Brannon L. Cahela

Noah C. Campbell

Mayson N. Chadwick

Samantha R. Chamblee

Freddianne T. Chandler

David A. Cherry

Joseph B. Clark

Zachary T. Clark

Keaton Clay

Caleb D. Cody

Jonathan T. Cole

William Brock Colvin

Cara E. Cornutt

Alejandro Corona

Sabria Cotton

Brian L. Dansereau

Kevin D. Derrick

Emily Tomie Duncan

Hunter A. Dunn

Emily K. Gaskins

Whitney L. Gladden

Audrey Anne Glitzer

Payton E. Golden

Mitchell B. Gore

Liliana Guevara

Danielle L. Havis

Hannah E. Hayes

Mandy J. Henderson

Christine M. Hendrix

Brandon G. Holland

Danielle Renee Hopper

Brooke Anna Hubbard

Taylor Nicole Ishee

Shannon Nicole Jackson

Natalie M. Jumalon

Adzovi Dzodzina H.
Kassegne

Hannah M. Kelley

Jodie T. Kennamer

Erik Lemus Zapata

Cassie H. Long

Haley E. Long

Cecilia T. Lopez

Abigail C. Maltbie

Dustin B. Mason

Hannah E. Mathis

Matthew T. Mayberry

Jordan S. McCarver

Corey M. McKinney

Christine H. Nguyen

Duyen Nguyen

Savannah D. Ogletree

Corey L. Orr

Almadelia Ortiz Hernandez

Jarrod M. Parker

Reyna T. Pedro

Duong Thuy Nguyen Phan

Tabitha D. Poe

Ryan T. Prickett

Savanna F. Rains

Natasha A. Ray

Luke I. Riffle

Ulises C. Rios

Sarah A. Roberts

Lauren N. Scales

Madison Sewell

Lauren Shaffer

George T. Shipman

Ra'Shaun T. Showers

Brittany B. Sims

Tabitha E. Singleton

Kimberley Spicher

India R. Steele

Coti S. Stewart

Chandler A. Tarvin

Stephen C. Tarvin

Brittney S. Taylor

Alicia B. Underwood

Macie L. Upchurch

Maria G. Vidal

Taylor B. Wagnon

Matthew S. Washington

Macy L. West

Heather N. Willbanks

Presley R. Willoughby

Gabrielle Wilson

Sara E. Womack

Malik L. Woodard

Lindsey N. Wright

Sergio Zavala

SOMERSET COMMUNITY COLLEGE, SOMERSET, KY

Judy Carol Absher

James Bradley Bailey

Justin Wallace Barnes

Brianna Michele Burdette

Kayla H. Chadwell

Rachel Dean Claborn

Travis Dills

James Stephen Eldridge

Whitney Nicole Ellison

Katharine Taylor Estep

Jason Eric Fox

Rebecca Jordan Franks

Timothy Lee Grills

Laura Marie Groce

Jacob Ryan Gross

Hannah Lane Haycraft

Ashley Nicole Hopper	Katherine E. Linville	Taylor Nicole Robinson	Whitney Lynn West
Matthew Nelson Jones	Hannah McAlpin	Ronnie Logan Skipworth	Kaitlyn Marie Whitaker
Christopher Oneal Kent	Abigail Alisa Perkins	Ira Robert Turner Jr.	Rick James Winstead

SOUTH ARKANSAS COMMUNITY COLLEGE, EL DORADO, AR

Chardia Marcedia Carroll	Latosha A. Gatson	Dawn R. Tucker	Janeen Louisa Renee
Lesley Drummond	Stephanie A. Pruitt		Watkins

SOUTHEAST ARKANSAS COLLEGE, PINE BLUFF, AR

Raisa Ama Afakia	John Cottrell	Shayla Grimmett	Cody Strom
Rose Beck	O'Linza Lue Eddington	Carolann Powers	
Kerry Coleman	Kiara Maureen Gray	Patrick Shelley	

SOUTHEASTERN BAPTIST COLLEGE, LAUREL, MS

Michael Beasley	Joshua M. Daniels	Justin W. Rhodes	Patricia A. Wilkins
Jeffrey A. Carney	Maston Anthony McMahan	Lindsey B. Walker	
Jeremy R. Clearman	Christopher Sean Piper	Jeremy M. Wilkerson	

SOUTHEASTERN BIBLE COLLEGE, BIRMINGHAM, AL

Amanda J. Ashton	Charmaine Camille	Molly Susanne McLain	Chase Daniel Ravenscraft
Michelle Dawn Beardsley	Holloway	Molly Susanne McLain	Tammy Reeves
Matthew Aaron Bryson	Jordan Lance Hughes	Sarah Anne Munroe	Levi S. Reynolds
Casey Nicole Cisco	Samuel J. Jones	Jonathan Jacob Naumcheff	Junggil Seo
Casey Nicole Cisco	Jeffrey David Kersh	Alyssa Nicole Nichols	Steve Wade Slaten
Gladys Delight Davis	Megan Elizabeth Krueger	Marguerite Parker	Sarah Anne Snyder
Gladys Delight Davis	Megan Elizabeth Krueger	Samantha Dawn Parsons	Alajujuan A. Sparks
Steven William Denney	Adriana Lee Lombard	Samantha Dawn Parsons	Leamon Kyle Sullivan
Steven William Denney	Jessica Elaine Mayfield	Justin Archer Pollock	Leamon Kyle Sullivan
David Jeffery Harrison	Lisa McGalliard	Sheila Quarles	
	Lisa McGalliard	Chase Daniel Ravenscraft	

SOUTHEASTERN FREE WILL BAPTIST COLLEGE, WENDELL, NC

Destanie Spring Aycock	Francisco Rodolfo	Nathaniel Ray Peoples	Allison Nicole Rager
Joshua Adam Butler	Manriquez	Briana Dawn Phillips	William Matthew Tilghman

SOUTHEASTERN ILLINOIS COLLEGE, HARRISBURG, IL

Alexandria Hope Armstrong	Nicole Campbell	Clinton Murphy	Peyton Robinson
Kelsey Bartok	Olivia Tamblyn Christian	Gianni Otto	Jayden Roper
Larissa Kaitlin Bond	Brooklyn Paige Lewis	Kennedy Phelps	Brittney Suits
Preston Boone	Ryan Abbott Luce	Autumn Pritchett	Kyle Steven Upchurch
Brenna Nicole Butler	Mitchell Masterson	Jacob Richerson	Jacob Vaughan

Jillian Wallace   James Adam Wasson   Cassandra Watkins

SOUTHEASTERN LOUISIANA UNIVERSITY, HAMMOND, LA

Krista N. Achor	Regan M. Cascio	Quintele M. Jackson	Mollie Mae Norton
Tamara E. Alexander	Fernanda Saliba Chagas	Kelsey Condon Johnson	Amy E. Purvis
Justin W. Bankston	Nicole Marie Cousins	Suyogya Karki	Alexis Nicole Quackenbush
Brittany Leigh Bates	Taylor Morgan Drude	Meredith Anne Keating	Katie Allain Simmons
Whitney Nicole Bell	Zachary Michael Edwards	Nisha Lama	Megan Nicole Simon
Neil A. Bourgeois	Kaitlin Noelle Farkas	Harli Angelle Manuel	Angele Mary Thibodaux
Emily Jean Bushnell	Paul Gerard Haddican Jr.	Morgan A. Miller	

SOUTHEASTERN OKLAHOMA STATE UNIVERSITY GRADUATE SCHOOL, DURANT, OK

Kelis Ayn Whisenhunt

SOUTHEASTERN UNIVERSITY, LAKELAND, FL

Colton Ryder Albright	Kristyn Elaine Eversole	Natalie Elaine James	Kirsti Danielle Mutz
Amy Diane Anderson	Hannah Evangeline Flores	Bethany Ann Johnson	Steven Luis Nieves
Kaitlynn Renee Andrews	Ana Lucia Forero	Emily Barrett Johnston	Andrew David Partridge
Jake Dean Archer	Kelly Rebecca Freed	Kristen Elizabeth Jones	Tapan Ashok Patel
Bailey Phillips Baeder	Leandra Lucia Furtado	Anna Elizabeth Kabrich	Marina Alyse Pawlaczyk
Mary Katherine Barnes	Jacob Michael Fusek	Jennifer Lynne Kimball	Micah Sharon Perry
Amy Nicole Bergey	Shayla Jo Fyfe	Jessica S. Kurbatov	Barbara Boursiquot
Cassidy McKenna Block	La Raey A. Galati	Michael James Kuzma	Perttula
Vonciel Tiffany Bryant	Rachel Marie Galbreath	Emily Ann Larkins	Erica Kristin Piper
Anna Elizabeth Burghardt	Jeremiah Paj Gallego	Justin Michael Lemke	Kelly Marie Prahl
Blake Everett Cason	Brittany Shanae Garcia	Jessica Lynn Logue	Sofia Victoria Ramos
Katlyn Rochelle Cervone	Alexis Janée Gauthier	Emma Grace Marie Loucks	Kristen Elizabeth Ray
Savannah Catherine Coates	Nicole Renee Geiger	Crystal Lee Lowery	Kellie Marie Recio
Monica Cordero	Jon Michael Geniesse	Taylor Ashley Lyon	Rhonda Crider Reed
Melissa Craw	Clayton Richard Gilbert	Kayla Danielle Malizzi	Marissa Nicole Reid
Dionysius Alexander Culver	Gabriella Hunter Gold	Katie Lynn Marki	Marc Dylan Renfro
Dana Marie Davis	Taylor Noel Grice	Sarah Nicole Marki	Kaitlyn Gaetana Ricci
Katelyn Jessica Deck	Robert Christopher	Scott Christopher Mautz	Traylor Lane Roberts
Kristen Johanna Deck	Hammond	Molly Kate McCann	Leslie Ann Robinson
Hannah Margaret Demarest	Rebekah Anne Harkness	Annisa Mary McElhenny	Kami Rashauna Rose
Marci Lynn DeShong	Kelton Keith Heckman	Curran James McQuade	Abbey Ann Ruben
Alyssa Diane Dillon	Michael Robert Hirschi	Rylan Michael McQuade	Cassedy Jené Rymer
Derek Matthew Drummond	Cody Scott Hoffman	Joshua Alan Minerella	Kalyn L. Safreed
David Dee Duron	Elsa Elizabeth Hoglund	Shelby Beatrice Mooney	Danney Morgan Samson
Kayla Michelle Ellis	Tyler Jay Hoitsma	Samuel Clint Moyer	Lorenzo Lazaro Sanchez
Caitlynn Mae Ensley	Terrah Lynne Holly	Kayle Marie Mullenix	Christian Phillip Santiago
Erica Joy Eschbach	Michael C. Hughes	Ryan Patrick Murray	Rachael Brooke Satalino

Christian Elise Serfass
Hannah Lee Sfameni
Luke Scott Shemeth
Samantha Renee Silver
April Kay Skipper
Sterling Shellie Smith
Kimber Natasia Stepp

Naomi Lynn Suchy
Jennifer Ann Swygard
Katherine Amber Swygard
Frederic Andre Thiriez
Anik Simone Thomas
Mercy Ohunene Ahuoiza
Toma

Kathleen Marie Trenski
Erika Marie Valdes
Rachel Marie Van Dyke
Vincent Stephen Veach
Raeanne Elizabeth Watkins
Brooke Ellen Williams
Isaiah Daniel Williamson

Zachary James Wolf
Zachary Paul Wolfe
Calen David Wood
Kaylyn Gabrielle Wren
Lauren Marie Yafanaro
Ariana Noelle Yap

SOUTHERN ADVENTIST UNIVERSITY, COLLEGEDALE, TN

Ryan Becker
Guilherme Brasil de Souza
Jose Briones
Jared Callaway
Ian Carney
Alexandria Center
Kevin Christenson
Ellen Chun
Jessica Davis
Emmylou Drusky
Roy Drusky
Cris Dutra

Caitlin Faber
Thomas Flynn
Albert Gonzalez
David Grau
Laura Joan Green
Loren Hall
Ellainna Hart
Emily Henson
Natalie Herrera
Adam Johnson
Vicki Johnson
Mariana Kaplan

Prescott Khair
James Lee
Sarah Maine
Judit Manchay
Adele Marsh
Erin Messinger
Emily Oliver
Chevon Petgrave
Nancy Pham
Eloise Ravell
Amy Risinger
Ryan Roberts

Astrid Irene Rodriguez
Trish Sausa
Heroes Sical
Zakeya LaVonnya Sisco
Brandon Strachan
Cassie Van Barriger
Dianne Wagner
Alyssa Williams
Elizabeth Wilson
Rachel Wilson

SOUTHERN ARKANSAS UNIVERSITY, MAGNOLIA, AR

Bethany Brooke Barney
Haley Nicole Bird
Heather Lynn Gorman

Mia Nashawn Hyman
Cameron Keith Imler
Amanda Lee Levin

Cashae' Janea Louden
Joshua William
Misenheimer

James Sorrell Perry Jr.
Mallory Nichole Selman
Lindsey Adelle Wood

SOUTHERN ARKANSAS UNIVERSITY TECH, CAMDEN, AR

Nicole M. Boer
Amanda L. Mosley

Vonisha D. Murphy
Caleb N. Pryor

Logan G. Shaw

Lisa M. Sledge

SOUTHERN COLLEGE OF OPTOMETRY, MEMPHIS, TN

Katie Allen
Katie Araiza-Brown
Heather Nichole Atcherson
Feyi Aworunse
Marie Bolin
Alison Kate Bozung
Joseph Brewer
Daniel Brigham
Andrew David Brown
Frank Carusone

Carissa Michelle Chambers
Hunter Chapman
Fallon Nichole Cone
Halie Cottrill
Kevin Davis
Brooke Dugas
Elizabeth Fioravanti Ellison
Stephen Ellison
Emily Jane Evans
Gabe Fickett

Tony Fioravanti
Trent Gaasch
Molly Marie Goodman
Virgilio Palma Gozum Jr.
Angela Haas
Dahlia Haddad
Kevin Michael Hart
Andrew James Hawkins
Jessica A. Haynes
Hannah Holtorf

Craig E. Hossenlopp
Barbara Allane Jodoin
Daniel Kelly
Alanna Marie Khattar
Aja Leigh Kimrey
Tyler Kitzman
Elena M. Lopez
Scott McIntosh
Kirsten McKnight
Mark G. Miriello

John L. Moonan III	Enrique Palacios	Scott R. Ronhovde	Danyetta Thomas
Jacob Walter Muller	Jigna Arun Patel	Jordan Dirk Rothlisberger	Brittany L. Tounsel
Andrew Neighbors	Robert Phyfer	Jennyffer Smith	Preslee Trammell
Tri M. Nguyen	Michael Polo	Megan Stanford	Xuetong Wei
Brett O'Connor	Kay Powell	Gerald Stinson	
Nathan E. Osterman	Amy Arlene Puerto	Crystal Leigh Stone	

SOUTHERN NAZARENE UNIVERSITY, BETHANY, OK

Emily Margaret Bostick	Cheyenne JaRae Hornback	Andrew Leahey	Danielle Rouse
Andrew Griffin	Jacob Kyler Hubbs	Briana Raquel Mullens	Gentry Smith
Grayson Haws	Amy Lauver	Sierra Dawn Peak	Zachary Cole Trotter

SOUTHERN NEW HAMPSHIRE UNIVERSITY, MANCHESTER, NH

Caroline Elizabeth Fleming	Chelsea Gilmartin	Benjamin C. Harris

SOUTHERN UNION STATE COMMUNITY COLLEGE, WADLEY, AL

John Wesley Adcock	Paige Knight	Jada Ivana Russell	Eric Velasquez
Zoe Arrington	Alexis Wren Moore	Caroline Simpson	Gemelia LaSheena Welch
Lauren Carter	Quincy Morris	Catherine Simpson	Madison White
Ceara Cooper	Taylor Leigh Nappier	Colby Spears	Savannah Carol White
Winston Durbin	Calvin New	Leah Katlyn Stinespring	
Macie Alexander Edwards	Miranda Owens	Marina Sudduth	
James Howard	Auburn Taylor Potts	Melissa Talmage	

SOUTHERN VIRGINIA UNIVERSITY, BUENA VISTA, VA

Brenna Iris Aamodt	Brigham Scott Doxey	Wright Miles Noel	Reva J. Satchell
Gregg Benjamin Allen	Caleb Noble Dransfield	Rachel Elisabeth Northcott	Sarah Elizabeth Simar
Jacqueline Marie Barlow	James David David Drasbek	Jordon Zdzislaw Peterson	Linnea Faith Simcik
Cody W. Barnes	Katie J. Durrant	Ethan James Pike	Kailey Anne Simmons
Alicia Blackham	Desiree Gentry	Alan J. Porter	Scott D. Stoddard
Elizabeth Hope Bonney	Heidi E. Glauser	Nicholas Jay Porter	Rebekah Grace Taylor
Ashley Brooke Bryant	Lauren Hafen	Madeleine Gail Rex	Clayton Blair Trover II
Tyler J. Clark	Bronwyn Himes	Jose Roberto Rivas Cruz	
Larissa K. Conger	Leah M. Huber	Nathanael Benson	
Kathryn Wagner Crookston	William Samuel Mellor	Rodriguez	

SOUTHERN WESLEYAN UNIVERSITY, CENTRAL, SC

Jaden Bruce Aho	Monica Arms	Catherine Bradberry	Frank Thomas Campagna
Kalyn Kimberly Anders	Mona Lisa Arrington	Curtis Grey Brewer	Angela Faye Carlson
Antonio Anderson	Joseph Earl Banks	Kayla Lynn Britton	Bryan Wayne Carpenter
Lawanda C. Anderson	Joshua Michael Bishop	Sarah Melissa Bryan	MaryGrace Alyse Carter
Michael Grant Arblaster	Kaycee Adelle Blackwell	John M. Callaham	Carrie Regina Casali

Fallon Cierra Childress
Bryn Morgan Chuba
Reginald Lammer Clark
Daniel Walter Cochran
Haley Elizabeth Collins
Laura Marie Collyer
John G. Czarnick
Leslie Daniels
Jeanette Domingo
Ebony Renee Douglas
Elizabeth Ashley Edge
Anthony Leon Elmore
Britney Michelle Fernandez
Latoya Nasiya Gary
Shelby Loree Gilbert
Christina M. Gilliard
Yolanda Regina Green
Deborah Sheriba Greenlee
Jenna Marissa Griffin
Pamela Kay Grigsby
Jordan Douglas Hanner
Emily Paige Harper
Willie Anthony Harris
Matthew Joseph Heerschap
Angela Marie Herring
Joey Lynn Herring
Miranda Nicole Hill
Torey Hill
Benjamin Thomas
Hochhalter

Andrew Ryan Howard
Jonathan David Hunt
Stacey Louise Hunter
Brianna Ashley Hydes
Dwayne A. Ismail
Eric Adolph Jackson
Janene Sims Jackson
Stacy Marie Jackson
Wendell Lee James
Kara Shea Jones
Johnnie Alexander Julian
Sheldon Paul Juncker
Frank Allen Kelly
John Labrash
Chelsea Elizabeth
Lindaberry
Avanelle Addington
Littlejohn
Carsen Christian Long
Emilio Jose Lopez-House
Grayson Crews Lorenz
Jarrod Lee Lucas
Alexander Matthew Luna
Macy Lynn Martin
Patrice H. McCormick
Tammie E. McGowan
Margaret Anne McMenimen
Anna Kyle Moore
Nathan Reid Moore
Leah Joy Moorefield

Jacqueline Wayne Morgan
Cheyle R. Morris
Stephen Mullaney
Conikim Marie Nguyen
Alexandra Taylor Oakley
Laura McKenzie Page
John Franklin Peak
Cale William Peake
Jordan Elizabeth Peters
Samantha Hope Powell
Franklin Cole Price
Tamika M. Pringle
Michael George Quayle
Elizabeth Griffin Ranges
Sage Maddox Rebottaro
Christina Marie Reed
Samuel L. Richardson
Macee Leigh Riley
Kylie Joy Rovenstine
Cynthia Anne Rumsey
Tzarina San Pedro Salomon
Jeffrey M. Schultz
Mildred Elizabeth Shealy
Casey Elizabeth Shearin
Amanda Shannon Shirey
Avia Deneen Smith
Michael Corey Smith
Nicholas Turbo Starling
Stanley Orlando Stroman
Ronald Justin Taylor

Rebekah Thomason
Daniel F. Thome
Joshua Lee Tolan
Christopher Phillip Tubbs
Garry Turner
Lindsey Owen Turner
Michael Eden VanDorn
Sandra R. Vann
Barry Lewis Vaughn Jr.
Demetria B. Washington
Chelsie Nichelle Waters
Christina L. Webb
Kelsey Edwina Wheatle
Darren Keith White
Megan Jean Widener
Donna Lashun Williams
Harold L. Williams
Hope R. Williams
Kimberly Dawn Williams
Chanel Melissa Winbush
Andre Franz Winters
Erin Noel Winters
Monique Renee Wright
Monica Dori Young
Sentao Zhou
Wanda Diane Zorn

SOUTH FLORIDA BIBLE COLLEGE THEOLOGICAL SEMINARY, DEERFIELD BEACH, FL

Cristalia Anjos
James T. Cater
Kevin Clarke

Mark Linton
Fabio Mazzola
Daniel Mickles

Monica Alejandra Nieto
Michael Pettilli
Samantha Silva

Michelle D. Woodstock

SOUTH LOUISIANA COMMUNITY COLLEGE EVANGELINE CAMPUS, ST. MARTINVILLE, LA

Megan Ahlers
Latarya Alexander
Bryson John Allen
Shelly Arceneaux
Xavier Austin

Vanequa Bourda
Seth Champagne
Kristen Nicole Chautin
Joshua Clements
Riley Girouard

Jaliyah Lindon
Lainey Ann McNulty
Derrick Mitchell
Kiona Oliver
Suzanne Evette Parks

Kyra Rhines
Bergeron Robert
Mason Soileau
Alyssa Tiana Solomon
April Thiboudeaux

Grace Venable

Francois Victoria

Victoria Ward

Anthony Williams

SOUTH LOUISIANA COMMUNITY COLLEGE FRANKLIN CAMPUS, FRANKLIN, LA

Marqueline DeJean

Marlon Hawkins

Demetri Hines

Olveny Jacko

Ayana Jackson

D'tron James

Tina Johnson

Sade Lemon

Angelina Mack

Chance Medlock

Ronantranique Moore

Shareva Prince

Bella Robison

Angela Sophus

Maria Cristal Soria

Lacy St. Blanc

Taylor Alexis Thomas

Niyanna Tillman

Alexandria Walker

Aaron Charles Webber

Ashley Wilson

Wayne Yelling Jr.

SOUTHSIDE VIRGINIA COMMUNITY COLLEGE CHRISTANNA CAMPUS, ALBERTA, VA

Wade C. Bagley

Derrick Carpenter Jr.

Catandra M. Chavis

Kathy Robinson Drummond

Timothy S. Everman II

Colin M. Green

Cade A. Hamm

Monica D. McMillan

Faith A. Merricks

Jennifer Segura

Al L. Tucker

Richard N. Watson

Kaylin V. Weise

SOUTHSIDE VIRGINIA COMMUNITY COLLEGE JOHN H. DANIEL CAMPUS, KEYSVILLE, VA

Jessica L. Buchanan

John J. Butler

Michael D. Chewning

Roy A. Claiborne

Ellen C. Crowder

Elizabeth J. Dunn

Marcella A. Featherston

Trevor D. Goin

Christie S. Guillen

Dorothy Long

Eileen R. Ranck

Lisa M. Southall

Phillip L. Whitlow

Melanie R. Windsor

Ginger DeJarnette Yancey

SOUTH TEXAS COLLEGE, MCALLEN, TX

Abigail Alaniz

Adriana Alvarado

Adaylin Alvarez

Daniela Lizbeth Avilez

Esteban Arman Banda

Ana Barco

Shean Benares

Bianca Blanco

Matthew Callahan

Cynthia Lilliana Cantu

Daniel Cantu

Jazzmin A Casillas

Elias Castillo

Juan Castillo

Tamara Castillo

Yesenia Yvette Celestino

Paola S. Cepeda

Sarah Alexis Champion

Christopher Child

Michael Cortez

Jacob Covarrubias

Victoria Cruz

Gilberto Cuellar

Palmira Cusi Ramirez

Conor L. Davenport

Jesus Davila

Dalia Daw

Maria De Dios

Lizbeth De La Torre

Amanda Delgado

Gerald Delgado

Yesenia Ruby Diaz

Ariatna Flores

Cesia Elizabeth Flores

Cristina E Flores

Ivette Flores

Jose D. Flores Jr.

Heather Kristine Fry

Amanda Galindo

Cynthia Galindo Julian

Teresa Gallegos Campos

Liliana Lynette Galvan

Maria Galvan

Ali Josue Garcia

Juan Garcia

Christa Garza

Erika Garza

Joely Garza

Jorge Luis Garza

Julio C Garza

Sandra Lylia Garza-
Escamilla

Alexis M. Gonzalez

Jeanelly Alexis Gonzalez

Roman Gonzalez

Javier Octavio Gonzalez Jr.

Jennifer Guajardo

Kayla Carin Guajardo

Xitlali Yolanda Guerrero

Brandi Guevara

Erika Guzman

Andrea Hernandez

Cynthia Raquel Hernandez

Ariana Hinojosa

Cody Lee Hunt

Pedro Jimenez

Mary Johnson

Karina Juarez

Vit Kaspar

Patricia Kimmons

Katlyn Judith Kuruda

Lorena Ledesma

Joshua Little

Anthony James Lopez

Mara Lopez

Francisco Lopez Jr.

Fernando Martinez

Breanna Alexa Mata

Raul Medina

Stevan Mireles

Diana Moya

Juana M. Muniz

Jordan Navarro

Phuong Nguyen

Mayra Nunez Luevanos

Monica Nuno

Ana Ortega

Horus Ortega

Mariela Ortez

Geoffrey Pelletier

Alexis Pena

Priscilla Lee Pena

Monica Pena Lopez

Karla Lizeth Perea

Erica Perez

Javier Valentin Perez

Roberto Pina

Phillip Shayne Pruneda

Oluwaseun Quadri

Alexiya Ramirez

Anna R. Ramirez

Diana K Ramirez

Juan Ramirez

Karen Ramirez

Maggie Ramirez

Charles Reed

Melissa A. Renner

Adriana Reyes

Jonathan Reyes

Adrian Riojas

Lorena Rivera

Monica Rock

Alan Enrique Rodriguez

Antonio Rodriguez

Aylin Rodriguez

Claudia Rodriguez

Jose M. Rodriguez

Mark Rodriguez

Ethan J Saenz

Mariel Saenz

Aaron Salazar

Roberto Salazar

Viviana Salazar

Ryan Salinas

Amaris Judith Sanchez

Candy Sanchez

Conny Sanchez

Erik E. Sanchez

Lisa Sanchez

Arush Shekar

Stacie Solis

Stephine Solis

Michael Sorce

Weijun Tang

Erick Thompson

Leslie Marie Torres

Mark A. Tovar

Sara Vallejo

Amanda Vargas

Claudia Vasquez

Emily Vega

Liliana Vega

Miranda Vick

Karina Villanueva

Nicole Williams

Jessica Je Zamarripa

Karina Zamora

SOUTHWEST BAPTIST UNIVERSITY, BOLIVAR, MO

Miranda L. Abdo

Kacey M. Ayers

Dakota R. Bailey

Jeremiah O. Bechtold

Nick D. Bettis

Christian Hamilton Binger

Andrew P. Bryant

Katie K. Buzard

Cody W. Campbell

Miranda M. Carlin

Autumn L. Case

Leah K. Cleek

Darcy L. Cochran

Emily G. Cumpton

Tori L. DeClue

Ginger L. Dorrell

Reed E. Dressler

Jenna B. Durnell

Michael D. Dye

Lianne N. Elliott

Gretchen B. Endres

Wendy D. Farmer

Spenser A. Farr

Kathryn L. Fitzpatrick

Ashley N. Fox

Mary A. Fritchman

Travis H. Furtkamp

Erica M. Garcia

Aric Dale Gooch

Spencer R. Greathouse

Megan C. Hamilton

Tyler T. Hampton

Sandra M. Hatchell

Letty J. Hill

Ryan C. Hlousek

Betsy G. Jacobsohn

Austin M. Jenkins

Micah J. Jordan

Hannah J. Kirby

Tabitha L. Kohl

Brady R. Kornrumpf

Leann R. Lansdown

Catie E. Lathrop

Ashley A. Lawson

Julia F. Lewis

Stefanie C. Lischke

Patrick E. Love

Lindsey N. Major

Josh M. Mayfield

Marissa A. McClure

Davis P. McElroy

Caitlin E. McEwen

Christine L. McIntire

Tori K. Morris

Nathan I. Mourik

Courtney L. Munton

Olivia J. Newby

Abigail M. Norcross

James B. Norris

Daniel A. Ogunyemi

Caleb N. Olson

Blaise C. Onyiaike

Abraham L. Pascoe

Joshua D. Phipps

Abigail E. Porter

Hannah L. Rogg

Renae J. Sattazahn

Michelle R. Schulte

Matt S. Shaffer

Steven E. Skaggs

Aaron M. Sloan

Spencer T. Smith

Allison J. Sterling

Janie D. Story

Thomas J. Strubinger

Grant S. Teckmeyer

Maggie L. Thomas

Caitlin H. Tufts

Elijah P. Van Hoecke

Samuel Vergara

Emily J. Warren

Caleb P. Whaley

Joshua R. Wingerd

Beth Ann Winship

Michele N. Wyatt

Joshua A. Yuhnke

Ruoxi Zhang

SOUTHWEST COLLEGIATE INSTITUTE FOR THE DEAF, BIG SPRING, TX

Adel Khalid Al Hosani

Turki A. Al Mansoori

Abdul R. Al Nuaimi

Daysi N. Carranza

Wesley E. Diaz

Jacob P. Garcia

Diamonique V. Holmes

Nima Jafari

Aviv R. Levy

No Mi

Taylor H. Nguyen

Maydee F. Vande Hey

SOUTHWESTERN CHRISTIAN UNIVERSITY, BETHANY, OK

Ha Min Choi

Lisa Renay Chrystal-Pruiett

Hannah Glynn Hayes

Kodi Briana Celeste Horn

Taylor Toy Jordan

Andrew J. Leingang

Brenda Ann McClure

Kyle Jordan Mickleburgh

Steven Kindred Overstreet

Logan D. Palmer

Tanesha A. Ray

Renee Nicole Reeves

Tory Paige Sharp

Brenda O'Hern Six

Garrett Thomas Zollinger

SOUTHWESTERN COMMUNITY COLLEGE, CRESTON, IA

Cassandra Anderson

Teresa A. Arkfeld

Brenna L. Baker

Abigail R. Ballard

Makayla L. Boothe

London O. Collins

Chelsie R. Dukes

Sydney L. Dunphy

Samuel Eagan

Shelbie Sue Greene

Jordan A. Johnson

Tiffany R. Kinsley

Casey A. Ladd

Ashley Lucio

JoHanna M. McGuire

Chrystian William
Meisenheimer

Lane P. Miller

Paige M. Mitchell

Ahmad Newsome-Hyland

Gracie M. Russell

Chelsi J. Sams

Xochitl Santoyo

Jami S. Sickels

Josie L. Sickels

Madison M. Skarda

LaStella Slack

Sydney D. Suiter

Zoei T. Tonkinson

Kevin W. Torres

Fox M. Whitman

SOUTHWESTERN OKLAHOMA STATE UNIVERSITY, WEATHERFORD, OK

Kelsey Taylor Abernathy

Amanda Jo Ann Adney

Aileen Theresa Aiello

Megan Maree Allen

Emily Baalman

Shae Lauran Bates

Hunter Stevens Boatwright

Morgan Pearl Bressman

Caleb Everett Broce

Julie Brown

Feras T. Bukhari

Chance W. Bunch

Gwendolyn Erin Burgess

Kristi Lynn Burghardt

Austin James Cantrell

Samantha Rae Caudle

Kyle Stuart Chai

Valerie Anne Chain

Keely Ann Clements

Alison Leigh Clinton

Mackenzie Nicole Cochran

Kimberly Denise Coney

Lucas H. Coody

Casi Kennedy Cornell

Steven T. Cornell

Rachel Nicole Cowan

Thomas Tanner Crandell

Colton R. Danyeur

Brian T. Dao

Ethan T. Davis

Laura Mozelle Davis

Renee Davis

Selamawit A. Dejene

Kristina Dixon

Jessica Mae Drake

Kortney S. (Meyers) Duffy

James M. Ely

Sarah Nicole Evans

Kaitlyn Anne Feterly

Erin Elizabeth Fields

Diana Michelle Flood

Nathalia Francio Concenza

Mackenzie Nicole Gifford

Nathan Dewayne Godfrey

Michael-Joseph Gorbet

Jordan Alyssa Grubb

Ricardo E. Gutierrez

Samuel Grant Hale

Bethany Kate Hawkins

Yolanda Hilburn

Benjamin Dale Hill

Connor Claye Holland

Bryan Dean Holt

Taylor Michelle Holt

Sierra Genevieve Hopson

Clinton Dean Horn

Zachary Whitney House

Kristen Taylor Howard

Mason Ray Howe

Rhiannon Grace Jensen

Sawyer Nicole Johnston

Ashley Kaytlin Jones

Shelby Lynn Josey

Ashton Marie Jung

Andrienne Lapewe

Ngapepoua Epse

Tina Trinh Le

Somi Lee

Tzu-Chi Lin

Jesse N. Lingerfelt

Audrey Blair Little

Lucas D. Little

Karlee Jordan Loula

Maureen Franceska
Matousek

Baylee Cheyenne McBride

Jessica McClure
Brooke Ann McCullough
Nile DeLawrence
McCullough
Erin E. McGuire
Kody Z. McKay
Abby Ursula McKisson
Ashley N. McMahon
Christian Matthew Meeks
Nikole Mingura
Angela Lynn Morgan
Kendra Dawn Morgan
Brendan K. Moser
Krystina Rachelle Muralt
Jennifer Elise Nail

Morgan Nance
Khanh Kelly Nguyen
Phuong Thanh Hoai Nguyen
Xuan D. Nguyen
Amy Michelle Ousley
Jared Thomas Owens
Bethany Mae-Marie Peyton
Nathan Phillips
Ashley Noel Pickens
Hailee Ranee Platt
D'lisa Pool
Taylor Edward Rains
Jesus J.R. Ramirez Jr.
Travis R. Ratcliffe
Christopher Wayne Revard

Rebecca Reyes
Haley Nicole Rogers
Jeff E. Roland
Whitini Marie Root
Jordon Kaly Sage
Carla Renee Salcido
Anthony Mitchell Sanchez
Jason Edward Sanders
Britton Alexandra Scott
Brooklyn Elizabeth Scott
Steven Blake Scott
Nathan Philip Seigrist
Emily A. Selby
Autumn R. Sellers-Caldwell
Emma N. Siegmann

Otoniel Alexander Soza
Kourtney Speece
Colin James Stallcup
Patricia Dianne Steadman
Christopher James Stevens
Jay Scott Stinson
Rachel Taber
Canisia Bongfen Tatah
Shea Lynn Thornbrugh
Allison DieuThao Truong
Makenzi Alexis Wagner
Jesse James Wald
Suni Re Williamson
Lori Ann Young
Hui Yi Zhen

SOUTHWESTERN OKLAHOMA STATE UNIVERSITY SAYRE, SAYRE, OK

Cody Nicholas Boulware
Kurtis Donald Clark
Bailey R. Daugherty
Erick Jovany Garcia

Brittney Michelle Jones
Marketa Antoinette Jones
Morgan Rachel Jones

Xochitl Fabiola Marquez
Rodriguez
Dakoda Lane Patton
Rachel Allison Randall

Brandy Sanders
Kelsie Lynn Shockey
Britney Marie Widener
Jennifer Anette Wing

SOUTHWESTERN UNIVERSITY, GEORGETOWN, TX

Christopher Bryer Adams
Egan Cornachione
Christina Kimberly Crandall
Meili Criezis

Afsoneh Esfandiari
Patrick Garza
Amy Gu
Sebastian Gualy

Nyokabi Kamau
Emma McDaniel
Mitchell Petersen
Mihaela Radu

Allison Schmitt
Taylor Vickers
Mia Zozobrado

SOUTHWEST MISSISSIPPI COMMUNITY COLLEGE, SUMMIT, MS

Brady R. Anderson
Kelly Lane Arnold
Emily Noel Ashley
Kayla J. Baldwin
Maurey Bland Jr.
Justin Marquise Blue
McKenzie Lee Brock
Myandra K. Brown
Vincent Antwon Calhoun Jr.
Ashley Nicole Coleman
Aurora Diaz

Sanetra A. Forbes
Keasia S. Gray
Christian O'neal Green
Caitlin G. Harrell
Abigail C. Hooks
Reed Lawrence James
Kaylee C. Johnson
Tayler Danielle Jones
Earlisa Matthews
Jana Kristen McEwen
Christien M. McIntosh

Liliana Gina McKnight
Harley Marie Menard
Reagan M. Myers
Bernard N. Nichols Jr.
Seth Andrew Nieman
Georgia Mae Osby
Danaraye C. Parks
Jessica Drue Penton
Brandy A. Powell
Lacee Dalana Quiroz
Katelynn N. Roberts

Lafayette Rutledge
Joshua A. Samander
Kristen M. Scarberry
Jonathan Tyler Shell
Lillie Snowden
Matthew John Stillman
Sarah Henning Tanksley
Brookyln V. Westmoreland
Aaron J. Wilkinson
Benton Brady Wilson

SOUTHWEST TENNESSEE COMMUNITY COLLEGE, MEMPHIS, TN

Megan L. Buscher

Jeannie Dulay

Bryan A. Henson

Nichole A. Jones

Michael A. Leverett

Janal L. Mason

Mustafa A. Muhammad

Taylor Joseph Page

Cassie Richardson

Jennifer Richardson

Ashley R. Shores

Breanna Taylor

Valencia Williams

SPARTANBURG METHODIST COLLEGE, SPARTANBURG, SC

Emma Christine Alexander

Avery Ashley

Austin Bess

Robert Bryant

Jacqueline Carter

Frederic Daniels

Randy Duncan

Christina Earley

Elizabeth Gort

Esther Green

Brittany Halter

Alexa Kerley

Kaitlin Kizer

Alaina Kummer

Eliza Long

Robert McAbee

Ashley Newton

Nina Overton

Shameia Rosier

Cierra Smith

Grayson Smith

Hope Smith

Tyrone Smith Jr.

Amber Briana Sumpter

Jesse Turner

Deanna Unger

SPENCERIAN COLLEGE, LOUISVILLE, KY

Mallory Faith Biggs

Melissa Ann Coleman

SPRING ARBOR UNIVERSITY, SPRING ARBOR, MI

Molly Anderson

Shannon Balcer

Lucas Barres

Rebekah Bentz

Karen Chanchavac

Connor Cheyne

Elizabeth DeGraaf

Holly Doerner

Andrea Janelle Finkbeiner

Benjamin Frederick

Molly Gorczyca

Maria Gail Gray

Taylor Richard Hawkins

Katlyne Heath

Morgan A. Lee

Anthony Mayotte

Steven Patrick Murphy

Morgan Postma

Dillon Rahill

Joshua Riddick

Reuben Rubio

Bryan Zinn

SPRINGFIELD COLLEGE, SPRINGFIELD, MA

Tyler Joseph Abate

Jessica M. Beausoleil

Audrey B. Brown

Brittney A. Cleary

Kelly Ann Diurno

Oliver Figuereo

Solkeren Figuereo

Michael L. Fletcher

Stephanie N. Foster

Taylor A. Friedman

Emily Casey Gins

Elizabeth A. Hart

Samantha J. Hill

Chris J. Jurkowski

Denee Lazariel

Keziah S. Love

Bibiana Andrea Medina

Colleen B. Mistler

Paige Elizabeth Moran

Simone G. Morin

Abigail E. Mulligan

Gregory A. Neal

Courtney L. O'Connor

Marissa E. Puchalski

Ashley N. Randall

Donna Simpson

Audrey C. Smith

Niya R. Solomon

Joshua D. Swain

Amanda L. Upchurch

Natalie A. Waechter

Erin R. Washington-Martin

Mikayla D. Wysocki

Amanda V. Zacchia

SPRINGFIELD TECHNICAL COMMUNITY COLLEGE, SPRINGFIELD, MA

Simone Baptiste

Michael Caine

Juhi Anushka Dasrath

Victoria Gour

Melissa Rosario

ST. CLAIR COUNTY COMMUNITY COLLEGE, PORT HURON, MI

Nicole Christine Barth

Kristina Marie Bowen

Kathy Renea Brady

Nicholas Ryan Brandon

Clark

Nicholas Ryan Davis

Adrianna Lee Doutry

Elizabeth Ann Green

Jillian Renee Helsom

Katelyn June Hunckler

Alan K. May

Cole Thomas Meyers

Megan Maxine Pitts

Mark Ira Spencer

Julie Ann Tirakian

Tyler Scott Wessel

ST. JOHN FISHER COLLEGE, ROCHESTER, NY

Jill A. Alaimo

Emily M. Brenner

Mary A. Frazier

Tiffany A. Gregoire

Emily A. Jacque

Tim J. Johnsen

Kelly M. Lampman

Olivia J. Lopez

Briana M. Macaluso

Jan E. Marchetti

Jessica F. Monroe

Michael S. Montemalo

Colleen T. O'Connor

Lauren A. Owens

Michaella M. Pilla

Lindsey L. Rivet

Anthony S. Rodriguez

Cody A. Schweickert

Makenzi L. Swartwood

Natalie E. Tuites

ST. JOHNS RIVER STATE COLLEGE, PALATKA, FL

Raymond Antwan Anderson

Willie Clyde Beaton II

John S. Blackman

Teresa Ann Borzilleri

Brandon Scott Buzard

Gerald T. Cahalane

Maria Lourdes Diaz Sanchez

Kasey L. Driggers

Giselle Marie Feliciano

Gregory Arthur Francois

Ashely Nicole Gloyd

Joseph M. Grosso

Aaron Gregory James Harris

Elizabeth Ashley Harris

Harlan Griffin Harris

Lindsey Carlyle Hayes

Maureen Elizabeth Wright Hernandez

Julianna Augusta Hicks

Jessica Rachelle Jacobs

Averi Gabrielle Jones

Hunter R. Jones

Rebecca Kolb

Derrick L. Lee Jr.

Joseph Samuel Loe

Martine Louis-Charles

Savannah Lee Montgomery

Katelyn Marie Patterson

Carol Ann Schwartz

Gary Lavonne Scott Jr.

Ashley Brooke Smith

Hannah M. Sommers

Rebekah Sookdeo

Zachery B. Taylor

Tina Maria Terranova

Andrew Christian Toelken

Andy Arnold Tzul

Omar F. Villaman-Larancuente

Glehn Paul Von Loh

Wesley Michael Weeks

Lucas Wayne Welch

Sara P. Welch

Dalton Shane Whitaker

Anne Marie Widener

Haley Annemarie Wildes

Shannan Marie Wood

Catharine Amelia Yates

ST. JOHN'S UNIVERSITY, JAMAICA, NY

Melissa Amato

Damanjyot Kaur Anand

Nicole Ariza

Paige Felicia Band

Cody Joshua Barber

Sebastian Enzo Bonnici

Gabriel Carrilho Camara

Jordan Canela

John Carleton

Justine Nicole Caruselle

Daniel Guagliardi Chen

Kenneth Ryan Ciszak

Wendy Marilu Claros

Jasmine Arielle Clyde

Frederick Dai

Maria Filindarakis

April Renee Gardner

Kayla L. Geier

Kristen Marie Greto

Naila Habeeb

Sarah Maria Hanna

Seahrish Javed Hashmani

Lauren Marie Ippolito

Michael Timothy John

Lauren Jorgensen

Kiara Kevelier

Krystal Kim

Maurisa C. Li-A-Ping

Erin Lutley

Jasiel Kwame Nhyirale

Martin-Odoom

Ridge Duane McKnight

Colleen A. O'Brien

Della Jillian Rao

Kevin Roan

Jennifer Paige Ross

Marissa Ruotolo

Zubia Sagarwala

Anthony Paul Sansone

Megan Schoenberger

Perri Cierra Sweed

Victoria Rose Tenpenny

Talia Gloria Tirella

Leah Todd

Thalia Toro

Gregory Vella

DeAnna Young

ST. JOHN'S UNIVERSITY STATEN ISLAND CAMPUS, STATEN ISLAND, NY

Sabrina Alvarez

Joseph Anzalone

Julio Bedola

Bailey Cammarano

Mark D'Alicandro

Ramzy Dawoud

Valentina Gioffre

Chelsie Green

Dante Landi

Caralina Marie Lawless

Michael Lazzarotti

Joseph Marinaro

James McKeon

Marina Mikhael

Raffaele Montuori

Victoria Frances Volpe

ST. LOUIS COMMUNITY COLLEGE FOREST PARK, SAINT LOUIS, MO

Abenezer Adale

Komlan Mawuli Agnigni

Sinhareeb B. Aloleiwi

Almira Arnold

Jerome Arnold

Jennifer Auxtero

Michael Earl Bady Sr.

Stacey Bats

Anne C. Beach

Riquita Bible

Lauren Blagajcevic

Chelsea Booker

Steven Borthick

Renada Marie Bridgett

Stephanie Brown

Martin Cheng

Zhaohong Cheng

Timothy Cole

Astra Coleman

Walter Cornethan

Don Costales

Harold Crawford Jr.

Prince amoabeng Danso

Pserah Darling

Kayla Danielle Deevers

Grant R. DeFord

Melissa De Wever

Umer Dido

Makenzie Eidson

Jennifer Emery

Amber Eslow

Nicholas Adam Farace

Susan M. Furkin

Sarah Garavaglie

Lisa Garrett

Selamawit Ghirmai

Alyssa Nichelle Gibson

Vanessa Rae Hardin

Chester Henderson

Michael Hobbs

Laurie Ann Hofer

Khamh Bawi Hum

Abdullahi Issak

Twuna L. Jackson

Dione Jenkins

Essence Jenkins

Mia Jenkins

Angela Johnson

John Johnson

Romona Johnson

Leslie Johnson-Dailey

Diamond Jones

Sharay Jones

Sharay Jones

Sonia Nadine Jones

Jennifer Jordan

Chikumbutso princess

Kachiwaya

Nicole Kilbride

Dakota Kolb

Iryna Kucheryaba-Ryan

Kyndal Lawrence

Mandi Leonberger

John Lippard

Michael F. McCluskey

LuAnne R. McKenzie

David McLaurin

Crystal Nicole Melching

Samuel Paul Middeke

Alissa Miller

Haile Miller

Angela Minor

Araceli Mora

Joseph J. Mungoma

Frunwi Ndukum

Bee Hoang Nguyen

Marinda Nha

Melyn Niewoehner

Izuchukwu Okonkwo

Jennifer L. Oliver

Karen Penn

Emily Phillips

Joshua Piper

April Politte

Mallory S. Pruemer

Gilbert D. Ramirez

Kaylee A. Reagan

Mary-Theresa R. Roam

Chad Robinson

Anne-Marie C. Rohrbacker

Claudia Romero

Jamie Roper

Andrew Colt Ruger

Naomi Russell

Elizabeth Russom

Denis Sales

Sharon Sanders

Toni Sanderson

Elizabeth Scherer

Lauren Schiller

Meagan Schreiber

Najma Sherzamin Sherzoy

Jessica Simora

Amber Spangler

Porsha Stewart

Robert Taylor

Safal Thapa

Elvira Thomas

Myesha Thomas

Strickland D. Tonya

Felicia Topel

Sara L. Tracy

Kendall Troxel

Ishmael Tumpe

Jazmine Tutwiler

Suzanne Varda

Kristin R. Vo

Martuis Walker

Stephen Walker

Virginia Ward

Fiqow Wehliye

Dawn M. Williamson

Elizabeth Womack

James Wright

Abel Yajabi Niyayaegma

HyeonWoo Yang

ST. NORBERT COLLEGE, DE PERE, WI

Taylor Baltus

Brooke Elisabeth Draxler

Kelsie George

Sara Gionet

Gregory Grohman	Quincy Kissack	Allison Parra	Corinne Stingl
Tyler Hacker	Alexis Klismet	Brenna Theresa Rathsack	Gretchen Stutz
Elena Herrera	Erin Knipp	Nate Ruehel	Emily Vetter
Hannah Kestly	Olivia Koehn	Brittani Nicole Seidel	Nicole Zellner

ST. PETERSBURG COLLEGE, CLEARWATER, FL

Roberta Spathari

ST. PETERSBURG COLLEGE HEALTH EDUCATION CENTER, PINELLAS PARK, FL

Heidi Lynn Altonburg	Anthony Chang	Alexander James Kerekes	Adrienn Somogyi
Kathryne Anderson	Adam Cortez	Lindsey Metzler	Nida Stang
Andrew Ashmead	Bryan Ray Doehleman	Melissa Morgenstein	Jennifer Swartz
Ailyn Avila-Portal	Joanna Duncan	Patrick Murphy	Egle Vaitkeviciene
Ashley Bisson	Elizabeth Eannottie	Emily Anne O'Brien	Chinetanaphone Vixayarazh
Nicole Carney	Nancy E. Gribnitz	Laura O'Keefe-Fontaine	Chrystal Wiener
Marina Carroll	Emily Johnston	Alireza Parishani	Kyle Workman
Rachael Carson	Charles Jones	Crystal Saeger	Elizabeth Denise Yuravich
Veronica Castillo Jones	Charis Blake Kelly	Amber Smith	

ST. PHILIP'S COLLEGE, SAN ANTONIO, TX

Leah Vaughan Adams	William Larkin Derendorf	Kurt Thomas Kucera	Kevin Bruce Poole
Ali Mahmood Alazzawi	Stephen Aldie Dewese	Lisa Landin	Marissa Elise Ramey
Dayron B. Alvarez Hernandez	Tess D. Elliott	Brian Curtis Likens	Jessica Ramirez
	Michael Alexander Ferrer	Enoc Torres Lopez	Lindsay Renae Ridge
Stephen Patrick Aney	Albino Flores	Morgan Leilani Lucas	Brian William Roach
Matthew Jay Astudillo	Norman Dualan Flores	Christopher Stephen Martin	Isaac Humberto Rodriguez
Nicholas Jordan Bautizta	Vidal Franco	Irene Matimba Mukaina	Iuliana Rodriguez
Sabrina Michelle Bosquez	Alexis Nadine Freire	Judith Louise Mayrand	Kevin Joseph Rose
Amira Nicole Boyd	Glenn Gafford	Jay Mitchell Mccoy	Garrett T. Rouse
Clayton Gary Bridges	Ruben Matthew Garcia	Dawn Marie Mcgill	Shelby Marie Rumsey
Audrie Iliana Cabrera	Abigail Carol Grathwohl	Genevieve G. Mendoza	Jamie Suyapa Salazar
Cady Lois Calhoun	Antionette Grove	Megan Leigh Meyer	Francisco Saucedo
Ashley Diane Calkins	Carrie Renee Grubbs	Benjamin James Mickens	Nicholas Michael Scalercio
Stephen E. Canedo	Yolanda Nicole Guerra	Beatrice Eva Maria Monroe	Marlena Rose Schirmer
Jose Leon Cantu	Jesse James Guerrero	Vanessa Feleene Netherlain	James G. Sedillo
Brandy Kristen Cardona	Alyssa Ramirez Gutierrez	Christopher Olivarri	Michael Rene Serda
Jalyssa Estele Carranza	Max Bruce Hernandez	Alexander Ovalle	Steven Silva
Jesus Eduardo Castro	Bobbi Loreen Hill	Gabriella Paris Noel Pawelek	Esmeralda Rodriguez Staudt
Lydia Joy Congdon	Joey Jimenez		Aaron Michael Stevens
Kasey Tayler Crank	Marcus Dwayne Johnson	Tasheka Latrice Pearcey	Ruben Surles
Keibian J. Crumedy	Keith Jaymeal Jones	Scott Collin Petersen	Makenzie Lynn Taylor
Patrick James Delgado	Nathan Alexander Kilgore	Carla E. Ponce	Cassandra Alysa Valadez

Jose Villarreal

Malcolm Simon Ward

Cheryl Williams

Jeffrey Frederick Witt

Jonathan Louis Yantas

Jennifer J. Yoo

Elizabeth Irene Zavala

STATE TECHNICAL COLLEGE OF MISSOURI, LINN, MO

Austin Adams

Corey Adams

Roxanne Alden

Kollin Anderson

Ashley Asher

Mackenzie Ashmore

Spencer David Bachmann

Luke Baker

Bryan Bear

Lexi Boehm

Patrick Boessen

Dane Bonnarens

Elizabeth Grace Boyd

Jake Butts

Chancelar Carrender

Michael Chernookiy

Robert Clay

Ashley Colter

Jamieson Crockett

Mark Deutschmann

Daniel Dove

Tabitha Dye

John Fick

Gary Galeski Jr.

Nicholas Haslag

Jason Henggeler

David Hohenstreet

Cassidy Jacquin

Juliette Jaegers

Sherri Kennedy

Reese Kerlin

Joseph Kilper

Jonathan Klott

Zack Kucsik

Erica LaBoube

Andrea Monroe

Jacob Moseley

Peter Oliver

John Orf

Madison Perkins

Derek Peters

Clark Philbert

Britney Prenger

Cody Russell

Justin Lee Schaefferkoetter

Patrick Schau

Kevin Schilling

Russell Shoemaker

John Sommer

Tyler Loren Struemph

Tyler Troesser

Kyle Verslues

Michael Ware

Charles Watkins

Tanner Weyrauch

Collin Williamson

Wade Wilmes

STATE UNIVERSITY OF NEW YORK AT DELHI, DELHI, NY

Nicole Bishop

Seth Capela

Rachelle Cassatt

Megan Cheylyn Davis

Selena Catherine Deeley

Andrea Griebel

Chynah Harden

Caitlin M. Jones

Deanna Knapp

Kathleen M. Lennon

Alexis Alexandra Lowe

Yuka Matsumoto

Stephanie Peccia

Morgan Phelps

Alexia Deborah Quintina

Ploetz

Jessica Lynne Reimertz

Szarina Saunders

Elizabeth Simpson

Nicole Smith

Fuyuri Someya

Justin Terry

Tania M. Zuniga

STATE UNIVERSITY OF NEW YORK BUFFALO–GRADUATE SCHOOL, BUFFALO, NY

Traci S. Aladeen

Amanda Allen

Allison Altman

Jennifer Andrews

Archis Bagati

Kathleen Blackburn

Brittany Boland

Melina R. Bowdwin

Brian M. Bowman

Rachael Burganowski

Michael Burns

Daniel Cartwright

Bibaswan Chatterjee

Mary Coble

Robert Coleman

Crystal Collado

Sidney Coombs

Eric Coombs Esmail

Ari Darlow

Sarah Dascanio

Gauri Desai

Joel Destino

Nitasha Dhillon

Sara L. Ditursi

John Lewis Etter

Zeinab Farhat

Peter R. Fendt

Andrea Gentzke

Jacob A. Gertz

Joshua Gordon

Yvette Granata

Xiaosu Guan

Sarah Hayes

Adam W. Heiermann

Chloe Higginbotham

Anna Hourihan

Brittany Iannone

Katelyn Imagna

Neriy Izkhakov

David Jacobs

Shelby E. Janutol

Matthew Johnson

Stephanie Kellner

Junghan Kim

Kayla Kuehlewind

Jessica A. Kulak

Sree Kurup

Susan LaValley

Elizabeth Lessner

Morgan Lester

Lauren Litvak

Mia P. Magliazzo

Ceilia Mah
Alexandra Markus
Samantha Matthews
Michael Thomas Mauri
Dustin McCall
Kathryn Michalek
Albina Minlikeeva
Andrew C. Mocny
Bryan T. Mogle
Irene Isoken Osagie
Alexandra Oshinsky
Gregory Oswald

Srikanth Parameswaran
Ciera L. Patzke
Angela Pieprzak
Zuwena Plata
Carly Poccia
Samantha Rose Podlas
Emily Pukos
Laurie Rich
Kathryn Roberts
Ben Robinson
Patrick G. Rose
Ashley Rosenberg

Shannon Rudolph
Rajavi Sanghavi
Antara Satchidanand
Gopika Shah
Amy Shaver
Adam Sheppard
Tatiana Shilina-Conte
Ryan P. St. James
Kaitlyn Stayzer
Krysten Stoll
James Brian Szender
Gianna Taglioni

Carly Vandergriff
Stanzi Vaubel
Jun Wang
Youjin Wang
Wit Wichaidit
Anne Wilson
Natalie S. Winters
Alfred Yeung
Sultan Zain

STATE UNIVERSITY OF NEW YORK CORTLAND, CORTLAND, NY

Jess Barton
Tyler Bouvia
Stefania Buta
Elliott Michael Butler
Matthew Castoral
Caysea Cohen
Rebecca Cornell

Matthew Cretaro
Brittnie Daugherty
Kyle Davis
Ricardo Destinvil
Corrine Edick
Connor James Griffin
Jeffrey Hock

Brooke Hughes
Kristen Ann Kircher
Lindsey Leclair
Kristie Marie Mauro
Kelly Marie McKenna
Deanna Meunier
Matthew Oswald

Natalie Perrigo
Meghan Peysson
Stephanie Rice
Jennifer Scheu
Karyn Lyn Scott
Kathryn Slattery

STATE UNIVERSITY OF NEW YORK NEW PALTZ, NEW PALTZ, NY

Rami Abouemira
Dani Ackerman
Jacqueline Aguilar
Rabih Ahmed
Chabreah Alston
Jenna Marie Anzalone
Giselle Benitez
Stephanie Faye Black
Rebecca Borquist
Jenisse Bouret
Sarah Broughton
Ariana Carbonaro
Kimberly Cincotta
Marie D'Apice
Nearlyse Anne Dandas
Rachel Dragos

Adriana Dulmage
Stephanie Inez Fernandez
Christopher Fusco
Elizabeth Gottlieb
Nicole Gottschalk
Michael James Grossman
Ian Hart
Morgan Hennessy
Helen Huang
Colleen Murray Jones
Kimberly Lynn Kallansrude
Raquell Kissi
Dylan Ann Krakowski
Kathleen Rose Leach
Nicholas Magnanti
Amanda Maldonado

Kerry E. McKeever
Diana Metz
Caitlyn Morris
Paige Olscamp
John Alan Owens
Hannah Phillips
Jesse Michael Pilnik
Shelby Leigh Platia
Devorah Price
Rachael Purtell
Alen Quints
Tusha Devi Ramnarine
Jessica Marie Restivo
Paola Rodriguez
Daniel Rosado
Christina Rose

Dylan Louis Rose
Joseph Russo
Akeem Samuels
Emily Sarra
Sabrina Courtney Sarro
Forrest Schaffer
Emily Susan Vanderpool
Paola Vargas
Alyssa Volpacchio
Chelsea Rose Weir
Betsy Wiener
Brett Wisner
Erica Yu
Jacob P. Zyskowski

STATE UNIVERSITY OF NEW YORK PLATTSBURGH, PLATTSBURGH, NY

Kathryn Aguilo

Fredrica O. Appau

Brianne Lynn Bello

Sonia Elizabeth Bennett

Olivia Kaitlin Cahill
Allyson Centola
Maria Emanuele
Danielle Farron
Jennifer Greenberg
Robert Greenspan
Cari Lewis

Molly Lundgren
Jessica Manning
Joseph Manzione
Veronica Marchello
Claire Marie Martuscello
Kelsey Elizabeth Mitchell
Samuel Brian Mozingo

Liana Nobile
Kelli Proscia
Shannon Rudy
Steven Gabriel Segarra
Amy Sheldon
Shanae Tiara Spruill
Alexandra Noel Stockman

Breanna Marie Syslo
Carly Tarullo
Daniel VanPatten
Lateef Wearrien
Dorian Abigail Yablin

STEPHEN F. AUSTIN STATE UNIVERSITY, NACOGDOCHES, TX

Amy Renee Allen
Elizabeth Anglin
Samantha Baker
Sydney Lynne Baker
Halee Balser
Da'Kecia Berry
Ashley S. Beverly
Zane Edward Bora
Courtney Reed Branton
Ryan Brewer
Berenice Saez Briceno
Audra Bridges
Symone S. Brooks
Lauren Brown
Alexandra Burke
Alexandra Caballero
Alyssa Capin
Gwendolyn Carmichael
Henry Balmore Chica Jr.
Katelyn Daniele Childress
Berkelely Church
Brianna Marie Clark
Elizabeth Clark
Elizabeth Crist
Megan Briana Curtner
Zachary Daugherty
Jordan D. Day
Carley Dewitt
Morgan Dison
Whitney Dugat
Alhajie Kwasi Dumbuya

Daniel Fansler
Courtney Danielle Flynn
Jacob Fripp
Lucina Garcia
Caitlin Gerval
Veronica Gilliams
Matthew Rudy Gonzalez
Brandi Mae Gouldthorpe
Haile Granberry
Tatum Mallory Greer
Claudia Yvette Guzman
Whitney Leigh Haddox
BreAnna Hall
Madison Beth Head
Kyle Edward Henkel
Jacqueline Hernandez
Ciara Holiday
Shonda Hortness
Brianna Durel Horton
Bryan L. Humphrey
Sarah K. Hutchins
William Huynh
Mara Ingersoll
Jordan Jeffreys
Mercedes C. Jones
Aundra L. Joyce
Rickelle Jacqueline King
Marc Klekar
Aubrey E. Laurent
Jazzlyn Charnae Layton
Jaydriana D'Shae Lister

Shelby D. Little
Katie Elizabeth Long
Brent Loving
Micaela Ruth Lumpkins
Victor Hugo Maciel-Contreras
Emmanuel G. Malana
Ashleigh Nicole Martin
Curt D. Mathis
Macie Mattila
Megan McCombs
Lahanna Lanae Miguez
Madelyn Minton
Jenny Nance
Amanda Lynn Nedbalek
Megan Katherine Nichols
Lilly O'Shay
Vanessa Yvonne Orellana
Dharti Badrish Patel
Nicole Amber Pennington
Rebecca Prince
Diana Guadalupe Ramirez
Maria Cristina Ramos
Laken Ray
Sydney Taylor Reed
Jared Ricks
Kyle R. Ripley
Ray Robberson
Denise Rocha
Danielle Denise Rogers
Ashley Nicole Schuenemann

Rebecca Ann Showalter
Brionne Smith
Emily Michelle Smith
Florina Soto
Julie Regan Spivey
Timothy Robert Stephenson
Cynthia Cryer Stewart
Timothy J. Swift
Tara Talley
Timothy Tang
Meaghan M. Tannehill
Haley Kay Tate
Katherine Taylor
Kareene A. Telesford
Chisolm Tessem
Ryan H. Thomson
Taylor Alan Todd
Doran Triggs
Amanda K. Tucker
Rosie Elizabeth Vega
Mary Dru Dru Wagner
Brittany Nicole Whiting
Samantha Nycole Wilkinson
Erin Michelle Williams
Katelyn Windham
Charise Sabah Wolo
Ryleigh Yates
Andrea Rodriguez Zermeño

STERLING COLLEGE, STERLING, KS

Melissa Rose Abousamra
Isaac Barnhardt
Chad Bennett
Emma Birky
Micah Black
Kate Brickell
Lacey Buckwalter
Madison Caffrey
Jennifer Calderwood
Kristin Calderwood
Brionna Clayton

Haley Davis
Isaiah Delsi
Amanda Del Toro
Caleb Ray Gaeddert
Matthew Garrett
Kacie Hastings
Elizabeth Herrington
Amanda Hood
Joshua Hoover
Esther Jenkerson
Stephanie Keith

Abigail Landis
Joshua Landis
Evelyn Mandell
Christina Leah McFerrin
Austin Mettling
Katie O'Brien
Paul Oswald
Rachel Padro
Keith Price
Troy Quenzer
Hayley Ray

Matthew Rich
Erika Rojas
Jacob Schimenz
Grant Speer
Summer Stanley
Jamie Tilton
Tennissa R. Williams
Megan Yoder

STEVENSON UNIVERSITY, OWINGS MILLS, MD

Nicholas Adams
Jessica Laura Arminio
Issa Bangura
Edward Alfonzo Bennett
Emily Jayne Benton
Linnea Alice Bleacher
Allyson Elizabeth Bowers
Grace Elizabeth Bowman
Revae Marchelle Boykins
Elisha Charlise Bradsher
Kristen Glenne Brooks
Lexus Renee Brooks
Shawn Donte Brown
Shannon Breana Burt
Justin Wendell Butler
Yasmine Aquiesha Byrd
Ryan Dillon Callinan
Joseph Michael Carlineo
Angel Monique Carter
Corinna Danielle Carter
Ruth Adelina Casadevall
Kristen Nicole Cassetta
Carli Taylor Castiglia
Tyler Nicole Chaney
Kaveri Chhabra
Brooke Elizabeth Clariday
Rachel Sujata Clein
Alexis Kimberly Cohen

Julia Cooke
Jacqueline Albertha Cooper
Kimberly Simone Crout
Abigail Patricia Czajkowski
Matthew Robert Daryman
Sharie Mae Gonzales David
Valerie Sagaoinit De Mateo
Ryan A. Diepold
Megan Lee Donovan
Charles Alfred Douty
Ryan Matthew Drazenovic
Daniel James Ebsworth
Aishani Eggenberger-
Lipschitz
Jessica Norton Eisenberg
Marisa Lee Elrick
Shaunae Monique Evans-
Wheatley
Alexis Shantel Fitch
Casey Scott Fitzgerald
Blake Andrew Ford
Larry Douglas Fort
Gerald Isaiah Foster
Clayton Reid Foxwell
Megan Elizabeth Garrahan
Kali Diane Gill
Brianna Ormena Glen
Allison Leigh Goodwill

Calvin James Granger
Alicia Carol Greene
Andrew James Grimm
Erick Christopher Guzman
Prince Kwabena Gyamfi
Emily Carole Haas
Kimberly Rose Hahr
Meagan Elizabeth Hardesty
Corrin Marie Harris
Erica Camile Hatcher
Ashlyn Taylor Hawbaker
Rachel Haley Haywood
Amanda G. Hinch
Molly Beatrice Hoyt
Matthew John Hughes
Robert Everett Hunt
Antonio Clyde Johnson
Sarah Catherine Johnston
Adrianna Vivien Kamosa
Elizabeth Glenda Kamosa
Alexis Rose Kapp
Samiya Andrea King
Lauren Kimberly Kiper
Kaitlin Marie Kirkwood
Jeremy Tyler Kline
Ashley Anne Koepping
Kevin Ogden Kopas
Katlyn Alexis Lamp

Elizabeth Ashley Lau
Thao Uyen Mai Le
Kenneth McCoy Lewter
Heather Kristine Lopiano
Emily Anne Losquadro
Sade Tiara Lucas
Ni N. Lwin
Jessica Lynn Mahla
Ryan Daniel Martin
Stephanie Marie Martinez
Elizabeth Pen Marx
Paige Elizabeth Maykut
Michelle Lee McDonald
Kevin Michael McDonough
Kelly Rebecca McKenzie
Mollie McGrain Meeder
Grier J. Melick
Stephanie Alyce Miele
Hannah Maree Milburn
Gretchen Mattingly
Milchling
Margret Grace Miller
Emily Ann Mills
Jon Stephen Moffett
Sara Magaly Morales
Zachary Justin Morris
Kristen Marie Mueller
Matthew Wayne Myers

Abdallah Malik Naanaa	Ashley Lynn Raup	Brooke Elizabeth Sexton	Sarah Marie Tweedle
Abbey N. Neuberger	Chloe R. Redmond	Danielle Terese Shanahan	Sherrie Andrea Wallace
Shahrose Noman	Kijon Antonique Renfroe	Amanda Reed Shetterly	Kameron Lynn Ward
Estefania Giron Nunez	Matthew Jong Roberts	Lauren Marie Shields	Deneen Joyce Watson
Hannah Joy Nusbaum	Emily Lynn Rosenthal	Marisa Elisabeth Sigler	Regina Lee Weber
Amanda Gayle Oppenheim	Christopher Ryan Rothmann	Shelby Alexandra Skarda	Neil James Westdorp
Courtney Mae Parto	Caitlin Eileen Roy	Alena Avi Solanki	Katlyn Denise White
Rachael Lorraine Patterson	Rachel Gabrielle Rudo	Gregory Scott St. Clair	Mackenzie Gene Wieder
Nicholas Alexander Peifer	Tyler Alexander Rutherford	Tavon Jamaal Stanley	Taylor Elizabeth Wiley
Megan Kylee Polis	Arwa Mahmoud Salhab	Kelsey Louise Stave	Robert Philip Wingert
Joshua William Powell	Erin Samantha Schapiro	Sarah Jean Swan	Emily Frances Wolf
Tyler Daniel Price	Claire Elizabeth Schindler	Kathryn Rose Thompson	Paige Alexandra Worthy
Leanne Mary Rafferty	Brittany Noelle Schultz	Lydia Arnall Tippett	Jason Michael Yingling
Emma Nicole Ragon	Colleen M. Scobie	Megan Brooke Toms	Savannah Kaye Yoder
Francesca Maria Raimond	Brett Daniel Louis Self	Christopher George Toth	Margaret M. Zimmermann

STEVENS–THE INSTITUTE OF BUSINESS & ARTS, ST. LOUIS, MO

Jessica L. Boewer	Derrick Smith	Brittni Whitaker	Sheriko White

STOCKTON UNIVERSITY, GALLOWAY, NJ

Carl Archut Jr.	Jessalee Rose Cruz	Theresa Margaret	Danielle Nicolette Simmons
Tahira Ayub	Ryan Earl Dever	McMackin	Cherie Marie Sloan
Aaron Bess	Christine Easton	Anh T. Nguyen	Alia Rae Smith
Marwah Bhatti	Leigh Fisher	Nicolas J. Persia	Nico Zane Smith
Liana Buccino	Nelson Gonzalez	Gabrielle Richardson	Patton Wayne Solowey
Jayson Cabrera	Cassandra Tiann Hrusko	Kristina Sabado	David William Somers III
Katelyn Clayton		Maryam Sarhan	Sarah Anne Voishnis

SUFFOLK COUNTY COMMUNITY COLLEGE, SELDEN, NY

Natanya Allen	Jamie Castro	Margaret Hartofilis	Bonnie Nielson
Derek Andersen	Adiba Choudhury	Jeff Hein	Peter Oliva
Ashley Andexer	Samantha D'Amico	Brandon Heinrich	Katrina Pilla
Colm Ashe	Olivia Del Vecchio	Samuel Imperato	Daniel Pritchard
Dean Bauer	Andreanna Diaz	Kristine Jankowski	Julie Quinn
Sonia Blue	Clarence Edwards	Deanna Keen	Juan Ramon
Robyn-Marie Bohne	Jill Franke	Justin Lerner	Alexander Rufrano
Vincent Bonilla	Amanda Friedman	Matthew Lofmark	Matthew Sclafani
Michael William Brenkert	Christina Georgia	John Lynch	Shezad Shah
Kerry Briscotti	Ricardo Gonzalez-Argoti	Lucia Mallozzi	William Smith
Carlos Cabo	Tatiana Alessandra	Hannah Michaelson	Brent Swike
Sarah Calire	Gonzalez-Argoti	Jessica Nelson	Cheick Sy-Savane
John V. Cannata	Alisha Hartmann	Brandon Nguyen	Emily Vaughan

| Ashley Vetter | Valerie Vogele | Cassandra Whelan | Emirhan Yeniduya |

SUFFOLK COUNTY COMMUNITY COLLEGE EASTERN CAMPUS, RIVERHEAD, NY

Chrstion Adams	Jacqueline Marie Frigano	Sydney Mackenzie	Bryan Passanant
Angelica Aguirre	Cinthia Gaitan	Alexis Melendez	Julia Petersen
Tatiana Banks	Lina Maria Garzon	Barbara Mellace	Celine Marie Rogan
Jennifer Elizabeth Brown	Christine Graf	Christopher William	Duane Silvera
Amanda Caliguiri	Aylin Eda Guvenc	Molchan	Cassidy Whelan
Natalie E. Camp	Tony Huynh	Evelyn Maribel Morales	
Sean Deery	Emily Jensen	Valverde	

SUFFOLK COUNTY COMMUNITY COLLEGE MICHAEL J. GRANT CAMPUS, BRENTWOOD, NY

Nkrumah C. Gordon	Michael Lindner	Joshua Robert Mendez	Maksym Tsar
Daniel Harper	Clarissa Marquez	Michael A. Porter	Leorelkys Villar
Rachel A. Heinicke	Christopher H. Melz	Anam Y. Rabbani	Briana Warnken

SUFFOLK UNIVERSITY, BOSTON, MA

Tiffany M. Alves	Zachary A. Fayne	Michael Jon Lapolla	Maaz M. Satti
Sarah K. Anderson	Nicole Fell	Jiaming Liu	Courtney Danielle Schopke
Adriana Bazoberry	Christopher P. Frangolini	Colin F. Loiselle	Shelby Nicole Somelofske
Monica Rose Caggiano	Daniela Coromoto Galindo	Elainy Mata	Theresa N. Stevens
Brendan J. Clifford	Patete	Connor M. McCarthy	Erika D. Tabares
Erin G. Cooper	Thomas C. Gaudet	Kara A. McCormack	Tamara Fabiana Fernandes
Amy E. DalCanton	Nathan R. Giordano	Enuamaka Mkparu	Tavares
Colleen O'Connor Day	Andrea Gonzalez Corleto	Caitlyn R. Mockler	Joy W. Thairu
Rachelle H. del Aguila	Serina K. Gousby	Molly E. Morris	Alicia M. Villett
Aayush H. Desai	Megan K. Graves	Megan N. Murphy	Zachary C. Werth
Ralitza D. Dountcheva	Reed T. Guerino	Rebecca Jeannick Ndawana	Jennifer L. Wilczynski
Danisha Mikah Dumornay	Xenia W. Hersey	Christina Pellegrino	Morgan L. Williams
Rebecca K. Eshoo	Elizabeth A. Hurley	Kanika Rajiv	
Kristen Nicole Farah	Amy Lyn Kerr	Andrea P. Ravikumar	
Christopher S. Faria	Felicia M. Krentzman	Lyndsay M. Reese	

SUL ROSS STATE UNIVERSITY, ALPINE, TX

Laura G. Cardona	Guadalupe M. Harris	Adrian J. Maldonado	Reba C. Smith
Arilene Carrasco	Aaron Herrera	Jacqueline M. Moses	Casey D. Sonier
Cencee S. Gordon	Christina L. Kile	Karina B. Rodriguez	Krystal D. Tanner
Dustan A. Greer	Ryan C. Kubena	Alejandra Ruiz	Meagan L. Thompson
Meghan Alanna Hammack	Danielle M. Lucero	Allyson A. Scown	Yancarlo Villa

SUL ROSS STATE UNIVERSITY GRADUATE PROGRAM, ALPINE, TX

Timilehin David Alake	Asrelle A. Anderson	Karlee D. Cork	Ernesto Garcia-Ortega

Matthew C. Hall

Alexandria M. Hassenflu

Christopher D. Jackson

Ashlee D. Krebs

Mitchell A. May

Billy W. Overton

Aryel C. Ramirez

Clarissa R. Stolte

Melissa Wallace

John S. Wilkins III

Ruoxi Wu

SUL ROSS STATE UNIVERSITY RIO GRANDE COLLEGE, UVALDE, TX

Kathylina L. Acosta

Beatriz Avila

Krystal S. Ballesteros

Brandy L. Callis

Roberta Susan Coleman

Alicia G. Dowell

Christa M. Flores

Walter Galindo

Alejandra G. Gonzalez

Luis J. Huerta

Gerardo A. Lopez Jr.

Faith M. Musquiz

Emmauel B. Odin

Jesus A. Ortiz Jr.

Joselyn Ponce-Romo

Darlene Quintero

Alyssa R. Quiz

Gerardo Ramirez

Maria L. Reyna

Ricardo L. Vasquez

Daniela Velazco

SUMMIT CHRISTIAN COLLEGE, GERING, NE

Dustin Daniel Amack

Sarah Amack

Stephen Hayner

Emilie Lorraine Jones

SUMMIT UNIVERSITY, CLARKS SUMMIT, PA

Ciara Altieri

Joy Angelica Faith Baxter

Adam C. Benjamin

Amanda J. Benton

Kathryn Rose Borne

Drew Bundy

Karen Butler

Liam Degnan

Diane Ebert

Caroline Grace Farrar

Jeremy Fodge

Robert J. Greathouse

Chelsea Hanna

Andrew Joel Hartley

Josiah Hayden

Michaela Height

Joelle Howard

Rachel Janho

Allison N. Kelley

Bliss Anne Lecea

Kevin Lorow

Marissa Martindale

Daniel Timothy McDivitt

Megan Miller

Jorge Molina

Aaron James Morin Sr.

Rachel Morris

Garrick Paden

Nicholas Emerson Peters

Keegan Pulz

Jason Regnier

Alyssa Rockefeller

Sarah Schlenker

Lauren Shepherd

Alaina M. Stevens

Emily Thompson

Zachary Alan Thompson

Daniel Trout

Kayla Underwood

Peter A. VanVolkingburgh

Anthony Vincent

Kirsten Weber

Hannah M. Westphal

SWEET BRIAR COLLEGE, SWEET BRIAR, VA

Brittany Nicole Agee

Charlotte Rives Barbour

Katelyn Ashley Craig

Madison Mae Cromwell

Emily Morgan Dallas

Morgan Nicole Deal

Julia Friend Eckstine

Lydia Nichole Fleck

Kiersten Jade Johnson

Garcia

Meredith Elizabeth Haga

Megan Kaitlyn Johnston

Shaniqua Clinnie' Jones

Katriana Nicole Jorgensen-

Muga

Madalyn Nicole Lee

Briana Lynae McCall

Shannon Margaret

McCarthy

Mary Stuart McDevit

Hailey Beaudry Montalbano

Jessie Ruth Schuster

Torrey M. Schwartz

Caroline Paige Shepard

Megan Ellen Shuford

Molly Elizabeth Van Buren

Calee Nicole Whitten

TABOR COLLEGE, HILLSBORO, KS

Dylan J. Algra

Spencer J. Baalman

Catherine E. Christie

Jennifer A. Crist

John J. Jedneak

Tena L. Loewen

Kristen E. Martens

Matthew W. Molden

Garrett D. Nikkel

Daniel J. Quiring

Carly M. Rowan

Kaleigh M. Troxell

Katey L. Whitesell

Joshua C. Wiebe

Celeste M. Worthy

TALBOT SCHOOL OF THEOLOGY, LA MIRADA, CA

John Barnewall
Trevor D. Behrns
Derek N. Brover
Andrew W. Campbell
Michal Lea Casement
Alysha P. Choi
Andrew S. Choi
Ji Hyong Hyong Choi
Analicia J. Davis
James W. Davis
John Do

Joel S. Elies
Michael S. Giesenhagen
Samantha K. Guzzi
Joel D. Hampton
Nicholas D. Harmon
Susan K. Heath
Janelle D. Henson
James Kiju Jang
Taeho Jung
Andrew Kang
David Kim

Myunghun Kim
Peter B. Ko
Ji W. Lee
Joshua Lim
Kyle C. Lundquist
Angel Meiyee L. Mang
Todd M. Morehead
Jean S. Park
Nicholas R. Perkins
Craig S. Petrovich
Paul S. Rheingans

Steven J. Schultz
Hayden C. Stephan
Daniel R. Stermer
Emily A. Stevens
Nicolas S. Tam
Zachary W. Taylor
Elizabeth A. Ward
Kari E. Watrous
Brent M. Worthington

TALLADEGA COLLEGE, TALLADEGA, AL

Lawrence Allen
Andrew Ashraff
Victoria Bates
Jamie Binns
Imari Blackwell
Marvin Braden
Kanila Brown
Derek Brumfield
Daniel Bryant
Derrick Calvin
Naeshaun Collins

DaJoseph Crawford
Briel Dawson
Augusto Garcia
Johnny Garcia
Sophia Harmon
Terrance Harris
Skye Hendon
Katelyn Hester
Gabriel Matias
Clinton McCoy
Maria McElderry

Laterria McKinney
Rasaunti McKinney
Pamela Miller
Maiya Minor
Audrey Morgan
Drake Mosley
Shala Owens
Myron Parker
Tia Peralta
Famel Restrepo
Theodore Thompson

Kelli Tipton
Ashlie Volpe
Charles Walker
Ronald Wallace
Craig Whatley
Blair Wheeler
Wanda Williams
Reginald Wills
Brionna Young
Eduvigis Zapata

TARRANT COUNTY COLLEGE NORTHEAST CAMPUS, HURST, TX

Mohamed Fahad Aboosally
Cesar A. Baltazar
Jack Tuiasi Burgess
Jeff Bruce Cantrell II
Scott Franklin Collins
Donna de Lisser
Meagan Kendall De Weirdt
David Foust

Joan Cesar Garcia
Emily Beth Hildebrand
Micah Hybarger
Erin Kitching
Manav Lamichhane
Joshua Michael Lynn
Benjamin Materne
Steve McCarty II

Michael Sekasozi
Muwanguzi
Juliet Mukiri Mwirigi
Nyanak Ngouth
Quynh Nguyen
Matthew Alexander
Pandolfo
Carlos Reyes

Rebecca Marie Reyes
Hannah Rachelle Rodriguez
Tiffany Lynn Smith
Jeni D. Talkington
Patricia Paulina Tiscareno

TARRANT COUNTY COLLEGE NORTHWEST CAMPUS, FORT WORTH, TX

Okiemute S. Aganbi
Dania K. Albashiti
Lissete Alcozer
Mary A. Alex
Anvaar Al-ghaziani

Haley M. Allen
Ronni Robyn Allen
Pirouz Allivand
Gerardo Zepeda Andrade
Ximena Arista- Zapata

Esther Azubike
Elizabeth F. Balderas
Summer A. Barrett
Nicholas G. Bonavia
Travis L. Brents

Madeline A. Brown
Jamie A. Burres
Andrew W. Burson
Jennifer L. Cantu
Christian A. Cardona

Altwin Carter
Amber C. Chadwick
Stephanie A. Chavez
Obinna R. Chibueze
Deana M. Cleger
Roger A. Courtney
Nicholas J. Crowder
Quinten L. Cruse
Daniel Cruz Villalpando
Garmai H. Cummings
Asheal A. Davis
Leslie C. Deal
Traclyn A. Deck
Vuong D. Do
Nang K. Dong
Courtney L. Duet
Hunter A. Filson
Natalie Flores
Franklin Edwin L. Fontelera
Steven S. Ford
Robert G. Frazier
Angel Gallardo
Annie N. Garcia
Juan R. Garcia
Jacob T. Gehringer
Weiwei Geng
Carlos A. Gomez
Austin J. Gonsoulin
Juan J. Guzman
Danielle L. Haley
Sean B. Haltom
Eric K. Hays Jr.
David W. Heller
Brian A. Hernandez
Andres Herrera
Jason Hinostroza
Thach N. Hoang

Emily Katherine Hopkins
Christopher R. Houston
Joel H. Howard
Lisa S. Hubbard
Jimmy Huynh
Kristine G. Jacobs
Justin W. Jordan
Tyler C. Kerns
Jonathan A. Kilgore
Cody M. Landers
Laura L. Langwell
Travis G. Lavoie
Laura J. Lee
Raen E. Levendoski
Eddie A. Lopez
Sierra A. Lopez
Jay C. Love
Rebecca G. MacDonald
Franchesca J. Magana
Christian J. Maize
Allison Claire Manning
Shane A. Marshall
Zynthia S. Martinez
Kirk A. Mathews
Michael A. Mayfield
Autumn V. McGaha
Marcia M. McGown
Morgan A. Michael
Lisa D. Miley
Donna L. Mills
Terry L. Mills
Jimmy E. Minero Reyes
Lawrence Mnang Kembuh
Erick E. Moreno Mendoza
Robert J. Morrell
Elizabeth N. Moss
Kafui A. Nadjombe

Giau T. Nguyen
Phuong N. Nguyen
Donna G. North
Israel Valentin Olivo
Lilian Ongaki
Claudia F. Ortega
Brenda Y. Ortiz
Emmanuel A. Ortiz
Emmiliany M. Ortiz
Monica M. Patak
Thomas E. Patty
Natalie L. Perez
Heather L. Perry
Colin T. Petty
Sean T. Pfarr
Joseph A. Piccola
Gavin M. Porter
Brent A. Rachall
Hugo Ramirez
Evelin Z. Reedus
Diego Rey
Cristian G. Rivera
Rosa M. Rodriguez
Jan L. Rogers
Neil A. Rohan
Jessica Ruiz
Colleen C. Rupert
Julie A. Sainer
Rosa E. Saldivar
Michael J. Salvador
Julian M. Schneider
Cody R. Scogin
Chassidy D. Seidmeyer
Cherryll S. Sipe
Aden R. Slay
Allison N. Smith
Jason P. Smith

Whitney C. Smith
Zeltzin A. Soto
Jeremy D. Spivey
Elizabeth R. Stephenson
Savannah G. Sutton
Azarah C. Swayne
Alexander G. Tidwell
Veronica Torres
Cindy L. Tran
Nhan Tran
Phuong Tran
Tuyet Tran
Jose I. Urvina
Kyle Valenti
Lizette Valenzuela
Veronica Valles
Juan C. Vasquez
Grant Vaughan
Matthew Vinson
Alyson Waddell
Benjamin J. Wagner
Hannah E. Wall
Peyton Marye Wallace
James D. Webster
Benjamin Webster-Brockette
Laney B. Wicker
Rachel Wieda
Chase B. Wiley
Catherine Williams
Diane M. Wood
Morgan Wood
Sarah M. Wynns
Kaylin Yochum
Jarett S. Zimmerman
Ben Zoltner

TARRANT COUNTY COLLEGE SOUTHEAST CAMPUS, ARLINGTON, TX

Qussai Abuawad
Samantha Alvarado
Ogechi Beauty Amadi
Anisa Avalos

Lauren Sydney Butaud
Daniela Castro
Huong T. Dinh
Precious Dunamis

Sahar Javed
Saran Kaba
Hong Thi Le
Rubi Macias

Shalaundra Antanette
Clarice Manning
Reginald Mckenzie
Kiela Moseby

Joel Tsasa Ngoma
Phat Nguyen
Quinn Nguyen
Vinh Nguyen

Adedoyin Esther Opara
Dawn Osborn
Jaymin J. Patel
Amanda Gayle Roach

Laura Rodgers
Taylor Arleene Smith
Elizabeth Nkemdilim Ukaa
Nathan Wade

Bilkis Alolade Wahab
Lysa Young

TAYLOR UNIVERSITY, UPLAND, IN

Megan E. Adams
Nate Aeilts
Wilson Hunter Alexander
Tyler Harrison Amann
Jessica R. Arbuckle
Nicole Ann Arpin
Kayleigh Danae Avery
Tobi Elisabeth Ballantine
Brian Danae Ballinger
Shayna Dale Balting
Deborah Joy Barnett
Keith William Bauson
MacKenzie Gabrielle Bedor
Joseph Patrick Bedwell
Abbey Joy Benson
Caitlin Elizabeth Bergman
Leah N. Blachaniec
Brennan Lucas Bookmyer
Avery Jackson Boxell
Abigail T. Brewer
Lydia G. Burchett
Megan Ann Bushman
Keith Logan Cantrell
Grace B. Carver
Chris Su Chang
Bryan Alexander
Charbogian
Camila Chiang
Emily J. Cho
Noah M. Clayton
Taylor M. Coats
Wynn W. Coggin IV

Alexis Jade Colón
Rachel Florence Cook
Zach Cook
Erin Beth Cooper
Eric Cameron Croft
Aaron Michael Crull
Noah Edward Cutshaw
Sam Monroe Davies
Katie DeHaan
Rachel E. Diamond
Abby L. Dyer
Ryan Sentman Ericson
Djamina Chrismene
Esperance
Rebekah Ruth Estes
Tia E. Etter
Grace E. Fairfax
Daniel J. Ford
Hanna E. Foster
Mary G. Fox
Austin Thomas Friesen
Meghan Nicole Gamble
Delaney Kathryn Getz
Kerri Ann Guffey
Matt Michael Hall
Jane Catherine Hawks
Samuel Thomas Ellis Hill
Erin R. Hoeft
Hannah Mae Hood
Elyse Janee Horb
Patrick Mark Hubbard
Taylor Hughes

Will C. Hussey
Alex Jackson
Ruth Marie Jansen
Chris Steven Jordan
Justice Alexander Juraschek
Joel Peter Kiers
Felissa J. King
Kaitlin R. Kinnius
Evan M. Koons
Haley Marie Kurr
Shawn Andrew Lashbrook
Kasey B. Leander
Mara J. Lombardi
Anna Kathleen Lothe
Katherine Marquez
Sarah A. McLeester
Mackenzie Marie Miller
Evan T. Miyakawa
Alex Wesley Moore
Daniel Joseph Morrison
Austin James Munn
Leah Renee Murphy
Julia Rose Oller
Samantha A. Petersen
Lauren N. Pfeifer
Maggie Michelle Plattes
Parker Maxwell Rea
Charlie O. Richert
Morgan A. Riessen
Hannah R. Schaefer
Katie E. Schantz
Jessica E. Schulte

Courtney A. Selle
Garrett Wyler Shanks
Jennifer Marie Shepherd
Natalie Lane Smiley
Emily Grace Smith
Katherine C. Smith
Danielle Marie Spoutz
Landon Alexander Stuart
Lathan Andrew Stuart
Jesse L. Stutzman
Savanna A. Sweeting
Elisa Ruth Tanquist
Zack S. Taylor
Lukas A. Thill
Blythe E. Todd
Veronica June Toth
Gabby Carole Trudeau
Morgan Marie Turner
Josh W. Urban
Nicole Alexandra Walker
Davis Allen Wetherell
Jillian Nicole Wilhelm
Lizzie L. Wilson
Rachel Katherine Wisz
David W. Wright
Chris M. Yingling
Brooklin Rae Young
Luke S. Yrastorza
Rachel Joy Zandee

TEMPLE UNIVERSITY AMBLER CAMPUS, AMBLER, PA

Victoria Uritsky

TEMPLE UNIVERSITY BOYER COLLEGE OF MUSIC & DANCE, PHILADELPHIA, PA

Sean Bailey
Kendra Balmer
Adam Barth
Maria Bauman
Michelle Bell
Eldon Blackman
Jennifer Borgwardt
Julie Grace Boyd
Daniel Brooks
Thieny Bui
Abby Carlozzo
Chen Chen
Long Cheng
Heeyoun Cho
Hee Jin Chung
Mariela Sofia Cifuentes
Jesse Clark
Sabrina Clarke
Mitchell Davis

Sean Davis
Madelaine Dijs
Alexandra Noelle Dovgala-
Carr
Kailey Dowd
Katherine Elizabeth
Dufendach
Marissa Renee Emmerich
Chad Fothergill
Brandon Frankenfield
Ronnal Freeman
Paul Futer
Casie Marie Girvin
Marianne Lee Gruzwalski
Olivia Gusmano
Sam Harris
Gretchen Hull
Tammy Huynh
Emily Kirsh

David Koh
Brooke Lemchak
Nicole Leone
Andrew Litts
Emily Mahoney
Sean Patrick Markey
Francis Markocki
Meghan McFerran
Mack Meyer
Chelsea Lilliana Meynig
Kathryn M. Moore
Aviva Muskin
Timur Mustakimov
Isabella Ness
Michael H. Newman
Andrew Payne
Marly Paige Pred
Dylan J. Principi
Nicole Renna

Susan Riley
Ajibola Jeremy Rivers
Sarah Rosenberg
John Saint Clair
Christopher Schelb
Kyle Scheuing
Stephen Selfridge
blythe Erica Smith
Victoria Tamburro
Jeffrey Torchon
Pamela Turowski
Andrew Unger
Austin Wagner
William Whalen
Zachary Winger
Daniel Richard Young
Muyu Yuan

TEMPLE UNIVERSITY SCHOOL OF PODIATRIC MEDICINE, PHILADELPHIA, PA

Jessica M. Arneson
Thomas B. Birdwell
Gurvikram S. Boparai
William H. Brownell
Anthony G. Brutico
Kristen R. Cadieux
Jared J. Cicero
Francois V. Dijour
Matthew J. Dougherty
Emmanuella M. Eastman

Arwa M. El-Sayed
Robert N. Ezewuiro
Chinenye Q. Ezike
Mark A. Fillari
Katherine Anne Florio
Tayyaba T. Hasan
Scott J. Hudzinski
Wesley A. Jackson
Margaret T. Kerins
Matthew C. Kujat

Woojung Lee
Elena S. Manning
John A. Martucci
Adam R. McDonald
Melissa R. Millili
Samantha A. Miner
Katlin A. O'Hara
Kevin P. Patel
Gledi Peco
Kevin J. Perry

Brian S. Rougeux
Joseph D. Rundell
Phillip M. Savage
Urja J. Shah
Jodene B. Shwer
Ethan A. Simoneau
Jennifer A. Skolnik
Kimia Sohrabi
Alexandra R. Spangler
Jeffery C. Zimmerman

TEMPLE UNIVERSITY SCHOOL OF THEATER FILM & MEDIA ARTS, PHILADELPHIA, PA

Cara Aguado
Guillermo Alonso
Razan Al-Salah
Jaad Asante
Daniel Barland
Madeleine Bishop
Amy Blumberg
Allison Boyle

Joel Chroscinski
Vanessa Crespo
Jon Diaz
Madeleine Ehrlich
John Fahey
Francesca Gallucci
Hannah Gold
Brice Goldberg

Kathryn Hannahan
David Jannetta
Cody Knable
Nathan Landis Funk
Nicholas Ligon
Tianyao Ma
Eli Marsh
Lian McFalls

Alexander Monsell
Christopher Murray
Kevin Murray
Kristen O'Rourke
Mark Partridge
Mengxi Rao
Tyler Rudolph
Kristen Scatton

Paige Smallwood
Karol Valencia

Gabriela Watson Aurazo
Apollo Weaver

John Yearley
Emily Young

Zhuoying Zhang

TENNESSEE TECH UNIVERSITY, COOKEVILLE, TN

Jonathan Clark Abbotoy
Hannah K. Benjamin
Kimberly Diane Biggs
Ashley Lin Bybee
Stacey C. Clark
Cory Joe Fuqua
Shelby E. Fuqua

Matthew Curtis Hege
Serena Marie Ingram
Neng Yuan Lan
Elissa Marie Longfellow
Emily Sarah McCracken
Tyler W. McNew
Luke Nakamoto

Savannah Mary Nevans
Emilee Katheryn Robertson
Justin Alan Rose
Nicholas Alexander Russell
Emily Ellyse Schiller
William Wade Seagrave
Madison Taylor Stephens

Whitney Elaine Stevens
Miranda Elizabeth Stoltz
Sarah Ann Tate
Houston Allen Vincent
Alison Nicole Wheatley
Justin Brady Wiser

TENNESSEE WESLEYAN COLLEGE, ATHENS, TN

Gad Azulay
Karena Denise Baker
Shasteena Michelle Baliles
Hannah Marae Brazer
Samantha Dianne Breedlove
Stephanie L. Bridges
Thays Rodrigues Cardoso
Courtney E. Colson

Tiffany K. Dierden
Chase Vincent Freeman
Emily Lauryn Gay
Emily Michelle Green
Jill Melissa Howard
Rhonda Renee James
Brett Matthew Longwith
Jonathan Dustin Love

Brookelyn Nicole Martin
Bridgett Diane Matthews
Rachel Anne Offutt
Lauren Elizabeth
Oglesby-Stuart
Brittany LaShae Payne
Mariana Moraes de Lima
Perini

Kiana Spenial-Leigh Pickle
Jenna Lin Riemenschneider
Jacob Michael Simmons
Misty Dawn Smith
Rita Marie Trythall
Kira Nicole Wade
Marissa Michele White

TEXAS A&M UNIVERSITY, COLLEGE STATION, TX

Roland Matthew Alonzo
Morgan Elizabeth Anderson
Elora Francena Arana
Lance Badoni
Jaskirat Singh Batra
Andrew Dean Baxter
James Colton Beall
Kacy Elizabeth Beck
Kimberly Cae LaPearl Berry
Cameron Taylor Blizzard
Claire Theresa Brandt
Santiago Andres Ceron
Robert Kyle Cook
Mary Antonia Crimmins
Brendan Kaleb Crouch
Soheil Ebadat

Annalisa Augusta Erder
Evan Anthony Flores
Elizabeth Marie Freeman
Peyton D. Fry
Kallie Nicole Fuchs
Thomas Aaron Fuller
Alexander Fabian Garcia
Brian Henry George
Sarah Elizabeth Gibson
Yucheng Guo
Hunter Alan Heaton
Robert Alexander Hill II
Jessica Michelle Hoffman
Alexandria Coszette Howard
Layeeka Mohamed Ismail
Adam John Kellen

Sarah Alexandra Knop
Colleen Marie Konetzke
Collin Matthew Kruger
W. Hayden Troy Lander
Kristi Marie Leonard
Mark Thomas Lutz
Maura Kramer Lytle
Maddison Ryan Malone
Abel Steven Mathew
Jordan Asher McKinney
Conner McQueen
Alyssa Marie Michalke
Michelle Althea Mitchell
David Jacob Moore
Karlie Rose Mueller
Nicholas Ryan Page

Jennifer Rangel
Laura Danielle Reid
William Walker Ryan
Cesia Margarita Sanchez
Callie Anne Scheffler
Taylor Nicole Stolt
Jenna Lynn Sutton
Matthew Harrison
Vanderbloemen
Derek Christopher Vincent
Nicholas Phillip Warner
Scott Michael Weaver
Sean Gabriel Whitney
Zachary John Roger
Williams
Connor Thomas Yancy

TEXAS A&M UNIVERSITY CORPUS CHRISTI, CORPUS CHRISTI, TX

Yuliana Isamar Almanza

Shanice Armstrong

Katherine T. Blake

Brandi Lynn Brast

Cole Castleberry
Katarina Chapa
Ronisha Christie
Sylvia Del Bosque
Derek Drozd
Rachel Edwards
Alexis Samantha Enriquez
Edelmiro Garcia Jr.
Alexandra Corrin Gittings
Jeremy Gonzalez
Rita Marie Guerra
Larry Guerrero
Rebecca L. Holmes

Emily Margaret Gayle
Howard
Oluwatoyosi Florence Idowu
Anthony L. Jaramillo
Hunter Johnston
Carl Wayne Juenke
Yunjoo Kim
Elena Kobrinski
Juan Martinez
Aaron Daniel Moss
Andrea Multer
Huong Nguyen
Ivette Perez

Maria Alejandra Puentes
Austin Reed
Joseph William Reustle
Mayra Rodriguez Gomez
Avery Elizabeth Scherer
Cassidy Scott
Kimberly Smoots
Shellby Soto
Nicholas Spalt
Erin Spann
Mara Rose Stonebrook
Nicole Stotts
Kayla Ariel Stovall

Hailey Sutton
Becca-Lee Frances Thomas
Erica S. Thompson
Conner Tichota
Uma Maheshwari
Venkatesan
Lauren Walker
Kelsey Lorraine Willems
Sophia Zaner
Arlene Zuniga

TEXAS A&M UNIVERSITY KINGSVILLE, KINGSVILLE, TX

Xenia Liza Adrian
Isabella Aguirre
Rawan H. Alhaddad
Carson Alsop
Achiaa Attakora
Amaniampong
Sambhavi Amarapalli
Javier Arizpe Rodríguez
Zachary Arnold
Juan Arreola
Illiana Avila
Scott Ayala
Luis Antonio Balderas
Trevor Baldwin
Hunter Balzen
David Barrera
Jessica Barrera
Iliana Guadalupe Bernal de
Contreras
Snehaben Bhakta
Vineeth Bharadwaj
Mrutyunjay Bhavanam
Mitchell Bro
Francois Brou
Joshua Burke
Clayton Campbell
Meagan Victoria Cantu
Marissa Carabajal

Rina Jeanette Castillo
Mikayla Cepeda
Jay Chaudhary
Flor I. Contreras
Isabella Patricia Cordova
Jazmine Coronado
Brandon Darr
Boukary Diallo
Marija Dimitrovska
Dylan Dimock
Kaley Dodd
Kenneth Dsouza
Nnana Edmund
Nancy Espinoza
Whitney Yewamide
Fakolade
Damian Martin Feeney
Caitlin Fleming
Aidan Flores
Corina Fuentes
Patricia Galindo
Razil Garbacz
Matthew Garberding
Ashton Garcia
Christian Garcia
Theresa Elizabeth Garcia
Audrey Garza
Onelisa Garza

Synthia G. Garza
Jared Gillam
Anthony Gonzalez
April Gonzalez
Claudia Gonzalez
Eric Gonzalez
Trevor Gonzalez
Alexis Greene
Daniel Gress
Elyse Grilli
Damian Guajardo
Benjamin Guerrero
Clarissa Danielle Guerrero
Landen Gulick
Samantha Catherine Haas
Lewis Haynes
Natalia Henao
Breanna Henderson
Maria Ximena Herrera Rea
Alyssa Monique Hinojosa
Wiktor Jakub Hudyka
Morgan Hunter
Michal Idziak
Kelly Nyuydini Jifon
Erica Justice
Richard Leos
Faustino Limon
Quintin A. Long

Amanda Longest
Desiree Renee Lopez
Ida Lopez
Marytza Lopez
Anthony Martinez
Ashley Martinez
Christopher L. Martinez
Guadalupe Martinez
Javier Martinez
Shannon Matis
Dennis Tyler Mays
Jorvis McGee
Francesca Mercado
Maximiliano Monsivaiz
Christina Montemayor
Beatriz Morales
Naomi Moreno
Zachary Naegelin
Uchenna Okakpu
David Ortegon
Odunola Funmilayo Oyeniyi
Abigail Oyervides
Ariel Ozuna
Ashley Palacios
Javier Palacios
Jacelyn Perez
Jacob Perez
Joel Perez

Odette LaNell Perez
Atchuta Valli Sravanthi Pilli
Gregory Pitre
Ashleigh Popek
Pablo Portillo
Erich Potthast
Jesus Prado
Shelby Purdy
Lourdes Ramirez
Sunjeet Singh Rathore
Briana Reyna

Monica Vianey Reyna
Luis Alberto Riojas
Hailee Roberson
Ashlea Rosenbaum
Christopher Oscar Ruiz
Coralie Saenz
David Salinas
Idalia Salinas
Nicholas Salyers
Brenna Seams
Jessica Leigh Sellers

Nadia Sherman
Michael Shervo
Brittney Lafayette Soliz
Enzo Soza
Ana Thompson
Tom Tiet
Rowena Lorene Trevino
Tiffany Trevino
Elisabeth Valadez
Amy Valdez
Brianna Vallejo

Sandy Viviana Vargas
Jesus Villegas
Michelle Elizabeth Wagner
Deven Westmoreland
Christina Whitney
Kyle Wilson
Amanda Marie Zuniga
Deedra Lynn Zuniga

TEXAS TECH UNIVERSITY, LUBBOCK, TX

Robyn Adams
Chloe Regis Alexander
Diana Aranda
Traci Jade Bailey
Maura Solange Yohana
Ballard
Cash Hearty Barker
Carly Elizabeth Barksdale
Bianca Nicole Barrera
Sara Baumgardner
Bailey Bell
Brittany Blakey
Anna Ruth Boyles
Andrea Britten
Caitlyn DeLane Brown
Amanda Calvert
Alicia Renee Castillo
Megan Bernadette Christian
Chirae Christie
Chelsea Ryanne Clark
Wendi Rhena Coats
Molly Ellen Craft
Lauren Nicole Cruz
Kaitlin Marie Danis
Nikita Dhir
Megan Lacy Dillon
Benjamin Chase Dossett
Brooke Downing
Ashley Nicole Duenes
Shannon Durkin

Benjamin Taylor Finlayson
Blaire Elizabeth Flora
Amanda C. Flores
Matthew Frosoni
Megan Marie Furlong
Jordan Ashlee George
Kaitlyn Anne Gerde
John Getz
Emily Kaitlyn Gilmore
Brandy Noel González
Alicia Madeline Goodman
Toddrick LeSean Gotcher
Samantha Tess Greenlees
Marguerite Katherine Grubb
Brenda Isabel Guardiola
Loren Hall
Jennifer Beth Harris
Nathanael Alton Havens
Jenna Hay
Katie Dawn Heffron
Emily Anne Hellman
Claudia Maria Hernandez
Andrea Leigh Hess
Shelby Renee Huber
Angga Khoirul Imam
Sabrina Sue Jamal
Amber Rene Jamerson
Erin Elizabeth Jarvis
Annabelle Louise Johnson
Reed Edward Johnston

Allison Jones
Lauren Joness
Julie Reun Jun
Nayane Yohanna Kennerly
Sydney Kate Kim
Emily Cawood King
Morgan Kinloch
Kristen Knight
Casey Ann Kopp
Emily Latham
Jennifer Nhu My Le
Jessica Anne LeFors
Jacob Dean Lieb
Ani Celine Mangold
Meredith Mansour
Ashley Maveddat
Nathan Thomas McCarty
Kayla Reilly McKinnis
Mallory Mathis Miller
Jackson Milone
Sarah Hartline Muncy
Paige Alexandria Murphy
Jadyn Taylor Newsom
Caitlin Erin Norris
Miguel Nunez
Chiamaka Thelma Obianyor
Kelsey Marie Orsak
Jonathan Andrew Ortiz
Jaclyn Francis Paul
Nicole Elizabeth Peacock

Emily Pellerin
Courtney Thuy-Ngan Pham
Lindsey Phillips
Nia Symone Pierce
Yasmin Rey
Courtney Michele Reynold
Emma Anne Riggs
Stephanie Dawn Riley
Carsen Joseph Roach
RaeAnn Lynn Rubenthaler
Lucely Santillan
Andrew John Schobelock
Rebecca Seitz
Aubrey Denae Servantez
Chloe Victoria Shelton
Simran Rachel Singh
Adrian Lynn Smith
Elizabeth Avery Smith
Sara Katherine Stewart
Taylor Symmank
Tessa Mae Talsma
Cameron Erin Taylor
Makenzie Hope Thomas
Patrick Alan Tone
Brooke Denise Walterscheid
Arren Wells
Holton Lane Westbrook
Bailey Brooke White
John Alexander White
Mackenzie P. White

Tanna Blair Wieler
Hannah Katherine Wilhite

Michaela Li-Yan Yarbrough
Shelby Young

Jaqueline Yareli Zavala

Evelyn Gabriela Zirena

TEXAS TECH UNIVERSITY SCHOOL OF LAW, LUBBOCK, TX

Shahzeb Atta
Christopher James Baker
Jasmine Denise Banks
Candice Leigh Barnard
Imogene Lucretia Boak
Regina C. Bost
Carter Bowers
Trevor Miles Brown
Andrew J. Cavazos
Jessica E. Chapman
Macy Ann Cotton
Jessica Nichole Eaton
Amber L. Fly
Sean Bartholomew
Galloway
Josue Joel Galvan

James Goff
Jamie Escamilla Gonzales
Daniel Joe Graves
Allison Brenna Grayson
Kimberly Catherine Marie
Grinnan
Miranda Blake Grummons
Catherine Aubrey Hansard
Jennifer Susan Hartman
Jaime Hernandez
Nicole Suzanne Holland
Stephanie Marie Ibarra
McKenzie Lee Jordan
Chelsie Alese Kidd
Robert Duncan Killian
Matthew G. Loving

Bryson Alan Matthews
Morgan Leigh McCorvey
Jeri Leigh McDowell
Joseph C. McNulty
Julio M. Mendoza-Quiroz
Ronald Lee Miller
Brenda Montoya
Alexandra N. Morris
Aubrey Katherine Noonan
Tara Elissa Parker
Niravkumar
Narendrakumar Patel
Spencer Cole Peeler
Brendan Sean Reeder
Stacy D. Riker
Kyle Andrew Rose

Jake Ryan Rutherford
Spencer Mark Salmon
Catherine Alexandra
Schraegle
Amanda Jean Schwertner
Austin Paul Smith
Kevin Christopher Smith
Ross Daniel Smith
Ashley Marie Snell
Shannon Brianna Spizman
SaraNeil Stribling
William James Strong-Ott
Adonia Tan
Sara Christine Thorton
Kristen Reid Vander-Plas
Alyssa Starr York

TEXAS WOMAN'S UNIVERSITY, DENTON, TX

Erika Loreyn Agpawa
Sandra Awad
Angela Bell
Diane Boles
Kaitlin Briggs
Aaron Castilleja
Megan Cornelison
Nicholette Custable
Rhianna Marie Doran
Alexa Lee Duysak
Kimberly Lynn Fazzone
Sarah Gerken

Emina Gibic
Rachel Gillis
Mariana Gonzalez-B.
Maritsa Guerrero
Hannah Hogg
Sarah Hou
Kayla Jenkins
Katherine Kellett
Jordan Kiefer
Emilyann Kinlaw
Ashlyn Lee
Cory Lee

Erica Cox Leone
Andrea Mapua
Abigayle Martinez
Monica Mathis
Sara May
Monserrat Moreno
Nicole Nordie
Desiree Patterson
Madeline Potter
Kristin Rhoden
Raechelle Marie
Torralba Robles

Delanie Marin Sager
Alexis Diano Sikorski
Karen Smith
Sarah Smith
Dennis Sorto
Katy Stephens
Chloe Terrell
Kelsie Turman
Bailey kaye Whatley
Lydia Williams

TEXAS WOMAN'S UNIVERSITY GRADUATE SCHOOL, DENTON, TX

Dena Abbott
Rasha Jamal Abdelrazzaq
Kristin Alder
Daniel Allen
Jessicca Allen
Amjad Almalaq

Arti Arti
William Ash-Houchen
Jeannine Birkenfeld
Aaron Bonnett
Anita Braddock
Tyriesha Brashae-Williams

Holly Browning
Marian Marie Browning
Erin Bruggeman
Kathryn Eleanor Caldwell
Rebekah Carl
Scott Carman

Christine De Angelis
Justin Decoux
Tri Dinh
Robyn Dobbs
Tamra Dollar
Nadia Dosal

Noura Moh'd Bandar Elwazani

Pamela Farley

Sarah Folkening

James Fuller

Jennifer Gerard

Diana Carolina Gonzalez

Marsha Gossett

Kirsten Guerra

Eric Gumm

Dana Guy

Kelly Hale

Tamanna Hamal

Danica Harris

Haleu Holt

Maureen Johnson

Melissa Johnson

Jamie Jones

Kourtney Kober

Elizabeth Larkin

Tawny Lebouef-Tullia

Paloma Linda Lenz

Brittany Lerma

Emily Macleod

Kristen Mathes

Heather McIntyre

Stephanie Mikus

Lauren Miller

Holly Diane Mitchell

Haley Mowdy

Marianella Nunez-Delgadillo

Kathryn O'Connell

Raluchukwu Ogbazi

Laura Ouimette

Kayla Pedroza

Lauren Perry-Norris

Yolanda Pimentel

Lynne Richardson

Sheila Richburg

Gabrielle Ricky

David Joel Rios

Brooke Rogers

June Rosdahl

Natalie Rose

Bethany Rothamel

Jaymie Sickling-Sparling

Breanne Sill

Stephen Simpson

Sheri Smith

Gabriela Solis

Angelia Renae Spurgin

Lisa Stewart

Michael Tam

Amber Nicole Thomas

Shivangi Vakharia

THE BAPTIST COLLEGE OF FLORIDA, GRACEVILLE, FL

Vastie Alexis

Leah N. Alligood

Joshua James Barkley

Melody Faith Barney

Nicholas L. Bishop

Sydney Brianna Bodden

Edward Calvin Booth

Shawn LaMonte Branham

Austin Cole Brinkley

Matthew Kyle Bryan

Leah G. Calhoun

Amanda Grace Carnley

Melissa Chambers

Moultrie Clement

Alainna Erin Davis

Shelsea Jane Denson

Katrina Jane Diamond

Natalie Cosette Fernandez

Colt Hunter Hudson

Hunter McKenzie Johnson

Elizabeth Keppel

Jonathan Robert Ketner

Andrew King

Joshua Robert Larson

Kate Lawhorn

Jeremy Meetze

Rachel Ann Miller

Terry Clyde Mills

Briana N. Monrose

Korey Adam Morrow

Ryan David Pickwick

Jonah D. Powers

Kate Hollis Prange

Brad Price

William Christopher Priest

Gregory Bryant Pruitt

Jennifer Crystal Ruiz

James E. Russ

Anne Marie Sapp

Misti Rose Solomon

Phillip Cory Solomon

Julian Eugene Strickland

Kathryn M. Taylor

Skylar J. Teel

Hannah VanLandingham

Kristen Marie Wanamaker

Christopher M. Wasson

Bobby Waynick

Ryan Carter West

Rebecca Lynn Whaley

Roselyn Jean Zaiter

THE CITADEL, CHARLESTON, SC

Nicholas Lee Alford

Spencer Avery Allen

Dane Andrew Anderson

Joshua Stephen Apsitis

Donald Owen Argy

Samuel Steven Benecke

Joseph E. Benson

Scott Austin Bidwell

Brian D. Bilbo

Ryan Evan Blagburn

Wade E. Bosley

Justin Alexander Brownlee

Danny Monroe Bruce II

Matthew Robert Bryant

Walter Dodson Bryson

Matthew Bungarden

Donald Birch Chestnut III

Ashley Nicole Claypool

Benjamin Thomas Cohen

Ryan Parker Davalos

Jessica Clementine DeWitte

Miller McVey Dial

Savannah Grace Duan

Ross Gaines Evatt

Chandler Harvin Fleck

Garreth J. Floyd

Zachary S. Ford

Franklin Tyler Fox

Ryan Jacob Glatz

Edward Traywick Godowns

John Eric Goins

Fernando Ulises Gonzalez

Kenny Gonzalez

John William Hope

Joe S. Hoying

Russell George Johnson

Joshua Duane Jordan

Brent Steven Kiefer II

John Nicholas Kouten

Matthew Charles Kraft

Daniel A. Larimore

Alexander Gerard MacDonald

Andrew Scott Mai

Madison M. Mayleben	Michael Hardy Nelems	Kelsey Leeann Schlegel	George Mitchell Taylor
Robert G. McClam	Johnathan Macon Overcash	Michelle Lynn Schoenfeld	John Luke Tippetts
Andrew C. McCluskey	Keisha Marie Hye Pendery	Taylor Meredith Scott	James Richard Urban
Thomas Looney McGuire	Luke N. Pittman	William Christian Sloane	Christopher William
Andrew Brett McMahan	Christian Tyler Potts	Augustus Towns Smith	Vanacore
Kane Patrick McManus	Brannon Jantzen Price	Mark Joseph Smith	Brooks Stallworth Wagstaff
Andrew John McSorley	Kyle William Price	James Andrew Stephens	Matthew Hunter Watson
Jamie Peter Meyer	John David Raad	George Tyrel Stevenson	Kathleen Elizabeth West
Craig Levar Miller	Carlos Israel Ramos	Cameron D. Summers-	Ashley Lorenzo Williams Jr.
Amber Renee Mills	Richard John Santorum	Powell	Austin Pierce Winkler
Matthew James Nedolas	Matthew C. Scalise	Nicholas Loring Sweat	Justine Casey Zukowski

THE COLLEGE OF NEW ROCHELLE ARTS & SCIENCES, NEW ROCHELLE, NY

Anissa Figueroa	Amanda Hernandez	Claudia Morales	Nohemi Payano
Emily Fontoura	Darielle Hickson	Jessy Ouseph	Carolyn Reichert
Marie Stephanie Gomez	Ja'Nasha King	Megan Adela Pasko	Paola Rodriguez

THE COLLEGE OF NEW ROCHELLE SCHOOL OF NEW RESOURCES, NEW ROCHELLE, NY

Raquel Cantre	Theresa Freeman	Kangela Moore	Lisa Ramcharan-Campbell
Sheryl Clarke	Darrell Inniss	Shawn Patterson	Garrett Stokes
Verna Diggs	Phylathia Monroe	Munoz Price	Sharon Venosa

THE COLLEGE OF NEW ROCHELLE SCHOOL OF NURSING, NEW ROCHELLE, NY

Chenel Bennett	Zanyl K. M. Farrell	Genesis Mota	Vyanna Leshel Todd
Keisha-Ann Bryan	Lea Jung	Andrea Restrepo	
Ros-Gassandre Cassamajor	Ashley McGillicuddy	Deanna Christine Rivera	

THE CROWN COLLEGE OF THE BIBLE, POWELL, TN

Kevin Jerome Barber	Marissa McKenzie Helton	Justin Daniel Ludka	Jacob Eric Samples
Brandon Gregory Brooks	Hannah M. Holbrook	Emily Katherine Moeller	Travis James Smith
Brittany Lynn Brown	Carl Blaine Houser	Samantha Mae Perkins	Victoria Rose Stover
Kyle R. Cox	Rebecca L. James	Carolyn Adelle Rhyner	Natalie Thomas
Shasta Rae Curtis	Kelsey Lee Jones	David James Royal	David Valazquez

THE MASTER'S COLLEGE, SANTA CLARITA, CA

Luke Abendroth	Natalie Boston	Elizabeth Castaneda	Grace Cypert
Luke Phillip Anderson	Emily Brayne	Caleb Chandler	Rafael Eduardo Dajer
Dina Archila	John Brazil	Hudson Christmas	Guerrero
Carissa Arend	Kimberlyn Bridges	Troye Christmas	Samantha Del Rio
JoyAnna Baker	Steffi Gayle Bullecer	Nicholas Covello	Daniel Dewey
Canon Baldridge	Aaron Bush	Andrew Croy	Samantha Dick
Jordan Bolde	Heather Marie Casey	Sabrina Cruz	Austin Jacob Doucette

Romain Drai
Samuel J. Eisenhuth
Morgan Fox
Erin Michelle Frye
Amelia Gaddy
Daly Gates
Hailey Gomillion
Elise Grangetto
Christian Hedland
Kathryn Heldridge
Jordan Hubbs
Julia Ingoldsby
Bethany Johnson
Eileen Kawamoto
Kara Kim
Taeyun Kim
Elisabeth Claire Kindlund

Amanda Kinney
Morgan Koch
Liza Koval
Dinah A. Laguna
Hollie Larsen
Natalie Lebkuecher
Chi Ung Lee
Rebekah Marie Leigh
Hannah Lokos
Stefanie Marie Loporchio
Hannah Lugg
William Lynch
Bethany Malievsky
Daphnee Jaymee Dae
Manderson
Morgan Maycumber
Stephanie McVicker

Rebecca Meitler
Mackenzie Morgan
Joshua Nelson
Brandin M. Nesbella
John R. Nesbella
Annie Ownbey
Kaelyn Elizabeth Peay
Benjamin M. Powell
David Martyn Ramos
Maya Rauch
Bethany Reeves
Connor Rhoden
Aaron Rose
Blake Roseberry
Leo Sakai
Noel Sakai
Amy Seaman

Joseph Paul Seitz
Joshua Sherfey
Taylor Scott Sinclair
Meghan Alexis Sowers
Kaitlyn Joy Stire
Susanna Kathleen Stixrud
Elrica Paramita Suhertan
Michael David Swartz
Timothy van Wingerden
Gabriel Varela
Karen Vivas
Katelyn Walter
Miranda Rae Wert
Michelle Wong

THE UNIVERSITY OF AKRON, AKRON, OH

Richard Dean Angeletti III
Isabella Kathryn
Bartholomew
Megan Brophy
Andrew Derhammer
Jessica Gonda

Josh Hillegass
Sarah Insull
Hannah Marcum
Layne Elizabeth McKinley
Natalie Miller
Chandler Mueller

Melissa Anne Paydo
Travis Pero
Billie Radcliffe
Jessica Repko
Paige Schertzinger
Kathryn Schneider

Allie Stanley
Jenna Aileen Strauss
Anna Tombazzi
Joan Wood
Erik Zito

THE UNIVERSITY OF ALABAMA, TUSCALOOSA, AL

Ky'Era Actkins
Marshall Anderson
Jacqueline Andreano
Catherine Ann Angelo
Rebecca Beasley
Steven Lasean Becton II
Sam Bellestri
Elizabeth Bersson
Crystal DeAnn Bice
Liza Helen Bollinger
Deanna Kaylin Bowen
Jacob Brackmann
Ashley Buchanan
Bryneth Buckner
Judith Nicole Burroughs

Taylor Nicole Byrd
Rachel Elise Carlson
Danielle Francine Cassady
Joseph Samuel Centeno
Amanda Chambers
Magdalena Chavez
Allison Cirenza
Michael Clark
Carrie Alicia Clower
Ciara R. Cooley
Robert Cope
Colton Cumbie
Lauren Alyssa Davis
Rachel Deeb
Whitney Deyo

Shazia Dinath
Kenya Donovan
Meghan Dorn
Clare Farrow
Catherine Faust
Fallan Frank
Kayla Frederick
Anna Gant
Allexa Gardner
Elissa Marie Gargiulo
Chelsie Alexis Gates
Doran George
Allison Glover
Nivory Gordon III
Robert Grady

Branden Andrew Greenberg
Alexandra Hagg
Anthony Hall
Kacie Hattaway
Luke Haynes
Tatum Higginbotham
Logan Holley
Brandon Hooks
Madison Marie Hooper
Emily Huynh
Siera Crimson Jann
James Slade Johnston
Hilary Jones
Alexcis Keenan
Frances Kyle

Jennifer Marie Lamberth
Christopher Lancaster
Madeleine Lewis
Mary Lewis
Thomas Lind
Gabrielle Kathleen Lindley
Haley Royar Loflin
Jessica Luker
Russell Macoon
Ciara Louise Naomi
Malaugh
Keeli Lanae Mallory
Lauren Mathews
Kathryn Mary Frances
McCoy
Genevieve Miller
Brianna Milner
Alexander Mitchell
Caroline Montz
Kelsey Joy Moore
Rodger Michael Moore
Jessica Morgan
Virginia Morgan

Brett Patrick Norris
Rachael Nowack
Kerri O'Connor
Jessica OBrien
Rachel Paikoff
Kara Diane Parks
Katie Elizabeth Parks
Anna Peeler
Justin Pendleton
Jessica Perkins
Ashley Perry
Allison Peters
Evan Phillips
Brandon Chase Poole
Peyton Dees Presto
Sarah Elizabeth Puckett
Orion Recke
Alex Reeder
Adam Eric Richey
Laura Ritchie
Emma Roberson
Carson Wright Roberts
Alexa Roe

Ashley Anne Ross
Danielle Sahud
Regina Salup
Erik Andrew Schatz
Eric Schulz
Alexander of Serman
Christian Shannon
Courtney Elizabeth Shows
Margaret Shuster
Haley Siddall
Grace Bethany Silverstein
Taylor Sims
Catherine Cammille Skelton
Brandon Skinner
Brianna Smiley
Emma Smith
Moriah Simone Smoot
Lauri Katherine Springer
Dylan M. Stephenson
Devin Stevens
Lindsay Madison Steves
Hunter John Stewart
Taylor Suydam

Eric Samuel Terrell
Benjamin Seth Tibbs
Alexis Ann Unger
Forrest Charles Walker
Caitlin Sims Wall
Ashley Warren
Emily Warwick
Justin Wells
Madeline West
Daniel Westfall
Sidney Ray White III
Rachel Wilburn
Michaela Jo Wilcox
Emily Elizabeth Williams
Joshua Williams
Kindle Shea Williams
Lauren Elizabeth Williams
Sierra Wilson
Alexander Vincent Wolf
Mai Yamane
Jordan Yazbec
Shuwen Yue
Megan Zartman

THE UNIVERSITY OF FINDLAY, FINDLAY, OH

Kyle J. Ames
Lana Attar
Kate M. Bauer
Heather J. Beck
Darnise Bembry
Caroline Joy Billings
Zac Binkley
Dylan Blunk
Karli M. Bonar
Sabrina M. Braunlich
Zachary K. Brown
Allison Christine Bunsey
Daniel A. Butler
McKenzie K. Butterman
Tyler J. Carroll
Megan N. Cleve
Charity C. Clum
Randolyn F. Cooper

Spencer M. Cooper
Kelsey M. Dager
Allison M. Dilbone
Hannah M. Dunbar
Kaitlyn R. Duskin
Brittany E. Eaches
Alyssa R. Ebbeskotte
Tyler M. Ellerbrock
Sean M. Farmer
Jessica T. Fletcher
Clay T. Fogle
Kadee K. Foote
Jordan Garcia
Emma R. Geis
Erin L. Gilbert
Haley A. Gray
Alyssa A. Grevenkamp
Lydia T. Guagenti

Jenny Hanf
Coyne Hopey
Levin James Hovest
Victoria C. Huber
Dylan J. Kaufman
Lexa L. Kessler
John Michael Kidd
Taylour A. Kidd
Elizabeth M. Kniss
Samantha J. Kolar
Meredith G. Kovener
Bennett A. Lamczyk
Djordje Ljubinkovic
Julie A. Lyons
Eric Manning
Britney M. Mcintosh
Lindsay D. McKee
Jacob S. Miller

Nathaneal J. Mol
Erin N. Mott
Caitlyn M. Murphy
Eun Young Young Na
Alex A. North
Allison C. Parker
Clay B. Parlette
Kacie M. Pohlman
Kathryn Poorman
Sara R. Postic
Kayla J. Prater
Shanon L. Romano
Shannon R. Roof
Cole Leon Ryan
Catherine A. Schnipke
Brandy B. Smith
Conner Spaeth
Christopher T. Stang

Elizabeth R. Streacker
Diane E. Susdorf
Timothy J. Szabo
Samantha T. Szwejbka

Nicholas J. Thompson
Taylor C. Trice
Taylor Renee Tweed
Teaona L. Wadsworth

Jessica M. Ward
Erica R. White
Traci E. Willis
Janelle M. Wiser

Elizabeth A. Wisma
Margaret Brunswick
Wuebker
Samuel J. Yates

THE UNIVERSITY OF MISSISSIPPI, UNIVERSITY, MS

Hillary Ake
Bjad Khalaf Almutairy
Kaitlin (Kate) L. Aspinwall
Jack A. Badger
Ethan RB Baker
Destinee A. Ball
France P. Beard
Silas G. Beebe
Alexandra Claire Bensel
Mary Kate Berger
Robert E. Bobo
Mary M. Bracken
Denae Bradley
Allison M. Bradshaw
Robert "Brady" Bramlett
Rod Bridges
Lauren Briscoe
Brianna F. Burse
Kristin Buskirk
Brittany R. Byrd
Melissa Capocaccia
Alix Cawthon
Brittany L. Clark
Laura Cline
Jeremy K. Coleman
Mary Chandler Cossar
Maia Cotelo
Joe Mack Curry II
T'Keyah Davis
Anne M. DeLee
Daniel S. Drummond
Emily Rose Duhe
Maggie K. Durnien
Mary Alex England
Callie A. Entwisle
Austin C. Ezell
Katherine K. Farese

William J. Fisher
Madeline O. Friedmann
Hunter A. Gabbard
James R. Galloway
Terrian Garvis
Kristina Gautier
Cassidy Gills
Alexandria E. Gochenauer
Whitney Jane Griffin
Melissa S. Griffith
Colleen R. Haadsma
Maggie Hall
Dana Hanley
Gretchen Harknett
Cynthia Harris
Jamille R. Hartfield
Ann-Marie Herod
Claire Nelson Hick
Mary Caroline Hitt
Tanetra M. Howard
Erin K. Hudnall
Lauren M. Hughes
Austin L. Ivy
Kaylee A. Jacks
Carole F. Jennings
Mary Kakales
Su Kim
Sara Kiparizoska
Logan T. Kirkland
William B. Kneip
Sabrina A. Kosloske
Lindsey S. Landrum
Mary G. Langford
John A. Larkin
Joseph Randall Latham
Elizabeth P. Leary
Elizabeth C. Lee

Mallory Simerville
Lehenbauer
Michelle Taylor Ley
Caroline C. Loveless
Kevin J. Mahalak
Mary V. Martin
Natalie Martinez
Chastity M. Massengill
Gabrielle M. Matthews
Haley E. McFall
Jennifer M. Miller
Jacqueline A. Morris
Mary Caroline Morris
Amber L. Murphy
Quinn H. Murray
Gabrielle Mykytyn
Vinayak K. Nahar
Heather L. Neilson
Abigail E. Newton
Allison Lea Nooe
Matthew F. Oellerich
Tori L. Olker
Madison Osias
Vivian B. Paris
Anna Leigh Phillips
Lyda Victoria Phillips
Paul A. Pohto
Mary Virginia Portera
Mallory K. Pullman
Allison Melissa Ramsey
Claire E. Rearick
Joseph A. Rebentisch
Chandler S. Rhea
Brandi Rhoden
Emily N. Richmond
Alexandra N. Robbins
Hart Elizabeth Robbins

Rachel Robertson
Julie Roher
Elizabeth G. Romary
Paige Rucker
Georgia T. Russell
Kelsey L. Sanders
Kelly E. Savage
Emily Anne Sharpe
Shawn Wesley Skinner
Brownlee S. Smith
Kelly K. Smith
Ryan T. Snow
Laura J. Speights
Alexander L. Spradlin
Kristen Lee Stephens
Anna Grace Stout
Ann Sutton Teichmiller
Sumudu Prasanna
Tennakoon
Madisen R. Theobald
Jamie L. Thomas
Justavian Tillman
Jenny Nguyen Tran
Rose E. Turner
Regan N. Tyler
Jennifer Ann Urban
Pierce T. Vaughan
Joella J. Vaughnn
Olivia B. Vinzant
Camille V. Walker
Katelin A. Wallace
Laura Kathryn Wegener
Anna Lee Whisenant
Debra L. Whitley
Elizabeth E. Wicks
Summer Wigley
Michael C. Wilkerson

Logan A. Wilson   Payton A. Winghart   Kathryn J. Wright   Ruth Zegel
Rachel Wilson

THE UNIVERSITY OF NEW MEXICO, ALBUQUERQUE, NM

Aaron D. Alexis-Destine	Jordan S. Dautenhahn	Quinci Legardye	Niharika Ravichandran
Jordan P. Allen	Matthew S. Davoudzadeh	Taryn B. Levels	Heather G. Rooke
Moses E. Allen	Laura E. Demers	Amelia M. Linde	Katie L. Rooke
Marlin Arriaga	Lauren E. Dennis	Chandler C. Livingston	Olivia Ross
Firas N. Ayoub	William M. Dole	Valentina L. Livingston	Joseph L. Sanchez
Matt Anthony Barstow	Katrina N. Edelmann	Kaitlyn D. Loafman	Stephanie A. Sarchett
Tia R. Benally	Mario J. Esparza-Perez	Patricia L. Lott	Travis Scholten
Kyle T. Biederwolf	Cheyenne J. Feltz	Arturo H. Lozoya	Jordan A. Scott
Rebecca L. Boddy	Allison A. Fetterolf	Layota Lozoya	Bradley R. Sedillo
Mandisa C. Bradley	Neigelle T. Francisco	Nicole M. Lucero	Cece E. Shantzek
Delia A. Brennan	Travis M. Gonzales	Benjamin G. Maggard	Victoria G. Shupryt
Darren G. Brown	Mariah E. Groll	Steven L. Maness	Alma T. Solis Vela
Marshall J. Broyles	Jorge Guerrero	Texanna L. Martin	Diane C. Sun
Nadia N. Cabrera	Jenna A. Hagengruber	Alyssa E. Martinez-Beltran	Cecille J. Thomas
Savana Carollo	Bisaan Hanouneh	Claire E. McNallen	Courtney A. Thornton
Darlene Castillo	James P. Hendrie	Amanda M. Miller	Lluvia A. Trevizo
Alexandra M. Cervantes	Alyssa N. Herrera	Jordan E. Monroe	Cheyenne M. Trujillo
Isabella A. Cervantes	Alexandra V. Hidalgo	Brianna S. Mulligan	Marika L. Trujillo
Brenda Chanez	Moises Ibarra	Bich-Hanh T. Nguyen	Elena C. Vigil
Harold U. Chang	Kyla B. Joas	John P. Ortega	Tyler Wafer
Danielle M. Chavez	Julian R. Juan	Amidooli J. Pacheco	Hilary R. Wainwright
William R. Chavez	Anabella King	Sabrina D. Pickle	Davilay D. Wells
James V. Clark	Shayla Ophelia King	Michael N. Pierce	April B. Yazza
Camilla F. Cluett	Aubriana L. Knell	Tori Pryor	
Angela Combs	Randy F. Ko	Mercedes R. Ramos	
Joseph P. Corazzi	Elizabeth D. Laydon	Maria Jose Ramos Villagra	

THE UNIVERSITY OF TENNESSEE AT MARTIN, MARTIN, TN

Nathan T. Allen	Christopher K. Coleman	Dezie E. Gude	Jordan L. Johnson
Jay S. Atkins	Joel T. Conway	Kayla R. Hargrove	Kaitlan V. Keel
Jenna H. Bailey	Megan C. Crow	Marne S. Helbing	Marabeth G. Kennedy
Samantha A. Beard	Dillon A. Davis	Lindsey P. Hendrix	Sydney A. LaFreniere
Dorothy J. Boyle	Haley R. Davis	Matthew K. Hirsch	Courtney H. McCaleb
Dimitric Carter Brown	Philip Clayton Dunivan	Catherine L. Hixson	Todd R. McDunn
Georgia L. Brown	Olivia L. Fernandez	Hailey B. Holcomb	Noah G. Melaro
Kaitlyn Brook Carlton	Jamal N. Glenn	Christian H. Holland	Lauren Paige Mooney
Christy A. Chicas	Matthew J. Granner	Rashunica T. Holland	Chloe Grace Mullis
Amelia S. Coalter	Mark C. Graubner	Temple G. Hughs	Tanna R. Norman

Sean P. O'Brien	Ashby J. Reed	Miranda N. Rutan	Brittany N. Twilbeck
Orren P. Ogg	Kristina M. Reed	Victoria L. Seng	David C. Walker
Bethany M. Orban	Hope E. Renfroe	Autumn B. Stallings	Meagan N. Walker
Elizabeth A. Packard	Andrea M. Richardson	Haley A. Swafford	Deven N. Wilson
Madilyn Peay	Jesse Luke Robinson	Alexandra D. Thompson	Rachael M. Wolters

THE UNIVERSITY OF TENNESSEE COLLEGE OF NURSING, KNOXVILLE, TN

Emeri Kaitlin Allan	Laura E. Eaton	Briana Ky-Mari Mcintyre	Megan Alyssa Seal
Samantha Taylor Anasky	Oksana Yemelyanova Fields	Taylor Armecia Medlock	Kari Michelle Self
Hannah E. Anderson	Tiffany Michelle Foster	Morgan Renee Meredith	Alesha Sells
Alex Ryan Bacon	Abby Bowman Goldston	Kayla Sheree Merritt	Jennifer Nicole Shearer
Christopher David Bailey	Sarah Elizabeth Greenway	Lindsey Estellan Miles	Andrew Christopher Sipf
Chelsea Marie Bales	Carlton Morgan Griffin	Ashley N. Mitchell	Austin Tyler Smith
Jacqueline Leduc Bennett	Elizabeth Jane Harpole	Alexandria Nicole Moore	Casey Elizabeth Smith
Ashley Jameson Bond	Eric Madison Hearn	Ashley E. Moore	Lauren Rae Speck
Jessica Lynn Bradley	Charles Leonard Hoffecker	Taylor Michael Mudd	Emily Grace Spence
Adrienne Liana Branch	Meredith D. Hudson	Matthew Townsend Mustard	Coleen Michele Spotts
Emily Marsh Breighner	Lauren Mitzi Ingleston	Madison Taylor Myers	Sarah Elizabeth Stevens
Carly Shannon Brown	Carmen Swabe Jeansonne	Anna M. Neglia	Faith Nicole Stewart
Marissa Garmon Bunch	Sarah M. Johnson	Kisan Patel	Kellye Stone
Karen Elizabeth Carcello	Samantha Paige Jones	Abigail Elisabeth Pirie	Madison Taylor
Andrea Elizabeth Carter	Avie Lynne Joyce	Sabrina Blair Ponder	Karis Abigail Terpstra
Robert Joles Carter	Robin McManus Keen	Tony James Poppel	Alyssa Thanasack
Zada Katherine Casey	Adaya Alexandra Kirk	Kerri Mychael Powell	Linda Winslow Trentham
Emily Hannah Clark	Michelle Lee Kixmiller	Kathryn Michelle Rack	Morgan Brooke Vantrease
Copeland Taylor Cobb	Cierra Simoneaux Lacour	Christine E. Ramsey	Daniel Scott Vickery
Sara Brianne Colby	Andrew Jeremy Ladd	Alexis June Reddish	Taylor Alan Warren
Christine Elizabeth Conner	Mallory C. Lanier	Nichole Justine Reed	Emma Carol Whatton
Adam Wade Curtis	Amy P. Larsh	Mary Alexander Richards	Virginia Williams
Michael J. Curtis	Jacob Andrew Lay	Olivia A. Riley	Mary Margaret Wilson
Diya Daswani	Maddison Matlock Lopez	Catherina Danielle Rinehart	Megan Elizabeth Woods
Ashley Noel Davis	Chelsea Shea Maute	Lauren Elizabeth Rucker	Hannah G. Yoder
Ryan Christopher Davis	Megan Kathryn McCarley	Lisa Michelle Russell	Paul Ashton Zanoni
Christopher Brent Delph	Bryanna McClure	John Andrew Schultz	Alexa N. Zarlengo
Sarah Morgan DeLung	Mallory Cameron	Stefanie N. Schumacher	
Shannon Eden Dorwart	Mccullough	Jean Bettencourtt Sconza	

THE UNIVERSITY OF TENNESSEE HEALTH SCIENCE CENTER COLLEGE OF PHARMACY, MEMPHIS, TN

James Scott Barker	Corrine Emma Evans	Brandon Merrill Ladd	Meredith Kristina Newsom
Cherish Lynn Bowman	Jeremiah Dee Glass	Whitney Richalena	Olabisi Omowunmi Jessica
Cathlyn Chan	Chantler Jones	McKinney	Olumuyiwa

Matthew Francis Reddin   Torrey Lee Smith   Kristin Leigh Summers   Rachel Elizabeth Triplett

Alicia Caston Sanchez

THE UNIVERSITY OF TEXAS ARLINGTON, ARLINGTON, TX

Destiny Brianne Adams   Jennifer Dela Pena   Jennifer Chika Okafor   Ryan T. Serio

Maryam Alam   Alyssa Anne Dequeant   Lillian N. Pena   Ryan Allen Stevens

Eligius Allan   Vedansh Gupta   David Timothy Rader   Margarita Takou

David Wayne Babbs   Alissa Danielle Hendricks   Madison Taite Reid   Stephanie Peebles Tavera

Denise Guadalupe Chavez   Laurie Ann Iliff   Kristina Ashleigh   Chandler Renee Tice

Onur Daskiran   Rachel Shavon Lewis   Reinschmiedt   Alison Torres Ramos

Amy Kristine Davis   Jasmine Lucero   Veronica Denise Sanders

THE UNIVERSITY OF TEXAS AT SAN ANTONIO, SAN ANTONIO, TX

Abdulbasit Abbasi   Katheryn Devore   Megan M. Jefferies   Aaliyah Maura

Christopher Edward   Tabitha Dhodapkar   Cierra Johnson   Jonathan Mayberry

Adkison   Sara Dibrell   Sonie M. Johnson   Andrea McDaniel

Oluwaseyi Alabi   Daniel Estrada   Kristen Keith   Briana Elizabeth Anne

Ashton Blake Alarcon   Reem Farra   Barbara Joan Kennedy   McFadden

Jenny Alfaro   Ian Faulk   Lance Paul Kimbro   Jalen McKee

Sarah Allred   Ashley Michelle Fazzini   Manojna Kintada   Ashley Medina

Jasmine Almazan   Anthony Flores   Andrew Steven Knight   Victor Melendez

Krista Noraa Anchondo   Vaughn Fontenette   Marie-Louise Koelzer   Amanda Midence

Daniel Ball   Chassidy Dominique Frelow   Alan Kosub   Donna Williams Miller

Molly Ballard   Suma Ganji   Joshua Taylor Kuehne   Krupa Rajendra Mistry

Kasey Barrett   Lucy Garcia   Elizabeth Keji Lajayi   Jahmilya Juanita Mitchell

Xabier Ignacio Basanez   Jose Ignacio Garcia   Kiana T. Lalau   Ndabezinhle Jordan

Estefania Bazan   Zambrano   Daniel Allen Large   Mkwanazi II

Susan D'Nae Brotherman   Sammar Ghannam   Mary Felicia Ledbetter-   Edward Joseph Mondragon

Krystal Brown   Anna Jessica Gomez   Gallagher   Sidney Montero

Julie Brozovich   Daniela Gomez Brana   Paul Lee   Ariel Britany Morales

Leighanne Butler   Gonzalez   Chelsea Monae Linwood   Brianna Morales

Gizelle Marie Cacho   Maria Elena Guerra Garcia   Katiuzca Isabel Loaiza   Jonathan Moreno

Amber Calvert   Jomari Guerrero   Baley Katherine Loera   Naomi Morgan

David Canales   Garrett Joseph Hall   Alejandra Longoria   John Louis Morin

Damien Xavier Cavazos   Kristen Annika Hamalainen   Alaina Marie Lopez   Lindsey Muenchow

Ndidi Cassie Chiedu   Regina Haua   Karen Lopez   Marian Murra Rodriguez

Valeria Colmenero   Ryan D. Himmelberg   Patricia Lopez   Matthew Mussenden

Ryan Conran   Jeremiah Edward Hobbs   Kelsea Leigh Louton   Cory Nguyen

Ashley Cooner   Tiffany Tarver Hunt   Erica Luke   Viet Hoang Nguyen

Vivian Cortez   Anusha Hussain   Yuting Ma   Vinh-Son Van Nguyen

Arielle Degueure   John Fayek Gerges Ibrahim   Lillian Martinez   Marco Ochoa

Gianna N. DeSalles   Andre B. Jeanjacques   Alpha Martinez-Suarez   Elizabeth Ochoa Chan

Claudia Magali Olivares
Latrice Denise Owens
Keerthana Reddy Pakanati
Christian Geronimo Pastrano
Alexa Patel
Kristina Patino
Lauren E. Patrick
Taylor Cezanne Pefferkorn
Saifa Pirani
Aaron David Pulido
Kevin Michael Pyles

Christopher C. Rendon
Blanca E. Rivera
Victoria Rosalinda
Rodriguez
Amit Kumar Saha
Vicky Salazar
Kimberlyne Sanchez-
Martinez
Kevin J. Simmons
Dwight Anthony Smith Jr.
Calandra Snowden

LaShonda Snowden
Aaron Sowle
Marc S. Stefonowicz Jr.
Justin Michael Stout
Pacer Cierra Swan
Michael Anthony
Thomas Jr.
Andrew Joseph Trautmann
Matthew Trevino
William Franklin Trynoski II
Oscar Tu

Michelle Nicole Vargas
Marcos Orlando Vargas Jr.
Victoria Anne Vaughn
Javier Alejandro Vazquez
Stephanie Aide Velazquez
Jorge Villarreal II
Otilia Antonia Webb
Brittany Welborn
Belinda Jayne Williams
John Thomas Wynkoop IV
Viktoria Taylor Zerda

THE UNIVERSITY OF TEXAS EL PASO, EL PASO, TX

Avery Aboud
Lizet Acuna
Javier Aguilar
Karen Aguilar
Desiree Heather Alegria
Valeria Altamirano
Alexandra Arciniega
Rachel Ann Arreola
Sidney Arrington
Brianna Barker
Alexandra Barraza
Zayra Barrientos
Brenda Barrios
Bethany Belmonte
Brittany Benavides
Megan Bermea
Alexis Bustamante
Jaime Aaron Cano
Marlene Cantu
Brianna Carmen
Oscar Casanova
Javier Castillo
Eduardo Jose Castillo Fatule
Yazmin Castruita
Giselle Cayme
Raymundo Contreras
Juan Corona
Roberto Corral
Blanca Carolina Correa
Ana Dominguez

Kim Dominguez
Cristina Enriquez
Edward Escobedo II
Edmundo Esparza
Angela mariajose Esquerra
Joseph Estalilla
Cecilia Alejandra Estrada
Lozoya
Janie Falk
Edna Judith Ferguson
Danielle Fincham
Danian Flores
Ana Melissa Garcia
Andres Garcia
Yuritze Alejandra Garcia
Marlyn Garcia Torres
Anthony Gardea
Eva Garza
Ilana Gomez
Alan Gonzalez
Kimberly Ann Gonzalez
Victoria Gonzalez
Jessica Gruver
Emily Guerra
Andrea Guerrero
Paulina Andrea Guerrero
Johnathan Gutierrez
Ana Delia Guzman
Joscelyne Guzman
Andrea Haddock

Caitlin Harmon
Ruby C. Hernandez
Amanda Herrera
Maria Hidalgo
Rachel Kern
Eden Klein
Elda Mitre LaBombarbe
Jacqueline Lechuga
Carlos Eduardo Lopez
Rodrigo Lugo
Karina Lujan
Bernadette Martinez
Catalina Adelise Mata
Larissa Mendoza
Laura E. Mendoza
Samantha Michelle Meza
Rogelio Montellano
Michael Andrew Montes
Ashley Munoz
Malvina Guadalupe Munoz
Elie Naddour
Monique Navarro
Alyssa Olivas
Caitlyn Olmstead
Chinedu Oputa
Jessica Oropeza
Joshua Perez
Marina Alicia Peveto
Sarah Ponce De Leon

Johanna Yvette Puga-
Martinez
Cristina Quinones
Gilberto Quintanilla
Jazmin Ramirez
Alexis Nicole Ramos
Jaqueline Ramos
Marissa Ashley Reyes-
Hernandez
Maida Ammi Rivas
Cristobal Ivan Robles
Tiffany Robles
Jose Rodriguez
Ileana Idally Rubio
Perla Rubio
Mayra Ruiz
Andrea Ruzic
Viridiana Saenz
Martin Salas
Carlos Salazar-Lopez
Amanda Sanchez
Ilse Sanchez
Valerie Serna
Denise Servo
Chyanne N. Smith
Jovanna Solis
Jesse Soria
Mariel Soto
Aileen Tapia
Marc Tarango

Abigail Tellez

Evelyn Torres

Karina Torres

Lizette Verenice Torres

Adan Valenciana

Carlos Valenzuela

Gigi Valles

Carlos Vazquez

Luisa Villasenor

THE UNIVERSITY OF TEXAS MEDICAL BRANCH–GALVESTON, GALVESTON, TX

Lauren Ashley Abeita

Daniel William Adame

Yetunde Omonola Akiwowo

Tracy Lynn Alexander

Syed R. Ali

Sierra I. Andreason

Bridget E. Andrews

Jeremy Bechelli

Lynn O'Dowd Bell

Leanne Elizabeth Benson

Kelsey M. Berg

Paul Vaughn Brown

Molly Beth Brownfield

Jill Norann Bryant-Bova

Gabriella Nicole Bunting

Jocelyn Callado

Gabrielle Casilang

Maria Mayela Chavez

Hunter Cherryhomes

Kailey Katherine Chua

Amanda Lynn Cormier

Elizabeth J. Crofton

Kara Cummings

Dalena Elizabeth Dekowski

Peggy L. Determeyer

Sara Elizabeth Dixon

Raymond Dayle Donato

Christian Gabrielle Donatto

Justin Alexander Drake

Demori Elizabeth Driver

Brandi Marie Dyess

Chijioke Cornelius Ezeana

Vicky Niannian Fan

Amanda Lauren Feilke

Kayla L. Floyd

Alison Fuller

Caitlin Godinich

Angela Ariana Gonzalez

Chelsea Marie Grigar

Jordan M. Hagen

Yvette M. Heflin

Amy Dawn Hermes

Katrina Mae Santos
Hernandez

Jessica Lynn Holik

LaToyia Ranell Holman

Austin Scott Jadloski

Christopher Michael Jones

Mark Thomas Jones

Joel Alexis Jurado

Stephanie Katzenmeier

Harjeet Kaur

Zachary Kennedy

Sheryar Khan

Kathryn Taylor Kuhn

Amit Kumar

Jessica Faithe Lee

John Michael Leger

Zakkoyya H. Lewis

Kristina Macias

Marissa Kay Mackay

Ennert Rutendo Manyeza

Brian Matthews

Lauren Ashley Miller

Faiza Amin Mohammad

Crystal Nicole Moody

Ana Cristina Nelson

Krystal Lynn Newell

Curtis A. Nutter

Rizah Arbiol Ouano

Malaney Ravae O'Connell

Michael J. Payne

Jennifer Renee Pazderny

Rachel M. Pearson

Ellen Elisabeth Petrucci

Hilary Rabago

Chelsey Roberts

Lyndsey Alana Roper

Monique-Muna Saleh

Mayukh Kanti Sarkar Ph.D

Katie Marie Schmitz

Madison Sikes

Jesus Silvas

Gabrielle Lynn Steele

Amy Millay Steinert

Christi Anne Sterling

Kathryn Michelle Stubbs

Jennifer Thedinga

John Thornton

Bethany L. Tiner

Milody P. Tran

Quynh Thi Diem Tran

Shirley Kung Tran

Charles Umbaugh

Dean Allen Vanek

Stephanie P. Vega

Ryan Edward Vick

Brian Watabe

Roxanne Jeanette Werley

Nolan Jeffrey West

Coryna M. Williams

Lauren Michelle Young

Katherine Tennell Zahodnik

Seth Zhanel

Yafang Zhang

THE UNIVERSITY OF VIRGINIA'S COLLEGE AT WISE, WISE, VA

Karley Louise Allen

Daria Blach

Cassandra Collette
Blackwell

Michael Ryan Blevins

Chelsea Paige Brummitt

Whitney Carico

Codi Daniel Collins

Melinda Marie Combs

Sierra Gabrielle Combs

Caleb Daniel Fast

Lyndra Abena Frimpong

Jacob Scott Garman

Ahliyah Curtrese Gavin

Jenna Nicole Gray

Sarah Louella Hall

Bailey Curtlan Helbert

Rebecca Kristen Blagg
Hopewell

Alana Grace Johnson

Lindsay Julanne Lawson

Erin Taylor Lee

Dustin S. McGill

Maurice Nathan McGlone

Hannah Nicole McNew

Timmy L. Meador

Jasmine Nicole Mitchell

Joy Noelle Mitchell

Jessalyn Gabrielle Mullins

Mark Mullins

John Alexander Nauss

Madison Niece

Junetta Paige Nuckels
Jessie Lynn O'Quinn
Madison Brooke Ray
Allie Jo Robinson
Kelsey Lenn Smith

Tyler Reid Stone
Sharmae Leigh Stringfield
Katelyn Danielle Sturgill
Zane Matthew Sturgill
Ashlee Sue Taylor

Molly Elizabeth Taylor
Derrick Scott Torres
Mackenzie Lauren Trent
Lindsay Frances Tucker
Shannon Christine Walker

Lauren Elizabeth Welborn
Chelsea Elizabeth
Whittington
Tanner Samuel Winesett
Hope Sierra Wymer

THE UNIVERSITY OF WEST ALABAMA, LIVINGSTON, AL

Khadijha Christine Abston
Shechinah Adams
Christian Adkins
Jess Wallace Allen
Abigail Ames
Brooke Roseann Ames
William Alexander Baldwin
Kylee Ryan Banister
Kaitlynn Marie Beaird
Ariana Kali Bentley
James Mitch Brumbeloe
Erika Alexandria Buckley
Jack Corbit Cockrum III
Raven Dakota Daniel
Laderius Devante Dumas
Emily Louise Edwards
Kelly DeVota Edwards
Emily Nicole Fast
Macy Lynn Fobbus
Alexander Lewis Franks
Magdalena Galvan
Coy Jefferson Graham

Mark Logan Grant
Rianna Jade Gurvitz
Katelyn Nicole Hand
Victoria Lorraine Henderson
Kimberly Ruberte
Hernandez
Mitchell Patrick Holgate
Jordan Ikner
Ashton Paige Ip
Erin Caroline Jimerson
Hannah Michelle Johnson
Chicko Rodriquez Jones
Jasmine Bianca Knox
Stedmon Keith Kugler
Laura Ann Mancin
Garrett Lee Mattix
John McClung
Latisha Juanita McCullum
Domonique Patrice
McDaniel
Tegan Irene McDermott
Luigi Mendez

Molly Taylor Merchant
Josh Millwood
Natalie Nicole Mooney
Caitlin Marie Moore
William Tyler Morgan
Christian Morris
Mariah Renee Mort
Callie Rochelle Murphy
Amber Nelson
Joya Bertice Peebles
Kieran William George
Pettigrew
Grace Catherine Pitt
Tyler Montana Jul Prescott
Morgan Ray
Savannah Elaine Reach
Ronald Jason Richardson Jr.
Lacey Nichole Ku'uipo
Santiago
Tranquil Shanquee
Shepherd
Severino Signa

Randa DeLane Simpson
Kesia Lachelle Smith
Kristina (Kristy) Ann Smith
Jessica Dean Smyth
Bailee Jordan Sparks
Ashley Stassin
Lydia Sutcliffe
Lauren Tate
Catherine Taylor
Deonmonique Alexius
Timmons
Allie Elise Tittle
Robert Lee Vetzel
Jessica Briann Voyles
Rashard Dekwanta Ward
Fhallon Chiara Ware-
Gilmore
Keith Alexander Watson
Andrew Perry Welch
Jacob Hunter Winborne
Savanna Paige Wooley

THE UNIVERSITY OF WEST FLORIDA, PENSACOLA, FL

Angela Adams
Monty Amelio Alcindor
Fernanda Luvizotto do
Amaral
Breeze Alexandra Arb
Prince-Kevin Ash
Matthew Bailey
Scott Adam Baker
Meghan Bang
Lauren Barnes
Kristina L. Boyd

Abigail Walton Bradley
Teresa Marie Brooks
Ryan Bullard
Steven Campbell
Rachel Elizabeth Capps
Victoria Cartee
Carrie A. Chavers
Ashley Ruth Sentell Christie
Catherine Cooper
Justice Cox
Alexandra Daneva

Kaley Dattilo
Nina Rickka de Guzman
Cynara Sherece Deveaux
Jennifer Diaz
Hakeem Douglas
Christian Lennon Dove
Devan Ellis
Kaitlin Marie Englund
Rebekah Ergle
Jessica Ann Evans
Jordan Nicole Ference

Mandy Babin Fernandez
Lucy Escamilla Flournah
Keyana Floyd
Rebecca Foglietti
David Franklin
Erica Lynne Garcia
Amanda Gerow
Tania Gerve
Namaz Habroun
Jeneice Hall
Brittany L. Hensley

Yasmin Marie Hernandez
Elizabeth Hewey
Christian Michael Hiebel
Holly Houghton-Brown
Diya Howard
Holly Hoyt
Georgia Huffman
Floyd Jackson
Rachel Johnson
Michaela Colette Jones
Jamie Lyn Kuhn
Ryan Lavoie
Diana Marie Lawless
Adrian William Lawrence
DaCotah Ledbetter
Kyla Beth Linn
Lori Lombardo
Alexandrea Loomis
Kaitlin Lott
R.A. Marionneaux
Andrew Marotta

Alicia Martin
Yuclenis Matias
Daniel McBurney
Anika McCray
Kari Anne McWhirter
Lauren Meadors
Alicia Morris
Carlos Pinto de Moura
Nam Nguyen
Tiffany Nisewonger
Anthony Noll
Elizabeth O'Connor
Kenny Parker
Kruti Nilesh Patel
Quintin Payton
Savannah Peyton
Mariah Pfleger
Tina Phan
Robert Prosser
Sarah Queiros
Courtney Radcliffe

Emilie Raistrick
Forrest Ray
Christina Rice
Rachel Richardson
Hermanda Robinson
Jasmine Romano
Brett Rowberry
Chance Russell Ryon
Twymun Safford
Shauna Sanders
Johnathan Shields
Katherine Silsa
Cameron Smith
Sigrid Solgard
Timothy Sowers
Stormy Speaks
Catherine Stainback
Thomas Edward Stombaugh
Ann Marie Stramanak
Ariel L. Sulejmani
Danielle Tavano

Jonathon Alexander Thomas
Linda Woodard Tierney
Xuan Loc Thi Tran
Karlie Trull
Rachel Truxall
Jessica Urquhart
Samantha Vaccarello
Shelby Vaughn
Stefan W. Vaughn
Janine Velez Vazquez
Melissa Wade
Jennifer Walters
Brittany West
Janae Williams
Jonathan Williams
Talisha Williams
Jeremy Wilson
Trisha Stenson Woods
Elizabeth Wright

THIEL COLLEGE, GREENVILLE, PA

James Russell Abbs
Ahlam Mohamad
Abdelrasoul
Brittany Irene Bates
Evialina Arkadyevn
Biarzhanina
Rebecca Campbell
Caitlyn Carney
Morgan Suzanne Chase
Brant E. Dencher
Mary Kathleen Dougherty
Stephanie Nicole Felix
Julia Renee Fink
Stephen Mark Formicella

Michael P. Germita
Allison L. Gloor
Cassie Marie Graham
Kristi Lee Guritza
Austin Carter Hall
Amanda K. Hautmann
Bailey L. Holmes
Loyal Matthew Jasper
Michael Allen Jeffers
Jeffrey Michael Jenkins
Nicole E. Johnston
Christian Nicholas Kafka
Lora Kay
Allanah Danielle Keisling

Trenton James Keisling
Jaclyn Kuzma
Tanner West Liptrap
Jessica L. Long
Shane J. Martin
Trevor William Martin
Yuki Matsuoka
Nicholas Alexander McNutt
Alyssa Dawn Mondi
Trent Lewis Mosely
Alexis Mowris
Alyssa Lynn Murphy
Joshua Nichols
Jaden Matthew Nozicka

Christopher Douglas Nuss
Sean Paul Oros
Samuel Frazier Passafiume
Kourtney Paige Polvinale
Tiffany Rohm
Derek Runge
Kelsey Dawn Schneider
Garret Bradley Schweitzer
Lauren Renee Stonebraker
Kelly Lyn Thompson
Kiara Lee Weltner
Kelsey Marie Wise
Bradley Matthew Wisnoski

THOMAS JEFFERSON SCHOOL OF LAW, SAN DIEGO, CA

Elizabeth L. Atkins
Sarah Brand
Joshua Brisbane

Jeffrey Martin Carr
Michael J. Christopher
Andrei-Vladimir Dumitrescu

Ricardo Elorza
Maggie Gaan
Christopher Godinez

Marisol Gonzalez
Melanie Guillen
Julie Lynn Hunt

Charlene Mayers

Narek Mnatsakanian

Erin Panichkul

Edith Polanco

Pua Jennifer Uyehara

Vanessa Valenzuela

THOMAS MORE COLLEGE MASTER OF ARTS IN TEACHING, CRESTVIEW HILLS, KY

Tonya Sue Hash

Lisa Caitlin Tieman

Chelsey Marquis West

THOMAS NELSON COMMUNITY COLLEGE, HAMPTON, VA

David Nicks

Victoria Ashley Viduya

THREE RIVERS COMMUNITY COLLEGE, POPLAR BLUFF, MO

Jacqueline Marie Alden

Truman Tyler Aldridge

Abbie Johanna Allen

Miranda LeAnne Armes

Tashema Tovah Arnau

Charles Calvin Edward
Arnold

Samuel Thomas Arnold

Callie LeShea Arrington

Lauren Alice Averell

Rebecca Ann Baker

Taylor Kahealani Baker

William Lane Below

Hayle Cheyenne Birdsong

Stephanie Cassandra Bishop

Ivory Megan Black

Katlyn Nicole Bolden

Luzviminda Romen Bowers

Adriane Lea Bowman

Cynthia Dianne Boyd

David Wiiliam Branch

Cynthia Grace Brannon

Marcena Danielle Briles

Madison Leigh Buhler

Kenneth Jarred Bullock

Mercedes Marie Butler

Tyson Lee Campbell

Brittney Nicole Cato

Rebecca Jean Cato

Juan Carlos Cazares

Judy Rae Chaffin

Katrie Smith Christopher

Cameron Patrick Clark

Katlyn Ann Clark

Stephanie Rae Colwell

Doris Jean Cook

Sarah Bethanye Cook

Charles Kenneth Cooley

Alisha Maria Coonce

Sandara M'Lynn Cornelius

Justin Case Cowart

Kendra Jade Crawford

Elizabeth Nichole Crow

Elizabeth Alice Crutchfield

Shelbie Eileen Darlin

Heather E. Davis

Jasmikia Rayshonda Davis

Miranda Lynn Deaton

Heather Anne DeRousse

Jessica Leah Dixon

Trevor LeGrand Dobbs

Drew Jason Dowd

Kellie Jo Duhon

Virgil Thomas Durrow

Jacklyn Elizabeth Eagle

Jennifer Lynn Esquivel

Montana Cheyenne Estes

Stephanie Elaine Eudaley

Kelcie Nicole Fahnestock

Bailey Jo Faries

Hunter Benjamin Frampton

Rachel Marlene Frazier

Stephani Denice Fulford

Justas Furmanavicius

Jamaica Cocaine Gannon

Ariana Garcia

Rosalyn Garner

Samantha Elizabeth
Gatewood

Jessica Brooke Gott

Hailey Jordyn Griffin

Jane Marie Ham

Emerald Briana Harris

Kayla Janea Hester

Brittany Ann Hill

Joesph Lane Hill

Seth Mason Hovis

Alexis Shea Jarvis

Takeia Barbara Jones

Beverly Sue Kennon

Courtney Nicole King

Taryn Joy Kingsbury

Rachel Suzanne Knowles

Samuel Kenneth James
Kraus

Starr Nicole Lawless

Miranda Nicole Leach

Alex Robert Lewis

Angela Christine Long

Misty-Love Lopez

Daniel Ray Lorentz

Anthony Norman Mann

Breanna Nicole Manns

Jordan Lucus Masterson

Ann Wanja Mati

Mara Naomi McClintock

Jacob Thomas McKuin

Ashley Ann Miles

Madison S. Miller

Alyssa Beth Moore

Alysia Nicole Musser

Karen Kay Nelson

James Edward Norman

Kaci R. Payne

John Sylvester Perkins

Emily Ranae Porch

Carson Tyler Priddle

Sarah Beth Ray

Shannon Leann Ray

Hannah Elizabeth Robertson

Dorthy Ann Robinson

Jessica Nicole Robinson

Raymond Sankitts

Maci Jo Shearer

Carole Mindy Sims

Jazzma Lannette Smith

Ashley Nadine Stonecipher

Autumn Eve Strickland

Gwendolyn M. Stroh

Joshua Logan Stromatt

Wesley Austin Stroud

Jessica Lynn Succaw

Kalie Dyann Tackett

Josephine Nichole Tallent

Amanda Jo Taylor

Joyce Elaine Teasley

Amber Jean Thompson

Alexis Charlyne Tipton

Brandy Marie Townsend
Joy L. Townsend
Kasity Ashlyn Twaddell
Jennifer Lynn Van-Es
Amanda Dawn Vinson
Chelsea Marie Vinson
Seth Atwood Wagner

Mindy Kay Walker
Declan Kyle Wallace
Chrystal Dawn Walsh
Holly Anne Walters
Mary Anna Ward
Sara Elizabeth Ward
George Marshall Warren

Kevin Kristopher Warren
Dallas Gregory Welling
Gabrielle Nichole Wheat
Bailey M. White
Khali Danielle Willis
Cheyene Kelly Wood
Tiffany Nichole Wood

Kathryn Alisa Woolard
Katherine Janelle Grace
Word
Lisa Jane Young
Brenna Michelle Ziegler

TOCCOA FALLS COLLEGE, TOCCOA FALLS, GA

Sullivan Scott Adams
Courtney Lynn Bechtold
Christa Ellen Blackaby
Megan Danielle Boylen
Micah Daniel Brewer
Joy Elizabeth Butcher
Nicole Cooprider
Amber Danielle Crank
Heather Day
Shanda Lee Elkins

Abigail Lynne Hansen
Brittany Ann Hedick
Tiffany Michelle Holcomb
Susannah Rose Hunter
Joshua David Jordan
Erich Brady Koenig
Melodie Priscilla Lamera
Hannah Lynn LeGrand
Rachel Elizabeth LeGrand
Joshua M. Lillie

Sarah Shepherd Lockwood
Benjamin Lincoln Witaya
Maxey
Maxwell Mathias Miner
Marilyn Mariah Mizenko
Julia Grace Nelson
Brooke Jayanna Oby
Caroline Frances Price
Sarah Jane Schaeffer
Brian Singleton

Michelle Diane Stephenson
Rebekah Marie Stillwell
Rebekah Marie Thompson
Matthew Davis Thorpe
Gabrielle Marie Torre
Conor W. Van Vranken
Ashley Brooke Wisehart

TOMPKINS CORTLAND COMMUNITY COLLEGE, DRYDEN, NY

Nicole Marie Augustine
Hannah Baker
Ernest Bell
Karen L. Betts
Anasthasia Blair
John T. Cannon Jr.
Kelly Doyle

Stacey Kay Eddy
Sophia Ezell
Angila Ferguson
Colton Arturo Griffith
Cecilia Hagen
Aneesa Hassell
Kevin Hernandez

Peter Karandeyev
Jessie Ke
Cassandra Kelly
Heather Ashley Skye
MacDonald
Lori Jean McKane
Jamie L. Myers

Deep Patel
Olu Hodari Khary Roberts
Aliyyah Sarvis
Jessi Kaye Thornton
David Lee Weaver
Colin Wood

TOUGALOO COLLEGE, TOUGALOO, MS

Blaise Adams
Jazmine Anderson
Lauryn Jaela Ashford
Trae Bell
Waynesha Equilla Blaylock
Brittaney Boyd
Khadijra R. Britton
Kiera Bronson
Timera L. Brown
Brandon R. Catchings
Nicole Collins
Wynisha Collins

Acacia Cooper
Laura K. Cooper
Antwan Courts
Breland Crudup
Spencer Davis
Amanda Dortch
Sonnetta Fields
Tierra Foster
Angel Garcia
Jessica Isabel Gutierrez
Torres
Billy Joe Hall II

Porshia Hardy
Jamila Harris
Venicelon Sacajawea Harris-
King
Aswad Jackson
Sherrall Jenkins
Khari Johnson
Shandell Marie Lewis
Tommie Mabry
Courtney Mangum
Danielle McGee
Jessica McKenzie

Laurin Olivia Mitchell
Jonathan Moore
Deja Patterson
Albert Payton Jr.
Christian James Ratliff-
Mason
Desiree Reed
De'Aris Rhymes
Johnny Robinson
Taralyn Alyce Rowell
Kira Seaton
Lauren Shelby

Naomi Short	Paula Thompson	Aurora Marie Washington	Dionne Wilson
Daneiqua Smith	Rasaan Turner	Victoria Marie Washington	Dorothy Elizabeth Woods
Daven Janeal Smith	Rasaan Sekou Turner	Jasmine Whipps	Hilary Micah Word
Rae'Jean Spears	Jameelah Walker	Iman Williams	Jonathan Zuniga-Hernandez
Jonathan Christian Taylor	Martinez Walker	Simeon Williams	

TOURO COLLEGE, BROOKLYN, NY

Bakhodir Abdullaev	Israel Feldstein	Rivka Herskowitz	Aliza Nabatian
Eli Aberbach	Miriam Felsenthal	Tzvi Hertzberg	Philip Nechamkin
Chana Yocheved Abrahkhaimova	Samuel Fieldman	Batsheva Hollander	Abraham Neuwirth
Tzvi H. Adams	Hilary Fink	Abbie Jakubovic	Talya Ovadia
Kevin Howard Alter	Avigail Fohrman	Tikva Kabbani	Leah Pacht
Abraham Altmann	Aryeh Forman	Bracha Kahn	Mendel Parnas
Moses Appel	Bracha Frank	Samuel Kahn	Prabhat Pathak
Elisheva Aufrichtig	Paul Fried	Tzvi Katz	Chana Pearl
Jacob Bakst	Hinda Friedman	Asael Kent	Aharon Pechman
Dan Bamshad	Rachel Frommer	Haddassah Kheradnam	Chana Pechman
Moshe Bedziner	Daniel Fuchs	Renata Khusainova	Yisroel Peikes
Sarah Beer	Temima Furst	Baila Kohn	Izzet Peksen
Yaakov Beiss	Esther Gellis	Mordechai Kuhnreich	Gabriella Pfeffer
Anaëlle Hanna Bensoussan	Raquel Gersten	Tara Kupchik	Ahuva Naomi Pollak
Abraham Bordon	Shlomo Ginsburg	Sara Langner	Avivah Rambod
Tatiana Brantsevich	Chaya P. Glazer	Debra Laub	Reut Raveh
Jonathan Burack	Shifra Glazer	Racheli Laub	Jacob Resnick
Tehila Chamani	Jonathan Glucksman	Yael Lazarus	Neeli Rhodes
Mark Cheirif	Adina Gold	Chaim Ozer Lederfeind	Daniel Romero
Dina Cohen	Dana (Shevi) Gold	Behgol Levian	Chaya Rosen
Gabrielle Tova Cohen	Meira Goldberg	Hannah Levin	Ann Rosenberg
Shaindel Cohen	Yael Davidowitz Goldberg	Abraham Levitman	Chaim Rosenfeld
Shoshana L. Cohen	Leah S. Goldberger	Chaya Levy-Haim	Avrohom Roth
Jeffrey Cynamon	Joshua Goldsmith	Daniel Lieberman	Aaron Rumpler
Simon Eliyahou Dadoun	Malka Goldstein	Jacob Lyss	Miriam Sabel
Hinda Dalfin	Yisroel Dov Goldstein	Ilya Mahilnitski	Brenda Salamon
Tehila Dasheff	Miryam Gordon	Rachael Mandelbaum	Yuliya Salanovich
Ruth Davidovits	Yisroel Green	Ari Mankowitz	Esther Schachter
Eli Derdik	Ayelet Greenberg	Yisroel Margolin	Aviva Schneider
Toby Diamond	Abraham Greenman	Gittel Markowitz	Yosef Schottenfeld
Jeffrey Drezner	Anna Grigoryan	Aviva Marquis	Tova Schur
Ari Eisenreich	Dov Grosser	Rachel Mayer	Hananya Schwartz
Naomi Englard	Chanie Grunwald	Leah Meth	Yehudis Segal
Aidel Ezagui	Yael Guttman	Esther Mizrahi	Chana Shakow
Baila Feldman	Esther Hecht	Chava Morgulis	Judah Siff
	Eva Hendler	Rivkah Moskowitz	Chana Sirota

Yaakov Slotkin
Bella Spira
Miriam Sussman
Rochel Tabi
Danielle Teitelbaum
Natalija Terehova
Rina Thaler
Yosef Yitzchak Tobi

Yosef Trachtenberg
Sara Trombka
Hannah Tsibushkin
Natanel david Tzion
Michael Ungar
Yishai Zvi Valter
Chaya Waxler
Renee Weinberg

Cynthia Weinberger
Faige Weinfeld
Hindi Weissman
Yaacov Wenick
Chana Wircberg
Richard Witkes
Kian Yaghoubnejad
Naftoli Yoffe

A. Young
Rachel Sarah Zdanowitz
Yaakov Zerbib
Adina Ziemba
Debra Zinn
Malka Zyman

TREVECCA NAZARENE UNIVERSITY, NASHVILLE, TN

Elizabeth A. Amick
Brian T. Anderson
Melody Rose Basinger
Sandy Brown
Wendy L. Bruer
Yolanda Y. Crutcher
Latisha Ann Dotson

Griffin Rees Dunn
Christopher Moriah Elliott
Daniel Seth Hare
Joseph Timothy Hare
Kayann E. Hare
Timothy Josiah Haynes

Sarah Elizabeth Claire Hogan
Kaylon MacKenzie King
Pamela D. Monjar
Rachael R. Nemiroff
Letrecia Lynn Parchman
Zachary Taylor Rayfield

Delois Reagan
Mackenzie Joy Rosenjack
Justin T. Schoolcraft
Sarah Elizabeth Wesley
Celina Mae Yates
Stephanie Michelle Young

TRIDENT TECHNICAL COLLEGE, CHARLESTON, SC

Linda Ash
Jonna Berry
Laurie A. Borcyk
Natalie Bristow

Rhonda M. Cox
Elizabeth Daughtry
Kimberly Anne Golde
Margaret Gombus

Lauren Grant
Tara Hirsch
Tracie Hopkins
Emily Jax

Laura Thomas
Justin DeGuzman Tomilloso
Krystal Welch

TRINE UNIVERSITY, ANGOLA, IN

Haley A. Agard
Mark A. Albert
Sydney T. Alley
Michelle J. Arce
Dustin A. Arvola
Shalisa V. Baxter
Betsy K. Beatty
Robin C. Beidelman
Kevin E. Berry
Wynn M. Bishop
Samantha F. Bortner
Zachary B. Bower
Dawn M. Bowers
Steven R. Bradford
Jayson P. Brennan
Deanna M. Buckley
Elyse R. Buehrer

Alec D. Burchard
Tammy L. Burgess-Kent
Trey D. Calver
Nicholas A. Cassidy
Michael A. Chernoff
William W. Connors
Lynda L. Crawford
Cameron A. Crenshaw
John L. Daniel
Olivia M. Deck
Barbara C. Dyrcz
Denise M. Easterday
Colleen M. Fair
Luke Riley Fimreite
Nicolas R. Flint
Courtney L. Forsythe
Alex M. Gillespie

Samuel D. Gilly
Garrett W. Gruenewald
Jacob S. Haller
Wade A. Hantz
Raeshone L. Harris
Christie Robyn Hasbrouck
Randall L. Haupert
Mitchell G. Herber
Brittany K. Herr
Zachary D. Hess
Daniel J. Hinde
Nicholas S. Hostetler
Katherine P. Hultquist
Jennifer S. Jackemeyer
Hunter N. Johnson
Amanda L. Kempher
Allison N. Kitson

Caleb J. Knust
Kyle J. Livingstone
Karly B. Lounds
Alexis E. Mack
Joshua D. Marty
Tyler C. Marx
Ethan M. Maust
Jaime L. McCarrell
Jordan T. McLain
Nicole C. Moan
Matthias B. Phillips
Catherine E. Porter
Taylor Keana Rabel
Susan D. Rarey
Jenna Michelle Rauch
Shawn J. Reiner
Andrew J. Rexroth

Nathan B. Riemer	Nicholas J. Shelton	Christopher A. Strauch	Steven Casey Walker
Jessica L. Riemesch	Ryan R. Skiles	Damian C. Tam	Lindsey Rae Welsh
Eric D. Roldan	Alexandra J. Slick	Brittany A. Taylor	Brandon J. Wilson
Niki L. Salzman	Whitney R. Stahlhut	Megan R. Verkamp	Amber R. Woods

TRINIDAD STATE JUNIOR COLLEGE, TRINIDAD, CO

Elizabeth Marie Aguilar	Samantha Renee Glover	Felipe De Assis Mello	Ainsley Ridgeway
Adam J. Aguirre	James Gruening	Machado	Sara Jean Rino
Ryan S. Ashbaugh	Nancy N. Guzman Diaz	Demetria Marie Madalena	Brandon Wade Robbins
Robert Edward Ayres	Jason James Guzzi	Kaitlin Frances Martinez	Katia Rocha
Jennifer M. Baca	Tannar T. Hanks	Robert Thomas Massarotti	Jeffrey Todd Rogers
Cam Lachlan Baird	Pamela Lynn Hennigan	Samantha R. McDonald	Caylene Romero
Rebekah L. Baquet-Holguin	Kelsey Rae Hernandez	Brylee Amber Medina	Lindsey DeRose Romero
Cody Basinger	Laura Andrea Herrera	Trent Delbert Milbrath	Zoe Ruff
Dante Amateis Begano	Saad Wady Hissien	Christopher Gabriel Mohr	Kimberly Anne Salapich
Lauren A. Bending	Steven L. Holdeman	Yasmin Eve Mookerdum	Helen A. Segura
Aleska Blagojevic	Eric Allen Household	Nicholas Allen Moore	Krissy Serra
Shane L. Boice	Austin Taylor Howard	Valerie Renee Morabito	James Edward Smith
Rebecca Dawn Bowman	William Robert Howe	Evan Chauncey Motlong	Jessica Leigh Smith
Jessica Sue Britt	Desiree Dinea Hyer	Kyle Joseph Neufer	Lukas Brooks Smith
Anabelle Celis	Kiera Brieanne Jackson	Cruz Nevarez	Kyle Lane Sowards
Cody Zeb Chavez	Raleigh Jackson	Garrett Hayden Nichols	Johanna Joy Spleen
Lina Chavez	Kevin A. Johnson	Chelsey Angel Nicol	Jennifer Ellen Stevens
Alexander Earl Chotvacs	Hope Marie Jones	Connor Alexander	Mark Tisdale
Ariana Catherine Coca	Jared John Jones	Nutterfield	Jayson Jerome Tuntland
Cheyenne R. Cron	Jordan T. Jones	Alec John Petterson	Phillip James Underwood
Amber Rose Dahl	Kyrie Mariah Joslyn-	Rachel Andrea Pirtle	Sierra Alicia Valerio
Aimee L. Davis	McCant	Stephanie Lynn Plata	Mark D. Vangemer
Adriana Lielua DeVille	Daniel Jurney	Anthony Carlo Porreco	Courtney Lee Vigil
Joshua W. Ellis	Justin Kamal	Riley Jacob Powell	Lee Benjamin Vigil
Torri Reynell Farrow	David Kangas	Caden Sean Pratt	Shandi May Waldroupe
Schady Fergeson	Hamza Karoumia	Colin Robert Pratt	Lacey Mitchell Washington
Katelynn Ann Findley	Nathaniel Patrick Kenyon	Eric S. Quan	Natoshia Wiederman
Kara Elizabeth Flores	Samuel Joseph Kounz	Laeticia Rambeau	Jack Henry Wilson
Donald Alfred Forland	Kenneth John Kowalski	Dorian Lord Ray	Marisa Kay Wilt
Kevin Foster	Daniel Lieberman	Carrie Jolene Reed	Holly Mari Woodbury
Alq Anton Fuierer	Flowerr Lopez	Herbert Wesley Reed	Adelphons Yephnick
Goeff Fullerton	Michael David Lowe	Hannah Marie Reynolds	Stephen Joseph Zmich

TRINITY BAPTIST COLLEGE, JACKSONVILLE, FL

Ashton Victoria Barnes	Katelynn Lola Crockett	Alexander Scott Dew	Joseph Donald Gaines
Leah Kay Brasher	Amber Marie Davoll	Michael James Duquette	Anna Rachel Gilkey

Taylor Nicole Keener
Elizabeth Ann Miller

David Lee Sears
Désirée Judith Smith

Gabriel Evan Stephens
John Wayne Sweat Jr.

Michelle Heidi Wise

TRINITY BIBLE COLLEGE, ELLENDALE, ND

Carly Anderson
Heidi Arin
Grant David Belgarde
Zach S. Crowe
Janae Droste
Kayla Folven
Cheri Froelich

Joshua Froelich
Jenna Hammontree
Sabra Rinnah Hoffman
Sarah Jefferies
Carissa Elsie Jost
Katelin Lindgren
Melissa Jo Lindgren

Anita Rae Morgenstern
Heather O'Brien
Rebecca Olsson
Neil Oravsky
SaraLi Petersen
Jessica Leigh Pryer
Jordan Rohrbach

Charitie Sandoz
Nathan Sandoz
Savanna Jean Schneider
Rachel Kaitlynn Seidel

TRINITY INTERNATIONAL UNIVERSITY, DEERFIELD, IL

Micaiah Andrew Burnett
Andrew Chally
Gina Collesano
Ryan Corcoran
Richard James Davis

Mariah Ferrier
Kelsey Gill
Sarah Harris
Nina Ingoglia
Andre B. Kimbrough Sr.

Adam Lange
Emily E. Loretto
Leotha Scott
Irene Strom Spejcher
Tiffany Stoiber

Reilly Todd
Cody Allen Voetmann

TROCAIRE COLLEGE, BUFFALO, NY

Arwa Al-Naji
Jamie A. Brayley
Rachel Bruso

Julie Jarka
Chelsea Kelly
Jerry Manuel

Christie Oak
Justin Rosie
Cynthia Runkel

Lindsey Wiza

TROY UNIVERSITY, TROY, AL

Jordan Adams
Mohammed Alsaid
Martha Anderson
Jeremiah Baky
Diana Barrett
Hailey Bates
Serena Bishop
Erica Bodiker
Katrina Moana Bokenfohr
Kristina Ka Pua O'kalani
Bokenfohr
Cierra Brinson
Adam David Brown
Victoria Brutlag
Abby Burch
Candice Butts
Kendall Carbonie

Courtney Chandler
Stephanie Clinton
Christoline Nichole Daniels
Payton Alexandra Donley
John Elmore
Jordyn Elston
Makenzie Ervin
Sarah Katherine Fleming
Kristen Frye
Farrah Nicole Gaston
Robert Gause
Adrian Janell Gee
Sarah Elizabeth Gilley
Quinta Goines
Lindsey Gordon
Autumn Griggs
Adrienne Gunn

Haley Alise Harris
Mary Elizabeth Heath
Kara Jane Runelle Henry
Kirsten Henry
Thuong Hoang
Alethea Hoffer
Cathy Huang
Danielle Humphreys
Jennifer Jayjohn
Jenyia Johnson
Mieah Shanice Johnson
MacKenzie Brooke Kayler
Angelene Kendall
Christian Knight
Ashlee Laramore
Emily Lincoln
Leah Livingston

Jonathan Eric Lowe
William D. Mangum II
Emily Brooke Mena
Brianna Rose Mendoza
Herman B. Mitchell Jr.
Whitney Nicole
Montgomery
Jane Morrell
Standria Alexis Moss
Ryan Parker
Raven Pasibe
Terrell Patrick
Jasmine Philyaw
Graham Pierce
Katie Pouncey
William Justin Ramirez
Knyra Ratcliff

Hannah Ray	Hallie Shannon	William Swicord	Erin White
Jaylan Reynolds	Dustin Sikes	Sierra E. Terrell	Rachael Wilkerson
Megan Roberts	Katie Sippel	Kennedy Thomas	Shelby Anna Wood
Patrick Rodgers	Jorge Solis	Tameron Alexandria Thorpe	Erin Woods
Ashley Rollins	Carlie Allison Spencer	Ansley Tucker	Alexandra Jade Worthy
Estephany Ruano	Kayla Sprayberry	Ngoc Vo	
Bria Rushing	Ronique L. Sutton	Chelsea Watson	
Shelby Scott	Jenna Lizabeth Swafford	Ivy Watts	

TROY UNIVERSITY GRADUATE SCHOOL, TROY, AL

Teaira J. Lindsey	Kimbrlei A. McCain	Kitty Amanda Smothers	Devangkumar L. Tandel
Qun Liu			

TRUETT MCCONNELL COLLEGE, CLEVELAND, GA

Rebekah Faith Atkins	John Thomas Bethel Justus	Jessica Starr Parker	Andrea Grace Towns
Lindsey Leigh Dyer	Penzi Kakoma	Thomas Philip Spivey	Stevi LaRie Williams
Bailey Elizabeth Jarnagin			

TULSA COMMUNITY COLLEGE SOUTHEAST CAMPUS, TULSA, OK

Brady W. Duncan

UNIFORMED SERVICES UNIVERSITY OF THE HEALTH SCIENCES, BETHESDA, MD

Evan Baines	Teresa Gilbride	Janette Noveras	Colin M. Smith
Ethan Bernstein	Joshua Krieger	Michael Pavio	Nicholas Szuflita
Jeremy Bolin	David Lin	Donovan Reed	Matthew Ward
Kaitlin Campbell	Raymond Michael Meyer	Haydn Roberts	Piotr Wisniewski
Mary Ford	Alexander Nissen	Alexandra Shams	

UNIFORMED SERVICES UNIVERSITY OF THE HEALTH SCIENCES DANIEL K. INOUYE GRADUATE SCHOOL OF NURSING, BETHESDA, MD

Mark Albright	Bethany Casper	John Kerns	Joseph Alan Melchi
Holly Archer	Danielle Kay Cuevas	Ann Ketz	Elizabeth Ann Poindexter
Samantha Elizabeth Bazan	Shinita La'Shay Burke	Jacqueline Marie Killian	Jennifer Lee Prosser
Jonathan Beatty	Favors	Rhonda Leary	Quinn Richards
Tara Blackwelder	Jennifer Fiandt	Lindsay Leskanich	Angela Shrader
Patrick Courtney Boyle	Stephen Gonsalves	Brittany Joyce Lozier	Kyong Winkler
Lisa Kim Buckles	Justin Hefley	Louis Magyar	
Kellie Casero	Kevin Jones	Lindsey Marquez	

UNION COLLEGE, LINCOLN, NE

Dorinda Afiba-Alimah Ackah

Sharyn Adams

Jah-Babe Aigbokhan

Edward Akioka

Jessyka Shana Albert

Ron Dale Ivan Ang

Amanda Joy Ashburn

Bryce Ashton

Kyle Berg

Adrienne Rae Maree Bohl

Natalie Alexandra Bruzon Mederos

Cesar Cabral Pestana

Bradley Allen Carlson

Janaya Cashman

David Castillo

Jessica Courter

Margrette Dallas

David Deemer

Kaelee Nicole Douchey

Victoria Edelbach

Kathy Edwards

Steven Foster

Gloria German

Ethan Griffith

Catalina Grigore

Hannah Gustafson

Kristina-Noelle Nanez Hammer

Joshua Hester

Rachel M. Jorgensen

Pemphero David Kandoje

Liana Kent

Mason Lazar

Timothy LeBard

Hannah Lechner

Rosalina Matheson

Benjamin Medina

David Meier

Andrew Mekelburg

Brittani Memsic

Tova Lynn Miller

Curtis Mishleau

Ryan Andrew Nelson

Rebecca O'Hare

Luis Olmedo

Chase Olson

Hyeon Park

Monica Pervis

Oscar Quezada

Bradley Roberts

Taylor Roberts

Stephanie Rubenthaler

Guanbo Shao

Arianna Rose Shay

Yuliya Shirokova

Sneha Taujale Shrestha

Cassandra Nicole Smith

Harrison Smith

Jordan Stolz

Kiley Thompson

Ashley Unterseher

Benjamin VandeVere

Sarah Christine Ventura

Madison Victoria Wagnaar

Megan Wehling

Ronnie Zanella

UNION UNIVERSITY, JACKSON, TN

Julia Danielle Berends

Courtney Danielle Berger

William Andrew Bigelow

Allen Richard Bradley

Grace Elizabeth Carbonell

Hannah Marie Conway

Chandler M. Cryer

BethAnne Lynnae Davis

Quinlan Kathryn Draper

Emily Elizabeth Easter

Joshua Mark Edgren

Lacie Alexandria Fink

Anna Jayne Goodman

Bonna Ruth Hardee

Holly Ann Johnson

Ruthie Ann Johnson

Kenan David Keller

Karis Patricia Kontilis

Rebecca Nicole Leet

Evan Michael Lewoczko

Gray Harrison Magee

Nathaniel Alden Magnuson

Jennifer R. Main

Allie Marie Malone

Sara Clarke Mason

Anna Lang McKelvey

Hailey Dawn Moore

Kaylene Vanessa Portell

Hannah Grace Richardson

Elizabel Ashby Sartin Riggs

Hannah Elizabeth Sewell

Caleb Tanner Shaw

Christopher Ryan Shaw

Abigail Nicole Thigpen

Elizabeth Joy Tomyn

McKinley Layne Tribble

Michelle Marie Undis

Jonathan Randolph Vailes

Heather Joy Vidal

Anna Katelyn Walls

Drew Alexander Wells

Clare Margaret Williams

Christina Danette Young

UNIVERSITY OF ARKANSAS AT MONTICELLO, MONTICELLO, AR

James B. Alexander

Jennifer L. Bailey

Frances A. Bellott

Hunter Alane Bennett

Reagan J. Dobbs

Robert L. Fletcher

Jimmy Tyler Harrison

Kenneth Walker Jarrett

Valeria A. Johnson

Aliyah R. Kennedy

Shelby M. Lane

Anna M. Lauhon

Julia M. Martin

Emily Mendiola

Nicole A. Mullen

Sarah B. Phillips

Destiny N. Randolph

McKenzie H. Rice

Shaynna R. Tanner

Eva S. Wallace

Danielle E. West

Donnell D. White

UNIVERSITY OF ARKANSAS AT PINE BLUFF, PINE BLUFF, AR

Leathan John Irvin

UNIVERSITY OF ARKANSAS COMMUNITY COLLEGE AT MORRILTON, MORRILTON, AR

Diana S. Bonilla Rivera	Jessie L. Kirkpatrick	Miranda G. Ponder	Justin M. Velte
Lena A. Couch	Brandon L. Klar	Matthew D. Post	Jonathan R. Wear
Gary W. Fryer	Jacob L. Long	Natalie M. Prall	
William H. Gwatney	Joshua W. McCrary	Joseph T. Ryan	
Sarah K. Hensley	Steven K. Perdue	Harold R. Spence	

UNIVERSITY OF ARKANSAS COMMUNITY COLLEGE BATESVILLE, BATESVILLE, AR

Aubrei Marie Adams	Jamie Rose Deken	Deborah G. Keller	Kimberly Licole Sample
Katie Lea Baker	Teresa A. Dodd	Kristie D. Kennedy	Roxanne Marie Scott
Brenda Balderas-Gonzalez	Carmen S. Duncan	James Samuel Lassiter	Crystal Denise Sharp
Jeffery Lynn Barker	Kristi Yvonne Fasse	Shane Anthony Lively	Jesse Rex Shoemaker
Megan Elizabeth	Debra K. Fletcher	Jackie N. Lowry	Cole L. Simmons
Blankenship	Marcy Ann Ford	Baylee Layne Mathews	Emily J. Smith
Akeyda Bowman	James N. Foster	Timothy William May	Heather S. Smith
Lynnette A. Bray	Selena A. Fouse	Joshua Keith McAnally	Tammy E. Smith
James R. Bridgeman	Rachael Marie Gifford	Jim McClurg	Kelsie Taylor Steele
Laci Ladawna Bridger	Jennifer D. Gilert	Joseph D. McDougal	Samantha Jo Stinnett
Kayla Dawn Brown	Stephanie J. Gladden	Kevin Lee McGee	Kayla Danelle Strother
Cherie Nell Buie	Allison Marie Green	Terry K. McGee	Alissa C. Sullivan
Karen Michelle Bush	Christin M. Hall	Robert A. Merritt	Micah D. Thatch
Nathan S. Christopher	Leslie N. Hitchcock	Christopher A. Middleton	Tyler W. Thomas
Nicole Louise Coe	Dohnny Jarrell Holley	Christian Eduardo Morgado	Lydia Marie Thorne
Leonard William Coles	Ashley N. Hudson	Laura Ivett Morgado	Lauren Elizabeth Wagster
Kristen Stazhia Cooper	Robert W. Johnson	Luz D. Ortiz-Roa	Lisa M. Watts
Candice R. Davis	Cari A. Johnston	Dianne L. Patterson	Miranda Williams

UNIVERSITY OF ARKANSAS COMMUNITY COLLEGE HOPE–TEXARKANA, HOPE, AR

Lindsey Braden	Amanda Kay Condon	Hannah Victoria Mattson	Rosie Richard
Lana Nichole Cherry	Shantel Rena Dennis	Heaven L. North	Sheria Ronshae Sanders
Kayla N. Collier	Jeffery G. Ladd II	Maryann Paredes	Samantha L. Smith

UNIVERSITY OF ARKANSAS LITTLE ROCK, LITTLE ROCK, AR

Ramya Deepthi Babbepalli	Clarissa A. Coleman	Adrian J. Hubbard	Tavleen Kaur
Kathryn R. Best	Connor P. Donovan	Cerise Inganji	Walter L. Kroptavich
Franklin L. Bick	Everett E. Elam	Caroline N. Johnson	Minghua Li
Bagwell L. Brandon	Lyndse L. Ellis	Marquise D. Jones	Grizel Macias
Latasha M. Briscoe	Jamie R. Gardner	Talyn N. Jones	Taurine C. Main
Kamesha N. Brooks	Morgan N. Gillum	Aliyah M. Joseph	Dillon W. Nash
Emily L. Bruner	Brandye N. Gilmore	Shahnawaz Gulam Yasin	Kunda Jean Pamphile
Taner Bulgak	Ali I. Hammoodi	Kapadia	Ndorimana
Anuia Chettipalli	Barasha Hiloidhari	Bayazit Karaman	LaChansity L. O'Gwinn

Shelby B. Owens
Micah P. Parker
Gabrielle C. Phifer
Shara M. Robbins
Autumn Rouse

Shatorya Shepard
Sankineni Shruthi
Rachel L. Smith
Alexa B. Treml
Jennifer L. Turnage

Ashley N. Wheeler
Michael H. White
Joanna Allison Whittaker
Tevin D. Wilborn
Desiree L. Williams

Kelsay A. Williams
Brittany C. Wright

UNIVERSITY OF BALTIMORE, BALTIMORE, MD

Kierra Brown
Benin Dakar
Jasmine Gibson
Stehle Harris

Tracey Hirsch
Hilary Keil
Caitlyn McNeill
Robert Jay Neuman Jr.

Fenose Osedeme
Shou De Shi
Amelia White
Danielle Suzanne Woyowitz

Sahar Zafar
Ann Margaret Zelenka

UNIVERSITY OF BRIDGEPORT, BRIDGEPORT, CT

Olumide Adebayo
Paul Alfaro
Bashar Alhafni
Imane Alou Issa
Ernest Joon Shiong Ang
Simon Arias
Samantha Baronavski
Ellen A. Belitzky
Vignesh Mandalapa
Bhoopathy
Steven Boitano
Ryan Carmone
Phillip Carroll
Edward C. Cirillo
Rebecca R. Ciullo
Clarens Clement
Kaila Crandall
Cristian Cuatzo
Angel De Los Santos

Diane Doodnauth
Gazi M. Duman
Alan Eskandar
Karissa Espada
Nancy Fagbene
Daniel Fernandes Lim
Karizma Jazmon Funnye
Alban E. Gaval
Sung Soon Gaval
Kwonsook Gerena
Fernando Gonzalez
Michelle Graboski
Shirlin Higgins
Kent Hoffman
Shamare Holmes
Anthony Huynh
Lalit N. Jagtiani
Edward Jeong
Gunsoo Kim

Hyeeun Kim
Angie Laguerre
John Dyls Leonidas
Jeff London
Amanda Rebecca Lynch
Rigel Mahmood
Cassie Mailhot
Terica Medwinter
Shiloh Morse
Desmond Nash
Jerry Olivier
Virginia Orman
Paige Owens
McKenzie Parent
Khrystian Pereira
Phylicia Zona Prince
Daniel Rabottini
Maheshwari Kumar
Rakkappan

Rebecca Marie Rieg
Emily Marie Riehl
Justin Sabo
Trina Scheie
Chernor Sesay
Ibrahim Shehadeh
Kristina Miju Smith
Ruta Miok Smith
Pham Tam
Dan Tenney
Ozden Tozanli
Perini Divya Deepika
Valla Malla
Larissa Vilaboim Oliveira
Brian Vo
Rishi Warokar
Takae Whitmore
Crystal Wilkins
Kajin Yousif

UNIVERSITY OF CENTRAL ARKANSAS, CONWAY, AR

Corry M. Adams
Erin Adams
Azeem Adebayo
Andrea Andrews
Allison Armstrong
Courtney Taylor Barrentine
Bertha Margarita Barrientos-
Valdivieso

Gunnar Alexander Bartlett
David Beale
Alyssa Kay Beaver
Hanna Betts
Amber Marie Breaux
Courtney Nicole Briggler
Natali Brown
Emily Burgess

Melissa Frances Burnley
Karrie Michelle Butler
Zach Carter
Tyaniah Sparkyl Cash
Samantha Scharolot Chase
Callie Clifton
Kayla Close
Stephanie Daigle

Aundrea Dorrough
Cody Charles Douell
Hailey Durham
Tara Elaine Dyer
Jassa Ferrell
Amber Fleming
Treslyn Fletcher
Mariel Forte

Jaimi Franklin
Chantelle Marie Giles
Jason Tyler Grady
Christina Griffin
Jerryll Elexander Hall
Lauren Kay Hall
Stephanie Nicole
Higginbotham
Logan D. Hirsch
Emma Claire Howard
Logan Rigby Howard
Hannah James
Cody Jefferson
Mariam Karamoko
Sinaly Karamoko
Emily Kibler
Dylan Kimery
Rachel Knowlton

Courtney Kordsmeier
Victoria LaFave
Trinady Alyssa Ledbetter
Ivana Lie
Travis Long
Malcolm Luster
Alexandria Mackey
LaDasia L. McCullough
Sydne Brenae McDade
Angel-Marie Faith
McDaniel
Sarah McDaniel
James McKay
Brittany M. McNeil
Whitney Alexis Meyer
Lori H. Monday
Jordan Lee Ann Moore
Jacqueline Bernice Moragne

Lauren Morris
Sarah Elizabeth Moss
Alesha Mount
Silas Michael A. Nellums
ZhuQing ZhuQing Nim
Corey Parks
John David Patterson
Kelsey Pope
Raven Symone Purifoy
Brittany Renfro
Camille Liberty Matias
Reyes
Taylor Morgan Richard
Nia Alyse Robinson
Aston Rosenberg
Ava Rumph
Tatsiana Savenka
Rylee Breanne Schwaller

Christian Scott
Emilie Shatto
Travis John Shaver
Sequoia Zhane' Snowden
Madeline Spickard
Abigail Strickland
Kirsten Tully
Aum'Arie Wallace
Kelsie Wasiluk
Skyler Colice Weinmann
Shonqualla Patrice West
Jacob Ian Wickliffe
Jarod Wickliffe
Seth Allen Wilson
Nikki Jo Wipplinger
Candace Danielle Young
David Zimulinda

UNIVERSITY OF CINCINNATI, CINCINNATI, OH

Manoj Ambalavanan

Ceejay Leota Boyce

Ashley Nkadi

Jose Carlos Liendo
Villarreal

UNIVERSITY OF DUBUQUE, DUBUQUE, IA

Stephen Adjei
Abbas Fayhan Alotaibi
Torrey Bahr
Klaudia Basierak
Kasandra Benson
Cassandra Berger
Sharon Boer
Emily Loretta Brinker
Caleb Chincoya
Tristan Conner Cortez
Alexander Eckes
Kristen Field
Icle Freeland

Melissa Gilstrap
Devin Rose Glenski
Gonzalo Hernandez
Cascante
Lucas Kahl
Andrew Kendell
Matthew Kilburg
Emily Konrardy
Joseph Edward Larson
Amonda' DezJohn Lawhorn
Jack Edward Lindsay
Megan Loes
Zachary Marotta

Joshua Michael Merritt
Abbey Christine Meyer
Dylan Michels
Daniel Morillo
Tatyana M. Mumm
Fabiola Ortiz
Edward B. Pablo III
Ashlyn Ptasienski
Chelsea Rangel
Ramon Riley
MacKenzie Robbins
Kristin Jean Robey
Laura Schauer

Amy Shook
Megan Siepler
Elissa J. Smith
Blaine Snitker
Paige Triervieler
Kimberly Trinco
Emielia Suzanne Turner
Robyn Wittkopf
Victoria Woltz
Hannah Zieser
Matthew John Zittritsch

UNIVERSITY OF GEORGIA, ATHENS, GA

Colin Asher Aaronson
Mitzi Anderson
Brittany Arnold

Diane Michel Arnold
Matthew Mark Arnold
Sylvia Ashley

Jayme Astarita
Shallum Atkinson
Stephanie Bacastow

Christen Baskerville
Kelly Marie Beavers
Danielle Bennett

Jessica Blaeser

Christine Brady

John R. Britt Jr.

Kelsey Brown

Tifara Brown

Mansur Ali Buffins

Lindsey Rae Bunting

John Branson Byers

Carson Byrd

Catherine Mahala Callaway

Jonathon Lynn Carter

Christina Joyce Chow

Briana Monet Clark

Chase Collum

Amanda Compton

Cayden Lanier Cook

Terence Curry

Kate A. Cushman

Lara Davis

Kiondre Dunnam

Alexandra Edquist

Steven Edwards

Dustin Ronald Ellis

Colin Fite

Shawn Foster

Houston Alexander Gaines

Hayden Elizabeth George

Martha "Meg" Gourley

Morgan Govatos

Elizabeth Faith Greene

Lance La'Broch Griffin

Dinesh Manohar Gurpur

Lori Hanna

Brendan Harris

Jordan Hill

Suzanna Harris Hodges

Betsy Holman

Derek Homrich

Melissa Jennings

Robert Glenn Johnson

Dylan Jolley

Mugdha Joshi

Alexa Lee Kelly

Pureun "Blue" Kim

Courtney Koval

Kimberly Lai

Taylor Lamb

Adam Lessner

Bruce Li

Christian Trevor Lisa

Louis Louis York

Emily Kathleen Maloney

Paige Marogil

Tori Martin

Sarah J. Mayer

Courtney McCune

Nicole Marie McEwen

Darby Elizabeth Miller

Larner Elizabeth Mills

Stephanie Mobley

Maria Munoz

Maria Susana Munoz

Richard Murray

Kim Tien Nguyen

Rachel Paleg

Thomas Paris

Trevor Ryan Paulos

Justin Payan

Adriana Perez

Erik S. Petrina

Katherine Frances Prather

Aaron Emmanuel Rawls

Clarice Reid

Nicole Riley

Rebecca H. Roth

Tucker Rubin

Miranda Russell

Nicolas Salyers

Francisco Sanchez

Mary Grace Sexton

Chinmaya Sharma

Sarah Frances Shor

Johnelle Simpson

Shaunteri Skinner

Cassidy Gail Sparkman

Tynan Stewart

Mary Beth Stinson

Anna Lee Studebaker

Cavender Steven Sutton

Stephanie Kah-Sin Tan

LaPorsche Thomas

Bert Ferguson Thompson Jr.

Sam Tingle

Esther Damaris Tonea

Kendall Alexzandra

Trammell

Madison Turner

Taylor Turnipseed

Nicole Marie Valerioti

Alexandria Jordan Van Dyke

Juhi Varshney

Sivakumar Venkatachalam

Melissa Mattie Visbal

Christina Wilson

Zari Desatrina Noel Wilson

Jennifer Woodward

Isabel Yanes

Cameron Saeed Zahedi

UNIVERSITY OF GEORGIA COLLEGE OF PHARMACY, ATHENS, GA

Ife-Atu Courtney Anachebe

Jaimie Amanda Bailey

Madeline Jane Burke

Andrea Michelle Clarke

Sarah Jane Clements

Allyson Alayne Cox

Shaily Tushar Doshi

Vidhi Ketan Doshi

Charlotte Lauretta
Dunderdale

Miriam Dalana Durden

Joshua Louis Foley

Sean Christopher Hawkins

Youn Jeoung

Jacqueline Jiayuan Liu

Mark Jonathan Miller

Corinne Marie Parker

Sara Terry Petron

Allison McCall Porter

Lindsey Ann Sellers

Abigail Taylor Shell

Cayla Noel Sinnemon

Katherine Marie Smith

Khushbu M. Tejani

Paige Nicole Wallace

Nathaniel Brett Wayne

UNIVERSITY OF GREAT FALLS, GREAT FALLS, MT

Lindsey Abramson

Garrett Adair

Rachel Altman

Aja Jewel Anderson

Annamaria Aquilino

Wendi Avila

Michael Ayala

Matthew Bartolotta

Dylan Berget

Tanner Boone

Christina Bruce

Iain Carr

Evalani Nicole Dahlin

Jordan Daugerty

Brianne Davis

Elyce Donaldson

Kyra Dorvall
Katelyn Duncan
Rowena FitzGerald
Katrina Greenlief
Cara Guderian
Kylan Hallett
Gena Handlan
Darah Huertas-Vining
Holly Johnson
Jace Kalbfleisch
Sadie Kieson
Marc Klimas

Erin Langdon
Erin Legel
Kyle Leir
Abby Linch
Darren Lockett
Jonathan Magana
Tiffany Marks
Katherine Martini
Mark Melton
Kathleen Monaco
Kelsee Montagna
Joseph Moser

Ijeoma Nneka Nnadi
Danielle Norling
Kelli O'Brien
Lauren Ozdowski
Shelby Pollington-Houska
Salvatore Principe III
Khaldoon Rashid
Jessica Ann Ream
McKinley Ridenour
Bryndee Ryan
Ciann Marie C. San Nicolas
Luke Schlosser

Pedro Simplicio
Sara Skinner
Andrew Sloan
Matthew Struzik
Peter Struzik
Keeley Van Blaricom
Taylor Vaughn
Nicole Wemhoff
Justin Whitman
Melvin Williams

UNIVERSITY OF HOLY CROSS SCHOOL OF NURSING, NEW ORLEANS, LA

Marissa White D'Antonio
Katie Lynn Escher

Aubree Gayle Lacour
Brittney Ann Montes de Oca

Alexa Shea Parria

Sanjay Muneshwar Murthi
Raman

UNIVERSITY OF HOUSTON CLEAR LAKE, HOUSTON, TX

Robin Michelle Aleman
Laeken Danielle Alswager
William Francis Althoff II
Cinthya Angeles
Carla Bradley
Julie Brenengen
Nancy Crumb
Elizabeth Davis
Asia Donald
Victoria Duffoo Tirado
Makayla Ellis
Ashley Fisher

Liane Friedberg
Nishok Vishnu Ganesan
Arlene Garcia-Chau
Michele Gibson
David Gonzalez
Amber Gross-Velez
Adriana Herrera
Brittany Hiett
Kevin Johnson
Paula Jones
Tho Le
Autumn Mason

Nisha Mathews
Juliana Munoz
Justin Murphy
Harsh Naik
Lilian Anna Nguyen
Tri Nguyen
Tri Tan Nguyen
Charan Pulipalupula
Sai Shankar Ramakrishnan
Gowri Amaranath Rapati
Katelynn Rivardo
Bianca Salinas

Wayne Alan Sallee Jr.
Sandy Samaan
Courtney Shaw
Darrell Ladon Stewart
Madison Stults
Truc Mai Tong Tu
Daniela Vazquez Klisans
Jose Daniel Velazco-Garcia
Bao Tran Thuy Vu
Jasmine Washington
Brianna Wilson
Leah Won

UNIVERSITY OF JAMESTOWN, JAMESTOWN, ND

Megan Baker
Ashley Barnhart
Emma Bellmore
Katianne Brockpahler
Alaina Brown
Levi Brown
Kaia Buck
Anthony Eric Gumarang
Buzzell
Beth Champa

Morgan Croves
Molly Ecker
Elizabeth Entzel
Mya Erickson
Brooke Grooters
Emerald Gyuricza
Jacob Hagler
Rachel Heuchert
Sarah Holen
Daniel Janu

Ashley Jenniges
Sydney Johnson
Joshua Knutson
Nathan Kopperud
Jessica Laddusaw
Nicole LaDouceur
Danette Larson
Kaylyn Lindstrom
Jana Lynch
Jordan Lynch

Bailey Nickoloff
Brook Rheault
Alphonse William
Schoeneberger
Markie Struxness
Brequan Tucker
Landon Uetz
Emily Wang
Nathan Willer
Bryn Woodside

UNIVERSITY OF LA VERNE, LA VERNE, CA

Hope Allen
Nysa Allen
Gregory Manual Amaya
Angelina Roxanne Arreola
David Judah Asbra
Tyler J. Bertao
Ryanne Bible
Jacob Bogdanoff
Kristina Bugante
Lauren Elizabeth Crumbaker
Sierra Rose Dasher
Breanna David
Desmond Rene Delgadillo

Theo Nina Doyle
Manlio Gamero-Rivera
Cari Ann Geiss
Christopher Alexander
Gonzalez
Celiana Vargas Guerra
Hayley Hulin
Ashley Mentie Johnson
Bradlee Michelle Johnson
Kassandra Lynn Jones
Sierra Jones
Jairian Clara Ka'ahanui
Megan T. Keller

Abby Marie Knight
Keith Kolb
Emily E. Lau
Melanie A. Loon
Stephanie Lopez-Ruvalcaba
Scott Davis MacKay
Anissa Francine Melendez
Jolene G. Nacapuy
Brenda M. Ornelas
Yareiry Giselle Pineda
Carla Quiroz
David Ritter
Juan Jose Rodriguez

Annabel E. Secaida
Kathryn M. Simonelli
Steve Richard Torres
Jeffrey D. Van Voorhis
Eden Elizabeth Vasquez
Sasha Lynn Webb
Kaila D. Williams
Joseph Emmanuel Yanez
Brittany Marie Yaxley
Selyna Carmen Ybarra

UNIVERSITY OF LOUISIANA AT MONROE GRADUATE DIVISION, MONROE, LA

Eric Bass
Brandi Decelle Hinton

Tonya Keene
Emily Barthol Myrick

Alvetta Lenoir Smith
Amanda Halley Tull

Asa Paul Warren

UNIVERSITY OF LOUISIANA AT MONROE UNDERGRADUATE, MONROE, LA

Christopher Adkins
Jameson Levon William
Alston
Tyler Gray Aulds
Molly Margaret Baggett
Jacqueline Faith Bonner
Christina Nicole Bruno
Marc Anthony Calhoun
Anna Cavalier
Morgan Elizabeth Chelette
Lara Catherine Crawford
Ashley Depaula
Caitlin Diana Dew

Christen Diel
Olivia Dixon
Dana Nicole Easterling
Katee Fairchild
Lacy Falke
Courtney Langley Flick
Amy Fontenot
Lindsey D. Fontenot
Lauren Renee Ford
Dalton Hamby
Lauren Frances Harper
Ashley Marie Hines
Helen Hughes

Catherine Ingram
Cameron Lee Irby
Dayton Dwain Landry
Trista Marie LeBeouf
Mason Copeland Liles
Rachael Maddox
Allena Brooke McCain
Hannah Kay Mosher
Geena Elizabeth Nellis
Lauren Norton
Allison Kelsey Ogden
Lauren Palmer
Lance Richard

Shelby Nicole Russell
Bria Iman Savage
Sarah Lynne Sellers
Kale Alan Shirley
Ann-marie Simon
Kelsie Stark
Halie Elizabeth Verret
Hamilton Stephens Winters
II
Whitney Wright
Chelsea Wyatt

UNIVERSITY OF LOUISIANA LAFAYETTE, LAFAYETTE, LA

Oluwakemi Ajala
Andrew Albritton
Kirsten Allen
Phillip Arceneaux
Alyssa Bienvenu
Bianca Blanco
Kelsey Brown

Taylor Brianna Brown
Melissa Burckhartt
Morgan Comeaux
Bianca Cook
Emily Nicole Covington
Paul Allen Cummins Jr.
Asia Dauntain

Aaren Faulkner
Victor Gaython Fields-
Meaux
Erin Fisher
Vince Frederic
Gabrielle Gallien
Brianna Gray

Kayla Hebert
Kelton Jessie
Matthew Juby
Shelbi King
Zach Francis Moran
Kunstman
Julia Lang

Meagan A. Lege
Allison Anastasia Marcel
Alana Marcello
Milen Matthews
Shashank Mishra
Steven Luc Nguyen
Austin Jude O'Connor

Wil Perkins
Annie Perret
Kristen Petitjean
Xiang Phung
Alexis Randle
Katherine Read
Giovanna Patricia Rocha

Stefanie Rodrigue
Christopher Rome
Charles Saloom
Jake Savoie
Seth Savoie
Gabrielle Semien
Thomas Shuff

Elvis Siripannho
Alfred Smith
Taylor Ann Till
Kelsey Vincent
Antoinette Watson
Tori Danielle Young
Zack Tee Yun Shan

UNIVERSITY OF MAINE PRESQUE ISLE, PRESQUE ISLE, ME

Oliver James Barratt
Mitchell Emerson Bartlett
Miranda Lois Bickford
Elizabeth Mary Bishop
Jessica Nicole Campbell
Kelsey Mae Churchill
Donald Francis Collins Jr.
Jordan Spencer Cook
Elizabeth Judith Day
Eric Steven Depner

Candy M. Easton
Theodore William Gilliam Jr.
Tonya Stella Godin
Margaret Alice Hart
Bethany Ann Heald
Erica Kaylyn Hemphill
Caleb Timothy Hobbs
Amanda Leigh Hotham
Errol Wilfred Ireland III

Jeffrey Lee Kiser
Amanda Martha Larrabee
Carrigan Kennedy Levesque
Melissa Marie Lizotte
Shawna L. E. McDonough
Marissa M. McGovern
Joshua Michael Morrow
Bobbi-Jo Oatway
Sara Katherine Packard
Kathryn Elizabeth Patenaude

Cody Gilbert Pond
Craig Donald Pullen
Abigail Mae Riitano
Idella Pearl Thompson
Crysania Harley Walker
Shulei Zhang
Ying Zheng

UNIVERSITY OF MARY, BISMARCK, ND

Mariah L. Benz
Ashley K. Bernhardt
Alexandra N. Brown
Anastasia M. Bruss
Ryan J. Buchholz
Brandon M. Carps
Alistair C. Crockett
Anne C. Dziak
Kendra M. Enget
Jean M. Gehrz
Morgan R. Glines

Erin N. Hamar
Brett J. Hample
Quinn A. Harmon
Maria I. Henke
Annie E. Hinnenkamp
Trisha R. Hoffart
Hannah N. Houle
Holly A. Krumm
Isaac A. Lindquist
Kelsey K. Meadows
Alexandra R. Montoya

Wendy R. Moore
Austin L. Phillips
Emily V. Rapkoch
Alexia D. Russell
Karen A. Schaaf
Matthew J. Schaefbauer
Brandon A. Schock
MiKayla R. Schuette
Matthew R. Schumacher
Courtney M. Sibla
Paige E. Smith

Mariah L. Sondrol
Megan H. Stamstad
Thomas J. Stevens
Elesha M. Tatro
Preston T. Tescher
Elizabeth K. Vogel
Morgan M. Wanner
Kendra L. Weigel
Andrea M. White

UNIVERSITY OF MARY HARDIN–BAYLOR, BELTON, TX

Aubri Adams
Grace Marie Adams
Carissa Araujo
Katie Ashworth
Allyson Baker
Clinton Barrineau
Mikayla Beebe
Shelby Lynn Brown

Taylor Cole
Gabriella Colurciello
Cristal Conner
Austin Lamar Conway
Nyanza Yvette Cook
Caleb Matthew Davis
Emma French
Benjamin Hammonds

Jessica Hardin
Abigail Joy Hoffman
Janet Holland
Jeffrey Ross Jones
Katrina Kastmo
Leah Kelley
Terrance Livingston
Lindsey Nicole Marek

Joel Ryan Maresh
Elise McDowall
Baylor Mullins
Patsy Lorena Orantes
Quinton Payton
Rebekah Renee Peyton
Payton Lauren Pierce
Shelby Prather

Beverly Price
Ryan Matthew Quinn
Jake Raabe
Estafani Ramos
William (Tripp) Reeves III

Lauren Rhea Ribera
Lindsey Brooke Roberson
Jeff Robertson
Sid Tucker Saxton
Camryn Schegel

Haden Seely
Veronica Shockency
Jessie Marie Simmonds
Will Stafford
David Matthew Twilleager

Kirstie Wallace
Gena Weeks
Bethanie Witte
Rachael Claire Wood

UNIVERSITY OF MARYLAND BALTIMORE SCHOOL OF MEDICINE, BALTIMORE, MD

Chelsea Camara

Rachel Kernizan

Kristi Lavin

UNIVERSITY OF MARYLAND SCHOOL OF DENTISTRY, BALTIMORE, MD

Laura M. Colmenares

Kristen M. Hammett

AnneMarie D. Pickett

UNIVERSITY OF MARY WASHINGTON, FREDERICKSBURG, VA

Sarah B. Campbell
Alexander W. Clegg
Kelsey Cunningham
Michaela Encinas De Asis
Anna E. DeMarr
Angela Tyann Dixon
Quinn Doyle

Margeaux Marie Ducoing
Thomas T.V. Ferrier
Kelsey Greenwood
Brittany K. Hylander
Diana Inthavong
Kristina Krumpos
Margaret Magliato

Miriam Tyler McCue
Abigail Sherwood Moran
Alexander Obolensky
Eynav Rachel-Ella Ovadia
Davarien Jeremiah Sayles
Ian Spangler
Zaire K.A. Sprowal

Aleksandra Szczesna
Ray Celeste Silverthorne
Tanner
Rachel Ann Thomas
Kayla vanWerkhoven

UNIVERSITY OF MASSACHUSETTS LOWELL, LOWELL, MA

Graham Arthur Allen
Steven Alves
Marianne Arsenault
Lauren Victoria Bennett
Lukas James Bernard
Lauren Bertolami
Katherine Bilodeau
Gerrit Boldt
Jonathan Cabot
Samantha Grace Cacciola
Kathleen Cameron
Shantelle Castle
James Christopher
Vanneyra J. Chum
Charlene Clerveau
Ashley Cochran
Sherine Farida Dao
Emily Dasey
Danielle Elizabeth DeGaspe
Matthew Desmond

James Patrick Donahue
Mercedes Dunham
Diana Estrella
Patrick Facendola
Eilish Faherty
Jackson Flynn
Jenna Mary Freitas
Kelly Freitas
Matthew Geary
Abigail Finda-Tengbeh
Gingrande
Kevin Michael Goddu
Nicole Hamel
Amanda Lee Hemond
Claudia Ho
Daniel Howell
Michelle Candice Janiak
Gladys Kibunyi
Alexa Lambert
Amy Lamont

Bianka Lazarus
Michaela Leach
Maria Loutraris
Nicole Lynch
MacKenzie Mahoney
Sonia Marcello
Kelsey C. Martin
Sara Mathieu
Matilda Matovu
Deepesh Moolchandani
Alyssa Mulno
Syndhia Mungalachetty
Kristina Murray
Erika Nadile
Somto Nnyamah
Christopher Nunez
Emily Elizabeth O'Brien
Kellie O'Brien
Travis James Overton
Stanley Ovile

Shivam D. Patel
Orquidia Paulino
Zofia Peach
Sabrina Pedersen
Nandana Penukonda
Vinhnguyenboi Pham
Marlon Pitter
Molly Post
Amanda Robinson
Pedro Rolon
John Romano
Alexander Philip Roy
Riley Ryan
Allison Mary Saffie
Bethsaida Saintvil
Danielle Sampson
Teresa Santana
Christine Schaffer
Kenya Semexant
Abigail Catherine Sheehan

Kaina Siffra
Marly Thomas
Shamilah Ulysse

Tyler Valila
Vanessa Vazquez
Jennifer Lynn Vivier

Jennifer Marie Wall
Niyah West
Denise Wheelden

Stephanie Wilson2
Zachary Zuber

UNIVERSITY OF MIAMI, CORAL GABLES, FL

Shawn E. Abuhoff
Chidera Anugwom
Stacie Maria Arechavala
Sarah Grace Aschebrock
Samuel Bookhardt IV
Teresa Marie Browning
Vinessa Burnett
Giovanni Calixte
Christine M. Castiglione
Nikita Chabra
Andreana Simone
Cunningham
James Czodli
Michael Deutsch
Caitilin Donahoe
Deandre Drummer
Ryan Durga
O'Shane Elliott
Stefani Fachini
Mikayla Farr
Kristina Francillon

My Hanna Fridell
Neelima Gaddipati
Matthew Getzoff
Christina Giles
Rhian Goolabsingh
Miranda Goot
Nicole Halmoukos
Brianna Hathaway
Jennifer Hollander
Alexandra Hussey
Kemi Ijitimehin
Jenna Johnson Johnson
Melissa Jordon
Zoe Kafkes
Bohdan Bohdanovich
Khomtchouk
Amanda Klaristenfeld
Natasha Koermer
Rori Kotch
Adam Lawrence
Douglas Hooper Lehtinen

Christian Lemon
Zachary Lipschultz
Emma Marzen
Shannon McCarthy
Paige Elizabeth McGlynn
Daniel A. Moubayed
Atara Muhammad
Micaela Nannery
Jessica Neer
Andrea Nickerson
Sunny Odogwu
Valerie Quirk
Sathvika Devi Ramaji
Ravika Rameshwar
William Ranson
Max Romanow
Robert Bradford Rowe III
Colin Ruane
Syed Hamad Sagheer
Briana Nicole Scott
Mary Selep

Ashley Serjilus
Faizah Shareef
Danielle Sheerer
Ishtpreet Singh
Jhanile Smith
Nicole Steinberg
Jeffrey Tyler Sznapstajler
Maureen Tan
Tequan Taylor
Katherine Thompson
Maite Veronica Torres
Nareka Trewick
Minnie Tsai
Alexander Wells
Mary Kristin
Westerhorstmann
Lexi Williams
Anthony Wolliston
Jacob Esper Yomtoob

UNIVERSITY OF MISSISSIPPI SCHOOL OF NURSING, JACKSON, MS

Grace Ann Agostinelli
Kristen Rebecca Berger
Kayla Noelle Clark

Brianna Jade DeWeese
Lucy Lennon Hall
Amy Elizabeth Heidelberg

Kathleen Nichole Meier
Mary Hope Phillips
Hannah Leigh Russell

Lauren Paige Teague
Tiara Emerald Turner
Davelin Deniece Woodard

UNIVERSITY OF MISSOURI SAINT LOUIS, SAINT LOUIS, MO

Negar Adl-Tabatabaei
Ala Al-Lozi
Lena Zaid Alsyouf
Abdulaziz Bashatah
Kaylyn Bauer
Katherine Bennett
Brandon Bishop
Paige Booker
Emily Bowman

James Michael Daniel
Bragado
Haley Brightwell
Timothy Burgess
John Bushur
Amy E. Cabanas
Anastacia Lynn Chambers
Mary Elizabeth Chickos
Andrea Ciarrochi

Brianne Clemons
Susan Cogan
Morgan Crane
Rebekah Cripe
Kelly Day
Kathryn Deeken
Chandler Duchaine
Alexander Colin Elias
Ryan Ely

Matt Fanning
Aixia Feng
Sean Patrick Fieser
Emra Gagulic
Michelle Gleich
Zach Goldford
Erin Graves
Amy S. Gregory
Jaylon Griffith

Rachel Marie Hanks
Sarah Harrison
Tyson Holder
Fatemeh Hossain Mardi
Mi-Hsuan Hsieh
Alex Idoux
Regina James
Jerrod Jaskot
Crystal Johnson
Eric'el Johnson
Nao Kawatei
Savannah Jade Kiser
Emily Klamer
Lingru Kong
Austin Lane
Sandra Lee
Yang Li
Alexandra Loehr

Michael Steve Mason
Jaclyn Mastroianni
Abdul-Kariem Matteuzzi
Rachel Elizabeth Matthies
Kelly McGovern
Lauren Elizabeth McJessy
Kourtney McKinney
Lyndsey McKinney
Celia Rose McManus
Christina Mertzlufft
Lindsay Meyer
Laura Annette Miller
Paula Henderson Miller
Kelley Lynn Moulton
Thong Nguyen
Tran Nguyen
Andrea Nichols
Tiffany Parrett

Dipa Patel
Kevin Petterson
Tessa Purcell
J. Amanda Rawls
Graham Renz
Kathleen Louise Riddler
Sarah Rizzo
Cameron Roark
Cara Sampson
Samatha Sandvoss
Anita Santiago
Danielle Marie Schaefer
John-Mark Scott
David Serati
Christopher Steven Shepard
Austin Stearns
William Stewart III
Kruti Surti

Beixuan Tang
Elias Toubia
Daniel Tracy
Melissa Triplett
Christina Usher
Cassidy Vangyia
Erin Michelle Walker
Gang Wang
Jamie Leigh Weiser
Li Wen
Beth Marie Wiese
Jheryca Williams
Paul Winter
Marcus Woodson
Kristin Wyninegar
Justin Yancey
Sisi Yang

UNIVERSITY OF MOBILE, MOBILE, AL

Katherine Becerly Alvernaz
Marianna Alves Dos Santos Velozo
Sara N. Armstrong
Brittany Shae Arndt
Audrey Lynn Birkhimer
John T. Borowski
Brian P. Boyle
Tammy Wadsworth Brown
Genevieve Gail Buaas
Brian J. Burkhardt
Lorie A. Bush
Kali R. Carver
Elissa Chamberlain
Hannah Elizabeth Cherry
Gregory C. Clardy
Taylor Danielle Clinkenbeard
Nathan Dakota Collier
Marcio Dal Pont
Alexa Marie Da Rosa
Brett Allen Davis
Victoria Dawson

Bethany Joy Douglas
Thomas P. Duke
Nicholas Matthew Dunkin
Rebekah K. Dye
Shaine Austin Edmondson
Kelsey L. Eiland
Paige Talley Ellison
Hyun Jung Eom
Katelyn E. Ewing
Korie Lynn Fontenot
Miranda J. Freeman
Tinsley M. Griffin
Delaney Noelle Grizzle
Lucia Alejandra Guajardo
Carol Ann Hall
Gary K. Hamner
Nicholas J. Hardeman
Catharine Quina Hardyman
Sandra D. Hayes
Sarah Noelle Hicks
Joshua Thomas Hill
Abigail Hitson
Joshua P. Holley

Santeria O. Howze
Josi Nadine Ingram
Brooke Alyse Jemison
Adrienne Alexis Johnson
Leslie E. Johnson
Amber Michelle Jones
Harthuya W. Jones
Linley Elizabeth Jones
Luke Brandon Jones
Paris Mercedes Jones
Dan Kawaguchi
Emily C. LaForce
Dakota Danielle Lancaster
Trinette M. Law
Amber Lawler
Heidi R. Little
Cody Claud Lockhart
Kristopher McAuley
Paige N. McAuley
Loretta R. McCleskey
Kathryn Anne McCollister
Kaysie Antoinette Meacham
Anna Jean Meherg

Ashley Michelle Middleton
Dylan Joe Miller
Nicole Michelle Molina
Daniel R. Moore
Bailey M. Nations
Megan Marie Nichols
Phoebe Rebecca Owen
Michaelyn Compton Parker
Christy Brown Parmer
Victoria Christian Parris
Seth Lowery Peacock
Cynthia Abigail Pennington
Joleigh E. Pigott
John Patrick Pledger
Wendi Nicole Poates
Aaron G. Pouncey
Abigail Elizabeth Pressley
Santiago Ernesto Quiros Casucci
Claire Morgan Richburg
Britni F. Rivers
Tiffany Craig Robinson
Zachary Wayne Robinson

John William Rogers
Christopher G. Rowell
Cody D. Scott
Leah Beverly Shepherd
Kavita Sherpa
Stacy R. Smith
Debra K. Story

Deborah Elizabeth Strausbaugh
Fredricka Monee Stribling
Brittney R. Swinney
Jennifer Ann Tart
Tameika L. Thomas
Blake Ellis Tims

Courtney D. Torrence
Brannen Jo Uhlman
Elizabeth Rose Ussery
LaKeisha Shuntae Williams
Schaquwa Renia Williams
Tiffany Monique Williams
Stefanie Lyne Willis-Turner

Scott Alan Wilson
Sheryl Lynn Wilson
Emley Maria Woodyard
Rhonda K. Wright
Deborah L. York

UNIVERSITY OF MONTEVALLO, MONTEVALLO, AL

Spencer Anglin
Ryan Anderson Baker
Zachary D. Brown
Carley June Bunch
Amanda Faye Currie
Stacy Daniels

Daniel Barron Deriso
Evan Allen Dixon
Shyanne Dawne Erickson
Morgan Gothard
Taylor James Kosman
Ondrea Khadija Lee

Emily Kirby Long
Victoria Marriott
Briana J. McDade
Kimberly McDade
Ashlyn Joy Morrison
Kayla Pilkington

Gabrielle S. Pringle
Nicholas Rivers
Crystal Roskam
Kayla Shelton
Matthew Turner Suddarth

UNIVERSITY OF MOUNT UNION, ALLIANCE, OH

Timothy Anderson
Reilly M. Augustine
Gabriela M. Botzman

Michael R. Cintron
Lauren E. Haines

Peyton R. Kranz
Paula A. Kyser

Khanh Linh Nguyen
Rebecca J. Rector

UNIVERSITY OF NEBRASKA MEDICAL CENTER COLLEGE OF NURSING, OMAHA, NE

Deana Andrew
McKayla Armstead
Veronica Behm
Joslyn Paige Brugh
Phillip Bullington
Caroline Burris
Martha Cochell
Raven Darnell
Sale Gentert
Genevra Graf
Taylor Gray

Chantal Heathers
Erika Hochstein
Julie Jordan
Ashley Kamphaus
Amanda Klein
Jennifer Kopp
Austyn Koppinger
Danica Lee
Kenzie Lentfer
Mara Maslowsky
Jessica McLellan

Michaela Miles
Sarah Michelle Mimick
Erica Minner
Jessica Pearce
Jenna Leigh Peterson
Sophia Przybylo
Abbie Rademacher
Eli Rodirguez
Blair Sanburg
Taylor Schelstrate
James Selvey

Nancy Leigh Silligman
Ann Catherine Smith
Taylor Straube
Beata Tabaka
Katie Tacke
Karin Vaughn
Sarah Wanek
Paige Wenske
Jessica Wooden
Lauren Zimbelman

UNIVERSITY OF NEW ENGLAND, BIDDEFORD, ME

Jacob G. Abel
Carlos E. Aguero
Peter M. Alfano
Joshua M. Allen
Ashley R. Anderson
Taxiarhia J. Arabatzis
Stephen G. Arsenault

Robert F. Aspinwall
Phillip J. Atherton
Maegan Auciello
Leslie A. Bardin
Janica E. Barrows
Alexandra L. Basiliere
Stephanie A. Beeckel

Mariah R. Benoit
Erin M. Bibber
Bronwen E. Boe
Jaclyn M. Bria
Haley C. Brooks
Mathew P. Brown
Victoria M. Bryan

Rebecca G. Buchanan
Megan M. Burns
Tanya D. Butts
Ryan B. Camire
Kristina M. Carlson
Adrienne L. Chase
Nicole M. Childers

Matthew J. Coelho
Cody L. Coolidge
Sarah J. Cooper
Emily L. Corey
Amanda L. Cressey
Hannah M. Cutting
Emily R. Cyr
Kendra L. Dawless
Kristin S. Dechene
Colleen M. DeCola
Kelly A. Dolyak
Abigail M. Donigian
Kaylee R. Doyle
Courtney M. Doyon
Colby Drost
Paul J. Dubuque
John J. Dusel
Matthew J. Eaton
Carly M. Emond
Alyssa A. Fabianek
Anthony D. Frangione
Shea M. Goudreau
Chelsea R. Grandinetti
Rebecca L. Green
Jessica L. Groleau
Kaitlyn L. Hall
Kayla B. Hamel
Lauren L. Hayden

Shamus G. Higginbottom
Caleb Robert Howard
Lauryn N. Huck
Holly A. Huntress
Jotham Taylor Illuminati
Alex F. Ingerson
John S. Jarvis
Morgan Jones
Ryan P. Juneau
Nicole E. Keaney
Jayne E. Kelly
Anni E. Kim
Ashlee Klemczuk
Chandler A. Knowles
Emma Louise Kokkinos
Rachael L. Koptik
Rebecca L. Krivitsky
Hannah E. Lachance
Rachel E. Lakin
My Tien P. Lam
Joseph Langan
Megan J. Lapointe
Kiera Latham
Catherine H. Leighton
Kayla L. Lindros
Tressa R. Loiko
Timothy A. Luttik
Emily F. Macduff

Alexandria D. Makucewicz
Alyssa N. Mazzariello
Joy M. McCarthy
Allison E. McFee
Thomas J. McManus
Aidan L. McParland
Francesca M. Medellin
Maxwell S. Metayer
Abriana E. Micca
Emily C. Mitchell
Lindsey K. Monaco
Shane P. Murphy
Chelsea J. Naylor
Korin M. Nickerson
Matthew G. O'Brien
Kiera L. O'Donnell
Paige J. Oliver
Ioana G. Panaitiu
Amanda E. Paradis
Michelle L. Pellegrino
Gwendolyn M. Pelletier
Ian J. Pelletier
Kailey A. Perez
Darcy-Lynn S. Perkins
Jessica R. Perkins
Megan E. Perry
Amy K. Phillips
Emma S. Pinard

Kaylee Pobocik
Jordan S. Porter
Mathieu Provencher
Hanna L. Pultorak
Xiomarah Y. Ramos
Brittani A. Roussel
Caroline A. Saban
Sarae A. Sager
Kaitlyn M. Savard
Wyler C. Scamman
Rachel Stephanie Schwaner
Jenna M. Selander
Matthew Sheehan
Janelle E. Sherman
Cassandra A. Simmons
Danielle Smerald
Tyler Stitt
Kerribeth A. Szolusha
Jordan Tate
Elizabeth Thompson
Shayne Toohey
Renee E. Violette
Christopher M. Watt
Taylor A. Watts
Alicia M. Wheeler
Carolyn R. Wheeler
Emily B. Zeimetz
Zethariah D. Zielinski

UNIVERSITY OF NEW HAVEN, WEST HAVEN, CT

Annalisa Rose Berardinelli
Natalie Rose Collins

Veronica Cruz
Amanda Rae Sigan

Glory-Jean Smith

Jonathan Spiegel

UNIVERSITY OF NORTH ALABAMA, FLORENCE, AL

Anna T. Glosemeyer
Mallory E. Hayes

Mariann J. Jahraus

Nicholas E. Lang

Allonda B. Leonard

UNIVERSITY OF NORTH CAROLINA CHARLOTTE, CHARLOTTE, NC

Lea Arapovic
Taylor Atwell
John Richard Auman
Natalia Barriga

John Alexander Beall
Maya Alexandra Black
Johnathan Blue
Jenna Rebecca Brown

Sharoyal Brown
Samantha Bruner
Marissa Bare Burchette
Diarra Butler

Phoenicia Butler
Domonique Byers
Lyna Cao
Kaitlyn Taylor Chapman

Erin Brianne Crissman

Dalton Jeffrey Culler

Anastasia Davis

Laura Danielle Diamond-Williams

Samantha Dietter

Katherine Hannah Fletcher

Victoria Sotonye Fubara

Nicolette Taylor Galo

Jessica Grenia

Meredith Hanes

Lashieka Hardin

Nicole Hardy

Crystal Harrell

Travis Higgs

Bradley Lane Hinson

Paula Ilonze

Ashley King

Brijesh Kishan

Bilqees Laghari

Robert Jake Lankford

Elise Katere McSwain

Katlynn Millette

Josie Moll

Emily Murphy

Yekta Nazari

Brandon Nixon

Ethan Norman

Obed Ohia

Joseph K. Okeiga

Kelly Denise Page

James Wellington Parkhill

Melanie Pflucker

Kelly Nicole Pittman

Danielle Porter

Christian Pridgen

Nicholle Rentas

Pamela Rivera

Jasmin Rivers

Natalie Rodriguez

Tiffany Shine

Sara Sibley

Sean Taylor Simmons

Kelsea Lane Smart

Melanie Smith

Christine Sorensen

Alexis Summey

Stephanie Sura

Rahma Syed

Anthony Tapp

Madison Walsh

Kyra Webber

Tynaiza Whitaker

Catherine Williams

Brittany Younts

UNIVERSITY OF NORTH GEORGIA, DAHLONEGA, GA

Erica Yvonne Barker

Patricia Bautista

Mark Raymond Beyrer

Collin Thomas Bezely

Jeannie C. Bradley

Rachael Anne Bryant

Aubrey Ward Bullock

Brianna Marie Carlan

Matt Bryan Caudell

Amberlyn Brianne Clark

Jana Leigh Coleman

Matthew Christopher Compton

Ruthanne Camille Conner

Michelle Lynn Correll

Chelsea Elizabeth Craig

Yvette Michelle Cromartie

Sean Edward Curry

Nathaniel Gordy Cutler

Mallika Dinesh

Brittnie Donzella

Mallory Anne Ellis

Robert Ross Ellison

Jacob Daniel Garcia

Maria Y. Garcia

Elton Garcia-Castillo

Itzel Garfias

Justin Patrick Grimaldi

Courtney Laine Hall

Danielle Nicole Hansel

Sawyer Cash Henderson

Joshua Gaines Hill

Steven Michael Hougland

Britni Jade Howard

James Eugene Howse Jr.

Kaitlin Leigh Hubbard

Ryan Nicholas Hudson

Kristopher Robert Irvin

Kierra Shante Johnson

Reed Alan Johnston

Elizabeth Vaughan Jordan

Mahnoor (Maha) Kamran

Alison Michele Kight

Cathlene Michelle Kirkpatrick

Jesse Tyler Ladanyi

Brittany Renae LeBlanc

Andrew Kevin Lewis

Marah Helen Lind

Lawrence Chadwick Loggins

Ayah Abdelmoneim Mansour

Katelyn Mathews

Andrena Brandy Mathis

Catrina A. Pingue May

Meagan Elizabeth May

Harlie McCurley

Amber Leann McHenry

Nelson Bladimir Moraga

Jessica Sara Moskowitz

Hannah Christine Myers

Austin Michael O'Neill

Paige Caroline Palmer

Sallie Jane Parker

Kyle Vincent Patterson

Larry Wayne Penrod

Megan Nicole Pepples

Catherine H. Pringle

Martha Gabriela Rodriguez

Emily Amelia Rom

Trevor Dirk Smits

Ian Thomas Sperin

Austin Lee Stewart

Bradley Austin Thompson

Adrianna Beatrice van Dongen

Kristin Lu Xiong

Christopher Chase Yarbrough

UNIVERSITY OF OKLAHOMA, NORMAN, OK

Katejoe Adaku Akabogu

Zeeneb Alsaihati

Jane Ngozi Obaji Anoke

Lauren Anto

Joseph Asante

Heidi Babin

Marla Bailey

Alexandra Baker

Michael Barnes

Marissa Beene

Micaela Benedetti

Hunter Birkhead

Breanna Bober

Jessica Lynn Bond

Sarah Bowdoin

Elizabeth Bryant

Chase Bukhair
Kendall Burchard
Laura Burns
Natasha Camacho
Rachel Campbell
Lauren Carmen
Jennifer Carmichael
Amanda Eve Carrick
Athena Chatzigiannidis
Charles Coker
Emily Elaine Cole
Amy Crone
Joseph D'Amato
Rachael Damon
Tayler Daniels
Emily DeSantis
Christina DeVincenzo
Brittny Dike
Ashten Ray Duncan
Aubrey Dwyer
Nathan Edmonsond
Elise Fast
Jessica Freeman
Dominic R. Granello
Lauran Green
Molly Hall
David Monk Haralson
Kaitlyn Holland
Kelsey Holtz
Amber Hubbard
Blessing Ikpa

Megan Ivy
Brent Janss
Andrea Jimenez
Alexandra Jones
Derrick Jones
Nathan Justus
Charity Leah Kennedy
Laura Kincaide
Nicole Knox
Kristin Lynne Kren
Yaaminey Kunderu
Darci Lambeth
Stephanie Lee
Ashley Leisten
Hannah Lobban
Victoria Loeser
Claire Malaby
Krishna Manohar
Avery Blair Marczewski
Conner Martin
Brandon McCabe
Katelyn McCarley
Julie McCloy
Reagan Metz
Reece Miller
Monique Mogilka
Andrew Moore
MaRiah Moore
Cameron Morgan
Daniel Moses
Thomas Murphy

Derek Nguyen
Richard Nguyen
Tina Nguyen
Tu Nguyen
Jimmy Ogden
Chase Ossenkop
Emily Arlene Owens
Aarol Parks
Darshit Patel
John H. Pham
Julianna Pianelli
Sarah Pitts
Haley Poarch
Hayden Lane Powell
Megan Pritchard
Anne Reburn
Ally Renfroe
Daniel J. Rennix
Colton Richardson
Amanda Lynn Rinchiuso
Justin Robbins
T'ata Roberts
Monique Rodriguez
Stephanie Schroeder
Maryum Shahzad
Emily Sharp
Kaitlyn Sigman
Keyana Simmons
Molly Sokolosky
Alexander Spens
Haley Stevens

Andrew Stewart
Julie Stockton
Nick Stowers
Keana Swadley
Emily Taylor
Kathleen Taylor
Kirsten Tharalson
Jason Thompson
Clara Thomson
Benjamin Toms
Cole Townsend
Elissa Ungerman
Mai Vangseng
Jillian Vaught
Joshua Wadler
Rachelle Ward
Lindsey Weiss
Olivia Jayne White
Madison Williams
Courtney Woltjen
Ross Woodard
Miranda Wright
Christina Wu
Nathaniel Yokell
Ryne Young
Keaton Zahorsky
Nafis Zaman
Lauren Zang
Bo Zhang
Cici Zhou
Meagan Zwahlen

UNIVERSITY OF PIKEVILLE, PIKEVILLE, KY

Kaitlyn T. Abdon
Brittany D. Adams
Bilal S. Ahmed
Joshua S. Akers
Kyle M. Allen
Aaron J. Asbury
Whitney M. Back
Jillian D. Bailey
Rebecca A. Baker
Wesley G. Barnett

Aileah K. Bartley
Autumn S. Billiter
Jobeth D. Bingham
Diego Blanco Reboredo
Stephen S. Boggs
Kenneth J. Bowling
Davina N. Bryan
Mark A. Carlson
Jesse James Coleman
Arianna C. Collins

Christina L. Compton
Finicia M. Compton
Eady E. Connally
Brent M. Cornette
Haley Makae Damron
Erin L. Edwards
Kelah L. Eldridge
Josi B. Estep
Savannah P. Estep
Karlee D. Evans

Valerie S. Eversole
Molly M. Frank
Jessica N. Gamble
Adam T. Hall
Autumn Victoria Hampton
Megan R. Hedgespeth
Donald L. Hensley
Jeffery D. Hensley
John A. Hopkins
Caitlyn M. Hunt

Jackson Peter Hussey	Logan E. Lucas	Nicolas Rodenbusch	Hannah N. Thacker
Kimberly A. Hylton	Sean Ly	Katelyn B. Simpson	Jarred D. Thacker
Gary Charles Johnson	Enrico Alexander Marino	Dustin E. Stacy	Mariah H. Tiller
Haley B. Johnson	Joshua H. Matheny	Daisy F. Stanley	Christopher B. Vance
Edward T. Joseph	Kristin C. Moore	Eric Corey Stump	James E. Williams
Derek A. Keller	Mary Elizabeth Moore	Courtney M. Taylor	Teddy G. Woods
Brianna L. Larson	Jammie D. Napier	Austin T. Thacker	Caroline M. Workman
Rachel E. Lee	Kyle J. Newsome	Ethan M. Thacker	Courtney N. Wright
Bradley S. Loader	Allie J. Paxton	Fayetta M. Thacker	

UNIVERSITY OF PITTSBURGH AT TITUSVILLE, TITUSVILLE, PA

Mark D. Crawford	Lyric Hill	Morgan L. Pittinger	Stephanie A. Thomas
Nina A. Curtis	Benjamin C. Hutcheson	Abbey R. Roach	Emily M. Wenger
Cassandra K. Davis	Denuel W. Jarba	Aisha Salami	Meghan A. Williams
Chelcy E. Douthett	Indiana X. Judy	Shannon L. Sanden	
Carla M. Ghannam	Sofia Kovacevic	Kelsey P. Smith	
Jeffrey C. Glass	Miranda Sue Ochs	Madison M. Stern	

UNIVERSITY OF PITTSBURGH BRADFORD, BRADFORD, PA

Alexander M. Acosta	Hannah Marie Fielding	Kayla Elizabeth Mascaro	Drew E. Sneeringer
Usman N. Ahmad	Benjamin R. Forney	Kaitlin Elizabeth McCann	Jon Austin Snyder
Hannah Marie Anderson	Emily Marie Fowkes	Nicholas McIntire	Kayla M. Stayer
Chevonne C. Bartlett	Justine Fox	Kyley J. Mickle	Josiephine Sweitzer
Erik S. Beeler	Anne Marie Garcia	Tyler D. Morris	Jordan Christine Taylor
Matthew Dean Bennett	Eric Thomas Gemmell	Ross E. Nelson	Allie R. Tress
Margaret C. Boehler	Katie Diane Gray	Rubie-Ann S. Nelson	Alyssa Raquel Vanasco
Gabrielle M. Bonheur	Alyssa Marie Gregg	Gabrielle A.S. Neuhof	Lori B. Vickery
Rachel Elizabeth Brune	Delaney R. Held	Allison Lee Osborne	Jordon L. Wagner
Jeffery L. Cattoni	Jordan N. Herberg	Kaserra A. Owens	Nashua W. Walters
Sara Marie Cohen	Anne Jiang	Steven A. Owens	Jetka Wanner
Rebecca Ann Coleman	Julian Joyner	Miranda Marie Ranelli	William A. Warren II
Phebean C. Davies	Jennifer Marie Lau	Alex J. Renwick	Cassondra E. Whittemore
William Dong	Falon L. Ljunggren	Brenda Santana Matis	Haley Jeanne Wilson
Elena J. Ehrentraut	Edith A. Lloyd-Etuwewe	Olivia F. Schrock	Nicole M. Wymer
Mark Emmens	Heidi Elizabeth Lucke	Aleia Scott	Melanie Yanetsko
Jordan Nichole Fargo	Brady M. Major	Joseph Sienkiewicz	

UNIVERSITY OF PUERTO RICO COLLEGE OF NATURAL SCIENCES, SAN JUAN, PR

Ruth L. Adames-Méndez	Rafael Portela Colón	Xiomara S. Molina Pérez	Lailiz Ortiz Ortiz
Diana A. Aponte-Colón	Richard Quintana Feliciano	Emmanuel Morales	Mariolga Masa Pereira
Juan A. Cantres Vélez	Diane L. Mankin Cruz	Monsanto	Carolyn Agosto Rivera
Gustavo Raúl Castro Ortega	Ingrid Pacheco Meléndez	Gabriela Firpi Morales	

Gabriel O. Rodríguez Narváez	Kevin M. Rodríguez-Santos Neysharie Sánchez Torres	Luis M. Taveras Grullón	Paulette Urrutia Villamil

UNIVERSITY OF PUERTO RICO MEDICAL SCIENCES CAMPUS, SAN JUAN, PR

Zoriely Amador Rios	Selimar Ledesma-Maldonado	Loida M. Portalatín Pérez	Idaliz Rodriguez Escudero
Julio A. Cedeño Alicea		Irwin Ramos López	Armando Silva Almódovar
Nicole M. Del Toro Pagán	Cathyria M. Marrero Serra	Christine M. Raymond Biaggi	Adriana Sota Avilés
Elsie A. Diaz Báez	Caroline Mejías De Jesús		Glendalis Vargas Vargas
Vanessa Estrada Rodríguez	Jeanmichael Meléndez Nieves	Jomir Rivera Rivera Keyla Michelle Rivera Ruiz	Ericka Vélez Bonet

UNIVERSITY OF PUERTO RICO SCHOOL OF LAW, SAN JUAN, PR

Julybeth Alicea Rodríguez

UNIVERSITY OF RIO GRANDE, RIO GRANDE, OH

Barbara L. Abels	April D. Davis	Leanna Grey	Amber N. Lambert
Kimberly R. Addis	Cynthia L. Davis	Stephanie A. Gruenberg	Kayte N. Lawrence
Harley Adler	Natalie J. Davis	Rachel Marie Haddad	Colby L. Lee
Halley J. Alberts	Kassandra N. Day	Dawn Michelle Hall	Stephanie N. Legg
Shameca R. Armstrong	Katelynn S. Dearth	Garret Hall	Rebecca Lipscomb
Bianca Claire Bailey	Pau Delgado Rodriguez	Rebecca Hall	Jaclyn L. Lowe
Amanda B. Baker	Jessica N. Delong	Kelsey L. Hamilton	Jacob D. Manning
Debora Barnhart	Heitor Schiavette Romariz De Melo	Samantha Jo Hammond	Amelia Marie Maxson
Jerri D. Bentley		Rachel Hannon	Jessica R. Mcclanahan
Joseph C. Bevens	Scarlett R. Denney	Dayton Palmer Hardway	Herbert A. Mcintyre
Sarah Bonar	Paul Victor Dennis	Dawn E. Helton	Amy R. Mckay
Braden Bowen	Melissa Dickerson	Jennifer Herzog	Tanisha D. Mckinney
Kimberly L. Bowman	Erica J. Dowell	Christopher A. Hill	Molly Meeks
Richard Lewis Bowman	Travis Elliott	Cassandra E. Holley	Andrea N. Mercer
Jessica Lynn Broderick	Alexandria N. Ellis	Adam M. Hollingshead	Dava N. Mershon
Morgan Brumfield	Randall D. Fite	Chandler M. Hoover	Stephanie Metz
Jan L. Carlisle	Ralene N. Fitzpatrick	Kyra Lashawn Howell	April D. Montgomery
Kaily E. Chamberlain	Sheri J. Foster	Allen D. Hudson	Ashley H. Morgan
Audra M. Clark	Thomas B. Foust	Kimberly C. Hurt	Paris Morris
Tonya L. Clark	Kody J. Fox	Amanda Michelle Imler	Edward F. Mussi
Chasidy L. Conley	Daniel S. Fraser	Shane Michael Ingles	Halee Myers
Carrie E. Coriell	Karla J. Garn	Ciara N. Jackson	Kenneth Michael Myers
Mckenzie M. Coriell	Megan E. Giffin	Adam R. Johnson	Samantha A. Myers
Emily Cox	Cherokee S. Gilkey	Nathaniel Johnson	Darian N. Napier
Lisa Cox	Hailee Danielle Golden	Kimathi Kaumbutho	Taylor D. Newland
Morgan Daniels	Samantha Graham	Cheryl R. Kerr	Jessica R. Northup
Atticus Joseph Davies	Breanna D. Grahame	Alexandria M. Kuhn	Judy Northup

Rachael L. Northup
Kiana C. Osborne
Rachel D. Payne
Britney Jo Pelletier
Brandy N. Perkins
Aaron L. Pletcher
Erin Polcyn
Samantha B. Proffitt
Brandi J. Ray
Cody L. Riffle

Kimberly L. Rollins
Kristen C. Rollins
Gwendolyn K. Rose
Dempsey Belle Rupe
Kyle W. Sanborn
Betsy J. Schramm
Judy A. Searles
Chobee L. Sheets
Peggy Dee Shiflett
John Anthony Sipple

Alyssa M. Smith
Ashley R. Smith
Kaylyn Spradling
Heather Thacker
Teresa H. Thomas
Grant W. Trimble
Jeni Lynne Tripp
Benjamin M. TRUE
Matthew C. Vitullo
James Wallace

Heather Ward
Timothy A. Warner
Wendy B. Wells
Breanna Reed West
Jessica L. White
Paula K. Williams
Nichole Renee Worsham
Courtney E. Young
Julian C. Young

UNIVERSITY OF SAINT MARY, LEAVENWORTH, KS

Nicholas S. Amerio
William G. Arnold
Russell C. Brown
Sarah J. Chavez
Lindee M. Clair
Anthony D. Clouse
Bonnie A. Cobb
Sarah J. DaMetz

Danielle M. Dowdy
Joshua J. Ervin
Ariana D. Frantz
Summer I. Frantz
Arcilia A. Gonzalez
Josue Omar Gonzalez
Mary A. Gregory
Keeton K. Krause

Andrew T. Kump
Gemma R. Maliszewski
Shirley A. May
Ashley M. Muldoon
Jasmine T. Nichols
Nathaniel O. Petty
Brice N. Plein
Aaron M. Potter

Patrick M. Rachford
Carla J. Ross
Brenna M. Seawalt
Olivia C. Silvey
Margaret G. Stewart
Keegan M. Towry
Elizabeth D. Walden

UNIVERSITY OF SAN DIEGO, SAN DIEGO, CA

Nicole Abraham
Alexa Argumedo
Alex Benson
Elley Berg
James Bried
Alaysia Brown
Karen Clark
Jordyn Corrington
Katie Coutermarsh
Elizabeth Creech
Rishika Daryanani
Rachael Emerick

Dante Enriquez
Lena Bianca Figueroa
Diana Fontaine
Nicole Forbes
Katherine (Katie) Fotion
Aidan Fouhy
Bryan Fox
Molly Gartland
Peter Greene
Keanu Gututala
Stephanie Halper
Alec Hartman

Angela Hessenius
Kevin Homaizad
Molly Humphreys
Zachary Jagielski
Kevin Karn
Rani Kumar
Juliana Mascari
Kaitlin Meyer
Austin Michel
Frances (Kristin) Mitchell
Sarah O'Connor
Morgan Offenheiser

Rosalie Plofchan
Shalin Shah
Michelle (Sydney) Smith
Lavanya Sridharan
Elizabeth Stenger
Marta Stojanovic
Leah Wargo
Brenna Wertzberger
Taylor Young
Laura Zollars
Anastasia Zuñiga

UNIVERSITY OF SCIENCE & ARTS OF OKLAHOMA, CHICKASHA, OK

Abbie Diane Alexander
Bretlin Allen
Sabrina Rene Atkinson
Alfredo Baeza Jr.
Justin Kyle Bennett
Rachel Bennett

Elizabeth Betzen
Jaci Denee Booker
Rhiannon Brewster
Sissel Brown
Aspen Burroughs
Halie Joyce Ann Cain

Hailey Nicole Camp
Connor Cheek
Courtney M. Cheesman
Shauntel Cornaby
Cynthia DeAnn Austin
Cunningham

McKenna Eubank
Kathleen Ezell
Katie Fikes
Brianne Alta Humphreys
Sonja Ingram
James Baley Kiper

Galela Kirkland
Dao Thong Lim
Jennie Danielle Linck
Jacinda Lovelace
Baylee Malone
Megan Malone

Kyle Maxwell
Thayne McCage
Jose Medina
Megan Myers
Robert Perez
Anthony Picinich

Manish Puri
Magdelene Quintero
Jordan B. Reed
Jordan Makaila Rhodes
Keaghlan Richmond
Shannyn Jean Spaulding

Kaylin Alyssa Taylor
Bailey Sue Vinsant
Shelby Wayland
Logan Webb
Joanna Ruth Weiss
Destiny West

UNIVERSITY OF SOUTH ALABAMA, MOBILE, AL

Shivani Ananthasekar
Hannah Elizabeth Brooks
Jessica Brown
Jennifer Clark-Grainger
Bethany Cobb
Mackenzie Coghlan
Roanna Coleman
Hannah Dawson

Forrest Edhegard
Fatima Hamade
Jamie Hanna
Adrianna Jackson
Hannah Victoria Kibby
Faith Deborah Kilpatrick
Ellisa Raye Long
Laura Lovett

Sayed Farhan Madni
Hilary McNeill
Kaylyn Neal
Taylor Marie P'Pool
Sarina Pakhamma
Mayank Patel
JuWan Robinson
Angelia Smith

Rodney Smith
Katherine Sweet
Holly Taylor
Jessica Nicole Taylor
Dylan Thorpe
Kendall Williams
Meredith Wyatt

UNIVERSITY OF SOUTH CAROLINA, COLUMBIA, SC

Carles Gambraie Anderson
Sango Huwaa Mosia Asante
Oyindamola Damilola Awe
Andrea Reanne Ayers
Allison Kimberlee Babcock
Joy Jael-Bee Barlow
Katherine Addison Barrack
Sarah Alyce Blomgren
Riley Xavier Brady
Alexa Ann Breeland
Alexis Marie Brewe
Eric James Bringley
Timothy Ford Bryson
Rozanna Catherine Buddin
Laura Rose Buescher
Matthew Alex Calcagno
Caroline Rose Caporossi
Chelsea Marie Clark
Chelsea Devan Coleburn
John Everett Craver
Elizabeth Ann Crummy
Clint Orlen Culver
Helen Elizabeth Darby
Jeffrey Laylon Davis

Khadijah Monique Dennis
Keenan McGrail Dunkley
Inemesit Charles Effiong
Kelly Lynn Faria
Alaina Rose Flanagan
Calli Nicole Fletcher
Taylor Lindsey Fontan
Sydney Elizabeth Ford
Ana Maria Gibson
Aaron Jacob Greene
Mary Hannah Greenway
Laquita Monique Grissett
Annie McCarthy Grove
Weston Cole Grove
Ryan Kelly Haltiwanger
Christina Marie Harkins
Lauren Jennie Harper
Olivia Hassler
Sabryna LaVerne Haynes
Taylor Ashley Haynes
Shelby Melanya Lyn Heary
Natalie Jean Hobson
Jonathan Shane Holt
Jaquon Edmar Irby

John Jacob Isenhower
Chardonnay Alexis Ismail
Davion Shabazz Johnson
Corey Todd Johnson Jr.
Cameron Gregory Kahn
Jonathan Mendel Kaufman
Rachel Diane Kitchens
Gabrielle Marie Kozub
Benjamin Starkey Lampe
Megan Nicole LaTorre
Jamie Lee Lawson
Nicholas Robert Lenze
Leeann Marie Leonhardt
Morgan Elaine Lundy
Shaina Nicole Manuel
Sarah Jessica Martin
Karra Waynette McCray
Mackenzie Alexandra
Meece-Rayle
Jarvia Breonne Meggett
Chance Lee Miller
Ryan Christopher Miller
Mariah Rose Minichello
Lorenzo Antonio Montali

Elizabeth Ellen Moore
Brooke Lynne Morton
Brady Christine Newell
Abbey Rose O'Brien
Rachel Lillian Odzer
Michael Carl Owens
Angelica Lauranette Palmer
Jessica May Parker
Rickeia Monaye Peterkin
Courtney Dora Petersen
James Frederick Weber Pike
Michael Steve Pina Gomez
Caroline Sydney Powell
Julia Anne Prodoehl
Sarah Elizabeth Puccio
Davide Chat Recchia
Cameron Elizabeth Reid
Eric Reyes-Bastida
Collin Drake Richardson
Elizabeth Christabel Riegel
Timothy Hunter Sabins
John William Sajovec
Tasha Nicole Sanders
Taylor Ann Santana

Olivia Christine Sargent
Emma Sophia Satzger
Lisa Lynn Schexnayder
Rachel Hope Scola
Joseph Emerson Setzer
Jacob William Sims
Lora Ann Stearns

Courtney Jean Swink
Tamaragail Calayo Tarrant
Kaleigh Summer Thomas
Brooke Lacey Turner
Christopher Jermane Turner
Anna Joline Tuten
Kady Beth Watts

Karli Janay Wells
Caroline Linnea Westberg
Addison Mae White
Julia Grace Whitehead
Andria Jamila Wilson
Ashley Elizabeth Wilson
Michelle Marie Wilson

Rose Mary Wilson
Joshua Cullen Wiltse
Davon Matthew Wright
Kiana Aleyah Wright
Grace Carroll Zimmermann
Victoria Welthy Zugehar

UNIVERSITY OF SOUTH CAROLINA AIKEN, AIKEN, SC

Derald Nicholas Adams
Katelyn Grisillo
Meredith Grace Hawcroft
Ayesha Nafesah Jihad
Giselle A. Johnson
Hazel M. Kelley

Lesley A. Koppert
Ajay Sivan Krishnakumar
Melissa Lane
Jennifer Law
Sophia Martinez
Ira Ellis Reeves IV

Eboni Cortessa Sanders
Nicole Sela
Taylor Leigh Shelley
Nikie Staley-Roach
Kara Elizabeth Summerlin
Hannah Taylor

Courtney Elizabeth
Templeton
Kayla Mari Victor
Nandi Ayana Wallace

UNIVERSITY OF SOUTH CAROLINA SUMTER, SUMTER, SC

Emma Wynn Betchman
Sherry Kay Burke

Alison Paige Coleman
Rachael Anne Horne

Mary Rachel Hudson
Taylor Nicole Jones

Devyn Wingard Youngblood

UNIVERSITY OF SOUTH CAROLINA UNION CAMPUS, UNION, SC

Emma Hodge Addison
Joseph C. Allen
Angela B. Bennett
Grady Biggerstaff
Braylin Kiere Brown
Amber Nicole Bumgarner
David Allen Burress
Brittany Kenyetta Davis
Lindsey Elizabeth Dawkins
Gage Jordan Eaves

Kayla Elizabeth Farr
Katie Nicole Ford
Michael Dalton Foster
Karla Lynn Franklin
Grayson Scott Garrett
Tracy Delynn Gatliff
Peggy A. Glenn
Kelsey E. Granger
Martha R. Grant
Alex Matthew Henderson

Addison Michelle Hill
Rachel Ann Hughes
Emily Brooke Ivey
Heather B. Johnson
Jacob Marcus Lee Jones
Jennifer Victoria Lankford
Timothy Marc Leigh
Brittney Victoria Moss
Adam Chance Parkins
Charles E. Pauley

Myranda Dawn Rhinehart
Briana Kiara Spencer
Christopher Allen Spencer
Jemochaine Shawne Stinson
Kevin Amonte' Sumpter
Timothy Scott Taylor
Brenda K. Tester
Kimberly Nicole Watson
Alana Dion Wright

UNIVERSITY OF SOUTHERN INDIANA, EVANSVILLE, IN

Lauren E. Abney
John T. Barton
Alicia M. Blackwell
Malana A. Boris
Jerry K. Boyd
Amanda L. Brown
Carlos E. Caballero-Ramirez
Maggie E. Comer
Faith H. Connell

Nathan D. Criss
Courtney I. Dressler
Brandon D. Edwards
Kayla M. Fein
Morgan N. Fields
Alexis K. Giannini
Samantha Leigh Harpenau
Megan Ann Heare
Kereston Lynn Hochgesang

Christopher M. Huber
Sarah E. Jackson
Allison June Kinney
Rebecca S. Koopman
Kaleb A. Kramer
Andrew M. Kuper
Jessica A. Litherland
Timothy N. Luczak
Alexander T. Martens

Aaron D. McCullough
Andrew L. McGuire
Chad E. McKinley
Coralys Miranda-Reyes
Alyssa B. Moore
Brianna D. Perry
Sara A. Poletti
Robert S. Rich
Mitchell A. Schnarr

Rachel A. Silliman
Evan K. Stieler
Claire M. Stover

Allen M. Thomas
Briony N. Towler
Katie D. Upton

Sarah N. Wagmeister
Taylor N. Washer

Megan E. Webster
Landen G. Weidenbenner

UNIVERSITY OF SOUTHERN MISSISSIPPI, HATTIESBURG, MS

Bailee Alexander
Joshua Aultman
Matthew Balcher
Anna Kate Baygents
Preston Bell
Matthew Bennett
Nick Bohte
Haleigh Rebekah Bradley
Katherine Lynette Brewer
Erin de los Santos
Samuel Dent
Blake Anthony Dunaway
Kristen Dupard

Lauren Duty
Bradley Floore
Candace Marie Franklin
Jeffrey Randolph George
JoAnna Gunnufsen
William Hewes
Kevreonna Hypolite
Mackenzie Deen Kelly
Danviona King
Sarah Lacoste
Amanda Ladner
Douglas McClure
LeBlanc Jr.

Lauren Mackenzie Lott
Morgan Mariel Lowe
Kayla Luedtke
Meredith McPhail
Catherine Mercier
Meredith Moody
Demetries Shawn Morrow II
Jordan Nettles
Ukamaka Nwaokorie
Perry Overstreet
Phoenix Pope
Haile Powenski
John Rimann

Alexis Lynn Nicole Sanders
Sarah Beth Selph
Lorenzo Spencer
Mary Spooner
Kyle Stoner
Bonishia Thomas
Eboni Thompson
Jessica Patrice Thompson
Alexis Tymkiw
Aleke Vehos
Christiana Whitley
Vaniecia Shantory Wilson

UNIVERSITY OF SOUTHERN MISSISSIPPI GULF PARK CAMPUS, LONG BEACH, MS

Lindsey Bell
Monique Marie Betting
Elizabeth Ann Bosarge
Alyssa Comfort
Megan Cromwell

Binesha Michelle Fairley
Jamie Henton
John Hubbard
Kimberly Nicole Lacap
Ashlei Lasha Lewis

Ashley Lewis
Elizabeth Mast
Kaouthar Mejdoubi
Heather Marie Miller
Nicole Miller

Rachel Moreno
Cara Rodgers
David Wayne Singleton
Victoria Roberts Smith
Bianca Stewart

UNIVERSITY OF ST. FRANCIS, JOLIET, IL

William P. Batsch
Brian C. Edwards
Andrew Finein

Brandon R. Ivins
Bryona Lavell Johnson

Justyna Weronika Jozwik
Precious McClain

Laura Munoz Lopez
Irma V. Sandoval

UNIVERSITY OF ST. THOMAS, HOUSTON, TX

Natalie L. Baker
Brittany Bigott
Jason Charles Brancato
Nhung Bui
Vladimir Davidiuk Jr.
Adriana Michelle
Dominguez
Rebekah Chantal-Jenai
Douglas
Ada Luisa Espinoza Suarez

Alexandra Marie Fernandez
Anna Rose Finnerman
Keagan Foss
Aliya Heise
Jennifer Hoang
Chante Trene Ellean
Jefferson
Sydney Christ Keller
Mackenzie Key
Kirstin Nicole Lee

Samantha Loos-Polk
Maghen Angelle Lormand
Jacqueline Mayoral
Taylor Eldora Mitchell
Elizabeth Ann Mussalli
Danny Santos Noriega
Erin Noel Novak
Krisly Sarah Philip
Gabrielle Rabosa
Angel Rivera

Mariana Sanches Viana
Alexandra Catherine
Summerour
Charlie Thai
Siyi Tian
Marianne Tran
TuyetLan Ngoc Vo

UNIVERSITY OF THE CUMBERLANDS, WILLIAMSBURG, KY

Brittany Sierra Marcella Anderson

Kellie Elizabeth Ball

Maggie Michelle Ballou

Rebekka Ann Bargo

Jamie Nicole Bell

Aaron Timothy Brewer

Mathias Richard Brewers

Todd Francis Campbell

Valerie Nicole Chavies

Keith LaMont Deveaux II

Trey Jehonnas Dick

Aneta Caprice Elliott

Anna Lynn Evdokiou

Haley Naomi Ferguson

Sara Jo Hampton

Haley Michelle Haygood

Miranda Caitlin Hedrick

Virginia Marie Jacobs

Heather Dawn Jolley

Sierra Elizabeth Jones

Candice Lindeque

Hunter McCain Martin

Josey Lee-Anne Mounce

Jessica Nichole Musgrove

Nicole Jasmine Nivison

William Holland Northern

Bonnie Joann Nutt

Brianna Shae Patterson

David Owen Poore

Sarah Jean Rainous

Hannah Elizabeth Ratliff

Katie Elizabeth Reid

William Jayson Smith

Jeffery Cameron Smoak

Makayla Elizabeth Tomblinson

Jon Kenyon Wilson

Ashley Victoria Wyatt

UNIVERSITY OF THE PACIFIC ARTHUR A. DUGONI SCHOOL OF DENTISTRY, STOCKTON, CA

Daniela A. Auerbach Jimenez

Dallin N. Harris

UNIVERSITY OF THE PACIFIC CONSERVATORY OF MUSIC, STOCKTON, CA

Sarah E. Antonsson

Robert Joseph Bassett

Makena Christine Clark

Alec Kendall Flatness

Sydney Frizzell Gorham

Bennett James Lopez

Julia Marie Ludwig

Jessica Taylor Rinehart

Rebekah Eileen Steiner

UNIVERSITY OF THE PACIFIC EBERHARDT SCHOOL OF BUSINESS, STOCKTON, CA

Mushel Fatima Kazmi

Jennifer Touma

Jesus Vega

UNIVERSITY OF THE PACIFIC GLADYS L. BENERD SCHOOL OF EDUCATION, STOCKTON, CA

Elizabeth Aguiar

Matthew Jensen Brewer

Tiffany Jolyne Field

Christiana Elizabeth Freiri

Siena Gerbert

Rebekah Jane Grabow

Ashley Michelle Keeline

Alexandra Figueroa Lopez

Heather Rose Quiñones

UNIVERSITY OF THE PACIFIC SCHOOL OF ENGINEERING & COMPUTER SCIENCE, STOCKTON, CA

Benjamin A. Aguilar

Abdulmohsen Y A A E Alshaiji

Hannah Reed Bettencourt

Evan Bomgardner

Andrew J. Bose

Cody Burkard

Samuel Costigan

Karla Patricia Duran

Zahi Paul Hakim

Logan Daniel Herche

Selena Dawn Kaffer

Austin Kimbrell

Timothy Lee

Selwyn Lehmann

Owen Curtis Lincoln

John Loomis

Laura Prange

Brianna Prebilic Cole

Lukas Anari Rickard

Dylan Anthony Saracco

Zeshawn Shaheen

Tanner Scott Shephard

Kathleen Shoga

Scott Snow

Peter James Tabada

Jason Tam

Mehal Vitthal

Jonathan Michael Wagenet

Muhammad Waqas

Timothy William Weatherwax

Christopher Wejmar

UNIVERSITY OF THE VIRGIN ISLANDS, ST. THOMAS, VI

Diana Ashhab

Alphea Glenyce Browne

Avanelle Lawn Alana
Carbon

Nakeshma S. Cassel

Nirisha Commodore

Deeno A. Cumberbatch

Clilia Z. S. Davis

Tarriesha A. Dawson

Chamara Alia Fahie

Aron A. Gumbs

Jared Alexander Hanley

Nathalia D. Henderson

Shaniqua Hodge

Shanee Isaac

Jernell A. Jerome

Lynesha Michelle Joseph

Tamika Grace Jude

Sequoia Lake

Sheneé Martin

DeWein Pelle

Trevesia A. Queeley

Kymberli Euanne Kecia
Simon

Omani Raheim Tuitt

Hannah N. Vogclina

UNIVERSITY OF THE VIRGIN ISLANDS ST. CROIX, ST. CROIX, VI

La Toya Benjamin

Augustus Laurencin Jr.

Niesha Mahepath

Crystal D. Peter

Samantha Roberts

Zoe' Theone Voya Walker

UNIVERSITY OF VALLEY FORGE, PHOENIXVILLE, PA

Kaylee L. Applegarth

Jaron J. Beadle

Emily K. Benco

Aaron Bishop

Anthony T. Blake

Micah Brugere

Elise N. Brunelle

Alexis M. Colon

David V. Cooper

Sorina A. Corkey

Justin Czubkowski

Lydia I. DeLeon

Patience Y. Ekuta

Roger C. Erdvig

Kaitlyn Faraghan

Jessica L. Fox

Matthew R. Godfrey

Julia D. Grant

Katherine A. Hewes

Ethan Q. Holmes

Kevin P. Landis

Timothy R. Lewis

Elicia MacTarnaghan

Brielle E. McKenzie

Gabriell E. Miller

Kristen Morgan Lindsey
Morrison

Kelsey L. Mosess

Kathryn E. Naylor

Rachel T. Nestman

Kristina Marie Padilla

Joshua M. Reedy

Rebekah Rosenberg

Kyler S. Sederwall

Renee A. Seler

Emily A. Stefanec

Rebekah L. Steinhour

Luke C. Stoltzfoos

James M. Tarpey

Corinne F. Twigg

Janna D. Weiler

UNIVERSITY OF WEST GEORGIA, CARROLLTON, GA

Renee' Michelle Bostic

Korbyn Boyd

Keisha Ann Boyle

Samantha Rose Bush

Anissa Teriona Lashun
Hobbs

Kelsey Christine Kennedy

Daija McElwee

Kayla Morris

Brandon Chance Reece

Ashley Viel

Carlene Williams

UNIVERSITY OF WISCONSIN EAU CLAIRE, EAU CLAIRE, WI

Lindsay Taylor Baczkowski

Carissa Kay Baier

Melissa Jane Beaupre

Katie Marie Beck

Leah Rose Beckman

Jesse Kyle Bluem

Kali Jean Boldt

Elizabeth Maura Brandes

K. Brellenthin

Shalaine Jean Buehl

Laura Elisabeth Crave

Nicole Lynn Egan

Caroline Anne Farrell

Steven M. Fuhrman

Andrea Janet Giachino

Katelyn Rose Haupt

Jody Lynn Herrmann

C. Hewitt

Heather Ann Hintz

Brandon Scott Hoege

Nicholas James Hora

Ellen Margaret Junko

Kayla Marie Knez

Jamie Lynn Kondro

Samantha Mary Kosel

Anna Maureen Kurilla

M. Leach

Laura Catherine Ley

Patrick Francis Moran

Alex Van Munger

S. Naegeli

Sidney Mariah Nelson

J. Nueske

Shelby Todd Owens

Alexander Vaun Padalino

Madeline Maria Parker

Hunter Joseph Promer

Leah Jean Radeke

Josephine Therese Reisner

Katherine Rose Robertson

Kari Louise Sarauer	Jennifer Rose Spata	Ariana Alicia Tellez	Cody Preston Waters
Laura Kristine Schlichting	Audrey Marie Steinman	Benjamin Jason Thompson	Cory Adam White
Jordan Marie Schwartz	Alicia Joy Swanson	Isaac	Jonathan A. Wieser
Patrick M. Smith	Annie Jean Szmanda	B. Wales	

UNIVERSITY OF WISCONSIN OSHKOSH, OSHKOSH, WI

Sara Ali Jamal Arafeh Jr.	Erin Quesnell	Kelsey Ann Sageser	Vishwajit J. Tuchscherer
Zachary Ryan Dunton	Todd M. Raley		

UNIVERSITY OF WISCONSIN OSHKOSH–GRADUATE SCHOOL, OSHKOSH, WI

Reginald Charles Parson	Kathryn Ann Scheeler	Matthieu Thomas Vollmer

UTICA COLLEGE, UTICA, NY

George Archundia	MaryEllen Fitzgerald Bord	Tanaesja Milligan	Morgan Reed
Frank Bartkowiak	Sara George	James Neeley	Matthew Rogers
Ignacia Bermudez	Janessa Haasbeek	Lana Marie Nitti	Anthony Michael Scalise III
Merissa Brillanti	Nikiya Harris	Opeyemi Ogunwomoju	Brittany Sieczek
Amarildo Ceka	Melanie Hicks	Steve Oliveira	Nicholas Alan Souza
Ann Ciancia	Laura Holmes	Amanda Paladino	Nicholas Surprenant
Elliott Coleman	Courtney Hryniowski	Rashida Patrick	Joel Wetmore
Nolan M. Cool	Cameron Jennings	Taylor Kristine Peters	Sarah Emily Wiatr
Rrezart Dema	Keari Little	Melinda Pfeffer	
Mikayla Dihrberg	Angela Malaspina	Cassandra Lynn Plows	
Issatou Fall	James McClendon	Morgan Rabideau	

UTICA SCHOOL OF COMMERCE, UTICA, NY

Zachary Babcock	Allison Melissa LaSalle	Bereny Paulino	Erich Stratton
Christine Emmerich	Patricia McCarthy	Patricia Anne Rodriguez	Kim Todd
Samantha Fay	Bruce Morgan	Jessica R. Smith	Ronald Van Duren

VALDOSTA STATE UNIVERSITY, VALDOSTA, GA

Sydney Ann Beckmann	Gloria De La Garza	Maya Phillips	Austin Strabala
Allison Bonanni	Summer Goff	Hunter Pope	Erinika Taliaferro
Kyle Bragg	Richard Hunnwell	Ashlie Prain	Tiffany Brianna Tanner
Eric Brantley	Bradley Joyal	Crystal Richardson	Tatiana Tsaruk
William Carraway	Emily Lovell	Ja'llen Ricks	Ann Williams
Noah Coil	Kalin Martin	Nolan Ripple	Maia Nicole Wilson
Phenix Culbertson	Clandra Newson	Abigail Shepherd	
Sky Dainty	Nikeshkumar Patel	Jasmin Solis	

VALENCIA COLLEGE WINTER PARK CAMPUS, WINTER PARK, FL

Victoria Alliji

Jacqueline Aubrey

Makayla Bullis

Sierra Lynn Collins

Keagan Fowler

Emily Jarjoura

Chloe Lomelli

Shelby Pickar-Dennis

Shanae R. Smith

Brandon Suggs

Cari Ware

Sierra Westfall

VALENCIA COMMUNITY COLLEGE OSCEOLA CAMPUS, KISSIMMEE, FL

Amanda Wendy Levya

Emmy Torres

VALLEY CITY STATE UNIVERSITY, VALLEY CITY, ND

Bradie A. Archbold

Alex Dawn Askerooth

Eve E. Axvig

Jamie M. Bartlett

Noele B. Blevins

Karyn E. Bomstad

Katarina C. Boychuk

Hailey I. Brevik

Cody O. Brooks

Amelia M. Brown

Matthew B. Bultema

David D. Burgess

Lyndsay M. Burns

Alicia B. Cebada

Tarah A. Cleveland

Jenna Lyn Coghlan

Amanda R. Cutts

Courtney J. Dixon

Barbara A. Ector

Cortney D. Edwards

Dacie I. Essig

Wendy M. Eszlinger

Andrew J. Evenson

Cassandra R. Fick

Jessica M. Georgeson

Alexis Anne Getzlaff

Megan A. Good

Bailey M. Goolsbey

Allison M. Hagerott

Michaela Elizabeth
Halvorson

Mackenzie J. Hamre

Shelby L. Hartman

Tiffany M. Hass

Misael Herrera

Kenneth A. Hodem

Shannon Dawn Hone

Emily J. Houmann

Staci A. Hovland

Miranda M. Hulm

Erin C. Jangula

Hanna L. Jepsen

Angie M. Johnson

Brianna L. Johnson

Jacob Ben Johnson

Jessica L. Jones

Ashley Nozomi Pascual
Kaya

Summer L. Keuler

Trevor J. Kleineschay

Lisa M. Klinkner

Emily R. Knoll

Adam L. Krueger

Caitlyn J. Krueger

Kelsey K. Labodi

Kaitlyn E. Langdon

Taran L. Langland

Nicholas Richard Lee

Alexis J. Lennon

Ashley M. Limesand

Ting Ting Lin

Colleen D. McNeill

Ashley Nicole Metcalf

Paige M. Meyer

Stephanie L. Miller

Tarra L. Miller

Sarah M. Odalen

Logan Edward Olesen

Megan Ann Olson

Elisabeth K. Ostrem

Heather K. Palmer

Courtney E. Pederson

Dallas D. Petersen

Kasaundra D. Peterson

Paul L. Peterson

Shelby D. Reiff

Morgan J. Rheault

Jennifer M. Riemann

Kate E. Roscoe

Courtney L. Rudolph

John E. Rutkowski

Shayna L. Ruzicka

Jessica A. Sanden

Jacob Nathan Schlecht

Karissa K. Schuler

Sara L. Schwanke

Leah A. Shepersky

Mariah J. Smith

Ben D. Sorenson

Cynthia M. Stahl

Maren K. Stegner

Baylee D. Swenson

Alessandra N. Taddeini

Megan Mae Trautman

Georgia Huntly Williams

VERNON COLLEGE, VERNON, TX

Hunter Abila

Alyse Almon

Abby Marie Anderson

Michelle Kay Allene
Anderson

Reid Armstrong

Edwin Bayudan

Kolton Burnett

Carly Cherry

Brook Conley

Raci Dillard

Emily Grace Durham

Monica Eslick

Shakota Field

Zack Bruner Lichtenberger

Carli Ann Maxwell

Boone Nees

Stephanie Nicole Otto

Anthony Pennartz

Ryan Puckett

Lari Robertson

Clay Rollo

Catherine Marie Ryan

Wherry Eteolia Tamara

Kaylee Breeann Taylor

Madison Templeton

Courtney Thayer

Sheena Worley

VILLA MARIA COLLEGE, BUFFALO, NY

Sarah Bond

Grace Gruarin

Jenifer Mack

VILLANOVA UNIVERSITY, VILLANOVA, PA

Christine C. Albert

Christopher R. Anderson

Claire M. Asmussen

Sarah T. Backenstoe

Nicholas E. Bayuk

Ana Becerra Taschetti

Christina M. Biancamano

Andrew C. Blazoski

Kyle J. Bowles

Thomas G. Brawley

Steven M. Buonomo Jr.

Jennifer L. Carillo

Nicholas M. Carney

Marianna F. Cesareo

Marissa R. Cucinotta

Brian F. Engelhart

Gabrielle Faragasso

Kaitlin N. Farinella

Ann M. Fazzio

Nicole M. Gambino

Casey M. Gatti

Sarah C. Hopkins

Christopher Kimito Hori

Gus L. Jenkins Jr.

Caroline A. Karanian

Shannon C. Lemmer

Meghan N. Long

Patrick Long

Evangelia J. Makrygiannis

Sarah A. McMahon

Andrew P. Moffa

Bailey M. Morley

Tatum E. Murray

Bryan R. Nardone

Andrew P. Orlando

Anika Pandit

Katrina A. Parsons

Stephanie L. Pastena

Meghan Kathryn Pawlak

Emily A. Persicketti

Molly C. Purnell

Patrick V. Ralph

Robert C. Reiff

Daniella P. Reimann

Thomas D. Rodriguez

Celina N. Santiago

Alyssa N. Sbarra

Jasmine C. Serano

Priya Shah

Elpitha L. Soussou

Sarah J. Stankiewicz

Eric W. Stoll

McKayla Swearer

Emily C. Tifft

Dylan Toolajian

Colleen M. Topper

Elizabeth R. Tyhacz

Brandon T. Wesley

Brian T. Whitehouse

VIRGINIA HIGHLANDS COMMUNITY COLLEGE, ABINGDON, VA

Kayla Renee Addesso

Michelle L. Arnett

Haley Brooke Ashley

Faith Mackenzie Booher

Emma Cheyenne Brewster

Kasey R. Burton

Cheyenne Geanene Calderon

Ashleigh Nicole Carnell

Kimberly Gail Trivett

Chapman

Aaron J. Dancey

Fred Daniel Day

Sara Anne Galliher

Jennifer L. Gibbs

Lionel William Grady Jr.

Isaac Rueben Grunstra

Timothy Eugene Hall

Trevor William Harrison

Ashley Brooke Hawk

Rebecca Erin Hockman

Heather Beverly Jeffreys

Andrea Denise Kaney

Mackenzie Alexandra

Kendrick

Victoria Lynn Kestner

Morgan Brianna Ledford

Elizabeth G. Lilly

Robin K. Linder

Jason T. Lovins

Abigail Louise Lyles

Krystal Marie Miller

Noelle Virginia Mutter

Stephanie Renee Necessary

Paula Marie Perry

Alyssa Marie Rainbolt

Kate Ann Reedy

Krista Shea Reynolds

Makenzie Ashton

Richardson

Kevin Rajesh Shah

Steve Brian Smith

Sheyanna Danielle Stillwell

Tabitha L. Thompson

Hannah Noel Torbett

Matthew William Trent

Justin Allen VanHoy

Kathleen Rebecca

VanNostrand

Brittany Hope Vicars

Kaylee Brooke Widener

Drew Elgin Williams

Adam Garland Wolfe

VIRGINIA POLYTECHNIC INSTITUTE & STATE UNIVERSITY GRADUATE SCHOOL, BLACKSBURG, VA

Nathan Andrew Carter

Matthew Yunho Chan

Shelley Lynn Cooke

Chelsea Rose Corkins

Saeed Izadi

Aaron Paul Johnson

Nicole J. Johnson

Shabnam Kavousi

Melissa Carol Kenny

Erin Suzanne Lavender-Stott

Tara Dawn Reel

Richard Rosario Rodrigues

Mohammed Saad Seyam

VIRGINIA WESLEYAN COLLEGE, NORFOLK, VA

Lauren Courtney Amos
Kiera Quineice Bell
Melinda Sue Bertram
Taylor Patrice Boyd
Tone' Marie Boykins
Ryan Matthew Breen
Andre Delsie Brummitt
Avriana Adonica Chavez
Joshua Joseph Currier
Fatima Breanna Davis
Joseph Michael DelPo III

Taylor Raye Doughtie
William James Edmundson
Tianna Tyanne Garland
Marlan Everett Hare
Stephanie Renee Harron
Tanasia Tara Hazelton
Courtney Louise Herrick
Jason Trevor Hoernke
Denisha Michele Howard
Khari Chaye Johnson
Whitney Frances Leliefeld

Robert Alexander McComb
Cassandra Renee McEwan
Victoria Mae O'Leary
Laura Elizabeth Robusto
Tenley M. Scott
Samantha Tate Small
Haley Jo Stromberg
Brittany Nicole Tasker
Audrey Syleste Lawrence
Thames
Andrew Michael Tomajczyk

Brooke Rae Totzeck
Tyler Demetrius Turner
Collette D. Vauthier
Austin Garret Von Ville
Chelsea Ann Washington
Stephanie Renee Williams
Michael Nance Willson
Courtni E. Wilson

VITERBO UNIVERSITY, LA CROSSE, WI

Emma Renee Akemann
Kirsten Marie Arm
Teryl A. Canada
Ryan Thomas Cook
Jennica A. Darcy
Danielle Rose Ducklow
Nathalia Duque Figueroa
Rebecca Fortek

Barb Grob
Sarah Hall
Delany Horton
Jessica Hundt
Ammie Jergenson
Dawn E. Johnson
Meredith Arden Jones
Jocelyn Klinkhammer

Corey Leonard Letizio
Jasmine Malouff
Kathryn Mormann
Marla Mulcahy
TheaMarie Jaton Peterson
Rachel Reeck
Dayna Roznowski
Brittany Santiago

Austin Sargent
Alyssa Sherwood
Paige Ashley Solie
Elizabeth A. Szymanski
Ashley Thornton
Kate Elizabeth Willadsen
Sadie Williams

VOLUNTEER STATE COMMUNITY COLLEGE, GALLATIN, TN

Barbara Harmon
Brandon Michael Herbert
Jenny A. Hernandez

Kaleb J. Kitchens
Brianna LaRhea Owen
Derek Powell

Megan Ratliff
Hannah Shepherd

Caleb Aaron Shupp
Stephanie White

WABASH VALLEY COLLEGE, MOUNT CARMEL, IL

Greta Claywell
Jeremiah E. Deckard
Peyton Rylie Farmer
Carrie Renee Gomez

Sidney Heldt
Kaela Hodges
Olivia Laurel Hunt
Kimberly M. Hutchcraft

Taylor Klein
Kaitlin Kralj
Shauna Mae Mitchell
Christopher Monasmith

Loan Ngoc Ngo
Mai Nguyen
Taylor Nicole Roosevelt
Bailey Nicole Winters

WALLACE COMMUNITY COLLEGE SELMA, SELMA, AL

Pulera Adamu
Jessica Allison
Guillaume Anthony
Taraya Bartell
Queneshia Beal
Ethan Bennett
Annie Berry

Crystal Bey
M Mostagir Bhuiyan
Claudette k. Blowe
Brittany Nicole Bowden
Karen Bradsell
Christopher Brady
Debra Brooks

Joseph Burke
Kyla Candies
Naomi Chappell
Brandon Childers
Leona Childers
Jessica Clark
Whitney Clay

Kadreika Clifton
Myaira Coleman
Brendan Collins
Ashlyn Cox
Ethel Craig
Lacey Crisman
Nolin Crowder

Floyd Crusoe
Vaierie Pandora Curtis
Thomas Dagostin
Logan Damoth
Diane Davis
Vanisha Davis
Monika I. Dedman
Whitney Denson
Ashley Deramus
Aubri' Dillard
Justin Driver
Africhinae Fikes
Jada Flanagan
Madison Flowers
Amber Ford
Eddie Ford
Kyle Friday
Tonya Glass
Arion Green
Latesha Greene
LaQuentin Gunn
Kristen Harre
William Harrell
Trendarius JaQuan Hill
Jesse Hogue

John Hood
Dexter Johnson
Jacob Johnson
Jalen Morrell Johnson
Regina Jones
Bridgette King
Quentika Lee
Mynesha Leonard
Jerry Light
Brittney Longcrier
Andrea Manzie
Kiara La'Shaunta Martin
Willie James Mason Jr.
Talisa Mccord
Lyndon Baine McGee II
Andrea McReynolds
Clara McWhorter-Light
Travis Miles
Demetria Lanise Minter
Avan Mosley
Pamela Moton
Beverly Owens
Kimberly Eileen Page
Tracey Perry
Stephanie Pettaway

Alden Pettway
Dakota Matthew Pittman
Carolyn Pounds
Taeyana Prevo
Kianna Reese
Kierra Reese
Sangita Reese
Imani Bri'sha Roy
Katrice Salone
Takia Sanders
Tamia Sanders
Stephanie Shannon
Demisha Shelton
Bonnie Lee Smith
Brandon Rashod Smith
Jakayla Smith
Wesley Smith
Shon Stallings
Justin Stanford
Crawford Steinberg
Hanah Stevens
Kalaisha Sullivan
Nathan Sykes
Lyshalia Taylor
Audriania Thicklin

Leon Thomas
Syreena Monique Thomas
Claudia Torres
Lucky Travis
Rekeshia Tyson
Victoria Vinson
Rebecca Waiker
Angela Ward
Sharon Waters
Brlttney White
Richard White
Samantha Wilkerson
Tamia Williams
Ahmad Wilson
Andrew Wilson
La'Ronda Witherspoon
Gabrielle Wood
Alexander Woods
Vonna Wright
Shelby York
Jennifer Youngblood
Courtney Zeigler

WALLACE STATE COMMUNITY COLLEGE HANCEVILLE, HANCEVILLE, AL

Patty Alexander
Whitney Alexander
Callie Allen
Amber Marie Allred
Terri Anders
Gregory Marshall Anderson
Staci Baker
Tyler Samuel Baker
Audrey Dawn Barnett
Cierra Marie Barrios
Sarah Ellen Battles
Cara Beasley
Mark Bland
Jessica Bradley
Ryan Bradley
Mallory Brannan

Emily Nicole Bray
Mark Brock
Mona Brown
Shelby Nicole Brown
Cindy Burchfield
Shasta Burke
Justin Burnett
Christopher Bynum
Kayla Byrd
Damon Calvert
Jennifer Campbell
Ricky Cason
Sheila Michele Chavers
Amanda Colson
Kristin Colvin
Kristen Cook

Lora Cottle
Amy Crowe
Julia Dailey
Sonia S. Datnow
Amanda Davis
Sandie Davis
Rosemary Dixon
Catherine "Malerie"
Drinkard
Erin Mckenzie Duncan
Hilary Ann Eason
Neely M. Franklin
Mackenzie Frederick
Hollye Spring Funderburk
Anthony Gann
Alexandria Paige Garner

Derek L. Gossett
Michael Gray
Hannah Gustin
Samantha Lois Hardisty
Melanie Kaye Harris
Lawrence Hartman
Olivia Henry
Hunter Zane Herron
Barbara Hoffman
Michelle Hogland
Katrina Holmes
Hannah Victoria Howard
Josh Luke Huddleston
Sarah L. Hughes
Porcha RaShae Hunter
Desiree Jackson

Hayley Johnson
Jonathan Johnson
Tammie Johnson
Caitlyn Kearns
Shaton Christine Kelley
Sanju Lamichhane
Lydia Latham
Jo An Letson
Erin Dorothy Lopez
Cesar Macias
Anthony Wayne Martin Jr.
Donald Wayne May
Treasure S. Mayfield
Tabitha Briana McCoy
Kristy Lee McKerley
Samuel Chavez Mendoza
Faith Moore
Daniel Moss
Ashlyn Storm Mullinax

Tonya Mullins
Micha Myers
Auston Davis Neal
Charles Nelson
Shannon E. Nichols
Alison Norris
Cody Trey Norton
Rebecca Lyn Oddo
Charles Paine
Michele Parker
Kaitlin McKenzie Parr
Taylor L. Pattillo
Joey Pilato
Jessica Nicole Pinyan
David Porter
Megan Joy Quimby
Ana Rameriz-Tomas
Jessica Leigh Ratliff
Macy Alexis Ray

Jennifer Vines Reed
Kalee Reid
Michael Richardson
Joel Robinson
Penny Rodgers
Kristen Rooker
Ashley Nicole Runions
Juan Sanchez
Zoey Nicole Scheetz
Lauren Nicole Seibert
Haley Self
Katherine Taylor Sexton
Hannah Shelton
Devin Sherrer
Jessica Simmons
Rachel Lynn Simmons
Erin Jackson Simpson
Brianna Sims
Haylee Brooke Sisson

Laura Smallwood
Ashley Smith
Lyndsey Breann Smith
Robert T. Smith
Alan Keith St. John
Cynthia Dawn Stricklin
Thomas Sullins
Lori Michelle Swann
Timotny Terry
Adrian Thomas
Shelby Till
Elijah David Tripp
Cyndi Lynne Turney
Christy Noelle Vaughan
Kaylynn Payge Ward
Misty Brianna Warren
Kaitlyn Aaron Wilson
Amanda L. Woodard
Charity Abigail Young

WALTERS STATE COMMUNITY COLLEGE, MORRISTOWN, TN

Joseph Lee Adams
William Parker Ashford
Bradley Wayne Backer
Jacob Straley Bartlett
Angel Dawn Beall
Mikayla Virginia Ruth Bell
Alyssa M. Bobalik
Peyton Skylar Booker
Daniel Jean Bradford
Kennedy Elise Branch
Jasmine Cabral
Laine Marie Coey
Jessica Lee Crawford

Matthew Jared Cureton
Tori Elizabeth Davis
Logan Norris Dickenson
Amanda Faith Drinnon
Lauren Kate Dunbar
Katrina Helen Eccles
Monica Garcia-Guzman
Stephanie Brooke Hammond
Summer Lynn Hayes
Lindsey Katelyn Haynes
Amber Ailene Hickey
Madison Rae Kilby
Brianna Ashley Lane

Alexis Hope Lowery
Christian Hunter Mallicoat
Kaitlyn RayAnne Martin
Mendy Kate Maxwell
Jade Victoria Merritt
Jacob Daniel Mills
Leslie Anne Odom
Kevin Lynn Parker
Noah Ray Parrish
Hailey McKenzie Pickett
Kathleen Ann Sargent
Gwendolyn C. Sheys
Gage Christian Smith

Meida Soto
Whitley Elizabeth Starnes
James Zackarrah Tackett
Amber Nicole Taylor
Jesse Dane Taylor
Allison Nicole Thomas
Tatiana Tikhonova
Krista Leann Trent
John Fredrick Wagner
Karly Brett Wells
Raven Lenise Wheat
Jeremiah Wimmer
Aaron M. Young

WARTBURG COLLEGE, WAVERLY, IA

Olayinka Ohotu Adetola
Selasi Tsitsi Ametewee
Joseph Thomas Amsberry
Robert James Anstoetter
Nolan James Asprey
Benjamin Joseph Bogard

Parker Jon Bolt
Kaitlyn Marie Brouwer
Heidi Lee Burgeson
Morgan Melissa Ciota
Leslie Michele Davis
Elizabeth Laura De Jardin

Angelo De Nubbila
Danica Marie Dickman
Emily Anne Eckberg
Jeanne Rose Edson
Nicole Marie Eick
Amalia Christine Emerson

Levi Andrew Endelman
Jamie Lynne Farley
Logan Marchall Goetzinger
Krystal Casandra Graves
Anthony Joseph Green
Nicholas Joel Green

Amanda Jo Groff

Mauricio Gutierrez Salazar

Daniel Lee Haack

Nicholas Jordan Hageman

Jared Joseph Hanus

Emma Louise Harmeyer

Jamie Jane Harrings

Emma Bernice Hellevik

Cole Steven Hinders

Wing Cheong Bryan Ho

Megan Elizabeth Howe

Derica Lynn Jakoubek

Cole William Jarrard

Melody Hazvineyi Jefita

Taylor Elaine Jensen

Rina Katsura

Ryan Lindner Kemp

Kaitlyn Rose Ketelsen

Madison Kay Kleve

Jennifer Rose Kuennen

Ashley Marie Lahti

Sean Harlow Lancaster

Benjamin Jeffrey Larson

Ngan Thai Le

Joey Leung

Brenna Marie Lien

Hannah Marie Long

Anna Elizabeth Mallen

Avery James Mason

Ashlee Nicole McGrown

Evelyne Cuthbert Mcharo

Michaela Ann McIlravy

Megan Lynn Neuendorf

Ella Marilyn Newell

Lauren Joyce Oberman

Tara Lynn Pape

Meghan Danielle Parman

Casey Lynne Pestka

Kelsey Lynne Peters

Kayla Polson

Jill Kathleen Powers

Megan M. Roedel

Ashley Nicole Rosa

Molly Jean Schares

Sarah Katherine Shirar

Lindokuhle Msimisi
Simelane

Carly Jo Sis

Victoria Kay Soat

Christopher Michael
Stauffer

Laura Marie Stenzel

Megan Marie Tapp

Elizabeth Marianne Trizzino

Andrew Lee Tubbs

Mackenzie Briana Walsh

Hunter Matthew Westhoff

Catherine Anne Wilcox

Chase Harrison Wilhelms

Allix Katrina Williamson

Trevor Davis Wood

Steven Douglas Zahn

Angela Ann Zook

WASHBURN UNIVERSITY, TOPEKA, KS

Colton B. Anderson

Nzingha I. Banks

Kyle Becker

Rachel N. Beiker

Alexa A. Bowen

Logan M. Brooks

Russell F. Budden

Stephanie E. Cannon

Brian C. Cervantez

Jena S. Dean

Mikayla M. Douglas

Sarah N. Edelman

Emily E. Engler

Kaylee J. Erickson

Natalie A. Flaucher

Christina J. Foreman

Mario A. Garcia

Alyssa R. Gerdes

Ellen E. Glasgow

Annastasia M. Glover

Dallas B. Hathaway

Donald D. Heiland

Kayla M. Herl

Hannah K. Howe

Kayla B. Johnson

Ryan P. Kelly

Kolin B. Klozenbucher

Courtney J. Koch

Blaire E. Landon

Rebecca Mary Maasen

Yangfei Mao

Olivia P. Marshall

Andy B. Massey

Kara M. Mazachek

Sharon K. McCourt-
Ostrowski

Monica K. McDougal

Evan R. Mietchen

Sarah M. Minneman

Chante R. Mitchell

Sarah P. Pederson

Blake K. Porter

Marina D. Quimby

Liandro Rodriguez

Katelyn S. Rollins

Jennifer L. Rosebaugh

Michaela R. Saunders

Christina M. Seeley

Connor E. Smith

Jack J. Van Dam

Kent A. Van De Mark

Madison A. Wiegers

Leanna R. Willer

Di Xie

Tae Yoo

Emily N. Zimmerman

Breona R. Zuchowski

WATTS SCHOOL OF NURSING, DURHAM, NC

Rachael V. Alexander

Leah Cagwin

Kristin Collis

Alaine Dean

Hannah Donahue

Crystal Lamarre

Briana Laures

Langston Preston

Chelsea Rhodenhiser

Jennifer Ritz

Ashley Roncaglione

Rachel White

Ciji Williams

Matthew Wilson

WAUBONSEE COMMUNITY COLLEGE, SUGAR GROVE, IL

Jevonnie Rémy Armistead

Jennifer Avila

Scott Bryan Brasel

Susan Burdette

Andrew Burton
Cassandra Camis
Michaela Jo Dearth
Katie Doherty
Anna Rose Dutton
Carol Fisher

Theresa Garcia
Kesha Dawn Henderson
Tyler Hill
Diana Lissette Iracheta
Shontal C. Jefferson
Christine L. Michaud

Kyle David Perkins
Yanru Pu
Claudia Resendiz
Britnee Saelens
Michelle Lynn Sakolari

Michael Alexander
Salamone
Kati Sibenaller
Emiliya Valcheva
Carlos Vazquez Acosta
Samuel Coleman Wuthrich

WAUKESHA COUNTY TECHNICAL COLLEGE, PEWAUKEE, WI

James J. Alsteen
Sarah Marie Barker
Michael D. Boehm
Vicki L. Boelter
Cortney M. Books
Karol J. Brennan
Alexandra M. Burgardt
Joseph P. Burnette
Michelle I. Cameron
Nina R. Clark
Alaina H. Cole
Ryan J. Corbin
Barbara J. Curry
Christina L. DeSautelle
Donna M. Dienhart
Michael L. Dufek
Joanne M. Edmundson
Erik J. Ennis
Jana L. Erdmann
Cassandra G. Ewert
Nina L. Fiedler
Jacqueline S. Gean
Cori A. Greenwald
Jessica D. Gregor

Molly M. Grennier
Sarah A. Guiliani
Paige Hanson
Kelly Haugen
Teraesa A. Hermanson
Andria L. Hernandez
Robert E. Hocutt
Shawn M. Hofstetter
Nicole L. Hunkel
James D. Johnson
Jeffrey D. Johnson
Robert R. Jones
Joseph R. Jorgenson
Matthew O. Karolek
Kyle C. Kielski
Robert A. Kincade
Jenna C. Koehn
Taryn A. Krause
Mitchell J. Kremel
Theresa B. LaMott
Douglas W. Lankford
Stephanie L. LeSage
William P. Maloney
Clinton J. Martinez

Michelle D. Mattheis
Dylan B. McCarthy
Christopher D. McGrath
Kelly A. McKeon
Delora A. Miksic
Christopher Morris
Jessica N. Niebler
Katie M. Parente
Jenna M. Parr
Jose I. Perez-Villa
Michelle L. Petrie
Jason S. Rehn
Maria L. Reyes
Brittany A. Rich
Jennifer L. Ries
Kurt J. Ritter
James A. Roderfer
Nathan P. Rogers
Brenda A. Rosman
Charles P. Russell
Shalimar J. Rydzik
Amy J. Sampson
Alyssa A. Schmick
Alysha L. Scholz

Heidi A. Seftar
Matthew M. Semrau
Jacquelyn E. Shaver
Julie A. Sheff
Andrew K. Sherwin
Troy A. Silbernagel
Mackenzie M. Slotty
Joy A. Sobie
Leah M. Socks
Logan T. Stigler
Jameson S. Studzinski
Leah K. Thornberry
Sara J. Torres
Yolanda M. Vogl
Alex D. Woodward
Joseph M. Wuenstel
Jordan Young
Rosemeena Zaman
Colleen E. Zeka
Becky L. Zingler
Nathan G. Zubke

WEATHERFORD COLLEGE, WEATHERFORD, TX

Juan Luis Aldape
Tina Ann Alford
Richard Sean Arbuckle
Jessica J. Archer
Mykayla Elizabeth
Armstrong
Sheila R. Barker
Kelley Nicole Belding

Kaylee Michelle Brooks
Jamie Renee Brown
Michael James Browne
Christy Lynn Butler
Isaac Chavez
Simeon Osoro Choi
Kodie Paige Cooper
Weston Decker

James Randolph Dixon
Shay Michele Douglas
Deris Deshaun Duncan
Phillip Duane Dyer
Kendell Lee Emmons
Krista Leigh Emmons
Whitney Maurine Ford
Eder Israel Frias

Makayela Elaine Fuller
Kelsey Maree Grottie
Chad Kendal Hartin
Joseph Gavin Herbel
Alex William Hitts
Matthew Jerome Hoerth
Lacy Bernice Jackson
Billy Cole James

Mikayla Marie Jennings
Jennifer Dawn Kamper
Fredrick Koinange Kimani
Heather Lanee King
Madeline E. King
Lane Garrett Livingston
Nicholas Anthony Lozano

Samuel Anthony Mahofski
Toni R. Martin
Peyton Louise Mccown
Christopher Lynn
Mccuistion
Dee A. McHenry
Nathan A. Mitchell

J'nae Melissa Mullen
Severija Narkute
Caitlin Marie Pastor
Bailee Jordan Pharis
Matthew Anthony Plusnick
Kaitlyn Renee Ridgeway
Donald Chace Sarchet

Kaitlyn Danielle Sessum
Mckinzie B. Shoush
Wesley Lane Sims
William Ryan Smith
Gregory Kent Talbot
Luis Torres

WEBBER INTERNATIONAL UNIVERSITY, BABSON PARK, FL

Botteron Benjamin
Viviane Buck
Stephanie Cabrices
Luka Coporda
Verity Crawley

Rachel Fredrick
Brandi Hazen
Jessika Hester
Krystal Ann Coral Huyler
Adam Jenkins

Kenny Overthrow
Edward Palmer
Henning Patricio
Steven Ritenour
Sophie Rossard

Sabrina Schumm
Stuart Snedden
Nicole J. Williams

WELCH COLLEGE, NASHVILLE, TN

Rachel Ann Burns
Nathaniel Austin Deel
Leah Carol Dell
Hannah R. Driggers

Joshua Daniel Dunbar
Michael David Hollis
John Daniel Newland
Leslie Blake Nichols

Emily Jane Parrish
Paula Melinda Stonerock
Larissa Cheree Thomas
Zachary Adam Vickery

Dustin Michael Walters
Rebekah Joy Zuniga

WELLS COLLEGE, AURORA, NY

Lindsay Achzet
Ariel Adams
Kyle Admire
Kimberly Bader
Navi Bal
Amanda Bottorff
Melissa Brewer
Courtney T. Brindisi
Alyssa Broome
Bailey Lynn Brown
Chelsea L. Carlin
Kaylee Anne Conner
Karinna Custer
Amelia Carol Flint

David Glidden
Andrea L. Gould
Leslie Green
Erin Nancy Hampson
Eric J. Hartmann
Aaron Heisey
Morgan Holtsclaw
Atiya Jemila Jordan
Ryan Kangas
Kailin Kucewicz
Michelle Lee
Anuhea-Emma Leite-Ah Yo
Scott Litvin
Nicole Loeven

Kamarie Maturine
Mikaela Mehlrose
Alexander Milliken
Tanner Mingen
Katherine Danielle
Mouradian
Anna Olczyk
Haylee Ouellette
Nadine Pershyn
Kelly Reppert
Alexandria Roberson
Nicole Sales
Valerie Schweigert
Catherine Anne Taylor

Deaven Theriault
Kendra Thomas
Mariah Elizabeth Thurston
Noa Tia
Justine Tibbits
Anastasia Toumpas
Zachary Tripsas
Erin K. Vallely
Marie Valliere
Lyndsey Wells
Molly Woods
Audrey Woolever

WESLEYAN COLLEGE, MACON, GA

Blaire Barnes Bagwell
Aahana Bajracharya
Brooke Frances Bosley
Thao T. Bui

Stephanie Shavonne Butler
Raleigh Catherine Chance
Sydney Elaine Davis
Sonya Dominique Dsouza

Jordan Alexandria Ealey
Sunada Khadka
Chelsea Leigh Lewis
Shujun Li

Chandra Tranelle Norman
Alannah Shelby Rivers
Maria Christina Rodriguez
Melissa Ivette Rodriguez

Wanda F. Rutland-Bond	Shamila Neemat Sarwar	Panyixiu Tian	Chau Minh Tran

WEST CHESTER UNIVERSITY, WEST CHESTER, PA

Jacquelyn Adeseye	Matthew Steven	Amanda Rae Long	Rich Schafer
Allison Marie Alexy	Dummeldinger	Rachel Lovell	Erika Schrock
Terell Bennett	Nicolas Anthony Dunn	Kathryn Ann Markovits	Jessica Schurstein
Sara Bennis	Courtney Dunne	Danni McGinty	Brian Schwabenland
Stephanie Binder	Henry David Eichman	Morgan Elizabeth	Stephen Sposito
Elizabeth Bishop	Crystalyn Marie Espinal	McMurtrie	Samantha Stalford
Alex Bowers	Anjelica Jean Finore	Kaitlyn Michalek	Devon Nicole Stroup
Lauren Brill	Jaclyn Giovinazzo	Amanda Louise Mooney	Matthias Szczepanek
Courtney Byrne	Tonya Kristy Ann	Andrew George Mudalel	Vanessa Thiel
Molly Byrne	Haderthauer	Shannon Patricia Nolan	Chan To
Laura Capehart	Andrew Hiles	Richard Lee O'Donnell Jr.	Jennifer Maureen Toby
Michael Cassidy	Michael Kalage	Danny O'Neill	Morgan TRUE
Nicole Susana Cattan	Kellen Kane	Joshua Oldham	Cristina Urena
Samantha Crabill	Elyse Anne Kistler	Jordan Wine Porr	Theresa Ann Whitehead
Michael Chayanne Diaz	Samantha Dorismay Lattie	Janice Rabian	Emily Zborowski
	Sara Leader	Robert Roulston	

WEST COAST BAPTIST COLLEGE, LANCASTER, CA

David Adams	Caleb Caviness	Arezoo Habibian	Sarah Janette Proctor
Nathan Albaugh	Morgan Daufen	Rebekah Harven	Mark Rasmussen
Ruth Alonso	Elizabeth Ee	Corey Heller	John Mark Ray
Jonathan Armstrong	Mychael Eikenberry	Elizabeth Hutchens	Jessica Roberson
Angela Berger	Marina Francisco	Tyler Nathanael Johnson	Jaritza Sabando
Jacob Bundy	Heidi Galyean	Patricia Lenz	Caleb Thiessen
Nathanael Robert Calvert	Connor Gaul	Nathan Longhofer	Nathan Walsh
Samantha Casequin	George Greene	Melissa Petersen	

WESTERN CONNECTICUT STATE UNIVERSITY, DANBURY, CT

Kaleigh Angela Cragan	Megan Elizabeth McCauley	Allison V. Vas	Kathryn Margaret Wichman
Francesca Marie Golightly	Lauren Alysse Muller	Krista Nicole Verrastro	Robert D. Zoccano III
Oscar Jean-Baptiste	Bianca D. Paolello		

WESTERN ILLINOIS UNIVERSITY, MACOMB, IL

Katherine Campagna	Kaylee Dianne McAllister	Nicole Ann Rybarczyk	Holly D. Stauffer
Karissa Marie Kouchis	Christie Elizabeth Millay	Kadidia Samassekou	Taylor N. Turner

WESTERN MICHIGAN UNIVERSITY, KALAMAZOO, MI

Emily Bamrick	Stephanie Beld	Lizzie Blasko	Ashley Bravo
Lauren Behmlander	Mary Bezinque	Beth Brandon	Ishara Brent

Emily Briggs
T'Ausia Bronson
Brianna Butler
Evelin Calderon
Rachel Callaly
Gina Cavanaugh
Li Cheng
Simbarashe Chirara
Emily Christensen
Adrienne Clabin
Cristina Cote
Marshell Cotton
Matt Coulson
Kendall Dixson
Dakota Mills Druley
Justin Eddy
Bertha Garcia-Rojas
Andrew Ryan Graeber

Katie Grinnell
Taylor Hall
Nathalie Hanson
Zachary Gilbert Henderson
Dominique Henry
Tu Ho
Ivory Hoang
Aaron Huntoon
Brandon Johnson
Autumn Kearney
Jaime Koehler
Tabitha Koppinger
Dale Kraai
Alec Kraus
Kimberly Laurent
Lauren Lenkart
Devon Lloyd
Aaron McClendon

Dennis Miller
Alainah Montemayor
Margarett Mooney
Edward Mulford
Salma Mumuni
Emily Nacy
James Nelson
Cecilia Nguyen
Adam Peterson
Joi Presberry
Lydia Pugh
Bryce Russell
Nayeli Sanchez
Nicole Satkowiak
Emily Scannell
Emily Scheffers
Taylor Schweyer
Silmang Sene

Anthony Skinner
Sarah Smeets
Cameron Smith
Connor Kenneth Smith
Ronnie Stephenson
Jacob Michael Stevens
Emma Logan Stuba
Joan Taveras
Victor Tran
Li Teng Voon
J. Gabriel Ware
Si'Ara Watkins
Kurt Wendland
Imani Whitby
Casey Wright
Peter Wyman

WESTERN NEBRASKA COMMUNITY COLLEGE, SCOTTSBLUFF, NE

Gladys A. Acosta Cardozo
Susan M. Albee
Blaise N. Alexander
Fabiana Andrade Da Silva
Musa Bah
Emily L. Bahmer
Garret Basler
Erin R. Baum
Shelton R. Blanco
Trae Blanco
Brandon Boardman
Josiah A. Bolyard
Abbey Boppre
Angela M. Borgmann
Ezekiel Bucks
Dianne L. Bunch
Matthew L. Cerny
Cody J. Childers
Lisa M. Christensen
Shawnee M. Christner
Jennifer R. Compton
Kathleen L. Converse
Larissa G. Converse

Cherry Cooper
Mindy E. Cress
Ryan L. Daniels
Katie Dannar
Kyle J. Debus
Mariah E. De Los Santos
Cassandra L. Dillman
Heather J. Doggett
Karianne I. Donnelson
Eklin Ehrman
Kathryn E. Ernest
Jenifer L. Evans
Whitney J. Fields
Sierra P. Frickey
Collette Marie Graham
Alexandra F. Green
Samantha K. Grimes
Shelby L. Grimes
Justin C. Hagerman
Maria Hilaria Hernandez
Serna
Brittany N. Hill
Regan J. Hinton

Marissa A. Holman
Dawn Holmes
Andrew J. Jackson
Ashlyn N. Jenkins
Chelsey G. Keefer
Seungin Kim
Joshua Alvin Kling
Richard W. Knott Jr.
Morgan A. Lamar
Jaime R. Landwehr
Tiffany N. Lewis
Michelle Maderak
Bakary Manneh
Fuatino S. Manu
Paula Markowski
Jolene R. Martin
Jasmine McLain
Courtney L. Medina
Rose K. Nelson
Courtney M. Noland
Ivette C. Ortiz
Marisa L. Plummer
Nathaly Poveda Ardila

Kimberly F. Powell
Kayla Roberts
Ismael Rodriguez
Jaime Kai Rohrer
Toni M. Rosado
Ashley M. Schievelbein
Brooke G. Schneider
Tyson A. Segelke
Alyssa B. Smith
Kelsey K. Southard
Hannah Sparks
Tristan C. Stephenson
Charles A. Stewart
Sarah Stull
Michelle M. Talbot
Sharon Tarus
Jeremy R. Torres
Elaine B. Tyree
Kierna B. Uthmann
Gabriela Valverde
Desirae Nicole Visser
Brooke R. Vogt
Brandon M. Wallace

Bryce B. Wasson
Lexi K. Webber
Darren D. Wells

Kelsey M. Westman
Carianne Renee White

Hannah Faith Wilke
Andrea T. Williams

Akofa Fiona Zannou
Kelly R. Zitterkopf

WESTERN NEW ENGLAND UNIVERSITY, SPRINGFIELD, MA

Nicole S. Ager
Joseph W. Baurys
Alisa Bekk
Erika L. Benlisa
Sarah Brauza
Kelly Anne Byrnes
Andrea B. Canales
Robert L. Caruso
Jasmine G. Chee

Julie Ann Cokotis
Alexandria N. Dean
Alexander N. DeFelice
Jeffrey M. DeManche
Jeremy C. Downs
Sylvia Drogosz
Stephanie R. Elizondo
Katie L. Farrell
Melissa C. Ferris

Emily A. Fliss
Jamie H. Franklin
Hailey B. Greenhalgh
Dawn E. Heideman
Anthony M. Kolakowski
Matthew S. LaCoille
Timothy J. LaFalam
Irmalie Lopez
Emily M. Lynch

Thinh Quoc Nguyen
Andres I. Otero
Gretchen L. Pancak
Abigail A. Powers
Sarah Anne Rup
Ellen J. Serra
Shaine G. Spencer
Lyndsey N. St. Jean
Danielle M. Torchia

WESTERN OREGON UNIVERSITY, MONMOUTH, OR

Emily Marie Allen
Maria Babiker
Jennifer Marie Bietschek
Gabrielle Boyle
Esther June Bruce
Megan Cabison
Andres Classen
Taylor Nicole Classen
Christiana Colasurdo
Lindsay Comella
Rachel Crawford
Patricia Desrosiers
Danica Drapela
Sarah Duhart

Stephanie Foster
Kauionalani Fukuda
John William Goldsmith
Shantell Guyton
Courtney Haess
Rebecca Jane Hazel
Joshua Logan Henderson
Katrina Henderson
Molly Marie Hinsvark
Noor Mustafa Ismael
Kelsie Johnson
Alexander Jones
Bryan Ross Kelley
Jimmy Khang

Audrey Klampe
Tyler Lewis
Kourtney Linebaugh
Alyssa Little
Zachary Martin
Mylisa McGill
Jaime Lynn Mendoza
Angelmary Joel Ndyetabula
Daniel Perez-Aguilar
Julie Ann Postma
Richard Prewitt
Cyntia Rodriguez
Tracy Romero-Rios
Sam Stageman

Amanda Stevens
Tori Stutzman
Katya McAuley Szigethy
Kaylyn Taylor
Daniel Thom
Richail Charnai Vail
Samantha Marie Valdez
Alexandra K. Vandenberghe
Tania Villanueva Reyes
Natalie Wallace
Matt Wines
Becki Nicole Wright
Josiah Wunsch

WESTERN TECHNICAL COLLEGE, LA CROSSE, WI

Mariah M. Deschler
Diedra M. Torgeson

Kimberly Kay Vaughter

Rozanna E. Weaver

Bao Xiong

WESTERN TEXAS COLLEGE, SNYDER, TX

Kaili Puakela Agabin
Greg Patrick Asher
Zachary Lee Barrientos
Kayla Deeanne Bartley
Brooke Margaret Berding
Carolyn Ruth Berry

Samantha Marie Bloom
Legrand Bouyi
Sydney Danielle Bowman
Vivienne Perez Dagalea
Andrea Delgado
Andres Delgado

Elliana Renae Doubleday
Darci Susanna Duncan
Heather Marie Dupree
Rachel Eva Gawdun
BreAnn Danielle Gotcher
Jasmine Dominique Green

Le'Ann Michelle Hall
Dylan Wess Hatley
Seth Francis Hubert
Billie Dian Jones-Hudson
Hunter Reagan Key
McKayla Jeanne Lucas

Shawna Lynn Mullinix
Jason Nunez
Malina Anselma Quezada
Jasmine Nicole Richardson

Sunny Ruiz
Morgan Leigh Scott
Ashley Dawn Semler
Jaden Rena Shoults

Clifford Zane Stafford
Yuliana Thamez
Laramie Dean Thompson
Kelsey Nicole Vasquez

Taliilagi Alohapumehana
Viliamu

WESTERN UNIVERSITY OF HEALTH SCIENCES, POMONA, CA

Jacob J. Adashek
Adel Aitali
Alina M. Amaral
David N. Ardakani
Cedric A. R. Bailey
Savannah E. Beauregard
Kristine N. Beetham
Brittinae Bell
Melissa R. Berg
Eugene J. Beville
Richard H. Bracken
Jacklyn L. Bradley
Kirsten L. Breslin
Jennifer E. Briggs
Ian P. Cahatol
Macey M. Camplair
Victoria T. C. Chan
Danielle N. Curi
Abdullah K. Dakhlallah
Christine L. Dang
Richard J. Delavan
Danielle M. Demel
Matthew Lawrence Diggory
Nnaemeka Daniel Diribe
Colin (Meng-Ju) Du
Stephanie Duckett
Caroline E. DuPee
Anna Dyurgerova
Amanda G. Emmert
Jenifer N. Fox
Ehssan Ghassemi
Zachary P. Giesen
Mindy J. Goh
Christle C. Guevarra
Katherine Ha
Chelsea E. Halprin
Laurie S. Hannan-reagan

Kristina M. Hart
Sarah E. Hassman
Kelsea Hazlehurst
Julia M. Healy
JoAnn M. Henwood
Stephanie L. Ho
Leo Holguin
Amy C. Huang
Amy Jee Hye Huh
Brittany G. Imlach
Shifteh Iranmanesh
Jennifer Israel
Sasha Rose Jensen
Calvin C. Jiang
Kristen D. Johannessen
Renata A. Jones
Olympia A. Kabobel
Mallory A. Kennedy
Emily M. Khatchaturian
Sei J. Kim
Pradhab Kirupaharan
Matthew M. Klein
Michele S. Ko
Stephanie Neal Kurica
Brian B. Lam
Ellen Lee
Jessica K. Lee
Patrick C. Lee
Meng Jie Li
Kimberly Lim
Xi Liu
Jaime Lu
Chan Luc
Cullen A. Mack
Kamran Mahramzadeh
Kevin V. Mai
Corby W. Makin

Lindsay S. Malcolm
Asya G. Marsh
TyIsa C. Marshall-Blanche
Blaine L. Massey
Brittany H. Mastin
Nathan R. McDonald
Kevin M. McEvilly
Radhika Mehndiratta
Sarah Mercer-Bowyer
Saul L. Miller
Sean Patrick Miller
Adam C. Mina
Lauren A. Molchan
Jessica Ann Moody
Kyle T. Mrohs
Gina H. Nalbandian
Timothy D. Naney
Syed Abbas A. Naqvi
Vitaliy P. Natkha
Todd R. Needs
Amy M. Nguyen
Elaine Nguyen
Phi T. Nguyen
Steven H. Nguyen
Jamie A. O'Connor
Gabrielle N. O'Garro
Marvin R. Ortiz
Eugene S. Pak
Christopher W. Parker
Juan L. Partida
Amie S. Patel
Himani K. Patel
Elyse K. Persico
Raksha Pradhan
Clarissa Prieto-Ayala
Yang Qiu
Jasmine Querubin

Lavanya Rajendran
Elizabeth A. Reischl
Erik M. Rueckert
Yesica Ruiz
Atul Saini
Israel Santander
Tara Sarabakhsh
Chandler P. Schermerhorn
Colby J. Seegmiller
Kyle T. Seko
Sakara Seng
Jennifer L. Seyffert
Avni A. Shah
Shahab Shahangian
Joseph P. Simmons
Grant G. Simpson
Stephanie C. Smith
Lauren K. Teichrow
Lidia Tekie
Casey J. Thompson
Kayla Uh
Marvin A. Vallejo
Emily L. Vandenberg
Melissa Marie Ven Dange
Jennifer M. Verba
Eric M. Vinceslio
Purvi Vira
Sahil F. Vohra
Douglas G. Wagemann
John R. Wagner
Whitney N. Wolfe
Andrew Taylor Yen
Shella Yu
Terry Yu

WEST KENTUCKY COMMUNITY & TECHNICAL COLLEGE, PADUCAH, KY

Sarah Jean Baird
Cyndel Leigh Bebout
Michelle Kayla Boss
Lindsey Michelle Briggs
Tracy Sue Burkhart
Desiree Chantelle Delapaz
Zachary Levi Everhart
Kelsey Marie Ferguson
Kristin Michelle Hardin
Brett Harold Hecklinger

Brandie Lee Hendrick
Cody Ryan Hollis
Mary Kate Hudspeth
Jacob Philip Hugenroth
Kaitlyn Nicole Hunter
Meaghan Rachelle Lawrence
Tiffany Paige McFadden
Susanna Marie Morrow
Corey Michael Nance
Selenia Marisol Ortiz

James Panosh
Jae Anne Rayburn-Trimble
Tasha Ana Redman
Bailey Elizabeth Robertson
Caitlin B. Rudolph
Amy Leann Runyon Dunlap
Benjamin Joseph Sandman
Matthew Alexander Snead
Kristie Dyan Starks
John R. Thompson

Kelli Lea Throgmorton
Stacey Lynn Tippin
Jade Leola Marie Townsley
Emily Renee Verbaere
Allison Lane Warford
Gwen Ellen Watson
Kaytlyn Paige Woodruff
Steven J. Wright

WESTMINSTER COLLEGE, FULTON, MO

Kelli M. Albrecht
Gordon Y. Allison Jr.
Olivia B. Andoe
Jon R. Antel
Krista K. Armontrout
Scovia Aweko
Amelia G. Ayers
Rachel E. Bade
Anne E. Baker
Abigail S. Bax
Meredith J. Bolen
Adam K. Brake
Alyssa K. Busken
Lejla Dervisevic
Erin J. DeVasto
Maria R. Donovan

Molly C. Dwyer
Steven Michael Ebert II
Mustafe M. Elmi
Megan R. Fitzpatrick
Ashley N. Flood
Nathan F. Fox
Kasey E. Gatson
Olivia C. Gibby
Mengdi Guo
Sombiniaina Herimpitiavana
Caitlin M. Higgins
Jeremy Cole Hill
Lori A. Hoertel
Ella M. Leslie
Danielle M. Lorenscheit
Ayush Manandhar

Mthobisi Maseko
Megan E. McCaul
Greta Morina
Allison N. Moulton
Harmony R. Nelson
Joseph M. Nieves
Spencer C. O'Gara
Brittany D. Paglusch
Ethan M. Parent
Robyn L. Parkinson
Erin J. Perry
Grant J. Peterson
Alexandra N. Rauscher
Mikaela R. Ruga
Steven Sakayroun
Grace A. Sanford

Samuel I. Schumacher
Da'Shaun Lee Scott
Haley J. Short
Blake E. Stonecipher
Jamie N. Striler
Veronica N. Tuthill
Kaitlin A. Valentine
Kristen A. Warncke
Jordyn E. Williams
Laura J. Wiltshire
Allison J. Wingert
Allison R. Wright
John E. York
Andrea M. Zalis

WESTMINSTER COLLEGE, SALT LAKE CITY, UT

Levi Rose Barrett
Hannah Baybutt
Kristina Benoist
Jessica Chellsen
Kaitlin Clements
Quentin Coppler
Selina Foster
Joshua Goldsmith
Trey Hansen

Joecee Heil
David Herzog
Alyse Horton
Hasib Hussainzada
Jane Jerman
Aamina Khaleel
Karissa Killian
Costa Lasiy
Kevin Martinez

Leesa McDill
Whitney Mecham
Marlene Mercado
Tanner Morris
Ghanashyam Neupane
Tallis Radwick
Rachel Roberston
Sydney Marie Sattler
Sierra Schoen

Jackson Shaver
James Steur
Elaine Michelle Thompson
Miguel Martín Villa
Whitney Walton
Thorne Warner
Leah Weisgal
Hannah Marie Williams

WEST SHORE COMMUNITY COLLEGE, SCOTTVILLE, MI

Norma Gonzalez Buenrostro

Jared Hanson

Cody Jensen

Tessa Kay Kriz

Maeve Lagerquist

Macy Marie Miller Kapala

Sean Pollock

Kendra Kay Schalow

Lindsay Scheffler

Hannah Catherine Stuck

Joseph A. Stuck

Brianna Nicole Walter

WEST TEXAS A&M UNIVERSITY, CANYON, TX

Alison B. Alexander

Anna R. Ceniceros

Michael J. Keough

Alexander Korn

Evans K. Langat

Jonathan Matthew Mitchell

Natalia B. Molina

Magali Moralez

Babar M. Mustafa

Sushil Paudyal

Fatima Maria Rebollar

Zahra H. Shihabuddin

Ganesh S. Sockalingam

Aileen M. Taylor

Casey R. Watson

WEST VIRGINIA NORTHERN COMMUNITY COLLEGE, WHEELING, WV

Rick L. Alleman

Chelsea Renea Arman

Rachel Jonell Arnold

Cerra Nicole Atkins

Amanda Caitlin Bailes

Leroy Barnett

Jacqueline S. Bartlett

Brandon Lee Bassett

Melisa Anna Beck

Kenneth Joseph Becker

Melissa Anne Beegle

Alorah Danan Beighey

Ashley Nichole Berardi

Chasity Rose Billingsley

Sarah Grace Blankenship

Maggie Marie Bonar

Tiffany Yavonne Braunlich

Jessica Brooke Burch

Breanna Elizabeth Cain

Brooke Lawren Capp

Heather Nicole Chaplin

Taylor Ryan Chappell

Amy M. Clay

MaryFrances Colabella-
Worklan

Jenny Lee Colaber

Elise A. Cowden

Emery Kate Curto

Lacey Anne Davis

Douglas Allen Debnar

Craig M. Dobbs

Rachel Dawn Doll

Stacey Nicole Durig

Haley Dawn Dyer

Nina Marie Elder ALP

Carolyn Anne Emery

Lee Ward Franklin

Michael Cody Gaunt

Victoria Kristen Gerst

Gina M. Granato

Melissa Ann Graziano

Joshua Robert Green

Christina M. Grindle

Krista Ann Habig-Klee

Lauren Jean Hall

Sydney M. Hanket

Brittany Marie Harrigan

Kelsey Alexandra Harris

Tracey D. Hartzell

Maci Marie Hascak

Janeen Denise Heath

Katie Lynn Heffner

Taylor Suzanne Himmelrick

Angel Mae Hines

Emily Sue Hobbs

Alice Marie Holstein

Kiersten Darlene Hores

Amy Josephine Howell

Patricia Lynn Hulderman

Tetiana O. Jackson

Savannah Renee Jasper

Jennifer Susan Kinder

Alexa Rae Kinemond

Jasmyn Marie King

Jonnielynn Allison Krieger

Erin Joy Lang

Deborah Ann Leech

Mary Ann Lemasters

Amanda L. Logston

Christopher Thomas Maher

Melody Louise Malolepszy

Kylee Marie Manypenny

Anna Christina Mason

Kristen Ciara McBee

Kelly Lynn McEwen

Carrie Samantha
McLaughlin

Katherine Olivia
McLaughlin

Andrew Richard Meighen

Deborah Sue Mercer

Joseph Daniel Mercer

Cayliana Renee Miller

Courtney A. Miller

Kelsey L. Miller

Nick D. Milone

Richard B. Miser

Tamara Kay Moore

Nicholas Charles Morris

Shannon M. Murphy

Beth A. Myers

Tyler Marshall Nally

Anna M. Otto

Tiffany Lynn Palmer

Jennifer Nicole Pennington

Jessica Renee Pennington

Laurie Ann Pickett

Donald Henry Possage

James Robert Powell

Michele Sahra Prudlo

Kelsey Rachael Renzella

Cassidi Paige Richmond

Jeffery Lee Richmond

Brooke Ann Robinson

Zoe Elizabeth Rogerson

Stephen George Rykowski

Susan M. Salonica Perdue

Devon Ann Satkowski

Mary Elizabeth Saunders

Austin Thomas
Schwanenberger

Carlie Nicole Sell

Janice J. Seyler

Lindsay Nicole Siburt

Mark A. Sloat

Kerri Ann Smith

Nathan William Snider

Dylan Andrew Stephen

Beth Ann Stocke

Valerie Louise Stoner

Mary Frances Tatich
Rose Marie Thomas
Traci Nicole Thomas
Tia M. Tomblin
Charles William Travis

Buffie Marie Turner
Laurie Ann VanDyne
Summer Lauren VanFossen
Kristin Rose VanScyoc
Melissa Renee Wasson

Susanne Marie Whipkey
Kimberley S. Whiteman
Allyson Marie Whorton
Samantha Nicole Williams
Brittany Nicole Wolfe

Savanna Grace Wolgemuth
Ryan M. Woods
Shataun Marie Wooten
Ashley Danielle Yoho
Lovie Elizabeth Zago

WEST VIRGINIA UNIVERSITY AT PARKERSBURG, PARKERSBURG, WV

Elijah Paul Adkins
Tierney Aldridge
Amber Alexander
Michael Archer
Faith Atkinson
Christopher Baker
Sevgi Bartlett
Danyelle F. Batton
Adam Beall
Bradley Beall
Lucas Beall
Samantha Jo Beaty
Kalob Bell
Adam Bennett
Christian Bettinger
Rachel Blankenship
Jennifer Blosser
Gregory allen Bly
Chelsey Boggess
Jerome Boley
Mark Boothe
Gregory Lee Bottenfield
Nancy Bowen
Harlan Bowser
John Boyles
Chase Brown
Ian Brownfield
Darin Sean Bryan
Luke Burkhammer
Flint Bush
Jeremy Lee Butcher
Kayla Byrd
Jacob Cain
Rebecca Campbell
James Carmichael
Melonna Amber Carmichael

Betty Carpenter
India Mary Carvell
Samantha Ann Casto
Joshua Cayton
Laura Cejka
Jose Chavez
Heather Dawn Chutes
Ashlee Coleman
Chad Conley
Kaitlyn Conner
Morgan Cook
Brandon Michael Corbitt
Quentin Corbitt
William Cornecelli
Caleb Cottrill
Brittany Nicole Cox
Levi Austin Cox
Donnie Crawford
Angela Cunningham
Anna Currey
Timothy Daniels
Dustin Daugherty
Marsha Davis
Tyler Dearien
Larry Manule Defrietas
Garrett Depergola
Briana Estrellita DeSouza
Kyle Andrew Deuley
Kristen Dietz
Ashley Digman
Bo J. Donaway
Barbara Dooley
Alan Dotson
Vanessa Jean Duffield
Brandon Michael Durback
Jared DuVall

Brandon Echard
Joshua Eggleston
Wesley Ellis
Amanda Nicole Ellison
Jenna Elmore
Sommer Fields
Alexis Fluharty
Raymond Foster
Cody Frederick
Kaitlin Garrett
Hayley Genger
Stephanie Gibbs
Kristelle Gumaru
Mark Hackathorn II
Corey Andrew Hager
Miranda Hall
Steven Hallett
Austin Handschumacher
Kaitlyn Harper
Jonathan Martin Harris
Katelyn Herrod
Alisha Hescht
Emily Higginbotham
Cody Hilling
Chelsey Hinkle
Shannon Brook Hopkins
Robert Horn
Timothy Allen Hornbeck Jr.
Kearsten Huffman
Aaron Jobes
Zackary Johnson
Mark Jumper
Amanda Jurkovich
Ashley Kedward
Peter Keiser
Cody Kennedy

Shannon Knight
Allen Lamp
Levi Lamp
Brian Lent
Melody Leonard
Amy Logue
Maggie Long
Taylor Lott
Kayla Lynch
Ryan A. Manley
Alex Martin
Joellen Masten
Steven Mays Jr.
Ryan McCoy
Candace Mellen
Joshua Miller
Geoffrey Mills
Amanda Minear
Connie F. Mollohan
Jenifer Renee Moore
Kenneth Moore
William Morris
Tonya Morrison
Sheynna Morton
David Mullins
Autumn Leigh Munday
Mackenzie Nestor
Caleb Norman
Codi Norman
Ivy Norris
Olivia Null
Emmanuella Onyekwere-Eke
Mary Onyekwere-Eke
Jacob Painter
Jennie Parks

Jordan Nicole Parsons
Emily Perdue
Clarissa Perkins
Katie Elizabeth Pifer
Marshall Polan
Sarah Popp
Crystal Post
Tashia Powell
Devin Maria Pryce
Lauren Christine Pursley
William Rader II
Susan Ramirez
Katherine Ratliff
John Ray
Lindsey Ray
Emily Katelyn Rhodes
Joshua Richard
Donald Ritchie
Deborah Robeson
Benjamin Ross

Rachael Ryan
Benjammin Sampson
Michelle Sandy
Kasey Schaffer
Evan Schoolcraft
Quinton Sells
Ashley Shamblin
Samantha Alane Shinn
Summer Sholes
William Shuman
Liticia Siers
Joseph Sikorski
Katherine Simmons
Brittany Sirk
Alexis Denise Smith
Deron Smith
Jacob Smith
Casey Snyder
Haley Snyder
Rebecca Lynn Snyder

Shaina Noel Snyder
Mary Ellen Sprouse
Daniel Steele
Logan Steele
David Stewart
Kaylee Dawn Stewart
Sarah Stewart
Amanda Stone
Regan Stout
Emily Strickler
Crystal Strothers
Kristen Michelle Suszek
Mark Tanner
Christopher Taylor
Emily Faith Thomas
Ronald Townsend
Carmel Ugim-Adie
Jordan Aaron Ullom
Shelby Valentine
Amber Vannoy

Vickie Vermilyen
Ashley Waggoner
Kaffie Nichole Waggoner
Ashley Walton
Wyatt Anderson Wamsley
Andrew Welsch
Jeremy Whipkey
LaRon White
April Whited
Magen Elizabeth Whited
Alexandra Danielle Wigal
Brandon Williams
Savanna Williams
Carolyn Wilson
Craig Wilson
Laura Wilson
Evana Marie Wise
Gina Workman

WEST VIRGINIA UNIVERSITY SCHOOL OF NURSING, MORGANTOWN, WV

Alan Alimario
Paige Erin Barker
Ian Mitchell Barley
Logan McKinley Barnett
Korrie Lee Barton
Casey Marie Batt
Adrianna Mickelle Bowley
Cecil Faye Burner
Kristen Glena Calebaugh
Gianna Marie Caromano
Cassidy Sharon Colston
Jacobi Krystalyn Cottrill

Rachel Nicole Cropper
Amy Leigh Davis
Danielle Ann Dawson
Katherine Anne Dayton
Cassidy Hope Dykes
Kristin Marie Elswick
Katie Lynn Foltz
Allison Leigh Fredenrich
Sarah M. Kennedy
Jacob Key
Lauren McKenzie Linton
Lindsay Michelle Marple

Maria Antonia Martino
Colleen Elizabeth
McCormick
Rose Frances Mcgonigle
Rachel Elizabeth Miller
Shannon Keats Miller
Marcelle Marie Murray
Michaela Kathryn O'Brien
Tia Jasmine Querrey
Michelle Elizabeth Rombro
Anna Mary Royek
Ashley Elizabeth Sauls

Cassidy Carrie Scott
Nicole Elizabeth Spindler
Grace Kathryn Stover
Rachel Marie Tonkin
Cortney Alyson Trickett
Jessica Jane Unmussig
Christopher Vance
Samantha Nicole Walton
Rica Elizabeth Wolfe
Nora Nicole Yokum

WEST VIRGINIA WESLEYAN COLLEGE, BUCKHANNON, WV

Elaine M. Ashman
Jackson D. Carey
Katherine L. Casey
Audrey Chefang Kemseu
Victoria P. Crise
Kimberly M. Culver

Carson O. Cunningham
Jordan N. Danko
Jessica A. Engles
Kortney B. Frame
Taylor L. Germain
Paula S. Gyamfi

Thomas A. Haines
Wilson R. Harvey
Bethany P. Jordan
Danielle B. Lancaster
Joshua S. Lopitz
Danielle N. Nehilla

Madison N. Ovies
Sarah L. Petitto
John H. Prentice
Kirsten M. Reneau
Corey R. Rhodes
Catherine G. Riggleman

Kaitlyn M. Romain
Nathan T. Ropelewski
Telena D. Sanson

Aurora C. Snyder
Scott P. Stoeckle

Philip A. Summers
Jordan L. Tate

Destinee J. Tunstall
Mason P. Winkie

WESTWOOD COLLEGE INLAND EMPIRE CAMPUS, UPLAND, CA

Laura Acuna
Nichole R. Addington
Natalie J. Amador
Erin Blankenship
Monica Brown
Bryan M. Carmona
Luis Castrejon Jr.
LaTiana Clark
Tyler Dresslar
Thomas Duval

Jennifer Estrada
Jesusa Estrella
Kijuana Guevara
Diana C. Gutierrez
Nicole Hanrahan
Martha Stephanie Herrera
Holly Hollosi
Tiffani M. Johnson
Lisamarie Jordan
Jessica Juarez

Martha E. Macias-Navarro
Karla Marin
Wytisha S. Miles
Cecilia Mucha
Gabriel Navarro
Mwamba Agatha Nguluta
Eleanor Charlotte Ann
Nieves
Gloria J. Patilla
Marion Payton-Carpenter

Bryan Peralta
Leslie Ramirez
Erika C. Saldana
Jaycee C. Samaniego
Ashly Jene'e Sinor
Isaac Thomas
Mimi Tran-Chavez
Flor Yslava
Juan E. Zuniga Medrano

WILKES COMMUNITY COLLEGE, WILKESBORO, NC

Shaun Michael Brooks
Ashley Elizabeth Carter
Brooke Alexandria Church
Kirstin Elizabeth Devlin
Esther Marilyn Fensterle

Laken M'Lynn Francis
Sabina Hernandez Gonzalez
Becky Govea
Anna Kristina Helms
Luke Mitchell Jarvis

Hannah Viola Jolly
Terry Dean Mahaffey
Kayla Austa McNeil
Donna Lynn Miller
Kayla Nicole Myers

Sandra A. Roten
Patrick James Simmons
Michaela Ann Todd
Kayte Marie Wiles

WILLIAM CAREY UNIVERSITY, HATTIESBURG, MS

Katelyne Alena Ball
Larson Todd Barkurn
Gleb Bilyalov
Balencia Sariah Crosby
Deon Latroy Cummings
Jaylen De'andre Eashmond

Ashley Nicholle Ford
Joseph Chad Goss
Casey Chantel Grinder
Brooklyn Paige Guillot
Ashlynn Nicole Hurst
Ashleigh L. Jones

Sean William Laird
Johnathan Trung Nguyen
Benjamin Patrick Salters
Houston Cole Saxon
Laura Bethany Scovel
Nigel Hayes Simmons

Alyson Marie Speights
Bethany Paige Truhett
Ian Thomas Turner
Lydia Terese Ulrich

WILLIAM JESSUP UNIVERSITY, ROCKLIN, CA

Zachary Adams
Jennifer Astwood
Stephanie Avila
Robert Todd Ballou
Natalie Barentson
Joeseph Briggs
Angela Brush
Schyler Jay Bryan
Rachel Burke
Cody Cantrell

Victoria Chon
David Coon
Danuta Dias
Monique Carol Dunievitz
Justin Dwyer
John Ebenezer
Stephen Eldredge
Maria-Jose Fernandez-Flores
Shelby Forbes
Rachel Nicole Gracey

Garrett Gregory
Antonina Grey
Krista Hallsten
Adam Hartigan
Margaret Hermle
Evan Hust
Sokol Irena
Trevor Jackson
Anna Kravtsova
Kayla Krogh

Bradley Allen Laws
Andrea Katharina Lindner
Jones
Abigail Llorente
Audra Lyons
Jessica Lyons
Danielle Mathiesen
Rebecca McConnell
Noelle Mueller
Dylan Neal

Olivia Whitney Nelson
Kyle Parrott
Parker Rea
Lauren E. Reierson
Jessica Rentz

Rina Rojas
Amanda Renae Schmidt
Claire Silva
Lindsey Singleton
Kalyn Switzer

Alexander Garrett
Thompson
Jessica Kaylene Titus
Kyleigh Turnquist
Dylan Valentine

Danien Walswick
Chad Joseph Wessling
Elizabeth Whitling
Riley Williams

WILLIAM PATERSON UNIVERSITY OF NEW JERSEY, WAYNE, NJ

Michelle Abril
Jennifer Baum
Emily Bruno
Tonee Burley
Mariela Capellan
Monique Castillo
Sarah Ciccarelli
Savannah Crippen
Jessica Daniels

Adams Desir
Jessica Nicole Ehnat
Jamal Fields
Christian A. Foti
Barbara M. Frace
Fredrik Hagbarth
Mohamed Ismail
Cheyenne Jacobs
Fatima Jamal Kanouni

Alessandro LoMartire
Mohammad Marey
Reinaldi Ariel Marquez
Alana Maya McCoy
Tyler Richard Mortensen
Anna Marie O-Connor
Julissa Ortiz
LaShae Robinson
Janice Rodriguez

Katiria Marie Rodriguez
Melissa Silvestri
Hassanah Smith
Jessica Margaret Super
Jada Toledo
Brandon Andrew Tyler
Kevin Vega

WILLIAM PENN UNIVERSITY, OSKALOOSA, IA

Lauren N. Abbas
Tori Lynn Albaugh
Michael Edward Aldeman
Michael John Applegate
Linnea Gavrielle Armus
Callie R. Arnold
Pacis Innocent Bana
Austin Paul Battreall
Bailie R. Benson
Natalie Jo Booton
Jerie Meagan Carson
Lane Taylor Colwell
Skip Michael Conner
Shania Danielle Cubit
Megan Lynn Dursky
Alexandria Sue Eckenrod
Alexander DW Edwards

Rebecca Catherine Eubanks
Nicole Marie Farrington
Amanda Marie Finkelberg
Jay Dillon Fresh
Santiago Goytia-Zamora
Emily Ann Hinnah
Tara Patrice Holdsworth
Alexa Ann Howard
Ryan Daniel Howard
Ariane Imulinde Sugi
Lauren Antonia Keen
Joseph Baxter Kminek
Alyssa Marie Kolberg
Alexis Kwizera
Ana Maree Lanphier
Titus Theodore Letzring
Logan Scott Loftus

Noelle Michele Luebbers
Esther Cecilia Lwakabamba
Connor Joe Menown
Jaden Annette Miskowiec
Madison A. Mitchell
Clarisse Mucyo
Claudien Bill Jean Mutabazi
Anne Niyigena
Montana Nicole Pence
Whitney Marie Reber
Markie Marie Roake
Jennifer Miracle Romas
Miranda Deanne Rozendaal
Alexi Rose Rule
Sabrina Rachelle Ryan
Joslyn Elizabeth Schaffner
Tanner Ryan Scott

Alora Ayrington Simmons
Heather Lynn Smith
Paige LeeAnn Smith
Zach Simon Smith
Jeremy Michael Swink
Lydia Grace Thury
Yves Tuyishime
Claire Ujeneza
Jesse Conner Utt
Christian Uwimana
John David VandeNoord
Holly Elizabeth Walker
Bethany Hope Waller
Lindsay Beatrice Wesely
Allison Taylor Williams
Jingye Yang

WILLIAM WOODS UNIVERSITY, FULTON, MO

Ashley LeeAnn Bauer
Caleb Bounds
Trevor Gruber
Samantha Harris

Billie Henry
Ashley Lauren Larkins
Alaina Leverenz
Isabella Long

Alyssa Marie McManus
Rachael Ostrem
Brandy A. Reagan
Emily Rogers

Joan Ryan
Ryan Ray Schmidt

WILMINGTON COLLEGE, WILMINGTON, OH

Eric Balash
Loryn Bryson
Jesse Donovan Buhrman
Nathan Earich Dean
Hannah Fetters
Erika Good
Dylan J. Hammond
Abigail Jude
Andreas Koyfis
Jamal McClendon
Joseph Njeru
Lindsay Marie Overmyer
John Parrett
Jadie Riewoldt
Tricia Steffen
Stryker Stock
Christina Lynn Veite
Louis Williams
Lydia Katherine Wolcott
Micaela Wright

WINGATE UNIVERSITY, WINGATE, NC

Carlos Abreu
Iris Brewer
AJ Guatlo Calpo
Madison Davis
Madison Dazey
Marguerite France
Joel Gashagaza
Jaclyn Gatton
Eric William Johnson
Mapoles
Griselda Martinez Valles
Jamie Mendoza
Timothy Nalesnik
Morgan Newman
Randy Lee Rutledge Jr.
Caleb James Skinner
Allyson Stone
Michelle Stumpff
Dustin Van De Veerdonk
Jonathan Lee Williams

WORCESTER STATE UNIVERSITY, WORCESTER, MA

Nicole B. Allain
Leanna F. Borges
Emma L. Canducci
Joshua D. Champagne
Jacqueline E. Channing
Courtney B. Chapin
Andrew F. Cienciwa
Matthew A. Cobuccio
Jennifer N. Collignon
Kurt M. Correia
Francisco A. Crisostomo
Brittany M. Desilets
Benjamin M. Dussault
Melissa E. Edberg
Marie K. Estabrook
Arianna D. Freeman
Cassandra E. Goncalves
Natasha N. Gonzalez
Nina J. Healy
Theresa H. Howe
Thomas M. Jacobsen
Kristen E. Kenney
Ashley A. Lameiras
Emily D. Lane
Daniel J. Livermore
Dana F. Perry
Alicia M. Pickering
Dominique A. Seles
Elizabeth M. Tarra
Kassandra M. Urena
Briana Leonor Vazquez
Heather Rose Vincequere
Tasneem M. Zawahreh

WYTHEVILLE COMMUNITY COLLEGE, WYTHEVILLE, VA

Amber Jeanette Ashton
Mariah Gabrielle Ayers
Lindsey Marie Blevins
Amanda Kourtney Bowman
Adam Daniel Bushlow
Chandra Carpenter
Shawntel Price Cox
Andrea Megan Dunford
Deja Lynn Edwards
Lisa Funk
Robin Renea Gibson
Chelsea Noelle Gunter
Morgan Elizabeth Hall
Sherry Joann Hinson
Audrey Sue Johnson
Brittany Lynn Jones
Chantel Brinna Kitts
Peter Kahto Lawrence
Austin James Puckett
Derek Quinn Rhea
Kayla Rae Rose
Jessica Danielle Shrewsbury
Bailey Grey Shumate
Zachary G. Taylor
Brittney Wojcik

XAVIER UNIVERSITY OF LOUISIANA, NEW ORLEANS, LA

Rayonna Adams
Nkemdi Agwaramgbo
Aizaz Ahmad
Evelyn Obawoye Ambush
Anthony Amerson
Chinelo Ananaba
Erin Ancar
Ashanti Anderson
Ganiat Amori Animashawun
Jacqueline Ewuraesi Baidoo
Ayanna Banks
Imani Bijou
Jasmine Blunt
Rosalind Borders
Edward Brooks
Laquel Renee' Brown
Sha'Nel Bruins
Kandis Carter
Manav Kumar Chakma
Cassandra Monique
Chambers
Bolden Charles
Usman Shahid Chaudhry
Frances Marie Cibilich
Eric Craig
Keajuana Alexus Crymes
Dahlia Daniel
Halima Dargan

Rosanna Dastoori

Jeremiah Davis

Brice Lavoysure Dean

Beverlin Del Rosario

Morgan Dillard

Bria Dixon

Amber Teresa Domingue

Lacey Douglas

Rose Duchane

Christopher Dunlock

Efehi Edomwonyi

Brea Edwards

Ajhia Ellis

Shikira Flounory

Hakeem Tonalli Frank

Terri Frazier

Alayna Joshalynn Freeman

Courtney Freeman

Ariele DeAnne French

Jarica Garner

Jasmine Geathers

Kelly Giardina

Teisha Goudeau

Simone L. Graham

Selena Gray

Erica Greenwood

Ralitsa Asenova
Hadzhistoyanova

Briana Hampton

Jodi Hill

Kiarra Hill

Danielle Hodges

Rasaan Hollis

Candace Hopgood

Moamen Ismail

Kayrah Jack

Nia Alexis James

Brianna Kentrell Jenkins

DeMone Johnson

Randall Johnson

Gabriel Jones

Kayla Jones

Leslie Jones

Jazzolynn Kelly

Leah Labat

Kevin Lam

David Le

Levon LeBan

Dominiqueca Brashaun
Lewis

Nicole Gaylor Little

Skky Martin

Caitlin Marie Mercier

Launa Metz

Glenda Doreen Middleton

Renee' Miller

Ryan Anthony Millon

DeMaurian Mitchner

Bianca Moore

Kos Mosley

Amira Muhsen

Catherine Camille Nash

Harold Nero

Anthony C. Nguyen

Daniel Nguyen

Dung Nguyen

Hoang Michael Nguyen

Kathy H. Nguyen

Tami Nguyen

Tracey Linh Nguyen

Tuan Nguyen

Angel Norwood

Chinyere Okafor

Lynda Osei

Alana Peck

David Phan

Nichelle Nicole Phelps

Anthony Poche'

David Powell

Derriyan Price

Kaila Pulliam Collins

Jeffrey Quach

Keegan Rayford

Keithan Rayford

Sherry Reddix

Evan Charles Reynolds

Tamara Richardson

Betool Ridha

Joseph Riles

Teri Robinson

Kaylan Elise Rogers

Devinn Rolland

Leanna Rucker

Autumn Leslie Saizan

Alinna Sam

Tanesha Sanchez

Chandler Schexnayder

Johlee Schinetsky

Yasmine Secrist

Stanley Sholtz

Bianca Shrestha

Alesha Smith

Amanda Smith

Jennifer Nicole Smith

Michaela Bernae Smith

Kennedy St Charles

Lauren Steele

Kayla Street

Rynisha Streeter

Ciaj Imani Strode

Bethany Tate

Jarvis Thibodeaux

Kevin Kahlil Thomas

Jennie Tran

Kayla Troxler

Jason Tucker

Destiny Vincent

Ashlynn Volpe

Janiece Ira Walker

Amanda Ware

Shannon Weatherup

Mariah White

Teneaka White

Marlon Williams

Andrea Willis

YORK COLLEGE OF PENNSYLVANIA, YORK, PA

Joshua D. Alwine

Brian E. Baker

Christopher M. Betzler

Ketsy Z. Caraballo-Garcia

Amanda C. Carman

Joel A. Copenheaver

Sonia K. Deel

James Francis Di Guglielmo

Brian W. Dix

Matthew D. Driscoll

Julie R. Dunphy

Jordan A. Elford

Lauren M. Enlow

Ashley E. Farren

Stephen M. Gannon

Kelsey J. Graver

Alexander Joseph Iula

Lindsay M. Jackson

Jason B. Keller

Ryker L. Kern

Abhijith Kudaravalli

Emily L. Kuhl

Parker D. Labrie

Chryssanthe Littos

Ashley L. McManus

Carissa E. McQuade

Shannon M. Meglathery

Ronald J. Mitchell Jr.

Lyndsey C. Mitchum

Lydia L. Moro

Zachary K. Myers

Chelsea L. Otis

Kelly M. Peck

Robin S. Prince

Kimberly V. Reed

Michael S. Rettew

Abbey L. Rhodes

Dani A. Robbins

Marisa Ada Sehested

Sarah Salome Sindelar

Alia T. Smith

Amanda L. Stagg

Rebecca M. Thomas

Makayla J. Thompson

Shannon M. VanDaniker

Heather N. Wilson

Alexandra S. Yambor

Sarah Y. Young

Terry L. Young

Anne Violet Zerull

YORK TECHNICAL COLLEGE, ROCK HILL, SC

Carol Elaine Barnes

Laura Beth Belcher

Edward Michael Bengivenga

Ronald Edward Bengivenga

Christian Adrian Bono

Hanna Belle Brabham

Shawn P. Brand

Jordan Elysse Brock

Richard James Carpenter

Paola Lizbet Castello

Kaira Lashawn Cloud

Christian Chase Cothran

Anna Claire Davis

Jonathan Earl Deadwyler

Amanda Valerie DeCarlo

Joshua William Dib

Kimberley A. Elkins

Andrew Corbin Faile

Destiny Marie Farrell

Bailey Michael
Faulkenberry

Teran LeeAnn Faulkenbury

Scherel Gambill Fisher

Joshua William Fogle

Danielle Lashay Gainey

Calib James Gioia

Ma. Guadalupe Guerrero

Jade Allyah Harkness

Victoria Brooke Harper

Kylie Raelinda Harris

Jonathan Michael Harwell

Joshua Farris Haws

Amber Mae Hayko

Atiya Michelle Henry

Jordan Lee Herbert

Delricka Latray Izzard

Kimberly Rodgers Jones

Christian David Kamke

Ashley Nicole Kane

James Winslow Kerber

Tanja Rachelle Krouse

Gregory Michael Lamb

Sean Michael Lary

Deborah A. Lawrenchuk

Siobhan R. Lovely

Jason E. Matthews

Allison Belle Maynard

Sabrina Shunta' McCoy

Michael Victor McKelvey

Roger Lee Moore

Shantia Naschelle Moorer-
Brown

Robin Nicole Moree Threatt

Ashley Ann Morris

Tammy Kiehl Nehls

Ashton Annette Nicholas

Robert Brian O'Dell

Ilona A. Okuneva

Roopa Palanisamy

Joseph Allen Peyton

Andrew-Gatlin Brett Pittman

Charity D. Povoa

Sarah Ki Rice

Andrew Martin Robbins

Alicia Renea Rogers

Kylan Damien Ruffin

Karla Y. Sanchez

Austin Terrell Savage

Jennifer Nichole Schroen

Cameron Xavier Sharp

Rachel Catherine Sharp

Patricia Denese Darty
Shuford

Amanda Christene Somani

Mark T. Stanford

Virgil D. Stevenson

Elizabeth Anne Stewart
Wiley

Sally Susanne Strickland

Tabitha Symone Strong

Heidi Salzman Surig

Mary Isabelle Taylor

Luz Amberly Thompson

Mandy R. Torres

Kortney Sue Wheeler

Michael K. Wilkerson

Aubrey Michelle Wilson

YOUNG HARRIS COLLEGE, YOUNG HARRIS, GA

Jacob Bennett

Stephanie Brady

Dorian Tiny Brunzelle

Sarah Burch

Shaw Carter

Zachary Champion

Diana Di Marco

Shaunmarie Alexandra
Dotson

Ivey Franklin

Jordana Cristina Freitas

Georgia Googer

Lauren Suanne Gray

Christian Drake Hambrick

Matthew Heard

Carolina Hernandez

Lauren Michele Hohn

Kristina Kauffman

Jaclyn Dianne Kernohan

Lindsey Koch

Jared Lee

Rachel Breann Lindsey

Steffan Lucarelli

McKenzie Nicole Lundgren

Sarah Magill

Taylor Moats Meier

Steven Melton

Stephanie Mills

William Moody

Elana Newman

Wade Orr

Jami Padgett

Irenee Payne

Homero Perez

Stephanie Rodock

Melisa Nicole Smith

Jaquelin Solis

Ashley Starnes

Chelsea Taylor

John-Michael Thomas

Karli Timms

Zachary Wagoner

Anna Walsh

Elizabeth Grace Williamson

Jordan Woodard

Madelyn Grace Youngblood

Ahmed Mohammed A. Alghamdi

Tara Rose Amero

Samantha Park Anderson

Demetrianna Maria Antonelli

Brooke Ann Ball

Nicole Lynn Balog

Victoria Irene Bankhead

Mia Brielle Barchetti

Michael Kevin Bellas

Roselynn Macala Betras

Lauren Ashley Bevan

Anthony Billet

Jamie Nicole Bogdan

Natalee Danelle Bommer

Julianne Borowske

Karly Rose Brogley

Jonathon Richard Burns

Jena Lea Bushong

Monica Ellen Busser

Zoey Olivia Butka

Jayne E. Catlos

Jasmine Dean Cecil

Shannon Lynn Chaffee

Nicholas Scott Chretien

Nicole Marie Cicozi

Catherine Marie Cooper

Anna Lisa Cowan

Mollie Catherine Crowe

Rae'ven Alexandra Crum

Roberta Michelle Cykon

Abhijit Raj Das

Rachel Alexis Davis

Stephanie Lynn Davis

Diana Louise Deehr

Mariah Denise DeFuria

Emily Jane Dixon

Ian John Dunlap

Jordan Ashley Edgell

Allison Michele English

Rebecca Marie Enlow

William R. Erskine

Paul Frederick Farbman

Gabrielle Fellows

Ian M. Friend

Augusta Eva Fronzaglio

Greta Frost

Gabriella Noel Gessler

O'Keal Mandela Gist

Mollie Danielle Golden

Aaron James Graneto

Taylor Lynn Greathouse

William Firmin Green

Madeline Kate Grimes

Allison Nicole Guerrieri

Jerrilyn Georgina Chessie Guy

Elizabeth Anne Hanna

Leanna Hartsough

Matthew Jay Hawout

Karina A. Hayek

Austin J. Hilt

Tarika Tahneen Holness

Courtney Christine Hunter

Jonathan Hutnyan

Josh D. Ivack

Jacob Anthony Janoso

Kylie Nicole Janoso

Jana Janson

David Anthony Jech

Sabryna Marie Johnson

Kelli McKensie Johnston

Georgia A. Kasamias

Audrey Ann Keleman

Maria E. Kenner

Abigail Elizabeth Kunce

Katina Eleni Landgraff

Josette A. Landis

Kaitlyn Marie Leonelli

Michael Joseph Leskosky

William Robert Ludt

Shannon Marie Lutz

Tyler-Alexis Chandler MacDonald

James MacGregor

Gianna Diane Marinucci

Ethan Francis Markowitz

Jami Elizabeth Mazei

Hallie McGee

Austin Taylor McLean

Matthew James Melito

Thomas James Merva

Emily Marie Metzgar

Jennifer Renee Miller

Tyler Antonio Miller-Gordon

Ashley Marie Milligan

Bryce Allan Miner

Samantha Ann Mock

Shawnna Marie Moore

Jason Franklin Morris

Marissa Ann Mraz

Matthew Allen Norris

Jarrod Jerome Novotny

Megan Rae O'Neill

Jacquelyn Kayla Oddo

Alyssa Anne Olmi

Emily Laura Orlo

Ashley Orr

Jennifer Marie Outland

Rodger Curtis Page

Sara Nicole Parry

Alexis Ann Patchen

Corey J. Patrick

Jacob Edward Penk

Taylor Ann Phillips

Nicolette Page Pizzuto

Samuel Michael Rakocy

Anna Virginia Reed

Jascelynn M. Romeo

Marisa Anne Rothbauer

Alyson Elizabeth Ryan

Korinne Elaine Sackela

Shalon Sharrieff Salters

Daniel Stephen Schaefer

Sarah Kathryn Schafer

Jacob Michael Schriner-Briggs

Carisa Lynn Sechrist

Dana Elizabeth Sidney

Evangelos Savas Sisalouis

Christina Alice Slavens

Jillian Smith

Sarah Cailin Smith

Kendra R. Sopshire

Kyle Robert Spickler

Alyssia Marie Springer

Mary Aileen Suszczynski

Ahmed Jamil Sutton

David Michael Tamulonis

James Michael Tancabel

Chynna Thompson

Abby Vitus

Abby Jordan Wateska

Jeffrey L. Wiltrout

Robert Paul Winner

Elisabeth Andrea Winston

Kristyn Wolf

Jordan Mark Wolfe

Stephanie Kay Wood

Trevon Jaquis Wright

Emily Rachel Young

Christina Marie Yovick

Stephen Harley Zaborsky

Jordan A. Zaluski

STUDENT BIOGRAPHIES

The annual publication of *Who's Who Among Students in American Universities and Colleges*® is intended to serve as a practical reference volume of generally accurate information. Information in this volume was secured directly from the students whose write-ups appear. Information is as complete as could be secured several months in advance of regular graduation time. All national organizations mentioned within student biographies refer to local chapters unless otherwise noted.

A

Aakol, Cletus Kpobari: Houston, TX; Regent University; DMin Clinical Pastoral Education, 2017; Chaplain Student Group; Food Services, All Nations for Christ Bible Institute International, Benin City, Nigeria; This award is dedicated to God and to my mom of blessed memory who inspired my passion for education.

Aaron, Matthew A.: Fort Worth, TX Midwestern State University; Mary and Danny Aaron; BS Computer Science/Mathematics, 2015; Upsilon Pi Epsilon Honor Society; Mortar Board Honor Society.

Abbott, Erica Ann: Clifton Heights, PA; Cabrini College; AnnaMay and Michael Abbott; BA Communication, 2016; Senior Honors Convergence Capstone, Senior Copy Editor; Society of Collegiate Journalists, President, Vice President, and Secretary; *Loquitur*, News Editor; *Her Campus Cabrini*, Editor-in-Chief/President; To my amazing parents, friends, and mentors, thank you for supporting me all 525,600 minutes of the year.

Abdur-Rahman, Haseena R.: Prince George, VA; Norfolk State University; Qahir and Mahasin Abdur-Rahman; BA Psychology, 2016; Student Activities, Vice President; This award would not have been possible without the support of my family and parents, Mahasin and Qahir.

Abillar, Jamina M.: Colorado Springs, CO; Ithaca College; Jessica and Dante Abillar; BA Communication Studies/Writing, 2016; Pi Kappa Delta National Honor Society; Relay For Life; Peggy R. Williams Award for Academic and Community Leadership Recipient, 2015–2016; Gamma Delta Pi Social Service Sorority President; I dedicate this award to my parents, Dante and Jessica Abillar.

Achor, Krista N.: Marrero, LA; Southeastern Louisiana University; Jennifer Nicole Vegas; BS Elementary/ Special Education, Mild and Moderate Grades 1–5, 2017; Resident Assistant, Resident Assistant of the Year; Order of Omega; Alpha Sigma Tau Sorority, Director of Ritual, Vice President of Organization Development, and Vice President of Member Development; I would like to thank my family for loving and supporting me in everything I do!

Ackah, Dorinda Afiba-Alimah: Lincoln, NE; Union College; David and Irene Ackah; BS Nursing, 2016; National Honor Society; Honor Society of Nursing, Sigma Theta Tau International; Union College Rees Hall, Dorm Nurse and Head Resident Assistant.

Adams, Benjaman Clayton: San Angelo, TX; Angelo State University; Carla Grigsby; BS Exercise Science/ Concentration in Athletic Training, 2017; This award would not have been possible without the support and love from my beautiful wife, Brittany Adams.

Adams, Haylie Christine: Celina, TX; Ranger College; Angela and Chad Adams; AS Nursing, 2018.

Adams, Taylor N.: Bartlesville, OK; Northeastern State University; Johnie and David Adams; BS Early Childhood Education, 2017; Student Oklahoma Education Association, Vice President.

Adelabu, Adegoke Joshua: Daytona Beach, FL; Embry-Riddle Aeronautical University Graduate; James and Naomi Adelabu; BS Aerospace Engineering, 2016; Task Force One, President; Peer Mentor for First Year Program, Teaching Assistant, Mentor for Freshmen, and Personal Tutor; College of Engineering Representative, Representative of the Month Award, Student Representative Board, Bookstore Liaison, Member of Academic Committee, and Forum Committee; This award is dedicated to God, thanking HIM for my family, everyone, and everything.

Adkins, Christopher: Natchitoches, LA; University of Louisiana at Monroe Undergraduate; Jennifer Threadgill and Michael Adkins; Pre-Pharmacy, 2019; University Academic Appeals Committee, Student Representative; Club Soccer Team, Vice President and Co-Founder; Interfraternity Council, Vice President of Judicial Affairs; Pi Kappa Alpha, Sargent-at-Arms, Campus Involvement Chair, and Assistant Social Director; Greek Week Steering Committee, Co-Chair; 31 Ambassadors, T-shirt Swap Committee Head, Public Relations Committee Head, and Vice President of Public Relations; Prep Staff, Parent Orientation Leader; SGA, Vice President; "You never know how strong you are until being strong is your only choice."

Aguilar, Javier: El Paso, TX; The University of Texas El Paso; BA Multimedia Journalism, 2017; Dean's List (2015–2016); Future Leaders in Public Relations, President; Gracias a mi madre Blanca, a mis suegros y a mi esposo por todo su cariño y apoyo.

Aguilar, Susie Vanessa: Junction City, KS; Barton Community College; Fernando Aguilar and Mayra Villalobos; AA Psychology; Alpha Sigma Lambda, Phi Theta Kappa; To the moment I broke my silence—we have the power to stop domestic violence and rape.

Agurs, LaQuayle Domonique: Colonial Heights, VA; Hampton University; Monica Robinson and Harry Agurs; BA Journalism, 2016; National Association of Black Journalists, Community Service Chair; *The Hampton Script*, Associate Editor; SGA, Student Representative to the Board of Trustees; Golden Key International Honor Society; Greer Dawson Wilson Student Leadership Training Program, Senior Co-Facilitator; Thank you, God. Thank you, family. Thank you, JLL. With each of you, I am whole.

Alessi, Nicholas Michael: Waukesha, WI; Carroll University; BS Nursing, 2016; Interfraternity Council, Vice President; Student Senate, Academic Affairs Member and Faculty and Student Ethics Board Member; Founding Father Pi Lambda Phi Fraternity, President and Vice President of Programming and Risk Management; I thank my mother and my fellow Pilams for helping me to succeed!

Alexander, Megan: Ponca City, OK; Northern Oklahoma College; AS Health Physical Education/Recreation, 2016; Criminal Justice Club; *The Maverick* Reporter; Fellowship of Christian Athletes, Leadership Team; I give God all the glory for this award and thank my professors for their support and encouragement.

Alexy, Allison Marie: Collegeville, PA; West Chester University; Bonnie and Eric Alexy; BS Marketing, 2017; Alpha Phi Omega, Inter-Chapter Relations Chair; American Marketing Association, Executive Board Member; Thank you to my family and friends for inspiring me to be the best I can be.

Alicea Rodríguez, Julybeth: Catano, PR; University of Puerto Rico School of Law; JD Law, 2017; "Academia Judicial Puertorriquena" Speaker; Law Clerk at Ferraiuoli, LLC 2015; National Women Law Student's Organization, Mentor; *Voto Inteligente*, "10 Competencias que debera tener un Gobernador?" November 2012; Collegiate Presidential Inaugural Conference, Student Assistant for Presidential Oath and Activities; Litigation Association; Golden Key Honor Society; National Society of Collegiate Scholars, Honor Member; SHRM Student Chapter, Vice President; BA Human Resources, Magna Cum Laude; Intellectual Property Pro Bono Member; This award would not have been possible without the support and love from my family.

Aliotta, Elizabeth Anne: Manchester, NH; Eastern Nazarene College; BS Clinical Psychology, 2016; Psi Chi Council, Vice President; Loving Hearts Ministry, President and Founder; Dance Ministry, President.

Allen, Boyd Derrick: Springfield, MO; Evangel University; BS Human Services, 2016. To my lovely wife, Sarah, thank you. I could not have done this without you. I love you.

Allinger, Crystal Elizabeth: Statham, GA; Kennesaw State University; BA Management, 2016; This award would not have been possible without my husband, family, and The University of Georgia.

Alonso, Bryant C.: Valdosta, GA; Augusta University College of Allied Health Sciences; Denita and Juan Alonso; MS Occupational Therapy, 2016; Student Occupational Therapy Association, Public Relations Chair; Special thanks to my professors, classmates, friends, and family! I could not have done it without you.

Alotaibi, Abbas Fayhan: Dubuque, IA; University of Dubuque; BS Aviation Management, 2017; Dean's List 2015; New Student Orientation, International Student Assistant for Admissions and Orientation Coordinator; Saudi Students Organization, Cultural Chair and Training Organizer.

Alshaiji, Abdulmohsen Y A A E: Stockton, CA; University of the Pacific School of Engineering and Computer Science; Yousef Alshayji and Shahla Dastenaei; BS Mechanical Engineering, 2016; Achieving this award could not have been done without hard work, my family support, and help from the Almighty.

Alshloul, Shams Nazzal: Boonton, NJ; College of Saint Elizabeth; MS Health Care Management, 2016; Health Services Department, Student Aide; Food and Nutrition Department, Student Aide; John Hill School, Volunteer; I am extremely honored to be a recipient of this award. Thanks to my family for the continuous support.

Alston, Jameson Levon William: Baton Rouge, LA; University of Louisiana at Monroe Undergraduate; Shawanza Alston and Kai Burrell; BS Kinesiology, 2016; STAART Campus Mentoring; Firestarters for Christ, President; Supplemental Instruction Leader, Stellar Performance Winner; Alpha Epsilon Delta, Pre-Professional; National Society for Collegiate Scholars; Phi Kappa Phi; Phi Epsilon Kappa (Honor Society); Association for Students in Kinesiology; ULM NAACP, Economic Empowerment Committee Head; Emerging Scholars, First Place Research Award Winner; 31 Ambassadors, Service Award Winner; Campus Activities Board, Secretary and Vice President; SGA, Senator and Melvin Rambin Backbone Award Winner; I want to thank God for this phenomenal award and opportunity. I am so thankful for this recognition.

Alswager, Laeken Danielle: Dickinson, TX; University of Houston–Clear Lake; Rodney and Ivonne Alswager; BA Biology, 2017; Texas State Teachers Association, Tri Beta Biological Honor Society; Hawks Spirit and Traditions Council; American Cetacean Society Student Coalition, President; This would not have been possible without my family and, most importantly, Drew Casey.

Altamirano, Valeria: El Paso, TX; The University of Texas El Paso; BS Electrical Engineering, 2017; Sigma Alpha Lambda; Institute of Electrical and Electronic Engineering; National Student of Collegiate Scholars; Kappa Delta Chi Sorority, Inc., Service Chair, Alumni Relations, Council Delegate, Officer of the Year, and Most Involved Award; Dedication pays off at the end—thanks to my family for never giving up on me.

Alvarez, Andrea: Dinuba, CA; College of The Sequoias; AA Office Assistant, 2018; College of the Sequoias; *Who's Who* Honoree; Thank you to my mom, Sally Villanueva, and my aunt, Rachel Martinez.

Amaral, Fernanda Luvizotto do: Curitiba, PR; The University of West Florida; Joao and Miriam Amaral; BS Business Management, 2016; Society of Human Resource Management, Winner of 2016 SHRM Student Case Competition; Dedicated to my family, tennis coaches, and professors who made this award possible.

Anderson, Ashley R.: Newton, NH; University of New England; Donna and David Anderson; BS Medical Biology/Pre-Physician Assistance, 2016; Cardiac Health Intervention Program, Researcher/Data Collector; International Medical Missions; Preble Street Soup Kitchens; Relay For Life; Habitat For Humanity; Rotaract; Biochemistry Laboratory Teaching Assistant; Diversity Leadership Certificate Program, One Diversity Leadership Certificate and Three Advanced Diversity Leadership Certificates; College Community Mentoring Program; Thank you to my wonderful parents, without whom this award would not have been possible!

Anderson, Brittany Sierra Marcella: Williamsburg, KY; University of the Cumberlands; Bev and Larry Anderson; BA Biology/Public Health, 2016; Tri-Beta, James Taylor Award; This award would not have been possible without the support and love from my family and teachers.

Anderson, Christopher R.: Oakland, NJ; Villanova University; Melena and Todd Anderson; BS Chemistry/Criminology, 2016; London Learning Community Abroad, Resident Assistant; Residence Life, Head Resident Assistant; Villanova Emergency Medical Service, Training Lieutenant and EMT/Driver; Many thanks to Mom and Dad for supporting me at Villanova and abroad—you helped make this possible.

Anderson, Lanna Nichole: San Francisco, CA; Bennett College; Enna Dials; BS Biology, 2016; This award would not have been possible without the love and support of my family and God.

Anderson, Octavia Renee: Columbus, OH; Duquesne University; Michele Thrower Shank; BS Nursing, 2017; Nationwide Children's Hospital, Volunteer of the Month Award; Chi Eta Phi, President, Vice President, and Mamie Garland Scholar; This award would not have been possible without the support of God, my family, and DU nursing school.

Aney, Stephen Patrick: San Antonio, TX; St. Philip's College; Eugene and Bernice Aney; AS Aircraft Technician Airframe/Powerplant, 2016; My family was always strong for me, and my strength reflects on this.

Antopia, Marissa: Von Ormy, TX; Palo Alto College; Sonia Aguilar and Roger Antopia; AA Psychology, 2017; TRIO Program, Palo Alto College Part-Time Honors Award for Outstanding Scholarship 2014; To all my family—thank you for all the support and love throughout my life.

Arant, Tiffany Carol: Pageland, SC; Northeastern Technical College; AA Nursing Program, 2016; This award would not be possible without the support, love, and encouragement from my husband and daughter.

Archer, Angelique Rosanna: Perryton, TX; Oklahoma Panhandle State University; BS Elementary Education, 2017; SOEA, Vice President.

Archuleta, Julissa: Pecos, NM; New Mexico Highlands University; James and Mary Jane Archuleta; BA Elementary Education, 2017; I would like to thank my parents, sister, and relatives for all of their support, love, and encouragement.

Arcy, Amanda Kalman: Dearborn, MI; Madonna University; William and Nancy Arcy, Shirley Arcy; BS Accounting, 2016; Madonna University's Bowling Team; "One Night Without a Home" Event Participant; University's Presidential Inauguration Participant; School of Business High Achievement Award; I would like to thank my family for all of their love and support throughout my life!

Arenson, Jillian Colby: Manalapan, NJ; Arcadia University; Allyson and David Arenson; BA Behavioral Biology, 2016; Ian Somerhalder Foundation College Board Advisor; Yearbook Senior Liaison; National Society of Leadership and Success, Vice President and Success Networking Team Coordinator; Real Certificate Program Mentor and Tutor; SGA, Chancellor, Senator, and Chair of Academic Committee; Class Officer, Vice President and Secretary; First Year Study Abroad Mentor; Hillel President; Knight Club, President and Performance Director; Thank you to my loved ones, especially my parents for always being my back bone! I love you!

Arredondo, Seanna: McKinney, TX; Bacone College; Patty and Tony Arredondo; BS Criminal Justice, 2016; Graduating with honors, Magna Cum Laude; Women's Basketball Academic Achievement; Big thank you to my parents for always supporting me.

Asche, Cody Wade: Okarche, OK; Northern Oklahoma College; Suzanne Clapper and Adam Asche; AS Agricultural Sciences, 2018; Phi Theta Kappa, All Oklahoma Academic Team; Young Republican's Club, Founding President; President's Leadership Council, President 2015–2016, Secretary 2014–2015), and Outstanding PLC Student; I could not have done this without my friends and family.

Ashmore, Jeffrey Alan: Bloomfield, IA; Indian Hills Community College; William and JoEllen Ashmore; AA Machine Technology, 2016.

Asthana, Samarth: Sugar Land, TX; Baylor University; Manish and Namita Asthana; BM Applied Music, 2016; Many thanks to all of the incredible educators who gave me the tools to succeed in life.

Atkinson, Sabrina Rene: Oklahoma City, OK; University of Science and Arts of Oklahoma; Vicky Atkinson; BS Business, 2016; Sigma Psi Omega, Historian 2015–2016; SGA, President 2015–2016 and Secretary 2014–2015.

Aube, Chelsea J.: Choctaw, OK; Oklahoma Baptist University; BS Biology, 2016; Blitz Week; Science Club, Council; Mortar Board Honor Society; Phi Eta Sigma National Honor Society; Campus Activities Board; Cargo Ranch, Volunteer and Mentor; Thank you to my family, fiancé, and friends for their love and support throughout my college career.

Ault, Aaron Christopher: Lewis Center, OH; Mount Vernon Nazarene University; Christopher and Deborah Ault; BA Urban Ministry, 2017; New Life Church Intern, Russellville Campus; International Travel, Italy/Vatican, Holy Lands, Germany, and Switzerland; Academic Excellence, Dean's List; Missionary Adventures, Guatemala, Peru, and the Amazon; SGA, Vice President of Academic Life 2015 and Ministry Director 2013 and 2014; "Truth can never be truth without grace, and grace can be nothing like grace without truth." —Rick Bezet

Austin, Brittany Ann: Highland Mills, NY; Dominican College of Blauvelt Graduate School; Timothy and Dorothy Austin; MA Students with Disabilities, 2016; New York State Council for Exception Children Student Board, Northern State Representative; Dominican College Track and Field Team, Captain and Most Valuable Player; Thanks to my family, friends, and a few special teachers who helped me along the way.

Autry, Cheyenne: Breese, IL; McKendree University; Cherie and Robert Autry; BA Athletic Training, 2018; Phi Eta Sigma National Honors Society; Concert Band, Fine Arts Scholarship Recipient; I am grateful for the support of my family while on my path to graduation.

Awwad, Haya Elise: Terryville, CT; Roger Williams University; Beverly Awwad; BA Psychology, 2016; Honors Program, Honors Advisory Council Student Representative 2014–2015; Student Orientation Coordinator 2015 and Orientation Advisor 2013–2014; Psi Chi, President 2015–2016 and Treasurer 2014–2015; Campus Entertainment Network, Board Co-Chair 2015–2016, Traditions Co-Chair 2014–2015, and Community Liaison Chair 2013–2014; None of this would be possible without the unconditional love, support, and encouragement from my mom.

Azoor, Hakeem: Arlington, VA; Northern Virginia Community College; Farahnaz and Amin Azoor; AS Business Administration, 2016; I'd like to thank my dear family for helping me through everything and dedicate this award to them.

B

Babcock, Cristine M.: Littleton, CO; Independence University; MA Health Administration/Technology, 2016; This award is an honor to receive, and I thank Mark and my family for their support.

Backus, Kelly Anne: Oceanside, NY; Long Island University-Post; Margaret and Kenneth Backus; BS Health/Physical Education; LIU Post Women's Lacrosse Team; The Ronald McDonald House of Long Island; The Cystic Fibrosis Foundation; Student Athlete Advisory Committee; This is dedicated to my support system who helped me get to where I am today.

Baeza Jr., Alfredo: Chickasha, OK; University of Science and Arts of Oklahoma; Alfredo Baeza; BSA Art, 2017; United States Marine Corps HIMAR Operator, Corporal; Green House Catholic Campus Ministry, President; Thanks to all of my professors, friends, and especially family for always supporting me.

Baidoo, Jacqueline Ewuraesi: Frederick, MD; Xavier University of Louisiana; Benedict and Jacqueline Baidoo; BS Dual Degree Chemical Engineering, 2018; Honda Campus All-Star Challenge; Golden Xcross Soccer Club; STEM NOLA; National Society of Black Engineers; Mahjong Club; I am truly grateful for the encouragement of everyone whom I have had the good fortune to meet.

Bailey, Lisa Ann: Orange Park, FL; Saint Leo University; Rosa Jean and WC Patterson; BA Psychology, 2016; This award would not have been possible without the support and love from my husband and children.

Baisden, Kevin: Falls Church, VA; Northern Virginia Community College; Olivia and Henry Baisden; AA Business Administration, 2016; United Negro College Fund, Anthem Corporate Scholars Award; Herblock Foundation, Scholars Award; Dean of Students Office, Administrator; Provost's Office, Public Relations Assistant; NOVA, Dr. Belle S. Wheelan Scholars Award; SEAL AWARD, Lois Corrol Scholars Award, Herbert and Marrion Zimmer Scholars Award, Fran O'Brien Memorial Scholars Award, Dr. Barnard D. Joy Scholars Award, and Deanna Bronder Scholars Award; Virginias Collegiate Honors Council, Scholars Research Award; SGA, Finance Officer; Finance Club, Vice President and Co-Founder; Honors Club, President and Founder; Exxon Mobil Symposium, Scholars Research Award; Thank you to all of those that helped me out along the way.

Baker, Kristin Nicole: Hazard, KY; Hazard Community and Technical College; BSW Social Work, 2016; President's Student Ambassador, President; Phi Theta Kappa National Honor Society, President; This award would not have been possible without the support from my family, especially my grandmother.

Baker, Ryan Anderson: Clanton, AL; University of Montevallo; Christopher and Melissa Baker; BS Biochemistry, 2017; Kappa Mu Epsilon 2016; *Who's Who* 2015; Order of Omega Greek Honors Society 2015–2016; Bass Fishing Team and Outdoors Association, President 2014–2016; University of Montevallo Master 2013–2016; Alpha Kappa Lambda Fraternity, Pledge Class of Alpha Si 2014 and Judicial Board Member 2015–2016; University President's Outdoors Scholars Program, President 2015–2016; SGA, Commuter Senator and Finance Committee 2013–2016; This award would not have been possible without my faith in my Savior and my wonderful family.

Banister Jr., Charles Ray: Douglasville, GA; Luther Rice College and Seminary; BA Ministry, 2015; The loving support of my wife, Lisa, and my precious children, Kinsey and Kaleb, have made this achievement possible.

Barbay, Brittany: Zachary, LA; Copiah-Lincoln Community College; Kathy and Tab Barbay; AA Arts, 2018; Graduation with Honors; Softball, 2nd Team All-State, Best Defensive Player; This award would not have been possible without the support and love from my family.

Barber, Kevin Jerome: Prince Frederick, MD; The Crown College of the Bible; Jerome and Cecilia Barber; BA Missions, 2016; SGA, Senior Class President; This award would not have been possible without my family and church.

Barberi, Michael David: Henrietta, NY; Roberts Wesleyan College; BS Organizational Management, 2015.

Barham, Tanesha "Niecy": Philadelphia, MS; East Central Community College; AS Nursing, 2016; Thank you to my family for lifting me up so I can reach the stars!

Barker Sr., Bryan-Daniel Stuart: Norfolk, VA; Norfolk State University; Yvette Barker; BA Psychology/General Special Education, 2018; Norfolk State University; Psi Chi International Honor Society in Psychology; Pi Lambda Theta National Honor Society for Educators; Golden Key International Honour Society; This award would not have been possible without the support of my family, Tammy, Danny, and Tamia.

Barksdale, Winston: Atlanta, GA; Saint Leo University; MS Criminal Justice, 2016; The unparalleled support from my family and the faculty have made this award possible.

Barnard, Rebecca Johanna: Hokes Bluff, AL; Gadsden State Community College; AA Accounting, 2016; I could not have done this without the love and support from my family and my awesome, powerful God!!!

Barnes, Carol Elaine: Lancaster, SC; York Technical College; Hattie Barnes and Larry Ingram; AA Surgical Technology, 2016; This award would not be without my Lord and Savior Jesus Christ, in Him all things are possible.

Barnes, Haley Logan: Adrian, MI; Adrian College; Cynthia and Kevin Barnes; BA Physical Education, 2017; Special Olympics Soccer, Assistant Coach; Phi Epsilon Kappa, President; It is an honor to receive this award, and I have been blessed with a phenomenal support system.

Barnewall, John: Yorba Linda, CA; Talbot School of Theology; MA Philosophy, 2016; I am both blessed and grateful to be able to share this award with my wonderful wife, Michelle.

Bartlett, Sara Lynne: Braintree, MA; Framingham State University; Helen and Russell Bartlett; BA English, 2016; Science State Street; ESL Tutor; Writing Tutor; Wildlife Club; Dean's List; Sigma Tau Delta; Hirt Literary Award; For my mom and dad—your belief in my possibilities helped make them probabilities and then, happily, facts.

Barton, Christol Lynne: Summerville, SC; Limestone College; Terri and Mike Newman; BA Social Work, 2016; Social Work Club; Dean's List Honor Roll; This award would not have been possible without the loving support of my husband, Jon, and my children.

Bates, Maegyn Danielle: Whitesburg, KY; Alice Lloyd College; BA Accounting/Business Manager, 2016; Alpha Chi; Top 10 Percent of the Class; Phi Beta Lambda, Vice President; This award would not have been possible without my Savior, my supportive parents, and my loving family and friends.

Batton, Danyelle F.: Parkersburg, WV; West Virginia University at Parkersburg; AA Business Technology, 2016; A special thank you to Marge and Chris Elrod for their support, love, and encouragement.

Baum, Jennifer: Monroe Township, NJ; William Paterson University of New Jersey; Arlene and William Baum; BA English/Secondary Education and Teacher of Students with Disabilities, 2017; Order of Omega National Honor Society, President; National PanHellenic Conference, Academic Chair and Recruitment Chair; Theta Phi Alpha, Social Chair, Fraternal Relations Chair, and Fundraising Chair; This award would not have been possible without the support and love from my family and friends.

Bax, Abigail S.: Jefferson City, MO; Westminster College; Buffy and Jeffrey Bax; BA Spanish Education/Spanish Language/Literature, 2017; Westminster Advisory Technology Team, Liaison and Mentor; Kappa Delta Pi, Historian; Alpha Gamma Delta, Property Coordinator, Greek House Manager, and New Member Leadership Award; I owe everything I have done to God, my family, my friends, and my sisters.

Baylon, Nicole Alexandria: Milwaukee, WI; Milwaukee School of Engineering; Ronald and Maria Luisa Baylon; BS Nursing, 2016; Intramural Volleyball; Honors List; Dean's List; Student Leadership Award Nominee, Student Employee of the Year, Spring 2014; Milwaukee Parks Renovation; Strides Against Breast Cancer; Tie Blankets for the Homeless; Spend a Day With a Child; A Week of No Excuses, Event Coordinator; Student Leadership Council, Secretary; Nursing Honor Society, Vice President; Student Union Board; MSOE Disc Golf Club, Founding Member and Secretary; Empty Bowls Milwaukee, Recruiter; Women's Connection, Committee Member; Lambda Zeta Nu Sorority; Student Nurses Association, Treasurer; National Student Nurses Association; To my family who nourished me with their love and selfless affection, Thank You!

Beach, Anne C.: St. Louis, MO; St. Louis Community College Forest Park; AA Health Information Technology, 2017; I wish to thank all those at Forest Park who made this possible, especially Patricia Stanford-Jones.

Beach, Jessica Danielle: Tulsa, OK; Oklahoma Baptist University; Tammy Beach; BS Nursing, 2016; OBU Nursing Quality Improvement Committee, Senior Student Representative; Mortar Board Senior Honor Society; Phi Eta Sigma National Honor Society; Student Nurses Association, Senior Representative; Student Success Center, Co-Chair and Nursing Coordinator; I am extremely thankful for this honor, and I would not be here without the Lord's guidance.

Beahm, Emily Catherine: Broadway, VA; Longwood University; Joe and Jennifer Beahm; BS Liberal Studies, 2017; Kappa Delta Pi; Historian 2015–2016; I would not be who I am or where I am today without my mom, dad, and brother.

Beasley, Brandon Martrel: Silver Spring, MD; Howard University; MA Divinity/Concentration in Ethics and Public Policy, 2016; Golden Key International Honour Society, Executive Board Scholarship Recipient; School of Divinity Book Scholarship Recipient; American Association for the Advancement of Science Grant Graduate Research Assistantship; School of Divinity Alumni Scholarship Recipient; Student Assembly Annual Ski Trip Co-Chair 2016; Student Assembly Secretary 2015–2016; American Association for the Advancement of Science Grant Graduate Research Assistant 2015–2016; Golden Key International Honour Society, Executive Board President 2015–2016; Financial Literacy SPARK Events 2015–2016; Alternative Spring Break, Memphis, Tennessee, 2015; Alternative Spring Break Radiothon 2015; WHUR Food2Feed 2014; Homeless Initiative, Veterans Appreciation Day 2014; MLK Day of Service 2014; Research Day Certificate 2014 Recipient; School of Divinity SGA, Vice President of Marketing 2013–2014, Vice President of Communications 2015–2016, Graduate Student Assembly Representative 2013–2016; Student Assembly Project Give Back 2013; This award would not have been possible without the love and support of Christ, family, and friends.

Beason, Thad Perry: Gaffney, SC; Limestone College; Charlotte and George Beason; BS Sport Management, 2016; Thanks to all of those who have helped me get to where I am today.

Beauchamp, Logan Andrew: Sherman, TX; Grayson College; Tim and Tonya Beauchamp; AS Sociology, 2016; SGA, Secretary 2015 and Service Coordinator 2016; Film Club, Co-Founder and President 2015–2016; Rotaract, President 2015–2016; History Club, Founder and President 2015; Success is not just about hard work, it takes people who want to see you succeed. Thanks to everyone!

Bebawy, Caroline: Walnut, CA; Azusa Pacific University; Nabil and Bahira Hanna; BS Biology, 2016; National Society of Leadership and Success; Alpha Chi Honor Society; This award would not have been possible without the support and love from my family and close friends.

Becerra, Elizabeth: Decatur, AL; Athens State University; BS Criminal Justice, 2016; This award would not have been possible without the support and love from my family.

Becker, Abigail M.: Manchester, IA; Iowa Central Community College; Sheryl Becker; AA Pre-Law, 2016; Bowling, National Runners-Up; This honor would not have been possible without the support of my family and friends.

Beekman, Angeleta Louise: Jacksonville, TX; BMA Theological Seminary; Marlin and June Epp; BA Religion, 2017; Being an older student, support from family, friends, professors, staff, and administration at BMA Theological Seminary has been indispensable!

Bell, Jamie Nicole: Burnside, KY; University of the Cumberlands; Lisa and James Bell Jr.; BS Psychology, 2016; Presidential Scholars Researcher, Influence of Locus of Control on Metacognition; Honors Day 2014, A.T. Siler Memorial Award Recipient; Student Services, Resident Assistant and Senior Resident Assistant; Women's Archery Team, Captain and Athlete; This award would not have been possible without the support of my family.

Bellin, Anthony Dwayne: Pawnee, IL; Benedictine University at Springfield; Jim Bellin and Nancy Lee Carson; BA Business Administration in Management/Organizational Behavior, 2016. You are never too old to get an education.

Beltran, Miranda Janelle: Laredo, TX; Laredo Community College; Gerardo and Maria Beltran; AA Physical Therapy Assistant, 2018; Laredo Community College Softball Program; Daniel B. Hastings Academic Scholarship Award; Thank you to God, my parents, and family for their continuous support and faith in me and for this recognition.

Bennett, Matthew Dean: Warren, PA; University of Pittsburgh Bradford; Cheryl Hand and Doug Bennett; BA Criminal Justice, 2016; International Justice Mission Club, Secretary; Christ in Action Club, President and SGA Representative; I thank God for giving me the love, strength, and wisdom needed to achieve this great award.

Bennett, Molly L.: Wagoner, OK; Northeastern State University; BA Communication Studies, 2016; 2015 Homecoming Court Queen; Rookie Bridge Camp, Emeritus Color Group Leader; The Big Event, Co-Fundraising Chair; Dance Marathon, Founder and Director; Alpha Omicron Pi, President and New Member Educator; NSU Fraternity and Sorority Life, Panhellenic President, Greek Woman of the Year 2015, Chapter President of the Year 2015, and True RiverHawk Award 2014; To my family, all I do is to make you proud—I love you.

Benton, Savannah Faye: Mount Vernon, IN; Ivy Tech Community College of Indiana Southwest; AA Surgical Technology, 2016; My accomplishments would not have been possible without the support of my wonderful husband, Jesse Benton.

Benz, Mariah L.: Bismarck, ND; University of Mary; Brian and Jami Benz; MS Speech Language Pathology, 2017; FOCUS Bible Study; University of Mary Leadership Academy, Ambassador; National Student Speech Language Hearing Association for Speech Pathology Students, President and Founder; I thank my family, friends, and professors who have supported me throughout my collegiate journey. Philippians 4:13.

Berding, Brooke Margaret: Round Rock, TX; Western Texas College; Tamara and David Berding; AS Pre-Nursing, 2016; College Softball; NFCA Scholar; Commissioner's Honor Roll.

Bernard, Caeleighn: Ocean Springs, MS; Mississippi Gulf Coast Community College Jackson County Campus; Melissa and Aaron Bernard; AA Biology, 2016; Phi Theta Kappa, Treasurer and Fundraiser.

Bess, Paula J.: Mapaville, MO; Missouri Baptist University; Nancy Marks; BS Business Administration, 2016; This award would not have been possible without the support and love from my family.

Bevagna Ospina, Holly Marie: Aguadilla, PR; Inter American University of Puerto Rico, San German Campus; Guadalupe Ospina Bevagna and Marco Bevagna; Medical Technology Professional Certificate, 2016; Civil Air Patrol, USAF Auxiliary; Cadet Executive Office and Cadet Drug Demand Reduction Officer; Ira C. Eaker Award Recipient; Commander's Commendation for Outstanding Performance; Science and Technology Association, Vice President; Asociacion de Salud Publica de Puerto Rico, Education Committee; American Red Cross, Communications, Public Affairs/Social Media, and Writer; Unwavering faith, support, and love— thanks, Mom and Dad, I could not have done this without you.

Bevis, Matthew Ryan: Waterloo, AL; Northwest-Shoals Community College; Terry and Crystal Bevis; AS Pre-Physical Therapy, 2019; SGA, Vice President; This award would not have been possible without the support and love from my family.

Bies, Jared Jack: Columbus, GA; Columbus State University; Jack and Leticia Bies; BA Biochemistry, 2017; Phi Kappa Phi, First Year Student Award; This prestigious award is dedicated to the loving support of both my mother and father.

Bihun, Catherine Rose: Levittown, NY; Long Island University-Post; Maureen Bihun; AA Psychology, 2016; Herstory Writers Workshop, Academic Intern; Sherman J. Tatz Memorial Award in Psychology for Outstanding Achievements Recipient; National Panhellenic Association, Panhellenic Delegate; LIU Post and Beyond Research Symposium, Presenter; Dean's List; Rho Lambda Honor Society; Order of Omega Honor Society; Omicron Delta Kappa Honor Society, President and Member; Alpha Xi Delta, Membership Vice President and Marshal; To Mom and Dad, whose love and guidance has made this award possible. I love you.

Biondolillo, Caroline Elizabeth: West Chester, PA; Immaculata University Undergraduate; BA Elementary Education Pre-K–4/Special Education K–8, 2017; Love Your Melon Immaculata University Campus Crew, Secretary; Kappa Delta Pi, International Education Honors Society, Secretary; Thank you to my mom, dad, Meredith, and Peter for your love and support.

Bishop, Elizabeth M.: Greenfield, IL; Columbia College; Russ and Lisa Bishop; BA Psychology, 2018.

Biundo, Amanda: Henniker, NH; New England College; Michael Biundo and Dawn O'Neil; BA Political Science/Communications, 2016; CiviCorps; *The New Englander*, Assistant Editor; Political Science Club, Co-President; College Republicans, President.

Bjornson, Chamaine A.: Midland, GA; Columbus State University; BS Nursing, 2016; Nursing Tutoring, Lead Tutor; Combat Veterans Motorcycle Association, Auxiliary Member and Treasurer; Student Nurses Association, Second Vice President; To my husband, Matthew, who found the best in me and never let it go.

Black, Kirsten Lea: Sellersburg, IN; Indiana University Southeast; Leah Phillips-Black and Randy Black; BS Criminal Justice, 2016; Undergraduate Research Fellowship 2015; Southeast Honors Program, Tier II Honors Scholar with Honors Research Track; This award would not have been possible without the support of my mentor, Dr. Walsh, friends, and family.

Blake, Courtney R.: Buffalo, NY; Buffalo State; Bruce and Kathy Blake; MS Exceptional Education, 2016; Autism Research Foundation; National Multiple Sclerosis Society; Educators with Disabilities Caucus; Division on Autism and Developmental Disabilities; CEC Teacher Education Division; Technology and Media Division of the Council for Exceptional Children; American Council on Rural Special Education; Association for Supervision and Curriculum Development; American Educational Research Association; Society for Research in Child Development; American Institutes for Research; Grantmakers for Effective Organizations; *The Qualitative Report*; American Evaluation Association; International Meeting for Autism Research; International Society for Autism Research; Association for Behavioral Analysis International; New York State Council for Exceptional Children; Graduate Student Amendment Committee; Graduate Student Social Media Committee; Kappa Delta Pi Honor Society; Graduate Student Social Welfare Committee; Graduate Student Budget Committee; Commencement Speaker Sub-Committee, Student Representative; Teacher Education Council, Student Representative; Commencement Committee, Student Representative; Graduate Student Association, Secretary; Phi Alpha Theta Honor Society, Secretary and Vice President; Ken-Ton Bus Safety Orientation; Multiple Sclerosis Walk, Team Captain, 2008–2016; TeachLivE Virtually Simulated Classroom Lab, Technology Assistant; 2015 SUNY C.I.T. Conference at Geneseo, Facilitator; Annual Westside Business and Taxpayer's Association Awards Ceremony; Multiple Sclerosis Monster Scramble, Participant and Donator; Fall Bash at the Tabernacle, Donator and Volunteer; Teacher's Desk Volunteer Service Day, Coordinator; Heritage Education Program School Supply Drive, Lead Coordinator; Kappa Delta Pi Honor Society, Graduate Liaison; My deepest gratitude goes to God and my Grandparents—I could not have done it without you!

Bloom, Kierstin Allana: Fort Dodge, IA; Iowa Central Community College; Rich and Christine Bloom; AA Science, 2016; My family's unconditional love and support made this award possible.

Blume, Johanna N.: Newtown, PA; Rider University; Valerie Sampson-Dunn and Charles Blume; BA Public Relations, 2016; The V.I.P After Party for 107.7 the Bronc, Host; Multicultural Student Leadership Institute, Mentor; Study Abroad; Track and Field 2012–2014, Athletic Academic Achievement Award Recipient; Omicron Delta Kappa; Leadership Development Program; Freshmen Orientation, Teacher; GLASS, Peer Mentor; Lambda Pi Eta, President 2015; To my mom—sorry for the times I've made you hurt, I hope this makes you beam.

Boetticher, Brooke: Lake Hopatcong, NJ; Centenary College; Janet Boetticher; BSW Social Work, 2018; Thanks to God and my family for always pushing me to be the most excellent me!

Bogdanoff, Jacob: Covina, CA; University of La Verne; Matthew and Christine Bogdanoff; BA Computer Science, 2016; Actor in Drama Productions; Computer Science Tutor; Editorial Cartoonist for School Newspaper; I would like to thank my family and the University of LaVerne for supporting me.

Bolden, Antonnea S.: Buffalo, NY; Buffalo State; Anthony and Sandra Bolden; BS Business Administration, 2016; Sigma Beta Delta Honor Society; Tau Sigma National Honor Society; US Army ROTC, S1 Administrative Officer/Mentor/Color Guard Member; This award would not have been possible without the love, support, and sacrifice from my family.

Bolden, Zoe C.: Buffalo, NY; Buffalo State; Anthony and Sandra Bolden; BS Business Administration, 2016; Tau Sigma National Honor Society; Sigma Beta Delta Honor Society; ROTC Golden Griffin Battalion, Peer Counselor, Mentor, and Cadet Intelligence Officer; This award would not have been possible without the support and love of God and my family.

Bolin, Jeremy: Gaithersburg, MD; Uniformed Services University of the Health Sciences; Debbie Bolin; PhD Medicine, 2016; Alpha Omega Alpha, National Student Director, Chapter President; I thank God and my family for their love and support!

Bonamassa, Alexis L.: Magnolia, NJ; Rider University; Paula and Michael Bonamassa; BA Radio, TV, and Film Communication, 2016; Rider GLASS Mentor Program; Rider Panhellenic Council, Vice President of NPC Recruitment 2014–2015 and President 2015–2016; Student Advisory Board for Film and Media Studies Minors, Co-Vice President; Residence Life Advisor, Olson Hall Wellness Community 2013–2015 and West Village A Premium Housing 2015–2016; Phi Sigma Sigma Sorority, Junior Standards Board Representative 2014, Scribe Executive Board 2014–2015, Parents and Alumnae Executive Council 2015–2016; Relay For Life, Committee Member; SGA, Bronc Aide 2013–2014, Events Coordinator 2014–2015, and Spirits and Traditions Chair 2015–2016; I could not have done this without the support of my parents, thank you.

Bonilla, Mariálix Cancel: Villalba, PR; Inter American University of Puerto Rico Ponce Campus; Félix Cancel and Maribel Bonilla; BS Biomedical Sciences, 2016; "Limpieza del Lago Cerrillos" Certificate; "Avancemos a grandes pasos, contra el cáncer del seno" Certificate; "Sembrando Esperanza" Certificate; I thank God and my parents for their support and commitment, without you this achievement is not possible.

Bookhardt IV, Samuel: Titusville, FL; University of Miami; JD Law 2016; *Race and Social Justice Law Review*, Staff Editor; Charles C. Papy Jr. Moot Court Board, John T. Gaubatz Competition Winner 2015; Receiving this honor was a highlight of my law school career. It brought tears to my eyes.

Bookout, Loren Hunter: Bremen, AL; Athens State University; BA Elementary Education/Collaborative K–6, 2016; This award would not have been possible without the support and love of my family and friends.

Booth, Hoyt W.: Holden Beach, NC; Brunswick Community College; Willie Booth and Linda Norris; AA Computer IT, 2017; This award would not have been possible without support of family, friends, and faculty.

Borne, Nathan Christopher: Winston Salem, NC; Brenau University; Christopher and Nancy Borne; MA Business Administration, 2015; This honor would not have been possible without the love and support of my mom and dad.

Bosarge, Elizabeth Ann: Ocean Springs, MS; University of Southern Mississippi Gulf Park Campus; Patricia Southern-Stork; MA Social Work, 2016; Mississippi Conference on Social Welfare 2015 Scholarship Recipient; MSW Club President 2015; Gamma Beta Phi Honorary Society 2015–2016; This award would not have been possible without the support and love of my husband, Randy.

Bosch, Katharine Noel: Cleveland, TN; Lee University; Donald and Patricia Bosch; BS Special Education, 2016; Theatre Productions, Lead, Supporting, and Stage Manager; Alpha Chi; Best Buddies; Phi Eta Sigma Freshmen Honor Society; Alpha Psi Omega, Theatre Honor Society, Secretary, Vice President, and President; This award would not have been possible without the continued support of my friends, family, and Lee Faculty.

Bostick, Emily Margaret: Edmond, OK; Southern Nazarene University; BS Elementary Education, 2016; Southern Nazarene University in Missions, Team Lead on Mission Trip to Romania; New Student Institute, Student Mentor and Family Group Leader; Kappa Delta Pi, SNU Representative 2014–2015 and Vice President 2015–2016; I am thankful for the support of a loving family, great friends, and above all an amazingly gracious God.

Boukas, James Evangelos: East Alton, IL; Bellarmine University; Kimberly and Vince Milazzo; BA Psychology, 2016; Bellarmine University Orientation Team, Member and Freshmen Focus Advising Assistant; Bellarmine Emergency Response Team, Vice President; This award would not have been possible without the support and love from my family

Bowman, Amanda Kourtney: Galax, VA; Wytheville Community College; Allen Bowman; AS Practical Nursing, 2016.

Boxell, Donna Gaines: Knoxville, TN; King University; BS Nursing, 2016; This award would not have been possible without the influences and loves of my life.

Boyce, Ceejay Leota: Mount Vernon, OH; University of Cincinnati; Corina Boyce; BS Biomedical Engineering, 2016; Engineers Without Borders, Historian and Design Chair; Sigma Phi Women's Honorary, Treasurer; Omicron Delta Kappa National Leadership Honor Society, Treasurer; GlobeMed, Co-President, Benefit Dinner Coordinator, Grassroots On-Site Work Intern, Campaigns Coordinator, and Global Health Summit Delegate; University Funding Board, Internal Vice President and Secretary; To my family, friends, and mentors, thank you for your love, support, and guidance over the years.

Boyd, Michele Marie: Abington, MA; Shenandoah University; Richard and Charlene Boyd; MS Performing Arts Leadership/Management, 2016; Teaching Artist, Dance Instructor for the Old Opera House, Italia Performing Arts, Rhythm N Motion, Urbanity Dance, and Clarke County Parks and Recreation; Many thanks to my family, friends, and mentors who encourage, challenge, and inspire me every day.

Boyle, Keisha Ann: Carrollton, GA; University of West Georgia; Ann and Kevin Boyle; BS Biology; 2016; Circle K; Tri Beta Biological Honors Society; Nation Society of Collegiate Scholars; WeTeach West, Event Planner and Community Service Coordinator; This award would not have been possible without the support of my friends, family, and instructors.

Bradley, Allen Richard: Hendersonville, TN; Union University; Ed and Susan Bradley; BS Accounting, 2016; University Ministries, Life Group Leader; House of Masters, Administrator 2013–2014; SGA, Senior Class Vice President; Phi Beta Lambda, President 2015–2016; Phi Alpha Theta, Senator 2014–2015 and Vice President 2015–2016.

Bradley, Denae: Jackson, MS; The University of Mississippi.

Bradley, Elizabeth A.: Lawrence, MA; Saint Michael's College; BA Psychology, 2016; Student Association Club Representative; Psychology Club, Vice President; Photography Club, President; This award would not have been possible without the love and support from my family. Thank you.

Bradley, Erica Leigh: Luverne, AL; Lurleen B. Wallace Community College; Sally and Tommy Bradley; AA Nursing, 2019; This accomplishment would not be possible without the love and support my family gives me.

Bradley, Haleigh Rebekah: Kingwood, TX; University of Southern Mississippi; Mark and Kathleen Bradley; BA Speech-Language Pathology, 2016; Eagle Connection Student Recruitment Team, President and Vice President; Kappa Delta Sorority, President and Vice President of Operations; This award would not have been possible without the unwavering support and love from my family.

Bradley, Jacob Tyler: Flat Rock, NC; Blue Ridge Community College; AS Film/Video Production, 2016; National Technical Honor Society; Ambassador Program, Student Ambassador; SGA, Public Relations Officer.

Bradshaw, Allison M.: Jackson, MS; The University of Mississippi; Marcia Bradshaw; BA Political Science, 2016; Relay For Life, Recruitment Team; Emerging Leaders, Program Planning Committee Chair; Omega Phi Alpha, Parliamentarian, Chapter Standards Board, and Financial Planning Committee; Students for a Safe Ride, Programming Committee; MOST Mentor, Group Leader; Sigma Alpha Lambda, Vice President; I owe everything to my extraordinary family and friends who inspire me to always go after my dreams.

Brakebill, Philip Austin: Allen, TX; Baylor University; Philip and Brenda Brakebill; BA Philosophy, 2016; Volunteer Special Olympics, Head Coach; Interfraternity Council Judicial Board, Justice; Pi Kappa Phi, Director of Philanthropy and Chief of Standards; For my folks.

Brasel, Scott Bryan: Batavia, IL; Waubonsee Community College; Dawn and Mark Brasel; AA History, 2016; National Society of Leadership and Success; Phi Theta Kappa; History Club, Vice President; Thanks to my family and friends for always pushing me to do better.

Brasher, Cynthia Kay: Brandon, MS; Belhaven University; BA Administration, 2016.

Brayley, Jamie A.: Niagara Falls, NY; Trocaire College; Duane and Clyde Brayley; BS Healthcare Informatics, 2016; This award would not have been possible without the support and encouragement from my father and grandparents.

Breaux, Chaz Michael: Florence, MS; Hinds Community College; Christine and Michael Breaux; BA Construction Engineering Technology, 2018.

Bredlow, Courtney A.: Tempe, AZ; Ashford University Clinton Campus; Tami and Chuck Bredlow; BS Business Information Systems/Business Administration, 2016; Golden Key International Honour Society; Junior and Senior Honor Society; This would not have been possible without the love and support from my family and friends! Thank you all!

Breen, Ryan Matthew: Norfolk, VA; Virginia Wesleyan College; Lisa and Robert Breen; BA Theatre, Minor in Communications, 2016; *Marin Chronicle*, Writer; Alpha Psi Omega, Business Manager; I would like to thank both God and my mother, without these two nothing would be possible.

Bregonzio, William P.: Thomaston, CT; New England College; Christine and Phil Bregonzio; BA Criminal Justice, 2017; Criminal Justice Club, Executive Board Treasurer; This would not have been possible without the love and support of my parents. Thank-you, Mom and Dad.

Brem, Sabrina Ann: Taylors, SC; North Greenville University; Steven and Sarah Brem; BA Piano Performance, 2019; Many thanks to the NGU faculty (especially Dr. Lillia Stoytcheva), fellow students, my parents, and God.

Brewer, Megan M.: Greensburg, PA; Robert Morris University; Donnie and Barbara Brewer; BS Nursing, 2016; Student Nurses Associations of Pennsylvania; Student Conduct Board; Office of Residence Life, Lead Community Advisor and Community Advisor of the Month; Alpha Phi Delta Fraternity, Sweetheart; Thank you to my wonderful family and friends. Most of all I thank the good Lord above!

Briggs, Ashley Marie: McNeill, MS; Pearl River Community College; Lisa and Daryl Keene; AS Nursing, 2016.

Bright, Aleah J.: Monroe, WA; Northwest University; BA Communication, 2017; *The Talon*, Assistant Managing Editor; Thank you to my amazing family for their constant support and love.

Bright, Crystal Leigh: Summerville, SC; Charleston Southern University; AA Criminal Justice, 2017; This award would not have been possible without support from my family, friends, and co-workers.

Briner, Crystal Leighanna: Greers Ferry, AR; Arkansas State University Beebe; Rita Clark; AA Liberal Arts, 2016; Trio, Student of the Week, November 23–29; Ecology Club, Treasurer; Gamma Beta Phi, State Vice President and Chapter Vice President; My award goes to the people who have believed in me.

Brinkley, Katherine Michelle Morris: Warner Robins, GA; Mercer University; BS Early Childhood Special Education, 2016.

Britland, Hana Agnieszka: Levittown, PA; Holy Family University; Teresa and James Britland; BA Secondary Math Education, 2016; Discovering Christ and Following Christ Program, Facilitator; Believe Lead Achieve, President; Honorary Degree Committee 2015–2016, Student Representative; Pigers Math Club, Secretary; I have to thank my family for the endless love, support, and encouragement over the years.

Brogan, Kathleen: Scranton, PA; Marywood University; Marlene and Joseph Brogan; MS Speech-Language Pathology, 2016; Thank you for giving me the world, Mom and Dad!

Brooks, Courtney R.: Boaz, AL; Snead State Community College; Kim and Stacey Brooks; AA Bio-Medical Engineering, 2016; Dance Team, Captain; SGA, Sophomore Representative; Snead State Community College Ambassador, Secretary; Phi Theta Kappa, Membership Director; I could not have come this far without the love and support of my family and friends.

Brooks, Edward: Luling, LA; Xavier University of Louisiana; Maryetta Lewis; BS Dual Degree Mechanical Engineering, 2018; Resident Hall Council, Parliamentarian; National Society of Black Engineers, Senator.

Brophy, Kelcie Katherine: Lexington, KY; Bluegrass Community and Technical College; Katherine Meyer; AA Business, 2016; This award is possible because of people who saw something in me even when I did not.

Brotherton, Caitlyn Rose: Boiling Springs, NC; Gardner-Webb University; Darlene Brink and David Brotherton; BA American Sign Language, 2016; Joyful Hands Ministry Team, Treasurer and Vice President; Student-to-Student: Peer Support, Founder and Peer Support Provider; Campus Ministries United, Worship Service Coordinator and All-Student Ministry Coordinator; SGA, Sophomore Class Vice President, Junior Class President, and Senior Class President; Thank you, Mother. I would not believe in myself if you had not believed in me first.

Browley, Peggy Elaine: Greensboro, NC; Guilford Technical Community College; Barbara Browley-King and Calvin Jones (Deceased); AA Culinary, 2016; President's List; Dean's List; Phi Theta Kappa; Culinary and Hospitality Club, Treasurer; This award would not have been possible without the support of my family, friends, and instructors.

Brown, Darren G.: Albuquerque, NM; The University of New Mexico; BA Psychology, 2016; Cognitive Resources and Computation Lab, Researcher and Research Assistant; National Society of Leadership and Success, Presidential Member and National Engaged Leader Award; Academic Coach, Level 1 Coach; Student Veterans of UNM; Psi Chi, Public Affairs and Historian; Golden Key; Mortarboard National Senior Honor Society, UNM Maia Chapter, Reading is Leading Chair; McNair/ROP Research Opportunity Program Scholars; Honor Society of Phi Kappa Phi.

Brown, Jessica: Mobile, AL; University of South Alabama; Joan and Jean Brown; BS Accounting, 2016; President's List, Honor Roll 2014 and 2015; Dean's List, Honor Roll 2000 and 2012–2013; Accounting Club, Treasurer 2015–2016; Beta Alpha Psi, Secretary 2015–2016; The future belongs to those who believe in the beauty of their dreams. To my family, Thank You!!

Brown, Julie Hannah: Mena, AR; Rich Mountain Community College; AS Licensed Practical Nurse to Registered Nurse, 2018; This award was made possible by the continuing support, love, and confidence placed in me by my family.

Brown, Kingsley Israel: Dunbar, WV; BridgeValley Community and Technical College; John D. and Tamra C. Brown; AA Dental Hygienist, 2016.

Brown, Lakeitha S.: Jackson, MS; Jackson State University College of Education and Human Development; Norman and Lillie Brown; BS Childcare/Family Education, 2016; Beacon of Service Award Recipient; Chi Alpha Epsilon National Honor Society, Diamond Key; NAACP, Civic Engagement Award; This award would not be possible without the support and love from God and my parents!

Brown, Misty Dawn: Spanish Fort, AL; James H. Faulkner State Community College; AS Nursing, 2016.

Brown, Tyler Sterling: Emmaus, PA; Rensselaer Polytechnic Institute; Donna and David Brown; BS Computer and Systems Engineering/Computer Science, 2017; Undergraduate Researcher; Eta Kappa Nu Honor Society; Tau Beta Pi Honor Society; Quidditch Team; Engineering Ambassadors, President Elect and Outreach Event Coordinator.

Browne, Alphea Glenyce: St. Thomas, VI; University of The Virgin Islands; Glentis and Vernice Browne; BA Accounting, 2017; CFBC Literary and Debating Society, Treasurer and Debater; St. Kitts and Nevis Student Association, Treasurer; Accounting and Business Professionals Association, President; Student Housing, Resident Assistant; Through Christ who strengthens me, I can do all things.

Bruffey, Claire Elizabeth: Lubbock, TX; Lubbock Christian University; BS Early Childhood Education, 2016; Alpha Chi Honor Society; GO! Orientation Leader; Kappa Delta Pi Honor Society; Women's Basketball Team; I am thankful for the Christlike support, love, and encouragement from my family, basketball coach, and the LCU community.

Brunson, Mauree Fore: Latta, SC; Coker College; Margaret Fore and Elijah Brown Jr.; BS Sociology and Criminology, 2016; SGA, Criminology Majors Representative; Dean's List; 2015 Coker Diamond Student of the Year; Thanks to all of my family, friends, and the Coker College staff for believing in me.

Buchanan, Stacy Drew: Locust Grove, VA; American Military University; MA Intelligence Studies–Cyber, 2016; Golden Key International Honour Society; This award was made possible by the love and support of my wife, children, and late mother.

Buckbee-Lutcher, Kelley L.: Elmira, NY; Nazarene Bible College; Jared and Beverly Buckbee; BA Christian Counseling, 2016; Crestmont College–School for Officer Training, AA Ministries, Graduated Magna Cum Laude; This award would not have been possible without the loving support of my husband, Michael.

Bugher, Michael G.: Hazleton, IN; Ivy Tech Community College of Indiana Southwest; AA Energy Technology, 2016.

Bundy, Wendy Lou: Luray, VA; Columbia Southern University; Larry and Lou Good; BS Criminal Justice Administration, 2013; This award would not have been possible without support from my family, mentors, and my husband, Chris.

Burke, Ronnie Allen: Viper, KY; Hazard Community and Technical College; Tonya and Jackie Logan; AA Applied Science–Human Services, 2016; Never give up no matter the obstacles facing you! The rewards you seek are near!

Burkeen, Heather Marie: Medon, TN; Austin Peay State University; David and Stephanie Burkeen; BS Medical Laboratory Science, 2016; Alpha Omicron Pi, Historian; I would like to thank my parents, other family members, and outstanding professor for their support.

Burlingame, Andrew R.: Huntingdon, PA; Juniata College; Patricia and L. Jay Burlingame; BA History/Politics, 2017; I want to thank my family and Juniata College for supporting me and helping me succeed.

Burnell, Mary B.: Pageland, SC; Northeastern Technical College; AA Applied Science in Business, 2015; National Technical Honor Society, Honor Award 2014; Phi Theta Kappa Honor Society, Honor Award 2014; Phi Theta Kappa All-State Academic Team, Honor Award 2014; SGA, Associate; My awards would not have been possible without God and the support and love from my husband.

Burns, Raquel R.: Jackson, MS; Jackson State University College of Education and Human Development; AA Elementary Education, 2017; I dedicate this award to my husband and my three boys.

Bush, Samantha Rose: Carrollton, GA; University of West Georgia; Kenneth and Rebecca Bush; BA Management/Marketing/International Business, 2016; Richards College of Business Dean's Council, Chair; International Services Program Fee Committee, Chair; Technology Fee Committee, Chair; National Society of Collegiate Scholars; Management Club, Vice President of Membership; Alpha Lambda Delta Honor Society, President; This award would not have been possible without the help of my family, UWG professors, and motivational friends.

Butcher, Jeremy Lee: Ravenswood, WV; West Virginia University at Parkersburg; Kenny and Donna Butcher; AA 3D Modeling, Simulation, and Design, 2015; Thanks to my grandmother and my whole family.

C

Cabibbo, Isabella Elizabeth: Spring City, PA; Delaware County Community College; Steven and Heidi Cabibbo; AA Education, 2016; Dance Team, Vice President; This award would not have been possible without the support and love from my family.

Cahill, Olivia Kaitlin; Plattsburgh, NY; State University of New York Plattsburgh; Katherine Cahill; BA Public Relations/English Literature, 2016; Rho Lambda Honor Society, Director of Finance; Alpha Phi Fraternity, Chapter President, Vice President of Risk Management, New Member Educator, Emerging Leaders Award Spring 2014, and Dedication to the Fraternal Excellence Initiative Award. This award is dedicated to my loving support system: my mother, Katherine, and my grandmother, Jane.

Cain, Halie Joyce Ann: Newcastle, OK; University of Science and Arts of Oklahoma; Stacey and Bart Daniel; BS Biology/Psychology, 2016; Drover Dancers, Captain; Drovers Against Cancer, President and Vice President; This award would not have been possible without the support and love from my family, friends, and teachers.

Calhoun, Payton Nichole: Tulsa, OK; Northern Oklahoma College Enid; BS Psychology, 2018; Presidential Leadership Counsel, Dean's Honor Roll; I would like to thank the PLC sponsors and my mother for supporting me on my journey.

Calvert, Courtney Greer: Spotsylvania, VA; Regent University; Janet and Greg Calvert; BS Psychology, 2016; Psychology Club, Vice President and Treasurer; Psi Chi, Inductee; This award would not be possible without the support, love, and encouragement from my family.

Camacho, David Keith: East Brunswick, NJ; Oakwood University; Marcia and Keith Camacho; BS Biomedical Science, 2017; Crunch-Time Tutors, Biology, Organic Chemistry, and General Physics Tutor; REACH 2013–2015; Honda Classica All-Star Competition Member 2013–2016; Oakwood University Youth Enrichment Association, Mentor 2015–2016; Tri-Beta Honor Society, Member 2014–2016 and Parliamentarian Elect; Alpha Chi Honor Society, Member 2015–2016 and President Elect; Oakwood's Biomedical Association, Member 2013–2015, Vice President 2015–2016, and President Elect; I am so grateful for this award. I thank God, my family, and my university for assisting me.

Campbell, Todd Francis: Whitby, ON; University of the Cumberlands; Kelly and Todd Campbell; BS Accounting, 2017; This award would not have been possible without the support from my family and faculty.

Camplair, Macey M.: Frederick, MD; Western University of Health Sciences; Robert and Rhonda Camplair; PhD Veterinary Medicine, 2016.

Cannon Jr., John T.: Dryden, NY; Tompkins Cortland Community College; Tom and Dottie Cannon; AA Business Administration, 2017; Phi Theta Kappa Honor Society, Vice President of Public Relations, Winner of All-NYS Academic Team Honor 2015; Theater Society and Performance; National Society of Leadership and Success, Presidential Member; Toastmasters International, President and Treasurer; SGA, Vice President of Student Involvement Committee; This award would not have been possible without the educational opportunities afforded me at Tompkins Cortland Community College.

Cantu, Cynthia Lilliana: San Juan, TX; South Texas College; Maricela and Luis Cantu; AA Interdisciplinary Studies, 2016; Honor Society; Chemistry Club; Biology Club; 4-H, Officer and Ambassador; President's Volunteer Service Gold Award; Mu Alpha Theta Math Honor Society; Choir, Soprano 1 Section Leader and Texas State Solo and Ensemble; Drama Club, Best Actress and All-Star Crew; Special Olympics Volunteer; March of Dimes Volunteer; Super Hero Project, Volunteer; Toys for Tots, Donor; National Down Syndrome Association, Volunteer; Future Farmers of America; Officer; PSJA North, Junior Class Valedictorian 2016 and Junior Candidate Class of 2016; Associates of Art Interdisciplinary Studies 2015; Alpha Lambda Delta; National Society of Leadership and Success; Sigma Kappa Delta, Vice President; Phi Theta Kappa, Vice President and Parliamentarian; Thank you to my family and friends for always being here for me. I love you all!

Cape, Karan Herrin: Supply, NC; Brunswick Community College; AA Business Administration, 2016; This award would not have been possible without the support and love from my husband, Eddie Cape.

Capps, Jordan Candace: Roxboro, NC; Meredith College; Jack and Beth Capps; BA Political Science, Interpersonal Communication, 2016; Class of 2016 Executive Committee, Publicity Chair; Student Life Committee Chair; SGA Executive Committee, Student Life Committee Chair; Special thanks from the bottom of my heart to my family!

Cardenas, Myles Christian: Conyers, GA; Kennesaw State University; Maurice and Chevron Cardenas; BS Construction Management, 2017; Sigma Lambda Chi Rho II; Golden Key International Honour Society; Society of Collegiate Leadership and Achievement; National Residence Hall Honorary; Odyssey Peer Mentoring Program, Mentor; National Society of Leadership and Success, National Engaged Leader Award Recipient; National Association of Home Builders Student Chapter, Vice President; I dedicate this award to my family, mentors, and friends as a thank you for their continued support.

Cardona, Laura G.: Ft. Davis, TX; Sul Ross State University; Javier and Sandra Luz Cardona; BA Business Administration, 2016; Freshmen Leadership Program; Delta Mu Delta International Business; Dean's List 2013–2015; Business Club, Vice President 2016 and Secretary 2015; This award would not have been possible without support and love from God and my family.

Carey, Kelly Marie: Holbrook, NY; Long Island University-Post; William and Teresa Carey; BS Forensic Science, 2017; Cheerleading Captain; Outstanding Achievement Award; I would like to thank my family, friends, coaches, and professors for their unconditional support.

Carlson, Jeremy Everett: Norfolk, VA; Norfolk State University; Cemeal and Eugene Carlson; BS Electrical Engineering, 2017; Army ROTC, C/1SG; German Armed Forces Proficiency Badge; Superior Cadet Award 2013–2014; Battalion Commanders Athletic Award 2014–2015; Color Guard; Ranger Challenge Team; Distinguished Cadet Award; I would not have gone this far if it was not for my mentors Eric Tyson, Christopher O'Sullivan, and Dale Ward.

Carlton, Kelsey L.: Ferrum, VA; Ferrum College; Anissa and Willis Garnett; BS Liberal Arts, 2017; Lambda Sigma, Vice President; Kappa Delta Pi; With the love and support from my family and friends, this award was possible!

Carnley, Amanda Grace: Graceville, FL; The Baptist College of Florida; Rick and Robin Carnley; BA Missions, 2019; I want to thank God and my family, without them I would not be who I am today!

Carosello, John Michael: Tempe, AZ; Embry-Riddle Aeronautical University Prescott Campus; Phillip and Colleen Carosello; BS Global Security and Intelligence Studies, 2016.

Carpenter, Hannah Elizabeth: Danville, IN; Marian University; Cindy and Jeff Carpenter; BA Visual Arts/K–12 Education, 2017; Kappa Delta Pi–Alpha Alpha Tau Chapter, Historian; I would like to thank my family, professors at Marian University, and God for my accomplishments!

Carrington, Janis Lynn: Gilmer, TX; LeTourneau University; BS Business Administration, 2016; Thank you to my family and friends, I would not have made it to graduation without your understanding.

Carter, Courtney Leigh: Olive Branch, MS; Blue Mountain College; Camey and Lee Carter; BS Elementary Education, 2016; This award would have not been possible without the love and support of my great family!

Carter, Denzel J.: New Kensington, PA; Robert Morris University; Tony and Jackie Carter; BA Accounting, 2016; Through everything I would not change anything. Reality is a humbling concept, thank you for the life lessons.

Carter, Jalynn Nicole: Sylacauga, AL; Central Alabama Community College; Marty and Jennie Carter; AS Nursing, 2018; REMOC Civic Club, Co-Sponsor; ANFRC AmeriCorps, Team Leader 2015–2016; CACC Jazz Band, Baritone Saxophone; I would like to thank my parents for always supporting me and encouraging to do my best.

Carter, Trisha Y.: Kingsport, TN; Northeast State Community College; Sam and Elizabeth Hicks; AS Medical Office Administration, 2016; This award would not have been possible without the support and love from my family.

Casadevall, Ruth Adelina: Lords Valley, PA; Stevenson University; BA Elementary Education, 2016; This award would not have been possible without the support and love from my family!

Cascone, Alexandra: Lisle, IL; Benedictine University; Stephanie Nocella; BA Marketing, 2016; American Marketing Association, President and Secretary; Family and mentors, thank you for your abundant support. This award would not have been possible without you.

Case, Lisa Jeanne: Daphne, AL; James H. Faulkner State Community College; Suanne and William Higgins; AS Nursing, 2016.

Casebere, Melanie Blair: Birmingham, AL; Huntingdon College; Cherly and Thomas Casebere; BA Political Science, 2016; Sigma Sigma Sigma; Sigma Tau Delta English Honors Society; Alpha Beta Honors Society; Women's Center, Panel Participant; Political Science Club, Panel Participant; Leadership Initiative, Hostess and Sponsor of Cyber Connection Day; I would not have made it this far without the work ethic my parents instilled in me.

Caselnova, Victoria Eleisa: Glens Falls, NY; Adelphi University; Eddy and Robin Caselnova; BS Nursing, 2015; Sigma Delta Tau, Secretary and Community Service Committee Chair; Adelphi University Cheerleading Team; Gamma Sigma Alpha Academic Honor Society; Rho Lambda Leadership Honor Society, President; Student Nurses Acting for Progress Club, Secretary.

Casey, Elizabeth: Elkhorn, NE; College of Saint Mary; Nancy and Joseph Casey; MA Occupational Therapy, 2018; Honors Biographical *Who's Who Among Students in American Universities and Colleges 2015*; Dean's List, Fall 2014–Fall 2015; American Occupational Therapy Association; Ladies Ancient Order of Hibernians; Student Occupational Therapy Association, Executive Board Member–Social Chair.

Casey, Maddisson Brooke: Van Lear, KY; Big Sandy Community and Technical College; Tracy and David Casey; AA Respiratory Care, 2018; This award would not have been possible without the support and love from my mom.

Castellano, Vitale Kyle: Cumming, GA; Kennesaw State University; Mike and Joan Castellano; BS Mechanical Engineering Technology, 2017; Golden Key International Honour Society 2015; National Society of Leadership and Success 2014; Martial Arts, Kickboxing Black Belt and Yondo Jiu Jitsu Purple Belt; I would like to thank my family for their support throughout my life. Hard work pays off.

Castiglione, Christine M.: Roslyn Harbor, NY; University of Miami; Lisa and Frank Castiglione; BS Public Health, 2016; School of Nursing and Health Studies Student Ambassador, Outstanding Student Award Recipient Class of 2016; Thelma Gibson Health Initiative; Upward Bound; Relay For Life; Clinton Global Initiative; Zeta Tau Alpha Sorority, Director of Philanthropy; Greek Week Executive Board, Greek God and Goddess Chair; United Against Inequities in Disease, Director of Marketing and Membership; SGA, Category 5 Spirit Programming Board, Marketing and Public Relations Chair; Mom, Dad, and Frankie—thank you for all of your love and support always.

Castillo, Karla Michelle: Laredo, TX; Laredo Community College; AA Business Administration, 2018; Phi Theta Kappa; This award would not have been possible without the support and love from my family.

Castillo, Monique: Harrison, NJ; William Paterson University of New Jersey; Tereza Botelho and Gerald Castillo; BA Liberal Studies/Women's Gender Studies, 2016; Caribbean Student Association, First Annual Scholarship Recipient; United Cultural Greek Council, Neophyte of the Year Award Recipient; This award would not have been possible without the unconditional love and support from my family.

Castillo, Rita Ann: LaFayette, GA; Belhaven University; BA Social Service, 2016; Cum Laude; Thanks, Roy Davis and Collin Petty, for pushing me and making me believe in myself. Love you guys!!!

Castle, Tracy Latrelle: Oakland, CA; American Public University; Inez Marshall; MA Intelligence Studies/Concentration in Intelligence Collection, 2016; Alpha Phi Sigma; Pi Gamma Mu; I thank God, my mother Inez, daughter Rachel, Dr. Drumhiller, and Dr. Barton for their love and support!

Castro, Gabriela Alejandra: Laredo, TX; Laredo Community College; Blanca Castro; AA Business Administration, 2016; Community Involvement in LBVEC and TRIO SSS Club; Community Service in College Sponsored Activities; TRIO SSS Club, Secretary Officer and TRIO Students Support Services Grant Aid Award 2014–2016; Phi Theta Kappa Honor Society; Scholastic Achievement 2014; Dean's List 2015; For those who inspire me, support me, and love me. Thanks to family, thanks to friends, thanks to the Lord!

Cavazos, Mercedes Caroline: Hanford, CA; College of The Sequoias; AA Social Work/Psychology, 2016; COS Foundation Transferring Students Award 2016–2017; Honors Graduate; Dean's List 2014; Student Worker; WestCare Volunteer.

Cerny, Matthew L.: Chadron, NE; Western Nebraska Community College; AA Auto Body Technology, 2016; This award would not have been possible without the support and love from my family and friends.

Cerra, Selena Rose: Fell Township, PA; Niagara University; Linda and John Cerra; BA Spanish/Education 5–12, 2017; Division 1 Athletics, Women's Golf; Bienvenidos Spanish Club, Service Trip Organizer; 4 Walls Project, Public Relations Chair; SGA, Freshmen Senator, Executive Communications Director, and Executive Parliamentarian; Sigma Alpha Sigma Presidential Honor Society Outstanding Freshman; Thank you, Mom and Dad, for teaching me to work hard and do what I love.

Ceruti, Koree N.: Laurelton, NY; Grambling State University; Leslie Ceruti; BA Accounting, 2016; Earl Lester Cole Honors College Student; I appreciate the love and support from my family!

Cervantez, Brian C.: Topeka, KS; Washburn University; Richard and Cynthia Cervantez; BA Mass Media, 2017; Tri-Bod Production 2014–2016, President 2015–2016; Hispanic American Leadership Organization 2014–2016; This award would not have been possible without the support and love from my family.

Cerveny, Katie Marie: Erie, MI; Lourdes University; John and Chris Cerveny; BS Adolescent to Young Adult Math Education, 2016; Member of SOMA College Community Northpoint Church, Volunteer and Outreach; Campus Ministry and College Board, Franciscan Pilgrimage to Italy; Dean's List; Women's Lacrosse, 1 Co-Captain and Student Athlete Athletic Conference Attendee; "In everything, give thanks." I will forever thank my family for their constant strength and support, always.

Chamberlain, Cindy: Snellville, GA; Kennesaw State University; BS Technical Communication/Information Design/Instructional Design, 2016.

Chamberlin, Rebecca C.: Oswego, NY; Cayuga Community College Auburn Campus; AAS Nursing, 2016; Nursing Club, President; Thank you to my family and instructors for supporting me and recognizing all my hard work.

Chambers, Anastacia Lynn: Bloomington, IL; University of Missouri Saint Louis; Blyth Chambers; BA Middle School Math Education, 2017; Weeks of Welcome, Crew Leader; Student Athlete Advisory Committee; Women's Swimming and Diving Team, Captain; This award would have not been possible without the loving support of my mom.

Chambers, Jonathan J.: Garden City Park, NY; Long Island University-Post; Michele and James Chambers; BA Finance, 2017; Beta Gamma Sigma 2016; Omicron Delta Epsilon 2016; Omicron Delta Kappa 2015–2016; Reserve Officers Training Corps, Cadet 2013–2016; National Society of Pershing Rifles 2013–2016; SGA, Senator and Parliamentarian 2013–2015; "Believe you can and you're halfway there" —President Theodore Roosevelt

Chan, Kah F.: Brockport, NY; Genesee Community College; Yeok Mun Chan; AS Computer Support and Operations, 2017; Computer Lab T207, Work Study Assistant; Diversity Club; Diversity Council; Photography Club; Student Advisory Board; Phi Theta Kappa Honor Society, President; Student Library Council; Academic Innovation Committee; I would like to thank my spouse, family, friends, and staff of GCC for making this possible.

Chandler, Harley J.: Hazlehurst, MS; Copiah-Lincoln Community College; Dana and Brent Chandler; AS Radiology, 2016.

Chang, Chris Su: Fishers, IN; Taylor University; Gary and Nami Chang; BS Elementary Education, 2016; Basics Junior Leader, Sharing the Gospel to Young People; Football, 2nd Team All-MSFA, All-Conference Academic, All-District Academic, Four-Year Starter.

Chapa, Katarina: Weslaco, TX; Texas A&M University Corpus Christi; Rosario Martell and Arkadio Chapa; BS Biomedical Sciences, 2018; Student Volunteer Connection, Service Events Committee Member; National Society of Leadership and Success, Community Service Co-Chair and National Engaged Leader Award; Special thanks to my family, friends, and God for guiding me through my academic journey.

Chaplin, Heather Nicole: Proctor, WV; West Virginia Northern Community College; Wayne and Tina Chaplin; Certificate in Small Business Management/Business Career Studies, 2016; Without the love and helpful criticism from my family, I would not have been able to receive this award!

Charnow, Michele A.: Mount Hope, WV; Bluefield State College; BA Social and Applied Sciences, 2017; In memoriam of Barbara S. Pacifico and Anthony M. Charnow.

Chatfield, Carissa J.: Muscatine, IA; Muscatine Community College; Janice Chatfield; AA Marketing, 2016; Phi Theta Kappa, Treasurer 2016 and All-Iowa Academic Team; I want to dedicate this award to my family and friends, without them this would not be possible.

Chavies, Valerie Nicole: Flat Lick, KY; University of the Cumberlands; David and Michelle Chavies; BA Accounting/Business Administration, 2017

Cherni, Samantha D.: Huntsville, AL; John C. Calhoun State Community College; Paul and Melissa Quick; AA Nursing, 2015; None of this would have been possible without God, my husband, and parents.

Childs, Aaron Jamal Toomer: Nashville, TN; Meharry Medical College Graduate School; Ishmael and Shelia Childs; MS Graduate Studies and Research in Public Health, 2016; Dean's List; This award would not have been possible without the support and love from my family.

Chin, Tiffany Gim-Yain: Lynnwood, WA; Seattle Pacific University; Ed and Mila Chin; BS Nursing, 2017; American Chemical Society, Treasurer; Asian American Christian Fellowship, Student Advisor; Thank you to my family, friends, and professors who have supported me in my educational and professional pursuits.

Chopra, Yuvraj: New Hyde Park, NY; Rensselaer Polytechnic Institute; Ravinder Chopra and Shalu Suri; BA Business Management/Computer Science, 2019; RPI Chess Club, Officer; Project Rishi, Secretary; Alpha Phi Omega, Pledge Class Fellowship Vice President and Freshmen Community Service Award Recipient; Nugent Hall Council, Treasurer; I am where I am because of my parents and my brother. This one's for them.

Christopher, Katrie Smith: Kennett, MO; Three Rivers Community College; Gary and Carol Smith; AA Mass Communications, 2016; This award is possible because of the love from my daddy, Gary Smith, and daughter, Zoe Christopher

Chuba, Kayla Ann: Shelton, CT; Bay Path University; BA Early Childhood Education, 2016; Field Work, Alice B. Beal Elementary School Longmeadow Montessori School; St. Mary School, Preschool Volunteer; Kappa Delta Pi Maroon; Key Honor Society; Stage Crew, *Little Women*, *Into the Woods*, *Steel Magnolias*, and Orientation Leader; Capitals of the World, Resident Assistant; Education Club, Chorale Executive Board; Chorale, Gaffney Memorial Scholarship Recipient; This award would not have been possible without the love and support from my parents and family.

Church, Brooke Alexandria: Purlear, NC; Wilkes Community College; Tracy and Heather Church; AA General Education, 2016; I would like to credit my family, my instructors, and everyone else who helped me along the way.

Chykugwu, Chidinma Favour Eunique Damilola: Lawton, OK; Cameron University; David and Mary Chykugwu; BA Journalism, Media Production, Marketing, 2016; Cameron University Broadcast Club; *Cameron University Collegian*, Staff Writer; CUTV, News Anchor and Television Host of the Year; Hot Button on CUTV, Co-Host and Co-Producer; Lambdi Pi Eta, Communication Association Honor Society Award Recipient; Outstanding Freshmen English Composition II Student Award; *Who's Who Among College Students In America* Award; Phi Kappa Phi National Honor Society Award; Phi Eta Sigma National Honor Society Award; International Club, Active Member Award and Nominee for Homecoming Queen 2015; Nigerian Students Association, Public Relations Officer, Active Member Award, and Second Runner Up Homecoming 2016; This award would not have been possible without the continuous love and support from my family.

Clark, Briana Monet: Athens, GA; University of Georgia; Debbie and Roderick Clark; BS Criminal Justice/Political Science/Sociology, 2017; Clarke County Mentor Program; Mock Trial, Captain; Undergraduate Black Student Law Association, Co-Founder and Vice President; Student Alumni Council, President; All that I am I owe to God and my angel mother. Thanks to everyone that supports me!

Clark, Stephen R.: North Richland Hills, TX; Hardin-Simmons University; Phillip and Linda Clark; BS Computer Science, 2016; President's List 2012–2016; Summa Cum Laude.

Cleavenger, Casey Jo: Philippi, WV; Alderson Broaddus University; Eddie Cleavenger; AA K–6 Education/Special Education, 2016; Thank you to my dad, nan, and boyfriend for continued support throughout my college career.

Clegg, Alexander W.: Fredericksburg, VA; University of Mary Washington; Kristin and Andrew Clegg; BA Communication/Digital Studies, 2017; Men's Rugby, Match Secretary, Captain, Most Improved, and Rookie of the Year; Center for International Education, Peer Advisor and Scholarship Recipient; Orientation Leader and Coordinator; Honor Council, Class of 2017 Elect; SGA, President; Without the opportunities my parents provided me, I would not be where I am today. I love you!

Clough, Justin Lee: Milwaukee, WI; Milwaukee School of Engineering; Christopher and Joanne Clough; BS Mechanical Engineering, 2016; Physics Department, Student Assistant; Campus Tutoring Center, Lead Tutor; American Society of Mechanical Engineers; This award would not have been possible without the support and guidance of my friends and family.

Clyde, Jasmine Arielle: Amityville, NY; St. John's University; Antoinette and William Clyde Jr.; BS Chemistry, 2016; Inorganic Research Student, University Research Day Participant; I'd like to dedicate this award to my incredible, caring, and devoted parents, Antoinette and William.

Cochran, Linda Ann: Coeburn, VA; Mountain Empire Community College; George Booher; AS Medical Office Specialist, 2016; PTK; PBL; I am so proud to graduate with my daughter, Rebecca. My husband, Fred, has supported both of us.

Cody, Toni Kaylen: Sulphur Springs, TX; Arkansas Tech University; Amber and Stuart Cody; BA Middle Level Education–Math/Science, 2016; Cru/Athletes in Action, Student Leader; Collegiate Middle Level Association, Secretary and Vice President.

Coffey, Amellia Nicole: Tucson, AZ; Oklahoma Baptist University; Tim and Betsy Coffey; BA Marketing/ Management, 2016; Mortar Board, Chapter President; Enactus, Chapter President; Track and Field, 2014 Team National Champion.

Cokotis, Julie Ann: East Longmeadow, MA; Western New England University; Nancy and Peter Cokotis; BS Finance and Management/Leadership, 2016; College of Business Outstanding Student Award; Academic Success Center, Academic Progress Monitor; Office of First Year Students, Orientation Group Leader, Student Ambassador, and Senior Office Assistant; Residents Hall Association, President of Commonwealth Residence Hall; Student Senate, College of Business Representative, Campus Relations Chair, Finance Committee Member, and Pioneer Valley Collaborative Ball Chair; Thank you, Mom, Dad, and Jen, for all of your love and support. I love you!

Cole, Sarah Elizabeth: Greenwood, MS; Northwest Mississippi Community College; Emily McPhail; BA Psychology, 2018; Psychology Club; Psi Chi, Treasurer; Phi Theta Kappa; Gamma Beta Phi; This award is very honorable. I owe my appreciation to all my awesome teachers and family!

Coleman, Jesse James: Raccoon, KY; University of Pikeville; BA Business Administration–Accounting and BS Arts Administration–Piano, 2016; Sigma Beta Delta; Pikeville Public Library, Volunteer Piano Instructor; UPIKE Concert Choir, Bass Choralist; This award would not have been possible without the support and love from my mother, Virna Lisa.

Collins, Julie Irene: Beaver Dams, NY; Schenectady County Community College; Julie and Joseph Collins; AA Culinary Arts/Baking Concentration, 2016; Bowling Team, NJCAA National Champions 2015 and 2016, NJCAA Regional Champions 2015 and 2016, Academic All-American 2015 and 2016, and All-Conference Team 2015 and 2016; Thank you to my parents and the excellent professors at Schenectady County Community College for this honor.

Collins, Natalie Rose: New Hyde Park, NY; University of New Haven; Sandra and Timothy Collins; BS Forensic Science, 2017; Delta Phi Epsilon Sorority, Vice President of Academic Affairs, Coordinator of Senior Programming, Coordinator of Scholarship Fund, and Coordinator of Alumni Affairs; Alpha Lambda Delta First-Year Honor Society, Executive Assistant; Gamma Sigma Alpha National Greek Honor Society, President; To my family and friends that have supported me throughout my life and made me who I am.

Colon, Alexis M.: Williamstown, NJ; University of Valley Forge; Alexsi Ortiz and Juan DeJesus; BA Deaf Ministries, 2016.

Combs, Angela: Albuquerque, NM; The University of New Mexico; BS Psychology and Anthropology–Evolutionary, 2016; Golden Key; National Society of Leadership and Success; Psi Chi; Mortar Board Senior Honor Society, Staff Appreciation Chair.

Combs, Taylyn Geneil: Whitesburg, KY; Hazard Community and Technical College; Gene and Deb Combs; AS Surgical Technology, 2016; Dean's List 2015; President's List 2015; Outstanding Appalachian Studies Student 2011; Associates in Arts Degree 2012; Associates in Science Degree 2012; Phi Theta Kappa Honors Society, Honors Night Presentation; Southeast Community and Technical College Honors Program; Miss Southeast Pageant, Crowned Winner 2012; I owe all of my accomplishments to God, my family, professors, and my heart, Robbie.

Cones, Julie D'Anne: Wagoner, OK; Connors State College; James and Diana Cones, Vicki and Robert Hill; AS Nursing, 2016; Toppers Volunteer Fire Department, First Responder; Relay For Life/Melee for Marks, Team Co-Captain; CSC Nursing Program, Jeopardy Award; Phi Theta Kappa, President's Honor Roll, Vice President's Honor Roll, and Associate of Applied Science; This would not be possible without your love and support, or the sum of my experiences. Thanks y'all!

Conway, Hannah Marie: Jackson, TN; Union University; BS Accounting, 2016; Historic Downtown Jackson Ghost Walk, Reenactor; Union University Campus and Community; Cantilena Women's Choir, Member and Section Leader; Union University Theater, Actor, Box Office Manager, and House Manager; Phi Beta Lambda; Phi Alpha Theta; Alpha Psi Omega, Business Manager and Secretary; Rutledge Honorary History Club, Vice President and Senator; Beta Gamma Sigma; Alpha Chi; To my family, I love you and I cannot thank you enough for being my rock and support.

Cook, Bethany N.: Seven Hills, OH; Case Western Reserve University; Kathy and Steve Cook; BS Materials Science/Engineering, 2018; Society of Women in Engineering; National Society of Collegiate Scholars; Relay For Life; Women in Science and Engineering Roundtable, Peer Mentor/Tutor and Youth Engineering Week Volunteer; Engineers Without Borders–Dominican Republic Division, Treasurer and Budget Lead, International Relations Committee Member; Alpha Phi, Director of Marketing, Peer Mentor, and Greek Scholarship Award; Mom and Dad, your endless love and support gives me the confidence to strive for greatness. Thank you.

Cook, Carla June: Waco, TX; Baylor University; Ken and Sharmon Edmonds; BS Secondary Life Science, 2016; School of Education Dean's List; Sigma Phi Lambda–Sisters for the Lord, Secretary; Thank you to my amazing husband, beautiful children, and Baylor professors for all of your love and support!

Cook, Nyanza Yvette: Killeen, TX; University of Mary Hardin-Baylor; BA International Business, 2016; I am extremely honored and incredibly appreciative for receiving this significant award. I love you, UMHB family!

Cooksey, Brett Daniel: Conway, SC; Coastal Carolina University; Michelle and Daniel Cooksey; BA Sociology and Political Science, 2016; Golden Key; Council for Exceptional Children, Chapter Media Chair; Pi Sigma Alpha, Chapter Vice President; Sigma Alpha Pi; This award would not have been possible without the support of my very loving family.

Copley, Connor M.: Manhattan, KS; Barton Community College; Robert Copley and Dena Krohn; AS Liberal Studies, 2016; Thank you to my parents, without whom I would not have grown into the man I am today.

Coppage, Chaste' L.: Oklahoma City, OK; Langston University; Carlos and Nacasaw Coppage; BA Accounting, 2016; Langston University Cheer, Head Cheerleader; Without the backbone of my family and friends, this award would be nothing more than incomprehensible.

Copple, Jordan Ann: Norfolk, NE; David and Shirley Copple; BS Occupational Therapy, 2017.

Coroiescu, Denise Nicole: New Caney, TX; Oklahoma Baptist University; Ronela and Adelin Coroiescu; BS Exercise Science, 2016; Track and Field, NAIA Women's Indoor Track and Field Team National Champions 2013–2015, NCCAA Women's Indoor Track and Field Team National Champions 2016, 60-Meter Hurdles Runner-up 2016; Volleyball, All-Academic Team 2014–2015 and Honorable Mention All-Conference Team 2015; Without the love and grace of God and my family, I would be lost in this world.

Correia, Alexandra: Woodsboro, MD; Frederick Community College; AA Business Administration, 2016; Phi Theta Kappa Honor Society; Spanish Department Student of the Year Language Award; Spanish Club, Vice President; Business Club, Secretary; "I can do all things through Christ who strengthens me." —Philippians 4:13

Cortez, Adam: Gulfport, FL; St. Petersburg College Health Education Center; Andrea Cortez Amado; AS Nursing, 2016; The Great American Teach in Azalea Elementary School, Nurse; Phi Theta Kappa; I thank God for all my blessings and my wonderful family for unconditional love and support.

Cortez, Araceli: Fontana, CA; California Baptist University; BS Nursing, 2018; Pre-Med Society, Vice President; Phi Theta Kappa; California Baptist University, Provost's List; Chaffey College, Dean's Honor List and Cum Laude; Puente Program, Secretary; Clinical Care Extender Internship; This award would not have been possible without the support and love from my family: Mom, Dad, Yecenia, Jordan, and Joseph.

Cortez, Geraldine Lissette: Framingham, MA; Framingham State University; Luis and Lilian Cortez; BS Fashion Design/Retailing, 2016; Fashion Design and Retailing Prospective Student Mentor, Dean's List 2014; With this award I want to thank God, my family, and friends for the unconditional love and support.

Costner, Jonathan Jacob: Shelby, NC; Cleveland Community College; Angie and David Costner; AS Broadcasting, 2018; I dedicate this achievement in honor of my faith, family, and friends.

Cousin, Courtney S.: Clarksville, TN; Austin Peay State University; Tongeia Farmer and Tucker Cousin; BA Business Marketing, 2017; NAACP; Changed Girls Organization; Habitat for Humanity; Governors Programming Council, Diversity and Variety Chair; Alpha Lambda Delta National Honor Society, Social Enrichment Chair; Alpha Kappa Psi Professional Business Fraternity, Director of Service and Service Award 2014–2015.

Cox, Courtney N.: Covington, VA; Ferrum College; Shannon and Mark Cox; BS Social Studies, 2017; Glen-Cairne Scholarship Award; Leadership Fellow Scholarship; Rotaract Club, Vice President; This award would not have been possible without the support of my parents, educators, and friends.

Cox, Graham Robert: Providence, RI; Providence College; Robert and Janis Cox; BS Computer Science, 2016; Army ROTC, American Legion Award 2015; As Grampy would say, "Persistent efforts, properly directed, always produce profitable results."

Craft, Courtney Ann: Millstone, KY; Alice Lloyd College.

Craig, Chelsea Elizabeth: Marietta, GA; University of North Georgia; Thomas and Elizabeth Craig; BS Psychology, 2016; Georgia Appalachian Center for Higher Education, Student Liaison 2014; Nighthawks Entertainment Activities Board, Committee Member 2013–2014, Senior Representative 2014–2015, and Outstanding Senior Representative Award 2015; Nighthawk Network, Developer and Coordinator 2015–2016; Orientation Leader and Staff 2013–2016; Theatre Guild, President 2012 and Vice President 2011; Delta Zeta Sorority, President 2014–2015, Vice President of Programs 2013–2014, Social Chair 2012–2013, Way and Means Internal Fundraising Chair 2015, Philanthropy Committee 2013, Open House Committee 2013, and UNG Sorority Woman of the Year Nominee 2015; "You're not in this world because you needed something. You're here because someone needed you." —Unknown

Crain, Tamlyn Marie: Port Orchard, WA; New Mexico Highlands University; BA History/Political Science, 2017; ASNMHU Student Senate, Senator; Gamma Alpha Omega Sorority Inc., Alpha Gamma Chapter Secretary; Thank you to my family by blood and by choice without whom I would not succeed.

Crandell, Thomas Tanner: Poteau, OK; Southwestern Oklahoma State University; Joyce Hall and Pete Crandell; PharmD Pharmacy, 2016; Phi Lambda Sigma, Alpha Psi Chapter Vice President 2014; Kappa Psi Pharmaceutical Fraternity Inc., Delta Beta Chapter Regent 2014, Vice Regent 2013, and Sergeant at Arms 2012; I credit my family, friends, teachers, and mentors for this prestigious award.

Crass, Cale Bradley: North Richland Hills, TX; Abilene Christian University; BS Business Management, 2016; Gamma Sigma Phi; A. B. Barrett Scholarship; Transfer J. C. Stevens Award; Virginia F. Heacock Scholarship; This award would not have been possible without the support and love from my family.

Crawley, Alecia Dawn: Henderson, KY; Henderson Community College; Tim and Lisa Crawley; AA Social Work, 2016; CROSS; Honor Roll; Thank you to my parents and teachers for the support and love throughout my life.

Crosby-Washington, Tysha Lyn: New Brunswick, NJ; Bloomfield College; Julius and Kathy Washington, Tysha and David Talton; BS Applied Mathematics, 2015; Excellence in Mathematics Award; Dean's List; Student Ambassador; Honors Program; SGA, Financial Advisor; Soccer Lead Judge for RoboCupJunior NY/NJ; Mathematics Tutor; International Student Services Intern; Residential Advisor; Sigma Alpha Pi Honors Society; Alpha Chi Honors Society; Thank you to everyone who's supported me in all of my years of hard work.

Cross, Keith Michael: Holden, MA; New England College; BA Business Administration, 2016; AA Business Administration, 2013, Cum Laude; This honor is dedicated to my family in recognition of their love and support.

Crowell-Graff, Jessica A.: Massapequa, NY; Rider University; Corinne and Robert Graff; BS Business Economics, 2016; This would not have been possible without the love and support from my family, my reasons.

Crudup, Breland: Jackson, MS; Tougaloo College; Maggie and Bobby Crudup; BS Biology, 2017; Honda Campus All-Star Challenge, Vice President and Vice Captain.

Cruz, Jessalee Rose: Hamilton Square, NJ; Stockton University; Mary Lopez; BS Health Science, Pre-Communication Disorders, 2016; American Legion Auxiliary Post 313, President; Alpha Phi Omega National Co-Ed Service Fraternity, Chair; Riding High Farm, Volunteer and Instructor in Training; Equestrian Team, Founder and President; Global Health Team, Fundraising Chairmen and Founder; This award would not have been possible without the support and love from my mom.

Culhane, Sara: Parker, CO; New England College; Gary and Lu Culhane; BA Kinesiology, 2017; Soccer; Honors Program; This award would not have been possible without the guidance and support of my loving parents.

Culver, Clint Orlen: Garden City, KS; University of South Carolina; Del Culver and Glenda Owens; BA Criminal Justice, 2016; US Army All-American Bowl, Assistant to Combine Director; Army ROTC, Distinguished Military Graduate, Superior Cadet Award, Battalion Executive Officer, and Ranger Challenge Team; SGA, Tau Epsilon Lambda Representative; Tau Epsilon Lambda Competition Team, Team Captain, First Place Individual Firearms Regional Competition, and First Place Team Firearms Regional Competition; Tau Epsilon Lambda, Freshmen Class President and Sophomore Class Vice President; This could not have been possible without the support of my beautiful wife, Denise. I love you!

Cumbee, Kristyn Leigh: Hollywood, SC; Lander University; BA Accounting, 2016; ZTA, Judicial Chair 2016, Most Valuable 2016, Student Advisory Athletic Committee 2015–2016, and Program Council Intramural Chair 2014–2015; Dance Team 2012–2016 and Coaches Award 2013 and 2015; This award would not have been possible without the love and support from my family.

Cunningham, Melisa Gayle: Laneville, TX; Panola College; Sheila and James Black; AA Medical Assistant, 2016; Community Food Bank Volunteer; I have to give credit to God and my husband for pushing and helping me this far.

Currier, Joshua Joseph; Norfolk, VA; Virginia Wesleyan College; Michelle Dunn and Roger Currier; BA Comprehensive Liberal Studies, 2016; Men's Lacrosse, First Team All-ODAC, All-Virginia, All-American, Player of the Year, and Rookie of the Year; I owe this award to the support of both sets of my parents, my Bubba, and Coach Stewart.

Curry, Dionye: Lithonia, GA; Regina and Tobias Howard; BS Sport Management, 2016.

Curry, Jacob D.: Lewisburg, TN; Columbia State Community College; Jay and Lisa Curry; AA History, 2017.

Curry II, Joe Mack: Stringer, MS; The University of Mississippi; Shirley Curry; BA Accountancy, 2016; National Pan Hellenic Council, 2015 Council President; KPMG Tax Intern; Alpha Phi Alpha Fraternity Inc., Nu Upsilon Chapter President; Hall of Fame Recipient; Columns Society; This accomplishment would have never been achievable without my mother. I love you, mom!

Cutts, Ezekiel X.: Tabernacle, NJ; Lipscomb University; Christopher and Renee Cutts; MS Sustainability/Business, 2017; YES Youth Encouragement Services, Tutor and Recreation; Ronald McDonald House Meal Fellowship, Coordinator; Intramural Sports, Referee Campus Club Volleyball, Softball, and Football; Student Activity Center, Facilities Manager and Graduate Assistant; Blood Water Mission, Campus Coordinator; Alpha Phi Chi, Treasurer and Vice President; Criminal Justice Club RCBC, Treasurer; SGA RCBC, Ambassador; Phi Theta Kappa RCBC, All NJ USA Community College Academic Team.

D

Dade, Vivian Yvette: Alexandria, VA; Northern Virginia Community College; AA Occupational Therapy Assistant, 2016; Staunch Supporter of Student Life Activities/Student Leadership 2014–2015 NOVA MEC Student Excellence Award Winner; Student Occupational Therapy Assistant Club, Occupational Therapy Assistant Student Tutor 2016; Phi Theta Kappa Society, President 2013–2014; My sincere gratitude to God, my husband, family, and friends for their unwavering love and support.

Dajer Guerrero, Rafael Eduardo: Antelope, CA; The Master's College; Maria Fuentes; BS Accounting/Finance, 2018; Accounting Society, Controller; The honor goes to the One who made this possible.

D'Andrea, Kelsey Amanda: Brick, NJ; Long Island University-Post; Eileen and Dennis D'Andrea; BFA Musical Theater, 2016; LIU Post Campus Life, Graduating Senior Award; Dean of Students, Years of Service Award 2016; Dean's List 2012–2016; Student Leader of the Month, September Recipient; Women's Achievement, Women's Recognition Award Nominee; Orientation Leader, Orientation Leader of the Year Award 2015; Phi Eta Sigma Honor Society; Order of Omega Honor Society; Rho Lambda Honor Society; Gamma Sigma Alpha Honor Society; Omicron Delta Kappa Honor Society; Panhellenic Association, President 2014–2015, Vice President of Recruitment and Marketing 2015–2016, and Greek Scholar of the Semester 2015; Alpha Xi Delta, Golden Quill Award 2016, Sister of the Year Award 2015, Heart Sunshine Award 2014, Greek Week MVP 2015, and Academic Achievement Social Chair; Post Theater Company, Company Coach; A big thank you goes to my parents and those who have inspired me at LIU Post!

Dang, Christine L.: Fontana, CA; Western University of Health Sciences; Eugenio and Bach Anong; PhD Nursing Practice, 2016; Community Health Improvement Program; Dean's List; This award is dedicated to my family, friends, and mentors for their love, support, and guidance.

Daniels Jr., Jerry L.: Fort Gaines, GA; George C. Wallace Community College; Catherine Daniels; AS HVAC, 2016; This award would not have been possible without the Lord, my family, and faculty at Wallace.

Daniels, Christoline Nichole: Headland, AL; Troy University; Sarah and Christopher Daniels; BS Athletic Training, 2017; Iota Tau Alpha, Secretary; This award would not have been possible without the love and support from my family.

Daniely, Rodney D.: Kingsland, GA; Jackson State University College of Science, Engineering, and Technology; Chernita and Rodney Daniely; BS Electrical Engineering, 2017; Louis Stokes Mississippi Alliance for Minority Participation, Student Researcher; Residential Hall Association, Dixon Hall President; This award would not have been possible without the support and love from my family.

D'Antonio, Marissa White: Covington, LA; University of Holy Cross School of Nursing; Charmaine Vosbein and William White; BS Nursing, 2016; This award would not have been possible without the love and support of my family.

Darling, Blake A.: Holt, MI; Albion College; Ben and Deanna Darling; BA Sociology, 2016; This award would not have been possible without the love and support of my friends and family.

Darling, Samantha: Succasunna, NJ; Centenary College; Lisa and Gary Darling; BA History/Secondary Education, 2018; Volunteer Activities, Jump Rope for Heart, Volunteer Softball Camp Coach, River Clean Up in Hackettstown, Community Plunge Food Pantry, and Volunteer Softball Coach; Softball, Second Team All-CSAC Pitcher, CSAC Pitcher of the Week, CSAC Honor Roll Pitcher, Cyclone of the Week, CSAC All-Academic Team, Athletic Director's Honor Roll, NSCA All-Academic Team, NSCA All-American Scholar Athlete; Thanks to my family for all of the love and support they give me every day.

Dashner, Amanda L.: Clarion, PA; Independence University; Tammy and Jamie Himes; AA Occupational Medical Specialties, 2016; This award would not have been possible without the support and love from my family.

David, Erica Lee: Jennings, LA; Louisiana State University School of Dentistry.

Davidson, Winston Guerney: Nashville, TN; American Baptist College; BA Bible/Theology, 2016; This award would not have been possible without the support of my church and my family.

Davila, Julie: Houston, TX; LeTourneau University Global; Onofre and Emilia Davila; BA Human Resources, 2016; I dedicate this award to my loving parents, Onofre and Emilia Davila. With all of my love.

Davis, Amber Brielle: Raymond, MS; Hinds Community College; Brenita and Rickey Davis; AA Elementary Education; Dean's Scholar; COGIC. Ministry, Choir Member; Wind Ensemble, Sixth Chair; Percussion Ensemble, Sixth Chair; IDEAL Women, Secretary; Hinds Hi Stepper, Squad Leader; I m honored and thankful for the love and support I had to make this award possible.

Davis, Bertram: Acworth, GA; Kennesaw State University; Ethel Jackson; BS Integrative Studies, 2016; Adult Learning Center, Book Subsidy; President's List 2013–2015; Dean's List 2012 and 2014; Carolyn Stovall Scholarship; Steven L. Lovig Endowed Scholarship; This recognition would not have been possible without the love from my family as well as extended family.

Davis, Calvin King: Bossier, LA; Centenary College of Louisiana; Casey Lanzillotti and Thad Davis; BA Sacred Music, 2016.

Davis, Carmen Ana: Sioux Falls, SD; Dakota State University; Maria and Dumitru Tofan; BS Network and Security Administration, 2016; This award would not have been possible without the support and love from my dear husband.

Davis, Gladys Delight: Calera, AL; Southeastern Bible College; Lois Diane Davis; BA Bible/Theology, 2017; Women's Ministry, President; Student Mission Fellowship, Secretary.

Davis, James Braswell: Carthage, TX; Panola College; Royce and Sharon Davis; AS Engineering, 2016; I dedicate this award to my family and teachers.

Davis, Jason Eugene: Martinez, GA; Augusta University The Graduate School; Eugene and Noelyn Davis; PhD Pharmacology, 2016; Biomedical Student Association, Vice President; Through loving support from El-Shaddai; my wife, Kristi; my parents, Noelyn and Eugene; my grandparents, Betty and Russ; and my advisor, Dr. Wu.

Davis, Julianne: South Hamilton, MA; Husson University; Len and Nancy Davis; BA Healthcare Studies, 2016; This award would not have been possible without the love and strength from all who support me.

Day, Colleen O'Connor: Boston, MA; Suffolk University; BA English, 2016; Boston Newspapermen's Benevolent Association, Resident Advisor; Sigma Tau Delta International English Honors Society, Dean's High Honors List; *The Suffolk Journal*, Editor-in-Chief; I am greatly honored and humbled by this award and the support I have received along the way.

Day, Kayla Ashlen: Milford, ME; Husson University; Jennifer and Corey Day; BS Legal Studies/Pre-Law, 2017; SGA, Vice President of Commuter Affairs and Executive Vice President; Legal Studies Organization, Treasurer and President; I m so grateful for my family's love and support. Without them, this award would not have been possible.

De Asis, Michaela Encinas: Fairfax, VA; University of Mary Washington; Roderick and Marcia De Asis; BS Psychological Science, 2016; Foundation for International Medical Relief of Children, Volunteer; Psychological Science Department, Elected Student Representative; Fredericksburg Counseling Services, Intern and Case Manager; Alpha Mu Sigma, Vice President of External Affairs 2014–2016; Receiving this award was the perfect end to my undergraduate career and I could not be happier. Thank you!

De Weirdt, Meagan Kendall: Keller, TX; Tarrant County College Northeast Campus; Lisann and Dave De Weirdt; AA English, 2016; Cornerstone Honors Program, Honors Degree; Psi Beta National Honors Society, Secretary.

Dean, Arden E.: Manalapan, NJ; Rider University; Stacy Poliner; BA Psychology, 2016; Greek Council, Vice President of Membership Development; Zeta Tau Alpha, Panhellenic Delegate, Director of Philanthropy, and Judicial Board Member.

Deckard, Jeremiah E.: Mount Carmel, IL; Wabash Valley College; Donna Deckard; AA Science/Arts, 2016; Players Guild Club, Co-President and Founder; I am thankful to all the friends, family, and faculty that made this possible.

Dedman, Monika I.: Clanton, AL; Wallace Community College Selma; LPN Nursing, 2018; This award would not have been possible without my God and husband.

DeDominicis, Nathaniel Alvah: Shelby, NC; Cleveland Community College; Nancy and Andrew DeDominicis; AS Associate in Science Degree, 2016; International Society of Automation Club, President; This great honor would not have been possible without my family, school faculty, co-workers, and my Heavenly Father.

Deeter, Caitlyn L.: Ringtown, PA; Shippensburg University; Dave Deeter; BS Exercise Science, 2016.

DeFelice, Alexander N.: Plymouth, MA; Western New England University; Michael DeFelice and Joan Buckley; BA Psychology, 2016; Peer Advisor of the Month 2014; Psi Chi International Honor Society, President; Psychology Club, President; I would like to acknowledge the unconditional love and support of my family, friends, and loved ones.

Defoe, Miranda M.: Fayetteville, TN; John C. Calhoun State Community College; AA Physical Therapist Assistant, 2016; This award would not have been possible without the love and support from my family and friends.

Delbalso, Andrea Erin: Pinola, MS; Hinds Community College; Christine DelBalso; AS Health Information Technology, 2016; Alpha Beta Gamma; Phi Theta Kappa; This award would not have been possible without my wonderful fiancé and my supportive mother and grandmother! Love you!

Dell-Bene, Deanna: Scotch Plains, NJ; Kean University of New Jersey; BA Psychology, 2016; Criminal Justice Club, President; BIG thank you to my mother for making me who I am and continuing to believe in me!

Deloach, Jasmine Monique: Bluffton, SC; Morris College; Ali and Irene Bozier; BA Criminal Justice, 2017; Chess Club; Criminal Justice Club, Secretary.

DeMarco, Robert Santino: Savoy, TX; Grayson College; Deborah DeMarco and William Berstler; AA Child Development, 2016; Future Educators Club, President; Evening of Excellence Award Recipient; President's List; Summa Cum Laude; Thanks to my mother, Deborah DeMarco, and my stepdad, William Berstler. I love you always.

DeMarr, Anna E.: Springfield, VA; University of Mary Washington; Glenn and Dianna DeMarr; BA Geography, 2016; Orientation Leader and Coordinator; Washington Guide, Director of Recruitment.

Demel, Danielle M.: San Diego, CA; Western University of Health Sciences; Jody Demel; DVM Veterinary Medicine, 2016; American Association of Equine Practitioners, Student Chapter President.

Denmark, Lisa: Rochester, NY; Monroe Community College; Charles Kramer and Susan Howell; AS Nursing, 2016; Phi Theta Kappa; 2015 Frank Lanza Memorial Scholarship Recipient; Student Nurses Association, President and Vice President of Mentoring; Thank you to my family for your unwavering support—this would not have been possible without you!

Denney, Krysten Raye: Shawnee, OK; Oklahoma Baptist University; Richard and Karen Denney; BS Biology, 2016; Festive of Fools Improv Troupe, Genie, Historian 2015–2016; College Players Theater Troupe, President 2015–2016 and Treasurer 2013–2015.

DeSalles, Gianna N.: San Antonio, TX; The University of Texas at San Antonio; Michael and Yolanda DeSalles; BA Interdisciplinary Studies, 2016; Junior Achievements, Teacher; National Collegiate Leadership Conference Participant; Civil Rights and Social Justice Trip Facilitator; To my awesome family and friends, YOU ROCK!! Thank you for all of your love!!

DeSecottier, Joel S.: Oklahoma City, OK; Mid-America Christian University; L. R. and Huni DeSecottier; BS Psychology/Pre-Med, 2017; Honor Roll; The pride which my father and family extends to me is my motivation to continue.

Deveau, Sadie Marie: Fort Erie, ON; D'Youville College; Christine and Walter Deveau; BA Psychology, 2016; This award would not have been possible without the love and support from my family.

Dever, Ryan Earl: Tabernacle, NJ; Stockton University; Jennifer and Earl Dever; BS Business Studies, Marketing, 2018; Thank you to my amazingly supportive family, friends, and mentors.

Dewanamuni, Udya Seneviratne: New York, NY; Queensborough Community College; Kithsiri and Kumudu Dewanamuni; AS Engineering Science, Concentration in Chemical Engineering, 2018; Chemistry Department, Tech Fee Student 2015–2016; Student Faculty Disciplinary Committee 2016–2017; STEM Research Club 2014; Emerging Leaders Program 2014; SACNAS Chapter, National Liaison 2016; Honors Program 2014, P. K. Wong Award, Queensborough 11th Annual Honors Conference Award, and Queensborough 12th Annual Honors Conference Award; Chemistry Club, President 2014 and Dr. Paris Svoronos Award; CSTEP Program 2016, CSTEP/STEP Regional Conference Award; CUNY Research Scholarship Program 2014, CUNY Research Scholarships 2014–2016; SGA, Executive Vice President 2016–2017; American Chemical Society 2015, Chemical Society National Meeting Award; This award was made possible with the support and love from my family and professors.

Dias, Sarah Elizabeth: West Palm Beach, FL; Palm Beach Atlantic University; Catherine Dias; BS Marketing, 2016; Impact Leadership Team, Co-Director; Micro-Finance Club, Marketing and Public Relations Officer; SGA, Election Chair; Sigma Beta Delta, Hospitality Officer.

Diaz, Yesenia Ruby: Alamo, TX; South Texas College; AA Advertising and Public Relations, 2016; President's Honor Roll; Thank you to my family and to my instructors for helping me achieve this award.

Díaz-Ferreira, Yamilette M.: Sabana Hoyos, PR; Inter American University of Puerto Rico, San German Campus; Jesús Díaz-Torres and Marvilla Ferreira-Casiano; BS Biology, 2017; Honor Program, Level Two, Rector's List Award; Tribeta Biology Honor Society, Zeta Beta Chapter; Without my family and my boyfriend's support, I would not have received this award. I owe them everything.

Diggory, Matthew Lawrence: Modesto, CA; Western University of Health Sciences; Larry and Diane Diggory; OD Optometry, 2016.

DiGianivittorio Sr., Nicholas A.: Sicklerville, NJ; Peirce College; John and Loretta DiGianivittorio; BA Professional Studies, 2016; This honor would not have been possible without the support and love of my wife, children, family!

Dignen, Timothy Wayne: Denton, MD; Chesapeake College; AA Nursing, 2017; Tutor, Algebra, Writing, Anatomy and Physiology1 and 2, and Psychology; 2016 Chesapeake Student Achievement Award Nominee; Phi Theta Kappa Honor Society, Bowdle Family Scholarship; TA, Psychology and Microbiology; Vice President CC/MGW Nursing Class of 2017; I would like to dedicate this award to my wonderful sons.

DiGrazio, Sandra N.: Barnegat, NJ; Rider University; Keith and Christine DiGrazio; BS Human Resource Management and Leadership, 2016; Order of Omega, Treasurer; Omicron Delta Kappa National Leadership Honorary, President; Human Resource Management Association, Public Relations Chair; Freshmen Seminar, Peer Mentor; Zeta Tau Alpha, President, Secretary, and Assistant New Member Coordinator.

Dillon, Layne Gregory: Ferrum, VA; Ferrum College; Greg and Debra Dillon; BS Political Science, 2016; Pi Sigma Alpha; Model UN, Delegation of the Year 2015–2016; Young Democrats, President; No Labels, Ferrum College Chapter President and Founder; This award would not have been possible without the support from my family, professors, and mentors.

D'Imperio, Catrenia Marie: Philadelphia, PA; Holy Family University; Helen Chomentowski; BA Psychology, 2016; Social and Behavioral Sciences Club, Events Coordinator and Club Core Values Award; To my dearly departed grandfather, who taught me the value of a big heart and good work ethic.

DiPreta, Stephanie Nicole: Franklin Square, NY; Long Island University-Post; Lily Eng and Anthony DiPreta; BA Health Science, 2016; 2014 Study Abroad Costa Rica, Universidad Veritas; USA Athletes International Lacrosse, England and Scotland 2015, Australia 2014; Hartwick College Women's Lacrosse, #13 Defense; Alpha Xi Delta Sorority, Social Media Chair; This dedication is to my parents and my sisters of Alpha Xi Delta, whom I love.

Dire, Glenn E.: Conyers, GA; Luther Rice College and Seminary; Harold and Linda Dire; MA Divinity, 2016; Short Term Missions, Africa, Haiti, Guatemala, Jamaica, and Wind River Indian Reservation; Love and thanks to Beth and Lee, God's two precious gifts to me in this life.

Dixon, Angela Tyann: Ruther Glen, VA; University of Mary Washington; BA English, Creative Writing Concentration, 2016; Mortar Board Cap and Gown, President; Commuter Student Association, Vice President; Theatre, Co-Star, Production of *Doubt* as Mrs. Mueller; In memory of my loving grandmother, Bernice Coleman. Thanks for your love, support and selflessness.

Dixon, Charla La'Tia: Jacksonville, FL; Jacksonville University; Yvette White-Dixon; BA Chemistry and Spanish, 2017; Chemistry Society; Sergeant at Arms; Resident Advisor 2014–2016; National Residence Hall Honorary, Secretary 2015; National Honor Society of Leadership and Success; I thank God for this honor and my loving mother and brother. I am truly blessed.

Dixon, Chereigna N.: Hazlehurst, MS; Jackson State University College of Liberal Arts; Beverly Steward and Donald Dixon; BS Criminal Justice, 2016; Wesley Foundation, Acting President; This award would not have been possible without God and my family.

Donaldson, Lindsay R.: Castro Valley, CA; Life Chiropractic College West; Gail and Tim Donaldson; PhD Chiropractic, 2016; Adjusting Ninjas Club; League of Chiropractic Women, Secretary; Network Spinal Analysis Club; International Chiropractic Pediatric Association, Pending Certification; Student Champions, Secretary; Thank you for your unconditional love and support, Gail and Tim Donaldson, and to my grandmother, Lois Donaldson.

Donohue, Virginia-Leigh: Vicksburg, MS; Jones County Junior College; Virginia Weaver Donohue and Robert Donohue; MA Elementary Education, Specializing K–3, 2019; Phi Theta Kappa, Director of Honors in Action.

Dorey, Mary J.: Port St. Lucie, FL; Indian River State College; AS Business Administration, 2016; Phi Theta Kappa Honor Society, Business Specialist; What a delightful surprise that could not have happened without the loving support of my family.

Dosdall, Joshua: Elk Point, SD; Dakota State University; BS Computer Science/Mathematics for Information Systems, 2017; Kappa Sigma Iota Honor Society; Pep Band, President; National Society of Leadership and Success, President.

Dotson, Shaunmarie Alexandra: Blairsville, GA; Young Harris College; Barry and Shay Dotson; BS Middle Grades Education, 2016; "Delight thyself also in the Lord; and he shall give thee the desires of thine heart." —Psalm 37:4

Dougherty, Mary Kathleen: Depew, NY; Thiel College; Margaret and Thomas Dougherty; BA Psychology, Sociology, and Criminal Justice, 2017; Dietrich Honors Institute, Dietrich Honors Scholarship; Student Athletic Advisory Committee, President; Thiel College Softball, President's Athletic Conference Academic Honor Roll; Thank you, Mom and Dad, for always encouraging me to do my best. I love you.

Doughtie, Taylor Raye: Suffolk, VA; Virginia Wesleyan College; Stuart and Ann Doughtie; BA Psychology/
Music, 2016; Presidential Scholar; Marlins Read, Tutor; Zumba(R) Instructor; Tenth Annual Winter Homeless Shelter, Manager; Omicron Delta Kappa; Neighborhood Tutoring; Psi Chi, Vice President; This award would not have been possible without support from my family and guidance from my professors.

Douglas-Perkins, Teylor Elicia: Kansas City, MO; Carthage College; Damon and Felicia Perkins; BA French, 2016; Carthage Fellowships, Study Abroad Fellow; United Women of Color, President and Secretary; Panhellenic Council, Senior Panhel Representative and Junior Panhel Representative; Intervarsity Christians; French Club; Gospel Messengers; Carthage Democrats; Carthage Allies; ResLife, Resident Assistant; Black Student Union; Sigma Omega Sigma, President, Vice President, Secretary, and Philanthropy and Social Chairs; Alpha Lambda Delta; All glory to God! Nothing would be possible without the love and support from my family and friends.

Douglass, Michael S.: Bentonville, AR; Case Western Reserve University; BS Biomedical Engineering, Engineering Physics, 2018; Humanitarian Design Corps and Engineers Without Borders, President and Project Lead; Zeta Beta Tau Fraternity, Director of Philanthropy; I owe everything I am to anyone who has ever known me.

Dovgala-Carr, Alexandra Noelle: Ewing, NJ; Temple University Boyer College of Music and Dance; John Carr; BA Music Therapy, 2017; Academy of Adult Learning for Adults with Intellectual Disabilities, Tutor; OwlCappella, Treasurer; Music Therapy Club, MARAMTA Conference Scholarship 2015–2016; Dedicated to my incredible support system, with utmost gratitude for the guidance and inspiration from my family.

Downey, Alayna Paige: Gaffney, SC; Limestone College; Lori and Scott Downey; BA Early Childhood Education, 2016; Miss Limestone College 2015, Overall Non-Finalist Swimsuit Scholarship Award, Duke of Edinburgh International Service Award, and President's Volunteer Service Award; SGA, Freshmen Class Secretary; Dance Team Member, First Place at Clash of the Carolinas Competition and National Championships in Variety and Hip Hop Categories; This award would not have been possible without my family. Thank you for everything you do.

Doyle, Clint: Nazareth, PA; Moravian College; BA Management, 2016; United Student Government, Parliamentarian.

Doyle, Theo Nina: North Hills, CA; University of La Verne; Greg and Kris Doyle; BS Psychology, 2016; Residence Hall Association, Programming Co-Chair and President; National Residence Hall Honorary, President; Phi Sigma Sigma, Treasurer, Parents Chair, and Faculty Chair; This award would not have been possible without the support of my mentors and family.

Dray, Theresa: Davison, MI; Marygrove College; BS Biology, 2017; Women's Basketball; Women's Track and Field; Sigma Zeta; Presidential Scholarship Award; This award would not have been possible without the love and support from my family.

Drazenovic, Ryan Matthew: Ellicott City, MD; Stevenson University; BS Chemistry, 2016; Gamma Sigma Epsilon Honor Society; Dean's List.

Dreszer, Emily Renee: Severna Park, MD; Anne Arundel Community College; George and Carol Dreszer; AA Political Science, International Relations, 2019; Center for the Study of Local Issues, Surveyor; Maryland General Assembly Internship, Delegate Intern; American Red Cross, Greater Chesapeake and Potomac Blood Services Region; Habitat for Humanity, Collegiate Challenge Participant with Alternative Spring Break Trip; Economics Club, Debate Participant; AACC Ambassador Program, College Ambassador; Leadership Challenge Participant; Student United Way at AACC, Vice President; Criminal Justice Association, Vice President; Legal Studies Association, President; SGA, Senator; I thank my family and friends for their support and encouragement, you all made this possible.

Driscoll, Matthew D.: York, PA; York College of Pennsylvania; Kevin and Tara Driscoll; BS Psychology, 2016; Thank you so much to my parents and everyone who has made my college experience great.

Drude, Taylor Morgan: Hammond, LA; Southeastern Louisiana University; Randy and Donna Drude; BS Integrative Biology, 2017; Dean's List; President's List; Green "S" Award; Vice President's Award of Excellence; TOPS Honors Scholarship; Southeastern Honors Scholarship; Division of Student Affairs Leadership Ambassador, Emerging Leaders Retreat.

Drummond, Lesley: El Dorado, AR; South Arkansas Community College; Bobby and Mary Rowton; AS General Business, 2016; This honor would have been impossible without the love and support of my family and instructors at SACC.

Dublin-Greene, Furo: Clarksville, MD; Howard Community College; Vivian Adeghe and Celina Dublin-Greene; AA Pre-Pharmacy, 2016; This award would not have been possible without the love and support from my family members.

Ducoing, Margeaux Marie: Fredericksburg, VA; University of Mary Washington; Darren and Lori Ducoing; BA Studio Art and Music, 2017; Mu Phi Epsilon; Bell-Acappella 2011–2015, Soprano 1; Student Art Association; National Society of Collegiate Scholars; Mortar Board; This award would not have been possible without the love and support of my family and friends!

Dudley, Heather Mae: Midland, TX; Midland College; Patricia Gray; AA Nursing, 2017; The support of my friends and family have helped me succeed while in school. Love y'all!

Duffoo Tirado, Victoria: Webster, TX; University of Houston–Clear Lake; Jose G. and Leyda M. Duffoo Tirado; AA Communication, 2017; Intercultural Student Services Strictly Speaking, Tutor; Office of International Admissions and Programs, IO Leader; University Christian Fellowship, SGA Representative; SGA, Vice President Outreach and Communication; Glory to Jesus for always guiding me to fruitful opportunity. Live life on purpose.

Dumitrescu, Andrei-Vladimir: San Diego, CA; Thomas Jefferson School of Law; Natalia Dumitrescu; JD Law, 2017; I owe everything to my mother and grandparents; they've given up everything so I could have more.

Duncan, Ashten Ray: Moore, OK; University of Oklahoma; BS Microbiology, 2016; Alpha Phi Omega; VPS; MBU Director; Gold Service Award.

Dunigan, Jamie Ann: Petersburg, IN; Oakland City University; BS Humanities, 2016; Pike County Little League, Past Coach; Pike County Youth Basketball, Coach; Pike County Youth Soccer League, Board Member, Secretary, and Coach; Community Volunteer, Petersburg Elementary School PTO Officer and Member; I dedicate this honor to my two children, Hayden and Dietrich. Teach to make the world brighter.

Dunn, Taylor Madison: Sturgis, MS; East Mississippi Community College; Todd and Melissa Dunn; AA Pre-Nursing, 2016; Phi Theta Kappa Honorary Society, Vice President; East Mississippi Honors Program, Highest Honors Graduate.

Duran, Karla Patricia: Stockton, CA; University of The Pacific School of Engineering and Computer Science; MS Computer/Electrical Engineering, 2016; Tau Beta Pi; Honor Society of Phi Kappa Phi; Society of Women Engineers; IEEE Eta Kappa Nu Honor Society, President; This award would not have been possible without the guidance and assistance given to me by Tony Duran.

Durham, Emily Grace: Crowley, TX; Vernon College; Becky Hayhurst; BS Nursing, 2018; Softball, All-Star Team and Academic All-American; Mentor at Local Boys and Girls Club; Thanks to my Grandparents and Mom for encouraging me to achieve my goals. Love to my family!

Dust, Casey Lynn: Rockville, IN; Saint Mary-of-the-Woods College; BS K–6 Mild Intervention Elementary Education, 2018; Student Senate, President; Dean's List, High Honors; Learning Resource Center, Tutor; Ethics Bowl, Member and Competitor; Honors Program, Outstanding Future Educator Award; Future Teachers of America, President; I have been blessed beyond measure; my cup overflows. I am so thankful for this honor.

Dutton, Anna Rose: Oswego, IL; Waubonsee Community College; Alecia and Bruce Dutton; AS Business, 2016; Oswegoland Park District; Sigma Chi Eta; Delta Sigma Omicron; Phi Theta Kappa, Vice President of Public Relations and Coca-Cola Community College Academic Team Bronze Scholar; Thank you, Mom, Dad, Emily, Tom, Alex, and Anthony, for endless encouragement through my first college adventure.

E

Earley-Wolfe, Donna Jean: Crystal Spring, PA; Allegany College of Maryland; Donald and Shirley Earley; AA Medical Assistant, 2016; Medical Assistant Department, Program Advisory Committee Member; Phi Theta Kappa Honor Society; To my family and friends for their support and encouragement and to Michael, my everything. Thank You

Easton, Candy M.: Presque Isle, ME; University of Maine Presque Isle; BSW Social Work Program, 2016; This award would not have been possible without the support and love from my sister, Sherry McGowan.

Eckstine, Julia Friend: Boonsboro, MD; Sweet Briar College; BS Psychology, 2016; Peer Health Educators and Advocates, Chair; BAM, President; Senior Class Officer, Secretary.

Eddington, O'Linza Lue: Pine Bluff, AR; Southeast Arkansas College; AS Accounting, 2017; Phi Theta Kappa; Dean's List; Trio, Student Ambassador and Vice President; This award would not be possible without the love, support, and encouragement from my family.

Eddleman, Jama L.: Dongola, IL; Murray State University Graduate School; MS Human Development and Leadership, 2015; Thank you to my family and my Lord and Savior for their unwavering support and love.

Edelmann, Kelsey: Hawley, PA; Keystone College; Richard and Nancy Edelmann; BA Psychology, 2016; Teaching Assistant in Social and Behavioral Sciences Division for Statistics of the Social Sciences, Research Methods, and Research Analysis; Peer Tutor; Dean's List Honors Award, All Academic Semesters; President's List Honors Awarded Spring 2014; Research Lab Manager of Howell Lab; Co-Author of Five Posters for the Annual Conference of the American Psychological Association and the Association for Psychological Science; This award was made possible by the faculty and staff at Keystone, my family, and my wonderful fiancé.

Edison, Kaitlyn: Enterprise, OR; Colorado Christian University College of Undergraduate Studies.

Edmaiston, Davey N.: Clarksville, TN; Austin Peay State University; Hollye and Jeff Edmaiston; BM Music Education, 2016; Mid-South Marching Invitational, Co-Logistics Director; NAFME Hillday 2015, Tennessee Collegiate Representative; National Association for Music Education, Secretary; Phi Mu Alpha Sinfonia, President, Secretary, Committee on Standards Chair Member, and Province Council Representative; I am honored to be chosen; it would have been impossible without support from family, friends and professors.

Edmisten, Shelby Vaughn: Spotsylvania, VA; Bridgewater College; Jeff and Carla Edmisten; BS Psychology, 2016; Active Minds, Leadership Team; Campus Crusade for Christ, Bible Study Leader; Spiritual Life Board, Community Team; Psi Chi Psychology Honor Society, President, Treasurer, and Outstanding Service Award; My parents and brother deserve the utmost thanks for supporting me emotionally, academically, and spiritually.

Edmonds, Lydia Jaclene: Tarboro, NC; Halifax Community College; Lafern Wilkins and Roosevelt Edmonds; AA Medical Laboratory Technology, 2016; This award would not have been possible without the support and love from my family.

Edwards, Ashley Marie: Marietta, GA; Kennesaw State University; Victoria Stolle and Paul Edwards; BA Entrepreneurship, 2019; Gordon State College Honors Society, Executive Board Member; Thank to my family, teachers, and friends, without which this award would not have been possible.

Edwards, Brandon D.: Evansville, IN; University of Southern Indiana; Shari and David Edwards; BS Health Services, 2016; Tau Kappa Epsilon, President, Vice President, New Member Educator, and Chapter Historian; None of this would have been possible without the support from family and friends, especially Granny!

Edwards, Liberty Mallare: Harrodsburg, KY; Bluegrass Community and Technical College; AS Industrial Maintenance Technology, 2016; AMT Program, Dean's List 2014–2015; I would like to dedicate this award in memory of my mom, Perla Huliganga Mallare-Silvano.

Edwards, Savanna Holly: Hartsville, SC; Coker College; BA Biology/Pre-Med and History, 2017; Thank you to my loving parents, without whom this award would not have been possible.

Edwards, Tonsa Evoria: Lakewood, WA; Limestone College; Daisy and Toney Edwards; BS Healthcare Administration, 2016; Assist Other Students; Honors Student; Without the love and support of my family and friends, this award would not have been possible. Peace!

Ehnat, Jessica Nicole: Edison, NJ; William Paterson University of New Jersey; Debby and Larry Ehnat; BA English Writing, Secondary Education, Endorsement in Special Education, 2017; Pi Lambda Theta; Sigma Tau Delta; William Paterson University Dance Team, President; I would not be where I am without the love and support from my family and friends.

Eichhorn, Vicky Marie: Otego, NY; Long Island University-Post; Kathy and Jeff Eichhorn; BS Forensic Science, Minors in Biology and Chemistry, 2016; Panhellenic Association, Vice President of Membership Development; SGA, Senator-at-Large, Senator of the Week; Forensic Science Club, President and Secretary; Delta Zeta, Ritual Chair; To my family and friends, thank you for all of your love and support through this journey!

Eisenstein, Rebecca H.: Patterson, NY; Moravian College; BA Marketing/Graphic Design, 2016; Alpha Sigma Tau Sorority, Vice President of Member Development, Nominations Chair, and Ritual Chair; Omicron Delta Kappa Honor Society, Treasurer and Outstanding Sophomore Leader; Habitat for Humanity, Co-President and Secretary; United Student Government, President; Special thanks to my family, Dean Loyd, and Dr. Desiderio for your love, support, and encouragement.

Elliott, Aneta Caprice: Acworth, GA; University of the Cumberlands; Gordon and Latricia Elliott; BS Business Administration/Fitness and Sports Management, 2016; Academic Resource Center, Tutor; Residence Life Staff, Resident Assistant; Track and Field, Runner and Team Manager; None of this would not have been possible without the love and support of my family and friends.

Ellisor, Chelsea Lynne: Newberry, SC; Newberry College; Todd and Sheila Ellisor; BS Nursing, 2016; Sigma Alpha Pi National Society of Leadership and Success; Student Nurses Association, President; This award would not have been possible without the support and love from my family and friends.

Erickson, Shyanne Dawne: Montevallo, AL; University of Montevallo; Yolanda Conn and Shane Erickson; BS Speech-Language Pathology, 2016; Chi Omega, Treasurer; Best Buddies, College Peer Buddy; National Society of Leadership and Success, Founding Executive Board and Treasurer; This award would not have been possible without the support of my family and friends.

Eriksen, Larissa Ashleigh Christine: Newark, DE; Lebanon Valley College; Paul and Linda Eriksen; BA English, 2016; Feminist Collective, Vice President of Activism and Service; Peer Mentor Program, Head Peer Mentor 2015; Wig and Buckle Theater Company, Class of 2016 Saltzer Award Recipient, President 2015–2016, Producer 2014–2015, Front of House Manager 2013–2014, and Director, Tartuffe, 2015; This award is dedicated to my dad who has encouraged me to be a strong, independent woman.

Escher, Katie Lynn: Meraux, LA; University of Holy Cross School of Nursing; BS Nursing, 2016; This award would not have been possible without the love and support from my family.

Espinoza Suarez, Ada Luisa: Houston, TX; University of St. Thomas; Luis Espinoza and Judith Suarez; MS Business/Finance, 2016; To my love ones, to Venezuela, and to all my fellow countrymen that have emigrated. There is hope!

Estep, Savannah P.: Grundy, VA; University of Pikeville; Donita and James Estep; BA Social Work, 2017.

Evans, Destinee Lynn: Lakewood, CO; Ottawa University; Debbie and David Evans; BA Elementary Education, 2016; Whole Earth Club; School of Education Work Study Student Worker; Fellowship of Christian Athletes; Big Brothers Big Sisters 2012–2016; Kappa Delta Pi, Membership Chair 2014–2015 and President 2015–2016; Kansas Teacher of Promise Award Recipient 2016; This award would not have been possible without the love and support from my family.

Evans, Monika Meyahna: Kennesaw, GA; Middle Georgia State College; Kim and Vashaun Jones; AS Psychology/Social Work, 2015; Relay For Life, Volunteer; The Knight Race, Volunteer; SPARC Atlanta, Certified Nursing Assistant Volunteer; Canterbury Club–Bleckley County Primary School Outreach Program, Volunteer Tutor and President; Middle Georgia State College Dean's List, 2013–2015; Sigma Kappa Delta English Honors Society, Vice President and Treasurer; SGA, Assistant Director/Senator and Outstanding Student Leadership Award Recipient 2014 and 2015; This award would not have been possible without the support and love from God, my family, and friends.

Eyer II, Jacob Stewart: Knoxville, TN; Flagler College; Keith and Sherry Eyer; BA Psychology, 2015; Social Sciences Club, Treasurer; Flagler College Research, First Author on Several Research Projects and Papers; Flagler College Trial Team, Captain and Top Ranked Witness; What's next?

F

Fairchild, Katee: Monroe, LA; University of Louisiana at Monroe Undergraduate; Connie and Doug Fairchild; BS Medical Laboratory Science, 2017; Campus Activities Board; American Chemical Society; Phi Kappa Phi Honor Society; Alpha Epsilon Delta Honor Society; St. Jude Up 'Til Dawn, Executive Director; Thanks for pushing me so hard all these years, mom. It has paid off!

Fanelli, Jordan Vincent: Washington, WV; Marshall University; BA Economics, 2017; Study Abroad Association; Pre-Law Club, Founder Spring 2016; Fraternal Values Society; Order of Omega; Lewis College of Business Dean's Advisory Board; John Marshall Emerging Leaders Institute, Retreat Leader/Organizer 2014 and Spring 2015 Graduate; THUNDER Dance Marathon, Executive Organizer 2015–2016 and ThunderWonder Award 2016; Alpha Tau Omega, Initiated Fall 2013, Pledge Class Treasurer, Executive Committee, Judicial Board Member, Keeper of Annals/Historian, and MU Greek Life Living the Ritual Award 2015; SGA, Lewis College of Business Senator 2013–2014 and Finance Chair/Treasurer 2014–2015; This award would not have been possible without the support and guidance from my family.

Farese, Katherine K.: Ashland, MS; The University of Mississippi; Karen and Anthony Farese; BA Political Science, 2016; Without my twin brother, Michael, my family, and my friends, this honor would not have been possible.

Farmer, Micah Lee: Murfreesboro, TN; Pensacola Christian College; Jeffery and Linda Farmer; BA Youth Ministries, 2016; Any educational success that I acquire comes directly from my Heavenly Father, who continually blesses me.

Farrar, Caroline Grace: Douglassville, PA; Summit University; Phil Farrar; BS Secondary Social Studies Education, 2017; Senior Citizens Ministry, Founder; Alpha Gamma Epsilon; Presidential Scholarship; 4.0 Mug; Student Leadership Council; Thanks to my parents who invested in my education, homeschooling me and supporting me throughout college.

Fellows, Shelley Lynn: Lawton, MI; Olivet Nazarene University; Karna and Lewis Fellows; BA Interior Design, 2016; This award would not have been possible without the love of God, my family, friends, and professors.

Figueroa, Anissa: Monroe, NY; The College of New Rochelle Arts and Sciences; Jesus and Antinette Figueroa; BA Communications, 2016; Study Abroad Program in Florence, Italy; Admissions Officer; Resident Assistant; Campus Ministry/Ursuline Leader, Ursuline Leader Award Recipient, Event Planner and Coordinator; Cross Country Team, Student Athlete Recognition, Most Improved; Blue Angels Cheerleaders; Hermandad de Sigma Iota Alpha Inc., Chapter President, Secretary, Social Chair, and Recruitment Chair; I'll always be grateful for everyone who made my college experience one of wisdom, joy, and blessings.

Finch, Savannah: Sherwood, AR; Arkansas State University Beebe; Angela Finch; AA Liberal Arts, 2016; Public Relations Department, Maintains Social Media Platforms and Photographs Student Activities; Psychology Club; Leadership Counsel; Resident Halls, Event Coordinator, Food Committee, and RA of the Year 2015; Plastic Bag Crocheting for Homeless; Foster Dog System; Freshman of the Year Award 2015; ASU Beebe Campus Award for Outstanding Achievement 2016; Thank you for the love and support from my family and my ASU Beebe campus mentors.

Finein, Andrew: Joliet, IL; University of St. Francis; Elaine W. and Read G. Finein; BA Mass Communication, 2017; Exploring Joliet, Assistant Producer; Daybreak Homeless Shelter; Illinois Residence Hall Association 2016 Host Team, Finance Chair; Residence Education, Resident Assistant and Senior Assistant; SGA, Class Senator; WCSF 88.7FM, Program Director.

Finkbeiner, Andrea Janelle: Freeland, MI; Spring Arbor University; Jeffrey and Karen Finkbeiner; BA Biology, 2016; E. P. Hart Honors Program, Honors in Biology Major, Summa Cum Laude; Track and Field, NCCAA All-American, Two-Time Student-Athlete of the Week, Crossroads League National Co-Field Athlete of the Week, NCCAA Indoor and Outdoor Scholar Athlete, and Spring Arbor University Individual Record Holder; This would not have been possible without God's grace and blessing and my supportive family.

Finn, Jennifer Lynne: Wind Gap, PA; Northampton Community College; Kathleen and Richard Finn; AA Psychology, 2016; 2016 Leadership Class; Academic Appeals Committee; Disciplinary Committee; Psychology Club, Secretary; Phi Theta Kappa: Tau Gamma, President; This award would not have been possible without the support and encouragement of mentors, friends, and family.

Fiscus, Nathan Kyle: Tuscumbia, AL; Northwest-Shoals Community College; Jim and Christy Fiscus; BS Geographic Information Systems, 2018; I would not have achieved this award without the support I received from my family.

Fisher, Ashley: Baytown, TX; University of Houston–Clear Lake; MA History, 2017; UHCL History Club, President; Distinguished Service Award; This award is dedicated to my mother, Wendy. Thank you for supporting me in my education.

Flagg, Lindsey Joreen: Crown Point, IN; Purdue University Calumet; BA Communication, 2016; Environmental Club, Recycling Committee and Reusable Cup Committee; Lambda Pi Eta; Purdue University Calumet Honors College, Outstanding Newcomer Award, Outstanding Committee Chair Award, Honors College Hall of Fame 2016, Newsletter Committee, Social Media Committee, and Social Media Committee Executive Board Chair.

Flaska, Makenzie LeeClair: Victoria, KS; Bacone College; Steve and Gail Flaska; BA Christian Ministry, 2016; Softball, Team Captain; I just want to thank my family for all the love and support they've shown me.

Flores, Alicia Ashley: South Bend, IN; Indiana University South Bend; Arthur and Alicia Flores; BA Mass Communications–Public Relations, 2017; *The Preface*, Staff Writer and Treasurer; This award would not have been possible without the motivation that comes from my daughters, Andrea and Danielle.

Folger, Guy: McAlester, OK; Eastern Oklahoma State College; AA Journalism/History, 2016; *The Eastern Statesman Newspaper*, Photographer, Staff Writer, Editor, Senior Staff Writer, and Won Numerous Awards in Oklahoma Collegiate Journalism Competitions; Photography Club, Vice President; This award would not have been possible without the inspiration of my high school journalism teacher, Inez Richmond.

Ford, Aimee Michelle: Aurora, IL; Benedictine University; AA Management, 2017; Benedictine 2016 Donor Breakfast, Speaker; Stewardship, Volunteerism, and Giving Back to the Community; Returning Adult Student and First Adult Student Scholarship Recipient; Four Different Leadership Certificates; Arthur J. Schmitt Future Leaders Award; Dean's List; I am grateful for the support, encouragement, and opportunities that the Benedictine University staff have provided.

Foss, Keagan: Houston, TX; University of St. Thomas; Bridgit and Rob Foss; BS Biology, 2016; American Chemical Society, Vice President; Tri-Beta Biological Honors Society, Treasurer and President; Thanks to my family who pushed me when I was strong and carried me when I was weak.

Foster, Stephanie N.: Woodbridge, CT; Springfield College; Linda and Howard Sadinsky; BS Health Science, Pre-Med, 2017; Women's Varsity Tennis, New England Women and Men's Athletic Conference 2014 Academic All-Conference Team Honors; I owe all of my successes to the love and support I receive from my family.

Foster, Zachary Tyler: Mentone, AL; Northeast Alabama Community College Social Sciences; Rodney and Pam Harper; BS Chemical Engineering, 2018.

Foti, Christian A.: Galloway, NJ; William Paterson University of New Jersey; BA Pre-Law, 2017; Legal Studies Club, President and Founder; Order of Omega National Greek Leadership and Academic Honor Society, Secretary; Haledon Fire Department, Firefighter; Absecon City Volunteer Fire Department, Firefighter; SGA, Tri-Term Senator of Student Life; Phi Kappa Tau Fraternity, Secretary; Greek Senate, President; To my family, thanks for your love and support throughout my college career. Love yas!

Fouse, Selena A.: Pangburn, AR; University of Arkansas Community College Batesville; AS Registered Nursing, 2015; I owe all my success to my husband, Patrick Fouse, and my sisters, Beckey Briggs and Brenda Wheeler.

Fowkes, Emily Marie: Franklin, PA; University of Pittsburgh Bradford; Denise and Ronald Fowkes; BS Hospitality Management, 2016; Woman's Tennis Team, Captain; Hospitality Club; Thank you to my parents and my sister, who helped and supported me throughout my four years of college!

Fox, Jason Eric: Somerset, KY; Somerset Community College; AS Physical Therapist Assistant, 2016; This award would not have been possible without the support and love of my wife, Tina Fox.

Franceschiello, Thomas M.: St Johnsville, NY; Schenectady County Community College; AA Culinary Arts, 2016.

Francis, Ramesh P.: Brandon, FL; Hillsborough Community College; Wilbert and Annalee Francis; AA Business Administration, 2016; Phi Theta Kappa, Alpha Lambda Alpha, Florida Executive Chapter, Chapter of the Year 2014–2016, and Five-Star Competitive Edge; SGA, Senator, Club Representative for Phi Beta Lambda, Collegiate 100, and Florida College System Leadership Training; I would like to thank Hillsborough Community College students, faculty, and staff for this award.

Frangolini, Christopher P.: East Boston, MA; Suffolk University; Pat and Angela Frangolini; BA Broadcast Journalism, 2016; Suffolk Broadcasting, Sports Broadcaster; Suffolk Free Radio, Board Member; *The Suffolk Voice*, Sports Editor; Just a young Boston kid trying to change the world.

Franklin, Neely M.: Mountain Brook, AL; Wallace State Community College Hanceville; Carol and John Miller Jr.; AAS Business Management, 2016; Thanks to Mom, Dad, Cody, Laura, and Lacy! This award would not be possible without them!

Fratterelli, Jenna Lynn: Williamstown, NJ; Immaculata University Undergraduate; Anthony and Terri Fratterelli; BS and ADD Exercise Science, 2017; PhD Physical Therapy, 2019; Thomas Jefferson University Class of 2019, Dean's Scholarship Award Recipient; Exercise Science Club, Vice President 2015–2016; Thomas Jefferson University Physical Therapy Club, Secretary 2014–2015 and President 2015–2016; Dean's List 2014–2015; Honor Society 2016.

Frayer, Brittany Michelle: Waldron, AR; Rich Mountain Community College; Carrie and Daniel White, Wade Frayer; AAS Information Technology, 2016; Rich Mountain Community College Student Ambassadors; SGA; Phi Theta Kappa; Thank you to my family for supporting me, especially to my mom, Carrie—I love you.

Frayer, Rebekah A.: Caraway, AR; Arkansas State University Jonesboro; Katherine Campbell; BS Interdisciplinary Studies, 2016; Delta Zeta, Academic Chair and Head Guard and 2015 Region XI Outstanding Senior; Student Activities Board, Student Union Events Director; Without my family and university, this award would not have been unattainable.

Frederick, Meghan: Trevose, PA; Holy Family University; Bernie and Bob Frederick; BA Early Childhood Education/Special Education, 2016; SeanMe Autism Awareness Organization, Program Coordinator; SGA, Class President; Education Connections, Vice President; This award would not have been possible without the constant support and love from my parents.

Freeman, Matthew Gordon: Gainesville, GA; Reinhardt University; Malcom Freeman and Wendy Harrelson; BS Mathematics, 2016; School of Mathematics and Sciences School Achievement Award 2015–2016; Reinhardt University Student of the Year Award 2015–2016; Alpha Chi; SGA, Commuter Senator 2012–2013, Chief of Staff 2013–2014, and Commuter Life Chair 2015–2016; This award would not have been possible without the support and love from my family. Thank you.

French, Christian Ryan: Corydon, IN; Indiana University Southeast; Donna and Chris French; BS Psychology, 2016; Associates in Counseling and Psychotherapy, Intern; Independent Research Project on Orthorexia Nervosa, Accepted for Publication; Independent Research Project on Graphic Horror Films, Accepted for Publication; Midwest Criminal Justice Annual Meeting, Student Travel Funds Award; Honors Program, Chancellor's Honors Program Scholarship 2014–2016; Undergraduate Research Conference, Continued Research Scholarship Award; Undergraduate Research Fellowship, Spring and Fall 2015; Psi Chi, IU Southeast Chapter; Castle Club, Vice President; Thanks to Kirsten Black for being a great research partner and Dr. Walsh's exceptional mentoring and dedication.

Fridell, My Hanna: Miami, FL; University of Miami; Jan Fridell; BS Public Health, 2016; Habitat for Humanity; Student Athlete Advisory Committee 2013–2016; Omicron Delta Kappa; Health Outreach Peer Educator Internship; School of Nursing and Health Studies, Research Assistant; Swim Team, Captain 2014–2016; Thelma Gibson Health Initiative Internship.

Friedberg, Nicole Holley: Sussex, NJ; East Stroudsburg University; Diane and Thomas Friedberg; BS Healthcare Administration, 2017; Sigma Phi Omega, Alpha Phi Chapter Secretary; ESU Honors Program, Treasurer; Hard work got me this far, but my parents are the inspiration and glue holding me together. Thanks!

Friedner, Eric: Marysville, WA; Embry-Riddle Aeronautical University; Lois Whitcomb and Alan Friedner; BS Aviation Maintenance Management/Minor in Safety, 2017; Alpha Sigma Lambda Honor Society; Thank you to my wife, Randi, for the support she has provided while I attend school.

Fries, Yvette Alice: Raisin City, CA; Biola University; Ralph and Leonarda Fries; BA Public Relations, 2015; This award is dedicated to my family and friends for their support through everything.

Fritts, Nathan R.: St. Louis, MO; Saint Louis University Doisy College of Health Sciences.

Frost, Travis Wayne: Edmond, OK; Oklahoma Christian University; Michael and Nancy Frost; BA Youth Ministry, 2016; Acappella Federation, Barbershop Chorus, Charter Member; Eagles Health Initiative, Charter Member; I truly owe this award to our faithful God, my wonderful wife, and my supportive family.

Frye, Jordan M.: Staunton, IL; Saint Louis University Department of Biomedical Laboratory Science; Darlene and James Frye; BS Investigative/Medical Sciences, 2016.

Frye, Skyler Kaitlyn: Hodgenville, KY; Murray State University; Tabitha Graham-Frye and Ron Frye; BS Nursing, 2016; Murray State Student Ambassadors, Executive Tour Coordinator; Panhellenic Counsel, Executive Treasurer; Alpha Sigma Alpha Sorority, Executive Secretary and Non-Voting Panhellenic Delegate.

Fryer, Jeffery Don: Eufaula, OK; Bacone College; BA Biblical Counseling, 2016; Baptist Collegiate Ministries, President; My motivation to succeed comes from my family, friends, military family, and my wife.

Fuchs, Kallie Nicole: Burton, TX; Texas A&M University; Paula and Dean Fuchs; BS Nutritional Sciences, 2016; Memorial Student Center Fall Leadership Conference, Director of Programming and Conference Delegate; Freshmen Leadership Experience, Program "Big," Assistant Director, and Community Outreach Committee Chair; American Medical Student Association Pre-Med Chapter, Gold Level Member and National AMSA Conference Delegate; College of Agriculture and Life Sciences Student Council, President, Vice President of Operations, Liaison to the Dean Committee Member, Farmer's Fight Committee Member, Nutritional Science Department Representative, and Finance Committee Member; SGA Executive Cabinet, Election Commissioner; Department of Nutrition and Food Science Directed Study of Nutrition Lab of Dr. Clinton Allred, Research Assistant.

Fujii, Keiko Christina: Boise, ID; George Fox University; Lorraine and Dave Fujii; BS Computer Science, 2016; Sakura Photography Owner, Three-Time "Photo of the Month" HP Oasis Display Winner, George Fox Annual Art Magazine Publication 2013 and 2015, and Multiple Western Idaho Fair Awards; Students for Innovation, Design, and Entrepreneurship Club, Council Member; George Fox Chapel Band, Pianist and Keyboardist; George Fox Swing Dance Club, Treasurer 2015; Association for Computing Machinery Women's Chapter, Chair and Founding Member; University Innovation Fellow; Thank you to my parents, fiancé, friends, and professors for all of their encouragement and love.

Fuller, Anthony: Norfolk, VA; Saint Leo University; BA Sociology, 2016; I am so grateful for the prayers, support, and love of my family, church family, and friends.

Fuller, Carrie: McDonough, GA; Luther Rice College and Seminary; AA Religion/Biblical Counseling, 2016; This award is dedicated to my daughters, Tonia, Audrey, and Tesha, and my sisters, Mary, Danette, Claudia, Ann, and Ella.

G

Gaither, Megan Nichole: Lonedell, MO; Missouri Baptist University; Jana Stein and Tim Presley; BS Secondary Education/English, 2017; Special thanks to my family, but especially my husband, Tyler, for believing in me. Love you all.

Galvan, Alejandro: Paterson, NJ; Passaic County Community College; Fernando and Vera Galvan; AAS Radiography, 2016; Phi Theta Kappa; Dean's List; My wife, Eva Villagrana, and my family's love made possible this awarding moment in my life.

Galvez Ospina, Esteban: White Plains, NY; Herkimer County Community College; Rosalba and Gustavo Galvez Ospina; AA Liberal Arts Science, General Studies, 2016; Herkimer Community College, Merit; This award would not have been possible without the love and support from my parents, Rosalba and Gustavo.

Galvez, Christopher T.: Olympia, WA; Columbus State University; Carlos Tadeo Galvez and Dina A. Firestine; MA Public Administration, 2015; National Infantry Association, Old Ironsides Chapter Member and Vice President; Young Professionals, Columbus Chamber of Commerce; Habitat for Humanity; Texas Ramp Project; Knights of Columbus, Fourth Degree Knight and Volunteer; Special thanks to my wife, Kritika S. Galvez, for her unwavering support in all my endeavors.

Galvez, Erik Enrique: Prescott, AZ; Embry-Riddle Aeronautical University Prescott Campus; Sylvia and Al Galvez; BS Aeronautics, 2016; I thank my parents for their love, support, and serving as my guides throughout college.

Galyean, Katelyn Lydia: Elizabethtown, NC; Barry and Michelle Galyean; BA Mass Communication, 2017; Big-Little Program, Founder and President; Chaplain Ministry, Chaplain and Chaplain Intern; Huge thanks to my parents, who supported and pushed me to be my best! Jeremiah 29:11.

Gamble, Dennis B.: Springfield, MO; Evangel University; BS Business Management, 2016; Adult Studies Award of Excellence 2016; Alpha Chi Missouri RHO Chapter 2016; This award would not have been possible without the support of my family and friends. Love you, Shannon!

Garcia, Yuritze Alejandra: El Paso, TX; The University of Texas El Paso; Gilberto and Lourdes Garcia; BS Health Promotion, 2017; To my hard dedication and support of my family.

Gardner, Dillon E.: Shawnee, OK; Oklahoma Baptist University; David and Teresa Gardner; BA Finance, 2016; Delta Mu Delta; Top Ten Percent of Business College at Oklahoma Baptist University; Enactus, CEO; Achieving this honor was only possible through the sacrifice and commitment of my peers and mentors.

Garner, Constance Michelle: Clarksville, VA; Longwood University; Donna Garner; BA Business Administration, 2016; Longwood Dining Services, Head Student Supervisor; Residential and Commuter Life, Resident Assistant and Desk Supervisor; Residential and Commuter Life Advisory Board, Treasurer; Residential and Commuter Life Mentors, Programming Committee Head; Longwood Conduct Board, Justice; SGA, Senator and President; I would be no where without my mother, who inspires me in everything I do.

Garrett, Jazmin Danyelle: Fort Deposit, AL; Lurleen B. Wallace Community College; Tina and Kelvin Garrett; AA Science, 2016; Thanks be to God, who makes all things possible, and to my Mom, my two siblings, and my loving family.

Garza-Escamilla, Sandra Lylia: Mission, TX; South Texas College; Jesus Saenz Garza and Rebecca Reyes Garza; BS Organizational Leadership/AAT Secondary Education, 2016; National Patient Safety Foundation; International Course Certificate, Organizational Leadership; Association of Texas Professional Educators; American Psychiatric Nurses Association; Texas Nurses Association; American Nurses Association; Texas Region Alumni Member, PTK 2016; NerdNation International Convention 2016; South Texas Health Systems Auxillian; Student of the Week 2014; Alumni Cohort 16 Leadership Development Studies–A Humanities Approach, International FB Forum 2014; Phi Theta Kappa International Honor Society Honors in Action, Committee Member 2013–2016; Texas Hall of Honor District V 2015; Phi Theta Kappa, Five Star Competitive Edge Scholar 2014 and 2016; GeroPsychiatric Specialty Unit; Kappa Beta Delta; Sigma Kappa Delta; Phi Theta Kappa; Latin@s Club, Communication Specialist 2013; Congressional Academic Recognition 2014–2015; Beta Epsilon Mu Chapter Phi Theta Kappa, President 2015–2016; Xi Epsilon Chapter Sigma Kappa Delta, President 2015–2016; Student Leadership Academy, Graduate 2015; AA Applied Science Associate Degree Nursing, Cum Laude Graduate 2015; AA Arts Interdisciplinary Studies, Cum Laude Graduate 2015; SGA, Senator 2016; Designated Texas Honor Scholar 2014–2016; *Who's Who Among Students in American College and Universities 2015*; All Texas Academic Team, Academic Achievement, Exemplary Community Service, and Expression 2016; Sigma Alpha Pi, Presidential Level 2016; AA Arts in Teaching Secondary Education, Cum Laude Graduate 2016; BS Applied Science Organizational Leadership, Cum Laude Graduate 2016;This recognition is possible with the support and love from my family, Ever, Levi, and Joel.

Gasow, Andrea Elizabeth: Mt. Zion,IL; Monmouth College; BA Biochemistry, 2016; Concert Band, Flute; Fighting Scots Marching Band, Feature Twirler; American Chemical Society, Presented Senior Research at 2016 National Conference in San Diego, CA; Mortar Board Honor Society, Philanthropy Chair; Alpha Lambda Delta, Junior Advisor; Pi Beta Phi, Senior Member Coordinator and Academic and Leadership Scholarship Recipient.

Gaston, Chelsea Nicole: Elm City, NC; Edgecombe Community College; Kim and Nick Gaston; AS Radiography, 2016; This award would not have been possible without the support from my parents and my fiancé, Doug Hunter.

Gaudet, Thomas C.: Peabody, MA; Suffolk University.

Gaynor, Benjamin: Sudbury, MA; Ithaca College; Deborah and Edward Gaynor; BA Spanish, 2017; IC Intercambios Bilingual Service Organization, President; Department of Modern Languages and Literatures, Teaching Assistant; *The Ithacan*, Chief Copy Editor and Proofreader.

Gayten, Halle: St. Rose, LA; Mississippi Valley State University Department of Teacher Education; Gilda Gayten; BA Elementary Education, 2016; Volleyball Team, Captain; This award would not have been possible without the guidance and encouragement from my family.

Gee, Adrian Janell: Tuscaloosa, AL; Troy University; Amanda Jackson and Eric Gee; BS Communications, Minor in Public Relations, 2016; Magna Cum Laude; Omicron Delta Kappa National Leadership Honor Society; Project EMBRACE, Public Relations Chair; Boys and Girls Club of Pike County; Noble Manor Retirement Home; Provost's List; Chancellor's List; Alabama Girls State, Delegate and Scholarship Recipient; Leadership Scholar and Scholarship Recipient; Outstanding Academic Performance, JRN 4440 and COM 4424; Conversation Partners, Lead Partner; University Activities Council; Career Services Office, Career Peer; Lambda Pi Eta National Communications Honor Society; Freshmen Forum, Student Delegate; Trojan Ambassador Association; M.I.S.S. Elite Society, Vice President and Public Relations Co-Chair.

Gentry, Darby Kathryn: Braselton, GA; Erskine College.

George, Ranell Lou: Scott City, KS; Independence University; Robert and Alma Dearden; BS Accounting/Emphasis on Forensic Accounting, 2016; A special thanks to my parents, ex-husband, sons, daughters-in-law, grandchildren, and other family members.

Gerber IV, Eric John: Aberdeen, SD; Northern State University; Thomas Gerber and Millie Gerber-Lockington; MS Clinical Mental Health Counseling, 2017; BS Psychology and Applied Gerontology, Certificate 2014; UCM Campus Minister, Director 2008–2010; Hu Ha Chinese Drum Group, Founder and Coach; Graduate Assistant, Psychology-101 Teaching Assistant 2014–2016; NSU NANTA Korean Drum Group, Founder and Coach 2008–2015.

Getzlaff, Alexis Anne: Minot, ND; Valley City State University; Daniel and Nancy Mahoney; BS Fisheries and Wildlife Science/Biology, 2017; This award would not have been possible without the support and love from my parents, Daniel and Nancy.

Ghelan, Elena: Staten Island, NY; College of Staten Island; Maria and Petru Ghelan; MS Accounting, 2016; BS Business Management, 2006; Sigma Beta Delta; The Academy of Economic Studies of Moldova 2012; Dean's List 2011–2012; National Society of Collegiate Scholars 2012; *Who's Who Among Students in American Universities and Colleges 2013*; College of Staten Island Scholarship Award 2012–2013 and 2014–2015; NYSSCPA Scholarship Award 2013–2014, 2014–2015, and 2015–2016; NYSSCPA Scholarship Graduation Award 2014; School of Business, The City University of New York, College of Staten Island, BS Accounting and Economics, Minor in Finance, Summa Cum Laude, 2014; School of Business, The City University of New York, College of Staten Island, MS Accounting, Summa Cum Laude, 2016; Vreau sa le multumesc mult parintilor, Petru si Maria Ghelan pentru sprijin si incurajari.

Gibson, Sarah Elizabeth: San Antonio, TX; Texas A&M University; William Gibson; BS Biomedical Engineering, 2017; Special Olympics; Physics and Engineering Festival; The Big Event; University and Engineering Honors Program, Scholarship Recipient; National Merit Scholarship Award; Tissue Microscopy Lab, Undergraduate Research; Tau Beta Phi, Laureate Award for Excellence Outside of Engineering; Aggie Swimming and Diving, National Champion, Collegiate All-American, Capital One At Large Recipient, and Scholar All-American.

Gilbert, April Dawn: Sevierville, TN; Pellissippi State Community College   ; AS Pre-Health Professions, 2016; Gamma Beta Phi; Dean's List; Thank you to my husband, Josh, Dr. Kover, Dr. Rumbolt, Robert Kalina, and my family.

Gilbert, Sierra Lynn: Yukon, OK; Oklahoma Baptist University; Clint and Regina Gilbert; BA Psychology, Pre-Counseling, 2016; Temple Baptist Church; Psi Chi, Vice President; This award would not have been possible without all of my incredible professors and friends at OBU. Thanks!

Giles II, Natascha A.: Sumter, SC; Central Carolina Technical College; Natascha Giles-Hunter; AA General Education, 2016; I would like to thank God and my supportive family for making this award possible.

Gilford, Tiffani L.: Selma, AL; Jackson State University College of Education and Human Development; BS Early Childhood Education/Family Education, 2016; This award is in honor of my parents, Linda and late father Willie, and definitely Caleb and Chloe.

Gill, Matthew Ransom: Brookhaven, MS; Copiah-Lincoln Community College; Diane and David Gill; AA Accounting, 2016; Phi Beta Lambda, Parliamentarian; Phi Theta Kappa, Vice President of Membership; This award would not attainable without sustenance from amazing family, friends, advisors, and teachers throughout my life.

Gilman, Christopher Joseph: West Newbury, MA; Roger Williams University; BS Finance, 2017; UFest Planning Committee; Coronation Committee; Golf Club, Founding Member; Delta Sigma Pi, Social Chair; Inter Class Council, President, Class of 2017.

Gilman, Ivala Lyn: Clarks Summit, PA; Keystone College; Robert and Rose Gilman; BS Criminal Justice, 2016; I am very thankful for my father's encouragement to succeed and the support from those around me.

Gimino, Abigail Frances: Rochester, NY; Roberts Wesleyan College; BS Nursing, 2015; A special thank you to my parents and fiancé for helping me achieve this great honor.

Gleaton Jr., Danny Richard: Pelion, SC; Midlands Technical College; Danny and Betsy Gleaton; AS Computer Technology, 2017; I would like to thank all my friends and family for your love and support.

Glenn Sr., David J. L.: Florissant, MO; Columbia College; Michael Elgin; BA Human Service, Psychology, and Sociology, 2018; Dean's List; This award would not have been possible without the love and support of my wonderful wife, Joy.

Glines, Morgan R.: Bismarck, ND; University of Mary; Monte and Errin Glines; BS Criminal Justice/Spanish, 2016; Spanish Club, Treasurer; Pre-Law Club, Vice President; Thanks to all of those that helped me strive for greatness.

Glover, Karen: Melbourne, FL; Embry-Riddle Aeronautical University; BS Aviation Business Administration, 2016; This award would not have been possible without the support of my husband, Houston. Thank you.

Goddu, Kevin Michael; Somerset, MA; University of Massachusetts Lowell; BM Music Studies Education, 2016; Play On Music Festival, Coordinator; Shadow Day, Program Coordinator; New Composer Festival, Festival Coordinator; Music Department, Audition Coordinator; Omicron Delta Kappa; Instrumental Music Outreach Staff, Assistant to Director; University Crossing, Building Manager and Welcome Desk Staff; New England Senior Youth Wind Ensemble, Saxophone Teaching Artist; New England Junior Youth Wind Ensemble, Saxophone Teaching Artist; Northeastern Districts, Junior and Senior, Collegiate Volunteer; All-State Collegiate Ambassador, Promising Future Music Educator Award 2016; Marching Band, Head Field Conductor, Assistant Field Conductor, and Equipment Manager; University Wind Ensemble, Ensemble Manager and Assistant Ensemble Manager; Performance Club, Founder and President; Collegiate National Association for Music Education, President, President Elect, and Treasurer.

Goldberg-Fenollal, Edna: Land O' Lakes, FL; American Public University; BS Space Studies, 2016; Golden Key International Honour Society; Dean's List 2013; Dedicated to my husband, my children, and my mother, whom I love with all my heart.

Goldstein, Yisroel Dov: Brooklyn, NY; Touro College; Steven and Miriam Goldstein; BA Psychology, 2016; Lander College Psychology Club, President; Lander College Dean's List; Yachad National Jewish Council for Disabilities, Summer Program Assistant Director and Weekend Retreat Adviser; This award would not have been possible without the support and love from my amazing parents.

Gomes, Bruna M.: Gainesville, TX; Oklahoma Baptist University; Marcello and Claudia Gomes; BA Marketing, 2016; Delta Mu Delta; Student Development Committee, Senior Female Representative; Campus Activities Board, Senior Director; Business Student Advisory Council, Senior Marketing Representative; I would like to thank my mom and dad for always feeding me—physically and mentally.

Gonzalez, Gabriel Jonas: Macon, GA; Mercer University; Denisse and Cesar Gonzalez; MS Biomedical Engineering/French, 2017; Engineering Scholars, Honors Research Program; Phi Sigma Iota Honor Society; Gamma Sigma Epsilon Honor Society; Sigma Xi Research Honors Society; Alpha Phi Omega Service Fraternity, Pledge Class Vice President; Order of Omega Greek Honor Society; Alpha Epsilon Delta Honors Society; Phi Eta Sigma Honors Society; Mercer Prosthetics and Orthotics Club; National Society of Leadership and Success, National Engaged Leader Award; Dean's List; Homecoming King 2015–2016; Lambda Chi Alpha Social Fraternity, Risk Manager, Standards Chair, House Manager, Executive Committee Member, Vice President, and Brother of the Year 2013–2014; International Bears Association, President and Founder, Most Improved Organization of the Year 2014–2015, and Recognized on Campus, Regional, and National Level by NRHH through OTM; Beta Beta Beta Honors Society; SGA, Senator At Large, Fiscal Affairs Committee Chair, and Student Correspondent; Society of American Military Engineers, Vice President; National Residence Hall Honorary, Recognition Chair; Omicron Delta Kappa Honor Society, President; Georgia International Leadership Conference, Staff-Student Board Coordinator; Office of Judicial Education, Student Justice; Office of University Advancement, Mercer Ambassador; Academic Resource Center, Lab Assistant and Peer Tutor in Math and Chemistry; National Residence Hall Honorary, Service Chair; Office of Residence Life, Resident Assistant, Staff Most Valuable Player Award, Special Projects Resident Assistant, and Senior Resident Assistant; Office of Admissions, Special Events Team, Student Admissions Team, and Student Leadership Team; Office of Career Services, Student Worker and Career Associate; University Center, Bearforce Worker; Thanks to my professors, advisors, friends, and family. Mercer is and always will be my home.

Gonzalez, Mary J.: Homer Glen, IL; Monmouth College; Linda Carrozza and Ramon Gonzalez; BA Biology/Psychology, 2016; Beta Beta Beta Biological Honor's Society; Dean's List; I could not have achieved this honor without support from Linda Carrozza, Lewis Carrozza, and Ramon Gonzalez.

Gonzalez, Natasha N.: Milford, MA; Worcester State University; Orlando and Natividad Gonzalez; BA Spanish, 2016; I am so honored to have received this award. All my hard work and dedication paid off.

Gonzalez, Tiffani Janiel: Bronx, NY; Nyack College Manhattan Campus; Ana Figueroa; BA Psychology, 2016; Open House for ATS/MBA/AGSC Master Programs; Open House for Undergraduate; Nyack College Scholars Symposium "The Meaning of Work!"; Thank you God for this award and everyone who supported and encouraged me along the way.

González-Vargas, Lynnette E.: Moca, PR; Inter American University of Puerto Rico, San German Campus; BA Secondary Education, Teacher of Mathematics, 2018; Achievements Night; Dean's List; I dedicate my achievements to my family, without them I would not be here.

Goodine, Quincy Aaron: Richmond, VA; Longwood University; Jerome and Monique Goodine; BS Kinesiology, 2016.

Goodman, Anna Jayne: Nashville, TN; Union University; Karen and Ronald Goodman; BA Communication Studies, 2016; Union University Student Leadership Award Program, Student Worker of the Month; Vocation Center Five-Star Applicant Program, Aspiring Pre-Professional 2015–2016; *Cardinal & Cream*, Freelance Writer and Magazine Feature Writer; *The Odyssey*, Social Media Director, Staff Writer, and Most Popular Article of the Week Award; Fellowship Student Ministries, Small Group Leader; Union University Debate Team, Seventh in the Nation and 2013 Novice Division; The Red Bus Project, Campus Visit Coordinator; The HUB Club, Tutor; Face of Justice, Veritas Abroad Missions Volunteer; Scarlet Rope Project, Communication and Projects Intern; International Justice Mission; Alpha Chi, President; Honors Student Association, Vice President and General Honors Program; SGA, Senior Class President, Sophomore Class Secretary, Senate Clerk, Senator, and Junior Class Council Member; I owe this award to the faithful support of loved ones and the grace of Christ.

Gordils, Rebecca Ashley: Bronx, NY; Mount Saint Mary College; Michelle Vazquez; BA Public Relations, Media Studies, and Journalism, 2016; Relay For Life, Team Captain 2013–2014; Writing Center, Writing Tutor; Orientation Leader; Improvology, Actress and Stage Manager; Theatre, Lead Actress; *Mount Messenger Newspaper*, Co-Managing Editor; Without the support of my outstanding professors, this award would have never been a possibility.

Gordon, Gabriel Nathaniel: Tulsa, OK; Oklahoma Baptist University; BA Anthropology/Cross-Cultural Ministry, 2016; Social Club, Pledge Master; Without the loving support and encouragement from my grandmother, I would not have received such an award.

Gordon, Kristin K.: Schenectady, NY; Schenectady County Community College; Shari and Tim Gordon; AS Performing Arts, 2016; Thank you to my family, loved ones, and teachers for being there every step of the way.

Gores, Ashton Mckinzi: Ardmore, OK; Oklahoma Baptist University; Jaynie and David Gores; BS Biology, 2016; Omicron Delta Kappa, President; The Fellowship of Christian Athletes, Leadership Team and Social Media Executive; Student Athletic Advisory Committee, Vice President; Color Out Oklahoma, Founder and Executive Board Member; Up Till Dawn for St. Jude, Executive Board Member; Varsity Women's Golf, Captain, National Association of Intercollegiate Athletics Champions of Character Award Recipient, Sooner Athletic Conference Academic All-Conference Team, and National Christian College Athletic Association All-American Scholar Athlete; Thank you to my family and OBU women's golf coach, Michael Manlapig, for making my educational journey possible.

Gorman, Heather Lynn: Hampton, AR; Southern Arkansas University; Donna and Steven Gorman; BS Animal Science, 2016; Make-A-Wish Foundation, Wish Granter 2015–2016; National Society of Leadership and Success, Vice President Spring 2014 and President Fall 2014–2016; Residential College Volunteer Activities, Columbia County Animal Protection Society 2012; Hampton Pee-Wee Cheerleading 2012–2013, and Eastridge Animal Hospital February 2013.

Gowans, Andrew Lee: Pensacola, FL; Pensacola Christian College; Lee and Kim Gowans; BA Pastoral Ministry, 2016; Ministerial Class President; Senior Class Chaplain; I thank my Lord Jesus Christ for giving me new life through His righteousness. All glory to Him!

Grady, Matthew Robert: Cedarburg, WI; Moraine Park Technical College; Janie and Jeffery Grady; AA CNC/Tool and Die Technologies, 2016; CNC Tool and Die Club, President; Many thanks to the people who helped me get where I am today. Thank you, Mom and Dad.

Graham, Rachel Lyn: Morton, PA; Immaculata University Undergraduate; Anessa and Paul Graham; BS Exercise Science, Concentration in Pre-Physical Therapy, 2017; Dining Services Committee; Phi Epsilon Kappa; Undergraduate Studies Honor Society; Mac Mentor; First Year Experience Mentor; Exercise Science Club, President; Head Resident Assistant, DeChantal and Marian Buildings; Delta Kappa Nu Sorority, President; I would like to thank my family, without their support this award would not have been possible.

Granello, Dominic R.: Dallas, TX; University of Oklahoma; Lynn and Greg Granello; MA International Area Studies, 2016; Sooner Curling Club, President; I am grateful for the love of my family and the support of my friends.

Grant, Julia D.: Lincoln University, PA; University of Valley Forge; James and Elaine Grant; BA Christian Ministry, 2016; Bless with a Dress Awareness Night, Leadership Team; Tutor; Peer Mentor; Confidence Week, Coordinator and Marketing; START Freshmen Orientation, Team Leader; I am thankful to God for His faithfulness and provision!

Grau, Hannah: Crestwood, KY; High Point University; BS Interior Design, 2017; University Ambassador, Mentor; Kappa Delta Sorority, Assistant of Recruitment; Alpha Phi Omega Service Fraternity, Secretary; Big Brothers Big Sisters, Event Planner; American Society of Interior Designers, Treasurer; International Interior Design Association, Treasurer; Interior Design and Home Furnishings Club, President; Order of the Lighted Lamp, First Sophomore Inducted; To everyone that never told me no but instead asked how they could make it possible.

Green, Christen BreAnn: Pine Bluff, AR; Mississippi Valley State University Department of Teacher Education; Ann Williams and Randy Green; BS Elementary Education, 2017; This award would not have been possible without my faith, my amazing parents, and Dr. T. Dumas.

Greenway, Miles: Weatherford, TX; Grayson College; Mick and Shirley Greenway; AA Education, 2015; Phi Theta Kappa.

Greenwood, Elizabeth Kathleen: Seaford, VA; Longwood University; Amy and James Greenwood; BA History, 2016; Conduct Board, Justice; SGA, Senator; *The Rotunda Newspaper*, Layout Editor; Lancer Productions, Street Team Marketing Director; Longwood Ambassadors, Activities Chair; This award would not have been possible without the support of my family, friends, and the Longwood community.

Gregg, Alyssa Marie: Kane, PA; University of Pittsburgh Bradford; Aime and Paul Gregg; BA Economics, 2017; Appalachian Teaching Project, Student Leader; Christ in Action Club, Vice President; SGA Executive Board, Parliamentarian; Resident Advisor, Section Leader; Thank you to family and friends who have supported and encouraged me.

Gregoire, Tiffany A.: Macedon, NY; St. John Fisher College; BA Mathematics, 2016; Teddi Dance for Love, Spirit Person; Fisher Players Drama Club, General Cast, General Crew, Vocal Director, and Orchestral Pit Director; Fisher Swingbirds Jazz Band, "Crescendo Award"; Colleges Against Cancer, General Committee Member; Service Scholars Program, Class Representative, Silver Presidential Recognition, and Service Scholar Application Committee E-Board; Varsity Volleyball Team, Player and Team Manager.

Gregory, Amy S.: Granite City, IL; University of Missouri Saint Louis; Judy Stroder and Ron Gregory; MS Education, 2016; Alpha Sigma Lambda, President.

Gregory, Raven Alexzandra: Raleigh, NC; Meredith College; Kenneth Gregory; BS Public Health, 2016; Silver Shield Honor Society; Peer Educators Advocating Responsible Lifestyles; White Iris Circle; Basketball, Captain 2015–2016 Season, Scholar NCAA Athlete 2013 and 2014, Most Improved Player 2012–2013, Dean Burris Coach's Award 2014–2015, Athlete Service Award 2012–2013, Women's Basketball Captain 2015–2016; "I am just a nobody trying to tell anybody about somebody who can save everybody." —Reese Kemp; God made this possible.

Greth, Kelsey: Salunga, PA; Kutztown University; Julia Wilson; BS Business Administration, 2016; College of Business Advisory Board, Student Representative; KUSSI Board of Directors, Student Representative; Alpha Sigma Tau–Gamma Lambda, Vice President of Finance and Director of Event Planning; Kutztown Student Government Board, Vice President and Secretary; Thankful for the support and love of my family and friends, especially my mother, Julia.

Grice, Steven: Greensboro, NC; Guilford College Center for Continuing Education; BS Business Administration, 2016; This award would not be possible without the love and support of my wife, Vivian.

Grieshaber, Kayla Renea: Saint Joseph, MO; Avila University; Scott and Kathy Grieshaber; BS Nursing, 2016; Campus Ministry, Service Team Member; Mother Fontbonne Award; St. Teresa of Avila Award; Spirit of Avila Award; Avila University Service Leadership Metal; Friends and family, thank you for supporting and shaping me into the person I am today.

Griffin, Misty M.: Livingston, TX; Angelina College; Peggy Griffin; AA Human Services, 2016; Without the love and encouragement from my family and friends, this award would not be possible.

Griffith, Colton Arturo: Maybrook, NY; Tompkins Cortland Community College; Steven and Jacqueline Griffith; AS Culinary Arts, 2016; This award would not have been possible without the support and love from my family and friends.

Grimes Jr., William Reid: Ruston, LA; Louisiana Tech University Graduate School; PhD Molecular Science/ Nanotechnology, 2016.

Grimm, Andrew James: Owings Mills, MD; Stevenson University.

Grizzle, Breanna Elizabeth: Royston, GA; Emmanuel College; Keely and Jeff Grizzle; BS Early Childhood Education, 2016; Women's Soccer, NAIA All-Academic Selection 2013–2015, NCAA All-American Selection 2013–2015; This award would not have been possible without the support and love from my parents, Jeff and Keely.

Grodzicki, Kayla Marie: Meriden, CT; Dominican College of Blauvelt; BS Social Work, 2016; Volunteer and Community Work, Keep Rockland Beautiful, Habitat for Humanity, People to People, United Way, Midnight Runs, and Rotary/Rotaract; Resident Assistant, Freshmen and Upperclassmen RA; Student Ambassador, Outstanding Contribution as a Student Ambassador Award; Campus Ministry, Vice President; Phi Alpha Honor Society, Senior President; Habitat for Humanity, President and Awarded Outstanding Contribution as a Member and President; This award would not have been possible if not for my supportive family at Dominican and at home.

Grossman, Michael James: Atlantic Beach, NY; State University of New York New Paltz; Robyn and Ira Frank; BA International Relations/Latin American Studies, 2016; Student Association Judicial Board; Chief Justice; Honors Program Liaison; Dean's List; I would like to thank my professors, family, and friends. Thank you for this honor.

Guajardo, Lucia Alejandra: Daphne, AL; University of Mobile; Javier and Lucia Guajardo; BA Early Childhood Education, 2017; Varsity Soccer; President's List Award; Kappa Delta Pi member, Secretary for Kappa Delta Pi; This award would not have been possible without the support from my family and professors.

Guerra, Emily Jayne: San Antonio, TX; Dallas Baptist University; BA Music Business/Concentration in Live Performance, 2017; DBU Choir Social Committee, President 2015–2016; Delta Theta Sorority; GrammyU; DBU Musical/Opera Workshops, Performer; Alpha Chi National Honor Society; Alpha Sigma Omega, Vice President 2016–2017; This award would not have been possible without the support from my family and God.

Guerrero Rivera, Dariana: Moca, PR; Pontifical Catholic University of Puerto Rico; Zoraida Rivera Acevedo and Jose F. Guerrero Roman; PhD Clinical Psychology, 2017; Relevo por la vida/Relay For Life-American Cancer Society, Volunteer; Proyecto Amor que Sana Organization, Volunteer and Food Service; Círculo de Premédica PUCPR Student Organization, Public Relations 2007–2008 and Secretary 2008–2009; Asamblea de Honores PUCPR-Ponce, Certification of Honor for Academic Excellence in Science Program 2009; Ronald E. McNair PUCPR Program, President of Group 19 2008–2010; To my family for their support, my professors for being my motivation, and to God for directing my life.

Guinn Sr., Ronnie Glenn: Chesterfield, SC; Northeastern Technical College; AS Business, 2016; A huge thank you to my family, who supported me on this honor.

Guzman, Jessica: Russellville, AL; Northwest-Shoals Community College; Jesus and Norma Guzman; AA Nursing, 2017; I would like to thank God and my parents for helping me accomplish my goals.

H

Hadley, Chloe Jo: Joplin, MO; Evangel University; Debbie and Virgil Brill; BS Biochemistry, 2015; Varsity Volleyball; NAIA Academic All-American.

Haessner, Kathryn J.: Moravia, NY; Daemen College.

Hagemann, Shannen: Lakeland, FL; Hillsborough Community College; Jerry Hagemann and Deborah Basso-Yoshimura; AA Medical Emphasis, 2016; SGA, President 2015–2016, Vice President 2014–2015, and Senator 2013–2014; Service Award; This award would not have been possible without the support of my parents and my dedication to school/SGA.

Hager, Corey Andrew: Ravenswood, WV; West Virginia University at Parkersburg; AS General Education/Pre-Professional, 2016; Thank you Mom and Dad for your never-ending belief in me, support, and love.

Hahne, Brooke Leigh: Warrenton, VA; Shenandoah University; Wendy and Brett Hahne; BA English, 1983; Fifth Global Conference on Trauma in Lisbon, Portugal, Presenter; Hirosaki-Gakuin Summer Intensive Program in Japan; S. Gordon Link Prize for Poetry Recipient; Going Global, First Year Seminar, Mentor; This award is for all those who helped shape me into the woman and teacher I am today.

Hakenewerth, Ellen M.: Jonesboro, AR; Arkansas State University Jonesboro; David and Melissa Hakenewerth; BS Strategic Communications, Public Relations Emphasis, 2016; JDRF Arkansas Chapter, Walk Committee Member; United Way of Northeast Arkansas, Communications Committee Chair; Community Health Education Foundation, Volunteer Committee Chair; Honors College Association, Public Relations Director, Freshmen Representative, and Ambassador; Volunteer A-State, Service Weekend and Volunteer Fair Chair, Servants Heart Award Recipient; Orientation Leader, Most Friendly, Helpful, and Spirited Orientation Leader Award; Alpha Gamma Delta, Philanthropy Coordinator, Most Outstanding Member, Woman of Purpose Award Recipient; National Panhellenic Conference, Gamma Chi, Most Outstanding Gamma Chi, Most Outstanding; St. Jude Up 'Til Dawn, Executive Director, Publicity Chair, Most Outstanding Social Media, Top Fundraising Participant; SGA, Public Relations Director, Action Fund Committee, Concert Lecture Series Committee, Communications and Alumni Committee, and University Diversity Committee; Public Relations Student Society of America, Vice President, Secretary, Treasurer, and Most Outstanding Member; Thank you to my parents, Zach Marsh, and Lisa Moskal for supporting me every step of the way.

Halbig, Carole Lorraine: Trappe, MD; Chesapeake College; AS Nursing, 2017.

Halcomb, Jessica Brooke: Hamilton, AL; Athens State University; Jeff Halcomb and Beth Rhea; BS Business Management, 2016; Head Athenian Ambassador; Delta Mu Delta National Honor Society; Provost's List; This award would not be possible without my amazing friends and family. I am forever grateful.

Hall Jr., James Earl: Siler City, NC; Guilford College Center for Continuing Education; Rebekah Hall; BA Psychology, 2016; This award would not have been possible without the love and support of Becky Dixon.

Hall, Austin Carter: Beaver Falls, PA; Thiel College; BA English–Writing/Literature/History, 2017; Lambda Sigma, Treasurer; Sigma Alpha Pi, Treasurer; Sigma Tau Delta; Editorial Board for *The Phoenix*; Alpha Chi, National Alpha Chi Scholarship Nominee; Kappa Sigma, Rush Chair, Communications Chair, Chapter Historian, and Treasurer; Alpha Psi Omega, Treasurer; Phi Alpha Theta, President, SGA Representative, 2016 Phi Alpha Theta District Conference Best Paper in a Panel Award, and 2017 Phi Alpha Theta District Conference Student Organizer; VAQ Humanities Research Honor Society, Founder, President, Vice-Chair of the 2015 VAQ Academic Conference, and Editor-in-Chief of the VAQ Undergraduate Research Journal *The Quill*; Without the support of my family and the Thiel College community, this award would not be possible.

Hampton, Sara Jo: Williamsburg, KY; University of the Cumberlands; Kelli and Joe Hampton; BA History/Political Science, 2017; Spotlight Singing Competition 2014, Third Place Winner; Spotlight Singing Competition 2015, First Place Winner; Phi Alpha Theta, Vice President 2016; Thank you to all my family and friends, I could not have done this without you!

Hancock, Wayne Austin: Robinson, TX; Lubbock Christian University; Rita and Steve Hancock; BA Biblical Text/Preaching, 2016; Alpha Chi; Kyodai Men's Social Club, Vice Chaplain; I want to thank the professors of LCU's Department of Biblical Studies for their guidance in my education.

Hanks, Rachel Marie: Saint Louis, MO; University of Missouri Saint Louis; Wayne and Nancy Hanks; MA Social Work, 2016; Thank you to my family, friends, professors, and classmates!

Harden, Julia: Elkton, MD; Cecil College; Janet and John Harden; AS Materials Management, 2016. I did it, and all for my daughter.

Hardig, Stephanie Marie: Statesville, NC; Pfeiffer University Misenheimer; BS Health/Physical Education, 2016; Student Teaching: School of Education; Servant Leadership Award 2016; The Village Church, Peer Ministries, Altar Guild; Residence Life Assistant and Programmer of the Year 2014–2015; Women's Soccer Team, Senior Leader 2015–2016, Conference Carolinas Academic All-Conference Team 2014–2015, and MVP 2015–2016; This award would not have been possible without the support and love from my family.

Hardin, Vanessa Rae: Saint Louis, MO; St. Louis Community College Forest Park; Leo and Bernice Hardin; AA General Transfer Studies/Psychology, 2017; Peer Mentoring, Certificate of Appreciation; CRN Honors Program, Board of Trustees Honors College Scholarship; This award is dedicated to my most profound teachers . . . my children, Paris, Pierson, and Gianna. I love you!

Harkness, Jade Allyah: Fort Mill, SC; York Technical College; Lewis and Kim Harkness; BA Business Management, 2018; Phi Theta Kappa, Academic Achievement.

Harmon, Barbara: White House, TN; Volunteer State Community College; Tony and Elaine Adams; AA Journalism, 2016; AS Songwriting; *The Settler*, Assistant Editor; National Society of Leadership and Success, National Engaged Leader Award; My family—Brent, Chandler, Courtney, and Gwendolyn—have contributed to all my accomplishments through their love and support.

Harmon, Lauretta A.: Terre Haute, IN; Saint Mary-of-the-Woods College; Marel and Billie Harmon; BS Human Resource Management, 2016; Thank you to all my family and friends who helped me achieve my goals.

Harmon, Tracy R.: Toledo, OH; Lourdes University; BA Middle Childhood Education, 2017; Collegiate Middle Level Association, President; I dedicate this award to those who support and believe in me: Mom, Dad, Mike, and Dr. Knaggs.

Harper, Lauren Frances: West Monroe, LA; University of Louisiana at Monroe Undergraduate; Bene and Kevin Harper; BBA Risk Management/Insurance, 2016; Beta Gamma Sigma, National Global Leadership Conference Attendee; Risk Management and Insurance Society, Vice President.

Harrell (Whitaker), Jenny Louise: Bainbridge, GA; Bainbridge State College; I'Lona Barrett and Roger Whitaker; AA English, 2017; Thanks, Daddy, CJ, Annabelle, Dustin, Chuck, Kristy, Tim, Tammie, and my family and friends—y'all made this possible!

Harris, Aqueelah: Philadelphia, PA; Peirce College; BA Accounting, 2016; Delta Mu Delta; This award is dedicated to everyone who supported and help me accomplish my goal.

Harris, Kendra M.: Portland, OR; Independence University; BS Graphic Design, 2016; This would not have been possible without Michael, my family, and God. Thanks for your belief and support.

Hart, Elizabeth A.: Chatham, MA; Springfield College; Jeffrey and Jennifer Hart; BS Athletic Training, 2016; Scholars in Action Day, Student Presenter; Sport Safety Day on the Hill, Student Representative; Leadership Summit, Nominee and Recipient; Humanics in Action Day, Volunteer; College Open House, Athletic Training Student Ambassador; Field Hockey, Captain; Outing Club; NATA; Athletic Training Club; This award would not have been possible without the support from my family, roommates, and athletic training classmates.

Hart, Margaret Alice: Stockholm, ME; University of Maine Presque Isle; Margaret and Stratford Cochran; BS Secondary Education, Social Studies, 2017; To my parents and the campus who have supported me and watched me grow these past years.

Hasbrouck, Christie Robyn: Terre Haute, IN; Trine University; Marla Hasbrouck; BS Mechanical Engineering, 2016; Trine University Mechanical Engineering Chair Tuition Scholarship 2011; Featured in Fall 2012 Issue of Allen School of Engineering and Technology; Featured on Trine University Website January 2013, Student Profile; Published in W. H. Freeman's 2014 Calculus Textbook; Trine University Math Club; Engineers Without Borders; American Foundry Society; Trine University Honors Student Association, Freshmen Mentor; Indiana Space Grant Consortium, Three-Time Scholarship Recipient; Foundry Educational Foundation, Four-Time Scholarship Recipient; Society of Women Engineers; American Society of Mechanical Engineers, Chapter Secretary; American Institute for Aeronautics and Astronautics, Chapter Vice President; Golden Key Undergraduate Honor Society; Phi Eta Sigma Freshmen Honor Society; Pi Tau Sigma Mechanical Engineering Honor Society; Alpha Chi Undergraduate Honor Society, Chapter President 2014; Tau Beta Pi Engineering Honor Society, Chapter President 2014, Vice President 2015, National Student Advisory Board Secretary 2015, and Scholarship Recipient 2014–2015; Sandia National Laboratories, Mechanical Engineering Intern; Lehigh University, Undergraduate Research Experience; Regal Beloit America Inc., Mechanical Engineering Co-Op; GE Aviation, Quality Engineering Intern; Trine University Multicultural Student Organization, Activities Board Member and Volunteer; I'd like to thank my teachers, friends, and family for their love and support throughout the years.

Hassan, Mona: Wilmington, DE; Goldey Beacom College Graduate School; MA Management, 2016; SHRM; This honor dedicated to my late father, who taught me the important of education.

Hassler, Olivia: Lake Harmony, PA; University of South Carolina; Ronald and Kathryn Hassler; BA Criminal Justice and Criminology/Women's and Gender Studies, 2016; The Fight Against Domestic Violence Speaking Engagements, Creator, Advocate, and Key Note Speaker; Wilma Rudolph Student Athlete Achievement Award; Athletic Department Inspiration Award 2015; International Justice Mission, Advocate; Congressional Advisory Board; Delta Epsilon Iota, President; Track and Field Student Athlete, Captain 2015–2016, Four-Year Letter Winner, SEC Academic Honor Roll, USTFCCCA All-Academic Status 2015, SEC Championships Competitor, NCAA East Regional Qualifier; None of this would have been possible without the encouragement from my family and my team. Thank you all.

Hassler, Victoria A.: Crossville, TN; Independence University; Doris and Steven Hassler; AAS Graphic Arts, 2016; This award would not have been possible without the support and love from my family.

Haughton, Sherry Lynn: Pearl, MS; Hinds Community College; AA Nursing, 2018.

Hauser, Joe William: San Angelo, TX; Angelo State University; Alysia and George Hauser; BS Nursing/Psychology, 2017; This award would not have been possible without the support and sacrifice from my family and other loved ones.

Hayes, Athena I.: Scroggins, TX; Northeast Texas Community College; Michael and Diana Hayes; AS English, 2015; President's Honors; Amigos Unidos; Sigma Kappa Delta; Phi Theta Kappa; *The Eagle Newspaper*, Staff Writer; I want to thank my parents for their unwavering love and support.

Hayes, Caitlyn L.: Hammond, IN; Purdue University Calumet; Lory Stucky and Benjamin Hayes Jr.; BA Accounting, 2016; Student Advisory Counsel, Advising Member; McNair Achievements, Academic Scholar; International Programs Office, English Language Mentor; SGA, Chief Financial Officer and Most Valued Member; Women in Business, Secretary and Outstanding Women Leader Award; Finance and Accounting Club, President; *Who's Who Among Students in American Universities*; This award would not have been possible without the support of my friends and family!

Haynes, Kedra Monique: Lynchburg, VA; Shenandoah University; Lester and Jacqueline Haynes; BS Biology/Public Health, 2016; Health and Life Sciences Club; Beta Beta Beta Biological National Honor Society, President and Member for Exemplary Achievements in Biology; Alpha Lamda Delta National Honor Society, Member for Academic Excellence and Community Service Project Volunteer; To my family and God who are my everything, this award would not have been made possible.

Head, Cortney Larane: Newnan, GA; LaGrange College; BA Religion, Philosophy, Global Missions with Asian Track Concentration, 2016; Provost's List Certificate; International Club, Secretary; I want to continue living even after my death, and now I shall!

Head, Madison Beth: Conroe, TX; Stephen F. Austin State University; Rick and Mary Head; BS Food Nutrition/Dietetics, 2017; School of Human Sciences Ambassador Award; Phi Upsilon Omicron National Honor Society; Nacogdoches Animal Shelter; Habitat for Humanity; Special Olympics; Nacogdoches Memorial Hospital Emergency Room, Physician Assistant Observer; Showcase Saturday, Tour Guide; School of Human Sciences Nutrition Ambassador; Biology Club; Allied Health Student Association, President; This award is dedicated to my family. Their love and support has made this achievement possible.

Heaton, Hunter Alan: Coppell, TX; Texas A&M University; Doug and Kim Heaton; BS Electrical Engineering, 2016; Advanced Course in Engineering, Distinguished Graduate; Undergraduate Research, Cadet Researcher; Special Tactics Squadron, Senior Pin Member; Ross Volunteers, Assistant Squad Leader; Air Force ROTC, Cadet Evaluator, Leadership Advisor, Squadron Commander, and Flight Commander; Corps of Cadets, SQ-11 Commanding Officer, SQ-12 First Sergeant, Most Outstanding Outfit Commander 2014–2015, Most Outstanding Junior, Sophomore, and Freshmen, Corps of Cadets Distinguished Student Award, and Corps 21 Scholarship; A big thank you to all my family, friends, and mentors who made me who I am.

Hebert, Andrew Todd: North Richland Hills, TX; Midwestern State University; Janet Hebert, PhD; MA Training/Development, 2015; A loving and supporting family has made me what I have become, and for that I thank you.

Hebert, Brianna Dean: McKenzie, AL; Lurleen B. Wallace Community College; Shannon Cauthen; BA Nursing, 2018; Student Support Services; Dean's List; This award would not have been possible without the support and love from my family.

Hebert, Corey Joseph: Acushnet, MA; Emmanuel College; Kenneth and Grace Hebert; BA Math/Management, 2016; Outdoor Track and Field, Captain; Indoor Track and Field, Captain; I would like to thank my parents, friends, professors, and, most importantly, God for their support.

Hecker, Melanie P.: Albany, NY; Hudson Valley Community College; Phyllis and Marc Hecker; AS Human Services, 2016; YOUTH POWER!; Motivational Speaking; Autistic Self Advocacy Network, New York Statewide Chapter Leader; Autism Campus Inclusion Academy; David A. Garfinkel Essay Contest of the New York State Court System, Honorable Mention; Not a Bit of Difference Club; Animal Outreach Club; Dedicated to my family, friends, my counselors who give me essential support, and professors who believed in me.

Heffron, Katie Dawn: Gainesville, TX; Texas Tech University; Donna and Mike Heffron; BA Education, 2016; National Science Teacher Association; *Who's Who Among Students in American Universities and Colleges.*

Helander, Jamie Nicole: Greensboro, NC; Guilford Technical Community College; AS Aviation Management, 2016; Women in Aviation First in Flight Chapter, Co-Founder and Outreach Chair 2015; Aircraft Owners and Pilots Association 2013–2016; American Business Women's Association 2014–2016; Experimental Aircraft Association Chapter 1083, ASCEND Camp graduate 2012, Camp Counselor 2013–2014, Lead Counselor 2015, and Youth Ambassador Award 2015; Youth Aviation Programs Association, Director of Youth Involvement July 2014; Co-Founded a 501c3 Non-Profit to Promote Youth in Aviation; Northern Guilford High School Women's Rugby, Co-Head Coach 2016; SGA, Aviation Campus Representative 2014–2015; Traffic Appeals Committee 2014–2015; Disciplinary Review Committee 2015–2016; Aviation Job Fair Planning Committee, Co-Lead 2014–2015; AV3 Building Dedication Committee 2015; Aviation Campus Events Planning Committee 2013–2014; Flight Team, Treasurer and Ground Events Instructor 2013–2015; Alpha Eta Rho, Gamma Theta Chi, Co-Ed Fraternity, President August 2014 and Vice President Spring Semester 2014; Thank you to all who have supported me in my academic and personal journeys! Many hugs!

Hemond, Amanda Lee: Methuen, MA; University of Massachusetts Lowell; Deborah and Michael Hemond; BA Psychology, 2016; Psi Chi, Treasurer; Residence Life, Resident Adviser and Assistant Resident Director; I could not have achieved this award without the love and support from my family and close friends

Henderson, Joshua Logan: Salem, OR; Western Oregon University; BA Anthropology, 2016; Peer Mentor Program Leader; Anthropology Club, President; This award is dedicated to my many mentors who have inspired me to achieve and continue learning.

Henderson, Marcus Robert: Albany, NY; Bryant and Stratton College Albany Campus; Lamont and Lateal Henderson; AA Business Administration, 2016; Special moments like this can be achieved through support, hard work, and dedication. "Nothing ventured, nothing gained."

Hendricks, Samantha N.: Huntingdon, PA; Juniata College; Susan and John Hendricks; BS Accounting and Financial Management, 2016; Omicron Delta Kappa; Tau Pi Phi Business Honor Society; National Society of Leadership and Success, President; Circle K, President; Women's Tennis, MVP; This award would not have been possible without the support and love from my family.

Hendrickson, Cristin Rebecca: Southlake, TX; Oxford College of Emory University; Cathy and Gabe Hendrickson; BS Biophysics, 2018; Office of Student Involvement and Leadership, Student Leader of the Month; Circle K, John C. Thompson Distinguished Member Award; Volunteer Oxford, Coordinator; Alternative Spring Break, Trip Leader; "What matters most in life are quotes and stuff that tell you what life is really about."

Henning, Brooke Nicole: Great Bend, KS; Barton Community College; Kristi and Dean Henning; AS Registered Nursing, 2017; Nursing Club, Projects Coordinator; "For all those who encouraged me to fly toward my dreams: Let's soar." —Anonymous

Hernandez, Eric: Baytown, TX; BS Psychology, 2016.

Hernandez, Rachel Marie: Colorado Springs, CO; Benedictine College; Gustavo Hernandez; BA Biology/
Biochemistry, 2017; Presidential Ambassador, Vice President; Ravens CARE; Student International Business Council, Administration Director; Atchison Community Health Clinic, Director's Assistant; Atchison Elementary School, Kindergarten Teacher Assistant; Women's Lacrosse Team, Scholar Athlete Award; Student Ambassadors, Spring Formal Committee; Thank you to all of my professors for their support.

Hernandez Serna, Maria Hilaria: Dalton, NE; Western Nebraska Community College; Petra Serna and Benigno Hernandez; AA Business Administration with Accounting Option, 2016; This award is dedicated to my mother's and fiancé's love and support. Thank you.

Herod, Ann-Marie: Abbeville, MS; The University of Mississippi; James and Ann Herod; BA Broadcast Journalism/African American Studies, 2016; Hall of Fame 2015–2016; Student Algernon Sydney Sullivan Award; I thank my Lord Jesus, my family, and church family for their love, guidance, and support.

Hershberger, Olivia Margaret: Butler, PA; Butler County Community College; Sheri and Keith Hershberger; AS Business Administration, 2016; Peer Tutoring; Student Employee of the Year 2016; Phi Theta Kappa Honor Society Rho Phi, Creativity Award 2016 and Vice President of Student Membership 2016; This award is a product of hard work and dedication by everyone involved in my education.

Hester, Jordan Bailee: Macon, GA; Mercer University; Timothy and Linda Hester; MS Electrical Engineering, 2017; Mobilize Mercer, Student/Faculty Planning Committee; Textron Inc., Intern 2014–2016, Advanced Concepts Intern, Test Engineering Intern, and Electrical Systems Intern; Alpha Delta Pi Sorority, Scholarship Chair; SGA, Sophomore Senator and Macon Connections Committee 2013–2014; SGA, Senator at Large and Campus Safety and Improvements Committee 2014–2015; SGA, Senior Senator and Chair of Academic Affairs 2015–2016; This award was made possible thanks to the support of my loving and hardworking family.

Hewett, Karalyn R.: Canton, MI; Olivet Nazarene University; Douglas and Kandra Hewett; BA English, 2016; Green Room Theater Company, Cast Member and Director; Sigma Tau Delta; Freshmen Connections, Mentor; Orpheus Choir, Officer; Thank you to my friends and family for their support over the last four years.

Heyer, Rebekah E.: Lucedale, MS; Mississippi Gulf Coast Community College Jackson County Campus; Lola and Chuck Heyer; AS Human Services, 2016; Human Services Club, President; This award would not have been possible without the love and support from my family, teachers, and friends!

Hickman, Emily H.: Jefferson City, TN; Carson-Newman University; Gail and Tony Hickman; BM Music/Outside Field in Religion, 2016; Alpha Gamma Chapter of Delta Omicron, Secretary and Historian; Marching Eagles, Head Drum Major; Wind Ensemble, Principal Clarinetist; I would like to thank my family, friends, and colleagues for their support and encouragement.

Hicks, Deavonte' Jarmole: Shreveport, LA; Centenary College of Louisiana; Jinaki and Adrian Thomas; BA Communication, New Media, 2016; Southern Collegiate Athletic Conference Basketball Representative and Media Specialist 2013-2016; Senior Committee, Event Coordinator; Multicultural Student Association, Vice President 2014–2015 and Vice President of Finance 2015–2016; Big Event Executive Counsel, Media Specialist; Pandora Design, Editor and Chief; Fellowship of Christian Athletes: Leader, Northwest Louisiana Christian Athlete of the Year 2014–2015; Resident Assistant, RA of the Year Spring 2015; Men's Division III Basketball, Sportsmanship Award 2014 and Community, Character, and Community Athlete Honoree Fall 2015; To those that have impacted my life, I am humbled. Thank you.

Hilburn, Yolanda; Clinton, OK; Southwestern Oklahoma State University; BS Management/Accounting, 2016; This award would not be possible without the support and love of my friends and family.

Hill, Devin T.: Madisonville, KY; Murray State University; Cathy and Paul Krejci; BS Biochemistry, 2016; To my family, thanks for the love, laughter, and prayers the last four years.

Hill, Jennifer: Glenolden, PA; Kutztown University; Kimberly Hill; BS Psychology, 2016; Psychology Club; Department of Disability Services Employee, Note Taker; Department of Anthropology, Sociology, and Philosophy Employee, Student Assistant; Department of Tutoring Services Employee, Program Assistant and Academic Coach; Performing Dance Portmanteau, Dancer; This would not have been possible without my loving family and friends and supportive professors.

Hill, Kiarra: Trenton, NC; Xavier University of Louisiana; Susie Smith and Lucius McRavin III; BS Speech-Language Pathology, 2017; National Student Speech Language Hearing Association, Community Service Chair; Mobilization at Xavier Pair Care; Thank you to my loving family for their unwavering support. I love you!

Hill, Tyler: Elburn, IL; Waubonsee Community College; Pat and Clifford Hill; AS Biology, 2016; Future Healthcare Providers of America, President; Delta Sigma Omicron, President; For all who support and push me.

Hilleshiem, Heath Ryan: Oak Harbor, WA; Embry-Riddle Aeronautical University; Derrik Hilleshiem and Barbara Harberson; BS Aeronautics, 2016; This amazing achievement would not have been possible without the love and support from my family.

Hite, Annalisa M.: Stoney Beach, MD; Anne Arundel Community College; James and Sharee Laubert; AA Communications, 2016; Orientation Leader 2014–2016; Campus Activities Board, Executive Board Member; SGA, Secretary 2014–2015 and President 2015–2016; I would not have received this award without God, my husband, and family.

Hodge, Alexis J.: Von Ormy, TX; Palo Alto College; Teresa Hilbig-Mendoza and Daniel Mendoza; AS Engineering/Computer Science, 2016; President's 4.0 Honor Awards 2013–2014; Trio Student Support Recognition Award and Scholarship 2015; Delta Sigma Omicron, Historian 2014–2016; Chi Alpha Epsilon, Honors Outstanding Scholarship Awards 2013–2016; PTK Honors Award 2013–2016; Thank you, Mom and Daddy (Daniel). My journey has just begun. I love you.

Hodges, Victoria Regina: Chesapeake, VA; Embry-Riddle Aeronautical University; John and Eileen Hodges; BS Aeronautics, 2016; God's unfailing help and the patient support of my family has been the "wind beneath my wings."

Hoeferlin, Erica Nicole: Wildwood, MO; Sinclair School of Nursing University of Missouri; Cheryl and Craig Hoeferlin; BS Nursing, 2016; Microbiology for Nursing and Health Professions, Teaching Assistant; Sinclair Success Mentors, Coordinator; Supportive Tigers Riding in Pursuit of Ensuring Safety; Mizzou Alternative Break; Emerging Greek Leaders Program; Dean's Advisory Council, Sinclair School of Nursing May 2016 Nursing Class; Greek Week Steering Committee, Blood Drive Coordinator; Alpha Delta Pi Sorority, Executive Vice President and Ronald McDonald House Philanthropy Event Co-Chair.

Hoff, Kristina Juliette: Indian Trail, NC; Catawba College; David and Francy Hoff; BS Sport Management, 2016; Sport and Health Sciences Society, President; This award would not have been possible without the continuous love and support from my family.

Holfelder, Annie Laurie Christy: Grove City, PA; Grove City College; Melinda and John Holfelder; BS Mathematics Secondary Education, 2016; Kappa Mu Epsilon, President; Grove City College Outing Club, Secretary, Alumni Secretary; With gratitude to Snail Hollow Homeschool. Soli Deo gloria.

Hollander, Jennifer: Clearwater, FL; University of Miami; Audrey and Shawn Hollander; BS Elementary/Special Education, 2016; Future Educators Association Honor Society, President; Thanks, Mom and Dad, for your love and support throughout my college career!

Holley, Logan: Demopolis, AL; The University of Alabama; Keith and Becky Holley; BA Civil Engineer, 2015; Shining Light International Volunteer Student Consulting Group, Co-Leader November 2014–January 2016; To my parents, Keith and Becky, I thank you with every ounce of my heart for your support.

Hooton, Frank Sharp: Weslaco, TX; American Military University; MA Intelligence Management, 2018; MICA RGV, Chapter President; Thank you, American Military University, Dr. Eduardo Martinez, and my family for your endless support!

Hopkins, Shannon Brook: Washington, WV; West Virginia University at Parkersburg; AA Business Administration, 2016; This award would not be possible without the support and love from my family.

Horton, Madison Brooke: Guntown, MS; Northeast Mississippi Community College; Marilyn Johnson; BA Optometry, 2016.

Houston, Felicia L.: Lancaster, TX; Cedar Valley College; AA Law 2017; Support Group for Moms, Founder; NBPP, Chief of Liaison; Phi Theta Kappa, Vice President of Leadership; Thank you, Pain, Struggles, and Obstacles for giving birth to Endurance, Persistence, and Dedication.

Howard, Joseph C.: Pittsburgh, PA; Saint Vincent College; Corey Howard and Anna Gitzing-Howard; BS Finance, 2016; I would like to give a special thanks to my sainted mother, Anna Gitzing-Howard.

Howard, Virginia Laura: Greenville, NC; Barton College; Don and Joann Howard; BS Business Administration, 2016; Conference Carolinas, Academic All-Conference 2014–2016; Phi Beta Lambda; Sigma Beta Delta Business, Management, and Administration Honor Society; Alpha Chi Honor Society; Delta Zeta Sorority; Women's Volleyball, Captain 2015–2016; This would not have been possible without the support and love from my family and friends!

Howell, Matthew D.: Flemington, NJ; Rider University; JoAnn and David Howell; BA Political Science/Spanish, 2015; 2015 Foreign Language Study Award; Rider's Presidential Award Nominee; Rider's Department of Languages, Literatures, and Cultures, Two Certificates of Merit for Writing and Achievement in Foreign Languages; National Political Science Honor Society; National Spanish Honor Society; Graduated Magna Cum Laude; Model United Nations Team, 2014 New York City International Competition "Top Delegation"; International Honor Society in Social Sciences; Rider Merit and Rider Advantage Scholarships; Dean's List 2011–2015; New Jersey Democratic State Committee, Rebovich Fellow; Intern for Representative Rush Holt; Intern for the New Jersey Assembly Majority Office; Intern for the United States Judiciary Committee; Intern for the Office of Senator Bob Menendez; Universidad de Alcala Semester Abroad, Volunteer Editor/Translator.

Hubbs, Jacob Kyler: Bethany, OK; Southern Nazarene University; Tracy and Deborah Hubbs; BS Biology, 2016; SIMS, Leader of Swaziland 1 Team; SGA, Senior Class Vice President of Campus Ministries; Thank you to my family, who have done more for me than I could ever imagine.

Hubisz, Devon Justus: Peabody, MA; New England College; Carrie-Lynn and Jeoffrey Hubisz; BA Criminal Justice, 2017; Project Genesis, Leader; Student Senate; Student Entertainment Committee, Vice President.

Huddleston, Matthew S.: Amarillo, TX; Amarillo College; AA Computer Information Systems, Programming, 2016; This is award is in memory of my parents.

Hudspeth, Mary Kate: Brookport, IL; West Kentucky Community and Technical College; Bonnie Grace and Greg Stamme; AS Culinary Arts, 2016; This could not have been possible without all the love and support from my family. Especially my momma!

Huff, Hope Katherine: Forest, MS; Copiah-Lincoln Community College Simpson County Center; Clayborn and Carolyn Huff; AA Ultrasound Technician, 2016; Homecoming Maid, Sophomore Maid; Trailblazer, Recruiter; SGA, Sophomore President; This award would not have been possible without the support from my family and boyfriend.

Hughes, Candace V.: Wichita Falls, TX; Midwestern State University; Linda Hughes (mother) and Martha Tempelmeyer (aunt); MS Biology, 2016; Honor Society Memberships, Golden Key, Alpha Chi, Sigma Tau Delta, Beta Beta Beta; Graduate Student Association, Secretary; Teaching Assistant, TA of the Year for Biology; Adjunct Instructor of Biology at Vernon College; Nursing Advisory Committee; Dental Advisory Committee; Science Club, Public Outreach Consultant; Community Garden; Thanks for the fantastic support from my family, friends, students, and professors!

Hughes, Derek Alexis: Madison, IN; Northern State University; Cindy and Chuck Hughes; BA Political Science/Psychology, 2016; It's called hard work for a reason; but that's what makes the results so worthwhile.

Hughes, Helen: Crossett, AR; University of Louisiana at Monroe Undergraduate; Sandra Raynard; BS Medical Laboratory Science, 2016; LSCLS Student Forum, Secretary; ASCLS Student Forum, Region VII Student Representative; Medical Laboratory Science Society, President; I would like to thank my family for the support and my wonderful professors for nominating me.

Hulderman, Patricia Lynn: Lancaster, CA; West Virginia Northern Community College; AS Pre-Psychology, 2016; SCARSY, Vice President; This would not have been possible without the support of my family, friends, instructors, and amazing tutor.

Hull, Liesl: Schenectady, NY; Hudson Valley Community College; AS Dental Hygiene, 2016; Dental Hygiene Gala, Student Ambassador; First Advantage Dental Hygiene Scholarship; Troy Study Club Scholarship; Sociology Department Research and Writing Award; Dental Hygiene Department Peer Tutor; Dental Hygiene Department Learning Lab, Teaching Assistant; Local Homeless Shelter, Food Service and Oral Self-Care Educator; Super Hero Smile Day, Presenter and Volunteer; Children's Dental Health Day, Presenter and Volunteer; Phi Kappa Theta; Thanks to my whole family, especially Reuben, Momma, Ethan, Reese, Darcy, and my amazing Lizer Girls!

Humphrey, LaLonne Chantel: Huntsville, AL; John C. Calhoun State Community College; Gloria Humphrey; AA Business Administration, 2015; Calhoun Warhawk, Student Ambassador and Assistant Treasurer; This award would not have been possible without the support of my family, loved ones, and friends.

Hunter, Danielle D.: Clarksville, TN; Austin Peay State University; Gina and Dwight Hunter; BS English and Political Science, 2016; Tennessee Equality Project, Campus Coordinator; Planned Parenthood of Middle and East Tennessee, Community Action Team Coordinator; Gay-Straight Alliance, President, Vice President, and Secretary; Center of Excellence for the Creative Arts, Social Media and Creative Planning Intern.

Hunter, Emily Brooke: Newark, DE; Campbellsville University; Jeff and Tammy Hunter; BS Math/Middle School Math Education/Minor in Secondary Education, 2017; Math Major, Alpha Chi National College Honor Society; Campbellsville University Swim Team, Qualified and Competed at NAIA Swimming Championships, Making it to Finals; Academic All-Mid-South Conference Award, and NAIA Women's Swimming and Diving Scholar-Athlete; This would not have been possible without my loving, supportive parents who home-schooled and prepared me for college.

Hunter, Precious Shekinah: Chattanooga, TN; Bennett College; Tina Reid and Ernest Hunter; BA Psychology, 2016; Student Ambassador, Tour Coordinator 2013–2014; Spirit of David Dance Ministry, President 2013–2015; SGA, Miss Royal Blue and White 2015–2016; Student Marshal Board, Head Marshal 2015–2016 and Assistant Head Marshal 2014–2015; This award would not have been possible without God, family, friends, and my Alma Mater Bennett College!

Hursh, Tember Lenn: Chesterfield, MO; Logan University; Kris and Sherri Dannenberg; PhD Chiropractic, 2016; Logan University Student Ambassador, Vice President, Founder, and Treasurer; This award would not have been possible without the endless love and support of my friends and family.

Hurst, Joseph C.: New Roads, LA; Grambling State University; Karen Holmes-Shaw, Richard Shaw, and Claude Hurst; BS Education, 2019; Professional Learning Experiences, President's List Honor Student; Honor Roll; Actively Attends Church; This award would not be possible without the blessings of the Lord Jesus Christ, my family, and friends.

Husted, Hannah M.: Lincoln, NE; Nebraska Wesleyan University; Linda and Ken Husted; BS Exercise Science, 2016; NWU Society of Scholars, Academic Honors List; University Jazz Ensemble, Rhythm Section Leader; I am deeply honored and would like to thank my amazing family and professors.

Huyler, Krystal Ann Coral: Babson Park, FL; Webber International University; Ken and Melonie Huyler; BS Hospitality and Management, 2017; Webber International Honor Society; Phi Beta Lambda, Secretary and Fourth Place State Awardee; QEP Committee, Student Delegate in the Co-Curricular Committee; Rotaract Member; Resident Assistant, Head Resident Assistant; I would like to thank God, my parents, family, and friends, who pushed me and made this possible.

Hyndman, Melissa R.: Merrick, NY; Rensselaer Polytechnic Institute; Marla and Scott Hyndman; BS Chemical Engineering, 2018; Society for Women Engineers, Outreach Director 2015–2016 and Knowledge Source Director 2016–2017.

I

Iliff, Laurie Ann: Fort Worth, TX; The University of Texas Arlington; BSN Nursing, 2016; Student Mentor for BSN Accelerated Program Foundations of Nursing Class; National Society of Leadership and Success; Arlington Student Nursing Association; New Student Panel Member; Sigma Alpha Lambda; All the glory belongs to God. Special thanks to my amazing husband, Dan, and our five children.

Infante, Kendrick Paul Manabat: Greenville, SC; Bob Jones University; Remedios Infante; BS Music Education, 2016; Literary Society Sidney Lanier, President 2014–2015; I want to thank God, my professors, my family, and my friends for their love and support.

Infante, Natasha Ariel: Tampa, FL; Hillsborough Community College; Sandra and Aristonico Infante; AA Biology, 2016; Hillsborough Community College Honors Institute, Honors Student and Presidential Honors Scholarship; All-Florida Academic Team; STEM Science Majors Club; Keep Tampa Beautiful–Keep America Beautiful; Metropolitan Ministries; Arete Honor Society; National Society of Collegiate Scholars; Phi Theta Kappa Honor Society, Vice President of Fellowship; Phi Beta Lambda Business Leadership, Secretary; I have received this honor and award due to the support of my family and friends. Thank you.

Irons, Darian P.: Canyon, TX; Amarillo College; AS Nursing, 2016; Phi Theta Kappa Honor Society, Academic Excellence; "The LORD is my strength and my shield; in him my heart trusts." —Psalm 28:7

Irvin, Leathan John: Little Rock, AR; University of Arkansas at Pine Bluff; Deborah Robinson and Earl Irvin; BS Regulatory Science/Agriculture, 2017; Founders and Honors Convocation Award Recipient Spring 2013–2015; School of Agriculture and Home Economics Scholarship 2015; Pulaski County Chapter Award Fall 2016 and Spring 2017; Honor Roll 2013–2015; Gama Sigma Delta Agriculture National Honors Society 2015; Alpha Kappa Mu National Honors Society Scholar 2015; ROTC, Cadet Honors Awards 2013–2015, Field Training Exercise 2013–2015, Drill Team, Military Ball Committee Fundraising Chair, Battalion Commander's Spirit Award Spring 2015, Recruitment Effort 2013–2015, and Fundraising Effort 2013–2015; York Award 2014–2015; Alumni Endowment Scholarship 2014–2016; Animal Science Club 2014–2015; Homecoming Assembly Speech 2015; National Alumni Conference 2015; Orientation Assistant 2015; Recruitment Team 2014–2015; Collegiate 4-H Club 2014–2015; Psychology Club 2012–2015, Co-Founder; Agriculture Scholarships Fall 2016 and Spring 2017; Dean's List 2013–2015; Biology Mentor and Tutor 2014–2015; Phi Beta Sigma Fraternity Inc., Sleep Outside for the Homeless 2012–2015, Chair of Bigger and Better Business 2014–2015, Reading to the Youth 2014–2015, Campus Cleanup 2012–2015, and Grave Yard Cleanup 2012–2015; Chancellor Galleria of the Arts 2013–2015; Lab Tec 2012–2015; University Round Up 2012–2015; American Fisheries Society 2013–2015; Bee Club 2012–2015; Bell Tower Scholarship 2014–2015; NAACP at UAPB 2012–2015; J. C. Corbin Alumni Scholarship Award 2015; History Club 2012–2015; Ja Da Lam Des Social and Civic Club Scholarship Award 2015; Aquaculture and Fisheries Club 2013; Alumni Pulaski County Chapter Scholarship Award 2015; Biology Club 2012–2015, Vice President 2013–2015; Chancellor's List 2014–2016; President's List 2014–2015; Carolyn F. Blakely Honors College, Parliamentarian Fall 2015 and Spring 2016, Senior Banquet Presiding 2015, Alumni Convocation 2012–2015, SHRC Conference 2015, Delta Nature Center Boo on the Bayou 2013–2015, Mentor and Tutor 2013–2015, and Alumni Banquet 2013–2015; This prestigious award would not be a reality without my family, loved ones, administration, and faculty.

Ishee, Taylor Nicole: Walnut Grove, AL; Snead State Community College; Robin and Jason Ishee; AS Biology, 2016; Snead State Student Ambassadors, Vice President.

Ismael, Noor Mustafa: Salem, OR; Western Oregon University; Mustafa Al-Karawi and Maysaa Saeed; BA Political Science, 2015; WOU Ambassador, Certificate of Appreciation from Western Oregon University Ambassador Program; My family and friends always support me. Their support helped me get the award.

Ivey, Emily Brooke: Union, SC; University of South Carolina Union Campus; Donna and E. Byrd Ivey; BS Nursing, 2018; Thanks for the love and support of my parents and "Mammy" who encouraged me all the way.

J

Jackman, Amanda: Martell, NE; Doane College; Jacque and Jim Jackman; BA Spanish, 2015; Cheerleading and Track; Modern Language Award; A special thanks to my loving professors, friends, and family who made this award possible!

Jacks, Rebecca R.: Clarksville, TN; Austin Peay State University.

Jackson, Alesha RoChe': Jackson, MS; Jackson State University College of Science, Engineering, and Technology; Michael and Allia Jackson; BS Civil Engineering, 2016; Alpha Kappa Alpha Sorority Inc., Historian, Treasurer, and Volunteer; Scholars Academy, SROP Fellowship and Tutor; Society of Women Engineers, Treasurer; Institute of Transportation Engineers, Vice President; National Society of Black Engineers, BEYA Community Service Award and SGA Representative; American Society of Civil Engineers, President, Treasurer, and Deep South Conference Competition; President's List; Dean's List; Honors Convocation; *Who's Who*; Alpha Lambda Delta; I dedicate this award to my parents, sister, family, friends, and mentors who encourage and support me.

Jackson, Chandra Denise: Springfield, MA; College of Our Lady of the Elms; BS Social Work, 2016; Obstacles will inevitably come your way. Always remember, what's for you will not pass you.

Jackson, Hannah Noël: Goffstown, NH; New England College; Kevin and Maureen Jackson; BA Fine Arts, Focus in Drawing, 2017; Bridges Program, Peer Leader; The New Englander, House of Representatives; The Henniker Review, House of Representatives.

Jackson, Kierr Iman: Jamaica, NY; Niagara University; BS Criminal Justice, 2015; Alpha Kappa Delta Honor Society; This award would not have been possible without the love and support from my family and friends.

Jackson, Stacey Lynn Paquette: Fort Worth, TX; Embry-Riddle Aeronautical University; Robin and Cliff Paquette; BS Aeronautics, 2016; United Nations Assistance Mission Liberia, Captain; United Nations Assistance Mission Afghanistan, Captain; United Nations Assistance Mission South Sudan, Captain; Airline Pilot WestJet, Captain; Alpha Sigma Lamba, Nu Kappa Chapter; My success was facilitated by the love, support, and sacrifice of my family. Infinite thanks and love.

Jackson, Stephanie Anna-Marie: Winchester, VA; Shenandoah University; Kimberly Fiorucci and Gary Jackson; MS Occupational Therapy, 2017; Thank you, mom, dad, family, and professors past and present! You inspire me daily.

Jacque, Emily A.: Horseheads, NY; St. John Fisher College; Theresa and Earnest Jacque; BS Psychology, 2016; Orientation Team, Student Orientation Coordinator; Student Conduct Board, Student Representative; Student Ambassador, CORE Team; I am who I am today because of the love and support from my family—Thank you!

Jahraus, Mariann J.: Huntsville, AL; University of North Alabama; Jeanna and Rodney Jahraus; BA Secondary Education in Biology, 2017; Department of Education Research Students, President; National Society of Leadership and Success, Sigma Alpha Pi, President; Multicultural Education Club, Vice President.

Jamal, Sabrina Sue: McKinney, TX; Texas Tech University; Carla and Naj Jamal; BA Energy Commerce, 2016; Energy Commerce Association; American Association of Professional Landmen; National Society of Collegiate Scholars; Delta Sigma Pi, Beta Upsilon Chapter President 2015–2016, Vice President of Chapter Operations 2014–2015, Faculty Relations Officer 2013–2014, and Active Member 2013–2016; Thank you to my family for supporting me throughout my time at Texas Tech University. Guns Up!

James, Janell T.: Phenix City, AL; Columbus State University; Tiffany James; BA Chemistry, 2017; PAWS; Columbus Regional Hospital; American Chemical Society, Vice President; Honors College, President; Dedicated to my supporters: Mom, Granny, Calvin, Dr. Meyers, Cory, Servant Ladies, and Honors College. Thank you!

James, Natalee Natassia Teresa: Jamaica, NY; Long Island University Brooklyn; Felix and Margaret James; MS Taxation, 2016; Berkeley College, Certified Accounting Tutor; National Association of Black Accountants, President; NABA Student Convention 2015, Interview Committee; Accounting Society, Senate Representative; Volunteer Income Tax Assistant; Sigma Beta Delta, Recipient of the Dean's Recognition of Excellence Award 2016; Graduate Research Assistant, Philip Wolitzer and Dr. Myrna Fischman Endowed Scholarship Award; I would like to acknowledge Yolande Harley for believing in me, without her this award would not be attainable.

James, Tatjana Irene: Athol, MA; Mount Wachusett Community College; Donald Grenier; AS Graphic and Interactive Design, 2016; I am the women I am today because of the love and support from my parents and family.

Janicki, Rebecca M.: Hillsborough, NJ; Rider University; Barbara Janicki; BA Accounting/Entrepreneurial Studies, 2016; Best Times, LLC; Beta Alpha Psi; Accounting Society; Business School Honors Program 2013–2016; Rider Open House 2015–2016; HomeFront; VITA 2013–2016; Locks of Love Donor; Beta Gamma Sigma; Phi Beta Lambda; Honors Thesis, Presented 2016; AICPA Student Affiliate; NJSCPA Ambassador 2014–2015; Omicron Delta Kappa; Accounting Society, Community Service Officer 2014–2015; Beta Alpha Psi, President 2015–2016 and Community Service Officer 2014–2015; Dean's List 2012–2016; This award would not have been possible without the support and love from my Mother.

Jankowski, Kristine: Holbrook, NY; Suffolk County Community College; Carmella and Ken Jankowski; AA Psychology, 2016; Campus Activities Student Worker, Information Booth, Alcove, Quiet Lounge, Office, and Registrar; Orientation Leader Award; Disney Club, President and Instant Impact Award; Campus Activities Board, Executive; Many thanks to my friends and family. Frank Vino, thanks for always pushing and helping me through everything!

Jena, Johnathan P.: Pepperell, MA; Fitchburg State University; Deborah and William Jena III; BS Professional Writing, 2015; Relay For Life, Captain; Run a Self-Help Blog with over 770 Followers, Two Facebook Pages with a Combined 30,000 Followers; Raised over $500 for Greater Boston Area Foodbanks.

Jennewein, Brooke Shelton: Holts Summit, MO; Missouri Baptist University; Billy and Sherry Shelton; BS Behavioral Science, 2016.

Jennings, Jennifer HaleLee: Greenwood, SC; Erskine College; Amy and David Jennings; BA English, 2016; Theta Alpha Kappa, Graduated Magnum Cum Laude; Sigma Tau Delta International English Honors Society, President; Alpha Chi National College Honor Society, President; This award is dedicated to Granddad Glenn Sturdivant, who shared his love for reading and learning with me.

Jimenez, Jacqueline E.: Eagle Springs, NC; Montgomery Community College; AA Human Services Technology and Human Services Developmental Disabilities, 2015; Martin Luther King Jr. Challenge Day; Sandhills Community College, Human Services Substance Abuse AAS in Process; Minority Leadership Award; This award is the result of the support and love from my family, employer, and instructors.

Johnson Jr., Juan Antonio: Tarboro, NC; Edgecombe Community College; Dorothy and Juan Johnson Sr.; AS Criminal Justice, 2016; *Who's Who Among Students in American Universities and Colleges 2015* Honoree; President's List 2014–2015; Study Abroad 2015, Scotland; North Carolina Community College System Student Leadership Development Program, SLDP Graduate Class of 2016; SkillsUSA, Third Place 2015 State Competition Crime Scene Investigation; Empowering Males with a Purpose to Achieve and Celebrate, Male Mentoring Program; SGA, Parliamentarian, Executive Board 2014–2016, Vice President, Officer's Award, and President's Choice Award 2014–2015; A special honor to my Lord Savior Jesus Christ, my loving family, and to Edgecombe Community College.

Johnson, Alfred Wendell: Atmore, AL; Athens State University; Deloise and Alfred Johnson; BA Postsecondary Education, 2016; This award would not have been possible without the Lord Jesus and my family.

Johnson, Bradlee Michelle: Los Angeles, CA; University of La Verne; Staci Johnson-Williams and Timothy Williams; BA Speech Communication, 2016; Student Ambassador for the Office of Undergraduate Admission, Tour Guide; Black Student Union, President; I am thankful for all of the opportunities and support; I am truly honored to receive this award.

Johnson, Brandon Tyler: LaFollette, TN; East Tennessee State University; MBA 2017; Tennessee Intercollegiate State Legislature, Attorney General; Lions Club, Charter President and Melvin Jones Fellowship; SGA, President Pro Tempore and Four-Term Senator; College Republicans, Chair; Sigma Chi, Derby Dad, and Recruitment Chair; "If I have seen further, it is by standing on the shoulders of giants." —Sir Isaac Newton

Johnson, Caroline N.: Warren, AR; University of Arkansas Little Rock; MA Applied Communication Studies, 2016; First Presbyterian Church of Warren, Elder and Clerk of Session; Drew H.E.A.L.T.H. Coalition, Member, Committee Chair, and Past Chair.

Johnson, Christopher F.: Shawnee, KS; Calvary Bible College and Theological Seminary; BA Pastoral Ministries, 2016; I am grateful for God's grace and the love and support of my friends and family.

Johnson, Daria Ansley: West Roxbury, MA; Newbury College; LaTanya Leath and Darin Johnson; BS Healthcare Management, 2016; Phi Eta Sigma Honor Society, Treasurer; This award would not have been possible without the love and support of my family.

Johnson, James D.: Waukesha, WI; Waukesha County Technical College; AS Accounting, 2016; Thank you, Sara, Amber, and Autumn, for your support and love during this journey.

Johnson, Janay Alysah: Durham, NC; Bennett College; Blanca and Jeff Johnson; BS Computer Science, 2017; Academic Honors, Honors List and Dean's List; Major Honors, Outstanding Computer Science Major; Junior Class Executive Board, Junior Class Senator; I dedicate this award to all of the amazing individuals who have supported and motivated me.

Johnson, Janessa Mina: Poughkeepsie, NY; Bennett College; Josie and Jeff Johnson; BS Biology, 2017; Resident Assistant 2015–2016; Dean's List 2015; Miss Biology 2016–2017; Biology Club, Minorities Administration for Pre-Professional Students Club; All of my achievements are a reflection of my family, who support and love me.

Johnson, Jessica L.: Land O' Lakes, FL; Norfolk State University; Brenda and Glenn Johnson; BS Accounting/Finance, 2017; Varsity Volleyball, MEAC Player of the Week, MEAC Rookie of the Week, MEAC All-Academic Team, and Six-Time AD Honor Roll; This award would not have been possible without my amazing support system. I love you all!

Johnson, Khari Chaye: Virginia Beach, VA; Virginia Wesleyan College; Celeste Walker and Nelson Johnson; BA Theatre, 2016; International Studies Abroad, Global Ambassador; Global Scholars Program, Semester in London; Alpha Psi Omega, President; Virginia Wesleyan College Dance Team, Captain; Sigma Sigma Sigma Sorority Inc., Vice President of New Members, Alumnae Relations Chair, Parliamentarian, Ritual Chair, and Music Chair; To my mother, Celeste Walker, for all of her love and support during my college years.

Johnson, Kimberly G.: Missouri City, TX; Howard University; Linda and Robert Johnson; BA Film and Television, 2017; National Society of Collegiate Scholars; Annenberg Honors Program; Howard University Film Organization, President; School of Communications Council, Evolution Administration, Chief of Staff.

Johnson, Patrice LaShawn: Detroit, MI; Marygrove College; BA Social Work, 2017; Wayne County Community College Academic Achievement; Marygrove College *Who's Who Among Students* Academic Achievement; Thank you to my family and friends for all their love, support, and encouragement.

Johnson, Shlonda Evette: Longview, TX; LeTourneau University Global; BA Human Services, 2016; I thank God and LeTourneau University for making it possible for me to receive this award.

Johnston, Courtney Anne: West Plains, MO; Ozark Bible Institute; BA Biblical Literature, 2016; Physical Education Teacher for 6–11th Grade Girls in Christian School; Citizens Emergency Response Team; Overcomers Choir Member; School Photographer; Student Council, Secretary and Student Representative; College Practicum, Leader of Nursing Home Ministries; I give honor to God and to my family, college, and friends for making this award possible.

Johnston, Reed Edward: Waco, TX; Texas Tech University; Dana Johnston; BS Agricultural Economics, 2016; College of Agricultural Sciences and Natural Resources, Texas Cotton Boll License Plate Scholarship, Dr. and Mrs. Cal Brints Scholarship, Aggie of The Month–CASNR, President's List, and Dean's List; Mission Work with First Baptist of Lubbock; Wounded Warrior Project; Adopt-A-Highway; Soils Judging Team, Two-Time National Qualifier and Secretary; Relay For Life; Bible Study; Alpha Gamma Rho, Vice President, Activities Officer, and Member of the Semester 2015; Agriculture Economics Committee, Planning; Collegiate Future Farmers of America, Vice President; Agronomy Club, Secretary; When life hands you lemons, put a bull rope on 'em. POW POW, Ol' Son!

Jones, Averi Gabrielle: Jacksonville, FL; St. Johns River State College; Paul and Debbie Jones; AA Sociology/Biological Anthropology, 2015; Phi Theta Kappa, Alpha Epsilon Lambda, Cum Laude, Dean's List; Writers Society, President 2014–2015; Ballroom Dance Club, President 2014–2015; SGA, President 2015–2016; Thank you to my parents, Paul and Debbie Jones, my family and friends, Jim Rogers, Shari McGriff, and God.

Jones, Brandi M.: Jackson, MS; Jackson State University College of Public Service; BS Communicative Disorders. 2016; Honor and Award Convocation; Dean's List; Walk for Children with Apraxia of Speech, Co-Coordinator; National Student Speech Language Hearing Association, Undergraduate Chapter President; "In order to succeed, we must first believe that we can." —Nikos Kazantzakis

Jones, Cana Marissa: Van Alstyne, TX; Grayson College; Yvette and Matt Jones; AS Nursing, 2016; I would like to thank God and my family for their encouragement, support, and endless love.

Jones, Colleen Murray: Ardsley, NY; State University of New York New Paltz; Mary and Wayne Jones; BS Elementary Education/Concentration in Spanish, 2018; To my parents, who taught by example the work ethic that got me here: I am forever grateful.

Jones, Elizabeth H.: Germantown, TN; Auburn University; Susan and Ted Jones; AA Organismal Biology, 2016; Involvement Ambassadors, Director of Student Development; Freshmen Leadership Programs, Vice President of Communications, Director, and Assistant Director; Delta Gamma Fraternity, Junior Member of Honor Board and Vice President of Foundation.

Jones, Gabriel: Shreveport, LA; Xavier University of Louisiana.

Jones, Jeffrey R.: Estero, FL; Robert Morris University; Brenda and David Jones; BA Sport Management 2015; Hockey Team, 2014 Atlantic Hockey Championship Winner; I want to thank my family for all their love and support.

Jones, Jorrie C.: Jackson, MS; Jackson State University College of Education and Human Development; Lorrie Ann Chatman and Kenneth Shelley; BA English Education, 2017; *eXperience* Student Life Magazine, First Staff Writer; *Blue and White Flash* Student Newspaper; Staff Writer; Recruitment Office Blue Ambassadors, Tour of Captains; Thank you to every educator that has ever saw potential in me, this award is for you.

Jones, Natalie Brooke: Mendenhall, MS; Copiah-Lincoln Community College Simpson County Center; AA Elementary Education, 2016; Phi Theta Kappa; H. F. McCarty Jr. Endowed Scholarship; Wilson/Massey Scholarship; This award would not have been possible without the love and support from my family.

Jones, Terria Trana: Winchester, VA; Shenandoah University; Terry and Ella Jones; PhD Pharmacy, 2018; Delta Sigma Theta Sorority Inc.; Student National Pharmaceutical Association, President-Elect; Rho Chi Honor Society; I would like to dedicate this award to God and to my loving, supportive family and friends.

Jones, Victoria Susan: Greer, SC; Lander University; Jean Jones; BS Sociology, 2016; Blue Key Honor Society, 2014–2016; Sigma Tau Delta, Secretary 2014–2015 and Vice President 2015–2016; Department of Political and Social Sciences, Display of Outstanding Sociological Imagination Award 2015-2016 and Maybelle Coleman Scholarship; Lander University English Club, Secretary 2014–2015 and Vice President 2015–2016.

Jones-Hudson, Billie Dian: Roscoe, TX; Western Texas College; AA Art Education, 2016; Thank you to God, my family, and friends for the love and support.

Jordan, Melissa A.: Abbeville, MS; Northwest Mississippi Community College; AS Paralegal Technology, 2016; If you're going to dream; dream big, anything is possible. Thank my family for their love and support.

Joseph, Kellie: Staten Island, NY; College of Staten Island; BA Sociology/Anthropology, 2016; National Society of Collegiate Scholars, Star Status Coordinator and Vice President of Community Service; CUNY Service Corps; College of Staten Island Student Government Scholarship; Center for Student Accessibility, Tutor; Health and Wellness Services, Peer Educator; This award would not have been possible without the support and love from my family.

Joseph, Lynesha Michelle: St. Thomas, VI; University of The Virgin Islands; Lynette P. Petty-Amey; BS Criminal Justice, 2018; Virgin Islands Army National Guard, Specialist/E4; Zeta Phi Beta Sorority Inc.; Behind every great accomplishment there is an even greater support team!

Joseph, Maurice: Riverside, CA; La Sierra University College of Arts and Sciences; Marilyn Bell-Joseph and Jerome Joseph; BS Global Studies/History, 2016; I dedicate this award to my parents, my support through the entirety of my studies.

Joyner, April: Tarboro, NC; Edgecombe Community College; William and Carolyn Scott; AS Nursing, 2016; SNA Member; This award would not have been possible without the support and love from my family.

Juraschek, Justice Alexander: Woodbridge, VA; Taylor University; David and Sandra Juraschek; BS Computer Science, New Media/Systems, 2016; This award is due to the love and guidance of my God and the family He gave me.

Justus, John Thomas Bethel: Cleveland, GA; Truett McConnell College; Michael and Janis Justus; BA History, 2016; Truett-McConnell College Chorale, Minister of Music, Glade Creek Baptist Church, Mt. Airy, Georgia; Reagan Legacy Foundation Liberty Education Tour, Reagan Freedom Fellow; Oxford Distinguished Scholar, President's Club; Summa Cum Laude; Outstanding Graduate in History 2016; I owe my success to Jesus Christ, my family, and my church.

K

Kafkes, Zoe: Willowbrook, IL; University of Miami; BSC Public Relations and Political Science, 2016; Greek Week Executive Board, Sponsorship and Fundraising Co-Chair 2014–2016; Panhellenic Association, Head Rho Gamma 2015–2016, SGA Coordinator 2014–2015, and Coordinator of Philanthropy 2013–2014; Zeta Tau Alpha Fraternity, Apparel Chair 2016, New Member Assistant 2016, Judicial Chair 2014–2015, and Homecoming Co-Chair 2014; Orientation and Commuter Student Involvement, Orientation Leader 2013–2015 and Orientation Fellow 2013; Butler Center for Service and Leadership, IMPACT Retreat Facilitator 2013–2015; Undergraduate Student Government, Executive Board Chief of Staff 2015–2016, Senate Vice Chair of University Affairs 2014–2015, and Category 5 Vice Chair 2013–2014; Thank you to my parents, who have given me everything. You've made me who I am today.

Kahn, Cameron Gregory: Mount Pleasant, SC; University of South Carolina.

Kaleal, Jillian Ann: Erie, PA; Gannon University; Louis and Debra Kaleal; BS Environmental Science, 2016; Students Against Violence Everywhere, President; Activities Programming Board, Special Events Co-Chair; Thank you, Mom and Dad, for everything you've done for me. I love you. Miss you, Mom.

Kaltenhauser, Catarina Elizabeth: Stuart, FL; Indian River State College; Richard and Cathleen Kaltenhauser; AA Liberal Arts, 2016; SGA Representative; This would not have been possible without the unending support of my family and friends.

Kangalee, Renessa Kate: Arima, TT; Flagler College; Rachael and Rennie Kangalee; BA Psychology/Sociology, 2015; Flagler Enactus, Secretary; This award would not have been possible without the support and love from my family.

Karat, Zouka G.: Pittsburgh, PA; Robert Morris University; George Karat and Madlin Ibrahim; BA Hospitality/Tourism Management, 2016; Dean's List; I dedicate this achievement to my parents for their selfless support and lifelong guidance. Love always!

Kawalerski, Steven Michael: Elma, NY; Canisius College; David and Lisa Kawalerski; BS Finance, 2016; Accounting Society; Habitat for Humanity, Community Day Volunteer; Travel Soccer Coach, Assistant Coach; National Jesuit Student Leadership Conference, Sponsorship Co-Chair and Transportation Chair; Golden Griffin Fund, Student Analyst; Finance Committee; Economics and Finance Club; SGA, Senator; Thank you to my family for all of their encouragement that helped make this honor achievable.

Kayumova, Luiza: Staten Island, NY; College of Staten Island; Anisa Kayumova; MS Social Work, 2018; This award would not have possible without the support and love from my MOM and sister.

Keene, Katie Bea: Thomasville, NC; Guilford Technical Community College; Cynthia and Irvin Coble; AS Criminal Justice Technology Law Enforcement Track–Homeland Security Certificate, 2016; SkillsUSA 2016, First Place State Level, Attended National June 2016; Community Watch, Leader and Organizer; Criminal Justice Department, Student Excellence Award; Phi Theta Kappa, Honors Society; GTCC SkillsUSA, Excellence Award; SkillsUSA 2015, Second Place National Level; SkillsUSA 2015, First Place State Level; Life is not about waiting on the storm to pass. It is about learning to dance in the rain.

Kehl, Jeanna: Eureka, IL; Eureka College.

Keith, Kristen: San Antonio, TX; The University of Texas at San Antonio; Chad and Connie Keith; MS Nutrition/Dietetics, 2018; Por Vida Program and Aramark, Health Fair Student Volunteer; Sports, Cardiovascular, and Wellness Nutrition DPG; Texas Student Dietetic Association; UTSA Health Nest; South Texas Academy of Nutrition and Dietetics; National Society of Leadership and Success; Dietetic and Nutrition Student Association, STAND Representative; UTSA Recreation Center, Zumba and Kickboxing Instructor.

Keller, Kenan David: Glen Carbon, IL; Union University; Phil and Faith Keller; BA History, 2015; Boy Scouts of America, Eagle Scout; Englewood Baptist Church, Band Member; House of Masters, Administrator; Life139, Treasurer; SGA, Councilman and Senator; Rutledge Honorary History Club; Phi Alpha Theta, Secretary and Actor; Union University Singers, Bass Singer; I cannot thank my friends, professors, and family enough for their encouragement. To God be all the glory.

Keller, Sydney Christ: Houston, TX; University of St. Thomas; BA Political Science/Psychology, 2017; Tutorial Services Center, Psychology and Political Science Tutor; The Center; Phi Sigma Tau; Psi Chi; Pi Sigma Alpha; Mock Trial, Captain; This award is dedicated to my loving friends, family, and teachers, especially my parents, Leslie and Howie.

Kelly, Jesus: Virginia Beach, VA; Embry-Riddle Aeronautical University; Adela and Jesus Kelly; BS Aeronautics, 2018; This award would not have been possible without the support and love from my family.

Kelm, Curtis W.: West Plains, MO; Missouri State University West Plains; BS Mathematics, 2018.

Kendrick, Amanda Leann: Pollok, TX; Angelina College; Greta Herrington Maggard, Charles and Carolyn Maggard; AS Radiologic Technology, 2016; Dean's List; Phi Beta Kappa; Animal Rescuer; Thank you to my wonderful family for helping make my dreams come true! I love y'all!

Kennedy, Haylee Marie: Philadelphia, TN; Hiwassee College; Jan and Bob Kennedy; AS Criminal Justice, 2016; Theater, Best Actor Award; Hard work and dedication to education and self-improvement will eventually pay off in the end.

Keough, David Tobiassen: Nashville, TN; Lipscomb University; BS Information Security, 2016; Cyber Security Defense Team, Co-Captain; Every moment in my life is a providence from my Lord, Savior, and Friend, Jesus Christ.

Keough, Michael J.: Dumas, TX; West Texas A&M University; Jimmy and Tammie Keough; MEd Instructional Design and Technology, 2015; Prison Volunteer, Chaplin TDCJ; Outreach Ethiopia 2012; ESL China, From 2002–2009, Teacher and Leader; ESL Thailand 2013, Teacher; K–12 Robotics, Mentor; West Texas A&M Toastmasters, Founding Member 2005; Research Grant Award, Primary Researcher, Integrated Technology into Clarendon and White Deer Schools; Thanks to my loving wife Emily for her sacrifice, support, and encouragement. You inspire me!

Kephart, Scott Berman: Clearfield, PA; Pennsylvania State University DuBois Campus; BS Information Systems Technology, 2018; League of Legends Club, President; Anime Club, President; IT Club; Video Game Day; I would like to thank those responsible for nominating me—I greatly appreciated it!

Kerby, Desireé Nichole: Florence, AL; Northwest-Shoals Community College; Julie DiOrio and Dwight Kerby; AS General Education, 2017; Traumatic Brain Injury Awareness Month of March; Phi Theta Kappa; I want to thank Stacey, Devin, Tyler, Mom, Justin, Papa John, Dad, and Misti for their support!

Kerekes, Alexander James: Palm Harbor, FL; St. Petersburg College Health Education Center; Laurie and Jim Kerekes; AS Physical Therapist Assistant, 2016; This was made possible by my Savior Jesus Christ, family, school faculty, Bailey Foundation, and classmates.

Kerekes, Ashley: Feasterville, PA; Peirce College; BS Paralegal Studies, 2016; Legal Studies Student Association; Lower Southampton Fire Department, Firefighter/EMT and Vice President; I am blessed to have the love and support from my family, friends, and Fire Department. Thank you!

Kernohan, Jaclyn Dianne: Whitby, ON; Young Harris College; Larry and Leslie Kernohan; BS Biology, 2016; Student Athlete Advisory Committee 2012–2016, Vice President 2015; Women's Lacrosse Player, Captain 2012–2016, Second All-Independent Team 2012–2014; CLAW 2014–2016; SGA 2013–2016; My family, friends, coaches, and professors are the reason I feel I can accomplish anything. Thank you!

Khaimova, Rebecca Madeline: Brooklyn, NY; Long Island University Brooklyn; PharmD Pharmacy, 2018; Freshmen Honor's Trip, Orientation Leader; Rho Chi Honor Society; Pharmakon Yearbook, Co-Editor; The Pharmacy Newsletter, Writer; Alpha Lambda Delta, Vice President; Alpha Chi Sigma, Chapter Treasurer; APhA-ASP, Generation Rx Co-Director; This award is dedicated to my amazing parents, siblings, and boyfriend! Thank you for always believing in me!

Khang, Jimmy: Oregon City, OR; Western Oregon University; Ricky Khang and Yang Vang; BS Criminal Justice, 2017; WOU Food Pantry, Volunteer; National Society of Leadership and Success, Sigma Alpha Pi, Publicity Chair, Vice President, National Engaged Leader Award, and Excellence in Service to Students Award; Thank you to my family for all their love and support. I appreciate it very much.

Kimbrough Sr., Andre B.: Chicago, IL; Trinity International University; BA Christian Ministry/Business Administration, 2016; This award would not have been possible without the support and love from my family. Thank you all!

Kimmig, Elijah: Sanford, FL; Pensacola Christian College; Charles and Rose Kimmig; BS Mechanical Engineering, 2016; Machine Design Electrathon Car Competition, First Place Team Member, Junior Year; Tornadoes Collegian Softball, League All-Star Team, Junior Year; Tornadoes Collegian Basketball, Head Coach, Junior Year; Pensacola Christian College Eagles Basketball, Eagles Defensive Player of the Year Award, Sophomore Year, Team Captain, Senior Year, and Eagles Most Improved Player Award, Sophomore Year.

Kinard, Carlton LeVante': Newberry, SC; Newberry College; Larry and Brenda Kinard; BA Music Education, 2016; South Carolina Music Educators Association, Collegiate President; Board of Trustees, Student Representative; Delta Omicron, President; Kappa Alpha Psi, President; SGA, President; I am truly honored and blessed to receive this award.

Kincade, Katie C.: Greensburg, PA; Seton Hill University; Sherrie and David Maahs; BS Hospitality/Tourism, 2016; Student Ambassadors, Membership Committee; Skal International Scholar; Pennsylvania Restaurant and Lodging Association, Future of the Industry Award; Griffin Guide; Spanish Club, Secretary; SHU CRU Student Involvement Club, President; I owe my success in college to the unconditional support of my family and significant other.

Kinder, Jennifer Susan: Weirton, WV; West Virginia Northern Community College; John and Agnes Kinder; CAS Patient Care Technician/Nursing, 2016; Philippine American Performing Arts of Greater Pittsburgh, Youth President of Dance, Certificate of High Performance; Thank you to all that have made this possible!

King, Emily Cawood: Monahans, TX; Texas Tech University; Susan and Richard King; BA Marketing, 2016; Raiderthon, Chair of Marketing and Public Relations 2015–2016; Women's Service Organization, Treasurer 2015–2016 and Pledge Trainer Assistant 2015.

King, Natalie Christina: Virginia Beach, VA; Regent University; Anita and Christopher King; BS Elementary Education, 2016.

Kinner, Jonathan James: Eaton, OH; Clear Creek Baptist Bible College; Harry and Sharon Kinner; BA Pastoral Ministries, 2016; Dean's List; Thank you to my family for they have been praying for me and encouraging me in every step.

Kinney, Allison June: Salem, IN; University of Southern Indiana; David and Ava Kinney; BS Dental Hygiene, 2016; 2015 Basketball Homecoming Queen; Dental Clinic Student Worker; NODA Regional Conference; Student Housing Association, Assistant Programmer; Career Counseling Center, Secretary; American Dental Hygiene Association, Treasurer; Student Housing Association, Secretary and Treasurer; Orientation Leader AMIGO; Resident Assistant; Volunteer USI–Girl Scouts of Southwest Indiana.

Kinyanjui, Ruth: Sioux Falls, SD; Northern State University; BS Management Information Systems, 2015; International Business Conference, Certificate of Participation; Competitive Online Research, Runner Up; Undergraduate Competitive Research, Research Grant Winner; This award would not have been possible without the support from my family, friends, and professors.

Kiparizoska, Sara: Laurel, MS; The University of Mississippi; Gordana and Zan Kiparizoski; BA Biochemistry, 2016; Thesis Research on Schizophrenia and the Olfactory System; UMMC and SMBHC Clinical Shadowing Program; 2015 Gillespie Business Plan Competition, Finalist; Sally McDonnell Barksdale Honors College, Sophomore, Junior, and Senior Senator, Academic Integrity Committee; Delta Delta Delta Sorority, Assistant Academic Chair, Academic Chair, Officer Nominating Committee, and Standards Committee; Student Alumni Council, Events Committee; McGowan Institute for Regenerative Medicine, Summer Researcher 2015; The Big Event Day of Service, Team Leader 2013; National Pan-Hellenic Conference, Judicial Board Member; Associated Student Body, Freshmen Council; I am so thankful for Mississippi constantly encouraging its students to continue with progressive thinking.

Kirkpatrick, Cathlene Michelle: Suwanee, GA; University of North Georgia; Deborah and Steve Kirkpatrick; BS Psychology, 2017; I dedicate this to my Grandma Neely who taught me that love is the greatest achievement of all.

Klampe, Audrey: Stayton, OR; Western Oregon University; Teresa Klampe; BS Psychology, 2016; National Society of Leadership and Success Award; National Engaged Leader Award; To my mom, grandma, and brother, your love and support have meant the world to me.

Klein, Michael L.: Monroeville, PA; Community College of Allegheny County Boyce Campus; George and Edith Klein; AS Electronics Engineering, 2016; Psi Beta; Phi Theta Kappa; Much love and thanks to my wife, Joanne Shelby-Klein, for believing in and supporting me.

Kleynowski, Chet Alexander: Bridgeport, CT; Dominican College of Blauvelt; Cynthia Lagor; BS Biology, 2016; Alpha Lambda Delta Freshmen Honors Society; Tribeta Biology Honors Society, President; Collegiate Smash Team, Captain; Biology Club; Anime and Gaming Club, President and Treasurer; This is all thanks to my loving mother, who has been the most supportive influence in my life.

Klimp, Taeler Demoin: Columbus, GA; Columbus State University; Jennifer and Tracy Harrison; BS Early Childhood Education, 2017; This award would not have been possible without the love and support from my family and fiancé.

Klonis, Alexandra Theofania G.: Milwaukee, WI; Milwaukee School of Engineering.

Kluk, Ryan Allen: Hampden-Sydney, VA; Hampden-Sydney College; Steve and Wendy Kluk; BS Biology/History, 2017; Hampden-Sydney Poetry Review, Student Editor; Orientation and Transition Leader, Head OTL; Intramurals, Student Director; Baptist Collegiate Ministries, Secretary and Treasurer; I want to thank H-SC, my family, and friends. I could not have done this without you.

Knowles, Billie Jo: Toney, AL; Athens State University; Tina and Billy Harris; BS Elementary/Collaborative Education K–6, 2016; This award would not have been possible without the love and support from my family.

Knowles, Chandler A.: Gorham, ME; University of New England; Jamie Breen and Wayne Knowles; BA Communications, 2015; Alpha Phi Omega, Historian; Ketchin' Up with Kate, Segment Creator and Performer; Radio UNE, President and Founder; Military Appreciation Club, President and Founder; I am here because of my Mom, Dad, Spencer, Joe Habraken, and Bistra Nikiforova. Thank you.

Knox, Kari: Hayden, AL; Athens State University; Ken Knox; BS Elementary/Collaborative Education, 2016; President's List 2014–2015; Thank you to my Heavenly Father and to my family for your love and guidance. Love you.

Koci, Korina: Myrtle Beach, SC; Coastal Carolina University; Eranda and Artur Koci; BS Public Health/Philosophy, 2016; Ethics Academy for Younger Children, Group Leader; SGA, Senator Representing the College of Science.

Kohrs, Tyler Young: Trenton, IL; Greenville College; Sherry and Jimmy Jenkins; BS Social Work, 2016; Admission Ambassadors, Male Ambassador of the Year 2012–2013; Vespers, Welcoming Coordinator Sophomore and Junior Years, Co-Executive Leader Senior Year; I am incredibly blessed by this honor, thank you to my family and also my GC family.

Kolar, Samantha J.: Findlay, OH; The University of Findlay; Patricia and Robert Kolar Jr.; BS Adolescent/Young Adult Integrated Mathematics Education/Pure Mathematics, 2017; Woodrow Wilson Visiting Fellow, Student Ambassador 2014; Euler Math Club, Public Relations Officer 2015–2016 and Secretary 2016–2017; Marching Oiler Brass, Secretary 2014–2017; Dance is for Everyone, Secretary 2015–2017; Special thanks to my wonderful parents for their continued support.

Kordyban, Cristey Dawn: Swanton, MD; Garrett College; Dennis and Virginia Dillsworth; AA Business Administration, 2017; Phi Theta Kappa Honor Society, Treasurer; This award would not have been possible without the support and love from God and family.

Koszyk, Lauren: Bloomington, IL; Illinois State University; Lynne Koszyk; BM/BA Piano Performance and German, 2016; Thank you to my mentors, professors, family, and friends for their continued support and encouragement.

Kotsovos, Erica Nicole: Naperville, IL; Benedictine University; Nicholas and Stefania Kotsovos; BS Marketing, 2016; Feed My Starving Children; RGB Foundation, Intern; Institute for Business Analytics and Visualization, Intern; I owe this award to my loving parents and inspiring brothers. Thanks for believing in me.

Kowalski, Jessica Marie: Dallas, TX; Dallas Baptist University; Jennifer and Gregory Kowalski; MA Christian Education, 2016.

Krauss, Robert Arthur: Pompano Beach, FL; Embry-Riddle Aeronautical University; BS Aeronautics, 2016; This award would not have been possible without the loving support of my wife, Carol.

Kroptavich, Walter L.: North Little Rock, AR; University of Arkansas Little Rock; MA Public Administration, 2016; Juris Doctorate; Graduate Student Public Administration Society, President 2015; Student Bar Association, Honor Investigator 2014–2015 and President 2015–2016; I would like to thank the professors who have helped me in achieving academic success and this award.

Kulhanjian, Spencer Michael: Telford, PA; Cairn University; Michael and Jennifer Kulhanjian; BS Bible/Youth Ministry Concentration, 2015; Milestone Yearbook, Page Designer 2012–2013; Resident Assistant, Most Valuable Resident Assistant 2015; Chamber Singers; Chorale, Vice President 2014–2015; This award is gratefully accepted with thanks to family, friends, and my Lord.

Kunstman, Zach Francis Moran: Sister Bay, WI; University of Louisiana Lafayette; BS Architectural Studies, 2016; Louisiana Ring Committee, Chair; SGA, College of the Arts President, College of the Arts Senator, Community Outreach Chair, and Alumni Association Representative; Phi Kappa Psi Fraternity, Corresponding Secretary (AG), Historian (SG), Public Relations Chair, Re-Charter of Louisiana Beta Chair, and Founding Father; Association of Future Alumni, President, Vice President, and Public Relations Chair; American Institute of Architecture Students, President, Vice President, Public Relations Chair, National Board Candidate for Vice President and South Quadrant Director, National Communications Task Force, and CRIT Journal Editorial Team Member; Leadership is never possible without hard work and dedication from everyone, thanks to all who made everything possible.

Kurauskas, Alexandra L.: Dubuque, IA; Clarke University; Al and Brenda Kurauskas; BA Psychology, 2016; Psychology Club, Vice President and Treasurer; Clarke Student Association, Junior Class Vice President and Executive Board Vice President; Into the Streets; Clarke Ambassador; Thank you to my parents and everyone who helped me to become the person I am today.

Kurulgan, Jennifer M.: Staten Island, NY; College of Staten Island; MS Nurse Practitioner, 2016; Golden Key Society; Sigma Theta Tau; College of Staten Island Academic Excellence Award and Scholarship; My two sons, John and Paul, never give up on your dreams.

Kuzdzal, Nicole Kristina: Allegany, NY; Ithaca College; Sherryann and Mark Kuzdzal; BS Clinical Health Studies, 2017; Ithaca College Catholic Community, Social Committee Chair, Mass Coordinator, and Retreat Leader; Hands of Praise, Vice President .

Kuzmickas, Diane Wytenus: Windsor Locks, CT; Asnuntuck Community College; AS Criminal Justice, 2015; Alpha Phi Sigma; Dean's List; *Who's Who Among Students in American Universities and Colleges*; I am honored to accept this award and wish to be an inspiration to my daughter, Jess.

L

LaBombarbe, Elda Mitre: El Paso, TX; The University of Texas El Paso; BA Criminal Justice, 2016; My sincere thanks to God, my husband, and family for their endless support during this journey.

Labrie, Parker D.: York, PA; York College of Pennsylvania; Russell and Mana Labrie; BA Criminal Justice, 2016; Resident Assistant, Student Staff of the Month January 2015, February 2015, and September 2015; Alcohol Awareness Week, Outstanding Participant Award 2014-2015; York College Mixed Martial Arts Club, Treasurer; Campus Activities Board, Cabbie of the Month February 2015; Peer Support Network, President and Treasurer; To those of my past present and future, thank you for your love and support.

Ladd, Brandon Merrill: Murfreesboro, TN; The University of Tennessee Health Science Center College of Pharmacy; PharmD Pharmacy, 2016; World Outreach Church, College Small Group Leader; Advance Memphis, Faith and Finances Ally; Fellowship Memphis Church, Greeter and Welcome Team Member; Christian Pharmacists Fellowship International, Vice President; Pharmacy SGA, Class President, Class Representative, Student Services Committee, and Interviewing Committee; American Pharmacist Association–Academy of Student Pharmacists, Member at Large, Vice President of Membership, PharmFlix Video Contest Winner, and National Patient Counseling Competition Participant; This award would not have been possible without the support and love from my family and friends.

Lafon, Jacqueline: Douglas, AZ; Cochise College; AA Psychology, 2016; Holocaust Club; Club Trio, Vice President; Phi Theta Kappa Honor Society, President; I dedicate this award to my family for their devoted love, wisdom, and believing in my success.

Lahayne, Teletha Leah Deanne: Fort Payne, AL; Northeast Alabama Community College Social Sciences; AA Business Management/Supervision, 2016; Thanks, Dad and Mom, for your love and support. Thanks, Nicolas, for being my rock.

Lake, Sequoia: St. Thomas, VI; University of The Virgin Islands; Ornette and Colette Lake; BA Accounting, 2016; Golden Key Honor Society; Dean's List; Fashion and Design Club, Public Relations Officer; To God, family and friends, Mrs. Rogers, Mrs. Martin, Pernillia, Faviola, Guerline, Lucrecia, and Thiera, thank you!

Lam, Candice Coco: Franklin, MA; Dean College; Oscar Lam and Annie Wong; AA English, 2016; Harney Academy of Irish Dance, Dancer; Berenson Mathematics Center, Student Staff and Math Tutor; Morton Family Learning Center Student Staff and Student Note-Taker; International Student Association, Vice President; Student Activities and Leadership Development, Student Staff and Community Advisor of Wallace Hall; National Society of Leadership and Success, Membership and President's Award; Phi Theta Kappa; I am humbled and privileged to receive this honor and look forward to achieving even more in the future.

Lambert, Casandra: Oradell, NJ; Kean University of New Jersey; Nuria and Alexander Lambert; MS Occupational Therapy, 2017; United Cerebral Palsy, Fundraiser and Member; Relay For Life; Alzheimer's Association; Brain Injury Alliance of New Jersey; Nathan Weiss Color Run; New Jersey Occupational Therapy Association; American Occupational Therapy Association; Student Occupational Therapy Association, Fundraiser Chair; This award would not have been possible without the support from my parents, family, peers, and faculty.

Lampkin, Alexius KaDeshia: Headland, AL; Albany State University; Kim and Al Lampkin; BA Forensic Science/Chemistry, 2018; NAACP; Habitat for Humanity; Sigma Kappa Delta; Forensic Science Club, President; Velma Fudge Grant Honors Program, Vice President; Gamma Beta Phi, Secretary; Florida Georgia Alliance for Minority Participation; Alpha Kappa Mu; I am grateful for everyone in my life who has helped me become the person I am today.

Lance, Sharese M.: Spokane Valley, WA; Independence University; Charlotte Johnson and Todd Newport; AS Business Management/Accounting, 2016; Gratitude to my husband, Dad, Mom, Kiana, Aunt Rose, Ramee Rogers, Heidi M., and many others.

Landry, Dayton Dwain: Baton Rouge, LA; University of Louisiana at Monroe Undergraduate; Durward and Lisa Landry; BA Criminal Justice, 2016; Delta Sigma Phi Fraternity, Sergeant at Arms, GPA Award; I would like to thank my parents, family, fiancé, friends, and professors for helping make this award possible.

Lane, Kentaysha Anita: Brooklyn, NY; Hampton University; Tyesha Thomas-Gant and James Gant; BS Nursing, 2016; Peer Counselor Organization, Parliamentarian; Student Nurse Organization, President.

Langham, Emma E.: Greenville, IL; Columbia College; Kirk and Melody Langham; BS Human Services, 2016; American Red Cross Association; Room at the Inn; Committed and Serving Together Club, Service Project Volunteer; Student Support Services, Mentor; Human Services Club, Vice President; This award would not have been possible without the support of my family, friends, and Columbia College.

Langland, Jordan Marie: Lakewood, CO; Oklahoma Panhandle State University; Julie Schmidt and Jim Langland; BS Animal Science, 2016; Phi Theta Kappa, Alternate CAB Representative; Equestrian Team, Regional Qualifier; Thank you to everyone for the unconditional love and support. I could not have done it without you!

Langley, Nia Alexandria D.: Grand Ledge, MI; Oakwood University; Jonathan and J. Robin Langley; BA English, Professional Writing, 2015; COGME, Inc., Violin Teacher; Oakwood University Symphony, Violinist; *Spreading Oak Newspaper*, Copy Editor; United Student Movement Student Government, Supreme Court Justice; I owe a huge thanks to my parents, Robin and Jonathan; my sister, Aliya; and, most importantly, God.

Langley-Brady, Dawn L.: Martinez, GA; Georgia Regents University College of Nursing; Anne Boone and Dr. Harry Langley; PhD Nursing, 2017; This award was possible through the support of my family and Augusta University CON faculty and colleagues.

Larimer, Morgan: Knoxville, TN; College of Charleston; Reecy Payne and Steve Larimer; BS Biology/International Studies, 2017; Biology Club, Vice President and Public Relations Executive; Student Researcher at Grice Marine Laboratory, MAYS Grant Recipient; Honors Engaged, Co-Leader; Office of Sustainability, Sustainability Fellow and Intern; Rotaract Club, President, Founder, and Vice President; CofC Meira Belly-dance Troupe; Intramural Dodgeball; Students for Social Innovation, Public Relations Executive; Alliance for Planet Earth, President and Public Relations Executive; ECOllective Student Project Committee, Executive Chair; Women's Lacrosse Team; Green Heart Volunteer; This award would not have been possible without the support and love from my family.

Larkins, Ashley Lauren: Fort Lupton, CO; William Woods University; Roger and Michele Larkins; BS Equestrian Science/Equestrian Administration, 2016.

Lary, Kaylyn Michale: Northport, AL; James H. Faulkner State Community College; Kay and Jeff Lary; AS Pre-Medicine, 2016; Dean's List 2014; Fellowship of Christian Athletes; Softball; Phi Theta Kappa; Without my family and friend, this award would not have been possible. I love you all!

LaSalle, Allison Melissa: Chadwicks, NY; Utica School of Commerce; Scott and Lisa LaSalle; AS Health Service Management, 2017; This award would not have been possible without the love and support from my family and friends!

Laster, Debra J.: East Haven, CT; Albertus Magnus College; BS Management, 2016.

Latta, Robert Lightfoot: Stilwell, OK; Connors State College; AA Sociology, 2016; I can do all things through Christ which strengthens me.

Lattie, Samantha Dorismay: Downingtown, PA; West Chester University; Leean Riley and Owen Lattie; BS Biology, 2016; Leadership Consultant, Co-President; I credit all of my success to my loving family and loving parents. Thanks, Guys!

Law, Stephen Jason: Cowpens, SC; Limestone College; Stephen Law and Annette Ramsey; BA Criminal Justice, 2017; Thank you to my loving wife, daughter, and family who gave much support and encouragement.

Lawson, Katherine: Arlington, VA; College of Charleston; Katherine and William Barnes Lawson Jr.; BS Business Administration and Economics, 2017; Dean's Student Forum, Director; Order of Omega Honor Fraternity; Interdisciplinary Center for Applied Technology, Cohort Member; Real Estate Club; Kappa Alpha Theta Fraternity; Center for Public Choice and Market Process, Market Process Scholar; Honor Board, Board Member; To my family and David, without your support I would have not been able to receive this award.

Lawson, Shandolyn A.: Chicago, IL; Jackson State University College of Education and Human Development; Gwendolyn and Carlos Lawson; BS Education, 2016; Dean's List; Chi Alpha Epsilon; My goal is to earn a bachelor of science degree in education.

Lazarus, John Kevin: Mobile, AL; Auburn University; BA Psychology/Spanish, 2016; Student Eminent Society Liberal Arts Ambassador Program, President; Camp War Eagle, Parent Counselor; Auburn Wesley Foundation, Discipleship Chair; University Program Council, Director of Films.

Leahey, Andrew: Bethany, OK; Southern Nazarene University; Thomas and Teresa Leahey; BS Pre-Physical Therapy, 2016; Cross Country and Track, NAIA All-American, Varies School Records, Three-Time GAC All-Team in Cross Country.

Leal III, Leonel: San Antonio, TX; LeTourneau University; Gabriela and Leonel Leal II; BS Electrical Engineering, 2018; President's List; CAD Lab Assistant; Association of Robotic Science, President; I would not be where I am today without God's strength and my family.

Lebeduik, Allison Nichol: Ridgeley, WV; Allegany College of Maryland; AS Medical Assistant, 2016; Medical Assistant Club, Secretary; Thank you to my family, friends, and amazing teachers for all of your love and support!

Ledesma-Maldonado, Selimar: Carolina, PR; University of Puerto Rico Medical Sciences Campus; Nilda Maldonado-Román and Luis Ledesma-Martínez; PhD Pharmacy, 2017; Beta Beta Beta; PharmD, "Farmacia en tu Comunidad"; Poster Presentations Certifications in: PRISM, PRSM, ABRCMS, NEA, SciTeCC, and XV Sigma Xi; Magna Cum Laude; This award would not have been possible without God and the support of my family and boyfriend.

Lee, Kirstin Nicole: Houston, TX; University of St. Thomas; Sharon and Dean Lee; BA Nursing, 2016; This award would not have been possible without the support of my family, friends, professors, and coaches.

Lee, Ondrea Khadija: New Market, AL; University of Montevallo; Maureen and William Lee; BA Marketing, 2016; Phi Chi Theta Business Fraternity, Volunteer Coordinator; SGA, Executive Secretary, Vice President, and Treasurer; None of this would have been possible without God, my family, and my friends. Thank you all!

Lefkowitz, Dylan: Charleston, SC; College of Charleston; Bruce and Debra Lefkowitz; BS Exercise Science, 2015.

Lehman, Cory: Maricopa, AZ; Central Arizona College; Sheila McMillen; AA Business Administration, 2016; Youth Ministry, Pastor, Mentor, and Motivational Speaker; Juvenile Prison Ministry, Pastor, Mentor, and Motivational Speaker; Student Leadership, Special Events Coordinator; Phi Theta Kappa, Vice President; I thank God for the wisdom and His grace, and I thank my Mother for her love and support.

Leonard, Hannah Young: Salisbury, NC; Brevard College; Beverly and John Leonard; BA Psychology/Theatre, 2016; Psychology Department, Outstanding Research 2015; Theatre Production of "Sylvia," Best Actress 2013; Theatre Production of "Proof," Best Actress 2014; Theatre Production of "Not With a Bang, But a Whimper," Best Supporting Actress 2015; Alumni Advisory Board, Student Representative; Theatre Department, Outstanding Student in Theatre Studies 2014 and 2016; Office of Career Exploration and Development, Intern; Boys and Girls Club of Transylvania County, Intern; Psychology Department, Outstanding Student in Psychology 2016; Theatre Production of "Crimes of the Heart," Best Supporting Actress 2016; Campus Activities Board, President; This award would not have been possible without the support of my amazing family, I love you.

Leonowitz, Jacob R.: Birdsboro, PA; Duquesne University; BS Music Education, 2016; Choral Programs, Pappert Men's Chorale 2012–2013, Voices of Spirit 2013–2016, Voices of Spirit Secretary 2014–2015, Voices of Spirit Bass Section Leader 2014–2015, Pappert Women's Chorale Accompanist 2014–2015; Spotlight Musical Theater Company, Music Director for Several Productions; Mu Phi Epsilon, Epsilon Upsilon, Vice President 2015, Two-Time Scholarship Winner, and Published Article in Mu Phi's Quarterly Publication, *The Triangle*; National Association for Music Education Chapter #159, Treasurer 2013–2014 and President 2014–2015); NAFME Collegiate Professional Achievement Award, May 2014.

L'Esperance, Kara M.: Wichita Falls, TX; Midwestern State University; Robert and Mary Mansker; BS Special Education, 2017; Honor Roll; President's Honor Roll; Annual Faith Refuge Mother's Day Supply Drive, Creator and Coordinator; Key Spouse Program, USAF, Key Spouse and Key Spouse Mentor; Girls Scouts of America, Assistant Troop Leader; Boy Scouts of America, NWTC, Committee Member; Alpha Chi Honor Society; Tau Sigma Honor Society; Council for Exceptional Children, President; I would like to thank my husband, Adam, for his unending faith, love, and support.

Lessard, Jamey J.: Westfield, ME; Northern Maine Community College; AA Automotive Technology, 2016; With the unending support of my parents, I would not have made my accomplishment become reality.

Levenson, Jack Michael: Brooklyn, NY; New York College of Podiatric Medicine; Yves and Robin Levenson; BS Psychology, 2016; Education Committee, Bacteriology, Physiology, Functional Orthopedics I, and Functional Orthopedics II; ACFAS Surgery Club; ASPS Surgery Club; Diabetes Club; Orthopedics Club; Radiology Club; Marathon Medical Staff, Diva Half Marathon, NYCRUNS Central Park Marathon, New Jersey Marathon; *Podiatric Medical Review*, Peer Reviewer; Junior Surgery Clinical Clerkship, Student Coordinator; Thank you to all my family and friends for their unconditional support!

Levia, Richard Keith: Altamonte Springs, FL; Belhaven University; BA Biblical Ministries, 2015; Precious thanks to God, Allison Levia, and family, whose unrelenting support and love have made this achievement colorable.

Lewis, Amanda M.: Franklin, PA; Robert Morris University; Sandy Lewis and Willard Burns; BA Media Arts, TV/Video Production, 2016; RMU Bands, Marching, Pep, Jazz, Concert, and Fife and Drum, Marketing and Information Officer; Kappa Kappa Psi, Treasurer; This award would not have been possible without the support of my mother and grandparents.

Lewis, Jazmyne D.: Monroe, LA; Grambling State University; Decie Lewis; BS Electronic Engineering Technology, 2017; This award would not have been possible without the support and love from my family and friends.

LeZion, Alexandria Grace: Springfield, MO; Evangel University; Melanie and Wes Connell; BS Psychology, 2016; Leadership on Campus Scholarship Recipient; Commuter Council, Non-Traditional Student Representative; Psi Chi, Vice President and Treasurer; This award is only possible because of God, my friends, my mentors, and my spiritual family.

Libera, Maris Anna: Palos Height, IL; Bellarmine University; Teresa and Gene Libera; AA Respiratory Therapy, 2017.

Linck, Donna Teresa: Lawrenceville, GA; Georgia Regents University College of Nursing; PhD Nursing, 2017; Graduate Research Assistant; Sigma Theta Tau Nursing Honor Society; Phi Kappa Phi Honor Society; National Society of Leadership and Success; Many thanks for the loving support of my family, especially my husband, Jack, and mother, Sachiko.

Lincoln, Owen Curtis: Sunnyvale, CA; University of The Pacific School of Engineering and Computer Science; Craig and Leslie Lincoln; MS Mechanical Engineering, 2016; Tau Beta Pi, Vice President; Theta Tau, Regent, Vice Regent, and National Convention Outstanding Delegation 2014.

Lindaberry, Chelsea Elizabeth: Myrtle Beach, SC; Southern Wesleyan University; Kristine and Jeffrey Lindaberry; BS Special Education, 2016; The chisel for success is a committed heart. Thanks to my family and fiancé for being wonderful examples.

Lindley, Logan Rant: Hinton, OK; Northwestern Oklahoma State University; Steve and Tricia Lindley; BS Biology, 2017; My amazing parents have always supported me, without them I would not be who I am today.

Lindmark, Miranda P.: Overland Park, KS; Baker University Baldwin City; Sheri and Russell Lindmark; BS Elementary Education, 2018; Total Equality Alliance, Member of Founding Class; Student Senate, Freshmen Class Representative 2014–2015 and Executive Board Secretary 2015–2016; Zeta Tau Alpha Sorority, Sisterhood Chair 2014–2015, Vice President II, and New Member Educator 2015–2016; I am so very grateful for my friends, family, and teachers for the endless support and love.

Link, Caroline Susan: Fort Thomas, KY; Bellarmine University; Kristin Dierig and Kevin Link; BA Accounting, 2016; Accounting Association, Secretary 2013–2014; Beta Gamma Sigma, Global Leadership Summit 2015 Representative and First GLS Case Competition Participant; Delta Sigma Pi, Vice President of Scholarships and Awards 2015–2016, Chancellor 2014–2015, Vice President of Alumni Relations 2014, Mrs. DSP 2015, and Most Reliable Brother and Most Visible Brother 2015; This would not have been possible without the support of my amazing family, friends, and teachers.

Linneman, Amber Dawn: Salisbury, MO; Sinclair School of Nursing University of Missouri; BS Nursing, 2016; Honors College; Nursing Scholar; This award would not have been possible without the encouragement and support from my family.

Little, Allie Christina: Gaffney, SC; Limestone College; Christina and Quay Little; BA Early Childhood Elementary Education, 2016; Know(2), Rising Star Award; This award would not have been possible without support from my family, teachers, and Limestone College.

Litton, Jessica Samantha: Flowery Branch, GA; Georgia Regents University College of Nursing; Dr. Waldemar Karwowski and Mrs. Bernarda Karwowski; Gerontology Acute Care Nurse Practitioner, 2016; PhD Nursing Practices; Sigma Theta Tau International Society of Nursing, Beta Omicron Chapter; National Society of Leadership and Success, Sigma Alpha Pi Chapter; Phi Kappa Phi National Honor Society; American Association of Heart Failure Nurses; American Association of Critical-Care Nurses; Thank you to my amazing husband and family, whose love and support have guided me throughout this journey!

Loaiza, Katiuzca Isabel: Brockport, NY; The University of Texas at San Antonio; Willan and Yudy Loaiza; MA Educational Leadership and Policy Studies, Concentration Higher Education Administration, 2015; Alternative Winter Break 2015 Participant; Diabetes Run Volunteer; San Antonio State Hospital Volunteer; Challenger Baseball Volunteer; Leadership Story Telling Luncheon Facilitator; The Honor Society of Phi Kappa Phi; Higher Education Administration Student Association; Roadrunner Productions, Game Day Director; Graduate Student Association, Vice President and Downtown Liaison.

Locasto, Joelynn Marie: Oxford, NJ; College of Saint Elizabeth; Joseph and Stephanie Longo; MA Education, 2015; Thank you to my family for your love and support.

Lockhart, Shereitta: Harvest, AL; John C. Calhoun State Community College.

Lococo, Stephen: Atlanta, GA; Kennesaw State University.

Logston, Amanda L.: New Martinsville, WV; West Virginia Northern Community College; AS Clinical Medical Assistant, 2016; Thank you to all that supported me during this journey. I love you all.

Long, Emily Kirby: Hartselle, AL; University of Montevallo; Jonathan and Judy Long; BS Communication Studies, 2016; Department of Communication, Future Falcon Volunteer, Event Planning Intern, Student Registration Assistant, Commitment to the Discipline Award, and Martin Luther King Oratorical Contest Winner; Admissions Office, Maven Tour Guide; Honors College, Team Lead for Eco-Trail Restoration, Sustainability Fund Grant Recipient, and Peer Mentor; Public Relations Student Society of America, Vice President; Central States Communication Association, Assistant Newsletter Editor; Lambda Pi Eta Communication Studies Honor Society, President; Order of Omega Honor Society, Vice President and Selection Committee; National Communication Association, Panelist; To my family, for without your everlasting patience and kindness this would have never been possible.

Looney, Pamela Diane: Grundy, VA; King University; Donald and Loraine Ramey; BS Nursing, 2016; King University; Summa Cum Laude; This award would not have been possible without the support and love from my family.

Lopez, Desiree Renee: Orange Grove, TX; Texas A&M University Kingsville; Leticia Lopez and David Ramirez; MS Counseling Psychology, 2016; Psi Chi International Honor Society; Counseling Psychology Graduate Student Organization, President; This award would not have been possible without the support and love from my fiancée, Randy, and family.

Lopitz, Joshua S.: Leonardtown, MD; West Virginia Wesleyan College; Deborah Bailey and Stephen Lopitz; BA Communication Studies, 2016; Office of Admissions, Intern; BOOT Camp, Student Leader; Student Senate, Freshmen and Sophomore Class President; Wesleyan Ambassador, President and Weekly Ambassador; Men's Track and Field, Eighth Place in Conference; Theta Xi Fraternity, President, House Manager, Public Relations Officer, Recruitment, Brotherhood, and Alumni Relations Chair; I have accomplished everything at Wesleyan only because of my family's generous support.

Loppe, Teagan Marie: Alameda, CA; Minot State University; Brad Loppe; BS Special Education, 2016; MSU at the Dome, Coordinator between Optimist Club and SCEC Club; I can't thank my family and friends enough for their continued support throughout my time at MSU!

Lorentzen, Abigail Margaret: New Bern, NC; Meredith College; James and Tracey Lorentzen; BA Mass Communication/International Studies, 2016; Office of Study Abroad, Peer Ambassador; Class of 2016 Executive Board, Historian; First Year Experience, Student Assistant; I am "Going Strong" thanks to my family and Meredith College!

Loreto, Marrissa A.: Moon Township, PA; Robert Morris University; Anthony and Kelly Loreto; BA Media Arts, 2016; Patriot Yearbook, Staff Photographer; Nonprofit Leadership Association, Public Relations and Social Media Chair; This award would not have been possible without my dedication and determination to succeed.

Lorey, Demi Alexis: Lubbock, TX; Lubbock Christian University; Melissa and Bruce Davis; BA Psychology, 2016; Alliance Team, Event Coordinator 2015–2016; *The Duster Newspaper*, Student Editor 2014–2015; Behavioral Sciences Society, Secretary 2014–2015; Lubbock Impact Mentor Program; Lead Coordinator 2014–2015; Sunset Church of Christ, Student Action Leadership Team, Evangelism 2015–2016; Kappa Phi Kappa, Chaplain 2015–2016; All glory goes to God. Thank you to my family, the incredible LCU community, and sweet Davis.

Love, Denise C.: Jackson, MS; Jackson State University College of Education and Human Development; BS Child Care/Family Education, 2016; I would like to thank my family for their continued prayers, love, and support.

Lovekamp, Hannah Louise: Saint Peters, MO; Missouri Baptist University; Kathleen and Michael Lovekamp; BA Psychology, 2016; Academic Honor Roll; Dean's List; President's Citation; Thank you to God and my family for your continuous loving support through the good times and bad.

Lovelady, Alicia Marie: Tishomingo, MS; Itawamba Community College Tupelo; Julie and Timothy Lovelady; AA Respiratory Care Technology, 2016; "I can do all things through Christ which strengthens me." —Philippians 4:13

Lovett, Andrea: Stockbridge, GA; Kennesaw State University; Freddie and Veda Lovett; BS Middle Grades Education; 2017; Kennesaw State National Pan-Hellenic Council, Public Relations Coordinator 2015–2016; Sigma Gamma Rho, Chapter President 2015–2016; This award really helped me believe in myself, and I am thankful for all of the love and support.

Lowery, Jessica Lynn: Frostburg, MD; Allegany College of Maryland; AA Massage Therapy, 2016; Promote the Profession, Treasurer of Massage Club; I want to dedicate this award to my family, who made this achievement possible.

Lozada Martín, Alejandra: Cabo Rojo, PR; Inter American University of Puerto Rico, San German Campus; Gisela and Irving Miranda; BS Biology, 2017; Student Night Award; Honors Certificate 2014, 2015, and 2016; Recognition of Merit and Accomplishment Award 2015; *Who's Who Among Students* Award 2014–2015; Student Activities Leadership Award 2014; IX Exhibition of Scientific Investigation, Poster Participation Award; Student Body Organization, BBB National Biological Honor Society Spirit Award 2016; Department of Languages and Literature Creativity Slam Contest Award 2013; Siempre tendré dos grandes amores: mi familia y la medicina.

Lundgren, Molly: Highland, NY; State University of New York Plattsburgh; Eileen and Gary Lundgren; BS Accounting, International Business, Business Administration, 2016; School of Business and Economics VOICES, Accounting Representative; Student Committee on Teaching Excellence; Student Managed Investment Fund; Accounting Mentoring Program, Coordinator; Accounting and Finance Association, Treasurer; This honor would not have been possible without the love and support from my family, friends, and faculty.

Lunsford, Jennifer Rose: Columbia, SC; Columbia College; BA Psychology/Behavioral Health, 2016; Mcnair Fellowship; Annual President's List; I could only have made it here without you by my side, Aubree, Michael, Mom, and Dad.

Luttrell, Zachary Ross: Indianapolis, IN; Marian University; Lisa and Ron Luttrell; BS Nursing, 2015; IU Health Patient Care Intern 2014–2015; IU Health Student Volunteer 2013–2014; Work Study Student 2010–2012; Theatre Department Actor 2010–2013; Green Life Club, Vice President 2012–2013; Performing Knights Club, Secretary 2012–2013; Student Orientation and Registration, Orientation Leader 2014–2015; Nursing School Tutor 2012–2013; Sacred Choir 2013–2015; Chamber Singers 2013–2015; Knight Fusion Show Choir 2012–2015; A Capella Choir 2011–2012; Marching Band 2010–2015; Student Leader 2014–2015; This award would not have been possible without the love and support from my family and friends.

Lutz, Shannon Marie: Warren, OH; Youngstown State University; MA English, 2016.

LuVisi, Olivia M.: Kuna, ID; Gardner-Webb University; Philip and Debrya LuVisi; BA Broadcast Journalism/Writing, 2016; Peer Leader, Senior Peer Leader Award; Relay For Life and Rave to Save, Deejay and Emcee; Gardner-Webb Athletics Promotions and Marketing Department, Video Coordinator; WGWG.org Gardner-Webb Radio, Volunteer DJ and Student Volunteer Coordinator; Student Recruitment Ambassador for Undergraduate Admissions, Communications Student Recruitment Ambassador; Miss Gardner-Webb Pageant, Crowned Miss Gardner-Webb, First Runner-Up, and Top 5; I would not be where I am without the support of my family and the GWU community. Much love.

Lwin, Ni N.: Owings Mills, MD; Stevenson University; BS Nursing/Minor in Psychology, 2016.

Lyle, Rachel C.: Glasgow, VA; Dabney S. Lancaster Community College; Thomas Lyle and Dana Holmes; ADN Nursing, 2016; Great things can come from even greater adversity.

M

Macalena, Brianne E.: Congers, NY; Dominican College of Blauvelt Graduate School; MS Childhood Education, Students with Disabilities, 2016; Special Needs Movie Night, Coordinator, Creator, and Host; Kapa Delta Phi, Academic Honor Roll; Council for Exceptional Children, Co-President 2015; This award would not have been possible without the love and unconditional support from my beautiful family.

Macaluso, Briana M.: Cicero, NY; St. John Fisher College; Greg and Robin Macaluso; BS Biology, 2016; Camp Good Days and Special Times, Camp Counselor; SGA Awards, Junior of the Year; Teddi Dance for Love, Chair; This achievement would not have been possible without the support from my loving family.

MacNeil, Ronda Lynn: Palm Springs, CA; Independence University; Phillip Davies, Clyde and Marie Huffaker; MBA with Emphasis on Entrepreneurship, 2016; National Society of Collegiate Scholars; Student Advisory Committee; This award would not have been possible without the support and love from my family.

Madni, Sayed Farhan: Mobile, AL; University of South Alabama; Irfan and Arshiya Madni; BS Information Systems, 2016; I want to humbly thank my parents, siblings, and friends who have been a salient part of my journey.

Mahammoud-Salem, Ahmed Mohammed: Philadelphia, PA; Goldey Beacom College Graduate School; MS International Business Management, 2016.

Mahle-Talayumptewa, Lynnora: Flagstaff, AZ; Independence University; Verde Mahle-Polacca; BS Accounting with Emphasis in Forensics, 2017; Thank you to my mom, brother, and husband for all the love and encouragement. I Love You!

Mahon, Annette Mary: Mount Vernon, OH; Mount Vernon Nazarene University; Nancy and Michael Mahon; BA Criminal Justice and Psychology, 2016; Stitch-A-Niche Community Service Group, Co-President; Treble Singers Women's Choir, President; This award is dedicated to those who believed in and supported me.

Majani Sr., Gertrude Kavugwi: Omaha, NE; College of Saint Mary; Salome Majani; BS Nursing, 2017; Do Unto Others Service Club, Christian Appalachian Project Workfest 2016; Student Senate-Elections Committee Chair; Sigma Phi Sigma 2015; Dean's List 2014–2015; This award would not have been possible without the support of faculty and staff and of my religious and biological families.

Major, Brady M.: Port Allegany, PA; University of Pittsburgh Bradford; David and Marcie Major; BA Interdisciplinary Arts, 2016; National Society of Leadership and Success; This honor is dedicated to Emily Dietz, who showed me the value of love and hard work.

Malik, Sadik: Alva, OK; Northwestern Oklahoma State University; Malik and Mercy Abubakar; BS Biology, Health Science Option, 2017; Tenth Annual Ranger Research Day, Poster Presentation on "The Effects of Familiar and Unfamiliar Music on Human Heart Rates"; Theater Production *Godspell*, Actor; Art Society Art Show, Second Place for Elements of Design, Selfie, Still Life and Third Place for Conceptual and Still Life Categories in Digital Photography; Festival of Cultures, International Students Association; Volunteer at Hopeton Church; Volunteer at Share Medical Center; Biology Club; Chemistry Club; Sigma Delta Pi Honor Society; Concert Choir; Red and Black Scroll Honor Society, Reporter and Historian 2015–2016; Spanish Club, Vice President; Medical Sciences Club, President 2015–2016 and Public Relations Officer 2014–2015; Special thanks to God, my parents, Dr. Cynthia Pfeifer-Hill, and Nice Mutsipayi, who push me to excel.

Maliszewski, Gemma R.: Wichita, KS; University of Saint Mary; Lisa and James Maliszewski; BA Theatre, 2016.

Malone, Justin L.: Quitman, LA; Grambling State University; Keith and Velma Malone; BS Marketing, 2019; Office of Student Judicial Affairs, Student Representative; Royal Court, Escort; This award would not have been possible without prayers and the support from my family.

Mann, Elizabeth Grace: Finksburg, MD; McDaniel College; BA Sociology, 2016; Relay For Life; American Cancer Society, Fundraiser; House of Ruth, Fundraiser and Donator; International Programs Office Candidate Search Committee; Study Abroad, Budapest, Hungary; Heroes Helping Hopkins, Fundraiser; Phi Alpha Mu, Alumnae Advisory Board and Standards Board Senior Representative; Alpha Kappa Delta, Voting Member in the Maryland Kappa Chapter; Order of Omega, Secretary; Student Alumni Council; This award would not have been possible without the support of my sorority and my passion for learning.

Manner, Jeffrey: Coatesville, PA; Delaware County Community College; AA Mathematics/Natural Science, 2016; Honors Geology; Phi Theta Kappa.

Manuel, Harli Angelle: Gonzales, LA; Southeastern Louisiana University; Steven and Sonia Manuel; BA Communications, 2016; Recreational Sports and Wellness, Student Intern and Student Supervisor; Order of Omega Greek Honor Society, President; SGA, President's Cabinet, Director of Campus Involvement for Greek Life, Director of Student Involvement for All Student Organizations, and Big Event Committee Head; Division of Student Affairs Leadership Ambassador, Emerging Leaders Retreat Co-Chair and Leadership Development Co-Chair; Sigma Sigma Sigma Sorority, Panhellenic Delegate Officer, Greek Week, Homecoming, Strawberry Fest, Sisterhood, Recruitment Committees, Dunham Leadership Representative, and By-Law Committee; I attribute all my success to the support, guidance, and love my parents shared with me.

Manzini, Thomas Robert Ratcliffe: Las Vegas, NV; Rensselaer Polytechnic Institute; Robyn and Aldo Manzini; BS Computer Science, 2016; Science Undergraduate Council, Co-Founder; Ambulance, Captain, Event Supervisor, Driver, and Crew Chief; Upsilon Pi Epsilon, NY Eta Chapter, President.

Marcel, Allison Anastasia: Lafayette, LA; University of Louisiana Lafayette; Tammy and Albert C. Marcel Jr.; BS Sports Management, 2016; Susan G. Komen Race for the Cure Volunteer; DELTA Gems Reading Book Club; Festival International de Louisiane Volunteer; Alzheimer's Association Annual Race Volunteer; St. Joseph Dinner Volunteer; St. Anthony Catholic Church "Feed My People" Ministry and CCD Administrative Assistant; Martin Luther King Jr. Program and Day Volunteer; Faith House King Cake 5k Run Volunteer; Ernest Gallet Elementary Reading Volunteer; Ronald E. McNair Scholarship Program; National Association of University Women Scholarship; Kinesiology Professional Association; Louisiana Athletic Trainers Association; Ragin Peppers; American College of Sports Medicine; National Society of Leadership and Success; Delta Sigma Theta Sorority, Inc.; Black Women's Leadership Association Association of Future Alumni Ambassador; Ragin Cajun Ambassador; President's List; Dean's List; SGA, Senator; "Never stop dreaming and never stop believing." To my parents and family, thanks for your love and support.

Marcinek, Melissa Cay: Okeechobee, FL; Indian River State College; Paul and Mary Marcinek; AS Criminal Justice Technology, 2013; I dedicate this award to my family, to whom I owe everything.

Maready, Kassie Brooke: Warsaw, NC; James Sprunt Community College; Bryant Maready and Julie Hatcher; AS Business Administration, 2016; This award would have been possible without the support from my family and dear love, Bobby.

Marek, Lindsey Nicole: Little River, TX; University of Mary Hardin-Baylor; BS Social Work, 2016; NASW/Texas State Conference; Poverty Simulation; NASW/TS Central Texas Counties Branch Meeting, Co-Facilitator 2016; Our Youth at Risk: Sex Trafficking and Unaccompanied Youth, Co-Facilitator 2016; Social Work Club; Provost and Dean Honor Society 2015; Delta Upsilon, Phi Alpha Honor Society, President 2016; This award would not have been possible without the support and love from my husband, family, and mentors.

Marino, Sarah: Buffalo, NY; D'Youville College; Philip and Elizabeth Marino; BS Exercise and Sports Studies, 2016; Student-Athlete Advisory Committee, Secretary; Softball, AMCC Academic All-Conference Team 2014–2016; Women's Basketball, Captain 2016, AMCC Sportsmanship Award 2013–2015, Spartan Award 2014, and AMCC Academic All-Conference Team 2014–2016; To my family, friends, teammates, teachers, and coaches: thank you for the constant love and support.

Marlowe, Lea Jasmine: Greenwood, FL; Mary Baldwin College; Cosie and Leo Marlowe; BS Business with Emphasis in Accounting, 2017.

Marquez, Vanessa Mae: Seguin, TX; Howard Payne University; BA Social Work, 2016; Social Work Club, Secretary; I am truly blessed to have been honored with this award. All honor and glory be to God.

Marshall, Olivia Grace: Lexington, KY; Bluegrass Community and Technical College; John and Sabrina Marshall; AS Radiography, 2016; Radiography Advisory Board, Class Representative 2016; Dean's List.

Martin, Jessica P.: Elizabethton, TN; East Tennessee State University; Lisa Ledford; BS Political Science, 2016; Athletics, Mascot; National Collegiate Honor Society; National Society of Leadership and Success; Civility Week Committee Member; Relay For Life Committee, Spirit Coordinator; SGA, Associate Justice and College of Arts and Sciences Senator; I could never thank my mom enough for all her love and sacrifices.

Martin, Judson Alecander: Jacksonville, AL; Gadsden State Community College; James and Belinda Martin; AS General Studies, 2016; Student Support Services, Tutor; I want to thank my family and all of the incredible teachers at Gadsden State.

Martin, Michael Anthony: Lonoke, AR; Arkansas State University Beebe; Abigail Miller; AS Criminal Justice, 2018; Student Support Services, President; Gamma Beta Phi Society; Resident Assistant, Freshman of the Year 2014–2015; This award would not have been possible without the mentorship and guidance of Gabriel Martin and Cleo Miller.

Martin, Trevor William: Conneautville, PA; Thiel College; Karen Martin; BA Accounting and Business Administration, General, 2017; Varsity Football, Two-Year Letter Winner.

Martinez, Jesus Omar: Elgin, IL; Elgin Community College; J. Jesus and Vicenta Yolanda Martinez; AS Business Degree in Accounting, 2017; Phi Theta Kappa Honor Society; SGA, Co-Secretary and Presidency Nominee; Every one of my accomplishments is thanks to the support of my parents, sisters, and friends.

Martinez, Melissa Amanda: Waleska, GA; Reinhardt University; Maria Toruno and Jaime Martinez; BA Digital Art and Graphic Design, 2016; Student Tour Guide, Captain; Theta Beta Chapter of Kappa Pi Honorary Art Fraternity, President 2014–2016; Resident Assistant; SGA, Vice President for Administration, Junior Class Representative, Sophomore Class Representative, and Marguerite Thigpen Cline Leadership in Action Award; Thank you to my family and friends for all of their support.

Mason, Angel Lashawn: Hyattsville, MD; Bennett College; Jacinta Mason; BA Psychology, 2016; Sisters of Service, Parliamentarian; Psychology Club, Parliamentarian.

Mason, Michael Steve: Arnold, MO; University of Missouri Saint Louis; Karyn and Gerry Mason; BA Psychology, 2016; Phi Theta Kappa Honor Society, Vice President of Service, Transfer Scholarship Recipient, and Five Star Competitive Edge; USA Today/Coca-Cola National All-Academic Team Member Gold; Pierre Laclede Honors College Student Association, Honors Program Scholarship Recipient; Honors College Dean's List; Words cannot convey my deepest gratitude to my family, mentors, friends, and community; nonetheless, Thank-you!

Massey, Andy B.: Satanta, KS; Washburn University; Shawn and Renee Massey; BS Criminal Justice, 2016; Boy Scouts of America, Eagle Scout; Thank you to all the people who have supported me throughout my four years of college.

Mate, Gia Marie: Virginia Beach, VA; Saint Leo University; Janice Cronk and Charles Missias; BA Logistics, 2016; Chimney Hill HOA; Southeastern Virginia Food Bank, Food Distribution; Saint Luke's UMC, Church Trustee, Church Delegate for the Virginia United Methodist Conference 2015, Prayer Shawl and Card Ministry, and Council of Ministries Chair; Dean's List; Thank you to my family, friends, and the United States Navy for making this possible.

Mathews, Asheleigh Brooke: Stroud, OK; Seminole State College; AS Medical Laboratory Technology, 2016; I would not be where I am today without the love and support from my family.

Mathews, Nisha: Houston, TX; University of Houston–Clear Lake; Jos and Jacqueline Mathews; BS Accounting, 2016; Servant Leader Scholar Program, Platinum Award 2016; Omicron Delta Kappa; Beta Alpha Psi; National Society of Leadership and Success, Treasurer 2015.

Mathis, Anwar-Nasser Hutty: Philadelphia, PA; Chey-ney University of Pennsylvania; BA Accounting, 2017; National Society of Leadership and Success; Keystone Honors Academy; Football, Quarter Back, Wide Receiver, and Kick Returner; I would like to thank God first. This award would not have been possible without maintaining focus.

Mattano, Marie Christine: Mystic, CT; Emmanuel College; Leonard and Susan Mattano; BA Art Therapy, 2016; Charter Member of Kappa Pi International Honorary Art Fraternity; Dean's List; Italy Today Language; Internship at Children's Art Centre in Boston; This award would not have been possible without the love and support from my friends and family.

Matthews, Marla G.: Nashville, NC; Nash Community College; AS Nursing, 2016; Volunteer with Missions of Mercy Clinics, Nursing Student Pre-Op Workup; Volunteer with Baptist Men Association Dental Buses, Nursing Student-Pre-Op Workup; Local Student Nursing Association, Night Class Liaison; This award would not have been possible without the support of my loved ones throughout nursing school.

Matthies, Jessica: Elizaville, NY; Columbia-Greene Community College; AA Nursing, 2016; Health Promotion Club; Phi Theta Kappa Honor Society; Without the loving support of my husband, Jeremy, my college education and this award would not have been possible.

Mattie, Leanne C.: Lafollette, TN; Carson-Newman University; Melissa and Bradley Mattie; BM Church Music, 2016; This award would not have been possible without God, my family, friends, and my professors.

Mauri, Michael Thomas: Lockport, NY; State University of New York Buffalo–Graduate School; Anna and Michael Mauri; PharmD Pharmacy, 2016; School of Pharmacy Class of 2016, Vice President; Pressure makes diamonds.

Mays, Taneil T.: Washington, DC; Bennett College; La-wana Mays; BA Business Administration, 2016; Campus Life, Resident Assistant; Strength and faith kept me striving, family and friends pushed me through.

Mbalule, Maryana B.: Wichita Falls, TX; Midwestern State University; BS Nursing, 2018; This award would not have been possible without the support of my family and friends.

McAnany, Rachel Lee: Langhorne, PA; Holy Family University; Edna and Michael McAnany; BA Communications, 2016; Holy Family University's Newspaper *TriLite*, Staff Writer; Kappa Theta Epsilon, Vice President; Public Relations Student Society of America, Vice President.

McAuliffe, Erin Nicole: Pompton Lakes, NJ; College of Saint Elizabeth; Christine and Kevin McAuliffe; BA Education, Biology, STEM, Special Education (TSWD), 2017; This award would not have been possible without the support and love from my family and friends.

McCarty II, Steve: Bedford, TX; Tarrant County College Northeast Campus; Steve and Cindy McCarty; AA Business Management, 2016; This award would not have been possible without the love and support from my beautiful wife.

McClanahan, Jessica R.: Crown City, OH; University of Rio Grande; BS Education, Intervention Specialist K–12, 2017.

McClure, Brenda Ann: Prague, OK; Southwestern Christian University; MA Theological Studies, 2015; This was possible because of the love and support of my husband, Steve. Thank you!

McCluskey, Rita D.: Brownsburg, IN; Marian University; BA Business, 2016; This award would not have been possible without the support of my husband and my children.

McCraw, Candace Sloane: Hobbs, NM; New Mexico Junior College; Carla Payne; AA Accounting, 2016; Academic Achievement, Outstanding Student in Geology; I am blessed to receive this award, I thank my family for their support!

McCuistion, Austin Gabriel: Arvada, CO; Abilene Christian University; Traci and John McCuistion; BS Biochemistry, 2016; Trojans Social Club, Treasurer 2015–2016.

McCullough, Ronald Thomas: Atlanta, GA; Clark Atlanta University Isabella T. Jenkins Honors Program; Ronald and Arlesia McCullough; BS Biology and Biosystems Engineering, 2018; Dual-Degree Engineering Program, 2016 AUCC Outstanding Achievement Award and Scholarship; Student Ambassador, Executive Board Member; Provost Scholar; Dean's List; Isabella T. Jenkins Honor's Program, Student Chief of Staff; Becoming an 18-year-old junior would not have been possible without the love and guidance of my parents.

McDade, Mariah Joanne: Pittsburgh, PA; Community College of Allegheny County Boyce Campus; Susan and Dennis McDade; AA Cardiac Ultrasound, 2018; Honors Leadership, CCAC Honors; I would not have the passion I have if it were not for my amazing friends and family!

McElrath, Khari Lanning: Arden, NC; Luther Rice College and Seminary; MA Apologetics, 2016.

McEwen, Nicole Marie: Charlotte, NC; University of Georgia; Lisa and Mark McEwen; BS Human Development/Family Science, 2018; Hygiene Closet Founder; Phi Upsilon Omicron; McPhaul Child Development Lab, Substitute Teacher and Intern; Student Association of Family and Consumer Sciences, Service Director; I am so excited to be able to use this award to further my pursuits.

McFadden, Kiana De'Marius: Waynesboro, MS; Jones County Junior College; Joe and Demarius McFadden; AA Physics, 2016; Christian Food Mission; Charles Pickering Honors Institute; Phi Theta Kappa, Vice President of Leadership; 2016 All-Mississippi Community College Academic Second Team; Coca-Cola's 2016 Community College Academic Team, Silver Scholar; Jones County Junior College Band Program, First Chair Saxophone Symphonic Band, Section Leader, and Saxophone Quintet Member; This award would not have been possible without God and the support from my family and instructors.

McGuigan, Brian Thomas: Hawthorne, NJ; Dominican College of Blauvelt; Michael and Mary Ann McGuigan; BS Athletic Training; Golf Team, Captain, Men's Golf Coaches Award 2013–2014, and CACC All-Academic Team; A massive thank you to my family and friends for their love and support.

McGuire, Andrew L.: Evansville, IN; University of Southern Indiana; Brian and Jean McGuire; BA Computer Information Systems, 2017; Volunteer USI, Team Leader; Association of Information Technology Professionals, Public Relations Chair; Housing and Residence Life, Resident Assistant; Activities Programming Board, President, Vice President, and Stage Acts Committee Chair; I would like to thank my family for providing me so much opportunity throughout my life.

McGuire, Kelsey Taylor: Horsham, PA; Kutztown University; Kelly McGuire; BA Special Education Visual Impairment/Elementary Education Pre-K to 4, 2017; Student Athletic Advisory Committee, Cheer Team Representative 2014; Best Buddies of Kutztown, Chapter Vice President 2014–2015 and Chapter President 2015; Golden Bears Cheerleader, Team Captain; Thank you, mom, for always supporting and encouraging me as I follow my dreams.

McIntire, Nicholas: Blue Jay, CA; University of Pittsburgh Bradford; Rusty and Lee Ann McIntire; BA Early Childhood Education, 2016; Education Club, President; This award would not have been possible without the support from my family and loving fiancée, Megan.

McKee, Jalen: San Antonio, TX; The University of Texas at San Antonio; Daina and Michael McGee; AA Communication, 2017; Triathlon Club; Spectrum; Hispanic Heritage Month Planning Committee; Filipino Student Association; Council of Student Organizations, Director of Public Relations 2015, Executive Director 2016, and Roadrunners Live Committee Chair 2015; Multicultural Greek Council, President 2016 and Vice President External 2015; Thank you to all of my friends and family for all of the love and support. Love you!

McKinney, Jordan Asher: College Station, TX; Texas A&M University; Vicki and Randall McKinney; BS Finance, 2016; Prospective Undergraduate Medical Aggie Students, Co-Director; Executive Council of Health Organizations, President; Abide, Treasurer; Global Medical Brigades, IT Officer; Kappa Upsilon Chi, Rho Chapter Secretary and Communications Chair; Impact Retreats, Prayer Team; The Father Redeeming the Enslaved and Exploited, Social Media Director.

McManus, Ashley L.: York, PA; York College of Pennsylvania; Debra and Robert McManus; BA Behavioral Science, 2017; Sigma Delta Tau, Assistant to the Vice President of New Member Education; Student Ambassador, Head Ambassador; Student Senate, Treasurer Pro-Temp and Vice President of Organizational Development; I am so thankful for the people who came into my life to make this accomplishment possible.

McManus, Celia Rose: Ballwin, MO; University of Missouri Saint Louis; Alynn and Ken McManus; MA Social Work, 2016; My thanks to the MSW faculty at UMSL, as well as my family, friends, and colleagues.

McNeil III, Gerald Thomas: Quincy, MA; Eastern Nazarene College; Gerald and Merri McNeil; BS Biology, 2016; Wollaston Church of the Nazarene, Assistant Preschool Sunday School Teacher; Chess Club; IT Help Desk 2012–2016; Physics and Engineering Club 2013–2016; Commuter Council, Social Life Representative 2012–2013 and Vice President 2013–2014; Animal Care Takers Team, Head 2014–2016; Acapella Choir, Acapella Choir Chaplin 2014–2015; Shrader Club, Vice President.

McNew, Makayla Kennedy: Keavy, KY; Alice Lloyd College; Aileen McNew; BS Biology, 2017; Dean's List; I would like to thank all of the people who have helped me further my education.

McQueeney, Brendan J.: North Easton, MA; Roger Williams University; James and Jane McQueeney; BS Marketing, 2016; Beta Gamma Sigma; American Advertising Federation; National Student Advertising Competition, Co-Account Planning Director; Delta Sigma Pi, Audit Committee, WQRI, General Manager, Business Director, and General Member; Thank you to my family, friends, WQRI, Carol, Gerry, Dana, and Eileen.

McSherry, Lori Elizabeth: Newton, NJ; Centenary College; BS Accounting, 2017; Resident Assistant; Academic Excellence Award from MACUHO; Leadership Award; I would like to thank my loving family and friends who have supported me though my educational endeavors

Meacham, Kaysie Antoinette: Perdido, AL; University of Mobile; Shelly and Allen Jay, Blake Malone; BS Elementary, Early Childhood Education, 2016; Reading Council, President; Thank you to my amazing family for your support over the years. I love you all.

Meador, Courtney Ellen: Hatfield, AR; Rich Mountain Community College; AA History, 2017.

Medellin, Francesca M.: Nashua, NH; University of New England; Catherine Merrill-Medellin and Benito Medellin; BS Medical Biology, 2015; College Community Mentoring, Site Leader; I just want to thank my family and friends for all their love and support through it all!

Meegan, Mackenzie Alexis: Phoenix, AZ; New England College; Maureen and Charles Meegan; BA Kinesiology, 2017; Health Science Club; Women's Lacrosse, Rookie of the Week; Women's Ice Hockey, 2015 All-Academic Team; Women's Soccer, 2015 All-Academic Team; Student Athlete Advisory Committee, Secretary and Student Athlete of the Year; This award would not have been possible without the support and love from my family.

Meggett, Jarvia Breonne: Charleston, SC; University of South Carolina; Mevetta Meggett Scott and William Scott; BA Public Health, 2016; Ronald E. McNair Scholar, Second Place National Award at SAEOPP; My Carolina Association, Student Engagement Council; Homecoming Commission, Executive Board; Phi Sigma Theta Honor Society, Vice President; Sigma Alpha Lambda Honor Society, Vice President; SGA, Secretary of Multicultural Affairs; But God! This award would not have been possible without Him and the support of my love ones.

Mehring, Jason: Rochester, MN; Crossroads College; Joyce and Terry Mehring; BS Christian Ministry, Biblical Studies, and Theology, 2016; Valedictorian, Graduated with a 4.0; President's Circle; Honors Student; Youth and Young Adults Director, Evangel United Methodist Church; Upward Soccer, Startup Team; Autumn Ridge Church Startup College-Aged Ministry, Hospitality Services, and Sunday School Teacher; Student Council, President.

Mellick, Michele N.: Pittsburgh, PA; Seton Hill University; Cathy and Rick Mellick; BA Psychology, 2016; Project Irreplaceable Breast Cancer Awareness, Founder; Psi Chi Psychology National Honors Society; Psychology Club, Student Researcher; Alpha Lambda Delta National Honors Society; SHUCRU University Spirit Club, Board Member; Academic Achievement Center Tutor, Psychology Tutor; Griffin Dance Team, Captain; University Tour Guide, Membership Chair and Griffin Guide of the Year 2014–2015; Class of 2016, Class President; Thanks to my parents, Cathy and Rick, for always being my biggest fans—love you so much!

Mercier, Caitlin Marie: St. Martinville, LA; Xavier University of Louisiana; Adelia and Michael Mercier; BS Psychological Sciences, 2017; Dean's List 2013–2015; Iberia Comprehensive Community Healthcare Clinic, Intern; Lafayette Community Healthcare Clinic; Eligibility Screener; Division of Social and Behavioral Sciences Grant; Division of Social and Behavioral Sciences Peer Mentoring Program, Peer Mentor; Alpha Kappa Alpha Sorority Inc., Secretary; Psychology Club, Secretary; I thank my family and friends for their amazing support. Without them, the award would not be possible

Messitidis, Catherine M.: Chester, NH; Saint Michael's College; Angela Tsivolas Messitidis and Michael Messitidis; BS Biology/Environmental Studies, 2016; Dean's List 2013–2016; Fossil Free SMC Member; Love Your Melon Campus Crew, Public Relations Manager; Green Up Club, Vice President; Orientation Leader, Two-Year Executive Board Member and Three-Year Leader; Mobilization Volunteer Efforts, New Orleans, Louisiana, and Kolkata, India Service Trips; To my family and friends, this would not have been possible without your endless love, support, and encouragement.

Metz, Reagan: Plano, TX; University of Oklahoma; Carol Metz; BA Environmental Sustainability, 2016; Green Week, Vice Chair of Public Relations; SGA, Superior Court Justice; Camp Crimson, Small Group Leader; Alpha Phi, Vice President of Risk Management; The Oklahoma Group, Vice President of Nonprofit Engagement; Many thanks to my mom, sister, friends, and professors for always inspiring, empowering, and believing in me.

Meunier, Deanna: Boonton, NJ; State University of New York Cortland; Tracey and Chuck Meunier; BS Sport Management, 2016; City of Cortland Youth Bureau, Recreation Assistant; Women's Varsity Ice Hockey, Rookie of the Year 2012–2013, ECAC West Second Team 2012–2013, ECAC West Rookie Team 2012–2013, and ECAC West All-Academic Team 2014–2016; This award would not have been possible without the endless support and love from my family.

Mickles, Daniel: Dania, FL; South Florida Bible College Theological Seminary; BS Clinical Counseling, 2016; I am a devoted Christian. God saved my life so I could save another life.

Miguel, Jan Edlene Te: Fremont, CA; Mary Baldwin College; Helen and Edgar Miguel; BS Applied Mathematics, 2016; I wish to extend my deepest gratitude to everyone, especially my family, for all your love and support!

Mikols, Marie Ann: Germansville, PA; Moravian College; Carolyn and Greg Mikols; BA English, 2016; Omicron Delta Kappa; *The Comenian*, Editor-in-Chief; Sigma Tau Delta, President; Public Relations Office, Reporter; A special thank you to my family, friends, and professors for all their support.

Miles, Kandice Elizabeth: Elgin, SC; Converse College; BS Chemistry, 2016; SGA Traditions Council, Vice-Chair; Nisbet Honors Society, Class of 2016 Representative; Model Programs, Head Delegate, Secretary General of Model NATO, and National Chair; This award would not have been possible without the support and love from my family, friends, and professors.

Millen, Julianne: Staten Island, NY; College of Staten Island; BA Writing/Linguistics/Minor in Psychology, 2017; Sigma Tau Delta International English Honor Society; New York State Women Inc., Staten Island Chapter, Scholarship Recipient; AA Arts, Summa Cum Laude; College of Staten Island Scholarship Recipient; Dean's List; National Society for Collegiate Scholars; Linguistics and Speech Sciences Club, Vice President; This award would not have been possible without the love and support of my family.

Miller Kapala, Macy Marie: Mears, MI; West Shore Community College; AA Computer's for Business, 2018; Volunteer Elderly Caretaker, Driver, and Errand Runner; Volunteer Rideshare Driver and Participant; I want to thank Jeff Emery and Ashley Miller, without them this award would not have been possible.

Miller, Erin Ann: Chandler, AZ; Holy Family University; Bruce and Leanne Miller; BA Psychobiology, 2016; Student Athletic Advisory Committee, President 2014–2016 and 2015 NCAA Leadership Forum Attendee; NCAA Division II Volleyball, Team Captain 2015–2016, CACC All-Academic Team 2014–2015, Division II Athletic Director's Association All-Academic Achievement Award 2015, Sandra Michael Scholar Athlete Award 2015, and Vision Core Value Award 2015; My family and coaches inspire me to do my best every day, which made this achievement possible.

Miller, Kayte E.: Royal Center, IN; Ancilla College; Dale and Fay Miller; AS Elementary Education, 2016; Softball; Leaders for Life; SGA; Dean's List 2014; Phi Theta Kappa; I appreciate the love and support along the way that has guided me in achieving this award.

Miller, Kimberly Bates: Kinston, NC; James Sprunt Community College; ADN Nursing, 2016; This award would not of been possible without my loving husband and two wonderful boys.

Miller, Landon Lee: Eldridge, AL; Bevill State Community College; Jeff and Jana Miller; AA Electrical Technology, 2017; I am appreciative for this award. Thank you to my family and friends for supporting me.

Miller, Nicole: Biloxi, MS; University of Southern Mississippi Gulf Park Campus; Robert Bailey and Sandra Micheluz; BA Social Work, 2016; School of Social Work Student of the Year 2016; Bachelor of Social Work Club 2014–2015; SGA, Representative for the College of Health 2014–2015; My achievements are the fruit of my family's support. Thank you!

Miller, Renee': Luling, LA; Xavier University of Louisiana; Joyce and William Miller; BS Biology Pre-Med, 2017; Rousseve Scholar, Top 10 GPA; TriBeta Biology Honor Society, Secretary; A special thank you goes to my loving family for their support and motivation. I love you forever.

Miller, Sara L.: Newburgh, IN; Ivy Tech Community College of Indiana Southwest; Laura Harlen; AA Medical Assisting, 2016; I would not have been able to achieve this without my fiancé.

Milner, Philip: Greenwood, MS; East Mississippi Community College.

Minter, Eric M.: Cumming, GA; Brenau University; Sharon Baker; BS Pre-Occupational Therapy Health Science, 2014; I would like to thank my family for their love and support.

Misko, Jenilee Sarah Mary: Madison, SD; Dakota State University; Leifa and Robert Misko; BS Exercise Science, 2016; Phi Eta Sigma; Internship at Madison Community Center; Roblin Personal Care Home, Volunteer; Athletic Training Room, Volunteer and Intern; Dean's List 2012, President's List 2013–2015; Kappa Sigma Iota; Softball, Freshmen and Sophomore Years; I would not have been able to receive this award without the love and support of my family.

Mitchell, Brett Armand: Rockaway, NJ; Dominican College of Blauvelt; BA Criminal Justice, 2016; Residence Life, Resident Assistant; This award would not have been possible without the support from my parents, William and Karen.

Mitchell, Haley L.: Laurel, DE; Delaware Technical Community College Georgetown; Jacqueline Mitchell; AA Early Childhood Education, Birth to Second Grade, 2016; I owe my success to the love and support of my family.

Mitchell, Katie Jean: Lockwood, MO; Crowder College; Shirley and Terry Mitchell; AAS Management, 2016.

Mitchell, Kelsey Elizabeth: Plattsburgh, NY; State University of New York Plattsburgh; Kelly LaDue and Lindsay DeCoste; BS General Studies, 2016; I am thankful for the support of my family who have made me positive throughout my college experience.

Mitchell, Laurin Olivia: Greenville, MS; Tougaloo College; Byna and Larce Mitchell Jr.; BA Psychology, 2016; SGA, Miss Senior 2015–2016; Sigma Alpha Pi, National Society of Leadership and Success; FAME, Faculty Assistant Mentor 2013–2014; TAMS, Tougaloo Ambassador and Meritorious Scholar; Tougaloo College Scholar, President, Provost, and Dean's List Scholar; This award would not have been possible without the support of my family, friends, and administrators.

Mitchell, Myrna: Many Farms, AZ; Navajo Technical University; Ella Mae and Bobby Mitchell; BA Dine Culture, Language, and Leadership, 2016; I dedicate this award to Shima Ella and my family who inspired me to pursue my dreams.

Mitchell, Shauna Mae: Mount Carmel, IL; Wabash Valley College; Richard and Cheryl Mitchell; AS Early Childhood Education, 2016; TRIO, Student of the Year 2015; I was surprised and honored to have been nominated for this award.

Mocyk, Laura Lynne: Warners, NY; Cayuga Community College Auburn Campus; Kevin and Lauria Mocyk; AA LAS Humanities and Social Science, Humanities Division, Early Childhood Concentration, 2016; Church Choir, Cantor; Tutor Club, Secretary; Thank you to my wonderful parents, Kevin and Lauria Mocyk, for all their love, support, and dedication.

Mohamed, Elsayed Fathi Moussa: Newark, DE; Goldey Beacom College Graduate School; MBA/MA Management, 2015; I dedicate this award to: my dear parents, my beloved wife, Zahra, my dear sons, Khaled and Amr.

Mohamed, Sayed: Newark, DE; Goldey Beacom College Graduate School; AA Finance; Thank you to my wife, children and my professor Dr. Mohamed Samir Hamza.

Mohammed, Fatma Osama: Newark, DE; Goldey Beacom College Graduate School; Hoda Khandil; MA Human Resources, 2016; I want to thank my mum, Hoda, and my real dad, Fouad. I love you.

Mohler, Carson L.: Wayland, NY; Ithaca College; Kathleen Schafer; MS Occupational Therapy, 2017; My hard work and dedication has paid off! Family is forever.

Monahan, Christie Rose: North Charleston, SC; Converse College; Michelle and David Monahan; BS Biochemistry, 2016; Student Plant Genomics Researcher; Chemistry Lab Teaching Assistant; Alpha Lambda Delta Honor Society, Editor; BBB Biological Honor Society, Secretary; Converse College Honor Board, SGA Organization, Vice Chair, Secretary, and Representative; General and Upper-Level Chemistry Tutor; Peer Academic Coach; Nisbet Honors Program, Student Board Member; This award would not have been possible without the support and love from my family.

Monroe, Kelsee Beth: Lawton, OK; Cameron University; Chandra and Van Monroe; BS Psychology, 2017; Psi Chi, Southwest Regional Award Winner, SWPA 2015; Honors Students Society, President and President's Distinguished Scholar Scholarship Recipient; Thank you, mom and dad, for always celebrating my successes and sometimes lecturing me about my failures.

Montes de Oca, Brittney Ann: Metairie, LA; University of Holy Cross School of Nursing; Pedro Montesdeoca and Malisa Hulette; BS Nursing, 2016; Student Nurses Association University of Holy Cross Chapter; Student Ambassador Peer Success Program Tutor; Project Lazarus, Volunteer; Boo At The Zoo, Volunteer; National Alliance on Mental Illness Awareness Walk, Volunteer; Nursing I Clinical Nursing Award; Nursing Research Award; Nursing Honors Program; Brown Foundation Scholarship Award; This award would not have been possible without the unrelenting support and love from my family.

Montes, Michael Andrew: El Paso, TX; The University of Texas El Paso; AA Psychology, 2016; The Society for Collegiate Leadership and Achievement; Golden Key International Honour Society; Student Recovery Organization; Multicultural Greek Council UTEP, Delegate; Order of Omega Greek Honor Society; Psi Chi International Honor Society; National Alliance on Mental Illness, Member of the Year 2015, Mental Health Advocate of the Year, and Inaugural NAMI Scholarship; Sigma Lambda Beta International Fraternity Inc., Community Service Chair; Alpha Phi Omega International Co-Ed Service Fraternity, Sergeant at Arms and Pledge Master; I want to thank the educators who said I would not amount to anything, this is for you!

Monti, Brianna Michelle: Lodi, NJ; Seton Hall University; Gina and David Monti; BS Chemistry, 2015; Order of Omega Honor Society; AFROTC, Cadet Vice Wing Commander, Commendation Award, and High School Scholarship Award; SAVE Team, Peer Educator; Senior Class Council, Public Relations Chair; SGA, Arts and Sciences Senator; American Chemical Society, Co-Founder and Vice President; Leadership Development, Student Leadership Consultant and University Leadership Fellows Program; Collegiate Panhellenic Council, Secretary and Dedication to Council Award; Greek Municipal Assembly, Treasurer; Delta Phi Epsilon International Sorority, President and Fundraising Chair; I'd like to thank Leadership Development, AFROTC, and my sorority branch for making this award possible.

Moody, Jessica Ann: Glendora, CA; Western University of Health Sciences; Sharon Moody; BS Osteopathic Medicine, 2016; American Medical Women's Association, Coordinator; Girl Scouts of Greater Los Angeles, TOUCH Community Service Award and Coordinator; This award would not have been possible without the support and love from my family.

Moody, Rachel Hanna: Maryville, TN; Hiwassee College; Brian and Benita Moody; BS Dental Hygiene, 2017.

Moore, KeTyria A.: Memphis, TN; Jackson State University College of Business; Loria Walker; BS Accounting, 2016; Honors College Council, Public Relations; Honors College, Salutatorian Scholarship Recipient; Thanks for all the support and love. Special thanks to all who helped my evolution.

Moore, Monica A.: Jackson, MS; Jackson State University College of Liberal Arts; Alma Moore; BS Psychology, 2016; Dean's List 2012; 22nd Joint National Conference Proceedings 2014, Publication, Presentation, and Student Competition Win; Leadership Scholarship Recipient; JSIPH, Student Researcher; Zeta Phi Beta Sorority Inc., Vice President; Psi Chi Honor Society; String Ensemble; Chamber Orchestra Scholarship Recipient; Thank you to my grandmother, mother, sister, aunts, uncles, cousins, friends, and my church.

Moore, Nicholas Austin: Powder Springs, GA; Kennesaw State University; Joy Spence and Debarron Moore; BS Psychology, 2017; Resident Assistant, Community Builder; I love who I have become. I hope others follow their dreams and never give up.

Moore, Wendy R.: Byron, MN; University of Mary; Andrew and Rita Distad; MS Nursing Administration, 2016; Sigma Theta Tau, Scholarship Award 2015; With grateful appreciation for the support of my academic endeavors from my husband, children, and parents.

Morabito, Valerie Renee: Trinidad, CO; Trinidad State Junior College; Aaron and Patricia Morabito; AA Business, 2017; Thanks to my parents and mentors for all the support through the best years of my life.

Morales Valverde, Evelyn Maribel: East Hampton, NY; Suffolk County Community College Eastern Campus; Gloria and Julio Morales; AS Biology, 2017; Honors Program; STEM Club, Secretary; Phi Theta Kappa; With pride I take this award, thanking my parents for their unconditional love and support.

Moran, Abigail Sherwood: Moneta, VA; University of Mary Washington; Shelly and Tom Moran; BA Music, 2016; Young Life, Volunteer Leader, and Team Leader; Encore! Show Choir, Music Director; I am thankful for a loving and providing Savior, without Him none of this would be possible.

Moreaux, Beatrice Naa-Abashie: New Hope, MN; Bethel Seminary; MA Marriage and Family Therapy, 2016; To Nii-Adjetey, Kristin, Naa-Adjeley, Adjei, and Sowah, you are the best of heaven's gifts to me.

Moreno, Elijah Austin: Hot Springs, AR; Arkansas Tech University, Tammie Moreno and Eliseo Moreno; BA Psychology, 2016; Visual Arts Association, Vice President; Student Activities Board, Motion Pictures Team Leader with 50+ Service Hours; This was made possible due to my loving parents, guiding teachers, and caring friends throughout my life.

Morgan, Kathryn I.: Albuquerque, NM; Eastern New Mexico University-Roswell; Harriet and Alan Morgan; AA Office Skills, 2016; Roswell Animal Humane Association, Volunteer; Phi Theta Kappa Honor Society.

Morrell, Jane: Troy, AL; Troy University; Beth Bayens; BA Multimedia Journalism, 2016.

Morris, Caleb Neal: Midland City, AL; Mississippi College; Sue German; BS Kinesiology, Pre-Physical Therapy, 2016; Kinesiology Club KSA; Pre-Physical Therapy/Occupational Therapy Club; Baseball Scholarship; *Who's Who*; Dean's List; Academic Honor for Gulf South Conference; I am blessed to have a loving family and honored to have Jesus Christ as my Savior.

Morris, Claudette Elise: Rochester, NY; Monroe Community College; Blanche and Raymond (Deceased) Huggins; AA Liberal Arts, 2016; Student, Peer Advisor; Daughter, Mother, Grandmother and Great Grandmother; I would like to thank my mother, my children, and my grandchildren for their continued love and support.

Morris, Elizabeth Mary: North Wilkesboro, NC; Regent University; Bob and Helen Morris; BA Cinema-Television, 2017; Mom and Dad, thank you for being a constant source of encouragement and blessing.

Morrison, Ashlyn Joy: Pleasant Grove, AL; University of Montevallo; Paula and John Collins; AA Fine Arts Painting, 2016; Falconettes Dance Team; College Night, Purple Side Cheerleader; United by Dance, Dancer; Delta Gamma Fraternity, Choreographer; You never know until you try. I would like to thank God, my friends, and family!

Morrow, Jeffrey T.: East Peoria, IL; Midstate College; BA Business, 2018; Thank you to my wonderful wife, Amy. God has truly blessed me, and I am truly grateful.

Moses, Jacqueline M.: Alpine, TX; Sul Ross State University; BA General Studies, 2016; Thank you to my loving daughter, husband, niece, mom, and grandparents for helping me fulfill my potential.

Moses, Sierra Marie: Austin, TX; Panola College; Joanna and Hunter Moses; AA Science, 2018; Volleyball, Team Captain and NJCAA Academic All-Conference; I am so thankful for such loving support system that made this award possible.

Mote, Anastasia A.: Quincy, FL; Chipola College; Michelle and Gary Clark, Willie Mote; AA Psychology, 2016; This amazing award would not have been possible without the love and support from my family.

Moton, Shewunikki Q.: Windsor, CT; Albertus Magnus College; Mary Moton and Walter Nolden; MA Business Administration, 2016; Thank you for the love and support, Mary Moton, Darren Foster, Peyton Anderson, and the remainder of my family.

Mouser, Elizabeth Ann: Stigler, OK; Northwestern Oklahoma State University; Lisa and Randy Mouser; BS Early Childhood Education, 2017; SOEA, Vice President.

Mukashev, Amirkhan: Vienna, VA; Northern Virginia Community College; Akhat and Roza Mukashev; AS Systems Engineering, 2016; International Scholar Laureate Program, Student Delegate on Engineering and Technology, New Zealand; STEM Club; National Society of Collegiate Scholars; Muslim Student Association; SGA, Events Committee Chair and Senator; NOVA SEAL Award for Service-Excellence-Academics-Leadership; This would not have been possible without God's mercy and the support of my family.

Mullen, Allyson Grace: Wilder, VT; Colby-Sawyer College; James and Pamela Mullen; BA Child Development, 2017; Alternative Spring Break Trip, Community Service Trip to Florida; Community Service Club, Vice President; Field Hockey, NAC Player of the Week, NAC All-Academic Award, and NFHCA National Academic Squad; This award would not have been possible without my friends, family, teammates, coaches, professors, and all their support.

Mungoma, Joseph J.: Saint Louis, MO; St. Louis Community College Forest Park; Hilda Odundo; AA Computer Science, 2017; Phi Theta Kappa, Community Service Participation Certificate; With this, the basic expectation is hereby set for you. Go beyond. Dream. Believe. Achieve.

Munoz, Malvina Guadalupe: El Paso, TX; The University of Texas El Paso; Simon and Bertha Munoz; BS Biological Sciences, Concentration in Biomedical Sciences, 2018; University Scholars Society, Scholarship Recipient; Phi Kappa Phi, Top 7.5 Percent of Juniors; Medical Professions Organization, Member Award; National Society of Leadership and Success, Success Networking Team Facilitator and National Engaged Leader Award; Miners Against Hunger, Student Relations Officer; Thank you to my family and friends for inspiring me to explore possibilities and accept challenges.

Murdock, Micah E.: Groves, TX; Lamar University; Mitch and Mary Murdock; BS Chemical Engineering, 2017; Rising Cardinal Award 2012–2013; Ann Shaw Award 2013–2014; C. Robert Kembel Award 2015–2016; Lamar Brewing Club, President 2016; Knights of Columbus, Deputy Grand Knight 2016 and Founding Member; College ACTS Retreat Core Team, Core Facilitator 2015; Newman Catholic Student Center, Liturgy Director 2013 and Treasurer 2013; Men's Club Soccer, Goalkeeper and Treasurer 2013; College of Engineering Ambassador, New Student Tour Guide 2012; Lamar College Republicans, Fundraising Chairmen 2013; SGA, Supreme Court Chief Justice 2016; Greek Council, Public Relations Chair 2014; Interfraternal Council, Public Relations 2013 and Secretary 2014; Pi Kappa Alpha Fraternity, Recruitment Chair 2016, President 2015, Vice President 2014, and Community Service 2013; Alpha Lambda Delta Honor Society; Lamar Ambassador, Lead Ambassador and President's Circle Dinner; American Institute of Chemical Engineers, Secretary 2013; Special thanks to my parents, Mitch and Mary Murdock. Without them, I would not be who I am.

Murphy, Amber L.: Metairie, LA; The University of Mississippi.

Murphy, Blake Edward: Paragould, AR; Crowley's Ridge College; BA Biblical Studies, 2017; Baseball; President's List; Sigma Chi Eta; Dean's List; This award would have been possible without God's blessings and guidance.

Murphy, Heather: Lubbock, TX; Lubbock Christian University; Ted Murphy; MS Counseling, 2016.

Murphy, Paige Alexandria: San Antonio, TX; Texas Tech University; Theresa Bilotta; BS Interior Design, 2016; International Interior Design Association, Public Relations Chair; Zeta Tau Alpha, President, Vice President I, House Manager, Director of Philanthropy, Parliamentarian, White Violet Award, and MVP Zeta Award; This award would not be possible without the love and support from my family.

Murray, Emily Catherine: Boulder, CO; Columbus State University; Greg and Emily Jackson; BS Psychology, Minor in Art, 2015; Operant Blocking Research, Research Assistant; Cougars Psychology Association, Founding Member; Psi Chi International Honors Society of Psychology, Vice President.

Murray, Taylor Andrew: Newton, AL; Enterprise State Community College; Mark and Donna Murray; AS General Studies, 2017; ESCC President's Cup; Most Distinguished Student in the History Department; Cerebral Weevils Scholars Bowl, Team Captain, Third Place 2015 ACBL State Championship, Fourth Place 2015 NAQT CCCT, Third Place 2015 NAQT Sectionals, Second Place 2014 Goober Lindsey ACBL Tournament, First Place 2014 Kickoff Tournament, and First Place 2014 Wallace State ACBL Tournament; Phi Theta Kappa International Honor Society, Chapter President, Distinguished Chapter Officer Team Hallmark Award, and Distinguished College Project Award; History Club, Vice President; Thanks to my instructors, friends, and family for the help and support they have provided throughout this college adventure.

Mwirigi, Juliet Mukiri: Fort Worth, TX; Tarrant County College Northeast Campus; Moses and Leah Mwirigi; AA Biology, 2018; Phi Theta Kappa, Enhanced Member and Nominated for District II Hall of Honor; Math Infinity Club, Peer Tutor and Sixth Place 2015–2016 Jim Bolen Math Competition; Dedicated to my family, friends, and teachers who have shown great support throughout my journey.

Mykytyn, Gabrielle: Marietta, GA; The University of Mississippi; Angela and Joseph Mykytyn; BS Forensic Chemistry, 2016; Community Assistant Association, President, Community Assistant of the Year 2014 and 2015, and Staff of the Year 2014 and 2015; The love and support from my family and friends have gotten me to where I am today.

Myrick, Joseph: Hamtramck, MI; Marygrove College; BA English, 2017; DeVlieg Foundation Scholarship; Dr. Lynne Schaeffer Award; Christine K. and John C. Cavanaugh Endowed Scholarship; Sigma Tau Delta English Honors Society, Publicity Co-Chair; National Dean's List; *Who's Who Among Students in American Colleges and Universities*.

N

Nabors, Rebekah: Eureka, IL; Eureka College; Randy and Jeannie Nabors; BA Elementary Education, 2016; Delta Zeta, Public Relations and Vice President of Programming; Eureka College Band, Band President and Student Director; First Generation, Mentor; This award would not be possible without the love and support of my loved ones.

Nakamura, Stephanie Marie: Flowery Branch, GA; Georgia State University; Mandy and Richard Harris; MBA with Accounting Focus, 2016; CSU Accounting Club; Beta Gamma Sigma Award; This award would not have been possible without the support of my generous employer and loving family.

Naney, Timothy D.: Fort Lauderdale, FL; Western University of Health Sciences; Lea Adamitz and David Naney; PhD Osteopathic Medicine, 2016; Sharp Memorial Hospital Volunteer; Rady Children's Hospital Volunteer; COMP SGA, DO 2016 Class Representative; COMP Student Executive Board, Vice Chair; LEAD Office, Medical School Tutor, Dental School Tutor, and Podiatry School Tutor; This award could not have been possible without the time, support, and love from my wife and parents.

Napier, Jammie D.: Hazard, KY; University of Pikeville; BS Psychology, 2017; I would like to thank my family for their unconditional support during this magnificent journey.

Nardi, Elizabeth Nicole: De Pere, WI; Ashford University Clinton Campus; JoAnn Bartolameolli and Vince Nardi; BA Business Administration, Public Relations, and Marketing, 2016; Service Advisory Board, Vice President and Emerging Organization Award; Women's Basketball, NAIA Conference Championship 2014; Women's Soccer, AII Conference Championship 2015 and NAIA Champions of Character Award; This award would not be possible without the nomination from Ashford and the love and support from my family.

Narvaez Mena, Katherine Danabet: Doraville, GA; Mary Baldwin College; Isis Danabet Narvaez Mena and Nahum Lopez; BS Biomedical Sciences and Business Management, 2016; President's Society; SGA, Vice President 2016; Beta Beta Beta, Secretary; Cross Country, Captain; Virginia Women's Institute for Leadership, Executive Officer, nULL Committee Chair, Peer Adviser, Physical Fitness Cadre, and Drill Team Commander; Nada hubiera sido posible sin los sacrificios y el sudor y lágrimas derramadas por parte de mi familia.

Nash, Margaret Louise: Tarboro, NC; Edgecombe Community College; AA Accounting and Business Management, 2016; Student Ambassador 2014–2016; Phi Theta Kappa, Spring 2014; Thank you for the continuing love and support from my husband and family.

Nawa, Maggie JoAnne: New Lenox, IL; Murray State University; Karen and Michael Nawa; BS Animal/Eq-
uine Science, 2016; Honors College Student Council; All-Campus Sing Chair; Public Relations Committee; Class Representative.

Naylor, Kathryn E.: Middletown, PA; University of Valley Forge; Donna and James Naylor; BS Early Childhood Education, 2016; Homeless Outreach; Children's Church Volunteer.

Neal, Kaylyn: Pensacola, FL; University of South Alabama; Princella Neal; BS Professional Health Science, 2016; National Association for the Advancement of Colored People, Outstanding Member Award; African American Student Association, Membership Development Committee Member and Gospel Choir; Jaguar Productions, Dedicated Member Award; Women of Excellence, Outstanding Member Award; Abeneefoo Kuo Honor Society, Historian; This award would not have been possible without God and the support and love from my Mother!

Nedbalek, Amanda Lynn: Lufkin, TX; Stephen F. Austin State University; BS Psychology, 2016; This award would have been impossible without the love, support, and inspiration from my family.

Nelson, Brooke Christine: Aberdeen, SD; Northern State University; Lori and Greg Nelson; BA English; 2017; SGA, College of Arts and Sciences Senator; Psychology Club; English Club; German Club, Vice President, President, and Scholarship Recipient; Honors Program, Honors Student, Scholarship Recipient, and Honors Club; Thank you to my older sister for your words of wisdom: "Suck it up, buttercup."

Nelson, Jessica Lynn: La Porte, IN; Indiana University South Bend; Carla and Peter Nelson; BA Social Work, 2017; Social Work Student Association, Media Director 2015–2016 and Secretary 2016–2017; This award would not have been possible without the overwhelming support from my family and friends. Thank you.

Nelson, Katherine Marie: Woodstock, GA; Samford University; BS Nursing, 2016; Camp Braveheart, Children's Healthcare of Atlanta; Step Sing 2013, Freshmen Ladies Show Director; Panhellenic Council, Director of Service Programs 2014; Chi Omega Sorority, Model Initiate, Pledge Class 2012 and Emerging Greek Leaders Award 2013; Step Sing 2015, Overall Committee; Step Sing 2016, Overall Director; I would like to give a special THANK YOU to my parents for their unending support.

Nelson, Matthew Ryan: Elba, AL; Lurleen B. Wallace Community College; Serena and Elijah Praytor; AA Diesel Engine/Heavy Equipment Mechanic, 2016; Phi Theta Kappa, National Technical Honor Society; I am honored to receive this award and owe it all to God and my family.

Neuhof, Gabrielle A. S.: Hooversville, PA; University of Pittsburgh Bradford; Cathlene and George Neuhof; BS Exercise Science, 2016; Student Activities Technical Manager, Student Activities Annual Events Committee Chair; Student Activities Council, Student Activities Council Committee Chair of the Year 2014.

Neumann, Susan L.: Troy, NY; Bryant and Stratton College Albany Campus; Beverly Buckbee-Shuhart; AA Medical Assisting, 2016; This award would not have been possible without the support and love from my family and partner, Deborah.

Newcomer, Zachary Brock: New Paris, IN; Manchester University; Dale and Phyllis Newcomer; BS Sport Management, 2016; Spartan Sport Management Club, Director of Management; This award would not have been possible without the love and support from my family.

Newton, Samantha K.: Hackettstown, NJ; Bloomsburg University; Kim and Jeffrey Newton; BS Early Childhood Education, 2016; Dean's List; This award would not have been possible without the love and support of my family and friends.

Nguyen, Anh T.: Egg Harbor Township, NJ; Stockton University; BS Business Accounting, 2016; Event Services and Campus Center Operations; Dean's List; Excellent Transfer Award; Many thanks to my family and staff at Stockton University for the support and love for this achievement.

Nguyen, Lilian Anna: Houston, TX; University of Houston–Clear Lake; MS Counseling, 2017; Leading and Serving Together, Youth Leader; Student Leadership, Involvement, and Community Engagement Program, Bronze Award; Special thanks to my family and friends for always supporting me. Love you!

Nguyen, Tri Tan: Houston, TX; University of Houston–Clear Lake; Phuong Trinh Bui and Tri Nguyen; BS Psychology, 2016; Servant Leader Scholar Program, Gold Level; Day of Service, Hope Village Site Leader; SGA, Executive Council Vice President Committee Coordinator; Systems Day Participant; Intercultural and International Student Services, Peer Mentor; SHOSTS Peer Mentoring Program, Peer Mentor; Office of International Administrations and Programs, International Orientation Leader; Orientation and New Student Programs, Orientation Leader; Vietnamese Students Association, Vice President; Legal Studies Association, Vice President; Criminology Studies Organization, SGA Representative; National Society of Leadership and Success, SGA Representative; I dedicate my accomplishments to my Mother, Phuong Trinh Bui, and everyone at University of Houston–Clear Lake.

Nichol, Nicole D.: Robinson, IL; Saint Mary-of-the-Woods College; Christine Kilpatrick and Steve Carter; BS Human Services, 2016; This award would not have been possible without the support and love my family.

Nichols Jr., Bernard N.: Magnolia, MS; Southwest Mississippi Community College; Shelia Magee and Bernard Nichols; AA English, 2015; Bear Chorus, First Tenor; Whispering Pines Yearbook, Staff; Pine Burr Newspaper, Staff Writer; I am dedicating this award to my loving family, educators, and mentors who have supported me from youth.

Nichols, Jasmine T.: Kansas City, MO; University of Saint Mary; Elizabeth Correll and Mark Nichols; BS Biology/Psychology, 2017; Volleyball, 2015 Daktronics NAIA Scholar Athlete; I want to thank my mother and best friend for constantly pushing me to achieve more.

Nilsen, Kelsey Elizabeth: Rogers, AR; Arkansas Tech University; Eric and Susan Nilsen; BS Management/Marketing, 2016.

Nimako, Nana: West Hills, CA; Agnes Scott College; Juliana Adusah and Charles Nimako; BA Economics, 2016; African and West Indian Student Association, President and Distinguished Community Alliance Award; This award would not have been possible without the guidance from my family and friends.

Nissen, Alexander: Rockville, MD; Uniformed Services University of the Health Sciences; MD Medicine, 2016; Intramural Club Sports, Basketball and Soccer Teams; American Medical Student Association, Treasurer; Gold Humanism Honor Society, Student Selection Committee; Alpha Omega Alpha, Student Outreach Representative; Valedictorian, Class of 2016; Thanks to my parents, Larry and Maryanne Nissen, and the rest of my family and friends for their support!

Nitsch, Virginia L.: Lewes, DE; Delaware Technical Community College Georgetown; AA Medical Laboratory Technician, 2018; MALTA Del Tech, Del Tech Student Spotlight 2015–2016; Academic Recognition Del Tech 2014; A sincere, loving thanks to my husband, Bill, my daughter, Allison, my son-in-law, Charlie, and my three beautiful granddaughters.

Nkadi, Ashley: Cincinnati, OH; University of Cincinnati; Michelle and Emeke Nkadi; BS Neuropsychology, 2016; Children's Cognitive Research Lab, Research Assistant; The Irate 8, Founder and Spearhead 2015–2016, Undergraduate Social Activism Award 2016, and Spirit of Cincinnatus Award 2016; *Noir Magazine*, Founder and Editor-in-Chief 2014–2016; The Lambda Society, Week of Excellence Chair 2015–2016; Cincinnati Women in Excellence and Spirit Together, Red Rose Chair 2015–2016; Caribbean Student Association, Public Relations Director 2014–2015; Midwest Dhamaka, Marketing Director 2015–2016 and Liaison 2013–2015; Asian American Association, Public Relations Director 2014–2015; Omicron Delta Kappa, President 2015–2016; United Black Student Association, President 2015–2016, Information Director 2015–2014, Executive Board Member of the Year Award 2015, and Marketing Director 2013–2014; Thank God, my family, and the support of those around me.

Nobiva, Nompumelelo Mpumi: High Point, NC; Johnson C. Smith University; BA Interdisciplinary Studies, 2016; International Club, President 2015–2016; Dean's List 2016; International Motivational and Empowerment Speaker 2013–2016; Ethics Bowl Debate Team, Captain 2016; I dedicate this award to my grandmother, Vivian Nobiva. Thank you for raising me this way.

Norris, Crystal Nicole: Rose Hill, NC; James Sprunt Community College; AA Computer Information Technology, 2016.

Norton, Cody Trey: Cullman, AL; Wallace State Community College Hanceville; AA Criminal Justice, 2017; Phi Theta Kappa Honor Society; Without God this would not have been possible and the love and support from my family.

Ntewo, Ubong A.: Evansville, IN; Indiana Wesleyan University; BS Biblical Studies, 2015; Shelter Volunteer, Guest Speaker, Team Leader, International Mission Trips Participant, and Hospice Care Assistant; Glory to King Jesus! Mom and Dad, thanks for inspiring me. My darling, Heather, you made this possible.

O

O'Brien, Kelsey Morgan: New Paltz, NY; Mount Saint Mary College; Edith Weber and Joseph O'Brien; BA English, Childhood Special Education, 2016; Kappa Delta Pi; Office of Admissions, Tour Guide and Intern; Thank you to my parents for your endless support.

O'Connor, Colleen T.: Syracuse, NY; St. John Fisher College; Kathleen and David O'Connor; BA Anthropology and Criminology, 2016; Most Improved Resident Assistant, 2013–2014 Academic Year; Sustained Dialogue Moderator; Dean's List; Third year Resident Assistant; I could not have accomplished all that I have without the love and support of my grandparents.

O'Connor, Jenna L.: North Adams, MA; Massachusetts College of Liberal Arts; Lori O'Connor; BA Sociology, English, and Women's Studies, 2016; Sigma Tau Delta; Lambda Iota Tau Honor Society; American Sociological Association Honors Program; Travel Course Scholarship, Spring 2016; Dean's List 2012–2015; Sociology Society, President 2016 and Vice President 2015; I appreciate everyone who has supported me in my personal and academic endeavors. Thank you all.

Oddo, Rebecca Lyn: Indian Springs, AL; Wallace State Community College Hanceville; Dona Martin; AS Nursing, 2016; Let's Pretend Hospital, Most Enthusiastic; To Wallace State for the best education, my family for encouragement, and my determination for success.

O'Dell, Shannon: Jasper, GA; Kennesaw State University; Kent and Tammy O'Dell; BS Nursing, 2016; Without the support of my family and friends, I would not be where I am today. Thank you.

Odom, Allison Lynette: West Columbia, SC; Midlands Technical College; Lynn and Christopher Odom; AS Associate in Science, 2016; Phi Theta Kappa; Dean's List; This award would not have been possible without the love and encouragement of my family.

Odong, Boniface: Virginia Beach, VA; Regent University; MA Divinity, 2019; Bible Study Committee, Facilitator; Housing and Residential Life, Resident Director; Without Jesus Christ, family, and friends, this award would not have been possible. Thank you so much.

Ogg, Orren P.: Martin, TN; The University of Tennessee at Martin; Cheryl and Sammy Ogg; BS Agricultural Business, 2016.

Ogunde, Oluwayemisi Bolatito: Goodyear, AZ; Northern Arizona University; Abiodun and Bolan Ogunde; BS Exercise Science, 2016; Food Recovery Network; Student Support Services, Peer Mentor; Relay For Life Planning Committee, Mission and Advocacy Director and Fundraising Director; Student Philanthropy Council, Fundraising Committee Chair; I am who I am because you lift me up; thank you, Mom, Dad, and SSS.

O'Kane, Victoria Ashley: Wellesley, MA; Fitchburg State University; William and Donna O'Kane; BS Nursing, 2016; Student Nurses Association, Senior Class Representative.

Olearchik, Nicole Anne: Ewing, NJ; Kean University of New Jersey; Nell Anne and Don Olearchik; BA Music Education, 2017; International Society for Music Education Conference, Student Presenter; *TEMPO Magazine*, Published Author; Leadership Institute, Platinum Member; Deaf Jammers, Performer; National Association for Music Education, Chapter President; New Jersey Music Educators Association Collegiate, President; I would like to thank my family and friends for all their memories, support, laughs, and love.

Olivas, Johnathon Douglas: Fort Collins, CO; Colorado Mesa University; John and Tammy Olivas; BS Biological Sciences, 2016; Graduate Education and Medical Sciences, President; I am humbled to know how much support I have from my family, professors, and friends. Thank You.

Oliver, Jade M.: Gadsden, AL; Gadsden State Community College; Cornelia and Jimmy Roebuck Jr.; AA General Studies, 2016; Phi Theta Kappa, Vice President; Thank you, maw! Without you, this would have never been possible!

Oliver, Katina L.: Lawrenceville, GA; Saint Leo University; BS Health Care Management, 2016; To God be the Glory!!! I dedicate this award to my family! "An Ordinary Servant with an Extraordinary Purpose."

Ondracek, Chloe Lian: Minot, ND; Minot State University; James and Pamela Ondracek; BA Mathematics, 2017; Computer Science Club, Treasurer 2014–2015; Mathematics Club, President 2014–2015; I would like to thank my parents, professors, friends, and community for their continuous support.

Onovwerosuoke, Jane Otivere: Jonesboro, AR; Arkansas State University Newport; Fred Onovwerosuoke; Wendy Hymes; AA Restaurant/Food Services Management, 2016; This award was made possible by God through the support of Dr. Fred Onovwerosuoke and Dr. Wendy Hymes.

Opara, Adedoyin Esther: Arlington, TX; Tarrant County College Southeast Campus; John and Veronica Opara; AA Nursing, 2017; This award would not have been possible without the support and love from my family.

Opgenorth, Seth Ryan: Oostburg, WI; Milwaukee School of Engineering; Dale and Shawn Opgenorth; BS Computer Engineering, 2016; IEEE Student Body, Treasurer; Underwater Robotics, President and CEO 2012–2016; This award would have been possible without my passion for knowledge that was inspired by my parents.

Orellana, Jennifer Diana: Jersey City, NJ; Bloomfield College; Normita and Hector Orellana; BS Nursing, 2016; Chi Upsilon Sigma National Latin Sorority Inc., Vice President and Treasurer, Highest GPA Award, Woman of Wisdom Award; I owe this and everything else I have achieved thanks to you mami, papi, and brother.

Ortegon, Armandina: Laredo, TX; Laredo Community College; AA Accounting, 2019; Phi Theta Kappa; This award would not have been possible without the support and love of my family and professors.

Osomo, Deborah Oluseyi: Longview, TX; LeTourneau University; Oyebode A. and Elizabeth N. Osomo; BS Education, Elementary Generalist Certification, 2017; The Learning Community, Secretary; University Class Assistant, Leader in Team Projects; IMPACT Senator, University Student Administration Leadership Position; International Lead, Leadership Position; Lambda Omega Chi, Mentor; This award would not be possible without the support and love from God, my family, friends, and mentors.

Ostby, Pamela Lynne: Lake Saint Louis, MO; Sinclair School of Nursing University of Missouri; PhD Nursing, 2016.

Ostrem, Amanda M.: Eagan, MN; Carthage College; Lynette and Jay Ostrem; BA Primary Education, 2017; Alpha Lambda Delta, Freshmen Honors; Resident Assistant, RA of the Month, Program of the Month, and Bulletin Board of the Month; Colleges Against Cancer, President.

Ott, Caroline McKenzie: Alpharetta, GA; Pepperdine University; William and Patricia Ott; BA Sociology, 2016; Kappa Kappa Gamma, Marshall; This award would not have been possible without the support and love from my family and my professors.

Overstreet, Steven Kindred: Bethany, OK; Southwestern Christian University; MA Theology, 2016; This award would not have been possible without Jesus Christ and the loving support of my wife, Teri.

Owens, Casey Paige: Easley, SC; North Greenville University; Charlene Holliday and Bobby Owens; BA Elementary Education, 2018; Early Childhood Association, Vice President 2016–2017; This award would not have been possible without The Lord and the support from my family and teachers.

Owens, Emily Arlene: Edmond, OK; University of Oklahoma; Tomás and Tammy Owens; BA Economics, 2016; President's Award for Outstanding Freshman; President's Award for Outstanding Sophomores; Regents Award for Outstanding Juniors; Big Woman on Campus; Camp Crimson, Small Group Leader; Kappa Alpha Theta, Alumnae Engagement Director; Crimson Club, Ambassador; The Oklahoma Group, Consultant; Campus Activities Council's Oklahoma Creativity Festival, Chair, Vice Chair of Marketing, and Publicity Liaison; This award would not have been possible without the support and love from my family and friends.

P

Page, Nicholas Ryan: College Station, TX; Texas A&M University; Steven and Mary Page; BS Aerospace Engineering, 2016; Kappa Theta Epsilon; Lambda Sigma; Psi Chi; Tau Beta Pi; Sigma Gamma Tau; University, College and Department Honors Program, Honors Distinctions; Boeing Shape Memory Alloy and Morphing Structures Research, Undergraduate Researcher; AFOSR Active Materials Research, Undergraduate Researcher; Regional Engineering Conference, Team Lead and First Place Overall; SpaceX Hyperloop Competition Team, Structural Design and Analysis Team Lead; Society of Automotive Engineers International Aerospace Design Competition, First Place Regular Class, First Place Oral Report, and Second Place Technical Report; Committee to Evaluate Computer Access Fee Competitive Grant Proposals, SGA Representative; Academic Operations Committee, SGA Representative; Writing and Communication Course Advisory Committee, SGA Representative; National Aggie Scholar Ambassador; Aerospace Honors Student Advisory Board, Founder; Aerospace Ambassador; Phi Eta Sigma; American Institute of Aeronautics and Astronautics, Publicity Chair, Webmaster, Junior Representative, and Senior Representative; Theta Tau Professional Engineering Fraternity, Vice President, Corresponding Secretary, Inner Guard, Regional Academic Team Captain, First Place Nationally for Professional Development and Brotherhood, and Third Place Nationally in Community Service; Autonomous Robot Design Research, Undergraduate Researcher; Aerospace Student Advisory Board. President; Student Senate, Academic Affairs Committee Chair; Nicholas Page, the Loudest and Proudest of the Fightin' Texas Aggie Class of 2016, A-Whoop!

Palmer, Miata Marie: Chesapeake, VA; Norfolk State University; Wanda and Thomas Watkins; MS Social Work, 2018; BSW Social Work, 2016; Magna Cum Laude; Sister Circle, Executive Administrative; Alpha Delta Mu, Zeta Chapter Vice President; This award would not have been possible without the dedication, support, and love from my family and friends.

Palmiscno, Anthony Carlo: Avonmore, PA; Seton Hill University; Brian and Angela Palmiscno; BA Spanish/Education, 2016; ESL Interpreter at Kiski Area High School; Avonmore Public Library Volunteer; St. Ambrose Food Pantry Volunteer; St. Ambrose Church Sunday School Teacher ; Alpha Lambda Delta Honor Society; SGA, Representative of the Year; Education Club, SGA Representative; Spanish Club, President; Honors Council, Vice President; Admissions Department Tour Guide, Griffin Guide and Griffin Guide of the Month.

Pancani, Michele: Milwaukee, WI; Milwaukee School of Engineering; Alessandro Pancani and Lorenza Del Vecchio; BS Computer Engineering/Electrical Engineering, 2016; On-Campus Employment, Peer Tutor and Test Proctor; NCAA Division III Men's Lacrosse Varsity Team, Assistant Captain and All-Conference Academic Team; Admissions Department Student Campus Ambassador; SGA, Senator and International Students Representative; Dedicated to my family for the great support. So close, no matter how far.

Panella, Jonathan David: Stafford Springs, CT; Roger Williams University; Michelle and David Panella; BS International Business, 2017; Study Abroad, France and Germany Spring 2015, Barcelona, Spain Spring 2016; International Business Club, Treasurer; Delta Sigma Pi, Vice President of Pledge Education and Social Chair; Orientation Advisor, Float Chair; This award would not have been possible without the support and opportunities that RWU has provided me.

Parker, Tony W.: Ottumwa, IA; Indian Hills Community College; AA Nursing, 2016; This award would not have been possible without the support and love from family and friends.

Parrott, Olivia Christine: Greensburg, KY; Campbellsville University; Walt and Deana Parrott; BA Nursing, 2017; Golf, All-American NCCAA 2015; I would like to thank my parents for the encouragement. To Jesus Christ, who gives me strength.

Pasquariello, Melissa A.: Kendall Park, NJ; Peirce College; BS Paralegal Studies, 2016.

Patel, Dipa: Saint Louis, MO; University of Missouri Saint Louis; Kantibhai and Taraben Patel; BS Criminology/Criminal Justice/Psychology, 2016; Psi Chi Psychology Honors Society, Certificate of Induction; Emerging Leaders Program, Program Completion Certificate and Peer Mentor; National Society of Leadership and Success, Induction Certificate; Triton LEAP Program, Peer Mentor; Advanced Leaders Program, Program Completion Certificate; Criminology/Criminal Justice Undergraduate Student Associate, Treasurer; The ingredients to success are desire, dedication, determination, concentration, ambition, vision, luck, and hard work.

Pattillo, Taylor L.: Hanceville, AL; Wallace State Community College Hanceville; Kim Lambert and Scott Pattillo; AA Medical Laboratory Technician, 2016; Zina Stansberry Microbiology Scholarship 2015–2016; Allied Health Scholarship 2013–2014; Thank you: Ma for believing, Dad for encouraging, Ash for loving, and Chris for putting up with me.

Patton, William D.: Knightsville, IN; Saint Mary-of-the-Woods College; Jane and David Patton; BS Kindergarten/Elementary Education, 2016.

Pawlak, Meghan Kathryn: Villanova, PA Villanova University; Lloyd and Lori Pawlak; BS Biology, Honors, 2016; Service and Justice Experiences Volunteer; Student Musical Theatre, Developmental Director and Chair of Publicity; Special Olympics Pennsylvania, Volunteer Coordinator and Local Program Host; Blue Key Society, Chair of Recruitment, Candidates Day Committee Volunteers Chair, Family Head, and Tour Guide; Residence Life, Resident Assistant; Thanks, Mom and Dad! Could not have done it without you.

Paydo, Melissa Anne: Wadsworth, OH; The University of Akron; Ronald and Kathleen Paydo; BS Chemical Engineering, Cooperative Education, 2016; Chem-E-Car Design Team, Safety Student Advisor 2013–2016; Engineering Student Council, Vice President 2015–2016 and Chem-E-Car Design Team Representative 2012–2014; American Institute of Chemical Engineers, Coleman J. Major Award for Outstanding Scholastic Achievement in Chemical Engineering, Outstanding Work Ethic Award, and Outstanding Freshman Gold Award; Williams Honors College Peer Mentor, Top Ten Exemplary Williams Honors College Senior, Alumni Association Student Recognition Award; National Society of Leadership and Success, National Engaged Leadership Award, National Student President Advisory Board 2015–2016, and President 2014–2015; Tau Beta Pi, President 2015–2016 and Vice President 2014; Earned with the continuous love and support from Mom, Dad, Katherine, Elizabeth, Matthew, and Conner.

Payton, Quinton: Tomball, TX; University of Mary Hardin-Baylor; Ernie and Linda Payton; Christian Ministry, 2016; 77th Annual Easter Pageant, Portrayed Christ; River Rock Bible Church, Youth Director; Mr. Crusader Knights, Second Runner-up; Welcome Week Steering Committee, Spiritual Life Committee; Called to Play Sports Ministry, Co-Founder and Vice President; "The Lord is near to the broken-hearted and saves those who are crushed in Spirit." —Psalm 34:19

Peake, Cale William: Columbia, SC; Southern Wesleyan University; Charles and Connie Peake; BS Human Services, 2016; I give thanks to God, my parents, and friends for their love and support for this award.

Pearce, Josey Lyn: Okeechobee, FL; Indian River State College; Peyton and John Pearce; AA Business Administration, 2016; Phi Theta Kappa, Vice President, All-Florida Academic Team 2016, and Nerd Nation; Without my family or special friends, I would not be where I am today. Thank you.

Pedigo, Nathaniel Robert: Valrico, FL; Milwaukee School of Engineering; Leslie and Ryan Pedigo; BA Mechanical Engineering, 2016; Boy Scouts of America, Assistant Scoutmaster and Eagle Scout; SGA, Treasurer and Senator; Thank you to all of my family and friends for pushing me to go further.

Peeler, Eryn Jodell: Pomona, CA; Oakwood University; Evelyn and Barron Peeler; BS Physical Therapy, 2016; Dean's List 2012 and 2015, Honor Roll 2013–2015; White Ribbon Medallion Award; Yellow Ribbon Medallion Award; Blue Ribbon Medallion Award; Allied Health Club, President 2014–2016, Public Relations Director, and Mentoring Program; This honor would not have been possible without the love and support of my family, friends, and educators. Thanks!

Pena, Lirva A.: San Juan, TX; Del Mar College; Victor M. and Lirva Cerda; AA Dental Hygiene, 2016; Community Oral Health Prevention and Promotion; Student Chapter American Dental Hygienists Association Officer and Parliamentarian; Texas Dental Hygiene Association Student Delegate 2015, Dean's List; Este reconocimiento no fuera sido posible sin el apoyo que me brindo mi esposo y mi familia.

Penafiel, Eliana: Elgin, IL; Elgin Community College; AA Accounting, 2016; Spartan Food Pantry, Volunteer; Spartan Connection Mentoring Program, Coordinator; Honors Program, Honors Scholar; Rho Kappa Chapter of Phi Theta Kappa International Honors Society, Vice President; I dedicate this award to all those moms that do not give up on their families and dreams!

Pereira III, Miguel A.: Rochester, NY; Buffalo State; Mike and Lesley Pereira; MS Creative Studies, 2016; Residence Life, Resident Assistant 2014, Best in Building Award, Academic Excellence Award, Most Visionary Paraprofessional, Best Innovative Program, and Janelle Brooks Award; College Senate, Student Welfare Committee 2014–2015; Federal Trio Program Upward Bound, Summer Camp Counselor 2014 and 2015; United Students Government, Senator 2011–2012, Rules and Regulations Chair 2012–2013, and Recipient of President's Commendation Award 2013; Sara, Mom, Dad, coaches, family, and friends, this is not possible without you. Thank you, love you guys!

Perez, Justin Daniel: Washingtonville, NY; Mount Saint Mary College; Debra and Danny Perez; BS Business Administration, 2016; Ralph Scholar; Medici Scholar; I would like to thank the Higher Education Opportunity Program for the opportunity to go to college.

Perez, Nilmary: Philadelphia, PA; Pennsylvania Institute of Technology; AS Allied Health, 2016; This award would not have been possible without the support and love of my wife, Krissy, my family, and PIT.

Perry, Annie Alexandria: Rocky Mount, NC; Edgecombe Community College; AA Early Childhood Education, 2017; Phi Theta Kappa; Your Resource Center Advocate; Red Cross, Fred Turnage Chapter; This award would not be possible without Nan Hunter, who kept encouraging me to go for it.

Perry, Cailli C.: Wichita Falls, TX; Midwestern State University; Lisa and Robert Perry; BSW Social Work, 2017; Church Activities, Vacation Bible School, Sunday School Class Teacher, and Mission Trips 2002–2016; Jacksboro Volunteer Work, Concerned Citizens, Meals on Wheels, Jacksboro Healthcare Center Nursing Home, and Greystone Park Retirement and Assisted Living; National Organizations Volunteer and Fundraising: Jared Box Project, World Vision, and I'm ME; Wichita Falls Volunteer Work, Children's Aid Society/Teen Shelter, Meals on Wheels, Monterey Care Center, Faith Mission/Refuge/Resale Store, The Kitchen-Red Door, Habitat for Humanity, Food Bank, Wichita Falls Public Library, Patsy's House, WFISD, and Youth Opportunities Center; Social Work Department, Participant in EURECA Research Project 2015 and Social Work Month 2014–2016; National Society of Collegiate Scholars, Fundraising Chair 2015–2016; Sigma Phi Lambda–Sisters for the Lord, Secretary 2015–2016; This award would not have been possible without the love and support from my family, friends, and God.

Pessetti, Karra: Algonquin, IL; Carthage College; Laura Renda and Brian Pessetti; BA Criminal Justice, Sociology, 2016; Dean's List and Dean's Scholarship 2012–2016; Diskerud-Eller Scholarship 2014–2015; Faculty Honor Scholarship 2014–2015; Alpha Kappa Delta International Sociology Honor Society; Alpha Phi Sigma Criminal Justice Honor Society; Alpha Chi National Honors Fraternity; Chi Omega Fraternity, Panhellenic Delegate 2013–2014 and Personnel Chair 2014–2015; Thank you to family and Carthage College faculty and staff. Your guidance means everything to me.

Peterson, Dana Catherine: Woodbridge, NJ; Cabrini College; Jeanne and Edward Peterson; BS Elementary Education PreK–4/Special Education K–8, 2016; Women's Basketball, Captain, All-Academic Team, Second Team All-Conference; Women's Soccer, Captain, 2014 Player of the Year, and All-Academic Team; Thank you to my family, friends, coaches, and teachers for your continuous love and support!

Petrushesky, Kristen Rebecca: Lancaster, NY; D'Youville College; Eric and Pamela Petrushesky; BS Exercise and Sports Studies, 2016; SGA, Newspaper Committee Chair; Student Newspaper, Editor; Lambda Sigma Honor Society, President; Crew Team, Captain; This award would not be possible without the support of my family. I love you!

Pettiford, Beryl: Worcester, MA; Quinsigamond Community College; AA General Studies, Healthcare Medical, 2016; Thank you, Dr. Carberry, for your inspiration. Tatyana, this is for us!

Peveto, Marina Alicia: El Paso, TX; The University of Texas El Paso; BS Biomedical Science, 2016; National Society of Leadership and Success, Success Networking Team Facilitator.

Pfister, Scott Alan: Broomfield, CO; Oklahoma Baptist University; Barbara and Doug Pfister; BA Communication Studies, 2016; Intramural Flag Football, Third Place; Intramural Bowling, Champions; Intramural Basketball, Champions; Serve Shawnee 2015, Co-Coordinator; Herd, Student Ambassador; Men Tell All, Single Male Speaker; The Mentoring Project; Frontline Church Shawnee, Serve Crew; Intramural Co-Rec Softball, Champions; Lambda Pi Eta; Dean's List 2014–2015; Homecoming Court 2015, Most Servant-Like Male; Steering Committee Member, Subgroup Leader; Canterbury, Co-Chair; I am eternally grateful for God and my family, who have made this award possible.

Phillips, Danny Allen Bishop: Stillwell, OK; Connors State College; BA Wildlife Ecology/Management, 2018; This award would not have been possible without my coach, professors, family, and my Lord and Savior.

Phillips, Jackie A.: Monterey, LA; Copiah-Lincoln Community College Natchez; AA Culinary Arts, 2016; DECA; Phi Theta Kappa Honor Society; National Technical Honor Society; This award would not be possible without the support, help, and love of my family and school faculty.

Phillips, Jessica Mashaun: Fort Worth, TX; Dakota State University; BS Health Information Administration, 2016; Union Gospel Mission of Tarrant County; Texas BUC$ Conference 2016, Hostess; BLS/CPR Certification; Healthcare Information and Management Systems; American Health Information Management Association; I would like to thank God, without him shining on my life this award would not be possible.

Phillips, Sandra K.: West Bloomfield, MI; Madonna University Graduate School; Alvin and Mildred Phillips; MS Hospice/Palliative Studies, 2016; Kappa Gamma Pi; Summa Cum Laude; Gratitude and thanks to my parents and family for unfailing support and continuous encouragement. Love always.

Piech, Peter Daniel: Meriden, CT; Rensselaer Polytechnic Institute; Alisa and Martin Piech; MS Computer Science, 2016; Upsilon Pi Epsilon Honor Society, Vice President; Delta Kappa Epsilon Fraternity, Sergeant-at-Arms; I thank my friends and family for the love and support that made this award possible.

Pierce, Nia Symone: Montgomery, TX; Texas Tech University; Tony and Gayle Pierce; BA Accounting, 2016; Accounting Leadership Council; Mentor Tech, Protégé Advisory Committee Leader; Honors College Ambassador; Rawls Business Leadership Program, Inaugural Member; Mortar Board, Member and Top 50 Senior.

Pierpoint, Victoria Ann: Big Sandy, TN; Murray State University Graduate School; Dwayne and Peggy Pierpoint; MS Speech-Language Pathology, 2016; Richmond Residential College, Outstanding Senior for Academics 2014, Outstanding Female College Member 2011, and Dr. Ken Bowman Outstanding Residential College Freshmen Leader of the Year; Christ Ambassadors Ministry, Student President 2014; Gamma Beta Phi, Recording Secretary 2011; I have been successful only with the grace of my Savior and support of my family. Thank you.

Pines, Terri: Atlanta, GA; Georgia State University; BA Sociology, 2016; Georgia State Ambassador Core, Volunteer Lead; Delta Epsilon Iota Honor Society; Thank you, Alex, for all of your love and support. I DID IT!

Piper, Christopher Sean: Ovett, MS; Southeastern Baptist College; David Piper; BA Church Ministry, 2017; I would not have this honor if it were not for the support of God, family, and friends.

Pittman, Andrew-Gatlin Brett: Rock Hill, SC; York Technical College; Michelle and Andy Pittman; AA Digital Information Design, 2018; Eastview Baptist Church, Young Adult Ministry Organizer, Small Group Leader, and Youth Band Bassist; "Whatever you do, do all to the glory of God." —1 Corinthians 10:31

Plank, Laura Nicole: Orrtanna, PA; Shippensburg University; Julia and Frank Plank; BA Supply Chain Management, 2016; Mom and Dad, thank you for the love and support that made this award a possibility.

Plass, Shantal J.: Schenectady, NY; Schenectady County Community College; Lavern Fraser; AS Business Administration, 2016; Student Affairs Division, Front Desk Office Assistant Student Worker; ALANA Club, President and New York State Assembly Leadership Award and Citation; Business and Law Club, Vice President; Women's Crew; Campus Safety Council; Faculty Student Association; Student Activity Board, President; SGA, Vice President; This award would not have been possible without God and the support and love from my family.

Plott, Cheryl Lynn: Flat Rock, NC; Blue Ridge Community College; Patricia Roysdon and Timothy Plott; AA Office Administration, 2016; Thank you to my family and friends for the love and support.

Podlas, Samantha Rose: East Amherst, NY; State University of New York Buffalo-Graduate School; Mark and Sue Ann Podlas; MBA General Management, 2015; I would not be who I am without the love from my Mom, Dad, and two sisters.

Polinski, Rebecca L.: New Kensington, PA; Duquesne University; Darlene and Raymond Polinski; BS Health Management Systems, 2017; 2015 Orientation Team Leader; Pi Kappa Epsilon, Health Management Systems Representative; Thanks to my family for their support and love throughout my years of education.

Pollak, Ahuva Naomi: Brooklyn, NY; Touro College; Esther and Daniel Pollak; BS Management Marketing, 2016.

Ponce De Leon, Sarah: El Paso, TX; The University of Texas El Paso; BS Civil Engineering, 2019; Make-A-Wish North Texas, Wish Granter and Wish Ambassador; Undergraduate Learning Center Technology Support, Undergraduate Assistant; Student Enrichment Experience; Student Leadership Institute; One Campus Challenge, Recruitment Coordinator; University Honors Council; "Commit your work to the Lord, and your plans will be established." —Proverbs 16:3

Ponder, Caley L.: Piedmont, AL; Gadsden State Community College; AS General Studies, 2016; Phi Theta Kappa; This award would not have been possible without the love and support from my family and friends.

Pondexter, Frankie Laine: Southaven, MS; Northwest Mississippi Community College; AA Criminal Justice, 2016; Thankful to my family and the faculty of Northwest Mississippi Community College for their support.

Poole, Marlee Erin: Newberry, SC; Piedmont Technical College; Laurie and Mo Keenan; AA Veterinary Technology, 2016; Vet Tech Club, Secretary.

Pope, Tonjua Marie: Amarillo, TX; Amarillo College; Gary and Marti Highbarger; AA Occupational Therapy, 2016; Phi Theta Kappa, Academic Excellence Award; I wish to thank my family for their love and support, especially my husband, Kyle.

Porter, Michael A.: Levittown, NY; Suffolk County Community College Michael J. Grant Campus; AA Chemical Dependency, 2015; Advocated for Access to Treatment in Albany Twice; Dean's List; I would like to thank my mom, Betty T. Porter, and Professor Kathy Ayres and Professor Suzanne Smollers.

Portera, Mary Virginia: Memphis, TN; The University of Mississippi; Amy and Greg Portera; BA Biology and Spanish, 2016; Delta Delta Delta Sorority, Scholarship Chair; Young Life; Big Event; LeapFrog, Taylor Medalist; Phi Beta Kappa; Phi Kappa Phi; Omicron Delta Kappa; Golden Key.

Potts, Emily Lynn: East Carondelet, IL; Missouri Baptist University; Mark and Jill Potts; BS Elementary Education, 2015; This award would not have been possible without the love and support from my family.

Povoa, Charity D.: Rock Hill, SC; York Technical College; Robert and Sandra Nelson; AA Arts and Associates of Applied Sciences in Automotive Technology, 2016; To all the wonderful people who helped make my college journey a success! Love and gratefulness!

Powers, Maria D.: Pound, VA; Mountain Empire Community College; Susie and Lennie Powers; AA Environmental Science, 2016; SGA, Secretary; Environmental Science Club, President; This wonderful experience is possible thanks to the support of my parents and also my professor, Dr. Ogbonnaya.

P'Pool, Taylor Marie: Birmingham, AL; University of South Alabama; Lorrie and Chuck P'Pool; BA Communications, 2016; College Panhellenic Council, Junior Panhellenic President, Community Relations Chair on Panhellenic Executive Board, Phi Chi, and National Panhellenic Conference 2013 and 2014 Attendee Representing the USA Panhellenic Executive Board; Mom and Dad, thank you for everything. "Commit to the Lord, and your plans will succeed." —Proverbs 16:3

Prater, Kayla J.: Belle Center, OH; The University of Findlay; Shelly and Jon Prater; BS Biology, 2016; Board of Trustees in Advancement, Student Representative; SGA, Class President; Scholarship and Research Society, President; This award would not have been possible without the boundless support from my family, friends, and mentors.

Preaus, Luke G.: Tulsa, OK; Northeastern Oklahoma A&M College; AA Business Administration 2016; Baseball; Business Administration Student of the Year 2015–2016.

Presley, Shanna Nicole: Frisco City, AL; Alabama Southern Community College; Sandra and John Presley; BS Radiologic Sciences, 2018; Student Support Services, Tutor; Phi Theta Kappa, Regional Distinguished Member Award and International Distinguished Member Award; Ambassador, President.

Presto, Peyton Dees: Cullman, AL; The University of Alabama; BS Chemical Engineering and Finance, 2017; Society of Engineers in Medicine, Secretary; University Scholars Program, Master of Science in Finance Candidate; Student Judiciary, Executive Committee Chair, Associate Justice; Million Dollar Band, Trumpet Section Leader; I would like to thank my parents for their endless support and unlimited encouragement.

Prince, Na'eem E.: Savannah, GA; Saint Leo University; Samuel and Ruth Prince; BA Psychology, 2016; This award would not have been possible without the support and love from my family.

Pringle, Catherine H.: Evans, GA; University of North Georgia; Gary and Devorah Pringle; BA Biology, 2017; University Recreation Center, Facility Staff, Summer and Fall 2016 and 2017 Supervisor; I am beyond grateful for this opportunity and owe it all to God, my parents, and my university.

Prisk, Emily Beth: Amarillo, TX; Amarillo College; Ludustia and Jeff Prisk; AA Photography and Marketing Management, 2017; 2015 Common Reader Visual Arts Competition, Best in Show; 2016 Amarillo College Honors Convocation, Outstanding Photography Major; SGA, Historian and Sweepstakes Award; I am so thankful for my friends and family and their love, kindness, and support. I love you all!

Prosser, Robert: Pensacola, FL; The University of West Florida; Larry Prosser and Patricia Socha; BS Global Economics/Finance, 2018; Sigma Chi Fraternity, Assistant Quaestor/Treasurer and Horizons Leadership Summit Attendee.

Proulx, Olivia Katherine: Unionville, CT; Mount Saint Mary College; BA Hispanic Studies, Certification in Elementary and Special Education, 2016; Love Your Melon Campus Crew, Vice President; A big thank you to my parents for always supporting and encouraging me! Go Knights!

Puccio, Sarah Elizabeth: Fort Mill, SC; University of South Carolina; Trudie and Victor Puccio; BS Accounting/Finance/Management, 2016; Phi Beta Lambda, Co-President; Beta Alpha Psi, Reporting Secretary; Thank you to my family and mentors for supporting me, this would not be possible without you.

Q

Qualls, Andrea M.: Brookland, AR; Arkansas State University Newport; AS Business, 2016; Dean's List; This award would not have been possible without the love and support from my family.

Quiceno Jr., Wilson Emerson: Morristown, NJ; Ramapo College of New Jersey; Wilson and Alba Quiceno; BS Information Technology Management, 2016; Educational Opportunity Fund Office, Graduate Outstanding Achievement Award; Chi Alpha Epsilon; Real Man of Ramapo Calendar, Honoree; Office of Fraternity and Sorority Life, Student Aid; Information Technology Services, Residential Networking Student Support Technician; SGA, Secretary of Greek Affairs; Interfraternity Council, Public Relations Chair; Resident Assistant, Student Staff Advisor and Staff Member of the Year Award; Association of Latinos Moving Ahead, Treasurer, Community Service Chair, Senior Adviser, and Co-President; I want to thank family, friends, Ramapo staff, and Fraternity Brothers for continuing to push and motivate me

Quinlan, Billy: Gray, TN; East Tennessee State University; Carolyn and Dennis Quinlan; BS Interdisciplinary Studies, 2016; Athletic Department, Gameday Marketing and Promotions Volunteer 2012–2014; Relay For Life, Entertainment Coordinator 2013–2014; SGA, Homecoming Committee 2013, Concert Planning Committee and Volunteer Coordinator 2014, Senator 2014, and Secretary of State 2014; Sigma Alpha Epsilon, President 2014–2015; New Student and Family Programs, Program Assistant 2014–2016 and Preview and Orientation Leader 2012–2014.

Quinn, Michaela: Jefferson, TX; Panola College; AA Business, 2016; This award would not have been possible without the love and support from my true family.

Quintero, Nathalie E.: Daytona Beach, FL; Embry-Riddle Aeronautical University; Omar Quintero and Ruth Hernandez; BS Aerospace Engineering, 2015; College of Engineering Dean's List 2011–2015; Women in Aviation International, Delta Air Lines Engineering Scholarship; Society of Hispanic Professional Engineers, 2015 Best Paper Award on Mechanics of Materials and Fluids; McNair Baccalaureate Program, McNair Scholar; Society of Women Engineers, President 2013–2014 and Treasurer 2012–2013; I would like to dedicate my success to my mami and papi, los amo!

R

Radcliff, Marissa May: Caldwell, OH; Rio Grande Community College; Mark and Michele Radcliff; AS Diagnostic Medical Sonography, 2016.

Radebe, Warren Sithembeka: Charlotte, NC; Johnson C. Smith University; Princess and Sybil Radebe; AA Political Science, 2016; LGBT Student Activist, President of SAFE Pride; Warren is a progressive social activist in South Africa and USA and Ambassador for LGBT Rights Africa.

Raman, Sanjay Muneshwar Murthi: Metairie, LA; University of Holy Cross School of Nursing; Sachida and Karol Raman; BS Nursing, 2016; Many thanks for all the love and support of my family, Sachida, Jean, Karol, Diana, and Howie.

Rameriz-Tomas, Ana: Boaz, AL; Wallace State Community College Hanceville; AA Respiratory Therapy, 2016; This award would not have been possible without the Lord's help and from the support of my parents.

Ramsey, Kayla Renee: Lancaster, CA; Oakwood University; Lisa Graham and Melford Ramsey; BS Nursing, 2016; Oakwood University Student Nursing Association, Senior Class Representative; I dedicate this award to God, my family, and friends who supported me during my studies.

Rapkoch, Emily V.: Bismarck, ND; University of Mary; Joe and Nina Rapkoch; BA Computer Information Systems/Information Technology Management, 2016; Mariders, Project Lead; Church of the Ascension, Confirmation Small Group Leader; Ronald McDonald House; Computer Personnel United, Webpage Manager; Residence Life Assistant; Catholic Relief Services Student Ambassadors; Emerging Leaders Academy, Early Admit Mentorship Program Pilot Group; Collegiate DECA, Social Media Manager, Webpage Manager, President, First Place State Competition, and Top Ten International Career Development Competition; None of this would have been possible without the love, support, and prayers of those around me.

Ray, Spencer Wayne: Republic, MO; Evangel University; BA Communication Arts/Media, 2016; National Society of Collegiate Scholars; Tink, Pip, Boukie, and Boba: I could not have made it through this adventure without you. Love you.

Rayford, Na-Shaunda DaNice: Anderson, IN; Saint Mary-of-the-Woods College; Natalie and Eric (Deceased) Maxwell; BS Criminology/Psychology, 2017; Basketball Team, Hardest Worker 2015–2016; Resident Assistant, Outstanding Achievement and Leadership Award; This award would not have been possible without God and the sacrifices and support of my family.

Read, Shalane: DuBois, PA; Pennsylvania State University DuBois Campus; Kim Lee and Brad Read; BA Human Development/Family Studies, 2017; This award would not have been possible without my son, who gives me the motivation to do well.

Reagan, Brandy A.: Montgomery City, MO; William Woods University; Ronald Reagan and Gloria Koehn; BS Business Administration, 2016; Active Minds, President and Vice President; Student Alumni Council, Class President, Representative, Treasurer, and Outstanding Student Coordinator; Order of Omega, President and Service Chair; Omicron Delta Kappa, President, Vice President of Membership, Logistics Committee Head, and Circle Leader of the Year; PanHellenic Council, Recruitment Counselor and Outstanding Greek Sophomore; Alpha Chi Omega, Chapter President, Student Foundation Ambassador, Chapter Chosen Most Outstanding Member, Nominating Committee, Chapter Standards and Relations Board, Traditions Chair, and Risk Management Committee; This award would not have been possible without the continued love and support from my dearest family and friends.

Ream, Jessica Ann: Columbia Falls, MT; University of Great Falls; Allen and Michelle Ream; BA Psychology, 2017; University of Great Falls Research Project, First Place at University of Great Falls Symposium; Great Falls Rescue Mission Volunteer, Outstanding Achievement Award; Providence Formation Program, Outstanding Achievement Award; Honor Society, Leadership Team.

Rebottaro, Sage Maddox: Tecumseh, MI; Southern Wesleyan University; Tina and Charles Rebottaro Jr.; BS Exercise Science, 2016; Foothills YMCA, Soccer Referee; Day of Service Participant; New Student Orientation, Orientation Leader and Warrior Trainer; I would like to thank everyone who has supported me. All of the glory goes to God!

Recio, Kellie Marie: Ruskin, FL; Southeastern University; Gina and Kevin Recio; BS Psychology, 2015; Psi Chi, Treasurer.

Redband, Lisa Ann: Batavia, NY; Roberts Wesleyan College; Larry and Carol Redband; BS Nursing, 2016; Nursing Club, Chaplain; Varsity Soccer, Scholar Athlete; "I can do all things through Christ who strengthens me." —Philippians 4:13

Redditt, Laura: Grenada, MS; Mississippi Valley State University Department of Criminal Justice; MS Criminal Justice, 2017; Zeta Phi Beta Sorority Inc., Scholar Award and Honors Scholar Award; This special achievement would not have been possible without God leading my path and my daughter, Loran.

Reed Jr., John Wesley: Alexandria, VA; New England College; Jean E. Johnson; BA Business Administration/Management, 2015; 2015 Magna Cum Laude; AvalonBay Community Service Award; Ceridian Implementation Team, Louisville, Kentucky; *All About Jazz Digital Magazine*, Article Contributor; Omega Psi Phi Fraternity Inc., Mu Epsilon Chapter; Dedicated to the late Rev. Dr. John Wesley Reed Sr., the late Annie Bell Leak Reed, and my wife, Vivian Cross Reed.

Reed, Andrea Cheryl: White Plains, NY; Nyack College Rockland Campus; BS Interdisciplinary Studies, Pastoral Ministry, Psychology Concentration, 2017; I dedicate this accomplishment to the memory of my mother, Valeria Yvonne Reed.

Reese, Amberly Loren: Madison, AL; Athens State University; Pamela and Dean Reese; BA Graphic Design/Studio Art, 2016; Art Club, President; Kappa Pi, President; This award is dedicated to my family and professors for always encouraging me to follow my dreams.

Reese-Campbell, Christina Ejade: Monroe, GA; Emmanuel College; Cynthia Reese-Campbell and Gregary Campbell; BA Organizational Communication, 2016; SGA, Sophomore Class Secretary; Emmanuel Leadership Initiative, Year 1 Completion; I am so grateful. Thank you to everyone who has helped me along the way.

Regan, Matthew Gerard: Medford, MA; Roger Williams University; BS Security Assurance Studies, 2016; I would like to thank my family, friends, and mentors from RWU who have helped me succeed here.

Rego, Triana: Rutherford, NJ; College of Saint Elizabeth; Isabel and Frank Rego; MA Counseling Psychology, 2017; *The Journal of Psychology and Clinical Psychiatry*, Two-time Published Researcher and Writer; American Psychology-Law Society; American Diabetes Association; Psi Chi; This award would not have been possible without the support and love from my family. You are amazing! I LOVE YOU!

Reid, Katie Elizabeth: Chattanooga, TN; University of the Cumberlands; Daniel and Karen Reid; BS Human Services/Concentration in Adult Intervention, 2016; Tue Upsilon Alpha Chi Mu, Secretary and Treasurer; Radio Show WCCR, Guest Speaker; House Council, Floor Representative; I dedicate this award to my supportive mom and family.

Reierson, Lauren E.: Roseville, CA; William Jessup University; Timothy and Linda Wakeley; BA Psychology, 2016; William Jessup Psychology Club, President.

Reinhardt, Victoria Jayne: Paducah, KY; Harding University; Doug and Denna Reinhardt; BA Communication Sciences and Disorders, 2016; Rock Mentoring; Relay For Life, Organizer; Spring Break Mission Trip, Honduras and Tuba City, Arizona; American Studies Institute; Omicron Delta Kappa; National Student Speech-Language-Hearing Association; Student Speech and Hearing Association, Service Director 2014–2016; Thank you to my family for their constant love and support.

Reiss, Monica: Macungie, PA; Messiah College; Barry and Wendy Reiss; BS Education PreK–4, Dual Certification in Special Education, 2016; SGA, Student Senate; Thanks to my mom and dad for always being supportive and encouraging of me throughout my life.

Render, Terrance Bernard: Decatur, GA; Georgia State University; Bernard and Pamela Render; BMU Music Technology, 2017.

Reneau, **Kirsten M.**: **Grafton, WV**; **West Virginia** Wesleyan College; Julie and Paul Reneau; BA English Writing Track, Gender Studies, and Specialization in American History, 2016; Collegiate 4H, Vice President; Sigma Tau Delta, Vice President; Alpha Gamma Delta, Gamma Experience Coordinator and Vice President Recruitment; Thank you, dad, for pushing me to greater heights, and mom, for helping me up along the way.

Renn, Rebecca Elizabeth: Louisville, KY; Bellarmine University; Jodell and Robert Renn; BA Psychology, 2017; Phi Mu, Phi Assistant.

Rerich, Ryan Alan: Weimar, TX; Missouri Baptist University; Patrick and Irma Rerich; BA Journalism, 2016; **Phi Lambda Phi**; **Alpha Chi**; **Golf, Team** Captain and Varsity Starter; *Timeline*, Lead Editor; BS Communication Studies; A special thanks to my parents, Buck and Irma Rerich, for the love and support.

Reyes, Dan Wayne Ang: Los Angeles, CA; Pensacola Christian College; Pham Van Tai Reyes and Hensie Reyes; BS Engineering, Mechanical Concentration, 2016; Lead and Participated in Prayer Groups and Bible Studies; Leading Role in Welcoming and Helping International Students; Minor Sports Participant and Top 3; Over 500 Hours Tutoring in Math and Engineering; Thanks to family and friends who supported me in various ways. Ultimately, all glory and honor to God.

Reyes, Lexie M.: Amarillo, TX; Amarillo College; Renee and Raul Reyes; AA Psychology, 2017; Phi Theta Kappa; Texas Regional District One Vice President; I would not be here without the love and support from my family. This is for you!

Reynolds, Chanda Parker: Clarendon, TX; Oklahoma Panhandle State University; Paul Reynolds and Kimberlie Parker Reynolds; BS Agronomy, 2016; Crops Judging Team; Women in Agronomy; Alpha Zeta, President; Dean's List; Student Council Representative; Spring Homecoming Queen; Without the support of my family and my instructors, this award could not have been possible. Thank you!

Reynolds, Travon A.: Duncanville, TX; Langston University; Debbie Ford; BBA Accounting, 2016; Football, All-Conference, Pre-Season All-American; President's List; Dean's List; Intern at Jackson Hewitt; This award has been made possible with the support and love of my mom. Love You!

Rhodes, Justin W.: Soso, MS Southeastern Baptist College; AA Bible, 2017.

Richard, Rosie: Texarkana, TX; University of Arkansas Community College Hope-Texarkana; Hazel and Scottie Brown; AA Registered Nurse, 2017; Susan G Komen Race for the Cure; Heart Walk; Domestic Violence; Texarkana Community College; Cum Laude; Dean's List; Honor Roll; My first priority is to God and family. I am active in church life and family life and a dedicated nurse.

Richards, Amber Louise: Buxton, ME; Pensacola Christian College; Paul and Marge Richards; BS Nursing, 2016; I praise my God and Savior Jesus for His grace and mercy. Without Him, I could achieve nothing.

Richardson Jr., Randal Craig: Pawcatuck, CT; Roger Williams University; Ida Polverari; BS Criminal Justice, 2016; Criminal Justice Club; Paintball Club; I am honored to receive this award and thankful to my family, friends, and professors for their support.

Richardson, Jennifer: Memphis, TN; Southwest Tennessee Community College; Denise and Phillip Richardson; AA General Studies, 2016; It is not when you finish, but how you finish. My family and I are truly honored.

Ridley, Calvin Taylor: Alton, NH; Framingham State University; Ryan and Gayle Ridley; BA Painting, 2016; The Hilltop Players, Future Leader Award Recipient; Sexual Harassment and Assault Prevention and Education, Intern; Alternative Spring Break, Trip Leader; Justin D. McCarthy College and Community Service Scholarship; Office of Residence Life and Student Conduct, Administrative Resident Assistant; Arthur B. Mazmanian Art Gallery, Intern; A. Carolla Haglund Cultural and Fine Arts Award; Kappa Pi Membership; Campus Pride, Advisory Board Member; Massachusetts Commission on LGBTQ Youth, Commissioner; Center for Academic Success and Advising, Receptionist; SGA Gender and Inclusion Ad-Hoc Committee, Chair; Alumni Association Leadership Scholarship, John F. Kennedy Award, and Student Leader of the Year Nominee; Pride Alliance; Good vibes to my family, Amy, Kimmi, Tim, Ladonna, Vicky, Johnny, Cam, the Fords, and Levi, with love.

Riemenschneider, Jenna Lin: Knoxville, TN; Tennessee Wesleyan College; BS Business Administration, 2016; Phi Beta Lambda, Secretary 2013–2014 and Reporter 2014–2015; SGA, Christian Fellowship Representative 2013–2016; Student Activities Board, Calendar Events 2014–2015; Christian Fellowship, Lead Team 2013–2016; All honor and glory go to God for his help and understanding! Thanks Mom, Dad, Kim, and Jay!

Rifilato, Anna C.: Johnstown, PA; Saint Vincent College; Rose and James Rifilato; BA Early Childhood Education, 2017; Saint Vincent Challenge Summer Camp, Counselor; Orientation Committee; Alpha Lambda Delta; Kappa Delta Pi; Early Childhood Club, Treasurer and President; Thank you to those I love for their love, help, and support.

Riley, Stephanie Dawn: Lubbock, TX; Texas Tech University; Donna Price and Michael Riley; BA Music Education, 2017; Collegiate Texas Music Educators, Elementary Chair; Tau Beta Sigma, Secretary and Rules Officer; Thank you to God, my parents, family, and friends for getting me here. Love you all!

Riojas, Luis Alberto: Three Rivers, TX; Texas A&M University Kingsville; Raymond and Marisol Riojas; BS Chemical Engineering, 2017; Society of Petroleum Engineers, Vice President 2014–2015; American Institute of Chemical Engineers, ChemE Car Captain 2015, Southwest Regional Conference Champions, and National Finalists; American Institute of Chemical Engineers, Historian 2015; My achievements are owed to my loving mother. May your counsel forever inspire those who hear it.

Ripine, Vaigalepa: Tampa, FL; American Military University; Tafaoga and Fiamatai Foalima; MA Human Resource Management, 2016; Thank you, family, especially my husband and kids, for the support and sacrifices. Love you all!

Riva, Cassandra A.: Plainville, MA; Salem State University; Carla Taft and Albert Riva; BS Communications, 2017; WMWM Salem State Radio, Program Director; Lambda Pi Eta; Alpha Lambda Delta; National Society of Leadership and Success.

Rivers, Ajibola Jeremy: Lafayette Hill, PA; Temple University Boyer College of Music and Dance; Titilola Lakeru-Rivers; BA Music Performance, Cello, 2016; St. Jude and the Nativity Episcopal Church, Acolyte, Reader, and Musician; Montgomery County Youth Orchestra, Composer-in-Residence and Section Mentor; Boyer Shadowing Program, Founder; University Women's Chorus, Guest Composer; Who knows where I would be without my mom and dad. You guys are the best.

Robbins, Justin: Oklahoma City, OK; University of Oklahoma; Michelle Robbins; BS Biology, 2016; Padres Luchando por sus Hijos Town Hall; Medical Brigade to Honduras, Translator; Medical Mission Trip to Peru, Translator; Children's Interstitial and Diffuse Lung Disease Foundation; Latinos Without Borders, Participant Coordinator; Oklahoma Blood Institute, Planning Committee; Sigma Lambda Beta International Fraternity Inc., President and Founding Father; Integrity Council, Vice Chair of Adjudication, Peer Educator, Public Relations Committee, and Senior Councilor; Hispanic American Student Association, Latino Flavor Chair and Executive Committee; I would not be where I am today without my family's and friends' support.

Roberts, Katelyn Delanie: Bogue Chitto, MS; Copiah-Lincoln Community College; Shannon and Kala Roberts; BS Nursing, 2018; 2015 Election Campaigns and Events Volunteer; Brookhaven Little Theater Volunteer; Brookhaven Animal Rescue League Volunteer; King's Daughters Medical Center Volunteer; Student Voices; Lady Wolves Basketball Team, Statistician; Sigma Kappa Delta English Honor Society, Secretary and Treasurer; President's Council; Phi Theta Kappa, Eta Omega Chapter, Vice President of Service; Copiah-Lincoln Community College Republicans Chair; Alpha Omega Science Club, Communications Director and President; Trailblazers Student Recruitment Team, President.

Robidoux, Ashtyn Carol-Ann: Apple Valley, CA; California Baptist University; Carol and Shawn Robidoux; BS Accounting, 2017; Alpha Chi, National Convention Attendee; This award would not have been possible without the love and support from my whole family.

Robinson, Jesse Luke: McKenzie, TN; The University of Tennessee at Martin; BS Criminal Justice, Concentration in Courts and Law, 2016; Tennessee Court of Criminal Appeals, Summer 2015 Internship; Alpha Phi Sigma National Criminal Justice Honor Society, President 2015–2016 and Outstanding Criminal Justice Student Award 2014; Tennessee Intercollegiate State Legislature, Deputy Secretary of State 2015 and House Representative 2014; SGA, Chief Justice 2014–2016, Attorney General 2013–2014, Freshmen Council Secretary General 2012–2013, and Most Dedicated Award 2016; University Scholars Program, 2016 University Scholars Project "Stepping Through Death's Door: An Insider's Perspective on Capital Punishment in Tennessee"; University Scholars Organization, President 2015–2016 and Secretary General 2014–2015; Carr Elementary School, Volunteer Tutor 2014–2015; I dedicate this award to my parents. I could not have done it without you, mom and dad.

Robinson, Lakeisha Nicole: Greensboro, NC; Guilford College Center for Continuing Education; Annette Robinson and Paul Marshall; BS Psychology, 2016; This award would not have been possible without the support and love from my family.

Robinson, Malachi-Chaim: Marietta, GA; Kennesaw State University; Gloria Robinson-Munir; BS Criminal Justice, 2017; President's List 2015–2016; Dean's List 2014–2015; National Society of Collegiate Scholars; Alpha Phi Sigma Criminal Justice Honors Society; National Residence Hall Honorary; Delta Epsilon Iota Academic Honor Society; Golden Key International Honour Society; This award would not have been possible without the support and love from my mom and aunt.

Robinson, McKayla B.: Canyon, TX; Amarillo College; Scott and Vickie Robinson; AS Business Administration, 2016; Phi Theta Kappa Honor Society; SGA; I could have not achieved this award without the support of my family and friends.

Rodriguez, Richard: Prescott Valley, AZ; Embry-Riddle Aeronautical University Prescott Campus; BS Aeronautics, 2018; I am grateful to Embry Riddle and the support and love of my family and my wife, Jacki.

Rodriguez, Sherrie L.: Kennesaw, GA; Kennesaw State University; MS Applied Statistics, 2016; Analytics Conference Presenter, SAS Analytics Poster Winner 2015; Graduate Research/Teaching Assistant, SAS Student Ambassador 2016; This award would never have been possible without the love and support of my family and friends.

Rogan, Celine Marie: Wainscott, NY; Suffolk County Community College Eastern Campus; AA Business Management and Administration, 2017; This award is dedicated to my wonderful sons, reminding them to never give up on their dreams.

Rogers, Blair L.: Milton, DE; Delaware Technical Community College Georgetown; Linda and Lynn Rogers; AA Elementary Education; This would not be possible without the support, help, and love of my family, friends, and teachers.

Rogers, Daniel Anthony: Lexington, KY; Bluegrass Community and Technical College; Julia Morrison and Elbert Rogers; AA Psychology, 2016; Phi Theta Kappa, President, Distinguished Chapter Member Award, and Adviser Award for Service; This award would not have been possible without the support and love from my family and Ms. Baker.

Rogers, Garrett: Clayton, OK; Eastern Oklahoma State College; Adrena and Patrick Rogers; AA Communications, 2016; I am so thankful for this award! It goes to show that hard work definitely pays off!

Rogers, Russell Tyler: Ellabell, GA; Georgia Southern University; Russell and Jalaine Rogers; BS Psychology, 2015; ESOL Tutoring; Psi Chi; Georgia Southern Honors Program; Theos Logos Christian Apologetics, Founder and President; All that I have and will have is from and for the Lord.

Romanik, Shelby Kristoff: Mount Pleasant, PA; Seton Hill University; Natalie and Steve Laskey; BS Business Administration, 2016; Rotary Youth Leadership Camp, Girl's Counselor; This never would have been possible without the love and support of my family and friends.

Romano, Madeleine: Yardley, PA; High Point University; Joseph and Rachel Romano; BA Graphic Design and Digital Imaging, 2016; Campus Activities Team, Executive Committee Venture Head; American Institute of Graphic Arts, Chapter Vice President and Founding Member.

Romano, Sara K.: Norristown, PA; Pennsylvania Institute of Technology; AA Practical Nursing, 2016; This would not have been possible without the loving support of my husband, kids, and parents.

Romero, Kayleigh Danielle: Beaumont, TX; Lamar University; Rebecca Broussard; MA Education and Educational Technology Leadership, 2017; Lamar University Honors Program, Vice President; Phi Kappa Phi Honor Society; Kappa Delta Pi; I would not be where I am today without the support and love of my family.

Rooker, Kristen: Warrior, AL; Wallace State Community College Hanceville; Tonya Fetner; AA Human Services; I would not be here today without the support of Ms. Beck: thank you for everything you have done.

Rosa, Sonia E.: Georgetown, DE; Delaware Technical Community College Georgetown; AA Human Services, 2016; This award was possible with the support of my family, friends, and instructors. Thank you!

Rosado, Ivonne: Phenix City, AL; Athens State University; Gilberto Ramirez; BA Management of Technology, 2017; Chattahoochee Valley Community College Dean's List; Athens State University Honor Student; This award would not have been possible without the support and love from my dad, Gilberto Ramirez.

Rose, Justin Alan: Winchester, TN; Tennessee Tech University; Carey Rose and Greta Curbow; BS Business/Information Technology, 2016; Association of Information Technology Professionals, President; Pi Kappa Alpha, External Vice President, Alumni Relations, Philanthropy Chair, and IFC Representative; This award would not have been possible without the support from my family and friends.

Rosewell, Michelle: Grapevine, TX; Angelo State University; BA Business Management, 2015.

Ross, RuthAnn M.: Wichita Falls, TX; Midwestern State University; Wendy Scott; MA Health Services Administration, 2017; Caribbean Students Organization Alumni; Wesley Methodist Church Nursery; Graduate Students Organization; Student Ambassador; Golden Key International Honour Society, Secretary; This award would not have been possible without the support of my wonderful family.

Rossi, Heather Lynn: Waxhaw, NC; High Point University; Linda and Bob Rossi; BA Theatre Performance, Vocal Performance, 2017; Special Needs Children Volunteer; Dean's List; Mu Phi Epsilon Music Honor Fraternity, Secretary; Sigma Sigma Sigma, Music Chair; Junior Marshal, Top 1 Percent of Junior Class; To my wonderful support system consisting of remarkable friends and family, thank you!

Rossi, Marco Walter: Arlington Heights, IL; Saint Louis University Department of Biomedical Laboratory Science; Paolo and Virginia Rossi; BS Medical Laboratory Science, 2015.

Roy, Caitlin Eileen: Middletown, MD; Stevenson University; Donald and Christine Roy; BS Elementary Education, 2016; Women's Volleyball Team, 2012 NCAA Second Round Participant and 2012 MAC Champions 2012; Women's Basketball Team, 2016 ECAC South Champions, 2015 NCAA Second Round Participant, and 2015 MAC Champions; Thank you to my family, teachers, coaches, and friends who have supported and encouraged me.

Rubianes, Mark Phillip: Hendersonville, NC; Blue Ridge Community College; Hector and Elsa Rubianes; AS Engineering, 2016; Dean's List 2015; Dallas Herring Achievement Award Nominee   ; First Church of the Nazarene Soup Kitchen Volunteer; Henderson County Habitat for Humanity Fundraising Event Volunteer; National Honor Technical Society, President; I dedicate this honor to all my family. It represents what is achievable with your strong love and support.

Rubiano, Christina Gianna: Manchester, NH; New England College; Toni and Joseph Rubiano; BA Political Science/Criminal Justice, 2016; Softball, All-American Scholar Athlete; Thanks, mom and dad, for being my rock; without your love and support I would not be where I am today.

Rudisel, Serena Nicole: Hampton, VA; Hampton University; Rahn and Patricia Rudisel; BA Electrical Engineering, 2017; Career Center Ambassador; National Society of Black Engineers, Finance Chair; Institute of Electrical and Electronics Engineers, Secretary; Honors College; The Greer Dawson Wilson Student Leadership Program; This award would not be possible without the motivation from my fellow Student Leaders and Hampton U!

Rueff, Jenna Katherine: Louisville, KY; Campbellsville University; Sandy and John Rueff; BS Psychology and Educational Ministry, 2016; This award would not have been possible if it were not for my family, friends, and professors.

Rundberg, Ginny: Olathe, KS; MidAmerica Nazarene University; BA Applied Organizational Leadership, 2016; Without the love and support of my family, this award would not have been possible.

Runions, Ashley Nicole: Fyffe, AL; Wallace State Community College Hanceville; Neal and Sheila Kennamer; AA Respiratory Therapy, 2016; My academic success was possible due to my husband, Joseph Runions, and my family's support.

Runyon Dunlap, Amy Leann: Murray, KY; West Kentucky Community and Technical College; Patsy Hutson and Roger Runyon; AS Registered Nurse, 2016; I owe my success to my supportive and loving family, who never gave up on me!

Russell, Dana L.: Hot Springs, AR; National Park College; Wilmer James (Deceased) and Lou Walker (Deceased); AA Computer Information Systems with Emphasis in Networking, 2016; Love and support from my family and friends made this possible. Special thanks to Chauna, Dejah, and Royce.

Russell, John A.: Greensboro, NC; Guilford College Center for Continuing Education; BS Community and Justice Policy Studies, 2015; Trevor Project Suicide Detection and Prevention, Coach and Mentor; Autism Society, Tutor and Mentor; Pride Youth Collaboration, Co-Founder; Police Accountability Research Project and Community Meeting, Researcher, Presenter, and Round Table Leader; Glen Haven Refugee Community Center, Mentor and Teacher; Dean's List; Mock Trial Team, Defense Attorney and Opening Statement.

Rutledge Jr., Randy Lee: Frederick, MD; Wingate University; Randy and Patty Rutledge; BS Elementary Education, 2016; Intramural Sports, Flag Football Championship 2015; University Event Staff Leader; Pi Kappa Phi Fraternity, New Member Educator, Philanthropy Chair, and Fraternity Man of the Year; This award would not have been possible without the support and love from my family and friends!

Ryan, Chance Moeteaph: South Cairo, NY; Columbia-Greene Community College; Wendy and Richard Gregory; AA Individual Studies, 2016; Phi Theta Kappa Honor Society, All-USA Community College Second Academic Team; Chancellor's Award; Men's Basketball, Coach's Award; Student Senate, Treasurer; Board of Trustees, Student Trustee; Thank you to all that have crossed my path in some way. Especially family, friends, and Alicia Pena.

Ryle, Maria Theresa: Clay, NY; Marywood University; Karen and Paul Ryle; BA Graphic Design, 2016; Women's Field Hockey, 2015 All-CSAC Sportsmanship Team, CSAC Academic Honor Rolls 2012–2013 and 2015, SGI/NFHCA Collegiate National Academic Squad Gladiator 2013–2015; Thank you to my family for supporting me in everything that I do.

S

Safer, Rachel S.: Avon, CT; Rider University; Donna and Robert Safer; BA Political Science, 2016; Global Studies Society, President.

Sagarwala, Zubia: Jamaica, NY; St. John's University; Farzana Sagarwala; BS Biology, 2016; Certificate of Achievement for Demonstrating Scholastic Excellence and Significant Academic Achievement in Biology; Omicron Delta Kappa National Leadership Society; Honors Program; Phi Eta Sigma Freshmen Honor Society; Sigma Alpha Pi National Society of Leadership and Success; New York Presbyterian Queens Hospital, Research Volunteer; Hillside Medical Care, Office Manager; Dean's List; Dr. Charles Lacaillade Memorial Award; Silver Key Nominee; Tennis Club, President and Captain; Watson Pre-Health Honor Society, Vice President; I dedicate all my hard work and accomplishments, both present and future, to my Amazing Mom. I love you.

Sager, Delanie Marin: Denton, TX; Texas Woman's University; Michelle and Robert Sager; BA Music, 2016; Pioneer Music Educators Association, President and Secretary; Iota Omega Chapter of Sigma Alpha Iota, President, Vice President of Membership, Recording Secretary, and Sword of Honor Recipient; Thank you to my family, friends, and professors for your support and encouragement!

Saint-Elien, Tarah-Lynn: Rahway, NJ; Rider University; Chyler and Magalie Saint-Elien; BA Communication Studies, 2016; Miss Violet Pageant, Winner; The Shadow Yearbook, Writer; Lambda Pi Eta, Secretary; AdornedinArmor.com, Creator of Personal Fashion Blog; ELLE.COM, Fashion Intern; All thanks to Jesus and my loving family, you are all my biggest blessings.

Salcido, Carla Renee: Weatherford, OK; Southwestern Oklahoma State University; BA Criminal Justice, 2016; Criminal Justice Club, President's and Dean's Honor Roll; My college experience has been a great one thanks to all of my family support.

Salmon, Cody Young: Harrison, AR; Arkansas State University Beebe; Bruce and Nicki Salmon; AA Animal Science, 2019; Without the love and support of my family, this would never have been possible. Thank you!

Saltzman, Charli K.: Lincoln, NE; Nebraska Wesleyan University; Mark and Kris Saltzman; BA Communication Studies, 2015.

San Nicolas, Ciann Marie C.: Great Falls, MT; University of Great Falls; BA Elementary Education, 2017; My family is truly the reason why I am who I am, and for that I am grateful.

Sánchez Torres, Neysharie: Guaynabo, PR; University of Puerto Rico College of Natural Sciences; Myrna Torres; BS Molecular Biology, 2017; Active Member of the American Student Medical Association; National Society of Collegiate Scholars; Summer Seminar; Summer Medical and Dental Education Program 2014; Biochemistry Department, Researcher; VA Caribbean Healthcare System Veteran's Hospital Volunteer; Summer Neuroscience Undergraduate Research Fellowship 2015; Annual Biomedical Research Conference for Minority Students, ABRCMS Travel Award 2015; This award would not have been possible without the support of my family and friends.

Sanchez, Marilyn: Madison, AL; Athens State University; BA Psychology, 2016; Fiddler's Convention; International Honor Society in Psychology; International Honor Society in Sociology; Behavioral Science Club; Special thanks to my family for the love and support that made it all possible.

Sanderlin, Janet: Charlotte, NC; Brenau University; MS Business Administration, 2016.

Sanford, Kalsey: Brooklyn, NY; Adelphi University; Chantile Davis; BS Marketing, 2015; Birthday Wish Foundation, Planner and Fundraiser; Gamma Sigma Alpha Honor Society, President; University Cheerleading, Team Manager; Sigma Delta Tau, Vice President of Philanthropy, Vice President of Scholarship, and Vice President of Fundraising; Rho Lambda Honor Society; My mom and my family made this award possible for me. Thank you for always supporting and loving me. I love you.

Sanger, Meghan Marie: Parker, CO; Colorado Mesa University; Paula and Howard Sanger; Business Administration, 2017; This award would not have been possible without the love and support from my family.

Santana Matis, Brenda: Germantown, MD; University of Pittsburgh Bradford; Ramona Matis; BA History and Political Science, 2016; Bernie and Panther Scholarship Awards; Freshmen Leadership Award; Phi Theta Kappa, Secretary; Admissions Office, Student Ambassador; National Society of Leadership and Success, Fundraising and Community Service Chair; SGA, Vice President, Secretary, and International Student Senate Committee; TRIO Student Support Services, Peer Mentor; This award would not have been possible without the support and love from my family! God Bless.

Santos, Olivia: Crowley, TX; Hill College.

Sarchett, Stephanie A.: Concord, CA; The University of New Mexico; Mary and Bryce Sarchett; BS Emergency Medical Services, 2016; New Mexico Medical Reserve Corps 2013–2016; The University of New Mexico Hospital Medicine Bow 2013–2014; Health Sciences Student Council, Paramedic Program Representative 2014–2015; Students of Emergency Medical Services; Student Health Leadership Council; Thank you Mom, Dad, and Wesley for believing in me when I did not believe in myself.

Savio, Jorguino A.: Batavia, NY; Genesee Community College; Joao Aparicio Capelao and Iria Monica Savio; AA Food Processing and Technology, 2016; I believe a successful person is someone who can survive in any situation.

Scappatura, Emily Jane: Dalton, PA; Marywood University; Susan and Peter Scappatura; BA Interior Architecture and Design, 2016; I am so honored to receive this award. Thanks to my family for their love and support.

Scarborough, Shawnta Nicole: Schenectady, NY; Bryant and Stratton College Albany Campus; Deborah Scarborough; AA Medical Administrative Assisting, 2016; Bryant and Stratton Ambassador; Dean's List; Honors and Intern of the Semester Award; This award would not have been possible without the love and support from my family.

Schaeffner, Lena: Conway, SC; Coastal Carolina University; Birgit and Thomas Schaeffner; BS Recreation and Sport Management, 2016; Women's Golf Varsity Team, Big South Player of the Year 2015 and Coastal Carolina University Female Athlete of the Year 2015; Recreation and Sport Management Alliance, Conference Research Presenter; This **award would not have been** possible without the love and selfless support of my family.

Schimek, Samantha A.: Newtown, PA; Rider University; Janet Schimek; BS Psychology, 2016; Rider SERVES, Vice President; Omicron Delta Kappa National Leadership Honor Society, Programming Chair; Zeta Tau Alpha Sorority, Nominating Committee Chair and Programing Council Secretary; Leadership Development Program, Certificate in Leadership.

Schneider, Brandon R.: Bellmore, NY; Ithaca College; Sharyn and Howard Schneider; BM Music in Combination with an Outside Field, 2017; Colleges Against Cancer, Chair of Social Media and Online **Communication 2015–2016; Students** Today Alumni Tomorrow, Chair of "I Love IC Week" 2016–2017 and Outstanding Educational Program "Kickback to Give Back"; This award is dedicated to my loving family. With your support, I am truly living the dream.

Schoeneberger, Alphonse William: Jamestown, ND; University of Jamestown; Bill and Lynn Schoeneberger; BS Nursing, 2017; University of Jamestown Concert Choir, Baritone and Pianist; Resident Life, Assistant Resident Director; National Residence Hall Honorary, President; Alpha Chi, Vice President; North Dakota Nursing Student Association, Secretary; Nursing Student Association, Vice President; Student Senate, Senator; This award would not have been possible without the love and support from my family.

Schrader, Riley Colt: Higdon, AL; Faulkner University; BA History Education, 2018; Honor Roll; Dean's List; Academic All-American Mid-South Conference Football.

Schreiner, Michael C.: St. Albans, VT; Saint Michael's College; BS Accounting, 2016; Women Helping Battered Women, Run for Empowerment; Vermont Walk to End Alzheimer's Volunteer; Men's Ice Hockey, Assistant Captain, NEHC Honor Roll 2015–2016, and NE10 Honor Roll 2015–2016; I dedicate this award to my family and the boys for all of their love and continued support.

Schuster, Jessie Ruth: Camp Hill, PA; Sweet Briar College; Sam Schuster; BA History and Music, 2017; Alpha Beta Lambda Honors Society 2014–2016; Advanced Choir, First Alto, Second Soprano, and First Soprano 2013; SGA, Sophomore Class President 2014–2015, Junior Class President 2015–2016, SGA President 2016–2017; Varsity Softball, Catcher and Outfield 2013–2014; Honors Program Student Council, Chair 2016–2017 and Representative 2014–2016; QV, On-Campus Community Service Club 2014–2016; Sweet Peas 2014–2016, Student Health 101 Editor 2014–2015; Beautiful and Mysterious Community Service Club, Vice President 2014–2016; Alumnae Relations, Phonathon Worker; Office of Admissions, Ambassador, Student Worker, and Hostess 20142016; Residence Life Advisor 2014–2016; Student Life, Orientation Chair 2016; Academic Resource Center, History Department Tutor 2015–2016; This would not have been possible without the dedicated alumnae, students, staff, and faculty of Sweet Briar College.

Schwartz, Alison Catherine: Frederick, MD; Frederick Community College; Stuart and Michele Schwartz; AA General Studies, 2016; Book Club, Vice President; Honors Student Association Club, Secretary; Honors College Program; Phi Theta Kappa.

Schwartz, Rachel Elizabeth: Frederick, MD; Frederick Community College; Stuart and Michele Schwartz; AA General Studies, 2016; Book Club, President; Honors Student Association, Treasurer; Honors College Program; Phi Theta Kappa Honors Society.

Schwarzman, Felicya M.: East Rockaway, NY; Ithaca College; Samuel and Rosalia Schwarzman; BMEd Music Education, 2017; American String Teachers Association, Secretary; Italian Club, Co-Founder; National Residence Hall Honorary, Resident of the Month Award, September 2013; Sigma Alpha Iota, Corresponding Secretary; I am grateful to my family and professors who have guided me here with the most of love.

Scruggs, Heather Nicole: Chesnee, SC; Limestone College; BS Elementary Education, 2016; I would not be receiving this award without the encouragement and support from my family.

Seales, Natalie Beth: Hattiesburg, MS; Jones County Junior College; Suzanne and Stephen Seales; BA English, 2018; Sigma Kappa Delta Tutor; SGA, Humanities Department Senator; Phi Theta Kappa, Vice President of Service; Thank you to my family (first and second) for your constant support. I would be lost without you!

Sears, Matthew: Turtle Creek, PA; Duquesne University; Kathleen and Joseph Sears; PharmD Pharmacy 2016.

Sebold, Britani Paige: Oakland, MD; Garrett College; AA General Studies, 2016; Loar Auxiliary Volunteer, Volunteer of the Month and Assistant Office and Inventory Manager; Without my family and friends, I would have never made it this far.

Sebring, Ericka Lee: Sailda, CO; Colorado Mesa University; Douglas and Deborah Sebring; BA Social Work, 2017; Residence Life Student Staff, Resident Assistant and Senior Resident Assistant; Without my family, my friends, and my God for support, this award would not have been possible.

Sechrist, Carisa Lynn: Youngstown, OH; Youngstown State University; Cindy Davidson and Joseph Vujanovich; BS Business Administration, 2016; iPal, Serving Member; Enactus, Entrepreneurship in Action; Team-Building Facilitator, Certification in Facilitating Team-Building Trainings; Safe Zone Ally; Emerging Leader Program, Leadership Designation; William H. Battan Scholarship Recipient; Dean's List; Reading and Study Skills Center, Top 10 Peer Tutor; Sports Management Club, Vice President; Nontraditional Student Organization, President and Treasurer; Presidential Mentor Award; Society for Human Resource Management, Vice President and Treasurer; Without my parents, Taylor, and Zach, this designation would not have been possible. Love you all.

Sedgwick, Keirra Michelle: Mitchellville, MD; Bennett College; Keitha and Michael Sedgwick; BA Journalism Media Studies, 2016; Student Ambassador, Vice President; Sirius XM Radio Host; SGA, Public Relations Specialist; *Belle Magazine*, Managing Editor.

Segarra, Steven Gabriel: Clifton, NJ; State University of New York Plattsburgh; Milagros Santana; BS Biochemistry, 2016; Department of Biological Sciences; Research Assistant in Molecular Biology and Biochemistry; Department of Chemistry, Teacher's Assistant in Organic Chemistry; Housing and Residence Life, Resident Assistant; SUNY Plattsburgh Pre-Medicine Association, President and Vice President; Without undying support from my family, mentors, and God, this award would not have been possible. Thank you.

Seidl, Jessica L.: Pittsburgh, PA; La Roche College; Colleen and Edward Seidl; BA PreK–4 Education and Special Education, 2016; Kappa Delta Epsilon, Vice President of Scholarship.

Seldon, Alana Dion: Bloomfield, CT: Andrea and Derrick Seldon; BA Communications, 2017; National Council of Negro Women, Senator; Collegiate Sisters for Action, Leadership Manager and President 2014–2016; Golden Bulls Activities Committee, Publicity Chair 2015–2016; Delta Sigma Theta Sorority Inc., Gamma Lambda Chapter Financial Secretary; SGA, Vice President of Student Affairs and Speaker of the Senate 2015–2016; Without the undying love, support, and encouragement of my family, my accomplishments would not have been possible.

Self, Melanie A.: Appleton, WI; Maryville University; Chuck and Kimberlee Self; BS Mathematics and Pre-Engineering, 2017; Step Up, Treasurer; This award would not be possible without the support of my family and friends.

Selman, Mallory Nichole: Junction City, AR; Southern Arkansas University; Chantle' and Jack Selman; BS Psychology, 2016; President's Ambassador, Vice President; Phi Mu, President, Social Chair, Panhellenic Delegate, Recruitment Counselor, Greek Scholar, and Greek Woman of the Year.

Serba Jr., Thomas Daniel: Tonawanda, NY; Medaille College; Suzanne and Thomas Serba; BA Psychology, 2015; Blanket Drive for Cancer Patients, Event Initiator and Blanket Crafting Coordinator; Personalized Cards for United States Soldiers, Event Organizer; Stuffed Animals and Personalized Cards for Pediatric Patients, Event Organizer; Baseball Academic Captain; FAR Academic Award; AMCC Peak Performer; Chi Alpha Sigma National Honor Society; Dean's List; Medaille College Leadership Forum Founder; Medaille Athletic Department, Assistant to Sports Information Director; Psychology Club; Alpha Chi National Honor Society; Sports Management Assist Team; Baseball Team, Captain; Student Athlete Athletic Committee, Secretary.

Shalaby, Shaimaa Nagy: Newark, DE; Goldey Beacom College Graduate School; MA Management, 2016; To my lovely family, especially my mom, Mrs. Manal; this will not be achieved without your support. Thanks!

Shannon, Alexander J.: Nassau, NY; Hudson Valley Community College; James and Maureen Shannon; BA Business Administration, 2016; Food Pantry Committee; Entrepreneur's Club; Investment Club Treasurer; Sock Drawer Charity Committee; Student Senate President.

Shape, Alissa R.: Andover, MN; Minnesota State University, Mankato Social and Behavioral Sciences; Susan and Todd Shape; BS Gender and Women's Studies, 2016; Women of Action Committee, President; Sexuality and Gender Equality; Gender and Women's Studies Club; Protecting Animal Rights Committee; Alpha Lambda Delta; This award would not have been possible without my family, friends, and all the activists that have inspired me.

Shaw, Christopher Ryan: Columbia, TN; Union University; Tracey House; BA Computer Science, 2016; Union Band, Trombone Player; House of Masters Nerf Club, Head Administrator; Band Ensembles, First Chair; Association of Computer Machinery, Vice President; To my family and those in my life, thank you for always encouraging me to reach my goals.

Shawver, Ashley Lakeisha: Lewistown, PA; Bloomsburg University; Eric and Teresa Shawver; BS Nursing, 2016; This award would not have been possible without the love and support from my amazing family!

Sheaffer, Breck K.: Soddy Daisy, TN; Hiwassee College; Dawn and Craig Sheaffer; AS Equine Management and Training, 2016; Christian Student Ministries, Christian Service Award; Thank you to my family and friends for all your support, I could not have made it without you.

Shelley, Jacquelyne Rose: Dover, FL; Flagler College; James Randal Shelley; BA Deaf Education, 2016; This award would not have been possible without the support and love from my family and fiancé, Chris.

Shelton, Glenn Samuel: Eden, NC; Central Christian College of The Bible; BA Religious Studies–Christian Leadership, 2017; Thanks to my loving wife, Kat, my daughter, Rebekah, and Mt. Ivy Christian Church for their support.

Sherman, Christina Marie: St. Louis, MO; Murray State University; David and Marlene Sherman; BS Pre-Veterinary Medicine, 2016; Student Ambassador 2014; Racer Band, Member 2012–2014 and Band Ambassador to Residential Colleges 2013-2014; Swing Dancing Club 2015–2016; Honors College, Class Representative 2015–2016, All Campus Sing Choreography Chair 2014–2016, Student Ambassador 2015–2016, Social Committee Member 2015–2016, Public Relations Committee Member 2015–2016, and Member 2012–2016; So many thanks to my family, who have supported me all the way. I love you guys!

Shirley, Kale Alan: Winnfield, LA; University of Louisiana at Monroe Undergraduate; Kevin and Karen Shirley; BBA Risk Management, 2016; Campus Activities Board, Leadership Workshop Series Committee Head; Insurance and Risk Management Society, Vice President of Fundraising and Secretary; 31 Ambassadors, Vice President of Public Relations and Community Service Committee Head; This award would not have been possible without the support and love from my family and friends.

Shores, Ashley R.: Arlington, TN; Southwest Tennessee Community College; Rex and Leann Shores; AS Natural Sciences/Biotechnology Technician, 2016; Phi Theta Kappa, Tennessee All-State Academic Team 2014–2015; Student Ambassador 2014–2016, Leadership Institute Award Tier I and Tier II; *The Southwest Source*, Online Editor 2015–2016 and Secretary 2014–2015; Tennessee Intercollegiate State Legislature, Senator 2014–2016 and Supreme Court Nominating Commission and Election Committee Appointment; Honors Academy, President 2014–2016; SGA, President 2015–2016 and Vice President 2014–2015; Mom and Dad, your endless love and support has allowed me to believe in my dreams.

Shores, Kimberly Gold: Winston Salem, NC; Guilford College Center for Continuing Education; Daniel and Patricia Gold; BS Criminal Justice, 2016; Your love and your support made these honors possible, my daughter, my rock, Laeken Kimber!

Shropshire, Emily Jordan: Bridgeton, NJ; Cumberland County College; Robert and Stephanie Shropshire; AS Justice Studies, 2016.

Shudt, Erica L.: Melrose, NY; Hudson Valley Community College; Matthew and Angel Shudt; AA Clinical Psychology, 2016; Phi Theta Kappa Honor Society, Vice President of Membership; Psychology Club, Vice President; Women's Basketball Team, Head Captain; Special thanks to my family for all of the continuous love and support throughout my educational journey.

Shulman, Yevgeniya: Brooklyn, NY; Long Island University Brooklyn; Yevgeniya Stepina and Leonid Blank; MS Taxation, 2016; Accounting Society President; ACFE President; Sigma Beta Delta, Becker Ambassador; Happy to have this award and big thank you for supporting by my lovely family.

Sibley, Aaliyah T.: Brookhaven, MS; Jackson State University College of Science, Engineering and Technology; Manderson and Katasha Sibley; BS Electrical Engineering, 2017; Society of Women Engineers, Parliamentarian.

Siden, Hannah Elizabeth: Westminster, MA; Fitchburg State University; Diane and David Siden; BS Psychological Science, 2016; Fitchburg State University Community Orchestra, Second Violin; Psychological Science Club, President; Three things come to mind: amazement, elation, and profound thankfulness.

Sidney, Marcus D.: Tampa, FL; Jackson State University College of Science, Engineering and Technology; Steve and Wanda Sidney; BA Earth System Science, 2016; Physics Office Student Volunteer; Alpha Chi National College Honor Society; Golden Key International Honour Society; Alpha Lambda Delta Honor Society; Chi Alpha Epsilon Honor Society; I would like to thank my parents for blessing me with their guidance, love, and support.

Siebel, Arthur Russell: Pecatonica, IL; Milwaukee School of Engineering; AS Mechanical Engineering, 2016; Tau Beta Pi; FIRST Robotics, Mentor; American Society of Mechanical Engineers, Chapter President 2015–2016; My success would not be possible without the support of all of my friends and family.

Sikorski, Alexis Diano: Fort Worth, TX; Texas Woman's University; Theodore and Rebecca Sikorski; BAIBS English/Psychology, 2018; EDventure International; Poetry Published in *Pour Vida Zine*, *Off the Quill*, and *The Daedalian*; G-Force Go Center Program, Mentor; Athenian Honors Society, Social Cultural Committee, Publications Committee, Outstanding Creative Submission to *Off the Quill*, and Outstanding Honors Freshman; Thanks to my mom and dad for supporting me in my endeavors and for reminding me to relax.

Silcox, Elizabeth Ashford: Atlanta, GA; Presbyterian College; Hal and Deborah Silcox; BS Business Administration, Concentrations in Accounting and Management, 2016; Fellowship of Christian Athletes, Treasurer and Leadership Team Member; Zeta Tau Alpha Sorority, Judicial Chair and Philanthropy Director; Accounting Club, Secretary; Society for the Advancement of Management, President; Employee of the Department of Campus Life, Resident Assistant and Orientation Leader; To my wonderful parents, thanks for teaching me to always put Jesus first. 1 Corinthians 15:57.

Simeone, Alyssa Ruth: Mount Pocono, PA; East Stroudsburg University; Richard and Debra Simeone; BS Biology, Concentration in Pre-Medicine, Minors in Chemistry and Mathematics, 2017; People Representing Individual Diversity in Education Committee, Student Senate Representative; Autism Speaks U, 5K Head Organizer; Pocono Mountain United Methodist Church, Singer; Challenger Sports Association, Volunteer Coach and Scholarship Recipient; Chemistry Club, Community Service Chair; Math Club; Student Senate, Senator and Senator of the Month; Office of Accessible Services Individualized for Students, Test Reader, Scribe, and Note Taker; Tutoring Program, Calculus I, II, and III, Physical Geography, History, and Biology Tutor; Women's Soccer, Student Athlete Advisory Committee Representative, Warrior Athletic Auction Scholarship, Athletic Director's Honor Roll; Concert Band, Oboist, Flutist, and Saxophonist; African American Student Alliance; Biology Club, Pocono Lion's Club Annual Scholarship, Tannersville Lion's Club Scholarship, and William T. Morris Foundation Scholarship; National Society of Leadership and Success, President 2016, Treasurer and Community Service Chair 2015, Outstanding Leadership Scholarship, Excellence Award, and President's Outstanding Service Award; Biology Pre-Medicine Club, Community Service Chair, Margaret A. Rosa Pre-Medicine Scholarship, and Dental Chair of Affairs; Without the push and support from my parents, I would not have received this outstanding award.

Simonetti, Kristy Marie: Greensboro, NC; Guilford College Center for Continuing Education; Frank Simonetti and Marsha Faucett; BA Psychology, 2016; This award would not have been possible without the support and love from God, family, and friends.

Sims, Milagros Ivelisse: Millstone Township, NJ; Georgian Court University; BA Psychology, 2016; This award would not have been possible without the love and support of my husband.

Singleton, David Wayne: Biloxi, MS; University of Southern Mississippi Gulf Park Campus; MS Social Work, 2016.

Sinor, Ashly Jene'e: Alta Loma, CA; Westwood College Inland Empire Campus; Robert and Dorinda Sinor; AA Criminal Justice, 2016; Suma Cum Laude; Ready for More Silver Award; President's List; Perfect Attendance; This accomplishment is proof that hard work pays off! Thanks to my boys and family for the support!

Sjolander, Micayla Marie: Belleville, KS; Cloud County Community College; Marriah and Bob Sjolander; BSW Social Work, 2016; This honor would have never been possible without the support and encouragement from my friends, family, and teachers.

Skinner Jr., Craig William: LaGrange, KY; Bellarmine University; Anne and Craig Skinner Jr.; BA Business Administration/Economics, 2017; Supplies Overseas, Volunteer Hours; VITA, Volunteer Tax Services; Brown Leadership Community Park Clean Up Service Hours and Brown Leadership Capstone Project; Economics and Finance Club, Treasurer; English Conversation Club, Community Service; Thanks to my family, friends, and professors who made this award possible.

Skinner, Sandra Denise: Virginia Beach, VA; Regent University; BS Business, Concentration in Human Resource Management, 2016; This prestigious honor would not have been possible without the support of my loving husband, Darren Skinner.

Slaughter, Chrys Marie: Chester, VA; Norfolk State University; Omissa Darden; BS Business Marketing, 2017; School of Business Ambassador, Tutor; Sophomore Class SGA, Historian; Spartan General, Historian and President; Without the love and support of my close friends and family, this award would not be possible.

Small II, Charles Edward: Florissant, MO; Missouri Baptist University; Maxine Small; BA Ministry Leadership, 2016.

Smeltzer, Leigh Ann: Royal, AR; National Park College; Karen Smeltzer; AA Associate of Arts, 2015; This award would have been possible without the unconditional love and encouragement from my family.

Smith, Alexis Nicole: Huntington, WV; Marshall University; Denise and Ronald Smith; BA Spanish, International Affairs, 2016; Edible Book Awards, First Place; 52nd International Festival, Performer; This award would not have been possible without the love and support of my family and friends.

Smith, Alia Rae: Iselin, NJ; Stockton University; Scott and Pamela Smith; BS Hospitality and Tourism Management Studies, 2015; College Cheerleading Squad; Move-In Committee; Stockton Disney Association; Hospitality and Tourism Society; Alpha Lambda Delta First Year Honor Society; Eta Sigma Delta Hospitality Honor Society; Delta Delta Delta Sorority, Secretary, and Continuing Education Chair; Thank you to my family, who has supported me throughout my college career

Smith, Ashley Nicole: Musella, GA; Mercer University; BBA Accounting 2016; Salvation Army, Bell Ringer; Carlyle Place; Delta Sigma Pi, Special Olympics; Crawford County High School Mentor; Salvation Army Angel Tree; Total Grace Baptist Church, Financial Secretary and Bookkeeper; Becker Professional Education, Campus Ambassador; Delta Sigma Pi, Vice President of Finance and Vice President of Community Service and Fundraising Chair; Beta Alpha Psi, President and Vice President; Relay For Life, Accounting Lead; This award would not have been possible without the love from my church, parents, family, and professors.

Smith, Audrey C.: Rosharon, TX; Springfield College; Curtis and Vonnie Roberts; BS Human Services, 2016; This award would not have been possible without God and my family.

Smith, Brownlee S.: Oxford, MS; The University of Mississippi; Martha and Rob Smith; AA Exercise Science, 2016.

Smith, Christopher Robin: Decherd, TN; Motlow State Community College; Robin Smith; AA Accounting, 2016; Phi Theta Kappa Honors Society; Decherd Lions Club; Franklin County Fair Board of Directors, Board Member; Cowan Cumberland Presbyterian, Director of Worship; SGA, Freshmen Senator and Sophomore Senator; This award would not have been possible without the support of MSCC Accounting Professor, Dr. Ward Harder.

Smith, Clarissa: Philadelphia, MS; East Central Community College.

Smith, Emily Michelle: Jasper, TX; Stephen F. Austin State University; Gary and Kristin Smith; AA Food, Nutrition, and Dietetics and Pre-Occupational Therapy, 2017; Sigma Kappa Omega Sorority, Fundraising and Homecoming Committees.

Smith, Lyndsey Breann: Falkville, AL; Wallace State Community College Hanceville; Dannie and Regina Pennington; AS Medical Assisting, 2016; This award would not have been possible without the support and love from my family and friends.

Smith, Malcolm Q.: Gainesville, VA; Norfolk State University; Reginald and Sonequa Smith; BS Business Finance, 2016; Thank you to my entire family and friends for their love and support. I am truly blessed.

Smith, Nico Zane: Sewell, NJ; Stockton University; John Smith and Elizabeth Winterburn; BS Hospitality/Tourism Management, 2017; Office of Student Development, Programming Assistant; Office of Residential Life, Resident Assistant and Rookie of the Year Award; Stockton Entertainment Team, President 2016–2017; This award would not have been possible without the support and love from my family, friends, and mentors.

Smith, Quanesha Myniah: Philadelphia, PA; Peirce College; BS Criminal Justice, 2016; This award would not have been possible without the support and love from my family.

Smith, Richelle R.: Jackson, MS; Jackson State University College of Business; Michele Davis; BS Economics, 2017; Campus Activity Board, Director of Community Engagement; I am honored to be a part of this elite group.

Smith, Shelvey Elizabeth: Chesterfield, VA; Mary Baldwin College; Shelvey Smith and Michael Allen; AA Marketing Communications, 2016; President's Society; Class Officer 2014–2015, Vice President; I would like to thank everyone who taught and supported me throughout my life.

Smith, Sterling Shellie: Oxford, FL; Southeastern University; Debra and Kenny Smith; BS Elementary Education, 2015; Kappa Delta Pi, Outstanding Member; This award would not have been possible without the support and love from my parents.

Smith, Tiffany Lynn: North Richland Hills, TX; Tarrant County College Northeast Campus; Scott and Cynthia Smith; AA Biology, 2019.

Smithson, Brandon JaDarius: Nashville, TN; American Baptist College; Marlisa Smithson; BA Bible and Theology with Pastoral Studies Concentration, 2016; American Baptist College Ambassador; Dean's List; Presidential Award; Sophomore Class President; Without the love and support from family and friends, the motivation to excel would not have been possible!

Smoot, Moriah Simone: Mansfield, TX; The University of Alabama; Mr. Myron Smoot and Dr. Tonya Smoot; BS Metallurgical/Materials Engineering, 2016; Science Olympiad Event Leader 2013–2016; Crimson Tide Ballroom Dancers 2014; Black Faculty and Staff Association, Academic Certificate of Distinction 2012–2016; Engineering Council of Birmingham, 2016 Undergraduate Student of the Year in Metallurgical and Materials Engineering; Department of Metallurgical and Materials Engineering, E. C. Wright Outstanding Sophomore Award, Farabee-Tannehill Award for Excellence, and E.C. Wright Award for Excellence; National Society of Black Engineers, Membership Committee Member; Alpha Epsilon Delta Health Pre-Professional Honor Society; Tau Beta Pi Engineering Honor Society; RISE Stallings Center, Weekly Volunteer; Wow! That's Engineering, Volunteer, Presenter, and Activity Leader; Society of Women Engineers, Liaison 2014–2016, Webmaster 2012–2016, and Outstanding Freshman 2012; Thanking my parents, family, friends, and school faculty for their continued support of my academic endeavors.

Soares, Jessica: Westerly, RI; Roger Williams University.

Solomon, Niya R.: New Britain, CT; Springfield College; Georgia and Gary Tillison; BS Human Services, 2016; This award would not have been possible without the patience and endurance from my parents and extended family.

Solomon, Shannon Lee: La Feria, TX; LeTourneau University Global; BS Early Childhood–6th Grade Generalist, 2015; Hard work and the support of family and friends helped me to achieve my goals.

Sonderman, Shannon M.: Jasper, IN; Saint Mary-of-the-Woods College; John and Judy Sonderman; BS Kindergarten–Grade 6, Mild Intervention, 2018; St Joseph Campus Ministry Singer; Camp Ondessonk, Crafts Coordinator Leadership Staff; Student Orientation, Team Leader; Soccer, Goalie; Junior Class Officer, President; I wish to thank my family and friends for their support and encouragement.

Soro, Gninhinninchionni Fatima: South Bend, IN; Indiana University South Bend; Porolo and Madjeta Soro; BS Actuarial Science, 2016; Home Fire Preparedness Campaign Event; College of Liberal Arts and Science Dean List 2013–2016; Food Bank of Northern Indiana; Red Cross Club, Secretary; I especially want to thank God and my parents who supported me and made receiving this award possible.

Sorondo, Richard Paul: Fresno, CA; Central Christian College of Kansas; BA Criminal Justice, 2016; I give all praise, honor, and glory to my Lord and Savior Jesus Christ.

Soto Morales, Clarissa: Aguada, PR; Inter American University of Puerto Rico, San German Campus Graduate School; MA School Psychology, 2016; This award would have never been possible without the support and love from my family. Dedicated to Aramis.

Soto-Olmeda, Roberto A.: Sabana Grande, PR; Inter American University of Puerto Rico, San German Campus; Carlos and Juana Soto-Ortiz; BA Sports Technology, 2017; I dedicate this award to my family and people who helped me achieve it and living surprise.

Souther, Deborah Fay: Pottsboro, TX; Grayson College; AA Teaching, 2017; This award would not have been possible without the support of my husband, Alan Souther.

Sowers, Meghan Alexis: Signal Hill, CA; The Master's College; Gary and Eunice Sowers; BS Biology, 2016; Sudara Inc., Staff Volunteer; Sigma Zeta Honor Society, Science Award Recipient; Presidential Scholar, Summa Cum Laude; Crosspoint Church Youth Leader, Sunday School Supervisor; Medical Volunteer for Mission Trip to Mindanao, Philippines; This award would not have been possible without the love and support of family and friends—thank you!

Spangler, Kelly Melissa: Columbus, OH; Harding University; Ronald and Patty Spangler; BS Mathematics/Computer Science, 2017; Harding University Honors Scholar; American Studies Institute; Alpha Chi Honor Society; Girl Scouts of America, Assistant Since 2013 and Cadette Leader 2015; Delta Sigma Mathematics Club, Secretary 2015; Chi Omega Pi Social Club, Treasurer 2015; Thank you to my family and friends for their constant love and encouragement. It means the world!

Spann, Brian Kent: Allen, TX; Dallas Baptist University; BA Communication Theory, 2017; Pi Theta Tau, Chaplain and Spiritual Chair; SGA, Student Organization Member of the Year 2013; This honor was made possible through the support of family, friends, and the grace of Christ.

Sparks, Paige Nicole: Costa Mesa, CA; Newbury College; BA Psychology, 2016; Psychology Club, President; SGA, Executive Senator Class of 2016; Psi Chi, President and Founding Member; Alpha Chi; Phi Eta Sigma; This is dedicated to my friends and family who pushed me towards success! You are my inspiration.

Sparks, Stephanie Ann: Trinity, AL; John C. Calhoun State Community College; AA Business, 2016.

Spencer, Christopher Allen: Union, SC; University of South Carolina Union Campus; BA Liberal Studies, 2019; South Carolina-Union Players, Actor and Theater Award; Dean's List and President's List; I want to thank God, the United States Marine Corps, and my family. Own the Universe.

Spigner, Caroline Gracen: Rainsville, AL; Northeast Alabama Community College Social Sciences, David and Shawn Spigner; AS Biomedical Sciences, 2016; Peer Tutor 2015, Math and Science Tutor; Class Favorites, Freshmen 2014–2015 and Sophomore 2015–2016; All-Alabama Academic Team, NACC Representative; President's List, Academic Honor List; NACC Scholarship Faculty Committee, Student Representative; Student Learning Outcomes Faculty Committee, Student Representative; Developmental Studies Faculty Committee, Student Representative; Backroads Yearbook, Staff Member; Mu Alpha Theta, Parliamentarian; SGA, President 2015–2016 and Freshmen Representative 2014–2015; Being honored among outstanding students would not have been possible without the dedication of my family, friends, and instructors.

Spires, Patrick Demario: Greenwood, FL; Chipola College; Ruth Brooks and Danny Spires; BS Business Management, 2017; Habitat for Humanity Volunteer; Phi Beta Lambda, Homecoming Court Nominee and Homecoming Court Attendant 2016; Without God and my mom, this would not be possible. I am honored to be a recipient of this award.

Spivey, Brittany Ann: Fairfax, VA; Northern Virginia Community College; David and Elena Spivey; BS Biology, 2017; Pathways Program, Active Member; Women's Cross Country Team, NJCAA Regional Championship Athlete; NOVA Board, Student Representative; SGA, Vice President; Honors Program and Club, Active Member; Thank you, Dr. Fitzgerald, Professor Balbuena, Coach Mancini, Brian Anweiler, and President Ralls, for the support.

Spors, Jennifer M.: Tonawanda, NY; D'Youville College; Paul and Kris Spors; MS Occupational Therapy, 2017; College Residence Life, Resident Advisor; Office of Admissions, Student Ambassador; D'Youville Medal; Student Association, Senior Senator; Student Association Scholarship; Pi Theta Epsilon, President; This award would not have been possible without the love and support of my family and friends.

Spralls, Sterling Michael: Red Oak, TX; Cedar Valley College; Dianne and Dr. Samuel Spralls III; AA Performing Arts, 2016; DCCFA Scholarship Award 2016; All-Texas Academic Team 2016; Amidon/Beauchamp Memorial Award, Student Leader of the Year 2016; I express gratitude to God for profuse blessings and the love and support of my family.

Staggs, Morgan: Leoma, TN; Columbia State Community College; AS Teaching K–5, 2017; This award would not have been possible without the support of God, my family, and instructors.

Staley, Tammaka Oli'Shai: West Columbia, SC; Coker College; Della and George Staley; BA Social Work, 2014; The achievements would not have been possible without my fiercely supporting family, best friends, and poetry family.

Stanback, Morgan Alexis: North Highlands, CA; McDaniel College; Alicia and Del Stanback; BA Spanish, 2016; Selected Candidate for English Teaching Assistantship Fulbright in Panama; Phi Beta Kappa Honor Society; Study Abroad, Summer 2014 Heredia, Costa Rica, Fall 2015 Oaxaca, Mexico, and Spring 2016 Granada, Spain; University of Benito Juarez Oaxaca ESL Classroom; McDaniel College Resident Assistant, Community Developer of the Year Award; McDaniel College Admissions Student Ambassador Special Project Assistant; California State University Sacramento ESL Classroom Assistant; Sigma Tau Delta International English Honor Society; Phi Sigma Iota International Foreign Language Honor Society; Omicron Delta Kappa Leadership Honor Society; Center for Experience and Opportunity Career Ambassador; Sacramento County Superior Court of California Spanish Language Assistant; Alpha Lambda Delta First Year Honor Society; Global Fellows Program; Peer Mentor; Kappa Mu Epsilon Mathematics Honor Society; Palabras to Words; Call Center Volunteer; Honors Program First-Year Representative; Thank you so much to my supportive friends, family, and faculty at McDaniel.

Stanford-Galloway, Patrick: Huntsville, TX; Sam Houston State University; Michael Galloway and Carole Stanford; BS Psychology, 2016; Psi-Chi, Treasurer; I want to thank my loved ones for always believing I would persevere, and I have.

Stanislawczyk, Jessica R.: Kendall Park, NJ; Rider University; BM Voice Performance, 2016; Westminster Choir College, President's Award Recipient; Great Strides Cystic Fibrosis Foundation Walk, Team Captain and Organizer; Relay For Life, Team Captain; Peer Tutor; Cathedral Choir at St. Francis of Assisi Dioceses, Student Intern, Section Leader, and Cantor; Leadership Development Program, Student of the Month Award; Omicron Delta Kappa Honors Society; Cooperative Program, Performer; Westminster Summer Camps, Counselor; Baccalaureate Honors Program, Andrew J. Rider Scholar Award, Undergraduate Research Scholars Award, and Andrew J. Rider Speech at Convocation; New Jersey Repertory Theatre, Director and Musical Director; Caroling at Nursing Homes; Charity Nights for the Trenton Area Soup Kitchen, Project Organizer; Ecomusicology and Ethnomusicology Conferences, Presenter; Vox Mousai Choir, Section Leader; Westminster Players, Performer; Associate Dean of Students Office, Student Assistant; Williamson Voices; Student Orientation Staff, Orientation Leader; Alpha Lambda Delta; Sigma Alpha Iota, Service Committee; Student Activities Committee, President; Thanks, Mom and Dad. "The future belongs to those who believe in the beauty of their dreams."

Stanley, Ciara R.: Columbia, PA; Cheryl and Jeffrey Stanley; BS Exercise Science, 2016; Phi Sigma Phi National Honor Fraternity, Brother at Large; This award would have not been possible without my mother's support and encouragement.

Starr, Roy: Acme, PA; Jacksonville University; Roy and Bridget Starr; BS Marine Science, 2018; Kappa Theta Chapter of Sigma Nu, Recruitment Chair; Thank you for the support from all of my families: parents, Jacksonville University, and Sigma Nu.

Steadman, Barry A.: Craig, CO; Colorado Northwestern Community College Craig Campus; Adriana Robbins and Barry-Alen Steadman; AA Journalism, 2016; Journalism Internship 2013; *Spartan Times Newspaper*, Reporter; SGA, Vice President and Student Senate; Success is not determined by where you are from but what you do with what you have.

Stefanou, Efthimia: Oakhurst, NJ; Georgian Court University; Athanasios and Artemis Stefanou; BS Nursing, 2016; National Honors Society in Psychology; RESOLVE National Infertility Association, New Jersey Infertility Advocate; SGA, Class President; Nursing Club; This award would not have been possible without the support of my mentors at GCU and my family.

Stevens, Amanda: Monmouth, OR; Western Oregon University; Lee Stevens; BS Community Health, 2016; Gerontology Club, Co-President; Community and Family Health Organization, President; Abby's House Center for Women and Families, Advocate.

Stevens, Laura Faith: Bristol, VA; Bluefield State College; Rick and Rebecca Stevens; BS Applied Science, Pre-Dental, 2016; Pre-Med Club 2012–2013; CHOICES Committee, Co-Chair; Shadowed Dr. Miller, Dr. Perkins, Dr. Davenport, Dr. Ellis, and Others; Bluefield State Inspirational Community Singers 2014 and 2015; Undergraduate Researcher 2013–2015, Concord University Research Presenter, IDEA Conference Research Presenter, and WV INBRE Conference Research Presenter; Student Support Services, Tutor 2013–2014; SGA, Senator, Secretary of Records, and Senator of the Year 2013–2014; McNair Scholar at Concord University 2014; Newman Civic Fellow Award 2015; Board of Governor's Tuition Waver 2012–2015; President's List at Bluefield State College 2012–2015; Baptist Student Union, President; Homecoming Miss Bluefield State College 2014; Remote Area Medical and Mission of Mercy, Denture Team Volunteer; Biomedical Club, Founder and President 2013–2015; Thanks go out to my family, friends, Michelle Cofer, Dr. Walters, Dr. Miller, and The Good Lord!

Steward, Shannon LeAshley: Greensboro, NC; Bennett College; Karen Bebee and Joseph Steward; BS Social Work, 2016; Social Work Club, Parliamentarian; Spirit of David, President 2014–2015 and Vice President 2013–2015; Phi Alpha Honors Society; Marshal Board, Marshal in ACES 2012–2015; Queens Association Board, Miss Student Ambassador 2014–2015 and Miss Barge Hall 2012–2013; This award would not have been possible without the support and dedication from my family.

Stewart, Jared Christopher: Charlotte, NC; Lee University; Chris and Paulette Stewart; BA Biblical and Theological Studies, 2017; Kairos Honors College, Underclassmen Mentor; Alpha Chi National College Honor Society; Theta Alpha Kappa, Inaugural Induction of the University's Chapter; Intermediate New Testament Greek, Zondervan Biblical Greek Award; Elementary New Testament Greek, Department Greek Award Bowdle Endowment; Adopt-A-Grandparent, Chaplain and President; This award is totally dependent upon the Lord's faithfulness and my parents' commitment to me.

Stilwell, Amber Rose: Erie, PA; Gannon University; Paul and Karen Stilwell; MS Environmental Health and Engineering, 2016; Sustainability Action Plan Committee, Student Researcher; Environmental Club, Media Manager; I dedicate this award to my family, friends, and mentors who have supported me throughout my education.

Stomberg, Rachel Maree: Galesburg, IL; Midstate College; Michael Glasnovich and Regina Sornberger; BS Health Services Management, 2016.

Stone, Kimberly: Easton, PA; Marywood University; MA Social Work, 2016; Graduate Assistant; Social Work Honor Society; Graduate Student Honor Society; This award was possible because of the love and support of my husband and my amazing children.

Stone, Preston: Eustis, FL; Embry-Riddle Aeronautical University; Ray and Stacey Stone; BS Unmanned Aircraft Systems Science, 2017; Loyal Order of the Moose; Unmanned Aircraft Systems Technology Organization, Treasurer and Program Manager; This award would not have been possible without the sacrifices made by family, friends, and fellow veterans.

Stonebrook, Mara Rose: Copperas Cove, TX; Texas A&M University Corpus Christi; Mary Stonebrook and Frank Seffrood; BS Biomedical Sciences, 2016; University Council of Student Organizations, President; Campus Activities Board, Traditional Events Coordinator; National Society of Leadership and Success, National Engaged Leadership Award; This award would not have been possible without the support and love from my family and friends.

Stotts, Nicole: Southlake, TX; Texas A&M University Corpus Christi; Michael and Leslee Stotts; BA Accounting, 2016; Aloha Days, Student Coordinator and Counselor; Panhellenic Council, President and Vice President of Public Relations; Society for Advancement of Management, President, Vice President of Fundraising, Third Place Campus Chapter Performance Program, Second Place Management Case Competition, Outstanding Student, Largest Organization in the College of Business at TAMUCC, and Largest Chapter in the Country; Zeta Tau Alpha, Vice President II–New Member Coordinator, Treasurer, Historian, Fantastic Finance Award, and Most Participation Award; This award would not have been possible without the support of my family and friends.

Stouder, Caitlyn E.: Evans, GA; Georgia Southern University; Christoph and Sandra Stouder; BA, Chemistry, Concentration in Biochemistry, Minors in Mathematics, Biology, and Pre-Dental, 2016; Chemistry Research, Travel Grants 2014–2016, Bill Ponder Scholarship 2015–2016, and American Institute of Chemists Award 2016; Hearts and Hands Health Clinic, Volunteer Dental Coordinator 2014–2015; Pre-Dental Society 2013–2016, Treasurer 2014–2016; Alpha Chi Sigma 2012–2016, Treasurer 2013–2014 and Master Alchemist/President 2014–2016; Student Affiliates of the American Chemical Society 2012–2016, Secretary 2013–2014, Vice President 2014–2015, and Public Relations 2015–2016; This award was made possible by the love and support of my parents, family, and friends. Thank you!

Streckfuss, Dreena Lynne: Mina, SD; Northern State University; Lisa Streckfuss; BS Psychology, 2016; Psi Chi International Honor Society in Psychology; Dean's List; This award would not have been possible without the support and love from my family.

Stroup, Devon Nicole: Oxford, PA; West Chester University; Jacquelyn and John Stroup; BS Athletic Training, 2017; YMCA STRIDE TOO, Volunteer Coach; Honors Student Association, Historian and HSA Happenings Editor; Club Field Hockey, President.

Studds, Kassi McLaren: Melbourne, FL; Flagler College; Gregory Studds; BA Psychology/Strategic Communication, 2016; Omicron Delta Kappa; Lambda Pi Eta; Phi Alpha Delta; Psi Chi, Treasurer; Residence Life, Resident Advisor; Campus Activities Board, Programming Director and Vice President of Administration; I would like to thank my parents, family, friends, and Flagler College for their love and support!

Stulc, James A.: Grand Junction, CO; Colorado Mesa University; Richard and Annette Stulc; BS Biology, 2016; This award would not have been possible without the support of my beautiful wife, Risharra.

Suarez, Shadia: Athens, TN; Cleveland State Community College; Dharia Gloria and Winkar Yaroslav; AS General Transfer, 2016; Autism American Association; Pages Reading Club; National Academy of Future Physicians, Alumni and Award of Excellence Recipient; American Heart Association; Supplemental Instruction, Composition I SI Leader; Phi Theta Kappa; SGA, President; Norma Davis Scholar; TISL Best Reporter; Rotaract; To my family and friends who have encouraged me to keep going.

Sullivan, Erin Margaret: Schenectady, NY; High Point University; BA Elementary Education, 2016; Kappa Delta Pi; North Carolina Association of Elementary Educators ; Student Alumni Council; Tri Sigma Sorority, Co-Public Relations Chair, Vice President of Operations, and Tri Sigma Scholarship Ring; Big Brothers Big Sisters, President; Thank you to my family, friends, and professors who always encourage me to Dream Big.

Sumeriski, Cody Michaels: Basom, NY; Genesee Community College; BS Physical Education, 2018; Genesee Community College, Physical Education Award; I want to thank my fiancée, family, and friends for their love and support through the years.

Summerlin, Kara Elizabeth: Lexington, SC; University of South Carolina Aiken; Lance Summerlin; BA Communications, 2016; Thank you to all of my family, friends, and professors who have encouraged me to succeed at USCA.

Summerour, Alexandra Catherine: Houston, TX; University of St. Thomas; Alex and Donna Summerour; BA Music Performance/Philosophy, 2016; Palmer Episcopal Adult Choir, Secretary; Music Department, Choral Librarian; Holy Rosary Catholic Church, Cantor; Chapel of St. Basil, Cantor; University Singers Choir; Palmer Episcopal Children's Choir, Assistant Director; Palmer Episcopal Adult Choir; Bangladesh's Dharmarajika Buddhist School and Hostile for Children; Bangladesh's Apongaon Drug Rehab Centre for Young Boys; Bangladesh's Street Children's Project with the Oblates of Mary Immaculate; Missionaries of Charity in Bangladesh; Habitat for Humanity in Bangladesh; Bangladesh's Holy Spirit Major Seminary and Our Lady of Sorrows Convent, Music Instructor and English Tutor; National Association of Teachers of Singing, First Place in Women's Division 2013 and Second Place 2014; University Achievement Scholarship; The Republic Philosophy Club, Vice President; Mu Phi Epsilon, President.

Sumpter, Amber Briana: Georgetown, SC; Spartanburg Methodist College; Fred Sumpter and Natashia Felder; AA History, 2016; I just want to thank God and my family for all the support and love given to me.

Super, Jessica Margaret: Oaklyn, NJ; William Paterson University of New Jersey; William and Joan (Claudia) Super; BA Secondary Education/History, 2017; Theta Phi Alpha, Greek Senate Representative ; SGA, Freshmen Class Treasurer, Academic Affairs Senator, Allocations Senator, and Board of Trustees Student Voting Member; Field Hockey, National Field Hockey Coaches Association National Academic Squad 2013 and 2014 and Academic All-NJAC Honorable Mention 2014–2015; "Nothing great is ever achieved without much enduring" —Catherine of Sienna

Surace, Jessica Rachael: Franklin, NJ; Keystone College; Christine Coulman-Smith and Charles Smith; BS Psychology, 2016; Sodexo, Student Promotion Coordinator; Counseling Center, Student Affairs Coordinator; Student Success Center, Student Assistant and Study Partner; Key Choices, Treasure; The Keystone Players, Usher; Sophomore Year Experience, Mentor Coordinator; Student Leader of 2015; Student Leader of the Month Award 2015; Keystone Creativity Award 2014; Keystone Innovation Award 2014; Keystone Research Award 2014; National Conference on Student Leadership; Keystone College Leadership Conference, Organizer and Presenter; Psychology Chub, Vice President; This award is an honor that I would not have without my fiancé, family, and friends.

Surratt, Kayla Nicole: Lexington, AL; Northwest-Shoals Community College; Salina and James Surratt; AS Salon/Spa Management, 2016; SkillsUSA, Outstanding Leadership Award 2015 and 2016; Recognition of Highest Achievement 4.0 GPA; Recognition of Scholastic Honors in Salon and Spa Management; *Who's Who Among Community College Students*, Award for Academic Achievement and Outstanding Leadership; This would not have been possible without God and the love and support of my family.

Swanson, Kai Michael: Machesney Park, IL; Milwaukee School of Engineering; Arika and Michael Swanson; BS Mechanical Engineering, 2016; SAE Aero Design 2016, Sponsorship Coordinator; School of Engineering Honor's List and Dean's List; American Institute of Aeronautics and Astronautics, Treasurer; SGA, Senator; Sigma Phi Delta Fraternity, Chief Engineer; My collegiate career would not have been possible without the support of my loving mother, Arika Swanson.

Sweed, Perri Cierra: Schertz, TX; St. John's University; Valerie and Reginald Sweed; BS Adolescent Education, 2016; Kappa Delta Pi Educational Honor Society, Social Committee; Alpha Kappa Alpha Sorority Inc., Secretary, Programming Chair, and Vice President; I am truly honored to be presented with such a prestigious award.

Sweet, Daniel Joshua: Brandon, MS; Dallas Baptist University; Dennis and Kimberly Sweet; BS Communications, 2016; Florida Collegiate All-Star Team 2012; Florida Collegiate All-Star Team 2013, MVP; Suncoast Conference First Team 2013; Polk State College Male Athlete of the Year 2014; Suncoast Conference First Team 2014; Suncoast Conference Player of the Year 2014; NJCAA National Team 2014; Florida Junior College First Team and All-Tournament First Team NJCAA VIII 2014; Florida Junior College Player of the Year NJCAA Region VIII 2014; Baseball Team, Player and Outfield; Omicron Delta Kappa National Leadership Honor Society; Dallas Baptist University Honor Roll 2014–2015; Lambda Pi Eta Communications Honor Society; Dallas Baptist University Academic Excellence Award 2015; Missouri Valley Conference First Team 2015, Award Recipient; I am grateful to God, my family, friends, coaches and teachers for their support and this award.

Swenn, Ashtyn Leigh: Shattuck, OK; Oklahoma Panhandle State University; Kelly and Lorinda Swenn; BS Animal Science, 2015; Alpha Zeta, Vice President.

Symons Jr., Kevin M.: Schenectady, NY; Schenectady County Community College; Kevin and Margaret Symons; AS Business Administration, 2018; Business Club, Vice President.

Syslo, Breanna Marie: Poughkeepsie, NY; State University of New York Plattsburgh; Shelley and William Syslo; MS Elementary/Special Education, 2017; Autism Speaks U SUNY Plattsburgh, Founder and President; Kappa Delta Pi, Co-President; Omicron Delta Kappa, President; This award would not have been possible without the support and love from my family.

Szigethy, Katya McAuley: Long Valley, NJ; Western Oregon University; Neil Szigethy and Martha Post-Szigethy; BS Theatre Arts/Forensic Anthropology, 2016; Office of Disability Services, Student Panelist; Anthropology Club, Historian and Creative Advertiser; National Society of Leadership and Success; To all my friends, family, fellow students, and professors, thank you for all your support and inspiration.

Szopo, Samantha: Saint Paris, OH; Kettering College; Vicki and Joseph Szopo; BS Health Sciences, Advanced Imaging, 2016; George B. Nelson Award, *Who's Who Among Students* Honoree 2014; This award is one of my greatest accomplishments and it would not have been possible without dedication, family, and God.

T

Tanner, Krystal D.: Fort Davis, TX; Sul Ross State University; Gerry Wilkinson; AA Biology, 2016; Biology Club, President; My mom and step-dad are the people I thank the most for who I am today.

Tapia, Valencia Lynette: Puyallup, WA; Langston University; Selina and Joseph Cook; BA Business Administration, 2017; Sigma Gamma Rho Sorority Inc.; Dean's List; I give all thanks to the continuous support from my family and Jesus Christ himself.

Tarrant, Tamaragail Calayo: Simpsonville, SC; University of South Carolina; Gemma and Ricky Tarrant; BS Biological Sciences, 2016; NASPA BACCHUS Conference 2015; BLS for Healthcare Providers, CPR/AED/AHA Certified; Adult and Pediatric First Aid/CPR/AED Certified; ARC Certified; Trans* Advocacy Training 2014; Suicide Prevention Gatekeeper Training 2014; MLK Jr. Day of Service 2014–2016; Safe Zone Ally Training 2013–2016; A. Bevy Productions at USC, Chief Liaison; Student Leadership and Diversity Conference 2013–2016; Multicultural Leadership Conference; Community Partner Breakfast 2014; Project Condom, Model and Participant; LEAD Retreat 2014–2015; Students with a Responsible Message, Secretary 2013–2014; Serve Carolina Workshop 2013; Association of Minority Pre-Health Students 2014–2015; Changing Carolina Peer Leader, Peer Educator, and Interpersonal Violence Prevention and Healthy Relationships Chair; Golden Key International Honour Society; Phi Sigma Theta; Omicron Delta Kappa; CATALYST Leadership Program 2013; Leaders Engaging Across Perspectives 2014; Emerging Leaders Program 2012; Alpha Kappa Alpha Sorority Inc., Community Service, Standards, and Archives Chair; Leadership and Service Center Team, Community Service and Spirit Programing; Bedsider U, Campus Representative, Group Leader, and Vice President; Multicultural Assistance Peer Program, Mentee, Mentor, and Leadership Team; Made possible because of all those who believe in me and my dream, especially my parents.

Tatah, Canisia Bongfen: Weatherford, OK; Southwestern Oklahoma State University; Pamela and Edison Fru Ndi; BS Biology, 2016; Chi Alpha On-Campus Ministry; Research Excellence Club; Southwestern International Students Association; Tri Beta Biological Honor Society; Biology Club, Ottis and Buena Ballard Memorial Scholarship; Black Students Association; Medical Professions Club; Collegiate Activities Board, Executive Member; Immense Gratitude to God Almighty and my wonderful family for the continual love and support.

Taylor, Ashley Michelle: Appling, GA; Augusta University College of Allied Health Sciences; Michael and Danielle Taylor; BS Dental Hygiene, 2016; This award would not have been possible without the love and support from my family and fiancé.

Taylor, Cameron Erin: North Richland Hills, TX; Texas Tech University; Tedna and John Taylor; BS Special Education, 2016; TAFE, Judged High School for Family Consumer Science; Golden Key, Academic Achievement; TSTA-SP, STEP Conference; TSTA-SP, Professional Development for Student Teachers; This honor would of never been possible without the love and support from my family and friends.

Taylor, Ryan A.: Lewisburg, TN; Columbia State Community College; Marvina Buuck and Ray Taylor; AS Health Care, 2018; God, my beautiful wife, and my five amazing children are the ones that motivate me to succeed. Airborne!

Tembo, Makomborero: Mount Pleasant, TX; Northeast Texas Community College; Elliot and Lovejoy Tembo; AS Biomedical Science, 2017; This award would not have been possible without the support and encouragement from my family.

Tennakoon, Sumudu Prasanna: University, MS; The University of Mississippi; Anula and Sunil Tennakoon; PhD Physics, 2016; Buildings, Grounds, and Renovations Standing Committee, Graduate Student Representative 2015–2016; Sports Club Council, Member and Student Representative 2014–2015; Spooky Night of Physics Demonstrations at Lewis Hall, Student Volunteer 2009–2015; Ole Miss Badminton Open, Competition Coordinator 2012 and Organizer 2014–2015; Graduate School Dissertation Fellowship Award 2016; Fifth Annual Graduate Student Council Research Symposium, First Place Podium Presentation Category 2015; Sigma Pi Sigma; Physics Graduate Student Association, Co-Founder and President 2015; Graduate Student Council, Director of Academic and Professional Development 2015–2016 and Senator 2014–2015; Ole Miss Badminton Club, President 2013–2015), Vice President (2012-2013), Web master (2011-2012; This award would not have been possible without the support and love from my family, teachers, and friends.

Terrell, Sierra E.: Troy, AL; Troy University; Patricia and Gary Terrell; BS Psychology, 2016; Psychology Club, Senior Editor Newsletter and President; Trojan Outreach, Academic Liaison and Peer Educator; I could not have done this without the proper guidance. Thank you Lord, mom, dad, and all.

Tharp, Jessica L.: Dallas, TX; Angelo State University; Michael DeLira; BA Communication/History, 2018; Lambda Pi Eta Communication Honor Society, Iota Alpha Chapter Secretary 2016–2017; Student Film Club, Secretary 2016; Galilee Community Development Corporation Community Board, Student Liaison 2015–2016; Fort Concho Museum Community Board, Student Liaison 2014–2015; Thank you to my friends, family, and all those who encourage me to pursue my dreams.

Thibert, Lauren: Plantation, FL; Flagler College; Kathy and Richard Thibert; BA Deaf Education, 2017; Ketterlinus Elementary; Thank you to all of my family, friends, and teachers who helped me along the way!

Thibodaux, Angele Mary: Cut Off, LA; Southeastern Louisiana University; Angela and Lance LaPlante; BA Psychology, 2016; Université du Québec à Trois-Rivières, Study Abroad Student; Hammond Horror Festival, Stage Manager; No Shoes Allowed Improv Group; Moderator; Sigma Alpha Pi; Phi Sigma Iota; Sigma Alpha Lambda, Secretary; Alpha Psi Omega, Secretary, Treasurer, and Stage Manager; Le Cercle Français, President; This achievement is made possible by all my family, friends, and instructors who supported me through this journey.

Thibodeau, Britni Danielle: Pace, FL; Huntingdon College; Ron and Kristin Thibodeau; BA Sports Studies–Exercise Science, 2016; Student Athlete Advisory Committee, Women's Tennis Sophomore Representative 2013–2014; Chi Omega Fraternity, T-shirt Chair and Sisterhood and Social Teams.

Thompson, Kim R.: Angwin, CA; Pacific Union College; BA Religion with Biblical Studies Emphasis, 2016; This award made possible thanks to the PUC Religion Department and additional personal supporters in my life.

Thompson, Luz Amberly: Rock Hill, SC; York Technical College; AS Surgical Technology, 2016; This award would not have been possible without the support and love from my family.

Thompson, Tifanie Dee: Demorest, GA; Piedmont College; Dawn Hunnicutt; BA Political Science, 2016; *Trillium Journal*, Published 2013–2016; Academy of American Poets College Prize Winner 2015; Psi Chi; Sigma Alpha Pi; The Torch of Piedmont; This award was made possible by the unwavering support of my mother, Dawn, and sister, Kaylee.

Timmons, Tiffany Lynn: Hanover Township, PA; Luzerne County Community College; Brenda Timmons; AA Medical Office Specialist, 2016; I could not have achieved this award without the support and encouragement of my family.

Tims, Blake Ellis: Mobile, AL; University of Mobile; Tommy and Cathy Tims; MA Marriage and Family Counseling, 2017; American Association of Christian Counselors; Alabama Counseling Association.

Tobey, Mollie Delena: Greenfield, MA; Fitchburg State University; Hilary Ince and Robert Tobey; BS Nursing, 2016; Competitive Figure Skating, Senior-Level Moves-In-The-Field and Junior-Level Freestyle; Sigma Theta Tau International Nursing Honor Society, Elected Student Board Member; Thank you to my family, friends, and faculty for your unconditional support always and for making this award possible!

Toda, Brian: Olyphant, PA; Keystone College.

Tomlinson III, Robert Edward: Three Rivers, MI; Glen Oaks Community College; Bob and Julie Tomlinson; AA General Studies, 2015; Glen Oaks Community College Music Club, Secretary; Dedicated to my parents, Uncle Dan, Aunt Amy, Auntie Nick, my friends, and the MLB Power Pros Forum.

Torchon, Jeffrey: Philadelphia, PA; Temple University Boyer College of Music and Dance; Joyce and Alan Torchon; MM Music Education, 2015.

Torrey, Heather Lynn: Clifton Park, NY; Bryant and Stratton College Albany Campus; Edward and Nancy Stentz; AS Accounting, 2016; Alpha Beta Kappa; I owe this degree to my daughter and family's support. Thank you always.

Toye, Adera Evelyn: Washington, DC; Bennett College; BA Journalism/Media Studies, 2016; Belle Ringer Scholarship Presented by Sybil Wilkes of the Tom Joyner Morning Show; Belle Media Group, Outstanding Journalism and Media Studies Student Award, Producer, Videographer, and Editor; Pre-Alumnae Council, Miss United Negro College Fund; Junior Class President, Special Events Coordinator; All thanks to God and my loving and supportive family.

Trahan, Rachel Alexis: Peabody, MA; Roger Williams University; John and Adriana Trahan; BA Public Relations, 2016; WQRI, Music Director; Drastic Measures A Cappella, Secretary, Vice President, and Public Relations Chair; This award reflects the love and support I have received from family and friends. Thank you for everything.

Tran, Cindy L.: Fort Worth, TX; Tarrant County College Northwest Campus; AA Nursing, 2016; Thank you, mom, for your unwavering support. This would not have been possible without you.

Trautmann, Andrew Joseph: San Antonio, TX; The University of Texas at San Antonio; Paul and Charlotte Trautmann; BA Accounting, 2016; Omicron Delta Kappa, Historian; Thank you to my father, Paul Trautmann, for all the love and support.

Trevena, Laurel Brooke: Beachwood, NJ; Immaculata University Undergraduate; Barbara and Will Trevena; BS Physical Therapy, 2017; Alpha Psi Omega; Phi Epsilon Kappa Honor Society; Immaculata University Honor Society; National Society of Leadership and Success; Alpha Xi, Greek Counsel Representative; This award would not have been possible without the love and support of my mother, Barbara Trevena.

Triplett, Megan Denea: Wise, VA; Mountain Empire Community College; Angela Hicks and David Puckett; AS Nursing, 2016.

Tucker, Margaret Shannon: Methuen, MA; Colby-Sawyer College; Susan and Michael Tucker; BA History and Political Studies, 2016; Dynamite Steppers, President; I would like to thank my family and friends, without them this award would not have been possible.

Turbeville, Brianna Chantelle: Lakeland, FL; Florida Southern College; Susan and Tim Turbeville; BS Political Science, 2015; Colleen Burton Campaign, Volunteer and Intern; Rick Scott Campaign, Volunteer; Run4One, Volunteer and Social Media; Adam Putnam Campaign, Volunteer; Model United Nations Club, Treasurer; Political Science Student Advisory Board; Pi Sigma Alpha; Florida Southern College Republicans, Executive Director; My accomplishments would not have been possible without God and the loving support of my family.

Turner, Gary Jason: San Angelo, TX; Angelo State University; JoBeth Richardson and Gary Turner; BSS Intelligence, Security Studies, and Analysis, 2018; This award would not have been possible without the love and support of my family.

Turner, Raysa Amezquita: Orange Park, FL; Saint Leo University; BS Criminal Justice, 2017; This award would not have been possible without the support and love from my family.

Turner, Terence Michael: Goodlettsville, TN; Lipscomb University; BA Psychology, 2018; I would never have received this award if my parents had not supported me throughout my academic career.

Tyler-Sheriff, Mondria Yaneick: Jackson, MS; Belhaven University.

Tyree, Elaine B.: Alliance, NE; Western Nebraska Community College; AA Health Information Technology, 2016; This award would not have been possible without the support and love from my family.

U

Uhler, Erica R.: Cleveland, OH; Rensselaer Polytechnic Institute; BS Chemical Engineering, 2018; Terra Café, Public Relations; Student Sustainability Task Force, Outreach Coordinator and Project Lead; Thank you, Mom. Without your support and enthusiasm, this would not have been possible.

Ullom, Jordan Aaron: Evans, WV; West Virginia University at Parkersburg; Jon and Nancy Ullom; AA Healthcare Administration, 2019; Phi Theta Kappa; Graduating Summa Cum Laude; This recognition would not be possible without the love and support of my family and friends.

Umphrey, Brittany Lorene: Philadelphia, TN; Cleveland State Community College; Donald and Trish Umphrey; AS General Transfer, 2018; This award would not be possible without my Savior Jesus Christ, I am nothing without Him.

Upadhyay, Tripti: Malvern, PA; Goldey Beacom College Graduate School; Kajal Upadhyay; MBA Healthcare Management, 2016; Classical Dance Award; Extemporary Speech Competition Award; Slow Cycling Race Competition Award; Leadership Award; Dance Performance Awards; Stage Performance Awards; Annual Academic Excellence Awards; Elocutions Awards in English, Hindi, and Marathi Languages; National Olympiads Awards; Basketball Awards; I am grateful to my Mom, Kajal Upadhyay, my husband, Kartik, friends, teachers, and my Honda Civic to help me achieve this award.

Uram, Aaron J.: Natchez, MS; Copiah-Lincoln Community College Natchez; AS HVAC, 2016; Phi Theta Kappa Honors Society, President AAZ Chapter; I want to thank the teachers and staff at Co-Lin Natchez for making this goal possible.

Urban, Jennifer Ann: Oxford, MS; The University of Mississippi; Ann Urban; JD Law, 2015.

Urie, Linda Kaye: Roswell, NM; Eastern New Mexico University-Roswell; BS Nursing, 2016; Phi Theta Kappa Honor Society; Without the support, encouragement and love of my husband, Michael Urie, this award would not have been possible.

Utt, Jesse Conner: Cowgill, MO; William Penn University; Kim and Barry Utt; BS Industrial Technology with Emphasis in Business Management, 2017; Men's Basketball; Dean's List 2013; Alpha Lambda Delta Honor Society; This award would not have been possible without the support from my family and loved ones.

V

Vaillancourt, Jessica Lynn: Presque Isle, ME; Northern Maine Community College; Paula Vaillancourt and Donald Shattuck Sr.; AA Early Childhood Education, 2016; ECE Pinning Ceremony   ; Receiving this award would not be possible without my family and my two beautiful girls.

Vaitkeviciene, Egle: Saint Pete Beach, FL; St. Petersburg College Health Education Center; AA Registered Nurse, 2016; This award would not have been possible without the support and love from my family.

Van Natta, Randall "Milt": Wisconsin Rapids, WI; Indiana Wesleyan University; Gail Van Natta; BS Biblical Studies, 2016; Everything in my life is sweeter because of the loving presence of my wife, Kay.

Vander-Plas, Kristen Reid: Lubbock, TX; Texas Tech University School of Law; Kevin and Twila Vander-Plas; JD Law, 2016; Supreme Court of Texas, Judicial Intern for Justice Don Willett; American Inns of Court, Pupil Member of the Tech Law Chapter; Delta Theta Phi International Law Fraternity, Dean of the Lindsey Senate; Texas Tech Board of Barristers, Member and 1L Moot Court Champion; Tech Law Advocacy Program, Order of the Barristers, Three-Time National Champion (Joseph M. Perry Parliamentary Advocacy Competition, National Pre-Trial Competition, and National Moot Court Competition), and ABA National Best Advocate; *Texas Tech Law Review*, Published Student Writer and Comment Editor; Thanks to my amazing parents, Stephanie, my professors, and my coach, Rob Sherwin, for seeing me through!

Vanier, Jake: Beaverton, OR; George Fox University; BA; Global Business/Marketing, 2016; Resident Assistant; Associated Student Community, Vice President of Representation and Student Body President.

Varela, Gabriel: Flagstaff, AZ; The Master's College; BA Biblical Languages, 2019.

Varela, Mikala Elizabeth: Westbrook, ME; Husson University; Juan and Lisa Varela; BS Accounting/MBA, 2016; Husson Accounting Society, President; Thank you to my wonderful parents for always supporting me every step of the way. With love.

Vargas Vargas, Glendalis: Moca, PR; University of Puerto Rico Medical Sciences Campus; PharmD Pharmacy, 2017; Academic Senator, Student School of Pharmacy Senator Representative, Academic and Student Committee; CEBNAD, Children with Type 1 Diabetes Camp Leader; Red Cross, Child CPR Training Volunteer; Kmart Pharmacy Intern; Iniciativa Comunitaria Alianza Member, Operacion Compasion Group, Iniciativas de Paz in Haiti; General Student Council, Student Senator; Pharmacy Student Council, Vice President; Comision de Sistema de Salud, Colegio de Farmaceuticos de Puerto Rico, Health System Commission; ASHP, Class Representative; Farmacia En Tu Comunidad Association, Community Activities Coordinator; APhA, Vice President of Membership; This award would not have been possible without the support of my family that believe in me.

Veite, Christina Lynn: Milford, OH; Wilmington College; Robert and Elizabeth Veite; BS Chemistry and Biology, 2016; Solutions Community Counseling and Recovery Centers, Residential Care Associate; Alkermes Pharmaceutical, Part-Time Validation Department; Peer Advisor, 2013 Volunteer and Mentor to Incoming Freshmen; International Undergraduate Research Symposium Presenter at the Sixth, Seventh, Eighth, and Ninth Annual Conferences; Co-Author of "Introducing Global Issues" Chapter 12 in *Introducing Global Issues, Sixth Edition*; College Learning and Reading Association Certified Chemistry, Biology, and Physics Tutor; Bethesda North Hospital, Auxiliary Volunteer Scholarship; District 17 Science Fair, Judge; American Chemical Society; Eco-House Resident, Ecology Centered Resident and Volunteer; Cross Country, NCAA Runner; Sixth Annual Undergraduate Research Forum, First Place for Chemistry, Math, and Physics; Fifth Annual Undergraduate Research Forum, First Place for Chemistry, Math, and Physics; Kappa Delta Sorority, Relay For Life Chair; American Medical Student Association, President; Science Society, President; This award would not have been possible without the support and mentorship from the Wilmington College Faculty!

Velarde, Ilci Giraldine: Newburgh, NY; Mount Saint Mary College; Yma Retamozo; BA Biology/Hispanic Studies, 2016; Dance Team; Rotaract, Secretary; Latino Student Union, Vice President; I would like to thank my family and Damian for all the support and love.

Vélez Ruiz, Sebastián: Cabo Rojo, PR; Inter American University of Puerto Rico, San German Campus; Elizabeth Ruiz Astacio and James Velez Jr.; BS Biology, 2018; Rector's List; Academic Excellence; Medlife UIPR San Germán Chapter; Beta Beta Beta Biology Honor Society, Chapter TriBeta; Caduceus, Pre-Med Society; PolyNatura Ecological Club, Staff Member; Honors Program; To my family, without whose love, support, and acceptance, this award would not have been possible.

Vella, Gregory: Staten Island, NY; St. John's University; Vincenza and Paul Vella; BS Criminal Justice, 2015; College of Professional Studies; Bronze Certificate of Achievement; Annual Dean's Award; Dean's List; Honor Society; Alpha Phi Sigma National Criminal Justice Honor Society; Phi Eta Sigma Honor Society; Creative Writing Excellence Award; Italian Excellence Award.; Only through hard work and perseverance can greatness be accomplished. Love and thanks to my parents.

Verrastro, Krista Nicole: Oakville, CT; Western Connecticut State University; Trish and Mike Verrastro; BS Elementary Education Math, 2016; Festival of Trees, Volunteer; Western Day of Service; Course Scheduling Committee, Student Representative; Culinary Council; Graduating Class Affairs; Relay For Life Committee; Education Club; SGA, Senator; Thank you to my family and friends for all the encouragement, inspiration, and motivation throughout the years!

Vietti, Katelyn E.: Benbrook, TX; Midwestern State University.

Vigilia, Ryan L.: Angwin, CA; Pacific Union College; Judy and Larry Vigilia; BS Music, 2016; Recital Receptionist; National Association of School of Music Accreditation Recital; English Department Employee of the Year Award; Philippines Medical Mission; Life Group Leader; Love Conquers All Free Medical Clinic; "You're a Good Man, Charlie Brown" Musical, Pianist; Pre-Med/Pre-Dental Club, Sergeant at Arms and Culinary Officer; Stockroom Cleric; Asian Student Association Club, Vice President; This award would not have been possible without the support and love from my friends, family, and teachers.

Villarreal, Brandi M.: Huntsville, TX; Sam Houston State University; Patricia Delgado and Olegario Cardenas; BS Criminal Justice, 2016; National Society of Collegiate Scholars; Forensic Science Society; National Engaged Leader Award, Organization Award; College of Criminal Justice Scholarship Achievement Award; National Society of Leadership and Success, President; It is an HONOR to have this award. It would not have be possible without my family's support.

Villarreal, Jose Carlos Liendo: Woodbridge, VA; University of Cincinnati; Carlos and Diana Villarreal; MS Criminal Justice, 2015; Alpha Phi Sigma National Criminal Justice Honor Society; United States Border Patrol Agent; Texas A&M University Undergraduate, Texas Aggie Corps of Cadets; This award would not have been possible without my children: Gaby, Dani, and Toni.

Villegas, Richelle Anette: Tempe, AZ; Central Arizona College; Gildardo Villegas and Saundra Rodriquez Feather; AS Music Performance, 2018; Thank you to my family and friends who have made this award possible for me.

Vincent, Shelby Lynne: Felton, DE; Delaware Technical Community College Georgetown; Joelle Vincent Jr. and William Vincent; AA Physical Therapist Assistant, 2017; 4-H Kenty County Order of the Links; Physical Therapists Assistants Club, President.

Vinton, Madeline: Webster, MA; Quinsigamond Community College; AS Business Administration, 2016; Phi Theta Kappa International Honor Society; Vice President of Leadership; Women of Distinction Award; My academic accomplishments would not have been possible without the love and support of my family.

Visbal, Melissa Mattie: Athens, GA; University of Georgia; Jon and Donna Visbal; BA Consumer Economics, 2016; This award would not have been possible without the support of my family and the UGA faculty.

Vohs, Rebecca J.: Rockwell City, IA; Iowa Central Community College; AS Administrative Specialist, AA Business Management, AS Accounting 2017; Phi Theta Kappa; Business Professionals of America, President Assistant; This award would not have been possible without the support of my family, friends, and mentors.

Von Loh, Glehn Paul: St. Augustine, FL; St. Johns River State College; Austin and Victoria Von Loh; AA International Studies, 2015; Florida College System SGA, District 2 Legislative Liaison; SGA, Student Body President.

W

Wagner, Jason L.: Hobbs, NM; New Mexico Junior College; Larry Wagner and Lorraine Tedford; AA Business, 2016; Lea County Center for the Arts, Board Member; Project Management Institute, Project Management Professional Certification; Toastmaster International-Enriched Speakers, President; I wish to thank my loving wife, Heather, and my two wonderful supportive daughters, Rachel and Leah.

Wagner, Jeremy Ryne: Oklahoma City, OK; Eastern Nazarene College; Jerry and Kim Wagner; BS Sports Management, 2016; Mount St. Mary Baseball Camp; Wollaston Lutheran Church, Lay Reader, Usher, and Acolyte; Executive Decision Simulation in the Business Department, Leader; Student Athletic Advisory Committee; Men's Varsity Baseball, Captain, Three-Year Commonwealth Coast Conference All-Academic Team, and All-Commonwealth Coast Conference Third Team Honors; Men's Varsity Basketball, Captain, National College Athlete Honor Society Chi Alpha Sigma, National Association of Basketball Coaches (NABC) Honors Court, and Three-Year Commonwealth Coast Conference All-Academic Team; Huge thank you to my family, friends, coaches, teachers, and students for making all this possible.

Wagner, Justin Garrett: Oklahoma City, OK; Eastern Nazarene College; Jerry and Kim Wagner; BS Sports Management, 2016; Mount Saint Mary Baseball Camp; Wollaston Lutheran Church, Lay Reader, Usher, and Acolyte; Executive Decision Simulation in the Business Department, Leader; Student Athletic Advisory Committee; Men's Varsity Baseball, Captain, All-Commonwealth Coast Conference Third Team Honors, and Three-Year Commonwealth Coast Conference All-Academic Team; Thanks so much for the endless support and encouragement by my family, teammates, coaches, and friends.

Wagner, Leah Brooke: Hobbs, NM; New Mexico Junior College; Heather and Jason Wagner; AA Business 2017, Mu Alpha Theta Pi Day; Lea County Women's Network Scholarship; President's List; Phi Theta Kappa; I give thanks to God. Thank you to my family, I love y'all the most!

Wagner, Michael Celin: Alpharetta, GA; Mercer University; Michelle and Lee Wagner; BA Accounting, 2016; Sigma Alpha Epsilon, Recruitment Chair and New Member Educator; Beta Alpha Psi, Recruitment and Communications Chair; Varsity Football, Unity Counsel Representative; My family, friends, coaches, and professors have worked hard to ensure my success.

Wagner, Rachel Nicole: Hobbs, NM; New Mexico Junior College; Jason and Heather Wagner; BS Nursing, 2017; Dean's List; Vice President's List; President's List; National Pi Day Fair; Better World Book Drive; Lea Regional Hospital Auxiliary Scholarship Recipient; Lea County Women's Network Scholarship Recipient; New Mexico Junior College Foundation Scholarship Recipient; Hurst NCLEX Review for NCLEX-RN; ATI NCLEX Review for NCLEX-RN; All-State Academic Team of New Mexico; Academic Achievement Award in Nursing; Mu Alpha Theta Math Honorary Society; Phi Theta Kappa Honor Society, Psi Theta Chapter President 2014–2015; This would not have been possible without the continuous love and support from my wonderful family. I love you most!

Wagner, Ryan Tyler: Jacksonville, FL; Jacksonville University; Debbi Crandall and David Wagner; BS Kinesiology, 2016; Kinesiology Student Society, President; Order of Omega Honor Society, Treasurer; National Society of Leadership and Success, Founding Member, Treasurer, and Vice President; Omicron Delta Kappa Honor Society; Green Key Honor Society; Presidential Advisory Council; Student Alliance, Interfraternity Representative and College of Health Sciences Representative; Sigma Nu Fraternity, President, LEAD Chair, Athlete of the Year Award, Brother of the Year Award, and Man of the Year Award; Davis Student Commons, Student Building Supervisor; I dedicate this award to my mother, father, and brother. I love you all beyond measure.

Walker, Cassie Marie: Hernando, MS; Northwest Mississippi Community College; Betty Walker; AA Elementary Education, 2015; Dean's List; President's List; I CARE Ministry; Northwest Education Association.

Walker, Steven Casey: Angola, IN; Trine University; Stephanie Jackson and Gary Shock; BS Psychology, 2016; This would not have been possible without the determination and focus I found within myself along the way.

Walker, Zoe' Theone Voya: Frederiksted, VI; University of The Virgin Islands St. Croix; Cecily Walker; BA Mass Communications, 2016; Thank you for instilling greatness in me, your chosen one. Without it, I would be nothing.

Wallace, Nandi Ayana: Columbia, SC; University of South Carolina Aiken; Weldon and Franquelletta Wallace; BA Sociology, 2016; This award would not have been possible without the support from my family. I love you!

Walters, James Matthew: Broken Arrow, OK; Oklahoma Baptist University; BA Religion/Biblical Studies, 2016; My utmost gratitude to Alan Bandy, my mentor in scholarship and dearest friend in the faith.

Ward, Evan James: Waco, TX; Baylor University; Dean and Ginger Ward; BS Health Science Studies, Pre-Med, 2016; Welcome Week Leader; Excellence in Student Involvement Award Winner; Multicultural Association of Pre-Health Students, Public Relations Committee Member, Public Relations Executive Chair, and Service; Peer Leader Program, Steering Committee and Service; This was only possible with the love and support from my family and fam. Matthew 6:34.

Ward, Susan M.: South Bend, IN; Indiana University South Bend; BA Sculpture, 2017; International Studies, Work Study and Intern; Dean's List; Officer Honors Program, Arts College Representative; Sculpture Department Work Study; Ernestine Raclin School of the Arts, Arts in Excellence Award; This award is a result of the support from Dr. Karakatsanis, Leo Stafford, and my family.

Ware, Jacob L.: West Point, MS; East Mississippi Community College; Kenneth and Sandra Ware; AS Forestry, 2016.

Ware, Lawren Brianna: Gadsden, AL; Samford University; Anna and Lawrence Ware; BMF Piano Performance/Pedagogy, 2016; Birmingham Arts Music Alliance, Original Composition Performed at the Abroms-Engel Institute for the Visual Arts; Democrats, Vice President 2013–2014; Orchestra, First Violinist; Jazz Band, Keyboardist and Pianist; Wind Ensemble, Co-Principle, Alto Saxophone; Fellows Program, Honors Program; Omicron Gamma Chapter of Delta Omicron International Music Fraternity, Music Director, Secretary, and Historian.

Wasek, Alyssa: Lake Jackson, TX; Abilene Christian University; Donald and Daryn Wasek; BA Management, 2016; Society for Human Resource Managers; National Center for Children's Illustrated Literature; Phi Eta Sigma; Thank you to my mother, father, and brother.

Washington, Vivian A.: Madison, WI; Edgewood College; Karen Washington; BA Communications, 2017; Office of Student Activities, Office Assistant; *On The Edge News*, Multimedia Editor 2014–2015; Edgewood Gaming Organization, Secretary; Eagles Debate Team, Secretary; Thank you for everyone who believes in me, including my family, my professors, Jeanne, and God.

Watanabe, Hiyori: Kyoto City, JP; Avila University; BA Education in Japan/Psychology in the United States, 2015; Taichi Sasamoto Exceptional Performance in Psychology Award; National Engaged Leader Award; I devote myself to education and psychology so that I will peacefully change the world for the better.

Watkins, Anthony: Mechanicsburg, PA; Messiah College; Dale and Nancy Watkins; BA Digital Media, 2016; I want to thank my family for all of their love and support and for making this award possible.

Watkins, Caroline Grey: Stoneville, NC; Rockingham Community College; Carla and David Watkins; AS Mathematics, 2016; Thanks to my uniquely special aunt, Ann Hundley, for her subtle support and motivation.

Watkins, Emily Lynn: Taylor Ridge, IL; Monmouth College; Mary Beth and David Watkins; AA Business Administration/Public Relations, 2016; Order of Omega Greek National Honor Society, Vice President; ASMC Leadership Conference, Attendee; *The Courier*, Contributing Writer; 'M' Athletic Club, President; Student Athlete Advisory Committee, President; Business and Economic Commerce Club, Secretary; Kappa Kappa Gamma Women's Fraternity, Academic Excellence Committee; Blue Key Honor Society, Head of Marketing and Public Relations Executive Board; Women's Softball, Midwest Conference All-Conference, Midwest Conference Academic All-Conference, and Captain; Women's Basketball, Midwest Conference Academic All-Conference and Captain; This award would not have been possible without the love and constant support from my family.

Wear, Jonathan R.: Danville, AR; University of Arkansas Community College at Morrilton; AA AAS Surveying, 2016; I would not be where I am today without my father, Brad Wear, and my incredible family and friends.

Weeks, Gena: Arlington, TX; University of Mary Hardin-Baylor; Kay and Tom Weeks; BS Interdisciplinary Studies, 2016.

Weghorst, Logan: Pickerington, OH; Mount Vernon Nazarene University; Christopher and Brenda Weghorst; BS Biochemistry, Pre-Medicine, 2017; Alpha Chi Honors Society, Chapter Vice President; Cycling Club, Vice President.

Wehrstein, Shiloh Wree: Counce, TN; Blue Mountain College; Mark and Tammy Wehrstein; BA Fine Arts, 2016; Modernian Society, President; Center Stage, President; Alpha Psi Omega, Vice President; I would not have this award without the love of friends and family.

Weinmann, Mary Elizabeth Ruth: Murfreesboro, TN; Pensacola Christian College; Robert and Debra Weinmann; BA Music Ministries, 2015; Leader Volunteer at Carpenter's Creek Assisted Living Facility for Christian Service; All praise, honor, and glory to God for this award! Thanking Jesus Christ, family, and friends for support.

Weller, Jordan Tempyl: Wildwood, MO; Missouri Baptist University; Robert and Vickie Weller; BS Biochemistry, 2016; Missouri Stream Team, Ten Year Certificate; Honorary Page for the Missouri House of Representatives, Certificate of Recognition; Solae Company Scholar, Certificate of Excellence; Alpha Chi; Sigma Zeta National Science and Mathematics Honor Society, Vice President of Gamma Lambda; SGA, Senator; Introduction to Biology Lab, Teacher's Assistant; General Chemistry Lab, Teacher's Assistant; Organic Chemistry Lab, Teacher's Assistant; Math and Science Club, President.

Wellman, Jennifer Ann: Quincy, IL; Maryville University; Linda and Johnny Wellman; Occupational Therapy, 2018.

Wells, Alicia Ann: Natchez, MS; Copiah-Lincoln Community College Natchez; Sherry and Keith Wells; AA Pre-Nursing, 2016.

West, Danielle E.: Monticello, AR; University of Arkansas at Monticello; Julie and Daniel West; BS Biology and Biochemistry, 2016; Vacation Bible School and Youth Programs, Special Needs Group Leader and Children's Sign Language Instructor; School of Math and Natural Science, Student Worker, Lab Technician, and Teacher's Assistant; School of Business, Student Worker and Office Worker; 2015 Homecoming Court, Representative Maid of Sigma Zeta; Sigma Zeta National Science and Mathematics Honor Society, President; Alpha Chi National Honor Society, Treasurer, Web-Master, and President; Everything that I have accomplished would not have been possible without the support of my family and friends.

West, Judy Elaine: High Point, NC; Guilford College Center for Continuing Education; BS Criminal Justice, 2016; Friend to Friend Mentoring; Distinguished Leadership 2012 and 2013; This award would not have been possible without love and support from my family and friends.

Wetmore, Alexander Byron: Zionsville, IN; Marian University; Kerry Salem and Rick Wetmore; BS Exercise Science, 2016; Indiana Academy of Science; 21st Century Scholar Mentor 2013–2016; Peer Tutor 2012–2016; Rotaract Club 2014–2015; Football, NAIA National Champion 2012, NAIA National Finalist 2014, NAIA National Champion 2015, NAIA Scholar Athlete 2014–2015, and Champion of Character Award 2015; This achievement was made possible through the support of my coaches, teammates, professors, friends, and family.

Whisenhunt, Kelis Ayn: Valliant, OK; Southeastern Oklahoma State University Graduate School; MA Clinical Mental Health Counseling, 2016; This award would not have been possible without the love of my family.

White III, Alvin D.: Hickory, PA; Robert Morris University; Peggy and James White; BA Media Arts, Concentration in Television and Video Production, 2016; Intramural Deck Hockey Team, Captain; Intramural Basketball Team, Captain; Coalition for Christian Outreach, Leadership Team; SGA, President; Be the change.

White III, James Dinsmore: Hickory, PA; Robert Morris University; Jamie and Peggy White; BA Media Arts, TV Video Production, Minor in Documentary Studies, 2016; Intramural Sports Participant, Basketball, Hockey, Volleyball, Knockerball, and Team Hand Ball; Coalition of Christian Outreach, Leadership Team; Big Brothers Big Sisters, Treasurer; SGA, Vice President; Work hard . . . dream big.

White, Carianne Renee: Scottsbluff, NE; Western Nebraska Community College; AA Information Technology, 2016; Phi Theta Kappa, Vice President; I would like to thank my husband, my children, my parents, and my professors for their support.

White, Lucia Catherine: Milford, CT; Rider University; Rachel White-Reilly; BA Digital Media: Radio, Television, and Film, 2016; Disney College Program, Character Attendant; Relay For Life, University Event Co-Chair; SGA, University Affairs Team Leader; Orientation Staff, Two-Year Orientation Staff Leader; Resident Advisor, Rho Alpha Sigma Honor Society; Thank you to my mentors, friends, family, and especially my mom. I would not have achieved anything without you.

White, Markel A.: Peoria, IL; Midstate College; Charlotte and Quinton Johnson Sr.; BA Business Administration, 2016; Two things define you: your patience when you have nothing and your attitude when you have everything.

Whitehead, Chrishae M.: East Saint Louis, IL; Jackson State University College of Business; Amika Allen and Christopher Whitehead; BA Finance, 2016; Without God, devotion, and the strong foundation of my family, this award would not have been achievable.

Whitehead, Shelby Corene: Lumberton, TX; Lamar University; Susan and Sidney Whitehead; BA Chemical Engineering, 2018; Tiger Rock Martial Arts, Certified Tae Kwon Do Instructor; Society of Women Engineers, Discover Engineering Committee, Events Coordinator, and Vice President; I dedicate all my successes to family and friends who assured me I could do anything.

Whitlock, Sara Elizabeth: Lee's Summit, MO; John Brown University; Daniel Whitlock; BS Biochemistry, 2016; Undergraduate Researcher, Outstanding Undergraduate Research Award 2015–2016; Thank you to my parents, who inspired me to love learning and made possible my success.

Whitlock, Sheila Anne: Bay, AR; Arkansas State University Newport; AA Business Technology, 2016; This award would not have been possible without the support of my loving husband and wonderful children.

Whitman, April Margaret: Anderson, IN; Kettering College; BS Nursing, 2016.

Whitworth, Tammara: Zephyrhills, FL; Saint Leo University; BA Criminal Justice, 2016; Without the support of my family and friends, this award would not have been possible.

Wieser, Jonathan A.: Maiden Rock, WI; University of Wisconsin Eau Claire; Daniel and Mary Wieser; BA Operations Management, 2016; APICS, Socials Committee, Second Place at Great Lakes District Case Competition 2016; College Republicans, Chapter Chair 2014–2015, Freshman of the Year, and Senior of the Year; Student Senate, Senator, 2015 Senator of the Year, Campus Affairs Commission, Intergovernmental Affairs Commission, and Finance Commission; Could not have done this without Harvey Schofield, Dr. William Edwards Demming, and Daniel Ek.

Wilkerson, Sarah Michelle: Blanchard, OK; Oklahoma Baptist University; Ronnie and Dawn Wilkerson; BS Nursing, 2016; Academic Affairs Committee, Junior and Senior Student Representative; I could not have received this award without the lifelong love and encouragement from my parents and family.

Wilkes, Ethel M.: Saint Maries, ID; Independence University; Bernice and Charles McKay; AA Business Management and Accounting, 2016; Two President's Awards; This award is for myself and my sisters, Joyce and April. Let us continue God's work!

Wilkins, Patricia A.: Laurel, MS; Southeastern Baptist College.

Willhite, Todd Michael: Bisbee, AZ; Evangel University.

Williams, Bethany Lynn: Greenville, SC; Bob Jones University; Raymond and Teresa Williams; BA Journalism and Mass Communication, 2016; *The Collegian*, Editor-in-Chief; American Advertising Federation, Secretary; This recognition would not have been possible without the support of my family, friends, and faculty. Thank you!

Williams, Bethany Rose: Selma, IN; Indiana Wesleyan University; BS Pre-Medicine and Biology, 2016.

Williams, Bligh: Toronto, CAN; AIB College of Business; Joy Hewitt-Williams and Eugene Williams; BA Business Administration, 2015; International Student Association, Vice President; Student-Athlete, Baseball Academic All-Conference; This award is a reflection of the guidance of my parents and God. Shalom.

Williams, Brittany Mahalie: Mattapan, MA; Emmanuel College; Teannia Williams; BA English Communication, 2016; Film Club, Co-President and Co-Founder; This award would not have been possible without the love and support of my family.

Williams, Catherine: Wilson, NC; University of North Carolina Charlotte; Gloria Howard; BS Nursing, 2016; University of North Carolina at Charlotte Awards; Dean's List; Chancellor's List; Cum Laude; Coping Mechanisms at a Mental Health Hospital Unit, Presenter; Pedestrian and Bicycle Safety at an Elementary School, Health Fair Presenter; NC MedAssist; Bank of America Award for Teaching Excellence; Alumni Association Tailgates; Relay For Life; Habit for Humanity; The Pines at Davidson, Retirement Home; Spring Arbor, Residential Assisted Living and Alzheimer's Dementia Care; National Society of Collegiate Scholars; Student Alumni Ambassadors; Ebony, Scottiara, LJ, Elijah, Jase, Dominic, Kayla, Matthew, and Tristan—this is for you!

Williams, Charell ReJean: Washington, DC; Bennett College; Robin Allen and Charles Williams; BS Elementary Education, 2017; Aces Marshall; College Cheerleader; Spirit of David Dance Ministry; Student North Carolina Association of Educators, Secretary, Event Coordinator, and President; I am very grateful for this award. Thanks to my family, support team, and advisers!

Williams, Christopher: Edgewater, FL; Embry-Riddle Aeronautical University; BS Aeronautics, 2016; I would like to thank my family, Ms. Joyce, Mazar crew, Kabul crew A1-2-3, and Team5 Erbil.

Williams, Ciara B.: Jackson, MS; Hinds Community College; LaTonya Wells and Cleon Williams; AA Radiology, 2016; Band Manager 2013–2014; Dean's Scholar 2014 and 2016; I would like to thank all of my family and friends for their love and support.

Williams, Courtni Cecilia: Chesapeake, VA; Chowan University.

Williams, Greg: Jonesboro, AR; American Public University; Johnny Williams and Pam Godwin; MS Space and Planetary Sciences, 2017; Special thanks for my coworkers for their motivation and my friends and family for their unwavering support.

Williams, Jacque'Lyn Annette: Kansas City, MO; MidAmerica Nazarene University; Bobbie Sias; BS Nursing, 2016; This honor would not be possible without the love and support from my FAMILY. Love You ALL.

Williams, Janae: Pensacola, FL; The University of West Florida; Roxanne and Robert Williams; AA Public Relations, 2016; Homecoming Board, Hospitality Chair; Omicron Delta Kappa, President; Alpha Gamma Delta Theta Lambda Chapter Public Relations Officer, Strive for Pi, and Highest GPA in Pledge Class; This award would not have been possible without the support and love from my family and friends.

Williams, Jason Christopher: Roanoke, TX; Embry-Riddle Aeronautical University; Richard and Kay Williams; BS Aeronautics, 2015; Ignite Research Grant to Study Foreign Direct Investment in China and the United States; This honor is the result of the encouragement from my family while serving in the military.

Williams, Joyce A.: Durham, NC; North Carolina Wesleyan College; Beddie and Earl Williams; BS Computer Information Systems, 2014; This award would not be possible without the encouragement of my family, friends, and Raziya Fatteh.

Williams, McKenzie Renee: Columbiana, AL; Belhaven University.

Williams, Mesa Ann Grace: Cleveland, TN; Lee University; Kelly and David Pracht; BS Mathematics with Emphasis in Actuarial Science, 2016.

Williams, Savannah Marie: Council Bluffs, IA; College of Saint Mary; MS Occupational Therapy, 2017; Pi Theta Epsilon, Secretary; My collegiate success would not have been possible without the support from my family and husband.

Williams, Stratton M.: Rockport, TX; Dallas Baptist University; Darla and Michael Williams; BA Kinesiology, 2016; Fellowship of Christian Athletes, Leadership Position and Speaker 2014–2016.

Williams, Zachary John Roger: Weatherford, TX; Texas A&M University; Donald and Stephanie Williams; BS Aerospace Engineering, 2017; Corps of Cadets Marksmanship Unit, Commanding Officer; First Place Team and Individual at the Military College Combat Shooting Championship; Thank you to my Mom and Dad for always pushing me to challenge myself to excel.

Williamson, Rashida Ashlynn: Atlanta, GA; Clark Atlanta University Isabella T. Jenkins Honors Program; Audrey Williamson; BA Political Science, 2018; Isabella T. Jenkins Honors Program Operation Hope to the Hungry; Boys and Girls Club of Metro Atlanta; St. Jude Stay Up for Good Fundraising Campaign; Judge Penny Brown's Sister Talk Conference; AIDS Walk Atlanta and 5K Run; Springfest Committee 2015, Vice-Chair; St. Francis's Table Atlanta; Women's Volleyball Team, Southern Intercollegiate Athletic Conference All-Academic Honors 2014–2015, All-Academic Team 2014, and Three-Time Scholar-Athlete Academic Achievement Honoree; Dean's Scholars Scholarship Program, Dean's List and Freshmen Academic Achievement Award; Red, Black and Gray LEADership Series; Orientation Guide Corps; *Who's Who Among Students in American Universities and Colleges 2015*;Isabella T. Jenkins Honors Program, Peer Mentor; Political Science Association, Treasurer; SGA, Executive Board Secretary 2016–2017, Miss Sophomore Royal Court 2015–2016, and Department of Leadership and Student Development; Phi Alpha Delta Law Fraternity, International; Delta Sigma Theta Sorority Inc., Sigma Chapter; This award would not have been possible without the support and love from a phenomenal woman, my mom.

Williams-Powell, Tashie Noelia Marie: Moreno Valley, CA; Moreno Valley College; Stephen Williams and Janice Powell; AA English, 2016; First Annual Roaring Block Party Planning Committee, Student Volunteer; 25th Anniversary Birthday Celebration Planning Committee, Decorations Lead; Inaugural Diversity Summit, Student Panelist; ATHENA Student Leadership Program Scholarship Recipient 2015; Renaissance Scholars Program. To my son, Chancellor, whose birth encouraged me to pursue an education and a brighter future.

Willoughby, Jesse Lee: Vestaburg, MI; Columbia Southern University; Kelvin and Lilah Willoughby; AA Occupational Safety/Environmental Health, 2015; It would have been impossible to achieve this award without the support of my family and friends.

Willson, Michael Nance: Norfolk, VA; Virginia Wesleyan College; BA Communication/Political Science, 2017; Jane P. Batten Student Center, Hub Staff; *The Marlin Chronicle*, Opinion Editor and Second Place for Best Sports Column in the Society of Collegiate Journalists Awards; Iota Beta Chapter of Sigma Nu Fraternity, Lieutenant Commander and Housing Manager; I would like to thank my family, friends, brothers, and professors for all of their support.

Wilson, Abigail: New Oxford, PA; Immaculata University Undergraduate; Brian and Jodi Wilson; BA Nursing, 2017.

Wilson, Constance Leighann: Wagarville, AL; Alabama Southern Community College; Christy and Brian Sullivan; AS General Studies, 2016; Student Support Services Member; Academic Achievement Award; Highest GPA; Student Campus Ministries, Co-Secretary and Commitment to Student Campus Ministries Award; Rotaract, Secretary, Certification of Completion Service Hours, and Commitment and Dedication to Peers in Rotaract Award; Phi Theta Kappa, 2015 Wounded Warrior Veteran Project; Thank you, none of this would have been possible without God and my family's love and support.

Wilson, Darcie Rae: Guymon, OK; Oklahoma Panhandle State University; Lanna and Richard Mosburg; BA Health and Physical Education, Sports Management, 2017; Softball; Dean's List; President's List; This award would not have been possible without the support and love from my mother.

Wilson, Samantha Lorraine: Florence, AL; Northwest-Shoals Community College; AS General Education of Science, 2016; Volunteer Tutoring; *Who's Who Among Students in American Colleges and Universities*; Florence Soup Kitchen Volunteer; This award would not have been possible without God and support of my family and friends.

Windsor Jr., Tommy Harold: Gilbert, SC; Limestone College; BA Criminal Justice, 2015; "You can accomplish anything if you are willing to pay the price." —Vince Lombardi

Winters II, Hamilton Stephens: West Monroe, LA; University of Louisiana at Monroe Undergraduate; Stephens and Sandie Winters; BA Marketing, 2016; Kappa Sigma Fraternity, Grand Master of Ceremonies; Opportunities are often only short-lived, but the regret of not accepting one could last a lifetime.

Wise, Kelsey Marie: Washington, PA; Thiel College; Frank and Amy Wise; BA Psychology, 2016; Athena International, Women's Leadership Award; Habitat for Humanity, Vice President; National Speech Language and Hearing Association, Vice President; National Society of Leadership and Success, President and National Engaged Leader Award; This would not have been possible without the love and support of my family and fiancé.

Wise, Zachary: Elkton, MD; Goldey Beacom College Graduate School; Robert and Angela Wise; MS Finance, 2016; This award would not be possible without the support from my parents.

Wnuk, Amy Christine: Hamburg, NY; Niagara University; Dennis and Judith Wnuk; BS Biology, 2016; Beta Beta Beta; Biology Club, Secretary; Bienvenidos Spanish Club, Vice President; I appreciate my family and friends for giving me the support to strive for these accomplishments.

Wojciechowski, Ashley N.: Saxonburg, PA; Robert Morris University; Joseph and Christine Wojciechowski; BA Communications, Concentration in Public Relations, Minor in Advertising, 2017; Delta Phi Epsilon, Vice President of Membership Development, Public Relations Coordinator, and Formal Recruitment Coordinator; Thank you, mom and dad, for your love and support in everything I accomplish.

Wong, Gavin: Cupertino, CA; Biola University; Freda and Gregory Wong; BS Business Administration and Management, 2015; Student Orientation Services Program Leader; Forensics Speech and Debate Team, Captain, Speech and Debate Coach, and Three NCCFA National Championships; Business Association, Executive Board Treasurer; Epsilon Kappa Epsilon Honor Society; Thanks to my family, friends, and mentors who have attributed to my personal and spiritual growth.

Wood, Shelby Anna: Wewahitchka, FL; Troy University; Rebecca and Christopher Wood; BS Social Science Education/Spanish, 2017; International Student Cultural Organization, Secretary; To my parents, thank you for your love and support. To my professors, thank you for your guidance.

Woods, Cori Carolyn: Montgomery, AL; Faulkner University; BS Business Management, 2016; Accounting Society; Collegiate Entrepreneur Organization, Vice President; Mr. and Mrs. Faulkner University, Mrs. Faulkner Nominee; National Society of Leadership, Fundraising Chair; Band, Vice President; Students for Life Group, President; This award would not have been possible without the support of my sweet family and God.

Worm, Katie Lynn: Preston, MD; Chesapeake College; Debbie and Robert Worm; AA Liberal Arts, 2016; This award would not have been possible without the continuous support and love from my family.

Wos, Lisa Marie: McHenry, IL; McHenry County College; Kristin Baker and Anthony Wos; AA English, 2016; Max M. Liptrot Memorial Scholarship Recipient 2016; President's High Honor Roll 2015; McHenry County College's Twofer Program, Student Worker and Promotional Assistant 2014; *The Tartan* College Newspaper, Copy Editor 2013; To my family, Kate, J. Krueger, and Eastland, thank you for everything. I would not be here without you.

Woyowitz, Danielle Suzanne: Baltimore, MD; University of Baltimore; AA Government/Public Policy, 2017; Intern for Senator Catherine Pugh Mayoral Campaign 2016; Alpha Chi Honor Society Helen P Denit Honors; Example of Excellence 2014; All is due to an understanding father, an inspirational grandfather, a dear friend, and a supportive canine companion.

Wright, Cody Eugene: Dublin, VA; Hampden-Sydney College; Ricky and Gail Wright; BA Government, Foreign Affairs, 2016; Phi Alpha Delta, Vice President and Secretary; I would like to thank my family and friends for all of the support.

Wright, Daniel A.: Augusta, GA; Kennesaw State University; BS Nursing, 2016; 2015 KSU Foundation Scholar, Leila Anderson Nursing Scholarship; To God be all the Glory! I am grateful for support from my family and loved ones.

Wright, Davon Matthew: Sumter, SC; University of South Carolina; BA Criminal Justice, 2016; Thank you to all of my family and friends for their support!

Wright, Kiana Aleyah: Sumter, SC; University of South Carolina; BA Psychology, 2016; ROTC; President's List.

Wright, Rhonda K.: Irvington, AL; University of Mobile; MA Marriage and Family Therapy, 2016; This award would not have been possible without the love and support of my amazing husband.

Wright, Vanessa Helen: Raeford, NC; Sandhills Community College; Joan Nockelin and Ronald Ruther; AAS Early Childhood Education, 2016; Early Childhood Club, Vice President; Phi Beta Kappa; Work Study Student of the Year Award; Nola Arden Manning Memorial Award; I am grateful for the love and support from my family, friends, and SCC instructors.

Wyatt, Chelsea: Monroe, LA; University of Louisiana at Monroe Undergraduate; Earnest and Tiffany Wyatt; BA Psychology, 2016; This award is great. I am very thankful for my family and professors that led me higher.

Y

Yagan, Sara: Syracuse, NY; Ithaca College; Taima and Amer Yagan; BS Health Care Management and Business Administration, 2017; Resident Assistant, Best Campus Wide Even 2014–2015; Peer Mentor, Leadership Scholarship; This achievement would not have been possible without the endless support from my loving parents and sisters.

Yanez, Cody David: Springfield, MO; Evangel University; Stephen and Leslie Yanez; BA Music and Biblical Studies, 2016; Evangel Composition Collective, Founding Member and Published Composer; Music Department, Pi Kappa Lambda Honor's Society Nominee; Scott First South Honors Floor, Sigma Alpha Sigma Honor's Society Inductee; Onboard at Sanctuary of Praise COGIC, Minister's License, Musician, and Children's Bible Teacher; Gospel Choir, Lead Musician and Co-Leader; Concert Choir, Chaplain; Chorale, Section Leader; National Association for the Teachers of Singing Regionals, Two-Time First Place Division Winner; Soli Deo Gloria.

Yergeau, Ciera: New Bedford, MA; Saint Mary-of-the-Woods College; Fernand and Anne Yergeau; BS Business Administration, 2017; International Orientation Leader; Sustainability Club, Treasurer; This would not be possible without the support of God, my family and SMWC.

Yomtoob, Jacob Esper: Mokena, IL; University of Miami; Laura and Benjamin Yomtoob; BS Neuroscience and Biochemistry, 2016; Undergraduate Neuroscience and Biochemistry Research, "Beyond the Book" Award; President's 100 Program, President's Ambassador to the University; Big Brothers Big Sisters; Best Buddies, Executive Board Secretary; University of Miami Alternative Breaks, Co-President, Site Leader, and Volunteer; Thank you to my family, friends, UM faculty and administration, and the Stamps Family Charitable Foundation.

York, Jaime Lee: Paint Lick, KY; National College Richmond; AA Medical Coding and Billing, 2016.

Yost, Mary Katherine: Landisburg, PA; Lebanon Valley College; Sue Anthony; BA History and Political Science, 2015; Collegiate Symposium on Karl Popper, Student Assistant; Mid-Atlantic European Union Simulation, Head of Government; Valley Humanities Review, History Student Editor; Colleges Against Cancer, Treasurer, Advocacy Chair and Co-Chair; This would not be possible without the love of my family and the grace of God.

Young III, John Thomas: Bartlesville, OK; Oklahoma Wesleyan University; BS Pastoral Ministry, 2016; In all your ways acknowledge Him, and He will make your paths straight.

Young, Aaron M.: Tazewell, TN; Walters State Community College; Jerry and Mary Young; AS General Studies, 2016; I would like to thank all my family, friends, and professors for their continued support and fellowship.

Young, Catherine E.: Millstadt, IL; Blackburn College; Debra Teagle; BS Biology, 2016; Blackburn Tutors, Chemistry Tutor, Biology Tutor, Math Tutor, and English Tutor; Blackburn Work Program, Academics Department Manager.

Young, Courtney Marie: Knoxville, TN; Pellissippi State Community College; AS Pre-Nursing, 2016; TBR Student Leadership Conference 2016; Making Graduation Possible; TnCis Study Abroad, Italy Summer 2015; Creative Writing Club; New Student Orientation, Student Leader; Dean's List; Tutor, Psychology, Sociology, and English; Student Activity Board; Access and Diversity, Participant; Disciplinary Hearing Board; Fee Board; Magnolia Campus Drama Club, President; Phi Theta Kappa, Alpha Theta Xi Chapter Vice President of Communications and Magnolia Campus Representative; Academic Student Success, Magnolia Campus Student Success Mentor; This would have never been possible without my parents, brother, kids, or my PSCC family.

Young, Jennifer Kingsley: Ardmore, PA; Bloomsburg University BS Health Sciences, 2016; I would like to thank my family, my professors, and Bloomsburg University.

Young, Krystle A.: Saint Louis, MO; Columbia College; BS Accounting, 2016; This award would be void without love from God, Tremayne, Doni, Nic, and Angel. Thank you.

Young, Silvana: Sugar Hill, GA; Georgia State University; BA Real Estate, 2017; Thank you to my family and employer for their support in my career goals.

Youssef, Mirna: Brooklyn, NY; Long Island University-Post; Mouaid and Magda Youssef; BA Criminal Justice, 2017; Resident Student Association, President; Admissions Office, Student Ambassador; *The Pioneer* College Paper, Features Head Editor; Achieving recognition for my academics is only possible with the love and support from my family. Thank you.

Z

Zafiroff, Ryan Nathaniel: Swartz Creek, MI; Evangel University; Terry and Greg Zafiroff; BA Biblical Studies and Preaching, 2016; Floor Council, New Student Representative; Teacher's Assistant; Campus Discipleship, Discipleship Leader; Residential Honors Society; Alpha Chi; Apologia, Apologetics Fellowship; Phi Sigma Tau.

Zahedi, Cameron Saeed: Athens, GA; University of Georgia; Alex and Shawn Zahedi; MA Economics, 2015; UGA MATHCOUNTS Outreach, Head Coach; Department of Recreational Sports,Club Sports Executive Committee Member; Men's Rugby Football Club, Captain, President, and Match Secretary; USA Rugby National Collegiate Honor Roll 2012–2014; Honors Program, Honors Teaching Assistant; Center for Undergraduate Research Opportunities, CURO Teaching Assistant, CURO Honors Scholar Conducting Physics Education Research; College of Engineering Research Assistant, Research Presented at 2014 Future Energy Business and Energy Informatics Conference in Rotterdam, The Netherlands; I thank my family, friends, and professors for their support, without which my success would not be possible.

Zayas, Rachael Marie: San Bernardino, CA; New Mexico Highlands University; BA Business in Accounting, 2016; Gamma Alpha Omega Sorority Inc., Prospective Active Educator, Social Chair, and Fundraising Chair; Student Senate, Senator, Treasurer, and Finance Chair; Student Ambassadors, President, Vice President, and Treasurer; This would not have been possible without the love and support from my family, especially my mom.

Zelenka, Ann Margaret: Baltimore, MD; University of Baltimore; George Zelenka Sr.; MS Negotiations and Conflict Management, 2016; Philippines Study Abroad 2016; President's Award 2016; Pi Sigma Alpha; Phi Alpha Theta; Sigma Nu Tau; Lead 365! Conference 2015, Participant; St. Ursula Catholic Church, Pastoral Council Member; St. Vincent De Paul Society; National Association of Pastoral Musicians, Basic Cantor Certification; US Department of Homeland Security, ICE Internship 2015; Murthy Law Firm Immigration Law Internship 2015; US Commission on International Religious Freedom, Media and Government Relations Intern; The Washington Center's Federal Diversity Initiative Internship 2016; Kosciuzsko Foundation Scholarship; Personal Assistant to Ann G. Giroux, Author and Archivist 2013–2016; Greater Baltimore Center for Pregnancy Concerns, Board Member; Merit Scholarship; Omicron Delta Kappa Scholarship; National Society of Leadership and Success; Alpha Kappa Alpha Scholarship Grant 2015, Academic Excellence and Student Leadership Award; Polish American Arts Association Grant 2014–2015; MD Senatorial Grant; MD House of Delegates Scholarship; Foundation Scholarship 2016; Center for Educational Access, Disability Note Taker; Achievement and Learning Center, Tutor and Peer Coach; Office of Technology Services, Lead Student Assistant; Polish Heritage Association of Baltimore, Board Member and Volunteer; Circle of Omicron Delta Kappa, Membership and Recruitment Officer; Conflict Negotiations and Conflict Management Graduate Association, President and Vice President; Tutor Certification, Level One; Crafters, President; Corinthians of UB, President; Respect Life Club, President; "Inspire excellence, honesty, and integrity with all that you do." Dedicated to Rosemary Goddard, my mother in Heaven.

Zettner, Darren Taylor: San Antonio, TX; Palo Alto College; Darren Taylor Zettner; BS Biology, 2019.

Ziauddin, Hassan: Ashburn, VA; Shenandoah University; Muhammad and Muzna Ziauddin; BA Business Administration, 2017; I would like to thank my loving parents, Dr. Muhammad and Muzna Ziauddin, for all their support and guidance.

Zimmerman, Detrica la'Joy: College Park, GA; Saint Leo University; Barbara Ann Woodruff Moore and Robert Lee Knox; BA Criminal Justice, 2016; Delta Nu; Delta Epsilon Sigma National Scholastic Honor Society; National Alliance of Mental Illness; Alpha Phi Sigma Criminal Justice Honors Society; Dean's List; Community Service Mentoring, Community Services, and Volunteer Works Feeding and Clothing the Hungry and Homeless; Learning is a lifelong process that will continue until you take your final BREATH. Encouragement appreciated.

Zimmerman, Kathryn Eva: Leominster, MA; Fitchburg State University; Janis and Gary Zimmerman; BS Severe Special Education, 2016; Dr. Anne May Award 2014; Vincent J. Mara Award 2013; Lena Caron Award 2013; Emerging Leader Award 2014; Dean's List 2012–2016; Kappa Delta Pi International Honor Society for Educators, President 2015 and Vice President 2014–2015; Receiving this honorable award was made possible by the love and support of my family.

Zollinger, Garrett Thomas: Bethany, OK; Southwestern Christian University; Larry and Tara Zollinger; BS Kinesiology, 2016; Yeah, Buddy!!!

Zuniga, Amanda Marie: Weslaco, TX; Texas A&M University Kingsville; Sandra Flores; BS Interdisciplinary Studies, 2016; Golden Key, Fundraising Director; I owe everything I am to my family.

Zyskowski, Jacob P.: Altamont, NY; State University of New York New Paltz; Randy and Dorothy Zyskowski; BS Management, 2016; Honors Program, Outstanding Graduate 2015; Management Association, Director of Finance; Catholic Campus Ministry, Leadership Team; Students for Sustainable Agriculture, E-Board; Beta Gamma Sigma Honor Society, Director of Membership and Public Relations; To family and anyone who called me friend, you have so much to do with who I am.